P9-BZD-511

Houghton Mifflin Mathematics 12

Robert G. Dearborn
John J. Del Grande
Jeri Lunney
Les Dukowski
Dale McAulay
R. Geoffrey Roulet

Houghton Mifflin Canada Limited
150 Steelcase Road West • Markham, Ontario • L3R 3J9

Houghton Mifflin Mathematics 12

Authors

Robert G. Dearborn, Mathematics Dept. Head, Queen Elizabeth C.H.S., Edmonton, Alberta
John J. Del Grande, Consulting Editor, Houghton Mifflin Canada Limited
Jeri Lunney, Vice Principal, St. Paul's High School, C.R.C.S.S.B., Nepean, Ontario
Les Dukowski, Vice Principal, H.D. Stafford Jr. Secondary School, Langley, British Columbia
Dale Anne McAulay, Teacher, Stephen Leacock C.I., Scarborough, Ontario
R. Geoffrey Roulet, Special Assignment Teacher, Mathematics/Computers, Timmins (Ontario) Board of Education

Consultants

Charles C. Edmunds, Mathematics Department, Mount Saint Vincent University
Linda L.B. Wheadon, Mathematics Teacher, Horton District H.S., Wolfville, Nova Scotia
Connie Shaver , Mathematics Coordinator, St. James Assiniboia S.D. #2, Winnipeg Manitoba

Canadian Cataloguing in Publication Data

Main entry under title:
Houghton Mifflin mathematics 12

For use in grade 12.
Includes index.

ISBN 0-395-42688-X

1. Mathematics—1961- I. Lunney, Jeri

QA39.2.H693 1987 512'.14 C87-093557-7

Editorial Adviser

John J. Del Grande

Editor

Sindy Vertlieb

Assembly and Technical Art

Dave Hunter
Tom Sankey

Cover Art

Ziggurat (1985) by Ted Bieler
Design by Dragon's Eye

Printed in Canada 12345/9210898

CONTENTS

1 Relations and Functions

2 Exponential Functions

3 Logarithms

4 Polynomials and Factoring

5 Trigonometry and the Solution of Triangles

6 Trigonometric Functions

1 Relations and Functions

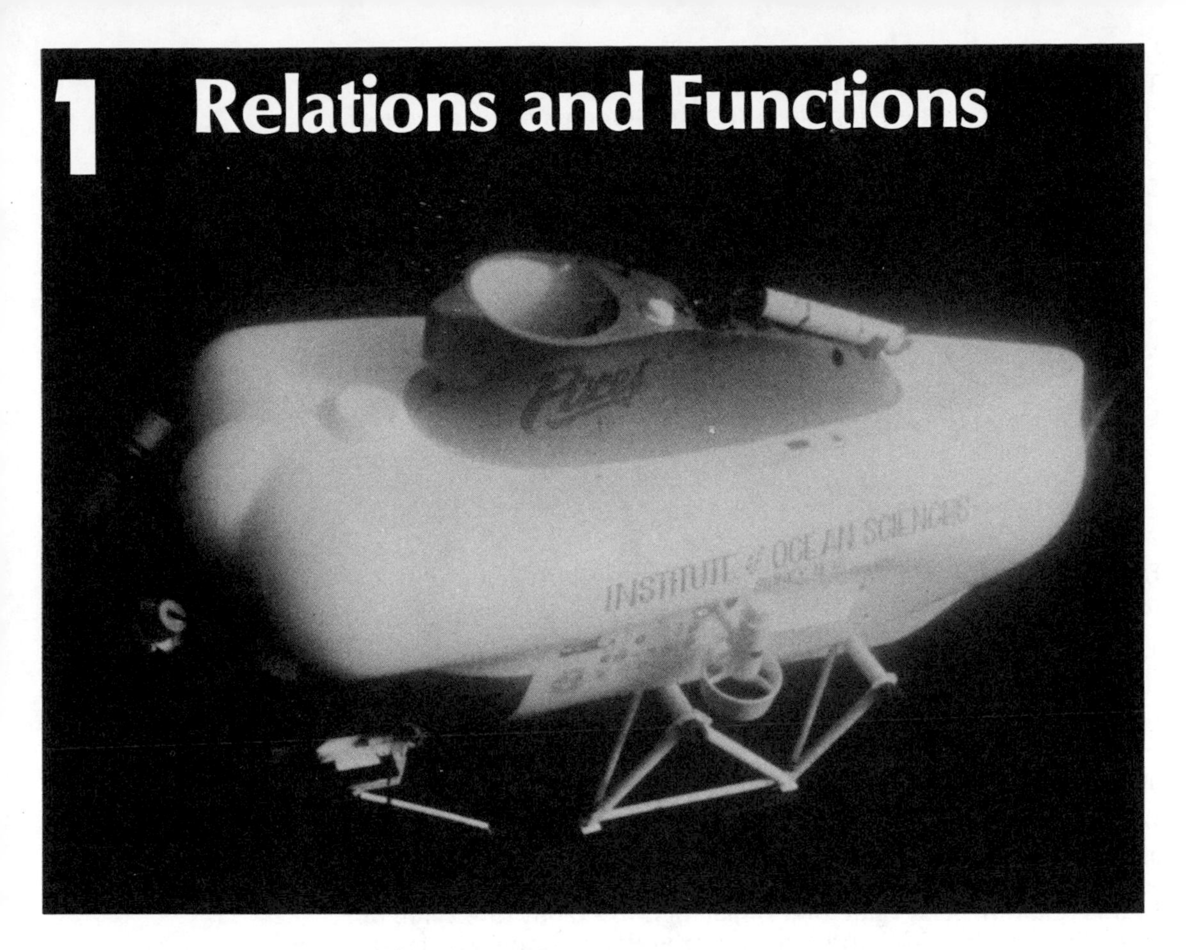

1-1 Relations and Functions

Mathematics can be used to describe, or model, events and situations in science, nature, and business. Engineers use mathematical models to predict the effects of physical processes and to make design decisions.

The graph shows the relationship between water depth and pressure as experienced by a sub-sea submersible. A sub-sea engineer could use information from such a graph to determine specifications on a new undersea vehicle. Such a graph defines a **relation**.

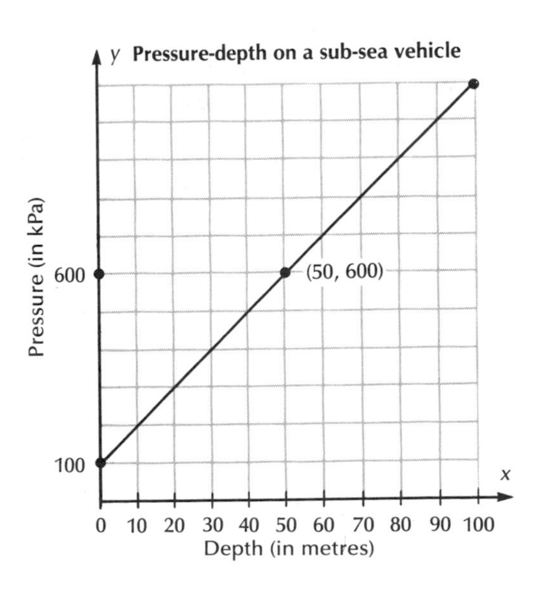

A **relation** is a set of ordered pairs.

The relation illustrated in the sub-sea pressure-depth graph could be defined in three other ways: by a set of ordered pairs, by a table of values, or by a matching diagram.

Set of Ordered Pairs: (0,100), (10, 200), (20, 300), (30, 400), (40, 500), (50, 600)

Table of Values

Depth d (m)	Pressure P (kPa)
0	100
10	200
20	300
30	400
40	500
50	600

Matching Diagram

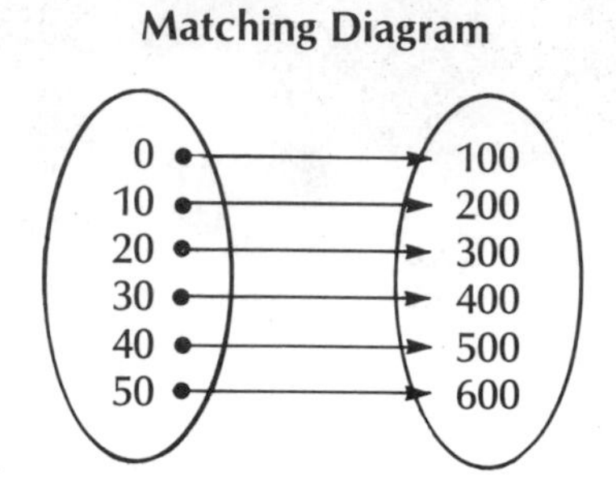

For a relation T, the **domain, $D(T)$,** is the set of all first members of the ordered pairs in the relation.

The **range, $R(T)$,** is the set of all second members of the ordered pairs in the relation.

Notice that the graph of the sub-sea vehicle relation is a straight line that passes through the points (0, 100) and (50, 600). Pressure, P, and depth, d, are related by the linear equation $P = 10d + 100$.

For the relation defined by $P = 10d + 100$, the domain is $\{d \mid d \in \mathbf{R}, d \geq 0\}$, and the range is $\{P \mid P \in \mathbf{R}, P \geq 100\}$.

$d < 0$ would not be appropriate for depth.

In this relation, each value of d is matched to exactly one value of P. A relation in which the ordered pairs are related in this way is a **function.**

A **function** is a relation in which each member of the domain is paired with exactly one member of the range.

The graph of a function has domain values placed along the x-axis and range values along the y-axis. Thus, for each point (x, y) in the graph of a function, each x is paired with exactly one y. That is, no two points on the graph lie one above the other. A vertical line will intersect the graph of a function in *at most* one point, as shown below.

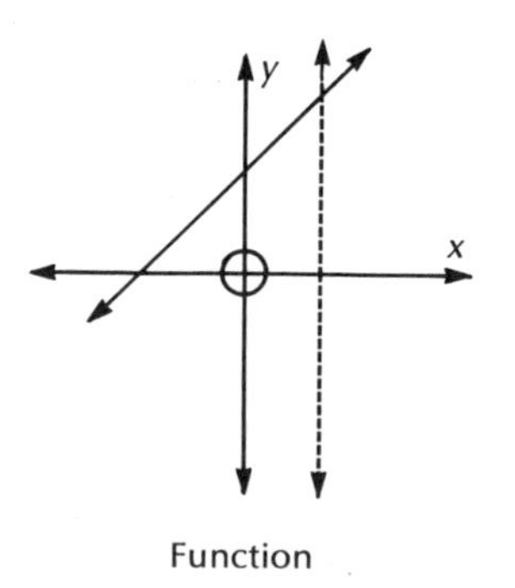

Function

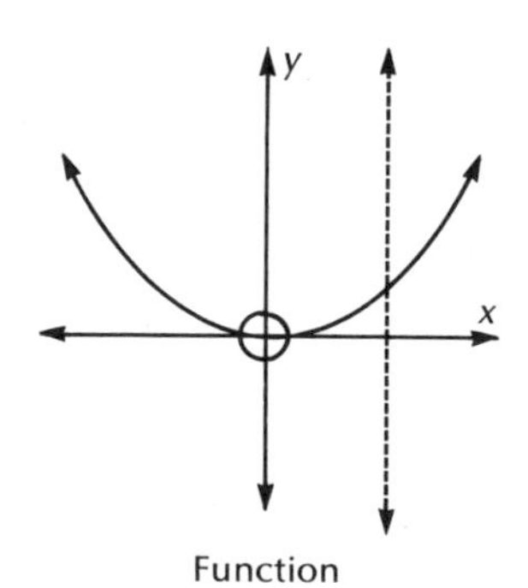

Function

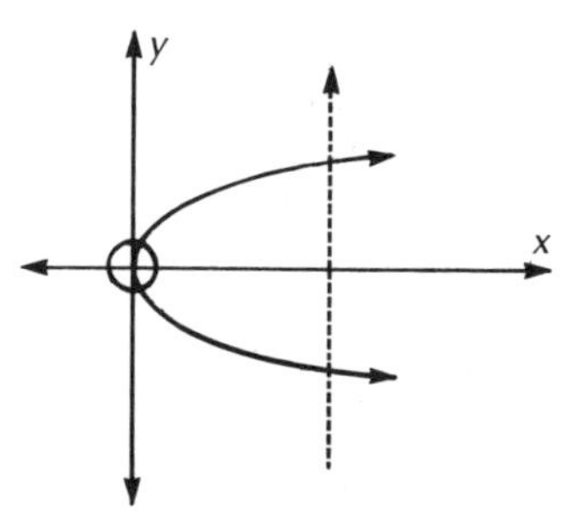

Not a function

Vertical line test for a function: Any vertical line will intersect the graph of a function in at most one point.

A function can be defined by using an equation, function notation, or mapping notation.

Equation	**Function Notation**	**Mapping Notation**
$P = 10d + 100$	$f(d) = 10d + 100$	$f: d \to 10d + 100$
$d \in \mathbf{R}, d \geq 0$	$d \in \mathbf{R}, d \geq 0$	$d \in \mathbf{R}, d \geq 0$

EXAMPLE 1: Find the domain and range of each function.

a. $S = \{(3, 2), (5, 3), (7, 4), (9, 5)\}$

$D(S) = \{3, 5, 7, 9\}$ — $D(S)$ is the domain of S.
$R(S) = \{2, 3, 4, 5\}$ — $R(S)$ is the range of S.

b.

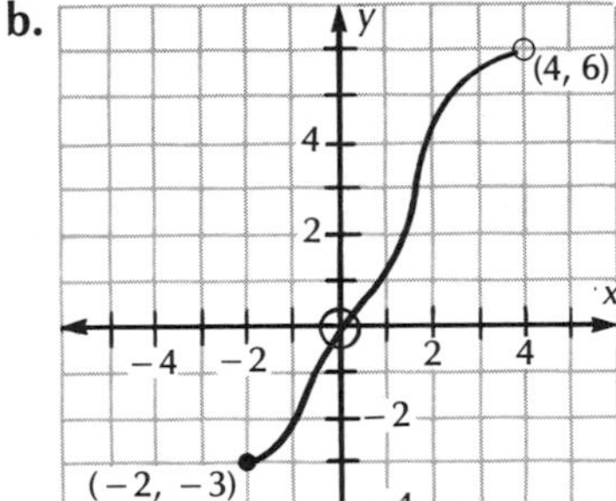

(4, 6) is not a point on the graph.

$D(T) = \{x \mid -2 \leq x < 4\}$

$R(T) = \{y \mid -3 \leq y < 6\}$

EXAMPLE 2: A function f is defined by $f(x) = \sqrt{3x + 1}$. If the domain is $\{1, 2, 8\}$, find the range.

$f(1) = \sqrt{3(1) + 1} = \sqrt{4} = 2$ $\qquad f(2) = \sqrt{3(2) + 1} = \sqrt{7}$ $\qquad f(8) = \sqrt{3(8) + 1} = \sqrt{25} = 5$

The range of the function is $R(f) = \{2, \sqrt{7}, 5\}$.

EXAMPLE 3: A function g is defined by $y = \sqrt{3x + 1}$, for $x, y \in \mathbf{R}$. Find the domain and range.

For $\sqrt{3x + 1}$ to be a real number, $3x + 1 \geq 0$, or $x \geq -\frac{1}{3}$.

$\therefore D(g) = \{x \mid x \geq -\frac{1}{3}, x \in \mathbf{R}\}$

Since $\sqrt{3x + 1}$ is never negative, then $y \geq 0$.

$\therefore R(g) = \{y \mid y \geq 0, y \in \mathbf{R}\}$

EXERCISE 1-1

A **1.** Determine the domain and range of each relation.

a. $\{(3, 1), (1, 9), (-1, 14), (2, 8), (0, 10)\}$

b.

x	y
-3	6
-1	2
1	2
3	6

c.

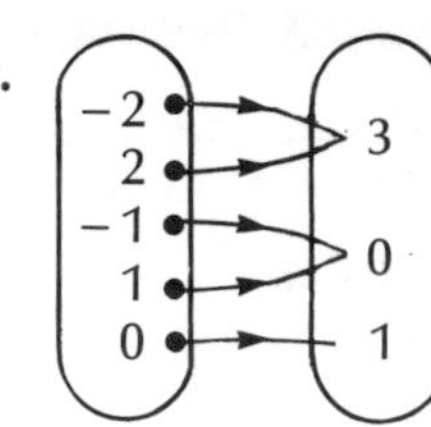

d.

2. Which of the given relations are functions? Explain.

a. $\{(5, 3), (3, 1), (1, 0), (-1, 2)\}$

b. $\{(6, 3), (4, 2), (3, 1), (4, 0), (5, 5)\}$

c.

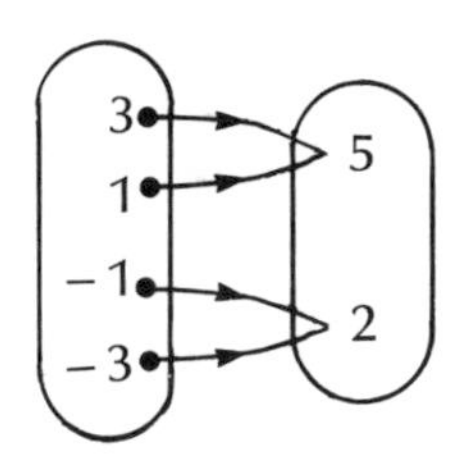

d.

x	y
-2	5
-1	3
0	-1
-1	-1
-2	-3

e.

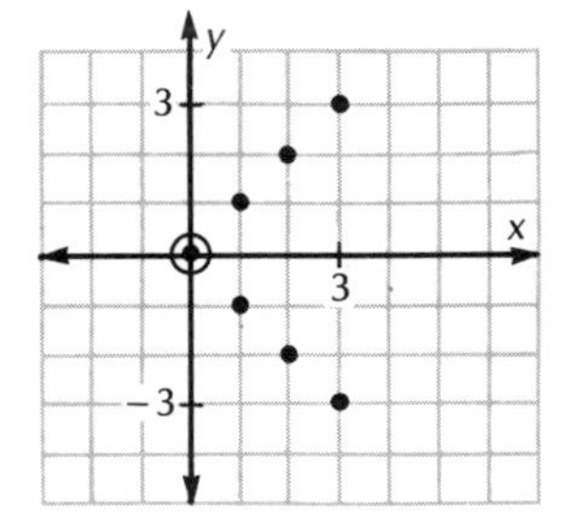

3. Which of the given graphs represents a function?

a.

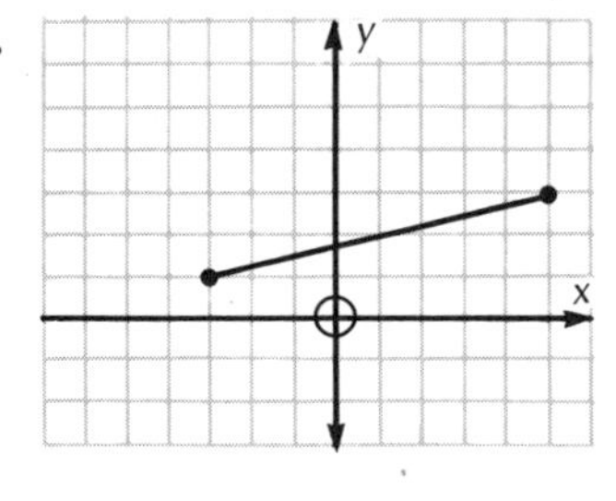

b.

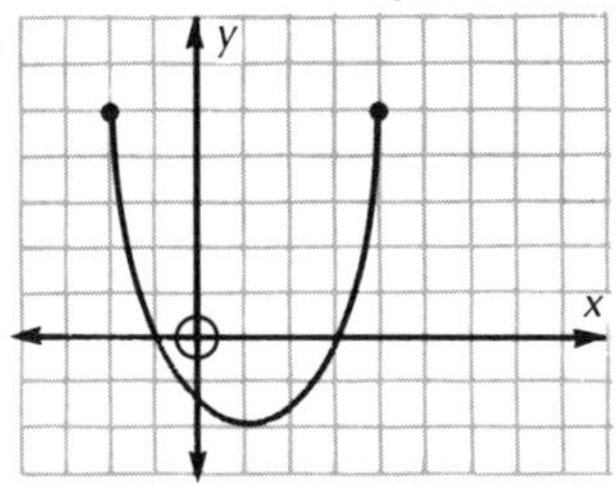

c.

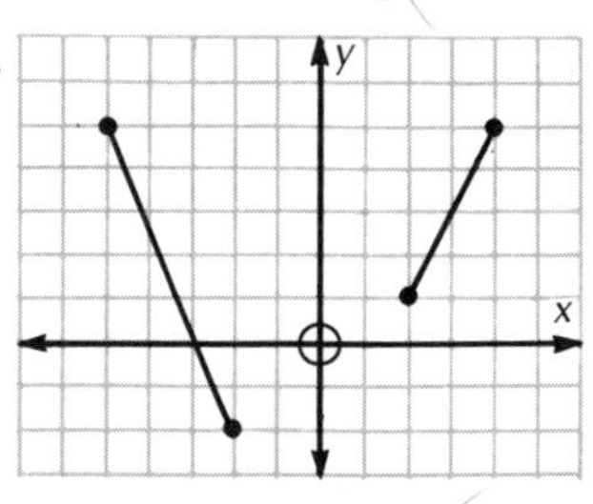

d.

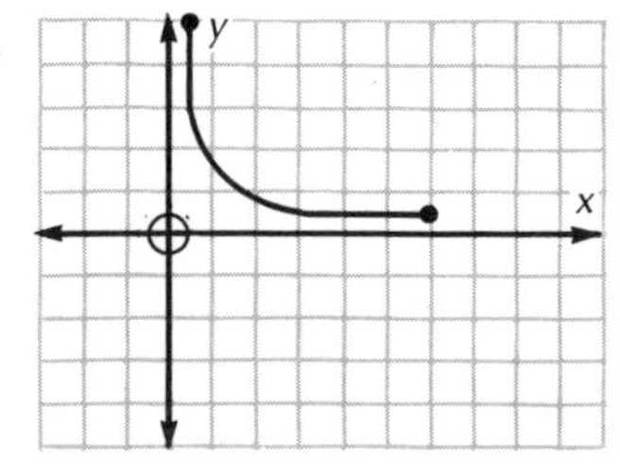

e.

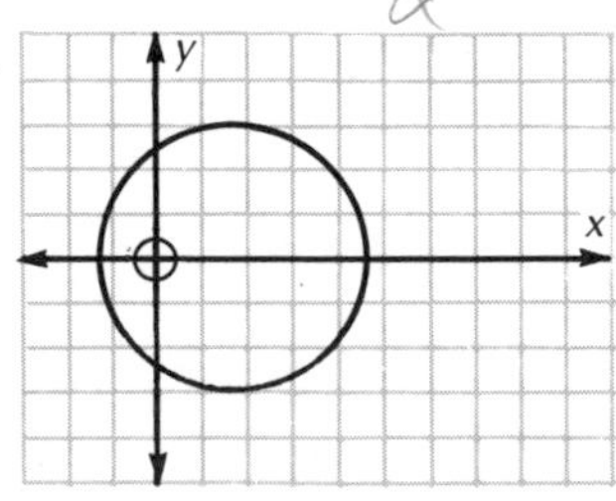

f.

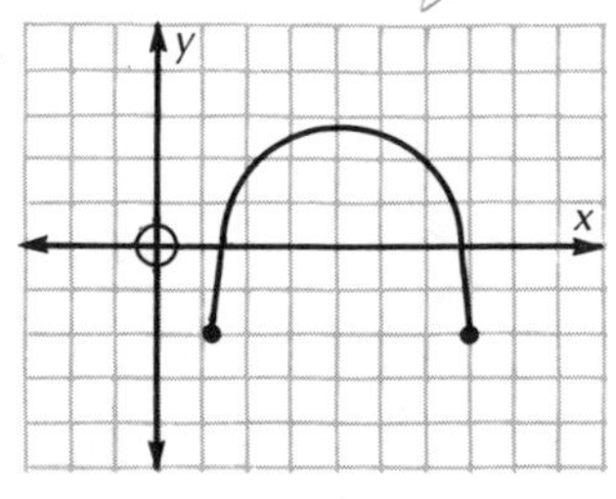

4. Evaluate each of the following, given that $g(x) = 2x^2 + 1$, $h(x) = \sqrt{x + 5}$, and $r(x) = \dfrac{6}{x - 3}$.

a. $g(5)$ **b.** $h(4)$ **c.** $h(-1)$ **d.** $r(2)$

e. $g(-3)$ **f.** $r(-1)$ **g.** $h(-5)$ **h.** $h(0)$

5. A function f is defined by the equation $y = 3x + 1$. Each given ordered pair is a member of f. Find the value of x and y.

a. $(3, y)$ **b.** $(-1, y)$ **c.** $(x, 7)$ **d.** $(x, -5)$

e. $(4, y)$ **f.** $(x, -8)$ **g.** $(x, 1)$ **h.** $(x, 0)$

B 6. Determine the domain and range of the function defined by each graph.

a.

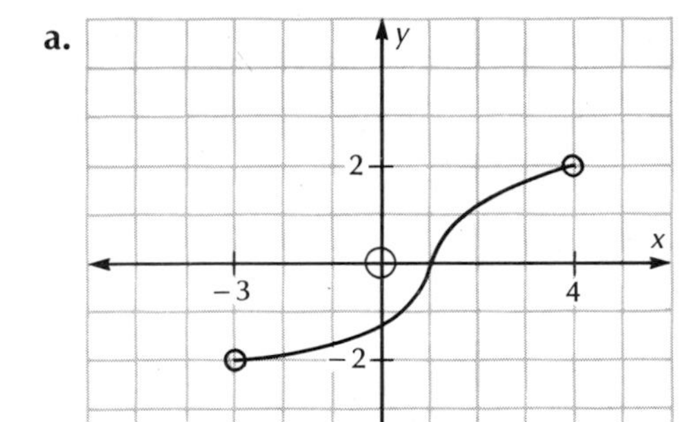

b.

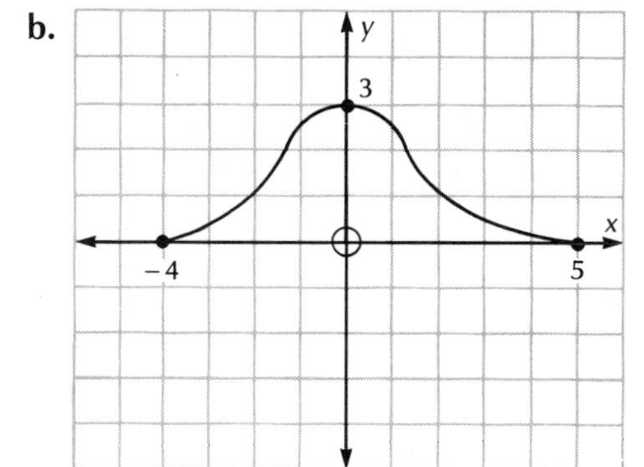

c.

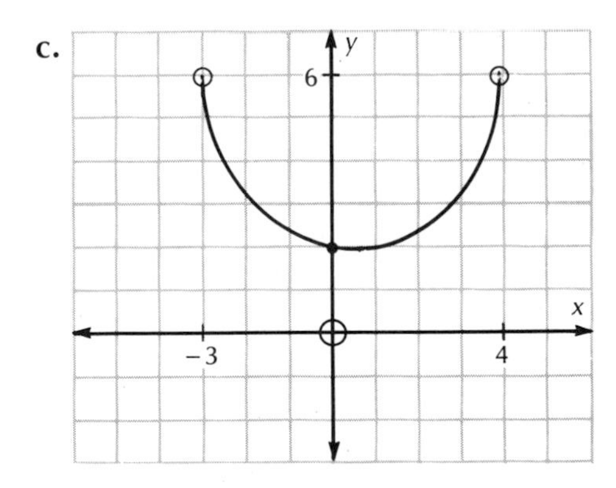

d.

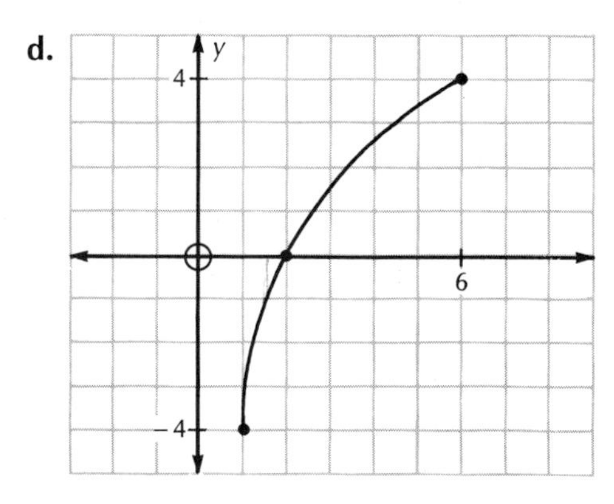

7. A function and its domain are given. Find the range of each function.

a. $f(x) = 3x + 5$, $D(f) = \{-1, 0, 1, 2\}$

b. $g(x) = x^2 - 2$, $D(g) = \{-2, -1, 0, 1, 2\}$

c. $h(x) = \dfrac{6}{x}$, $D(h) = \{1, 2, 3, 4\}$

d. $p(x) = \sqrt{x^2 - 1}$, $D(p) = \{x \in \mathbf{R} \mid 1 \le x \le 3\}$

8. Find the domain and range of the function defined by each equation. ($x, y \in \mathbf{R}$)

a. $y = x^2 - 5$ b. $y = 2x - 3$ c. $y = \frac{1}{x}$

d. $y = \sqrt{2x - 6}$ e. $y = \frac{2}{x - 1}$ f. $y = \frac{3x}{2}$

g. $y = \sqrt{x}$ h. $y = \sqrt{x + 3}$ i. $y = \frac{3x - 5}{4 - 2x}$

j. $y = x^2 + 2x + 1$ k. $y = -\sqrt{4 - 2x}$ l. $y = \sqrt{4 - x^2}$

9. If $g(x) = x^2 - 1$, find an expression for each of the following.

a. $g(2x)$ b. $g(x^2)$ c. $g\left(\frac{x}{2}\right)$

d. $g(x + 1)$ e. $g(-k)$ f. $g(2 - m)$

10. a. If $g(x) = \frac{x + 6}{2}$ and $g(k) = 0$, find the value of k.

b. If $g(x) = x^2 - 2x + 1$ and $g(n) = 0$, find the value of n.

c. If $f: x \rightarrow 3x - 5$ and $f(a) = 10$, find the value of a.

11. Graph the relation defined by each given equation and determine which is a function.

a. $y = x^2 - 3$ b. $3x - 4y = 12$ c. $x^2 + y^2 = 25$

d. $xy = 16$ e. $2x^2 + 2y^2 = 50$ f. $y = \frac{12}{x}$

12. Wages are often calculated as a function of time. Write an equation that represents each situation.

a. Sandy's hourly wage is $5.72. What are her gross earnings, E, for h hours worked?

b. A plumber charges a base fee of $37.50 plus $27.50/h. What will be the charge to repair restaurant appliances if it will take n hours to complete the work?

C 13. • Graph the relation defined by each equation, where $x, y \in \mathbf{R}$.

• Find the domain and range of each relation.

• Determine which is a function.

a. $y = x^2 + 1, -1 \leq x \leq 4$ b. $x^2 + y^2 = 25, x \geq 3$

14. A parking lot charges $2/h or any portion thereof for parking.

a. Graph the parking charges from 08:00 to 18:00.

b. The graph in part **a** is called a **step function**. Give a reason for this name.

15. **a.** The cost of renting a power saw is \$2.50/h or portion thereof, plus a \$5.00 maintenance fee. Draw a graph that shows the cost of renting the saw for a period of one hour to eight hours.

 b. An electronics company pays their sales representatives a salary plus a bonus. Each representative receives a salary of \$1500 per month plus \$500 bonus for each \$50 000 worth of merchandise sold in excess of \$100 000. Graph the total pay each representative earns for sales from \$0 to \$1 000 000.

16. Determine an equation that is satisfied by the members of each given set.

 a. $\{(0, 1), (-2, -3), (3, 7), (1, 3)\}$
 b. $\{(1, -1), (3, 7), (2, 2), (-2, 2)\}$
 c. $\{(-1, -8), (2, 4), (4, 2), (8, 1)\}$
 d. $\{(0, 0), (4, 20), (2, 6), (-1, 0)\}$

17. Find the domain and range of the function defined by each given equation, where $x, y \in \mathbf{R}$.

 a. $y = \dfrac{x}{x - 1}$ **b.** $y = \dfrac{x - 1}{x}$ **c.** $y = \dfrac{x - 1}{x^2}$

Biography

Radio Astronomer John Lambourne Locke

John Lambourne Locke was the first director of the National Research Council's Herzberg Institute of Astrophysics. He was born in Brantford, Ontario on May 1, 1921. After service in the Royal Canadian Navy during World War I, Locke graduated from the University of Toronto in 1946 and went on to receive his doctorate in 1949.

He has held a number of posts, including that of chief of the stellar physics division at the Dominion Observatory in Ottawa, officer in charge of the Dominion Radio Astrophysical Observatory near Penticton, BC, and radio astronomer at the National Research Council.

In 1967, Locke was a member of a Canadian team that took simultaneous observations from radio telescopes thousands of kilometres apart and combined them to produce a more accurate understanding of distant radio sources in space. The process was very complex, but essentially involved adding and subtracting functions. As a result of their work, the team was awarded the Rumford Premium from the American Academy of Arts and Sciences.

1-2 Transformation of Functions— Stretches and Reflections

The equation of a function changes in predictable ways when the graph of the function is transformed by stretching or reflecting.

EXAMPLE 1: Compare the graphs of $y = f(x)$ and $\frac{y}{2} = f(x)$, for $f(x) = x^2 + 2x$.

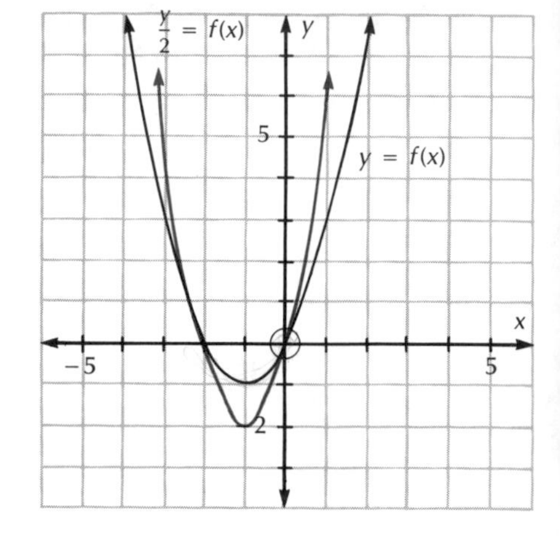

Since $\frac{y}{2} = f(x)$, then $\frac{y}{2} = x^2 + 2x$.

That is, $y = 2(x^2 + 2x)$.

Graph both functions on the same set of axes.

When y is replaced by $\frac{y}{2}$, the graph of $y = f(x)$ is stretched vertically by a factor of 2.
Notice that $(x, y) \rightarrow (x, 2y)$.

EXAMPLE 2: **a.** Compare the graphs of $y = f(x)$ and $y = f(3x)$, for $f(x) = x^2 + 2x$.

Since
$$y = f(x) = x^2 + 2x, \text{ then}$$
$$y = f(3x) = (3x)^2 + 2(3x), \text{ or}$$
$$y = f(3x) = 9x^2 + 6x.$$

The graph of $y = f(x)$ is "compressed" along the x-axis by a factor of 3, or stretched horizontally by a factor of $\frac{1}{3}$.

Notice that $(x, y) \rightarrow (3x, y)$.

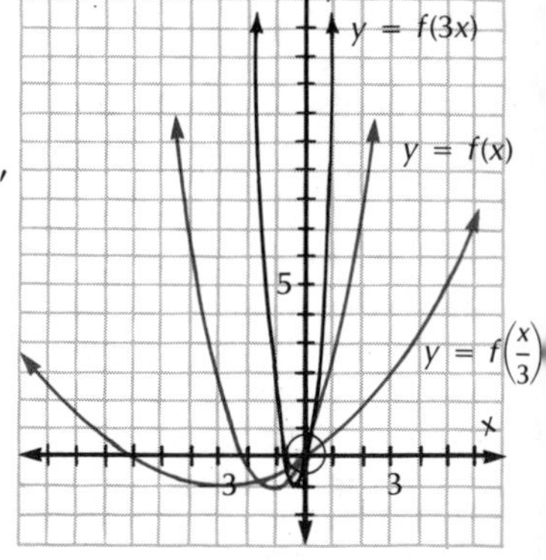

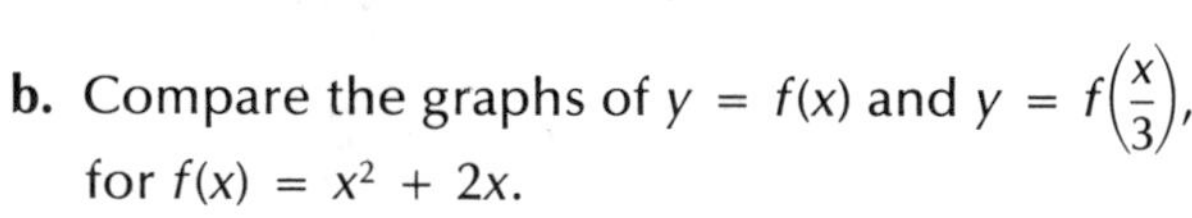

b. Compare the graphs of $y = f(x)$ and $y = f\left(\frac{x}{3}\right)$, for $f(x) = x^2 + 2x$.

Since $y = f(x) = x^2 + 2x$,
then
$$y = f\left(\frac{x}{3}\right) = \left(\frac{x}{3}\right)^2 + 2\left(\frac{x}{3}\right),$$
or
$$y = f\left(\frac{x}{3}\right) = \frac{1}{9}x^2 + \frac{2}{3}x.$$

When x is replaced by $\frac{x}{3}$, the graph is stretched horizontally by a factor of 3 along the x-axis.
Notice that $(x, y) \rightarrow \left(\frac{x}{3}, y\right)$.

SUMMARY

Vertical stretch by a factor of k: $(x, y) \to (x, ky)$ $y = f(x) \to y = kf(x)$

Horizontal stretch by factor of m: $(x, y) \to (mx, y)$ $y = f(x) \to y = f\left(\frac{x}{m}\right)$

EXAMPLE 3: Compare the graphs of $y = f(x)$ and $y = -f(x)$, for $f(x) = x^2 + 2x$.

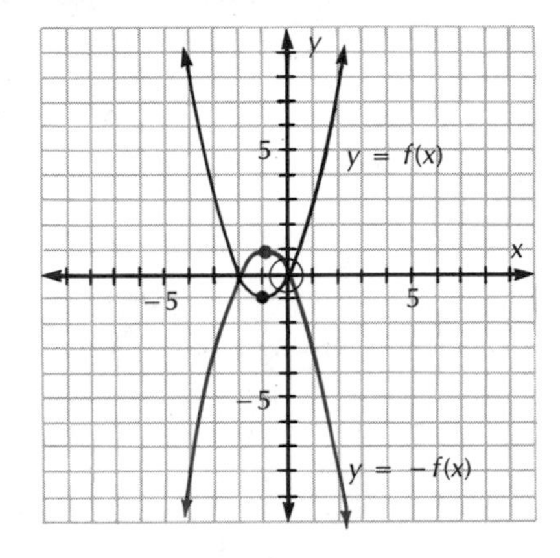

First, notice that $-f(x) = -(x^2 + 2x)$. That is, $-f(x) = -x^2 - 2x$.

Graph both functions.

The x-coordinates of each point on the graph remain unchanged, but the y-coordinates change sign.

Notice that $(x, y) \to (x, -y)$.

It appears that the graph of $y = -f(x)$ is a reflection of the graph of $y = f(x)$ in the x-axis.

EXAMPLE 4: Compare the graphs of $y = f(x)$ and $y = f(-x)$, for $f(x) = x^2 + 2x$.

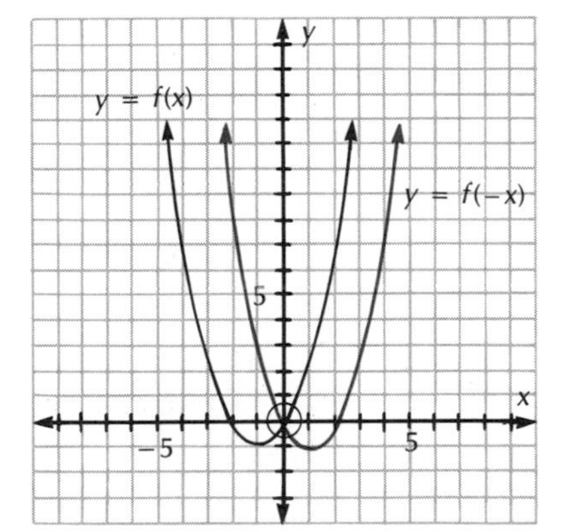

To find an expression for $f(-x)$, replace each occurrence of x in the original function with $-x$.

$f(-x) = (-x)^2 + 2(-x)$, or

$f(-x) = x^2 - 2x$

Graph both functions.

Notice that $(x, y) \to (-x, y)$.

It appears that the graph of $y = f(-x)$ is a reflection of the graph of $y = f(x)$ in the y-axis.

SUMMARY

Reflection in the x-axis: $(x, y) \to (x, -y)$ $y = f(x) \to y = -f(x)$

Reflection in the y-axis: $(x, y) \to (-x, y)$ $y = f(x) \to y = f(-x)$

EXAMPLE 5: The graph of $y = f(x) = x^3 - 3x - 2$ is shown below, along with its image under transformations. Find an equation of the image.

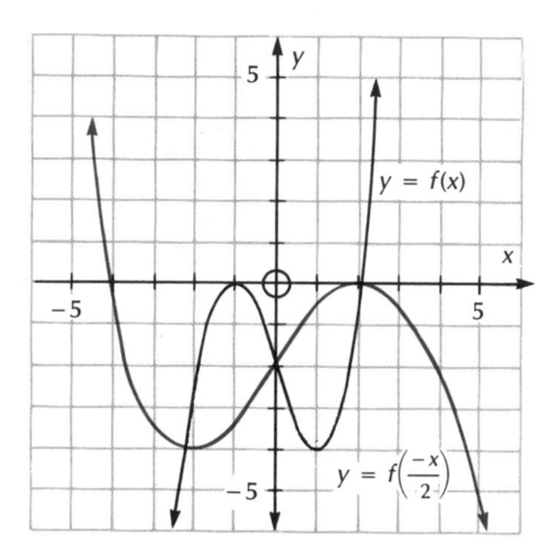

It appears that the graph of $y = f(x)$ has been reflected in the y-axis and then stretched horizontally by a factor of 2.

The new equation is determined as follows.

- Reflect the graph of $y = f(x)$ in the y-axis.

  $y = f(x) \rightarrow y = f(-x)$

- Stretch the graph of $y = f(-x)$ horizontally by a factor of 2.

  $y = f(-x) \rightarrow y = f\left(\frac{-x}{2}\right)$

Therefore, an equation of the image is given as follows.

$$y = f\left(\frac{-x}{2}\right)$$

$$y = \left(\frac{-x}{2}\right)^3 - 3\left(\frac{-x}{2}\right) - 2$$

EXAMPLE 6: The graph of $y = x^3 - 3x - 2$ is shown. Use transformations to sketch the graph of $y = -\frac{1}{2}x^3 + \frac{3}{2}x + 1$.

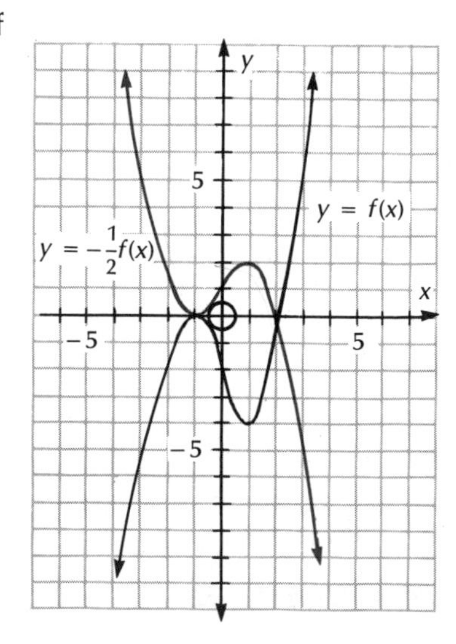

The new graph is an image of the graph of $y = x^3 - 3x - 2$ under a reflection in the x-axis and a vertical stretch by a factor of $\frac{1}{2}$.

The new function is $y = -\frac{1}{2}f(x)$.

Therefore, to sketch the graph of the image, reflect the graph of $y = f(x)$ in the x-axis and stretch it vertically by a factor of $\frac{1}{2}$.

XERCISE 1-2

1. Identify the transformations that have been applied to each graph to produce its image.

a.

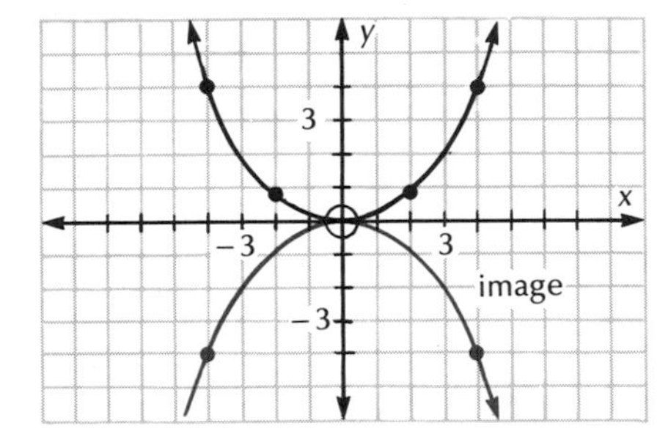

b.

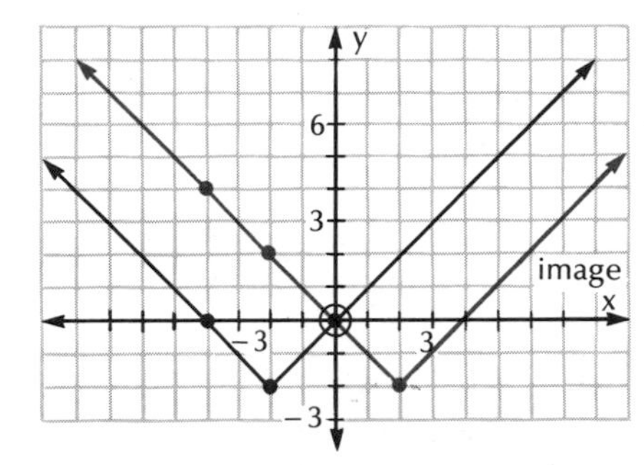

c.

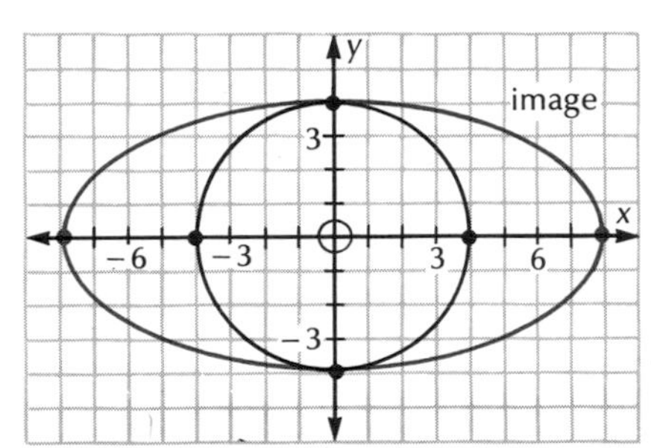

d.

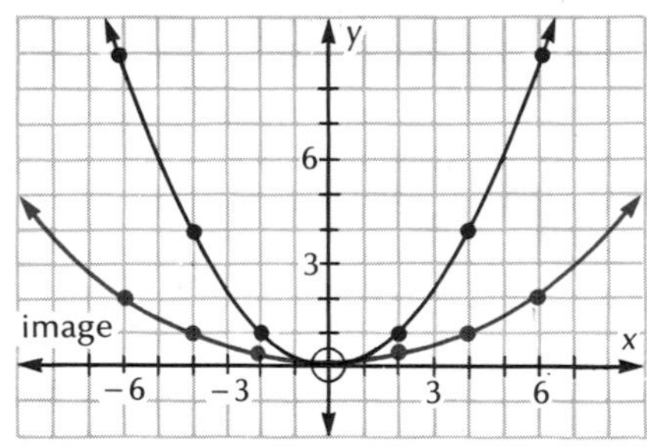

2. Copy each graph. Perform the indicated transformation to sketch a new graph.

a. Reflect in the y-axis.

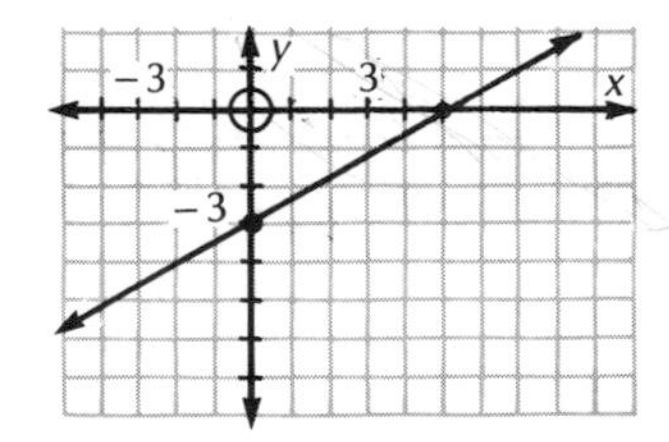

b. Reflect in the x-axis.

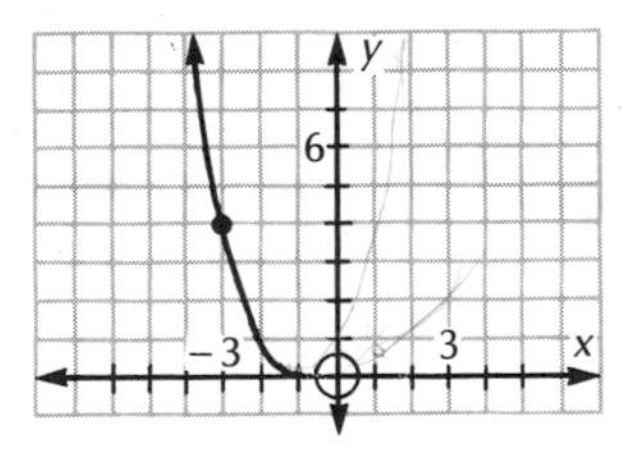

c. Stretch horizontally by a factor of 2.

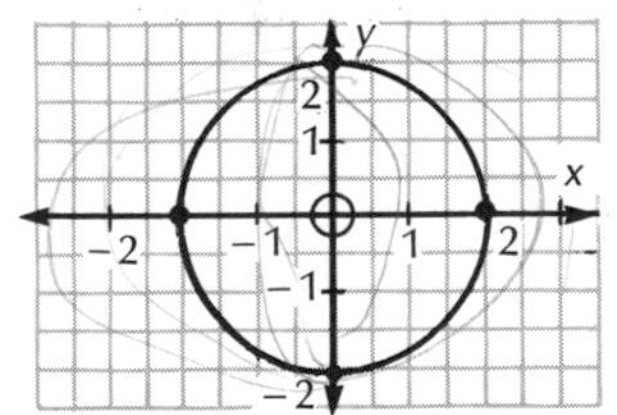

d. Stretch vertically by a factor of 3.

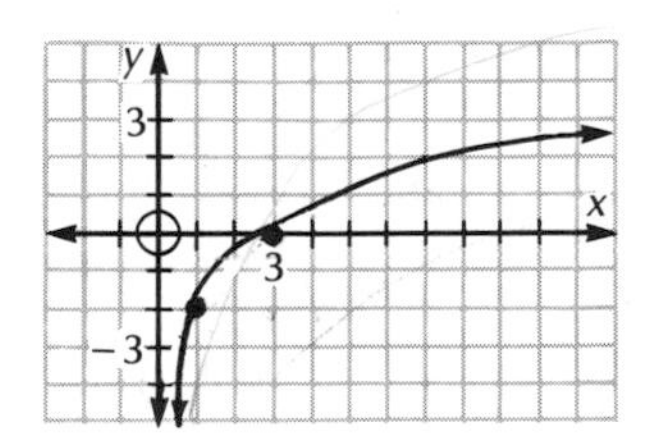

e. Stretch horizontally by a factor of $\frac{1}{2}$.

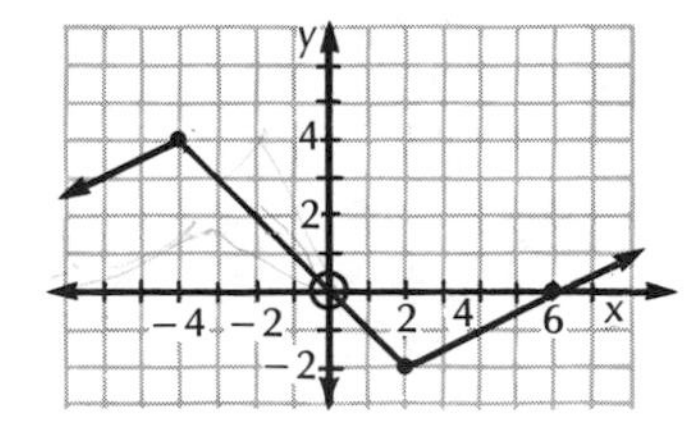

f. Stretch vertically by a factor of $\frac{1}{2}$.

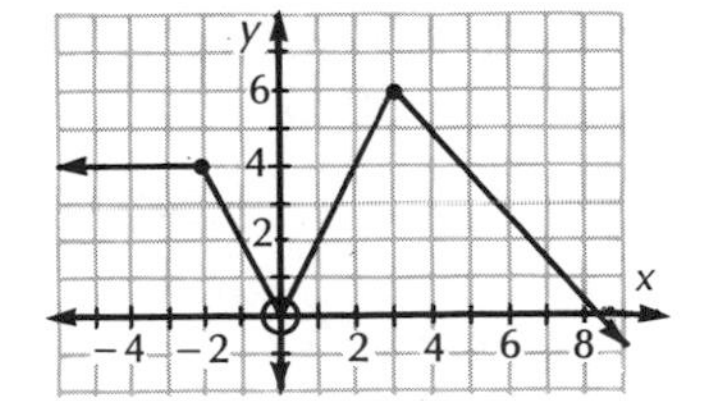

3. The graph of each given equation is transformed as indicated. Find an equation of each transformed graph.

a. $y = x^2$ Reflected in the x-axis
b. $y = x$ Stretched vertically by a factor of 3
c. $y = \frac{1}{x}$ Reflected in the y-axis
d. $y = 5x - 1$ Stretched horizontally by a factor of 3
e. $y = 2 - x$ Stretched horizontally by a factor of $\frac{2}{5}$

B 4. In each case, the graph of an equation and its image under transformation is given. Determine an equation of each image.

a.

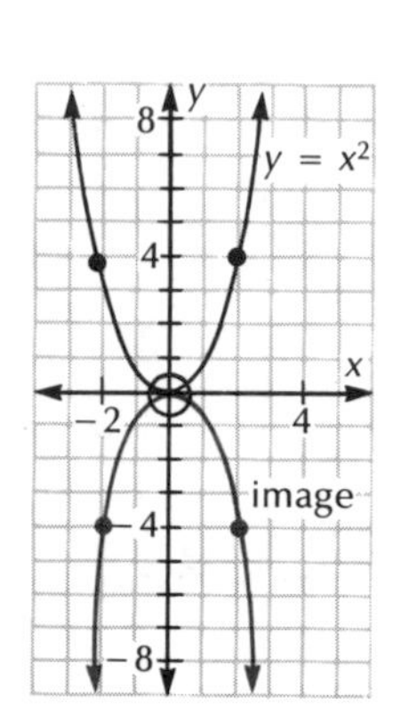

b.

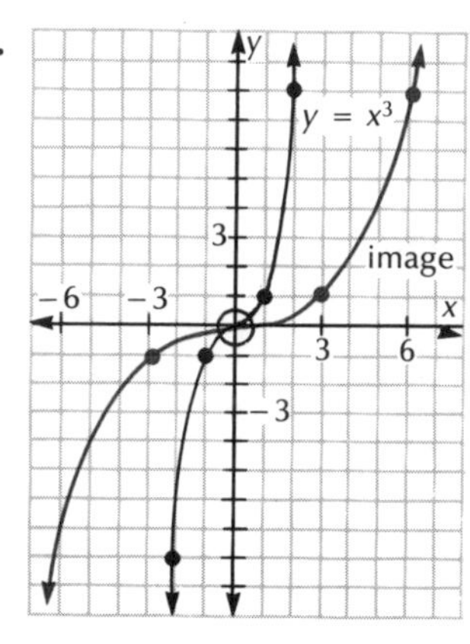

c.

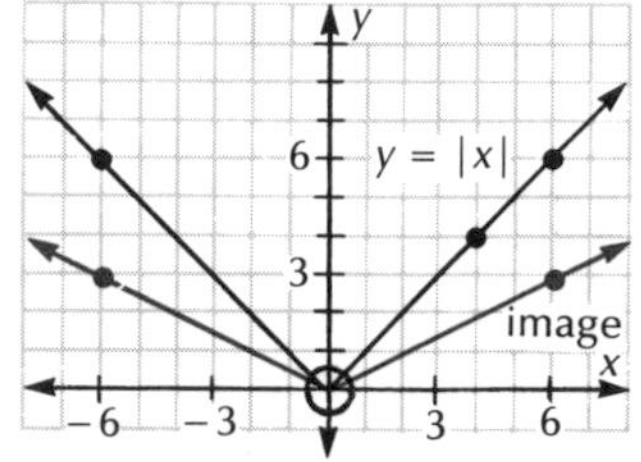

d.

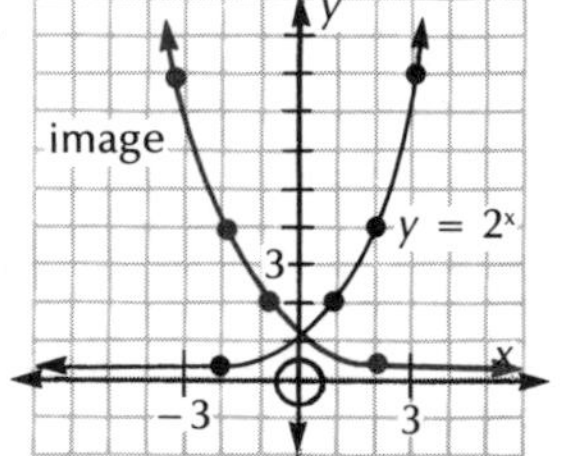

5. The graph $y = x - 5$ is given below. Use transformations to sketch the graph of each given equation.

a. $y = -x + 5$
b. $y = -x - 5$
c. $y = 3(x - 5)$
d. $y = \frac{x}{2} - 5$

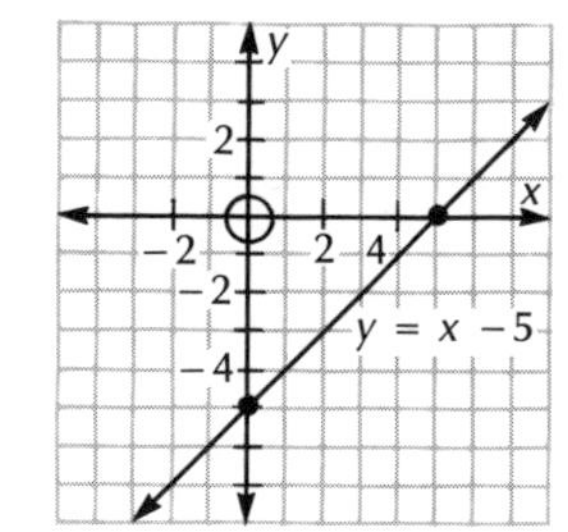

6. The graph of $y = f(x)$ is given below. Each given equation is a transformation of $y = f(x)$. Describe the transformation in words and then sketch each graph.

a. $y = f(-x)$
b. $y = f(2x)$
c. $y = 3f(x)$
d. $y = -f(x)$
e. $y = f\left(\frac{x}{3}\right)$
f. $y = \frac{2}{3}x - 2$
g. $y = -f\left(\frac{x}{2}\right)$
h. $y = -f(-x)$

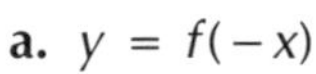

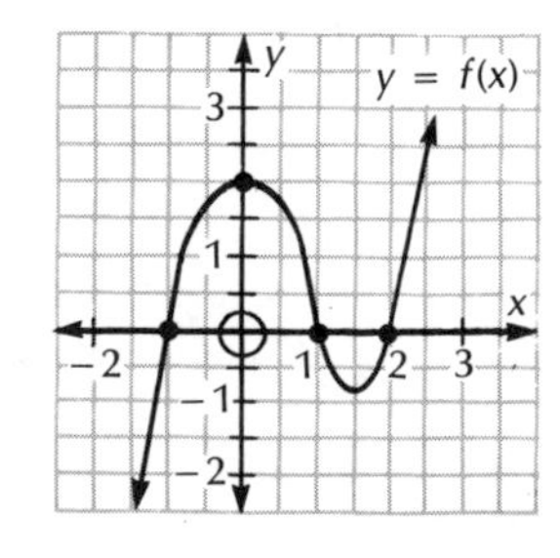

7. The equation of a function and its transformation image are given. Describe each transformation.

a. $y = x \rightarrow y = -x$

b. $y = x^2 \rightarrow y = \frac{1}{2}x^2$

c. $y = \frac{1}{x} \rightarrow y = \frac{-2}{x}$

d. $y = \sqrt{x} \rightarrow y = 3\sqrt{-x}$

e. $y = (x + 1)^2 \rightarrow y = \frac{(-x + 1)^2}{2}$

f. $y = x^3 \rightarrow y = -2(-x)^3$

C 8. Each given ordered pair defines a function. The graph of each function is transformed as indicated. Determine the function defined by each transformed graph and write it as a set of ordered pairs.

a. $\{(0, 5), (-1, 3), (2, 7), (3, 5)\}$ — Reflected in the x-axis and stretched horizontally by a factor of 3

b. $\{(-1, 3), (0, -5), (3, 1), (5, 6)\}$ — Reflected in the x-axis and reflected in the y-axis

c. $\{(7, 3), (5, 0), (3, -2), (1, -6)\}$ — Stretched horizontally by a factor of 2 and stretched vertically by a factor of $\frac{1}{2}$

d. $\{(-2, 5), (-1, 2), (0, 3), (2, 5)\}$ — Stretched horizontally by a factor of 5 and reflected in the y-axis

e. $\{(0, -5), (-2, 6), (4, 0), (-6, 1)\}$ — Stretched vertically by a factor of 3 and reflected in the y-axis

9. The point P is reflected in the point R. Label the image point I. The points P, R, and I are collinear and the distances PR and IR are equal, as shown in the diagram. Find the image of each of the following after reflection.

a. $P = (3, 5); R = (4, 1)$

b. $P = (-2, 1); R = (0, 3)$

c. $P = (-5, -1); R = (2, -2)$

d. $P = (0, 3); R = (-1, 0)$

e. $P = (-2, 3); R = (3, -1)$

f. $P = (4, 3); R = (4, -2)$

10. Show that the reflection of a graph through the origin is equivalent to a reflection in the y-axis followed by a reflection in the x-axis.

Historical Note

Leonardo da Vinci and Reflections

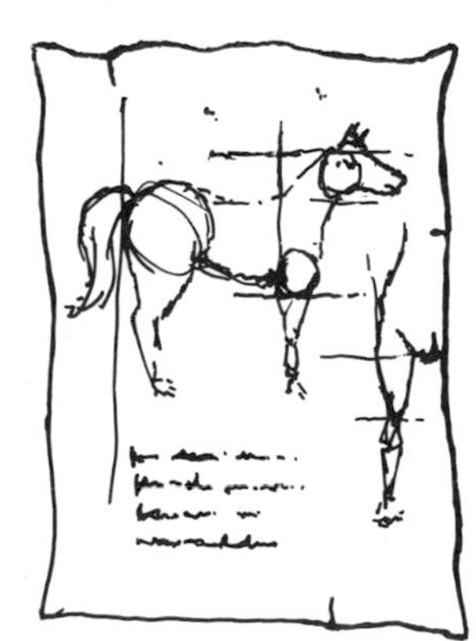

There have been many fascinating uses of symmetry and reflections throughout history. Leonardo da Vinci, a great thinker and inventor, wrote his notebooks in Latin, as did many scholars of his time. However, Leonardo also wrote notes backwards. Such notes can be read by reflecting them in a mirror.

1. Which letters of the alphabet are mirror images of themselves?
2. Identify any words that you know that are mirror images of themselves.
3. Identify uses of reflection in daily life.

1-3 Transformations of Functions—Translations

A **translation** can be represented by a slide of a real object. Under a translation, a graph can slide horizontally or vertically. The equation of a translated graph is a modification of the original equation.

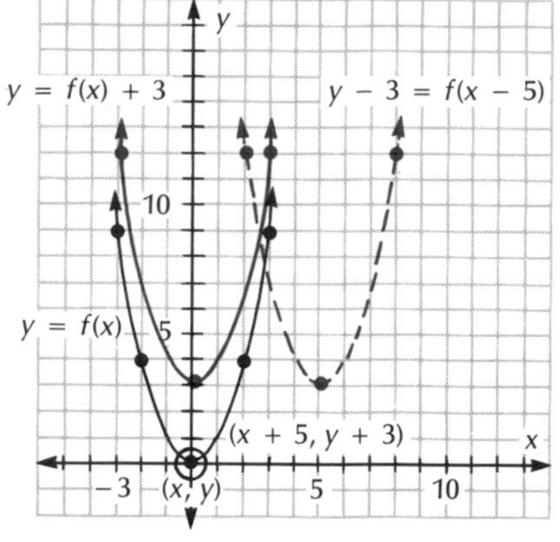

The graph of $y = f(x) = x^2$ is shown at the right. If the graph is translated 3 units up, parallel to the y-axis, then each y-coordinate is increased by 3.

That is, $(x, y) \to (x, y + 3)$.

If the new graph is then translated 5 units to the right, parallel to the x-axis, then each x-coordinate is increased by 5.

That is, $(x, y) \to (x + 5, y + 3)$.

Translations such as these can be represented in the equations of functions.

SUMMARY

- Translation parallel to the x-axis by a units: $(x, y) \to (x + a, y)$ $\quad y = f(x) \to y = f(x - a)$
- Translation parallel to the y-axis by b units: $(x, y) \to (x, y + b)$ $\quad y = f(x) \to y - b = f(x)$ or $y = f(x) + b$

Notice the opposite signs.

EXAMPLE 1: The graph of $y = x^2 - 1$ is given along with its image after two translations. Find an equation of the image.

Consider the image of the point $(0, -1)$.
The point $(0, -1)$ maps onto $(-3, 1)$ under a pair of translations:

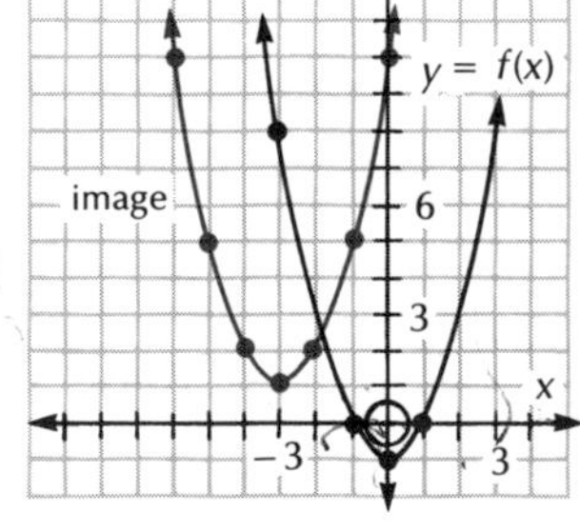

- a vertical translation $(0, -1) \to (0, 1)$ and
- a horizontal translation $(0, 1) \to (-3, 1)$.

For $(0, -1) \to (0, 1)$, the graph is translated parallel to the y-axis, 2 units in the positive direction (up).

$$y = f(x) \quad \to y = f(x) + 2$$
$$y = x^2 - 1 \to y = (x^2 - 1) + 2$$
$$y = x^2 + 1$$

For $(0, 1) \to (-3, 1)$, the graph is translated parallel to the x-axis, 3 units in the negative direction (to the left).

$$y = f(x) \quad \to \quad y = f(x - (-3))$$
$$y = x^2 + 1 \to \quad y = (x + 3)^2 + 1$$
$$y = x^2 + 6x + 10$$

Therefore, an equation of the image is $y = x^2 + 6x + 10$.

EXAMPLE 2: The image of the graph of $y = x^2$ is defined by
$\frac{y}{2} = (x - 3)^2$.
What transformations were applied to the graph of $y = x^2$ to produce the image?

Compare the form of the two equations.

$$y = x^2 \qquad \frac{y}{2} = (x - 3)^2$$

This indicates a vertical stretch by a factor of 2.

This indicates a horizontal translation, 3 units to the right.

Therefore, the graph of $y = x^2$ was stretched vertically by a factor of 2 and translated horizontally, 3 units to the right.

EXAMPLE 3: Apply the following translations, in sequence, to the graph of $y = \sqrt{x}$ and determine an equation of the resulting graph.

- First, stretch horizontally by a factor of $\frac{1}{2}$.
- Then, reflect in the y-axis.
- Finally, translate 5 units to the left, parallel to the x-axis.

Treat each transformation separately.

- First, stretch the graph of $y = \sqrt{x}$ horizontally by a factor of $\frac{1}{2}$.

$$y = f(x) \rightarrow y = f\left(\frac{x}{\frac{1}{2}}\right)$$

$$y = \sqrt{x} \rightarrow y = \sqrt{\frac{x}{\frac{1}{2}}}$$

$$y = \sqrt{x} \rightarrow y = \sqrt{2x}$$

- Next, reflect the graph of $y = \sqrt{2x}$ in the y-axis.

$$y = f(x) \rightarrow y = f(-x)$$
$$y = \sqrt{2x} \rightarrow y = \sqrt{-2x}$$

- Finally, translate the graph of $y = \sqrt{-2x}$ five units to the left, parallel to the x-axis.
  A translation of 5 units to the left is a translation of -5 units, parallel to the x-axis.

$$y = f(x) \rightarrow y = f(x - (-5)), \text{ or } y = f(x + 5)$$
$$y = \sqrt{-2x} \rightarrow y = \sqrt{-2(x+5)}$$

An equation of the final image is $y = \sqrt{-2(x + 5)}$.

EXERCISE 1-3

A 1. Determine what transformation has been applied to each graph to produce its image.

a. 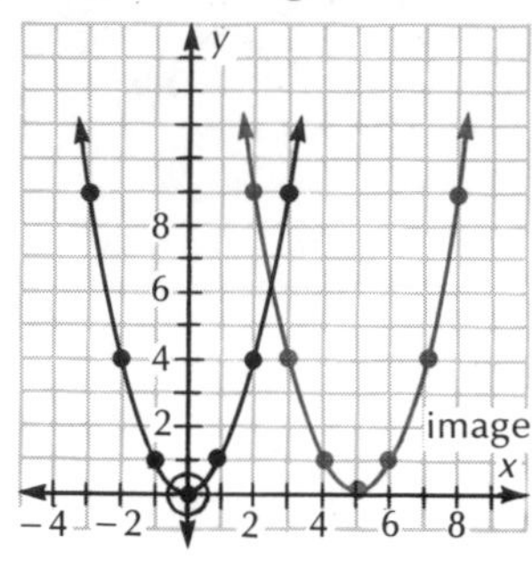

b. 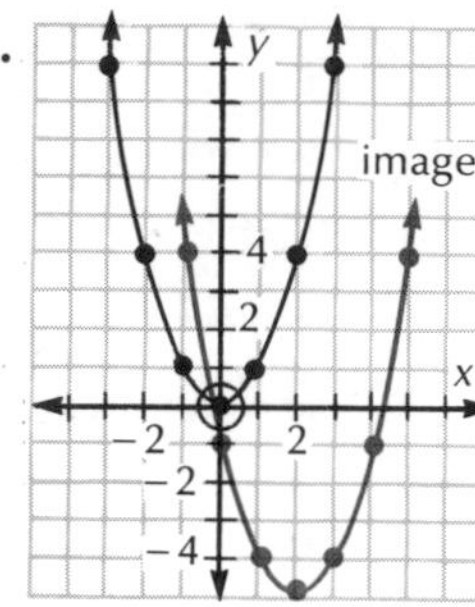

c. 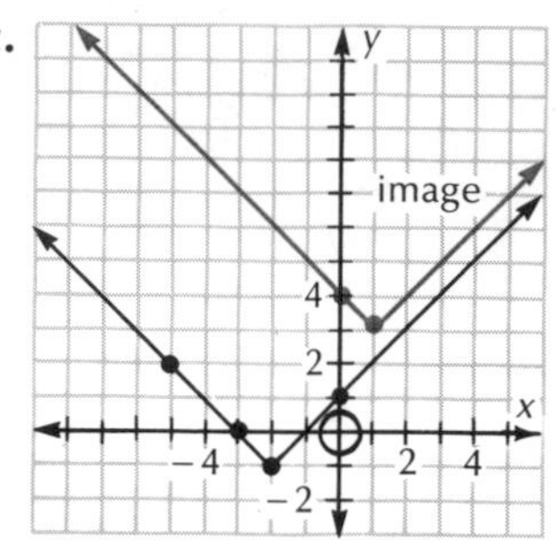

2. The graph of each given equation is transformed as indicated. Find an equation of each image.

a. $y = x^2$ — Translate 3 units to the right, parallel to the x-axis.
b. $y = 3x + 1$ — Reflect in the x-axis.
c. $y = x^3$ — Translate 3 units parallel to the x-axis and -2 units parallel to the y-axis.

3. Copy each graph and then sketch its image under the given transformations.

a. Translate -2 units parallel to the x-axis.

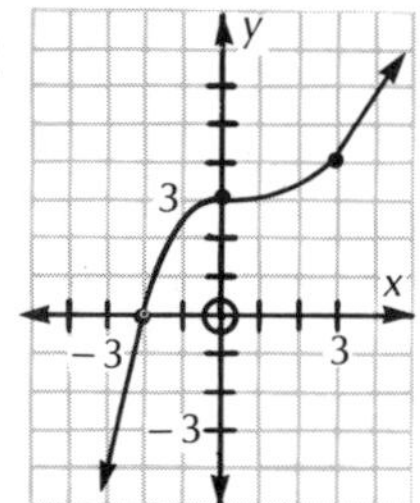

b. Translate 3 units parallel to the y-axis.

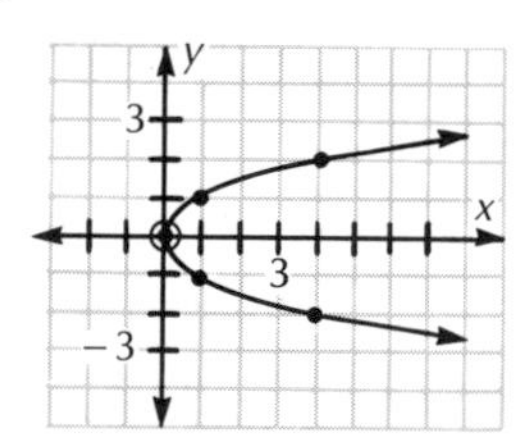

c. Translate -1 unit along the x-axis and -2 units along the y-axis.

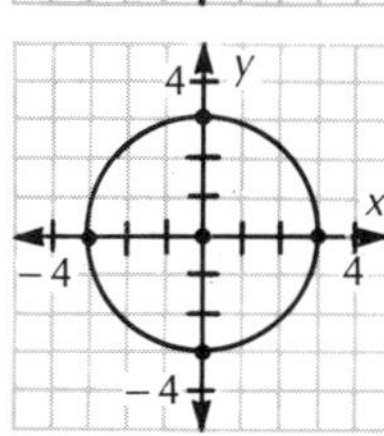

d. Reflect in the y-axis and translate -3 units along the x-axis.

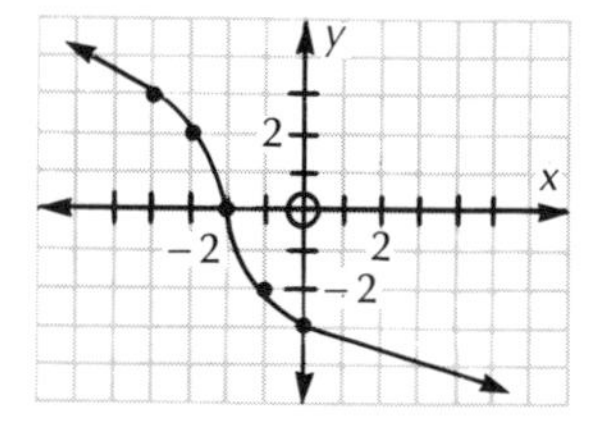

B 4. Given each equation, its graph, and its transformation image, write an equation of each image.

a. $y = x^2$

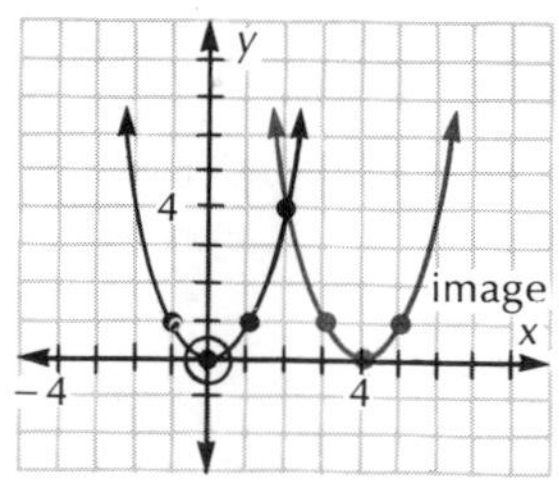

b. $y = x^2 + 2$

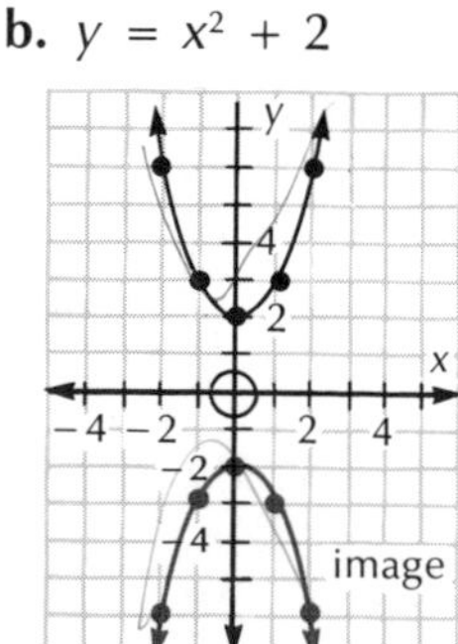

c. $y = \sqrt{x}$

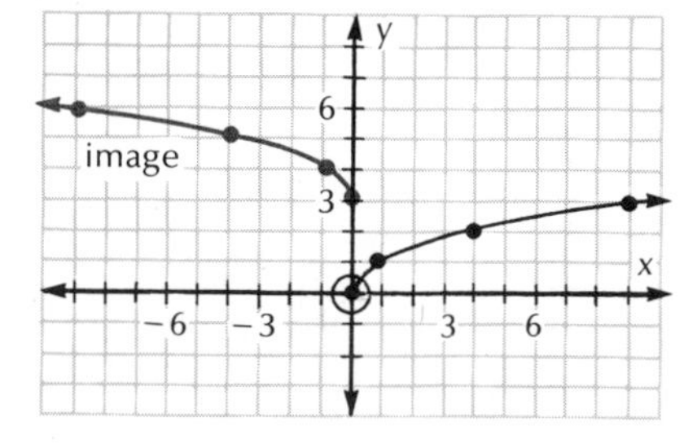

5. Each given equation represents a transformation of the graph of $y = f(x)$. Describe each transformation and then sketch each graph.

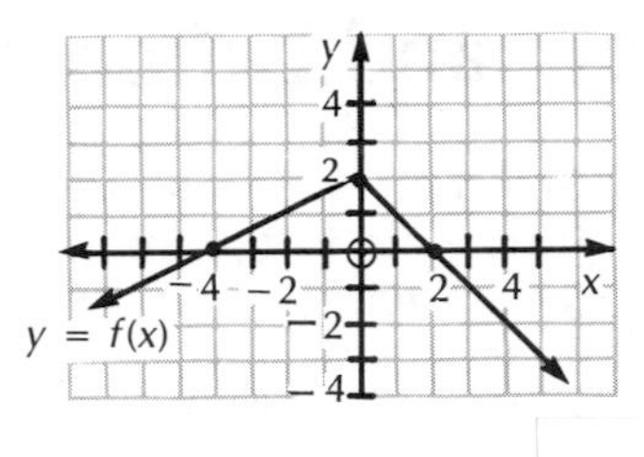

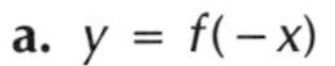

a. $y = f(-x)$ b. $y = f(x - 3)$

c. $y + 3 = f(x)$ d. $\frac{y}{2} = -f(x)$

e. $y = 3f(x)$ f. $y - 3 = f(x + 1)$

g. $y = -f\left(\frac{x}{2}\right)$ h. $y = -f(-x)$

6. Describe the transformations that map the graph of the first equation onto the second.

a. $y = x \rightarrow y = 3x - 2$ b. $y = x^2 \rightarrow y + 3 = (x - 1)^2$

c. $y = \sqrt{x} \rightarrow \frac{y}{4} = \sqrt{x - 1}$ d. $y = \frac{1}{x} \rightarrow y = \frac{1}{2x} + 1$

e. $y = x \rightarrow y = -x + 1$ f. $y = x^3 \rightarrow y = 2x^3 - 3$

g. $y = \sqrt{x} \rightarrow y = 5\sqrt{x - 1} + 2$ h. $y = x^3 \rightarrow y + 5 = (x - 2)^3$

7. The graph of each equation is transformed as indicated. Give an equation of the image under transformation.

a. $y = x^2$ Stretched horizontally by a factor of 2 and then translated vertically +3 units

b. $y = \frac{1}{x}$ Stretched vertically by a factor of $\frac{1}{2}$ and then translated along the x-axis by −1 unit

c. $y = 3x - 2$ Reflected in the x-axis and translated 3 units up the y-axis

d. $y = x + 5$ Reflected in the x-axis and stretched vertically by a factor of $\frac{1}{2}$

e. $y = x^2 - 3$ Stretched vertically by a factor of 3 and then stretched horizontally by a factor of 2

f. $y = \frac{3}{x - 1}$ Translated parallel to the y-axis by a factor of −2 and stretched vertically by a factor of $\frac{1}{3}$

g. $2y = x^3 + 1$ Reflected in the x-axis and translated −1 unit parallel to the x-axis

8. What point is invariant (that is, remains unchanged or is its own image) under any stretch?

9. The graph of any linear equation is a transformation of the identity function I: $y = x$. Explain how to transform the graph of each equation *back* to the graph of the identity function.

a. $x - y = -2$ b. $5x - y = 2$ c. $2x + 5y = 8$

d. $y = -1.5x + 3$ e. $4x - y - 3 = 0$ f. $y = \frac{2}{3}x - 2$

10. Under what transformation is the graph of $y = x^2$ invariant?

11. The graph of the relation $R(x)$ is invariant under a reflection in the x-axis. Under what conditions could $R(x)$ be a function?

1-4 Sum and Difference of Functions

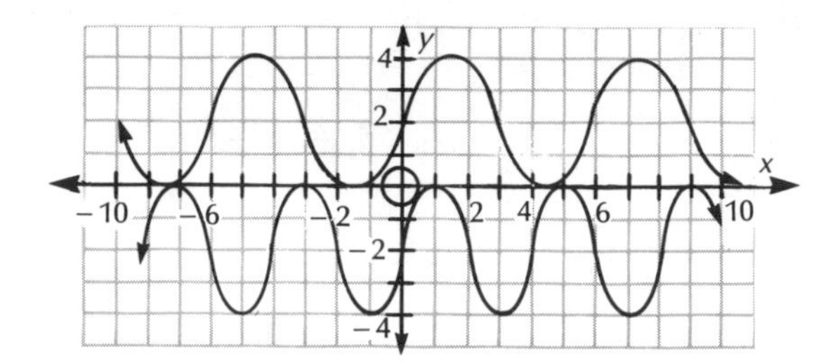

Musicians tune their instruments by comparing the sound to that of a standard note. If the instrument is slightly off tune, then a "beat" note will be heard. If there is no beat note, then the instrument is in tune with the standard note.

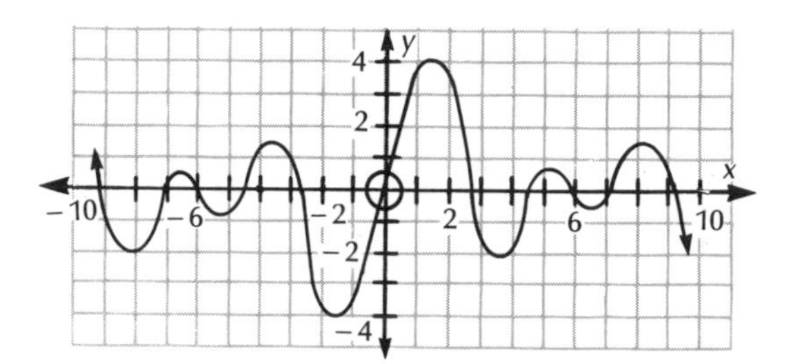

An oscilloscope shows the wave produced by sound. The standard note is shown in the top trace and the instrument's sound is shown in the bottom trace. The traces on the oscilloscope are graphs of amplitude (loudness), plotted on the *y*-axis, versus time, plotted on the *x*-axis.

The musician hears the combination of the two sound waves. The combined sound wave is the result of adding the *y*-coordinates of the traces at each instant. Note the shape of the combined wave.

The sum of two functions *f* and *g* can be easily found.

EXAMPLE 1: Four classmates participated in a two-day bike-a-thon. The distances (km) they cycled each day are given below as functions *f* and *g*.

$f = \{(\text{Kim}, 11), (\text{Jamal}, 10), (\text{Greta}, 9), (\text{Hannah}, 12)\}$ This represents day 1.
$g = \{(\text{Kim}, 17), (\text{Jamal}, 12), (\text{Greta}, 14), (\text{Hannah}, 7)\}$ This represents day 2.

Write the total distances cycled as a function.

The sum of the functions is found by adding the distances cycled by each person for both days.

$$f + g = \{(\text{Kim}, 11 + 17), (\text{Jamal}, 10 + 12), (\text{Greta}, 9 + 14), (\text{Hannah}, 12 + 7)\}$$
$$\therefore f + g = \{(\text{Kim}, 28), (\text{Jamal}, 22), (\text{Greta}, 23), (\text{Hannah}, 19)\}$$

> In general, for functions $f: x \to f(x)$ and $g: x \to g(x)$, the sum of *f* and *g* is given as follows.
>
> $f + g = \{x, f(x) + g(x)\}$, where $f(x) + g(x)$ is defined.

Note that $f(x)$ and $g(x)$ are defined if *x* is in the domain of *f* and *g*. Thus, $f(x) + g(x)$ is defined if *x* is in the domain of both *f* and *g*.

EXAMPLE 2: Given $f(x) = x^2$ and $g(x) = x - 2$, find a defining equation of $(f + g)$ and of $(f - g)$.

$$f + g = \{(x, f(x) + g(x)\}$$
$$= \{x, x^2 + x - 2\}$$

Therefore, a defining equation of $f + g$ is $y = x^2 + x - 2$.

$$f - g = \{(x, f(x) - g(x)\}$$
$$= \{x, x^2 - (x - 2)\}$$
$$= \{x, x^2 - x + 2\}$$

Therefore, a defining equation of $f - g$ is $y = x^2 - x + 2$.

EXAMPLE 3: Evaluate each of the following, given that $f(x) = 3x - 2$ and $g(x) = x^2$.

a. $f(3) + g(3)$

$$f(3) + g(3) = [3(3) - 2] + [3^2]$$
$$= (9 - 2) + 9$$
$$= 16$$

b. $f(2) - g(4)$

$$f(2) - g(4) = [3(2) - 2] - [4^2]$$
$$= (6 - 2) - 16$$
$$= -12$$

EXAMPLE 4: The graphs of functions f and g are given below. Graph $f - g$.

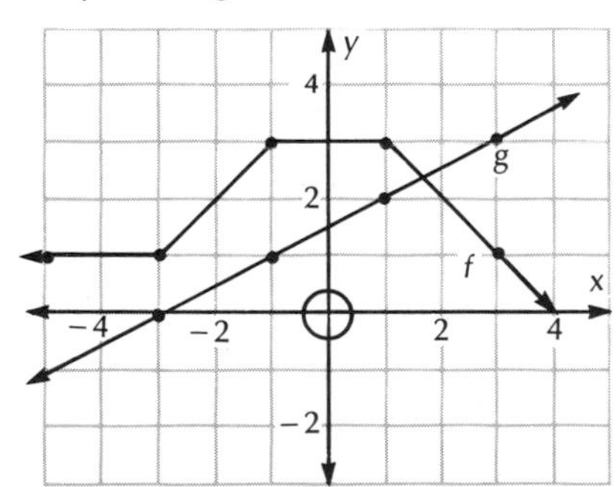

Identify several points of f and g from the graph. Use these points to find points of $f - g$. Then graph $f - g$.

x	f(x)	g(x)	f(x) − g(x)
−5	1	−1	2
−3	1	0	1
−1	3	1	2
1	3	2	1
3	1	3	−2

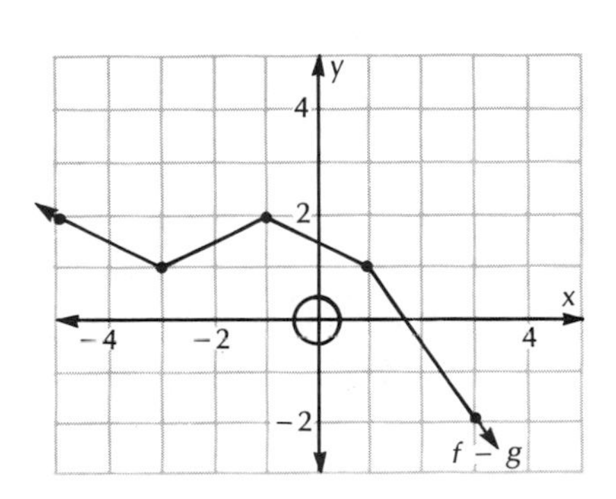

EXERCISE 1-4

A **1.** Given that $f(x) = 3x - 2$, $g(x) = x^2 + 3$, and $h(x) = \frac{1}{x}$, evaluate the following.

a. $f(3) + g(3)$ **b.** $f(0) - g(0)$ **c.** $f(2) + h(2)$
d. $f(1) - h(1)$ **e.** $g(-3) - f(-3)$ **f.** $h(-1) - g(-1)$
g. $f(-1) + h(-1)$ **h.** $f(3) + g(3) - h(3)$ **i.** $g(-2) + h(-2) - f(-2)$

2. In each case, the graph of a pair of functions is given. Copy each graph and sketch the graph of the indicated function.

a. Sketch the graph of $f + g$. **b.** Sketch the graph of $f - g$. **c.** Sketch the graph of $f +$

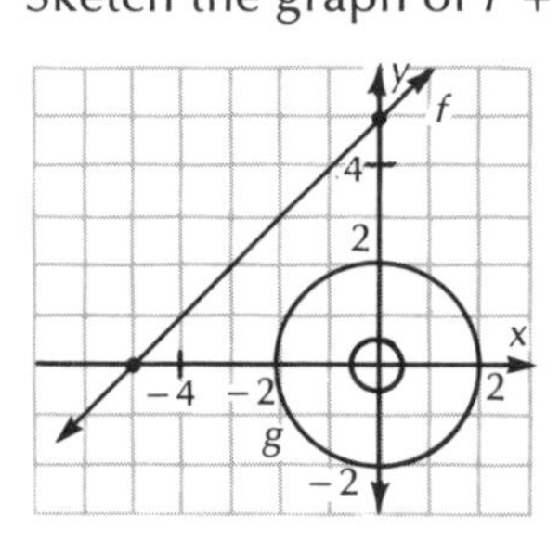

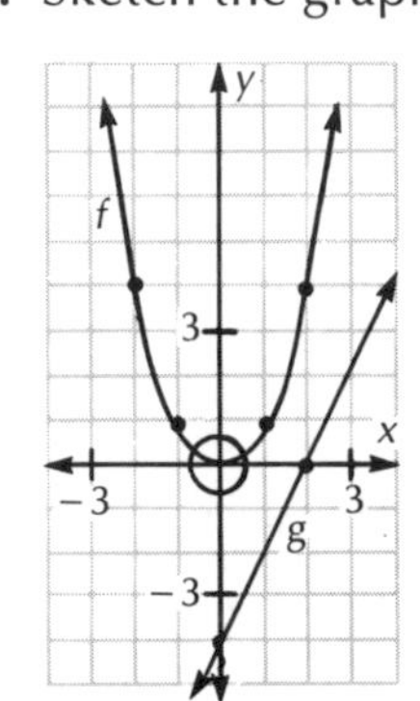

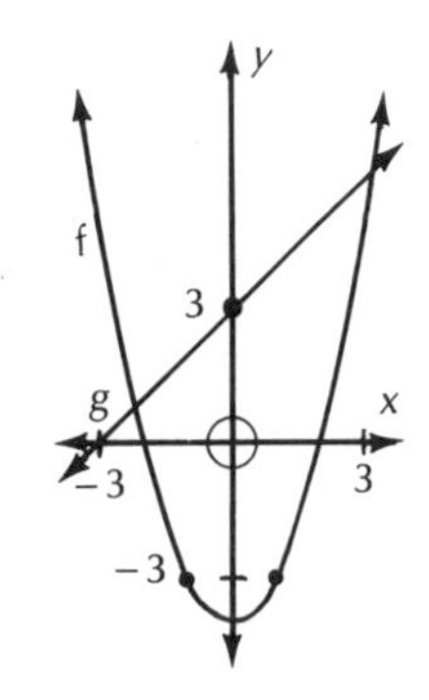

B **3.** Given that $f(x) = x - 1$, $g(x) = x^2 - 1$, and $h(x) = 3x^2 - 2x + 1$, find a defining equation for each of the following.

a. $f + g$ **b.** $f - g$ **c.** $f + h$
d. $g + h$ **e.** $h - g$ **f.** $f - g + h$

4. Evaluate each new function obtained in exercise 3 for $x = 3$.

5. In each case, the graph of a pair of functions f and g is given. Graph $(f + g)$ and $(f - g)$.

a.

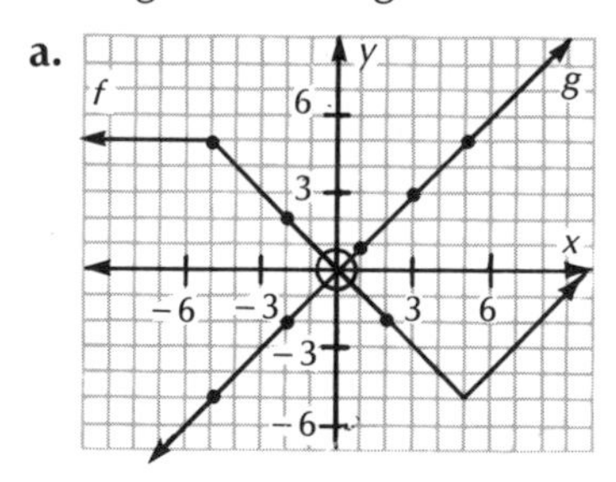

b.

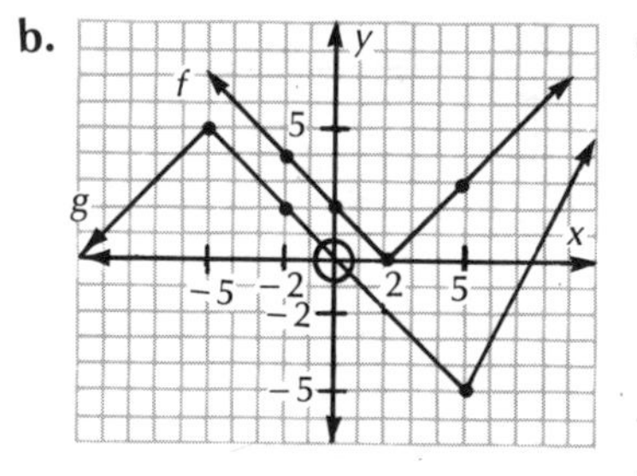

c.

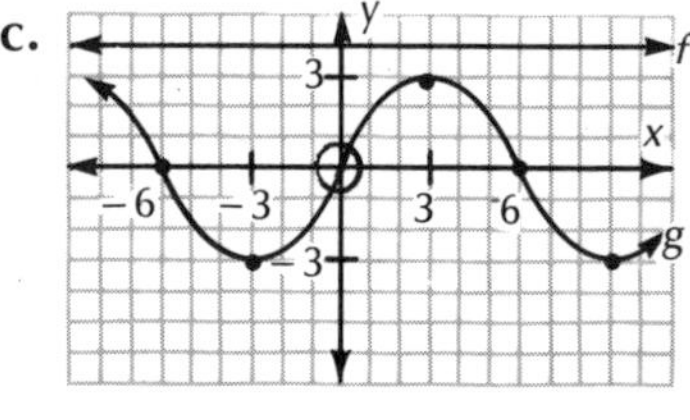

d.

e.

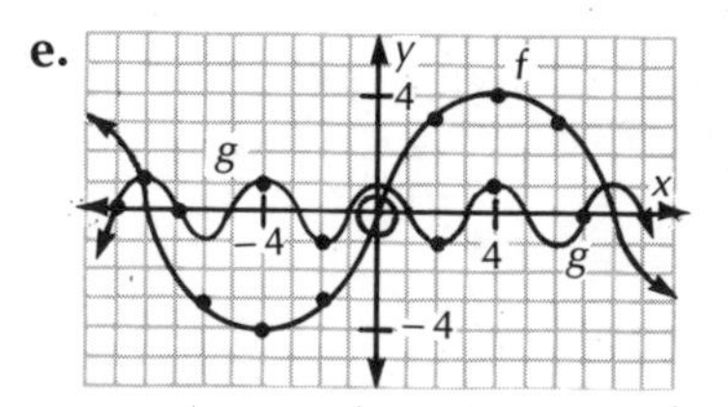

f.

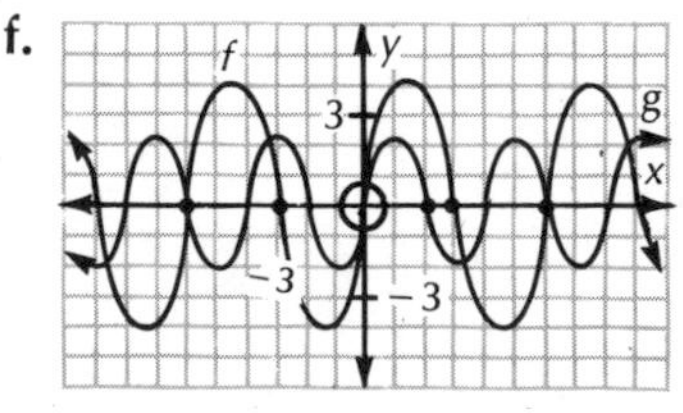

Review

1. Find the domain and range of each relation. Which are functions?

   a. $\{(3, 1), (2, -1), (0, -1), (-2, 5), (-1, 7)\}$

   b.

x	y
3	7
2	2
1	-1
0	-2
-1	7

   c.

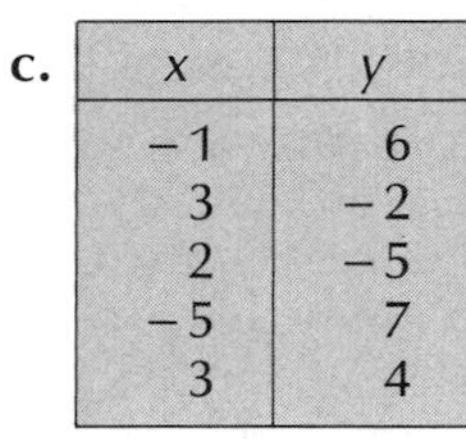

x	y
-1	6
3	-2
2	-5
-5	7
3	4

   d.

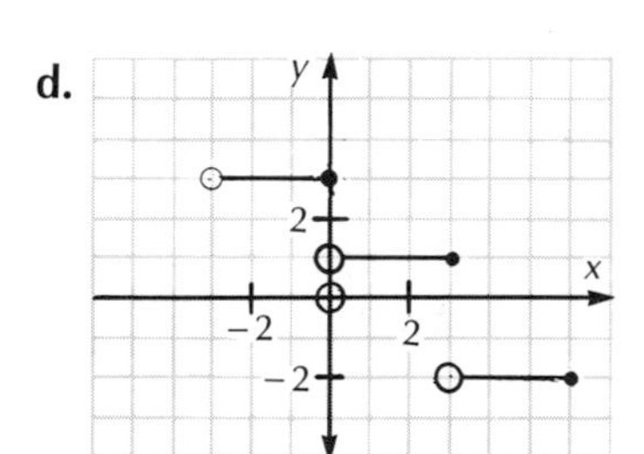

   e.

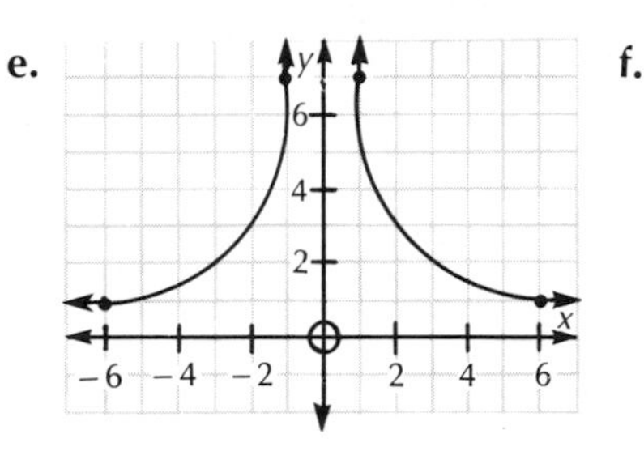

   f.

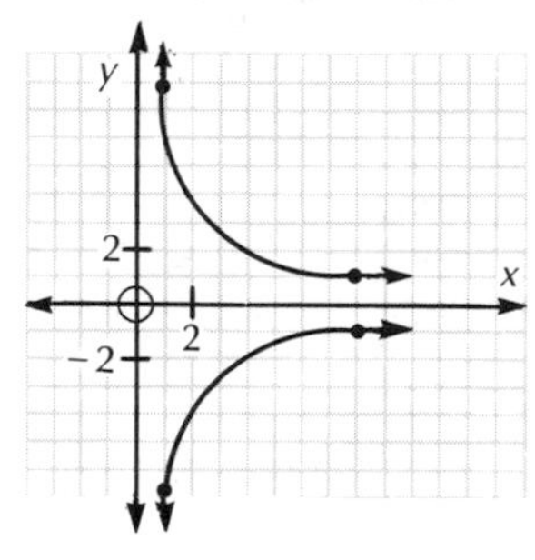

2. a. Given that $f(x) = 2x - 1$ and $D(f) = \{-3, -2, -1, 0, 1, 2\}$, find $R(f)$.

   b. Given that $g(x) = \dfrac{3x - 1}{x + 3}$ and $D(g) = \{x \mid -1 \leq x < 7\}$, find $R(g)$.

3. The graph of a function and its transformation image are given. Determine an equation of each image.

   a.

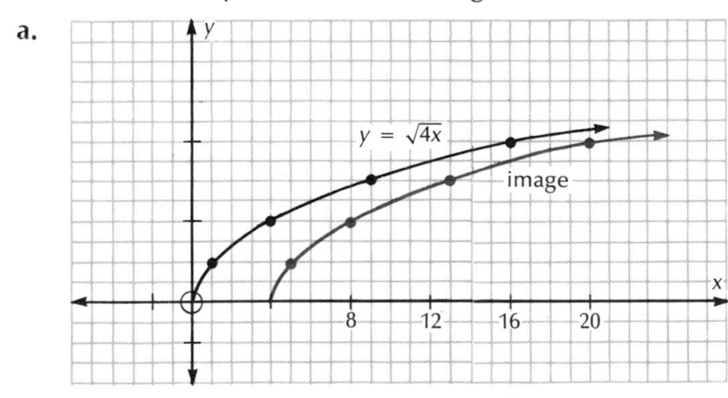

   b.

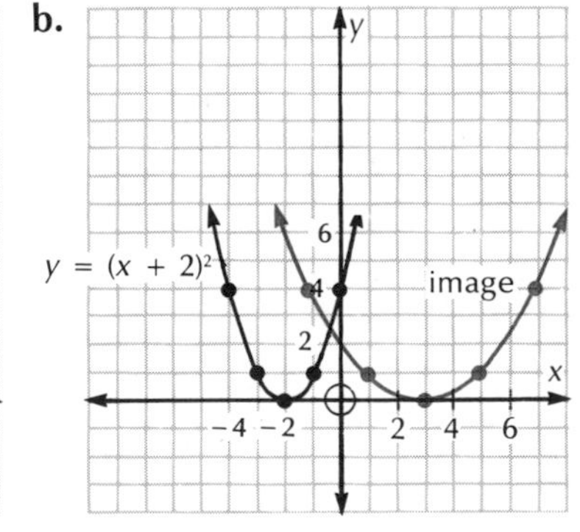

4. Each given mapping sends a function to an image under transformation. Describe each transformation.

   a. $y = 3x \rightarrow y = 3x - 1$
   b. $y = x^2 \rightarrow y = 2x^2$
   c. $y = x \rightarrow y = -x$
   d. $y = x^3 \rightarrow y = (x - 1)^3 + 2$
   e. $y = x \rightarrow y = -\dfrac{x}{2}$
   f. $y = \dfrac{1}{x} \rightarrow y = \dfrac{1}{2x} + 3$

5. Given that $f(x) = 5x - 7$, $g(x) = x^2 + 1$, and $h(x) = \dfrac{12}{x}$, evaluate the following.

   a. $f(2) + g(2)$
   b. $g(4) - h(4)$
   c. $h(-2) + f(-2) - g(-2)$
   d. $h(x) - h(x)$
   e. $f(x) + g(x)$
   f. $g(x) - f(x) - h(x)$

1-5 Composition of Functions

The walls of an undersea vehicle must be sufficiently thick to withstand pressure at greath depths.

The first two tables below define a function between depth and pressure, and a function between pressure and safe wall thickness of an undersea vehicle. The two functions can be combined or *composed* to define a function between depth and thickness, as shown in the third table.

Depth (m)	Pressure (kPa)
500	5000
1000	10 000
1500	15 000
2000	20 000

Pressure (kPa)	Wall Thickness (cm)
5000	2
10 000	4
15 000	6
20 000	8

Depth (m)	Wall Thickness (cr
500	2
1000	4
1500	6
2000	8

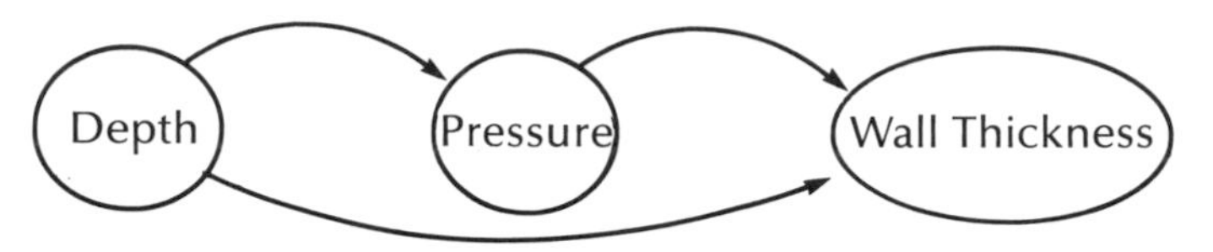

In general, for functions f and g, the **composite function, $f \circ g$,** takes elements from the domain of g and assigns them values in the range of f.

The domain of the composite function, $f \circ g$, is a subset of the domain of g.

The range of the composite function, $f \circ g$, is a subset of the range of f.

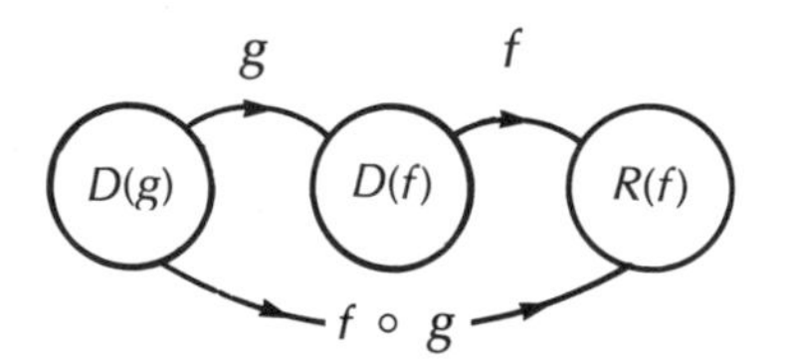

EXAMPLE 1: For the given functions f and g, find the composite function, $f \circ g$. Then find the domain and range of the composite function.

a.

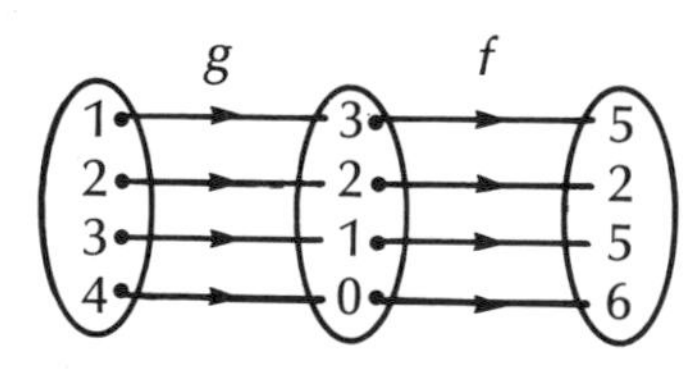

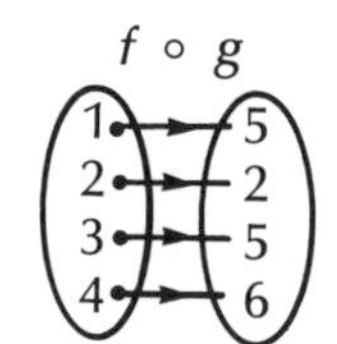

$D(f \circ g) = \{1, 2, 3, 4\}$
$R(f \circ g) = \{5, 2, 5, 6\}$

b. f: $\{(-3, -5), (-2, -4), (-1, -2), (0, 2), (1, 5), (2, 8), (3, 9)\}$
g: $\{(-3, -7), (-2, -5), (-1, -3), (0, -1), (1, 1), (2, 3), (3, 5)\}$

$f \circ g$: $\{(-1, -5), (0, -2), (1, 5), (2, 9)\}$

$D(f \circ g) = \{-1, 0, 1, 2\}$

$R(f \circ g) = \{-5, -2, 5, 9\}$

> For functions f and g, the **composite function, $f \circ g$,** is defined as $f \circ g(x) = f(g(x))$.
> The function is read as "the composite of f at g" or "f at g of x".
> The function g is evaluated at x and then the function f is applied to that result.

Also, $D(f \circ g) \subseteq D(g)$ and $R(f \circ g) \subseteq R(f)$.

$\subseteq$ means "is a subset of".

EXAMPLE 2: Evaluate the following, given that $f(x) = 3x^2 - 1$ and $g(x) = x - 3$.

a. $f \circ g(2)$

$$\begin{aligned} f \circ g(2) &= f(g(2)) \\ &= f(2 - 3) \\ &= f(-1) \\ &= 3(-1)^2 - 1 \\ &= 2 \end{aligned}$$

b. $g \circ f(4)$

$$\begin{aligned} g \circ f(4) &= g(f(4)) \\ &= g(3(4^2) - 1) \\ &= g(47) \\ &= 47 - 3 \\ &= 44 \end{aligned}$$

EXAMPLE 3: Functions f and g are defined as $f(x) = \dfrac{1}{x^2 - 4}$ and $g(x) = \sqrt{x - 2}$.

a. Find $f \circ g(x)$.

$$\begin{aligned} f \circ g(x) &= f(g(x)) \\ &= f(\sqrt{x - 2}) \\ &= \frac{1}{(\sqrt{x - 2})^2 - 4} \\ &= \frac{1}{(x - 2) - 4} \\ &= \frac{1}{x - 6} \end{aligned}$$

b. Find $D(f \circ g)$.

The domain of $f \circ g$ is a subset of g.

Since $g(x) = \sqrt{x - 2}$, then $x - 2 \geq 0$.
So, $D(g) = \{x \mid x \geq 2\}$.

But $f \circ g(x) = \dfrac{1}{x - 6}$, where $x \neq 6$.

$\therefore D(f \circ g) = \{x \mid x \geq 2, x \neq 6\}$

EXERCISE 1-5

A 1. Given f: $\{(-3, 5), (-2, 3), (-1, 1), (0, -1), (1, 1), (2, 3), (3, 5)\}$ and g: $\{(0, 2), (1, 3), (2, 6), (3, 1), (4, 18), (5, 27)\}$, find the following.

a. $f \circ g$ **b.** $g \circ f$ **c.** $g \circ f(-1)$ **d.** $f \circ g(1)$
e. $R(f)$ **f.** $D(f)$ **g.** $D(g)$ **h.** $R(g)$
i. $D(g \circ f)$ **j.** $R(f \circ g)$ **k.** $D(f \circ g)$ **l.** $R(g \circ f)$

2. Given that $f(x) = x - 2$ and $g(x) = x^2 + 1$, evaluate each composite function.

a. $f(g(2))$ **b.** $g(f(-1))$ **c.** $f \circ g(3)$
d. $f \circ g(-2)$ **e.** $g \circ f(5)$ **f.** $g \circ f(-4)$
g. $f \circ g(-3)$ **h.** $f \circ g(7)$ **i.** $g \circ f(-3)$

3. The functions f and g are defined by the given mappings.

a. Find $g \circ f(2)$.
b. Find $g \circ f(-1)$.
c. Find $f \circ g(0)$.
d. Construct a mapping diagram of $f \circ g$.
e. Construct a mapping diagram of $g \circ f$.

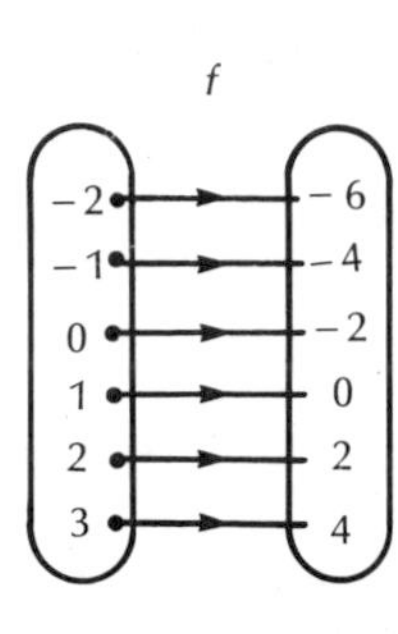

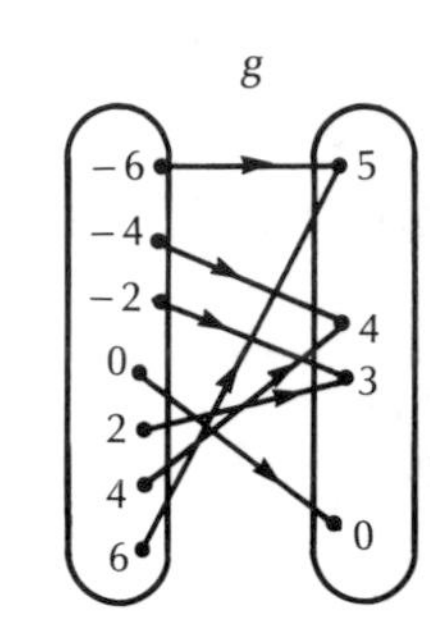

B 4. Given $f(x) = 2x - 1$, $g(x) = x^2 + 2$, and $h(x) = \frac{1}{x - 3}$, determine an equation of each composite function.

a. $f \circ g(x)$ **b.** $g \circ f(x)$ **c.** $h \circ f(x)$
d. $h \circ g(x)$ **e.** $f \circ h(x)$ **f.** $g \circ h(x)$

5. A country fair lasts for seven days. The predicted attendance for each day is determined by the following formula.

$N(d) = 3500 - 150\,(d - 4)^2, \{d \mid d \in \mathbf{Z}; 1 \leq d \leq 7\}$

The revenue is predicted as a function of the number of people in attendance and is found by the equation below.

$$R(N) = 11N - \frac{10\,000}{N}$$

Find an equation of a function that will predict the revenue for each day.

6. For each pair of functions, determine an equation for $f \circ g$ and for $g \circ f$. Then find the domain and range of f, g, and each composite function.

a. $f(x) = x - 1$, $g(x) = \sqrt{x}$
b. $f(x) = x^2$, $g(x) = x + 1$
c. $f(x) = x^2 - 1$, $g(x) = \frac{1}{x + 1}$

7. From a height of h metres, the unobstructed distance that you can see is given by the formula $d = 3.43\sqrt{h}$, where d is in kilometres. The CN Tower has a glass elevator that takes passengers up 342 m to the observation decks and restaurant. If the elevator rises at a rate of 3 m/s, find an equation that describes how far passengers in the elevator can see, t seconds after the elevator starts to rise.

8. The "weak link" in the Deep Rover sub-sea vehicle is the cast aluminum ring between two acrylic hemispheres. The thickness of the aluminum ring needed for a given pressure is given by the formula $T = \frac{PO}{2S}$, where P is the pressure in kilopascals, O is the outside diameter of the ring, and S is the tensile strength of cast aluminum.

An equation of the function that relates pressure to depth is $P(d) = 10.1(d) + 101$, where P is the pressure in kilopascals, and d is the depth measured in metres.

The outside diameter of the ring of the Deep Rover is 145 cm and the tensile strength of cast aluminum is 2.07×10^5.

a. Find an equation of the composite function that relates thickness to depth.
b. The Deep Rover is designed for a depth of 2800 m. What is the thickness of the aluminum ring?
c. Draw a graph of T versus d.

9. In a cable-stayed bridge, the length of each cable supporting the bridge deck is the hypotenuse of a right-angled triangle. The triangle is formed by the bridge deck, the supporting tower, and cable itself.

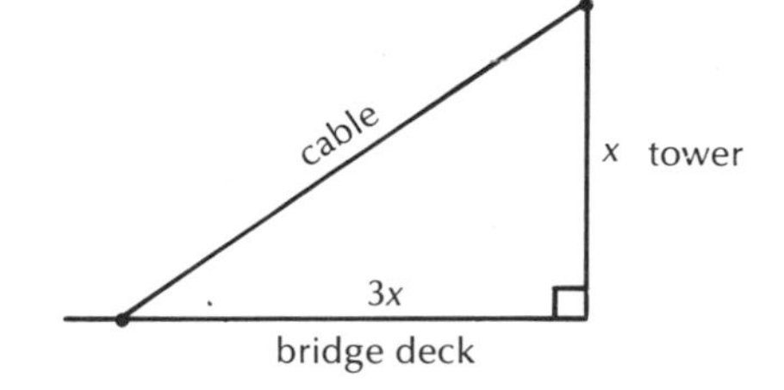

a. If the distance along the deck is three times the tower height, find a function that expresses the length of the cable as a function of the height of the anchor point up the tower.
b. The mass of the cable is 125 kg per metre plus 2700 kg for anchor hardware. Determine an equation that gives the mass of the cable as a function of the height of the anchor point above the bridge deck.

10. Given $f(x) = x^2 - 1$, $g(x) = x + 1$, and $h(x) = \frac{1}{x}$, determine each of the following.

a. $f \circ g \circ h(x)$ b. $g \circ f \circ h(x)$ c. $h \circ f \circ g(x)$

11. Write each given equation of a function as the composition of two simpler functions.

a. $y = \sqrt{x^2 - 4}$ b. $y = \frac{1}{\sqrt{x}}$ c. $y = 3x + 2$

1-6 Inverse of a Function

Many calculators have a key marked [INV]. Pressing the [INV] key modifies the action of other keys — it often "undoes" the action originally performed by the key.

For example, for the calculator key marked [x^2], pressing [INV] [x^2] is equivalent to pressing [$\sqrt{x}$].

In the diagram at the right, the first mapping is produced by pressing the [x^2] key. The second mapping is produced by pressing [INV] [x^2].

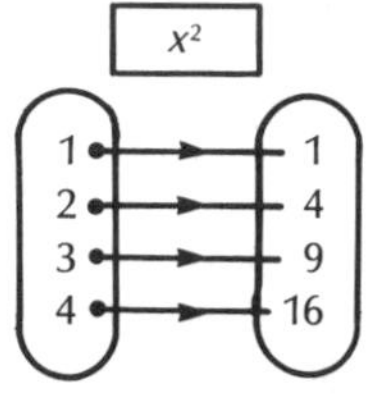

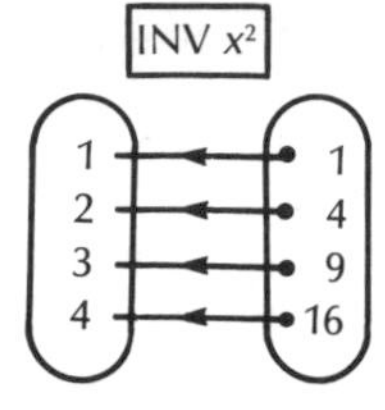

Notice that f maps its domain elements onto its range and that g maps the range of f back onto the domain of f.

The function g is called the **inverse** of f, and is denoted as $\boldsymbol{f^{-1}}$.

Note that f^{-1} is not the same as $\frac{1}{f}$.

> In general, f and f^{-1} are inverses if, and only if, for every $(x, y) \in f$, then $(y, x) \in f^{-1}$.

EXAMPLE 1: A function g is defined as the set of ordered pairs $g = \{(-2, 5), (-1, 2), (1, 0), (1, -2), (2, -5)\}$. Find g^{-1}.

Interchange the numbers in the ordered pairs to find g^{-1}.
$g^{-1} = \{(5, -2), (2, -1), (0, 1), (-2, 1), (-5, 2)\}$

EXAMPLE 2: Graph f and f^{-1}, given that $f: x \rightarrow x^2 + 1$.

First, make a table of ordered pairs for f.

x	$f(x)$
−2	5
−1	2
0	1
1	2
2	5

The graph of f^{-1} has the numbers of the ordered pairs reversed.

x	$f^{-1}(x)$
5	−2
2	−1
1	0
2	1
5	2

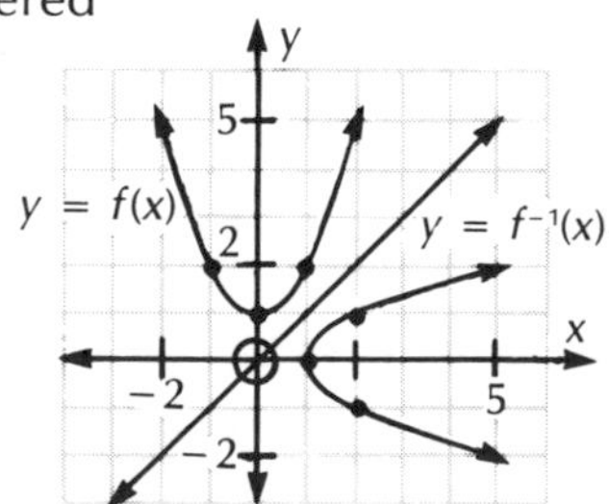

Notice that f is a function, but f^{-1} is not, since it does not pass the vertical line test.

The graph of f^{-1} is the reflection of the graph of f in the line $y = x$. For a point (x, y) on the graph of f, (y, x) is the corresponding point on the graph of f^{-1}.

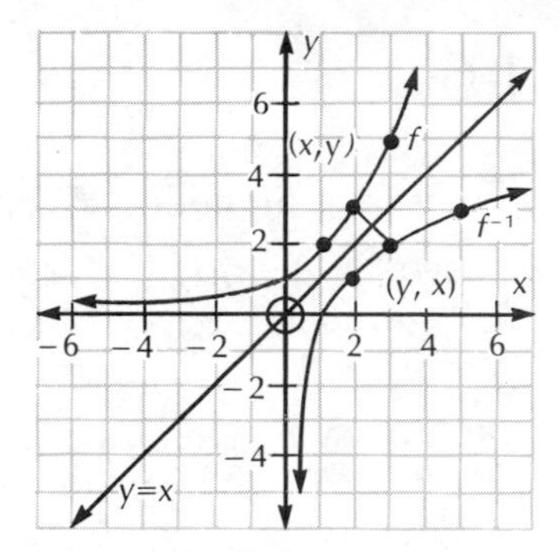

To show that $y = x$ is the reflection line between the graphs of f and f^{-1}, it is only necessary to prove that $y = x$ is the perpendicular bisector of the line segment with endpoints (x, y) and (y, x). The proof is left to the exercises.

To find an equation of the inverse of a function, think of "undoing" the function. Consider the function defined by the equation $f\colon y = 2x^3 - 4$.

f: (Take x.) → (Cube it.) → (Multiply by 2.) → (Subtract 4.) → ($y = 2x^3 - 4$)

($\sqrt[3]{\dfrac{x+4}{2}} = y$) ← (Take the cube root.) ← (Divide by 2.) ← (Add 4.) ← (take x) :f^{-1}

$f\colon y = 2x^3 - 4$ $\qquad$ $f^{-1}\colon y = \sqrt[3]{\dfrac{x+4}{2}}$

An alternate way to determine an equation of the inverse of a function is to interchange the roles of x and y in the equation of the function.

EXAMPLE 3:

a. For $f\colon y = 2x + 1$, find an equation of f^{-1}.

Interchange x and y and then solve for y.

$$f\colon y = 2x + 1$$
$$x = 2y + 1$$
$$y = \frac{x-1}{2}$$
$$\therefore\ f^{-1}\colon y = \frac{x-1}{2}$$

b. For $f\colon y = 2x + 1$, find $f \circ f^{-1}$.

$$f \circ f^{-1} = f(f^{-1}))$$
$$= f\left(\frac{x-1}{2}\right)$$
$$= 2\left(\frac{x-1}{2}\right) + 1$$
$$= (x - 1) + 1$$
$$= x$$
$$\therefore\ f \circ f^{-1}\colon y = x$$

The composite function in part **b** is the identity function I.

SUMMARY
- For a function f and its inverse f^{-1}, $(x, y) \in f$ if, and only if, $(y, x) \in f^{-1}$. Note that f^{-1} might not be a function.
- The graph of f^{-1} is the reflection of the graph of f in the line $y = x$.
- To determine the equation of f^{-1}, interchange the roles of x and y in the equation $y = f(x)$.
- The composite function $f \circ f^{-1}$ is the identity function $I\colon y = x$.

EXERCISE 1-6

A **1.** List the inverse of each function. Which inverses are also functions?

a. $\{(-2, -8), (1, 1), (0, 2), (3, 7), (-2, 4)\}$
b. $\{(-1, -1), (3, 27), (0, 0), (2, 8), (-2, -8)\}$
c. $\{(-2, 4), (3, 9), (4, 16), (1, 1), (-1, 1)\}$
d. $\{(9, 3), (0, 0), (1, 1), (4, 2), (16, 4)\}$
e. $\{(3, 3), (2, 2), (-1, 1), (-2, 2), (5, 5)\}$
f. $\{(8, 7), (3, 2), (7, 8), (8, -1)\}$

2. Reflect the graph of each given function in the line $y = x$ to find the graph of the inverse. Which inverses are functions?

a.

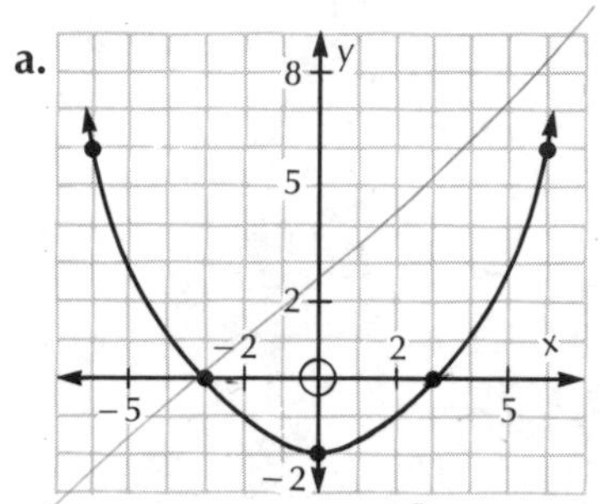

b.

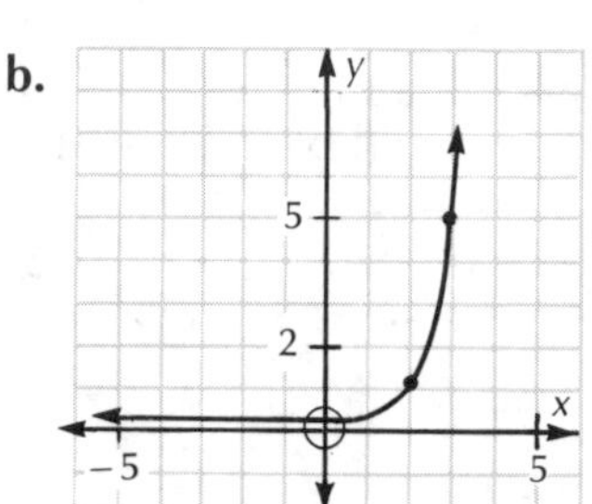

c.

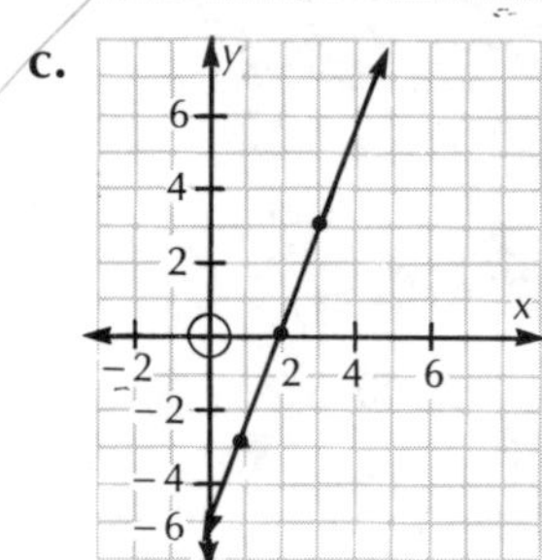

d.

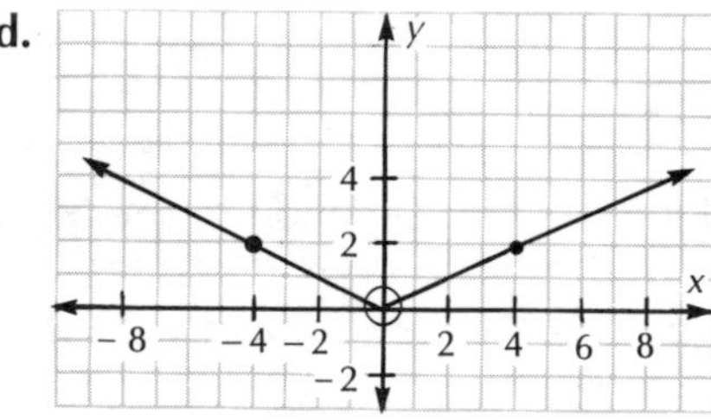
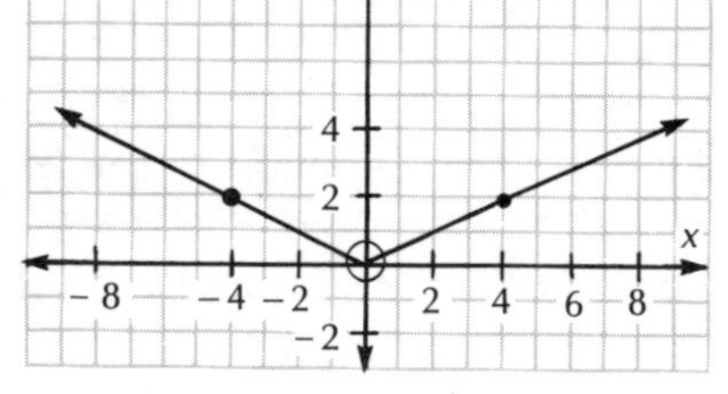

3. a. $D(f) = \{0, 1, 2, 3, 4, 5\}$
$R(f) = \{-3, -2, 5, 7, 9\}$
Find $R(f^{-1})$.

b. $D(f) = \{x \mid -3 \leq x \leq 3\}$
$R(f) = \{y \mid 0 \leq y \leq 6\}$
Find $D(f^{-1})$.

c. $f(x) = x - 2$
$D(f) = \{3, 5, 7, 9\}$
Find $R(f^{-1})$.

d. $f(x) = x^2 + 1$
$D(f) = \{x \mid -2 \leq x \leq 2\}$
Find $R(f)$, $D(f^{-1})$, and $R(f^{-1})$.

B **4.** For each pair of functions, determine $f \circ g(n)$ for the given values of n. Decide which pairs could be inverses of one another.

a. $f(x) = 2x + 2$

$g(x) = \left(\frac{x - 2}{2}\right)$

$n = -2$ and $n = 3$

b. $f(x) = 3x - 1$

$g(x) = \left(\frac{x + 1}{3}\right)$

$n = -1$ and $n = 0$

c. $f(x) = \frac{1}{x}$

$g(x) = x^2$

$n = 4$ and $n = -3$

d. $f(x) = \frac{1}{(x + 3)}$

$g(x) = \frac{1}{x} - 3$

$n = 1$ and $n = -2$

5. Find a defining equation of the inverse of each given function.

a. $f(x) = 3x - 2$ b. $f(x) = 3 - 4x$ c. $f(x) = \frac{3}{2}x + 1$

d. $f(x) = \dfrac{1}{x}$ e. $f(x) = \dfrac{2}{x - 1}$ f. $f(x) = \dfrac{2}{x + 3}$

g. $f(x) = \sqrt{x - 1}$ h. $f(x) = x^2 - 2$ i. $f(x) = -\left(\dfrac{x + 2}{3}\right)$

6. For each function graphed below, the inverse is not a function. Restrict the domain so that the inverse is a function.

a.

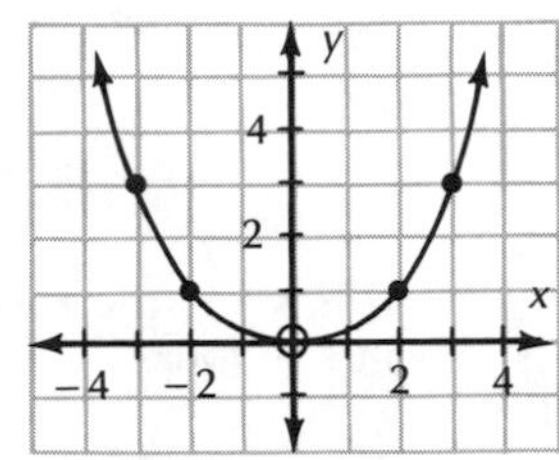

b.

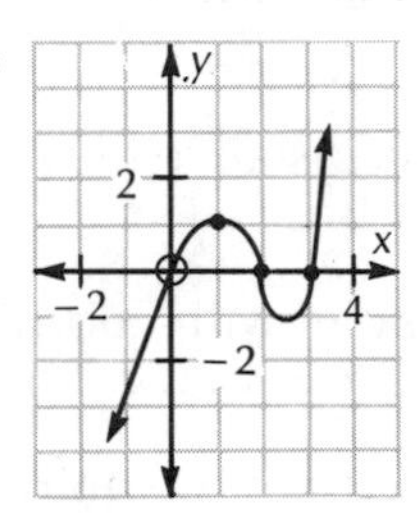

c.

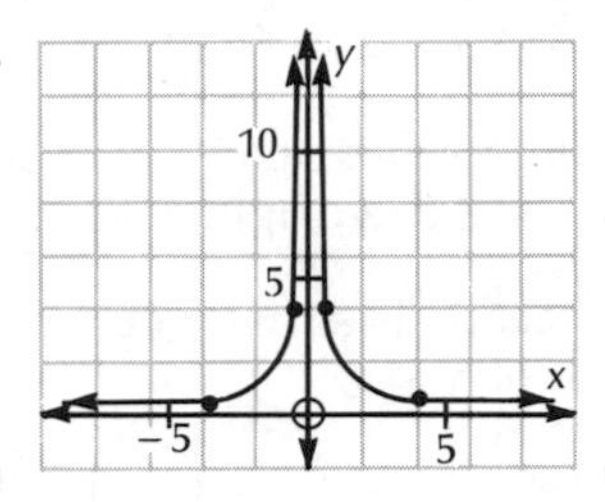

7. • Find f^{-1} for each given function.
• Graph f and f^{-1} on the same set of axes to show that the function and its inverse are reflections in the line $y = x$.

a. $f{:}y = 2x - 1$ b. $f{:}y = \frac{3}{4}x + 2$ c. $f{:}y = \frac{1}{2}x^2$

d. $f{:}y = x^2 - 3$ e. $f{:}y = \dfrac{1}{x^2}$ f. $f{:}y = \sqrt{x + 1}$

8. What test, similar to the vertical line test, can you perform on the graph of $y = f(x)$ to determine whether or not f^{-1} is a function?

C 9. The ordered pair (a, b) is an element of the function f.

a. Can (b, c) be an element of f^{-1}?
b. Can (c, a) be an element of f^{-1}?

10. To prove that the graph of f^{-1} is the reflection of the graph of f in the line $y = x$, it is only necessary to show that the line $y = x$ is the perpendicular bisector of the line segment joining corresponding pairs of points. If (x, y) is a point on the graph of f, then (y, x) is the corresponding point on the graph of f^{-1}.

a. Show that the midpoint of the line segment with endpoints (x, y) and (y, x) lies on the line $y = x$.
b. Show that the line $y = x$ is perpendicular to the line segment joining corresponding points by proving that the slope of the line $y = x$ is the opposite of the reciprocal of the slope of the line segment with endpoints (x, y), and (y, x).

1-7 Absolute Value Functions

Jan hits a golf ball straight for the flag on a green that is 150 m away. The shot might be long, short, or even in the hole. A shot that is short by 5 m could be recorded as -5, and a shot that is long by 8 m could be recorded as $+8$. The important consideration is the distance the ball is from the hole. The idea of *undirected* distance can be expressed by **absolute value.**

Consider two points, 4 and -4, on a number line.

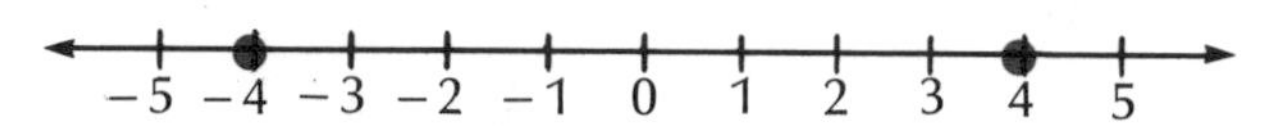

The **absolute value** of any number is the distance between the point and the origin.

$|4| = 4$ means the distance from the point with coordinate 4 to the origin is 4.

$|4|$ is read "the absolute value of four."

Similarly, $|-4| = 4$ means the distance from the point with coordinate -4 to the origin is 4.

The absolute value of any real number can never be negative. In particular, $|0| = 0$.

EXAMPLE 1: Evaluate.

a. $3|-7| = 3(7)$
$= 21$

b. $-|3 - 5| = -|-2|$
$= -(2)$
$= -2$

c. $||7 - 2| - |8|| = |5 - 8|$
$= |-3|$
$= 3$

> In general, for $x \in \boldsymbol{R}$, if $x \geq 0$, then $|x| = x$. If $x < 0$, then $|x| = -x$.

EXAMPLE 2: Solve $3x + |x| = -8$.

If $x \geq 0$, then $|x| = x$.
$\therefore 3x + x = -8$
$4x = -8$
$x = -2$
But $x \geq 0$, so x cannot be -2.

If $x < 0$, then $|x| = -x$.
$\therefore 3x - x = -8$
$2x = -8$
$x = -4$
Since $x < 0$, then -4 is a solution.

Therefore, the solution set is $\{-4\}$.

EXAMPLE 3: Graph $\{(x, y) \mid y = |x - 2|\}$, where $-2 \le x \le 4$.

Make a table of values.

x	$x - 2$	$y = \lvert x - 2 \rvert$
4	2	2
3	1	1
2	0	0
1	−1	1
0	−2	2
−1	−3	3
−2	−4	4

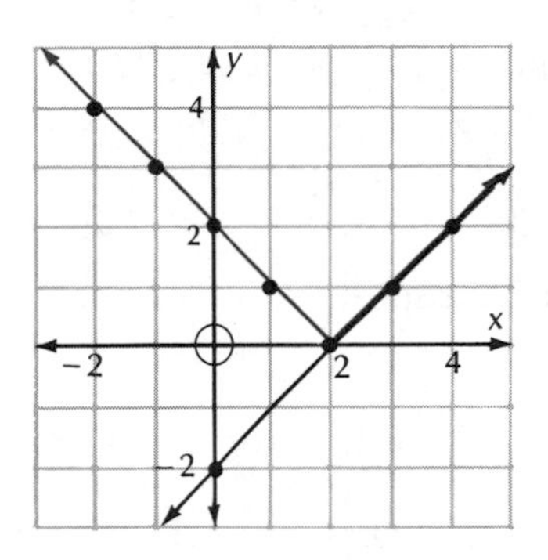

Notice how the graph of $y = |x - 2|$ is related to the graph of $y = x - 2$. Since $|x - 2|$ cannot be negative, then y cannot be negative. So the part of the graph of $y = x - 2$ that is below the x-axis is reflected in the x-axis to obtain the corresponding portion of the graph of $y = |x - 2|$. The part of the graph that is above the x-axis is left unchanged.

EXAMPLE 4: Solve and graph on a number line.

a. $|x| > 2$

On a number line, the distance between the origin, O, and a point with coordinate x is greater than 2.

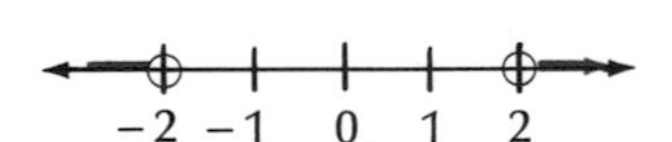

$\therefore x < -2$ or $x > 2$

b. $|x| < 2$

On a number line, the distance between the origin, O, and a point with coordinate x is less than 2.

−2 −1 0 1 2

$\therefore -2 < x < 2$, or $-2 < x$ and $x < 2$.

EXAMPLE 5: Solve and graph on a number line.

a. $|2x + 1| \le 3$

$$-3 \le 2x + 1 \le 3$$
$$-4 \le 2x \le 3$$
$$-2 \le x \le 1$$

−2 −1 0 1

b. $|5x - 3| \ge 12$

$5x - 3 \le -12$ or $5x - 3 \le 12$

$5x \le -9$ or $5x \le 15$

$x \le -\frac{9}{5}$ or $x \le 3$

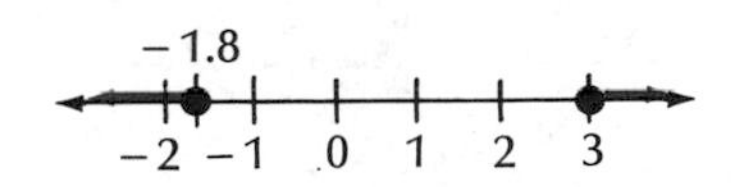

EXERCISE 1-7

A **1.** Simplify.

a. $|-8|$ **b.** $|3-5|$ **c.** $-|5-7|$
d. $-2|7|+3|-5|$ **e.** $|-5|-|-2|$ **f.** $3|8-7|-|2-6|$
g. $|4-7|-3|3-5|+|-6|$ **h.** $-3|5-2|+2|3-5|$ **i.** $-|3+|-2-6||$

2. Find the solution set for each equation.

a. $|x|=5$ **b.** $|z|=3$ **c.** $|x+3|=10$
d. $|x-2|=1$ **e.** $|5-x|=1$ **f.** $1-|-x|=4$
g. $|2x+1|=5$ **h.** $|4x+2|=6$ **i.** $|x-3|=7$

3. Given that $f(x)=3x-1$ and $g(x)=5-x^2$, evaluate the following.

a. $|f(1)|$ **b.** $f(|-2|)$ **c.** $|g(3)|$
d. $g(|2|)$ **e.** $f(|7|)$ **f.** $|g(-2)|$

4. Solve and graph each inequality on a number line.

a. $|x|>2$ **b.** $|x|\geq 5$ **c.** $|x|<6$
d. $|x|\leq 4$ **e.** $|x-2|\geq 4$ **f.** $|x+1|<3$
g. $|2x|>6$ **h.** $|3x|\leq 12$ **i.** $|3-x|<2$

B **5.** Find the solution set of each equation.

a. $2|x-1|=6$ **b.** $|3-x|+4=2$ **c.** $|3-2x|-1=4$
d. $3|x+5|=6$ **e.** $2|x-2|+5=9$ **f.** $6-3|x+1|=0$

6. Solve and graph each inequality on a number line.

a. $|2x+1|<5$ **b.** $|4x-2|\geq 6$ **c.** $|3-2x|>3$
d. $|6-4x|\leq 2$ **e.** $|3x+1|>5$ **f.** $|7-4x|<9$
g. $|5x-1|\leq 6$ **h.** $|3-5x|\geq 2$ **i.** $|4-2x|>0$
j. $4|3-x|+5\leq 9$ **k.** $3|5-2x|+1>10$ **l.** $3|4x+1|-7\geq 20$

7. Graph the function defined by each equation.

a. $y=|x+2|$ **b.** $y=|3x-2|$ **c.** $y=|x^2-4|$

8. Copy each given graph of $y=f(x)$. Then graph $y=|f(x)|$ on the same set of axes.

a.

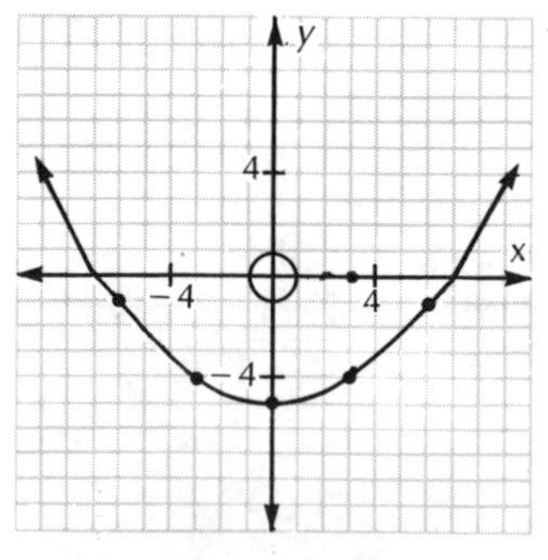

b.

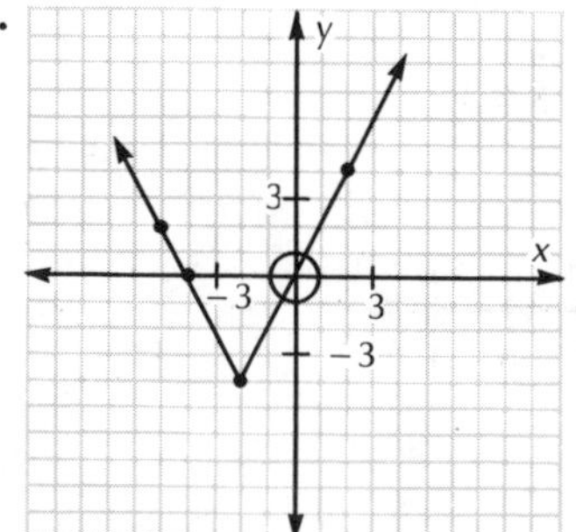

c.

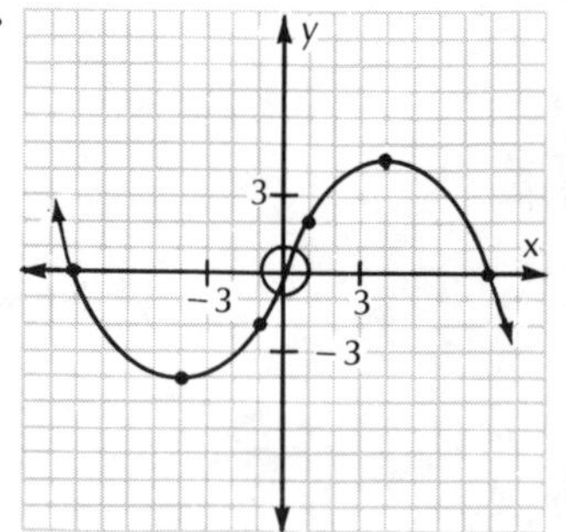

9. Given that $f(x) = 3x - 5$ and $g(x) = x^2 - 5$, graph the following.

a. $y = f(x)$ b. $y = f(|x|)$ c. $y = |f(x)|$
d. $y = g(x)$ e. $y = g(|x|)$ f. $y = |g(x)|$

10. Find the solution set of each equation.

a. $5|x| - 3|x| = 10$ b. $2|x| - 3 = |x|$
c. $2|x| + 3 = 4|x| - 1$ d. $3|x| + |x| - 5 = 2|x| + 9$
e. $4|x - 2| + |x - 2| = 15$ f. $|x + 1| = 2|x + 1| - 8$
g. $|2x + 5| = x + 6$ h. $|3x + 1| = 3 - x$
i. $|3x + 1| = 4x - 1$ j. $2|x - 3| + 5 = 9 - x$

11. Graph the solution set of each inequality on a number line.

a. $|x + 3| > 2x$ b. $|3x| \leq x + 4$
c. $|2x| \geq x + 6$ d. $|2x + 1| \leq 7 - x$

12. Solve.

a. $|x + 4| = |2x|$ b. $|3x| = |8 - x|$
c. $|2x + 5| = |x + 2|$ d. $|3x - 2| = |x + 4|$

13. Draw the graph of each equation.

a. $|x| + |y| = 1$ b. $|x| - |y| = 1$

EXTRA

The Triangle Inequality

he **triangle inequality** states that for
y two numbers a and b, the
llowing relation is true.
$|a + b| \leq |a| + |b|$

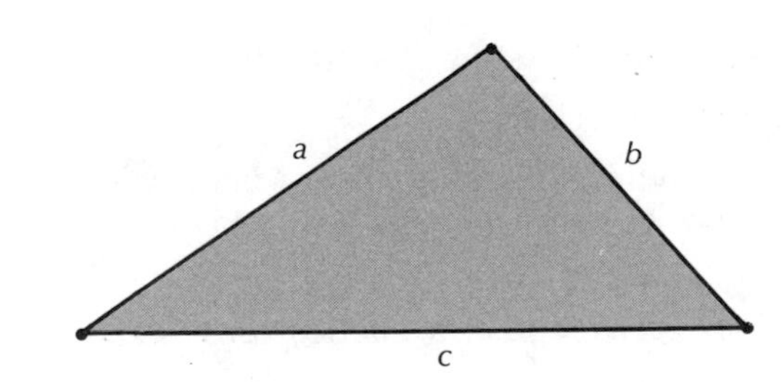

he name "triangle inequality" stems
om an associated theorem in
eometry. That is, if a, b, and c are
ree sides of a triangle, then the
ngth of any one side must be less
an or equal to the sum of the lengths
the other two sides.

For what values of a and b is it always true that $|a + b| < |a| + |b|$?
Under what conditions is it true that $|a| + |b| = |a + b|$?
A modification of the triangle inequality states that
$||a| - |b|| \leq |a + b|$. Prove that $||a| - |b|| \leq |a + b|$.
What other modifications of the triangle inequality can you state and
prove?

1-8 Rational Functions and their Graphs

A **rational function** is a function defined as $f(x) = \frac{p(x)}{q(x)}$, where $p(x)$ and $q(x)$ are both polynomials and $q(x) \neq 0$.

A simple rational function is $f(x) = \frac{4}{x}$. Its graph is shown.

x	$f(x)$
8	$\frac{1}{2}$
6	$\frac{2}{3}$
4	1
2	2
1	4
$-\frac{1}{2}$	-8
-1	-4
-2	-2
-4	-1
-8	$-\frac{1}{2}$

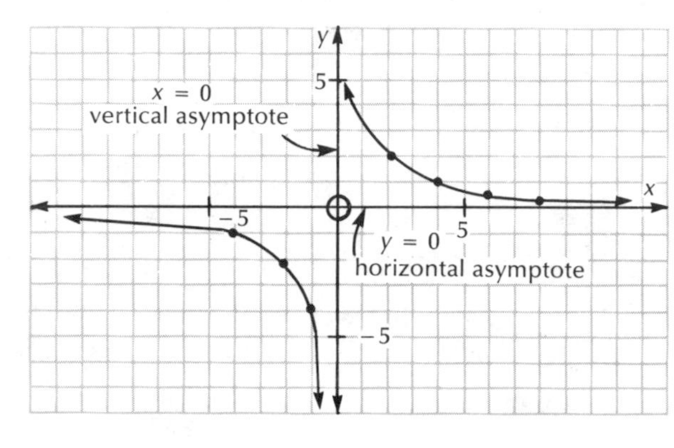

Since division by zero is not defined, zero is not in the domain of f. That is, $f(0)$ is not defined. Therefore, the graph of $f(x)$ does not cross the y-axis and the domain of f is $D(f) = \{x \mid x \in \mathbf{R}, x \neq 0\}$.

Of special interest is the graph of $f(x) = \frac{4}{x}$ as $|x|$ becomes very small or very large.

As $|x|$ becomes very large and $x > 0$, (or $x \to \infty^+$),
$f(x)$ is positive and approaches zero.

As $|x|$ becomes very large and $x < 0$, (or $x \to \infty^-$),
$f(x)$ is negative and approaches zero.

$\to$ is read "approaches"
∞^+ is read "positive infinity"
∞^- is read "negative infinity"

As x approaches zero but remains slightly larger than zero (or $x \to 0^+$),
$|f(x)|$ becomes very large and $f(x) > 0$.

As x approaches zero but remains slightly smaller than zero (or $x \to 0^-$),
$|f(x)|$ becomes very large and $f(x) < 0$.

SUMMARY x	$f(x)$
$\to \infty^+$	$\to 0^+$
$\to \infty^-$	$\to 0^-$
$\to 0^+$	$\to \infty^+$
$\to 0^-$	$\to \infty^-$

The range of the function is $R(f) = \{y \mid y \in \mathbf{R}, y \neq 0\}$.
The graph approaches, but does not cross the lines $y = 0$ or $x = 0$.
The lines $y = 0$ and $x = 0$ are the **asymptotes** of the function $y = \frac{4}{x}$.

- The line $x = a$ is a **vertical asymptote** of the function $y = f(x)$ if $f(x)$ approaches ∞^+ or ∞^- as the value of x approaches a and remains slightly larger (a^+) or slightly smaller (a^-).
- The line $y = b$ is a **horizontal asymptote** of the function $y = f(x)$ if $f(x)$ approaches b and remains slightly larger (b^+) or slightly smaller (b^-) as the value of x approaches ∞^+ or ∞^-.

EXAMPLE 1: Sketch the graph and find the asymptotes of $f(x) = \frac{1}{x^2 - 4} + 3$.

First, analyse the function to see what happens at certain *critical* values of x.

- Determine which values of x are excluded from the solution. $f(x)$ is undefined for $x^2 - 4 = 0$, or for $x = 2$ and $x = -2$.

- Determine the value of $f(x)$ near the excluded values and as $|x|$ becomes very large.

x	$x^2 - 4$	$\frac{1}{x^2 - 4}$	$f(x)$
$\to 2^+$	$\to 0^+$	$\to \infty^+$	$\to \infty^+$
$\to 2^-$	$\to 0^-$	$\to \infty^-$	$\to \infty^-$
(vertical asymptote $x = 2$)			
$\to (-2)^+$	$\to 0^-$	$\to \infty^-$	$\to \infty^-$
$\to (-2)^-$	$\to 0^+$	$\to \infty^+$	$\to \infty^+$
(vertical asymptote $x = -2$)			
$\to \infty^+$	$\to \infty^+$	$\to 0^+$	$\to 3^+$
$\to \infty^-$	$\to \infty^+$	$\to 0^+$	$\to 3^+$
(horizontal asymptote $y = 3$)			

- Use a table of values and the above information to sketch the graph.

x	$f(x)$
-3	$3\frac{1}{2}$
-1	$2\frac{2}{3}$
0	$2\frac{3}{4}$
1	$2\frac{2}{3}$
3	$3\frac{1}{5}$

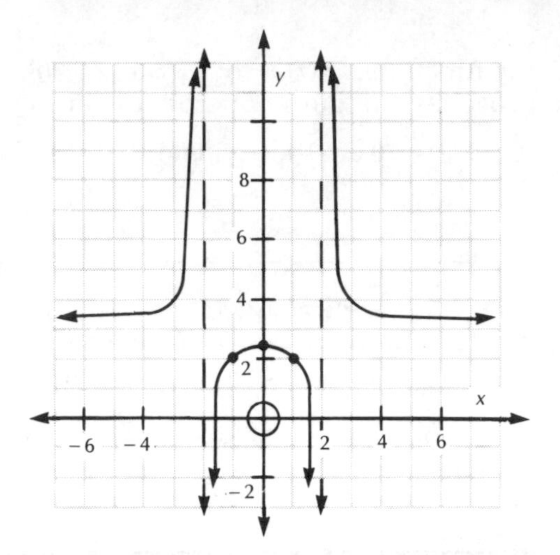

EXAMPLE 2: Find the asymptotes and sketch the graph of $y = \frac{1}{\sqrt{x^2 - 9}}$.

- Determine the excluded values.
  Since $\sqrt{x^2 - 9} \neq 0$, both 3 and -3 are excluded values.
  Furthermore, the square root of a negative number is not defined in the real numbers, so $\sqrt{x^2 - 9} \geq 0$.
  That is, $x \leq -3$, or $x \geq 3$.

  Consequently, the domain of the function is $\{x \mid |x| > 3\}$.

- Make a table to determine the asymptotes.

x	$\sqrt{x^2 - 9}$	$\frac{1}{\sqrt{x^2 - 9}}$
$\to 3^+$	$\to 0^+$	$\to \infty^+$
$\to 3^-$	excluded	*
$\to (-3)^+$	excluded	*
$\to (-3)^-$	$\to 0^+$	$\to \infty^+$
$\to \infty^+$	$\to \infty^+$	$\to 0^+$
$\to \infty^-$	$\to \infty^+$	$\to 0^+$

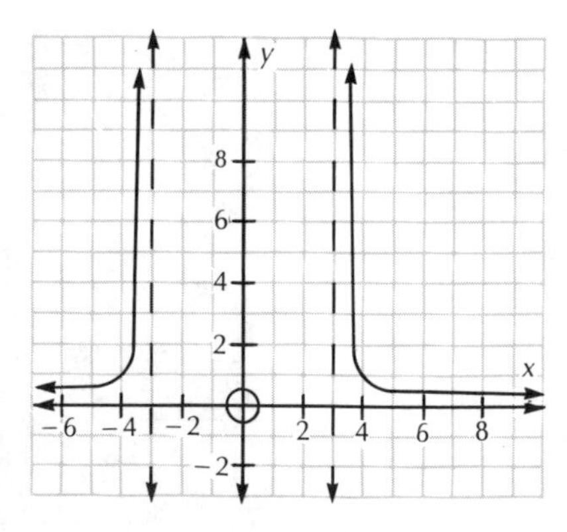

The vertical asymptotes are $x = 3$ and $x = -3$.
The horizontal asymptote is $y = 0$. The range is $\{y \mid y > 0\}$.

EXAMPLE 3: The graph of g is shown. Sketch the graph of $\frac{1}{g}$.

- The graph of g crosses the x-axis at -3 and 5. These are critical values of x because $g(x)$ is equal to zero at these values of x and therefore $\frac{1}{g}$ is undefined.

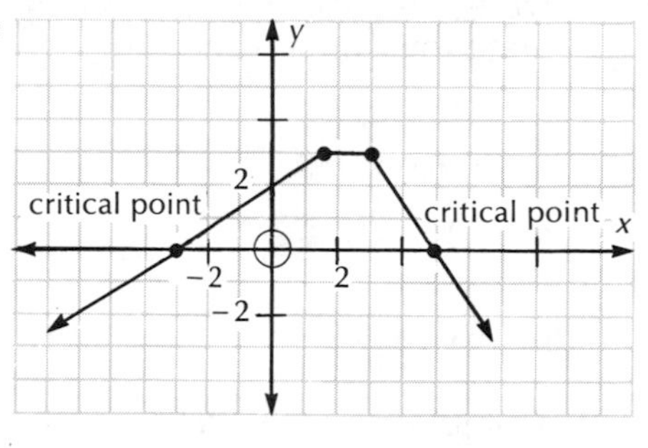

- Make a table to analyse the graph of $\frac{1}{g}$ near the critical values of x and also as x approaches ∞^+ and as x approaches ∞^-.

x	$g(x)$	$\frac{1}{g}$
$\to(-3)^+$	$\to 0^+$	$\to\infty^+$
$\to(-3)^-$	$\to 0^-$	$\to\infty^-$
$\to 5^+$	$\to 0^+$	$\to\infty^+$
$\to 5^-$	$\to 0^-$	$\to\infty^-$
$\to\infty^+$	$\to\infty^-$	$\to 0^-$
$\to\infty^-$	$\to\infty^+$	$\to 0^-$

- Make a table of values and sketch the graph.

x	$g(x)$	$\frac{1}{g}$
-6	-2	$-\frac{1}{2}$
-4	$-\frac{2}{3}$	$-1\frac{1}{2}$
-2	$\frac{2}{3}$	$1\frac{1}{2}$
0	2	$\frac{1}{2}$
$1\frac{1}{2}$	3	$\frac{1}{3}$
3	3	$\frac{1}{3}$
4	$1\frac{1}{2}$	$\frac{2}{3}$
6	$-1\frac{1}{2}$	$-\frac{2}{3}$

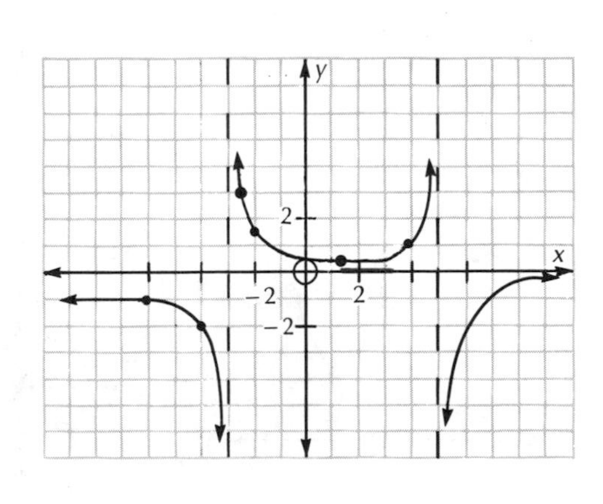

EXERCISE 1-8

A 1. Determine the excluded values for each of the following functions. State the domain and range.

a. $f(x) = \dfrac{1}{x - 3}$ **b.** $g(x) = \dfrac{1}{x + 2}$ **c.** $R(x) = \dfrac{1}{x^2 - 9}$ **d.** $p(x) = \dfrac{1}{x^2 - 16}$

e. $t(x) = \sqrt{x + 2}$ **f.** $r(x) = \sqrt{x^2 - 25}$ **g.** $m(x) = \dfrac{1}{\sqrt{x^2 - 9}}$ **h.** $s(x) = \dfrac{1}{\sqrt{x^2 - 16}}$

i. $q(x) = \sqrt{5 - x}$ **j.** $n(x) = \dfrac{1}{\sqrt{1 - x^2}}$ **k.** $k(x) = \dfrac{1}{\sqrt{1 - x}}$ **l.** $h(x) = \dfrac{1}{\sqrt{9 - x^2}}$

2. Complete each table.

a.

x	$\dfrac{1}{x-3}$
$\to 3^+$	$\to$ ■
$\to 3^-$	$\to$ ■
$\to \infty^+$	$\to$ ■
$\to \infty^-$	$\to$ ■

b.

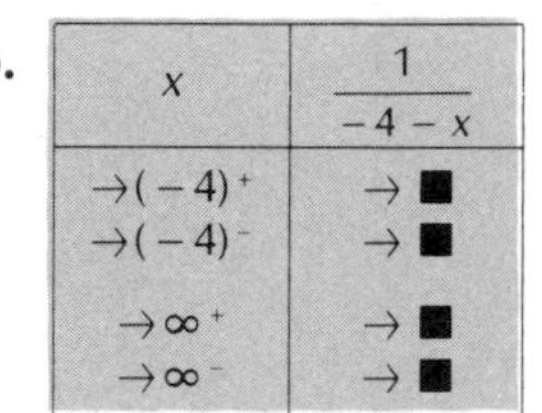

x	$\dfrac{1}{-4-x}$
$\to(-4)^+$	$\to$ ■
$\to(-4)^-$	$\to$ ■
$\to \infty^+$	$\to$ ■
$\to \infty^-$	$\to$ ■

c.

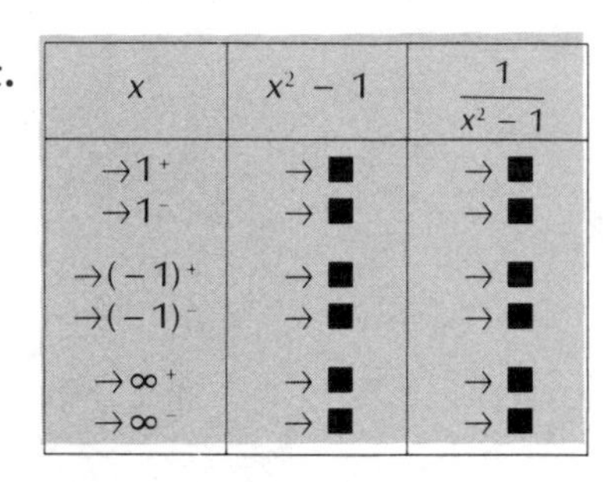

x	$x^2 - 1$	$\dfrac{1}{x^2-1}$
$\to 1^+$	$\to$ ■	$\to$ ■
$\to 1^-$	$\to$ ■	$\to$ ■
$\to(-1)^+$	$\to$ ■	$\to$ ■
$\to(-1)^-$	$\to$ ■	$\to$ ■
$\to \infty^+$	$\to$ ■	$\to$ ■
$\to \infty^-$	$\to$ ■	$\to$ ■

B 3. For each graph of $y = f(x)$ given below, determine the critical values of x for $y = \dfrac{1}{f(x)}$. That is, find the values of x for which $\dfrac{1}{f(x)}$ is undefined.

a.

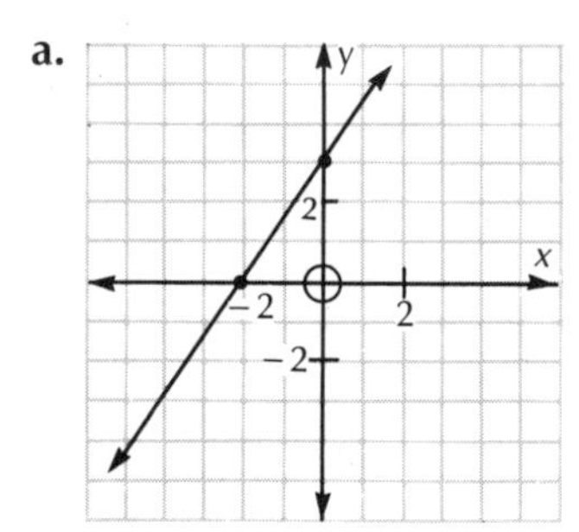

b.

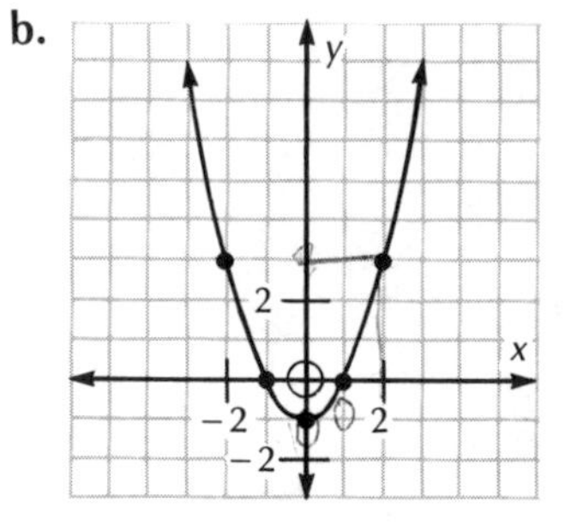

c.

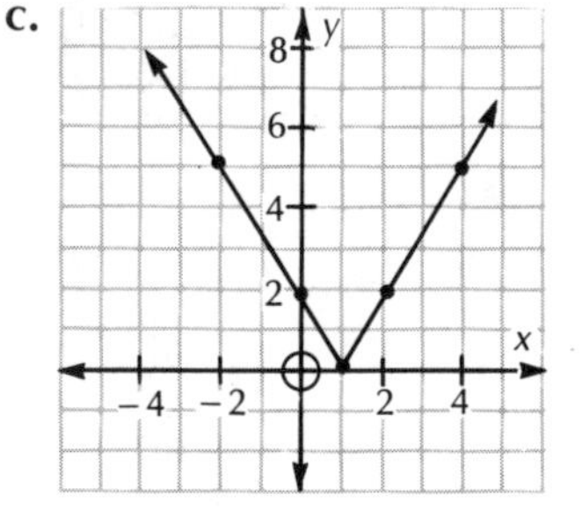

d.

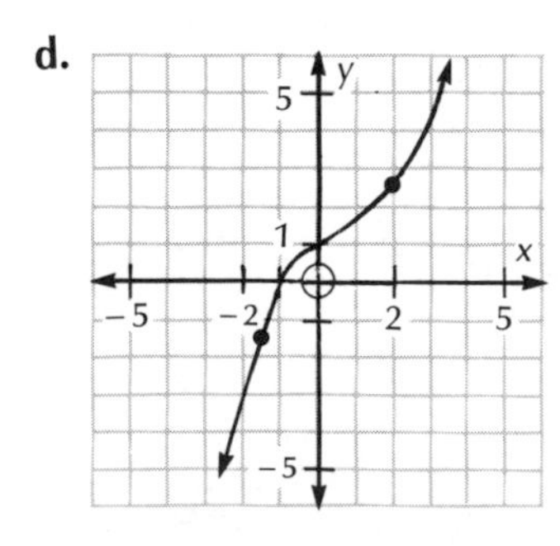

e.

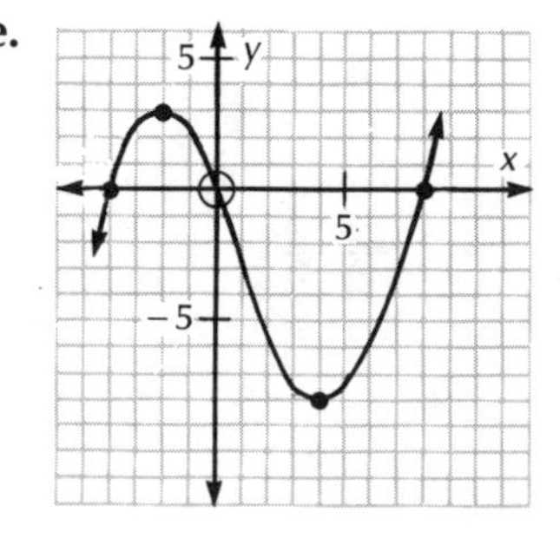

f.

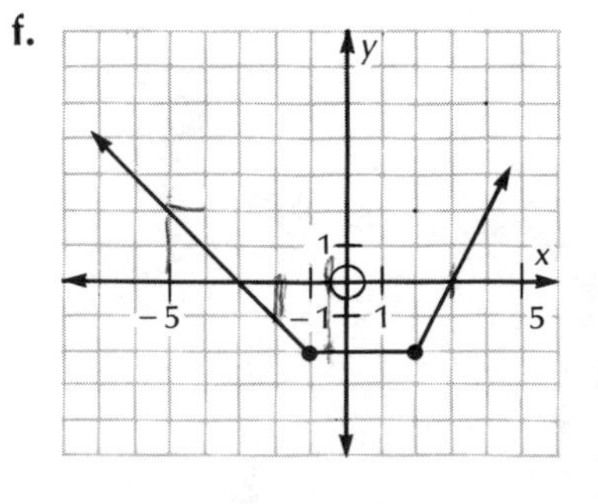

4. Graph the function defined by each equation and find each domain and range.

a. $y = \frac{1}{x + 1}$ **b.** $y = \frac{1}{x^2 - 16}$ **c.** $y = \frac{1}{\sqrt{x - 3}}$

d. $y = \frac{1}{x - 3}$ **e.** $y = \frac{1}{x^2 - 4}$ **f.** $y = \frac{1}{x} + 3$

5. Without graphing, determine the horizontal and vertical asymptotes and the excluded regions of each function. State the domain and range of each.

a. $y = \frac{1}{x - 5}$ **b.** $y = \frac{3}{x^2 - 1}$ **c.** $y = \frac{1}{\sqrt{x - 5}}$

d. $y = \frac{1}{x^2 - 25}$ **e.** $y = \frac{1}{x} - 6$ **f.** $y = \frac{1}{\sqrt{x^2 - 4}} + 5$

6. Copy each graph of $y = f(x)$ and on the same set of axes plot $y = \frac{1}{f(x)}$.

a.

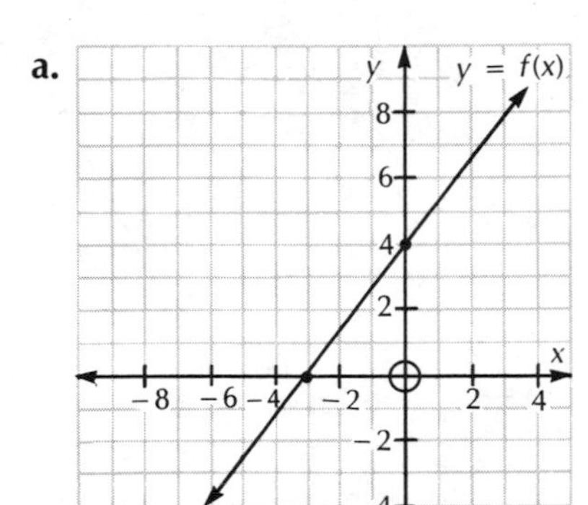

b.

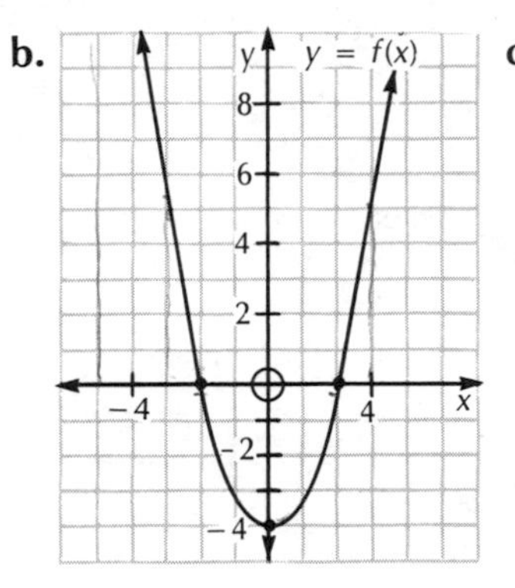

c.

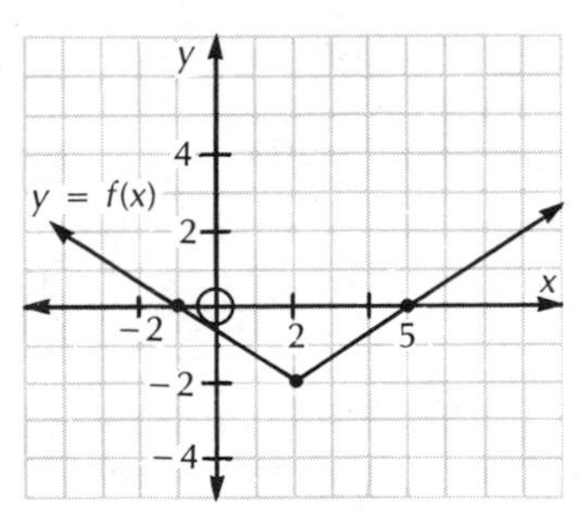

d.

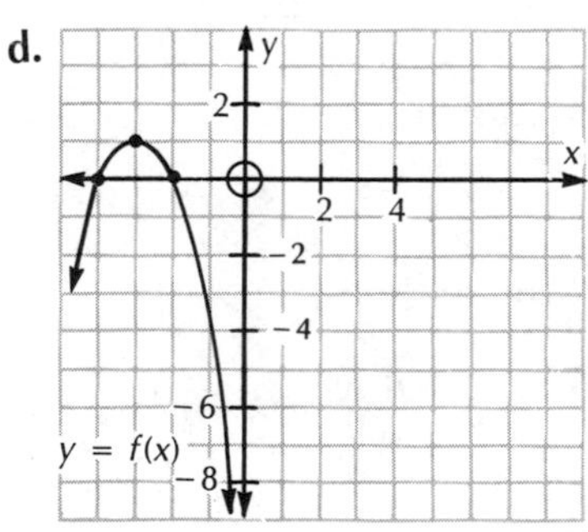

e.

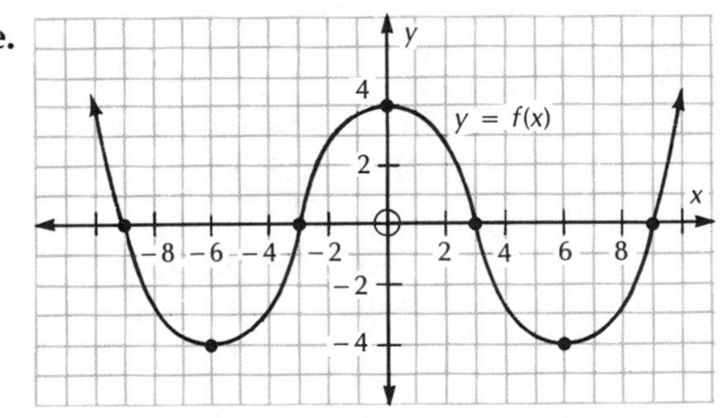

7. For the function f defined by each given equation, plot the graph of $\frac{1}{f}$ by determining asymptotes and excluded regions.

a. $y = 2x + 6$ **b.** $y = x^2 - 1$ **c.** $y = \sqrt{x^2 - 25}$

d. $y = (x - 3)(x + 5)$ **e.** $y = \sqrt{x + 5}$ **f.** $3x - 2y = 6$

8. Graph the function defined by each equation.

a. $y = \frac{x}{x^2 - 1}$ **b.** $y = \frac{3x - 1}{x^2 - 49}$ **c.** $y = \frac{x - 2}{x^2 - 4} + 5$

1-9 Periodic Functions

Tides are produced by the gravitational effects of the Sun and the Moon. Hydrographers prepare tide charts to provide ready access to the time and height of the tides.

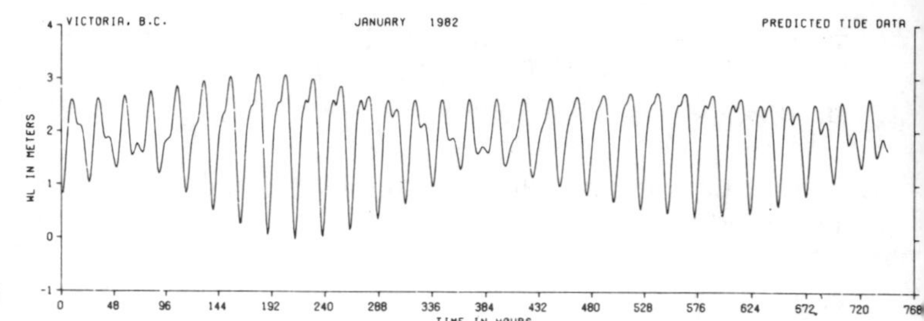

The movements of the Moon around the Earth and the Earth around the Sun are **periodic**. That is, the motions repeat at regular intervals. Tide calculations are based on these periodic motions.

The graph of a periodic function will be a series of congruent patterns that repeat.

Suppose a skier skis down a hill at a constant rate and then travels back up on a chair lift every 30 minutes. The skier's altitude from the bottom of the ski hill will be a periodic function of time.

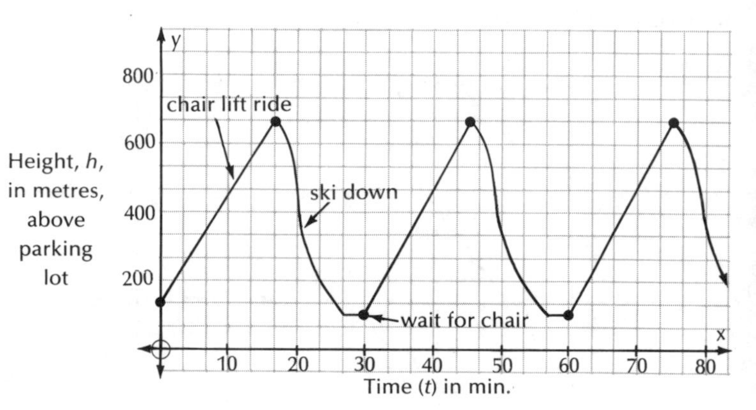

The skier repeats the same path every 30 minutes, provided the chair lift operates at a constant rate and the skier skis at a constant rate. At any time t, the skier will be at a height $h(t)$ from the bottom of the hill. Since the function is periodic, $h(t)$ will also be the skier's height 30 minutes from t, or $h(t + 30)$. That is, $h(t) = h(t + 30)$.

Also note that the skier gets on the chair at a height of 100 m above the parking lot and gets off at the top of the ski hill at 700 m. Half the difference between the maximum and minimum heights, 300 m, is the **amplitude** of the function h.

The **fundamental period** of the function is 30 minutes since it is the smallest positive value for which the function repeats itself. Any integral multiple of 30 will produce another period.

- A function f is a **periodic function** if, and only if, $f(x + p) = f(x)$ for some value p.
- The smallest positive number P such that $f(x + P) = f(x)$ is the **fundamental period** of the function.
- The **amplitude** of a periodic function is half the difference between the maximum and minimum values of the function.

XAMPLE Determine the fundamental period and amplitude of each function graphed below.

a.

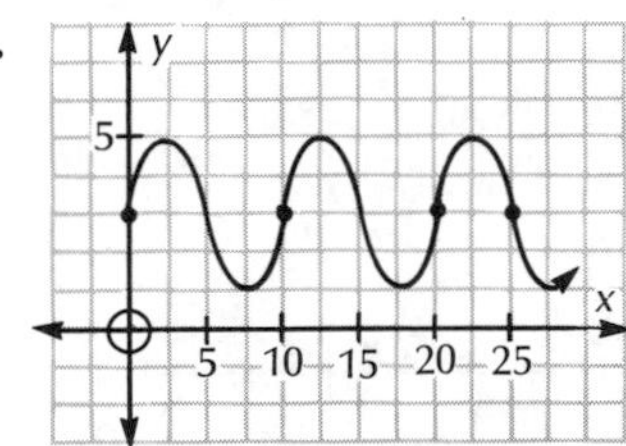

The graph repeats every 10 units along the horizontal axis. Thus, the period of the function is 10.
The amplitude is 2, half the difference between the minimum value, 1, and the maximum value, 5.

b.

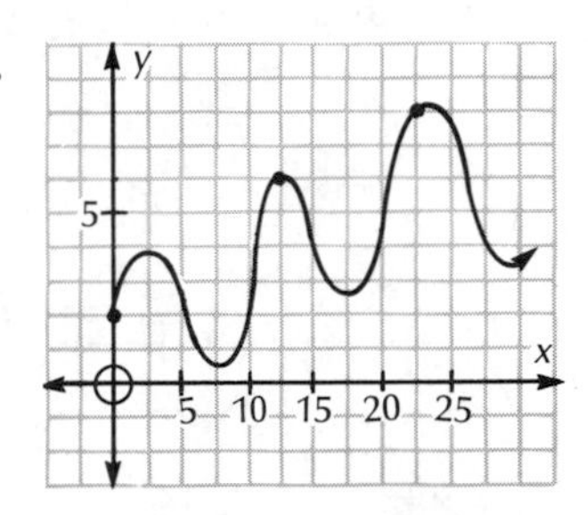

This is *not* a periodic function. Although the shape of the pattern appears to repeat, the values of $f(x)$ do not repeat—they increase steadily.

XERCISE 1-9

1. For each relation that is a function, classify each as periodic function or not periodic. If the function is periodic, then determine its period and amplitude.

a.

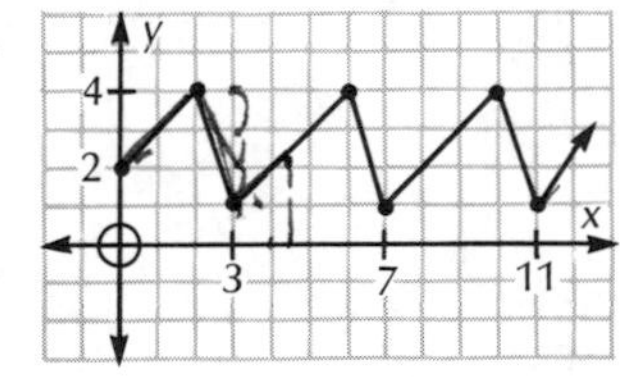

b.

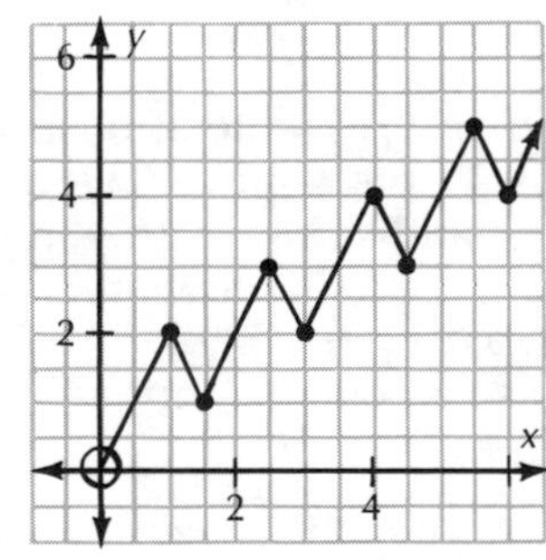

c.

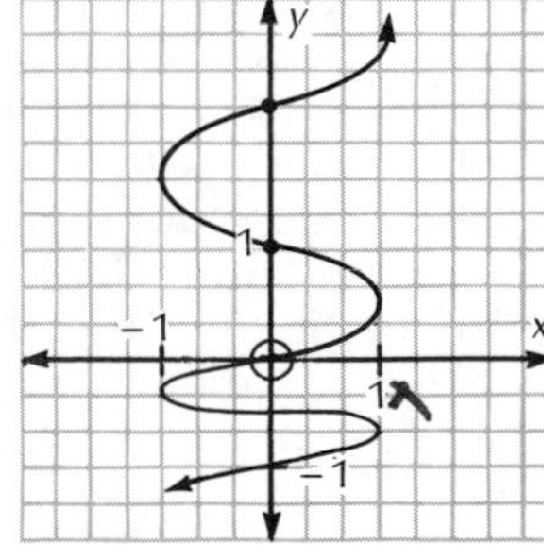

d.

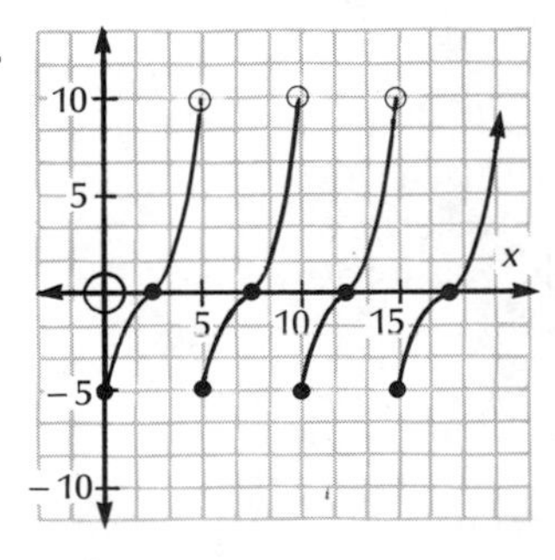

e.

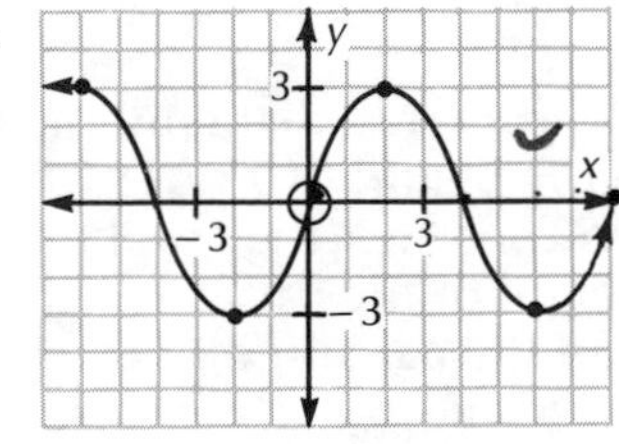

f.

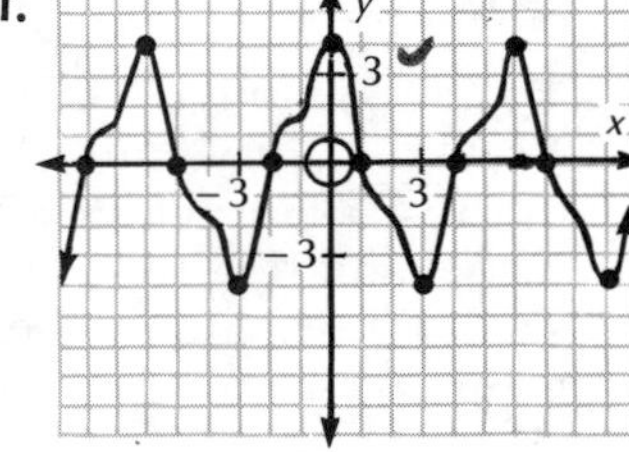

2. Functions f and g are defined by the graphs below. Graph $f + g$. Which of the function sums, $f + g$, is periodic? Give the amplitude and fundamental period.

a.

b.

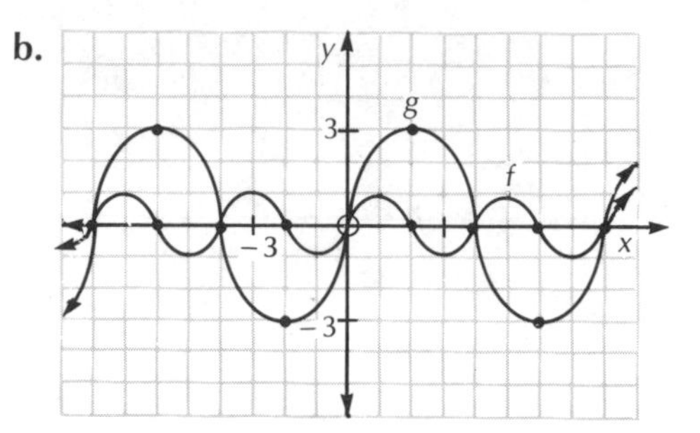

B 3. Plot the phases of the moon on a set of axes such as the one shown.

a. What is the period of the phases of the moon?
b. Predict the dates of the next three full moons.

New Moon	First Quarter	Full Moon	Last Quarter
Jan 10	Jan 17	Jan 26	Jan 3
Feb 9	Feb 16	Feb 24	Feb 2
Mar 10	Mar 18	Mar 26	Mar 3
Apr 9	Apr 17	Apr 24	Apr 1

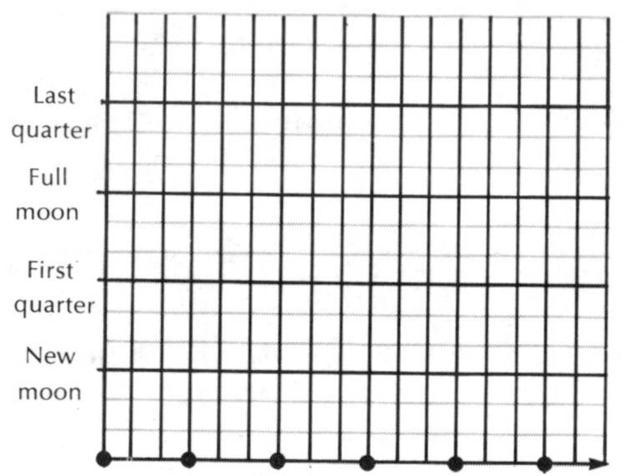

4. The amount of carbon dioxide (CO_2) in the atmosphere varies periodically with the seasons. Plants remove CO_2 from the atmosphere during the spring and summer growing season and subsequently release it during the fall and winter. The seasonal fluctuation is about 10 ppm (parts per million). In addition to the periodic variation, there is also an overall annual increase in the amount of CO_2 by about 1 ppm.

The concentration of CO_2 in April of 1980 was at an annual peak of 340 ppm. Sketch a graph of CO_2 concentration from 1980 to the year 2000.

C 5. An amusement park Ferris wheel has a diameter of 60 m and rotates at a rate of 0.5 rev/min. Graph the height of a rider who is riding in one of the cars for 0 to 5 min. (To construct the graph, sketch the Ferris wheel and determine the height of the car at 10 s intervals. From the sketch, measure the height of the car and plot the points on the graph.)

6. The graphs of functions f and g are shown below.

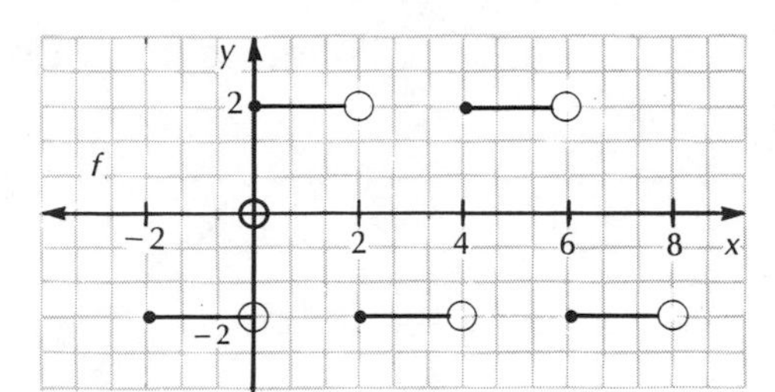

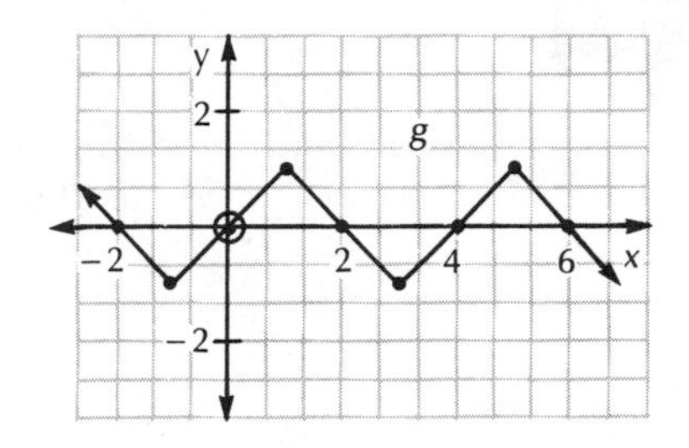

Graph each of the following. Give the period and amplitude for any that are periodic. **a.** $f + g$ **b.** $f \circ g$ **c.** $g \circ f$

7. A function f is periodic with $f(7) = 11$ and $f(12) = 11$.

a. Does this mean that the period of the function must be 5?
b. Must the period be a multiple of 5?
c. Must 5 be a multiple of the period?
d. Justify your answers to parts **a**, **b**, and **c**.

Application

The Tides

Ocean tides are caused by the gravitational effects of the Moon and the Sun. Although the Sun is far more massive than the Moon, the effect of the Moon is more than double that of the Sun because it is so much closer to the Earth.

At New Moon and Full Moon the Earth, Sun, and Moon are in line with one another. Tidal effects are strongest at these times. At the quarter phases of the Moon, the three bodies are out of line and the tidal effects are minimized.

Because the Moon's revolution around the Earth is periodic, as is the Earth's revolution around the Sun, tidal effects can be predicted.

Surprisingly, the height of tides is affected more by the geometry of the coastline than by gravity. Hence, the massive tides in the Bay of Fundy are primarily due to the particular shape of the bay rather than a particularly strong gravitational pull.

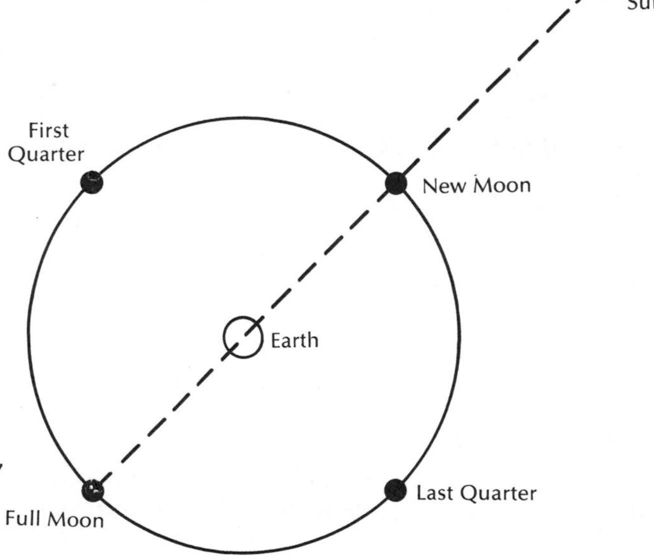

Look in an Earth Science text and find out how the rotation of the Earth and the inclination of the Moon's orbit affect the tides.

EXTRA

Slant Asymptotes

An oblique line l is a **slant asymptote** for a function f if the graph of $y = f(x)$ approaches l as $|x|$ becomes very large.

Consider the function defined by the equation

$$f(x) = \frac{x^2 - 2x + 1}{x}.$$

As long as $x \neq 0$, the equation can be rewritten as follows.

$$f(x) = \frac{x^2}{x} - \frac{2x}{x} + \frac{1}{x}$$
$$= x - 2 + \frac{1}{x}$$

The function $f(x)$, then, is the sum of $x - 2$ and $\frac{1}{x}$.

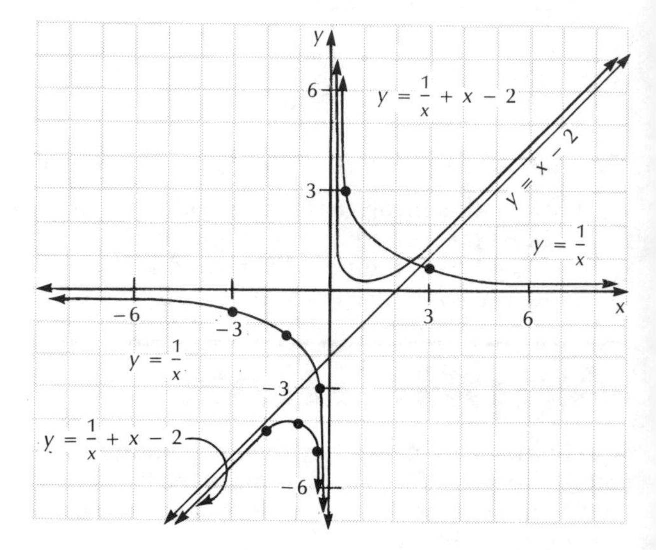

The graphs of $y = x - 2$ and $y = \frac{1}{x}$ are shown above. To find the graph of f, add the ordinates of $y = x - 2$ and $y = \frac{1}{x}$ at each point.

As $|x|$ becomes very large, $\frac{1}{x}$ becomes very small and the graph of f approaches the line $y = x - 2$.

The line $y = x - 2$ is a slant asymptote of f.

Determine the asymptotes, including the slant asymptotes, of the function defined by each equation. Use this information to sketch the graph of each function.

1. $y = \frac{2x^2 - 2x - 1}{x}$ **2.** $y = \frac{3x^2 - x + 1}{x}$ **3.** $y = \frac{2x^3 - 2x + 1}{x^2}$ **4.** $y = \frac{x^2 - 1}{\sqrt{x^2 - 1}}$

Review

1. Find the domain and range of each relation. Which are functions?

a. $\{(3, 7), (2, 8), (4, -3), (-1, 0), (-5, -3)\}$ **b.** $\{(x, y) \mid y = \sqrt{x^2 - 4}\}$

c.

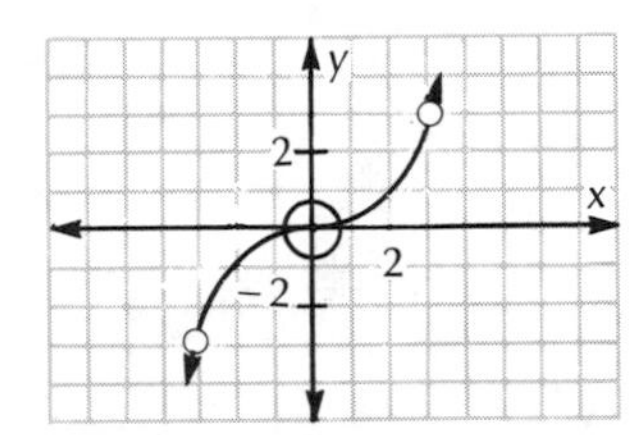

d.

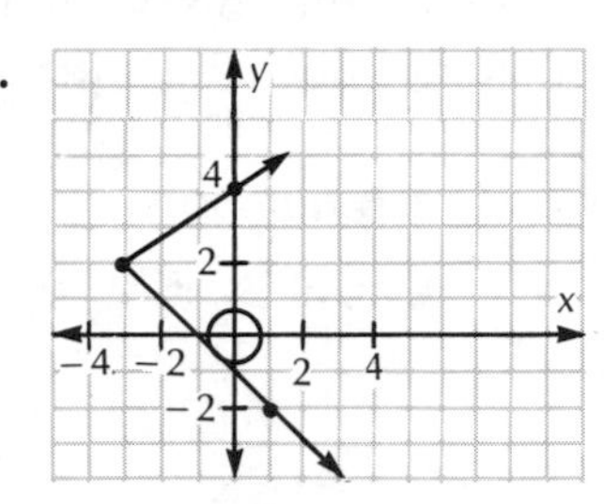

2. Given the graph of $y = \sqrt{4 - x^2}$, sketch the graph of each given equation.

a. $y = 3\sqrt{4 - x^2}$

b. $y = -\sqrt{4 - x^2}$

c. $y = \sqrt{4 - (x + 1)^2}$

d. $y = \sqrt{(4 - x^2) + 3}$

e. $y = \sqrt{4 - \left(\frac{x}{2}\right)^2}$

f. $y - 3 = -2\sqrt{4 - x^2}$

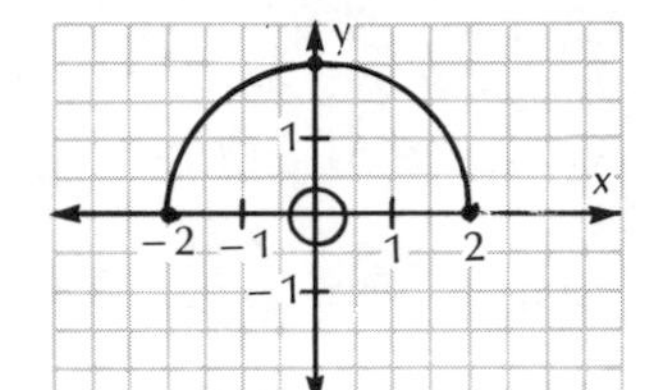

3. The graph of each equation is transformed as indicated. Determine an equation of each transformation image.

a. $y = x^2$ Translated 3 units up, parallel to the y-axis and 2 units left, parallel to the x-axis

b. $y = 3x - 2$ Reflected in the x-axis and stretched by a factor of 4, parallel to the y-axis

c. $y = \dfrac{1}{\sqrt{x - 1}}$ Translated 2 units down, parallel to the y-axis and reflected in the y-axis

4. Given the graphs of f and g at the right, sketch the graphs of $f + g$ and $f - g$.

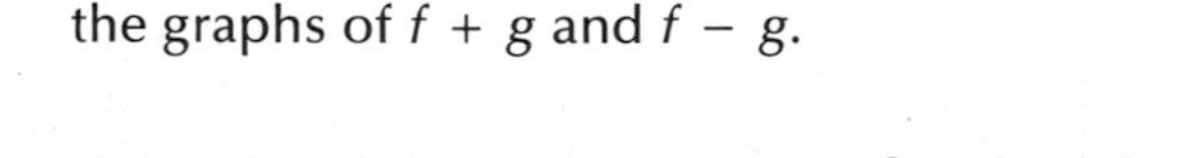

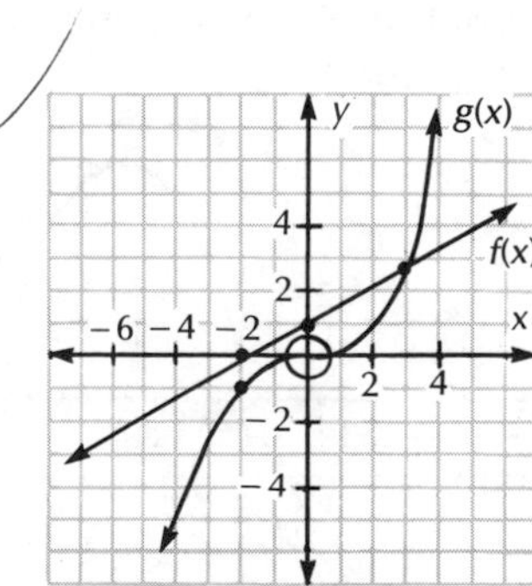

5. Given that $f(x) = 2x - 1$, $g(x) = x^2 - 3$, and h: $\{(2, 0), (1, 3), (0, -2), (-1, 5), (-2, 3)\}$, find the following.

a. $f \circ h(-1)$ **b.** $h \circ g(1)$ **c.** $f \circ g(2)$

d. $g \circ f(-1)$ **e.** $h \circ f(1)$ **f.** $f \circ g(x)$

g. $g \circ f(x)$ **h.** $R(f \circ h)$ **i.** $R(f \circ g)$

j. $D(g \circ h)$ **k.** $R(g \circ h)$ **l.** $R(g \circ f)$

6. Large photographic prints are made by projecting images onto sheets of photographic paper pinned to a wall. The exposure time, t, needed for a print is related to the area of the print, A, according to the equation $T: t = 0.01A$. The area of the print is related to the distance from the projector, d, according to the equation $D: A = 0.3d^2$.

   a. Find an equation for the composite function $T \circ D$.
   b. What two quantities does the equation in part **a** relate?

7. Find the inverse of each function.

   a. $f: \{(3, 7), (2, 1), (-4, 6), (0, 5), (-2, 1)\}$ b. $y = 2x + 3$

   c. $f: x \to x^2 - 2$ d. $f: \{(x, y) \mid y = \frac{2}{x - 1}\}$

8. Find the solution set of each inequality and graph each solution on a number line.

   a. $|2x - 1| \geq 7$ b. $|3 - 2x| \leq 3$ c. $3|x| - |x| > 6$
   d. $4|x - 1| - |x - 1| \leq 6$ e. $3|x - 5| - 1 > 8$ f. $3|2x - 1| + |2x - 1| < 12$

9. The graphs of $y = f(x)$ and $y = g(x)$ are shown at the right.

   a. Sketch the graphs of $y = |f(x)|$, $y = f(|x|)$, $y = f^{-1}(x)$, and $y = g^{-1}(x)$.
   b. Which of the graphs represent functions?

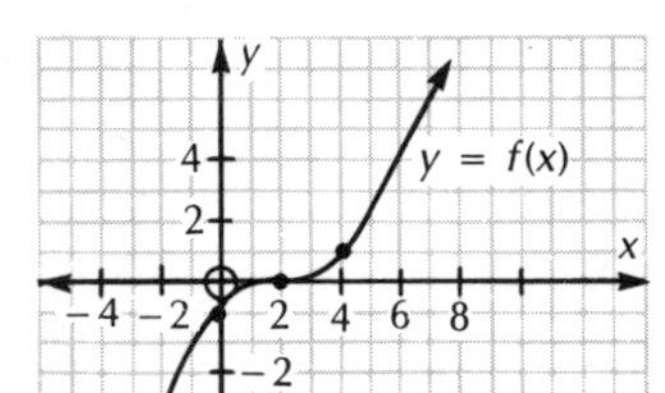

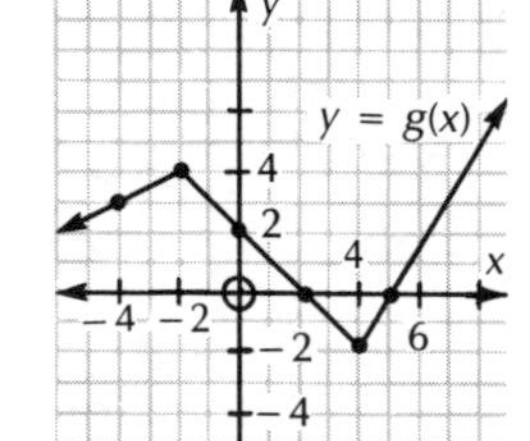

10. Sketch the graph of each function. Determine the horizontal and vertical asymptotes and the excluded regions.

   a. $y = \frac{1}{4 - x}$ b. $y = \frac{1}{x^2 - 1}$ c. $y = \frac{1}{\sqrt{x^2 - 4}}$

11. Determine whether or not each graph represents a periodic function. If the function is periodic, then give its period and amplitude.

a.
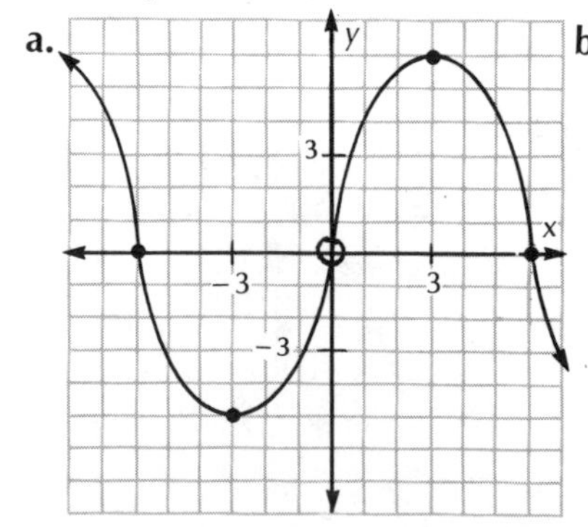

b.
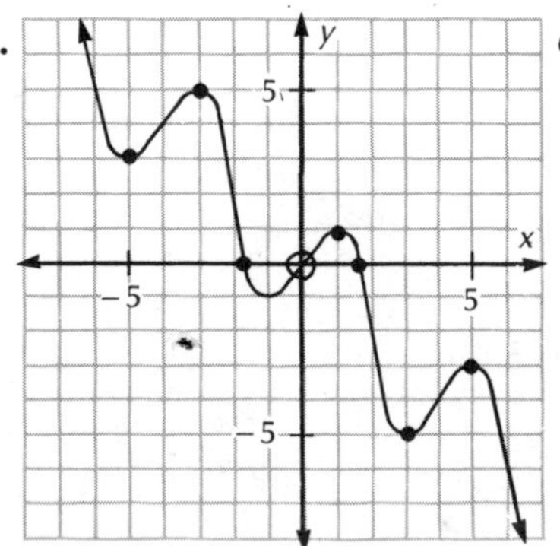

c.
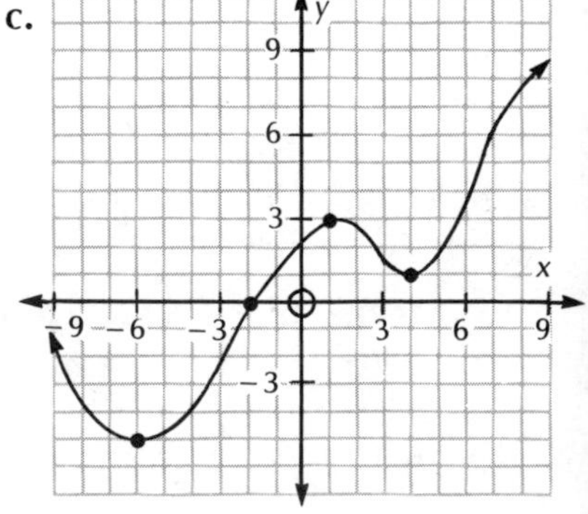

Test

Unit 1

1. Determine each of the following for the given functions f, g, h, and k.

f: $\{(-3, 1), (-2, 0), (-1, 3), (0, 5), (1, 6), (2, 8), (3, 10)\}$
g: $\{(0, -4), (1, -3), (2, -1), (3, 2), (4, 5)\}$
h: $\{(x, y) \mid y = 2x - 3, x, y \in \mathbf{R}\}$
k: $\{(x, y) \mid y = \sqrt{x^2 - 9}, x, y \in \mathbf{R}\}$

a. Domain of f **b.** Range of k **c.** Range of g^{-1}
d. $f(0)$ **e.** $f(g(3))$ **f.** $k \circ h(2)$
g. $f^{-1}(3)$ **h.** $k^{-1}(\sqrt{5})$ **i.** g^{-1}
j. $f \circ h$ **k.** $D(g \circ f)$ **l.** $R(h \circ k)$

2. The graphs of f and g are given.

a. Sketch the graph of the inverse of f and g.
b. Which of the inverses are also functions?
c. Sketch the graphs of $\frac{1}{f}$, $\frac{1}{g}$, and $f + g$.

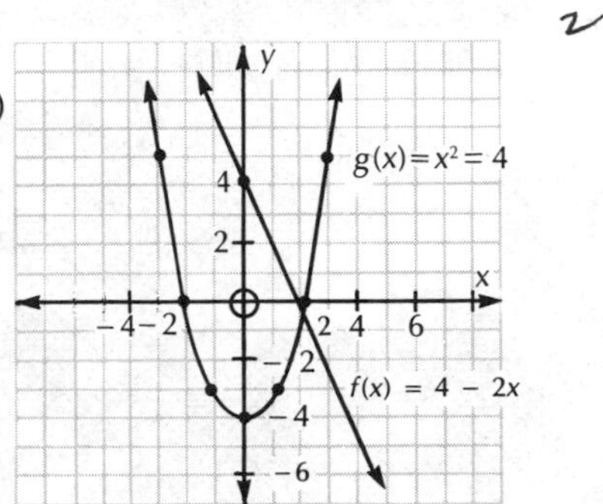

3. In each case a graph and its image under transformation are given. Determine an equation of each transformation image.

a.

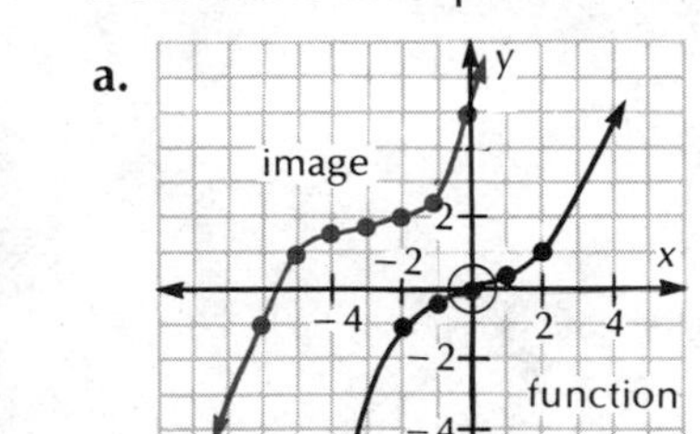

b.

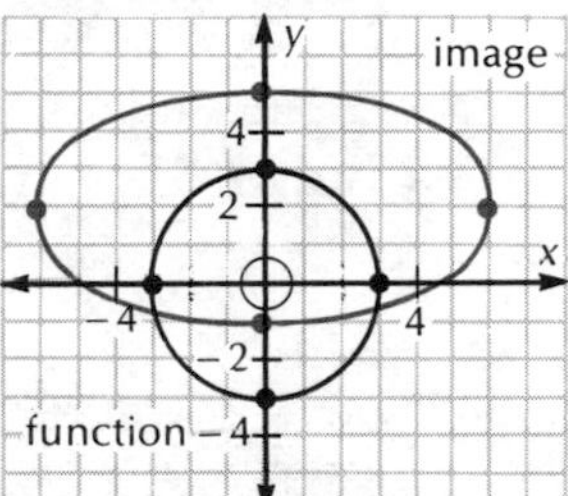

c.

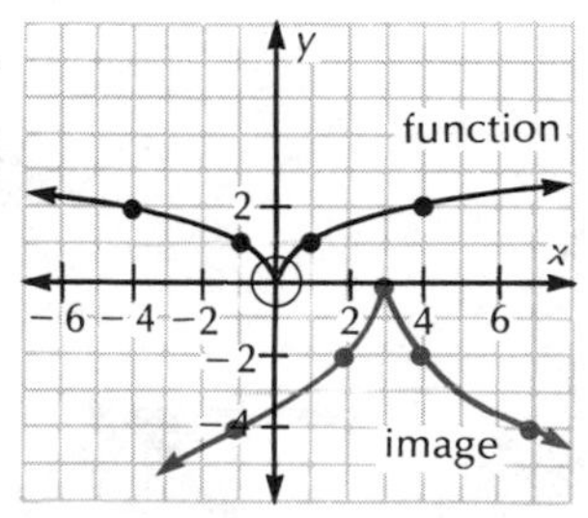

4. Graph the solution set of each inequality on a number line.

a. $|3 - 2x| \geq 5$ **b.** $5|x - 5| + 2 < 7$ **c.** $4|3x + 2| - |3x + 2| \geq 15$

5. Sketch the graph of the function defined by each equation. Determine the horizontal and vertical asymptotes and the excluded regions.

a. $\dfrac{1}{x - 3}$ **b.** $\dfrac{1}{x^3 - 8}$ **c.** $\dfrac{1}{\sqrt{4 - x^2}}$

6. A periodic function p has an amplitude of 15 and a period of 7.

a. If the maximum value of the function is 4, what is the minimum value?
b. $p(3) = 5$; What is $p(10)$?
c. Is it possible that $p(0) = 5$?
d. Is it possible that $p(-1) = 1$?

2 Exponential Functions

2-1 Rational Exponents

Mathematics can be applied to measure the loudness of sound by using a unit called a *decibel* (dB), which is one tenth of a *bel*. That is, 1 dB = 0.1 bel. The unit was named in honor of Alexander Graham Bell, the inventor of the telephone.

Decibels and bels are used to measure audible sound. Each 10 dB increase in loudness of sound results in the intensity of the sound being multiplied by 10. For example, the rustling of leaves in a tree may measure 20 dB, or 2 bels.

A sound that measures 30 dB, or 3 bels, is 10 times as intense as the sound of rustling leaves.

A sound that measures 40 dB, or 4 bels, is 100 times more intense than that of rustling leaves.

This relationship is illustrated in the following table.

Loudness of Sound in Bels	1	2	3	4	5	6
Intensity of Sound	10	10^2	10^3	10^4	10^5	10^6

The loudness of sound in normal conversation measures about 60 dB, or 6 bels. A lion's roar measures about 89 dB, or 8.9 bels. The intensity of the two sounds can be compared using powers of 10, and written as a fraction with rational exponents.

$\frac{10^{8.9}}{10^{6.0}}$

The numerator represents the intensity of a lion's roar.

The denominator represents the intensity of normal conversation.

Since the base of both the numerator and the denominator is 10, the fraction can be simplified using laws of exponents, which are reviewed below.

For $a \in \mathbf{R}$, $a > 0$, and $p, q \in \mathbf{Q}$, the following rules of exponents apply.

- **Product Rule:** $(a^p)(a^q) = a^{p+q}$
- **Power Rule:** $(a^p)^q = a^{pq}$
- **Quotient Rule:** $a^p \div a^q = a^{p-q}$
- $a^0 = 1$
- $a^{-p} = \frac{1}{a^p}$

EXAMPLE 1: Simplify.

a. $(2a^3)(3a^4b) = 6a^{3+4}b$
$= 6a^7b$

b. $10^{8.9} \div 10^{6.0} = 10^{8.9-6.0}$
$= 10^{2.9}$

c. $\frac{3mn^2p^3r^{-2}}{(3np)^2} = \frac{3mn^2p^3}{9n^2p^2r^2}$

$= \frac{mn^0p^1}{3r^2}$

$= \frac{mp}{3r^2}$

For $a, b \in \boldsymbol{R}$, $a, b \geq 0$, and $p \in \boldsymbol{Q}$,

$(ab)^p = a^p b^p$ and $\left(\frac{a}{b}\right)^p = \frac{a^p}{b^p}$.

EXAMPLE 2: Simplify.

a. $\left(x^{\frac{1}{3}}y^{\frac{1}{2}}\right)^2 = \left(x^{\frac{1}{3}}\right)^2\left(y^{\frac{1}{2}}\right)^2$

$= x^{\frac{2}{3}}y$

b. $\left(\frac{2a^2}{3b^3}\right)^2 = \frac{(2a^2)^2}{(3b^3)^2}$

$= \frac{4a^4}{9b^6}$

c. $(4m^2n^{-3})\left(\frac{3m^{-4}n^{-2}}{2mn^2}\right) = \frac{12m^{-2}n^{-5}}{2mn^2}$

$= \frac{6}{m^3n^7}$

d. $9^{\frac{1}{4}} \div 9^{\frac{1}{2}} = 9^{\frac{1}{4}-\frac{1}{2}}$

$= 9^{-\frac{1}{4}}$

$= \frac{1}{9^{\frac{1}{4}}}$

Expressions with rational exponents can often be written using radicals. For example, consider $\left(x^{\frac{1}{2}}\right)^2$ and $(\sqrt{x})^2$, where $x \geq 0$.

$\left(x^{\frac{1}{2}}\right)^2 = \left(x^{\frac{1}{2}}\right)\left(x^{\frac{1}{2}}\right)$

$= x^{\frac{1}{2}+\frac{1}{2}}$

$= x$

$(\sqrt{x})^2 = (\sqrt{x})(\sqrt{x})$

$= \sqrt{x^2}$

$= x$

Since $\left(x^{\frac{1}{2}}\right)^2 = x$ and $(\sqrt{x})^2 = x$, then $x^{\frac{1}{2}} = \sqrt{x}$, with the restriction that $x \geq 0$.

Similarly, $x^{\frac{1}{3}} = \sqrt[3]{x}$, $x^{\frac{1}{4}} = \sqrt[4]{x}$, etc.

If the denominator of a rational exponent is an even number, another restriction applies.

For example, consider $x^{\frac{1}{2}}$ and $x^{\frac{1}{3}}$ for $x = \pm 64$.

If $x = 64$, then $x^{\frac{1}{2}} = \sqrt{64}$ or 8.

If $x = -64$, then $x^{\frac{1}{2}} = \sqrt{-64}$, which is not a real number.

Therefore, $(-64)^{\frac{1}{2}}$ has no real solution.

If $x = 64$, then $x^{\frac{1}{3}} = \sqrt[3]{64}$, or 4.

If $x = -64$, then $x^{\frac{1}{3}} = \sqrt[3]{-64}$, or -4.

Thus, for a rational exponent with an even denominator, the base must not be negative.

> In general, for $a \in \boldsymbol{R}$, $\sqrt[n]{a} = a^{\frac{1}{n}}$, where $a \geqslant 0$ when n is even.

Powers with rational exponents can be written in a number of equivalent ways. Consider the following equivalent ways of writing $5^{\frac{3}{8}}$.

$$5^{\frac{3}{8}} = \left(5^{\frac{1}{8}}\right)^3 \qquad 5^{\frac{3}{8}} = (\sqrt[8]{5})^3$$

$$5^{\frac{3}{8}} = (5^3)^{\frac{1}{8}} \qquad 5^{\frac{3}{8}} = \sqrt[8]{5^3}$$

> In general, for $a \in \boldsymbol{R}$, $p, q \in \boldsymbol{Z}$, and $q \neq 0$, $a^{\frac{p}{q}} = (a^p)^{\frac{1}{q}}$ or $\left(a^{\frac{1}{q}}\right)^p$ and
>
> $a^{\frac{p}{q}} = \sqrt[q]{a^p}$ or $(\sqrt[q]{a})^p$, where $a \geqslant 0$ when q is even.

EXAMPLE 3: Rewrite and simplify.

a. $(-8)^{\frac{5}{3}} = (\sqrt[3]{-8})^5$
$= (-2)^5$
$= -32$

b. $(-81)^{0.75} = (-81)^{\frac{3}{4}}$
$= (\sqrt[4]{-81})^3$

This has no real solution since $\sqrt[4]{-81}$ is not a real number.

c. $\sqrt[3]{125^2} = (\sqrt[3]{125})^2$
$= 5^2$
$= 25$

Notice that evaluating in this form results in a calculation that is easier than evaluating $\sqrt[3]{125^2}$.

EXERCISE 2-1

A 1. Write each of the following as a rational number.

a. 2^{-3} b. $9^{\frac{1}{2}}$ c. $(3^2)^3$ d. $(-2)^0$
e. $(-3)^{-3}$ f. $(-7)^{-2}$ g. $8^{\frac{1}{3}}$ h. $8^{\frac{2}{3}}$
i. $\left(\frac{9}{16}\right)^{-\frac{1}{2}}$ j. $(\sqrt{5})^2$ k. $\sqrt{8}\,\sqrt{2}$ l. $\left(\frac{1}{1000}\right)^{-\frac{1}{3}}$
m. $\left(4^{\frac{1}{2}}\right)^3$ n. $625^{\frac{1}{4}}$ o. $\left(2^{\frac{1}{2}}\right)\left(18^{\frac{1}{2}}\right)$ p. $900^{0.5}$

2. Explain why $-(3^2)$ and $(-3)^2$ do not have the same value.

3. If x is an integer, then for what values of x is $-(3^x)$ equal to $(-3)^x$?

4. Which of the given numbers are real numbers?

a. $27^{\frac{2}{3}}$ b. $(-81)^{\frac{3}{4}}$ c. $32^{\frac{3}{5}}$ d. $(-125)^{\frac{2}{3}}$
e. $(-4)^{\frac{3}{2}}$ f. $(-6)^{\frac{3}{4}}$ g. $13^{-\frac{5}{3}}$ h. $(-17)^{\frac{5}{6}}$

5. Rewrite using only rational exponents.

a. $\sqrt[3]{5^2}$ b. $\sqrt[4]{15^2}$ c. $(\sqrt[3]{-25})^2$ d. $(\sqrt[3]{-8})^2$
e. $\sqrt[3]{\frac{8}{27}}$ f. $(\sqrt[5]{-32})^{-4}$ g. $(\sqrt[3]{-27})^{-2}$ h. $\left(\sqrt{\frac{36}{49}}\right)^{-3}$

6. Rewrite using only positive exponents.

a. $\frac{1}{(2^{-3})}$ b. $\left(\frac{1}{2}\right)^{-1}$ c. $\frac{3}{(1-3^{-2})}$ d. $\frac{1}{3^{-1}}+\frac{1}{2^{-1}}$
e. $1-3^{-1}$ f. $1-2^{-3}$ g. $2^{-1}-3$ h. $(2^{-1})^{-2}$

B 7. Simplify each expression.

a. $\left(x^{\frac{1}{2}}\right)\left(x^{-\frac{1}{2}}\right)$ b. $\left(a^{\frac{1}{4}}\right)\left(a^{-\frac{1}{2}}\right)$ c. $(x^3)\left(x^{\frac{2}{3}}\right)$ d. $b^{\frac{1}{2}} \div b^{\frac{2}{3}}$
e. $t^{\frac{5}{2}} \div t^{\frac{3}{4}}$ f. $\left(x^{-\frac{6}{7}}\right)^{\frac{1}{2}}$ g. $\left(y^{\frac{4}{5}}\right)^{-\frac{2}{3}}$ h. $\left(2x^{\frac{1}{3}}y^2\right)^3$
i. $\left(3a^{\frac{1}{2}}b^{\frac{1}{4}}\right)^2$ j. $(25x^4y^{-8})^{\frac{1}{2}}$ k. $(16a^2b^{-6})^{\frac{1}{2}}$ l. $(8a^3b^{-6})^{\frac{1}{3}}$
m. $(-8x^6y^{-9})^{\frac{2}{3}}$ n. $(-27x^6y^{-9})^{\frac{1}{3}}$ o. $(-32a^{-5}b^{10})^{-\frac{3}{5}}$ p. $(-27x^6y^{-9})^{\frac{2}{3}}$

8. Simplify each expression.

a. $\dfrac{\left(27^{\frac{2}{3}}\right)\left(16^{\frac{3}{4}}\right)}{8^{\frac{5}{3}}}$

b. $\dfrac{\left(a^{\frac{2}{3}}\right)\left(a^{-\frac{3}{4}}\right)}{a^{\frac{1}{2}}}$

c. $\dfrac{\left(x^2y^{-\frac{2}{3}}\right)^3\left(x^{\frac{1}{3}}y\right)^2}{\left(x^{\frac{1}{2}}y^{\frac{1}{3}}\right)^2}$

d. $\dfrac{\left(27^{\frac{1}{4}}\right)\left(3^{\frac{1}{2}}\right)\left(6^{\frac{3}{4}}\right)}{2^{-\frac{1}{4}}}$

9. You can use a calculator with a $\boxed{y^x}$ key to evaluate an expression like $1.5^{0.32}$, as shown below.

$\boxed{1.5}$ $\boxed{y^x}$ $\boxed{0.32}$ $\boxed{=}$ 1.138 542 3

$\doteq$ 1.14 (correct to two decimal places)

Use a calculator with a $\boxed{y^x}$ key to evaluate each expression. Round answers to the nearest hundredth.

a. $(1.7)^{0.52}$ **b.** $(4.2)^{0.87}$ **c.** $(0.3)^{7.2}$ **d.** $25(1.02)^{3.5}$ **e.** $0.75(1.72)^{1.6}$

10. Using a calculator, you can determine that $(0.86)^{-5.2} = 2.190\,826\,8$. Experiment with a calculator to determine which keys can be used to obtain this result.

11. Use a calculator to evaluate each expression.

a. $(9.62)^{-2}$ **b.** $(2)^{-1.5}$ **c.** $(3)^{-0.03}$ **d.** $50(1.02)^{-5}$

e. $70(0.5)^{-3.5}$ **f.** $0.3(14.5)^{-7.2}$ **g.** $(17.2)^{-0.3}$ **h.** $3^{-0.005}$

12. A calculator can be used to evaluate $8^{\frac{1}{3}}$, as shown below.

$\boxed{8}$ $\boxed{y^x}$ $\boxed{3}$ 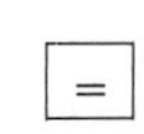  $\boxed{\frac{1}{x}}$ $\boxed{=}$ $\boxed{2}$

Use a calculator to evaluate each expression. Round answers to the nearest hundredth.

a. $27^{\frac{1}{3}}$ **b.** $\sqrt[4]{7.5}$ **c.** $\sqrt[5]{10.7}$ **d.** $\sqrt[3]{0.002\,16}$

13. A calculator can be used to evaluate $8^{\frac{2}{3}}$, as shown below. (Note: $\boxed{M+}$ is an "add to memory" key and $\boxed{MR}$ is a "memory recall" key.)

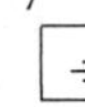  $\boxed{2}$ $\boxed{\div}$ $\boxed{3}$ $\boxed{=}$ $\boxed{M+}$ $\boxed{8}$ $\boxed{y^x}$ $\boxed{MR}$ $\boxed{=}$ 4

Use a calculator to evaluate each expression.

a. $(27)^{\frac{2}{3}}$ **b.** $(0.15)^{\frac{4}{7}}$ **c.** $(0.47)^{\frac{2}{9}}$ **d.** $(56.2)^{-\frac{2}{3}}$

14. If the sound of normal conversation measures 6.0 bels, determine how much louder each given sound is than that of normal conversation.

a. a lion's roar at 8.7 bels
b. Niagara Falls at 9 bels
c. a passing train at 10.5 bels
d. a jet engine at 11.3 bels

2-2 Real Exponents

Powers with *rational* exponents, such as $7^{\frac{2}{3}}$ and 5^{-3}, can be readily evaluated using rules of exponents and a calculator. However, evaluating powers with *irrational* exponents requires further investigation.

Does $2^{\sqrt{2}}$ exist? Can its value be calculated?

A graph can be used to show that $2^{\sqrt{2}}$ has a value in the real numbers. First, a table of values is used to graph $y = 2^x$, as shown below.

x	$y = 2^x$
−3	0.125
−2	0.250
−1	0.500
0	1.000
1	2.000
2	4.000
3	8.000

Then the Pythagorean Theorem is applied to determine that the segment joining points (0, 0) and (1, 1) has length $\sqrt{2}$.

A circle with centre (0, 0) and radius $\sqrt{2}$ intersects the x-axis at the point $(\sqrt{2}, 0)$.

Finally, the line $x = \sqrt{2}$ is drawn.

Notice that this vertical line contains the point $(\sqrt{2}, 0)$ and intersects the graph of $y = 2^x$ at the point $(\sqrt{2}, 2^{\sqrt{2}})$.

That is, when $x = \sqrt{2}$, the value of $y = 2^x$ is $2^{\sqrt{2}}$.

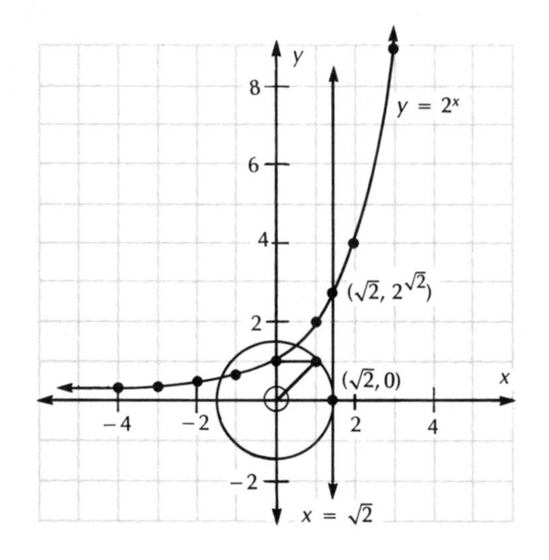

If the graph of $y = 2^x$ is *continuous*, or has no breaks in it, then *all* lines that are perpendicular to the x-axis will intersect the graph of $y = 2^x$.

Thus, 2^x has a value in the real numbers for every real value of x, and in particular for $x = \sqrt{2}$.

Since $2^{\sqrt{2}}$ has a real value, a calculator can be used to approximate the value, as shown below.

[2] [y^x] [2] [$\sqrt{\ }$] [=] 2.665 144 1 (correct to seven decimal places)

EXERCISE 2-2

A **1.** Simplify each expression.

a. $(7^{1+\sqrt{2}})(7^{1-\sqrt{2}})$ **b.** $(3^{\sqrt{5}})(3^{-\sqrt{5}})$ **c.** $4^{3\sqrt{2}} \div 4^{2\sqrt{2}}$
d. $9^{\sqrt{10}} \div 3^{\sqrt{10}}$ **e.** $(2^{3\sqrt{2}})^{\sqrt{3}}$ **f.** $7^{1+\sqrt{5}} \div 7^{\sqrt{5}}$

B **2.** Use a calculator to evaluate each of the following.

a. $(2.7)^{-0.35}$ **b.** $(0.54)^{-0.03}$ **c.** $3^{\sqrt{3}}$ **d.** $(0.65)^{\sqrt{2}}$
e. $\sqrt{7}^{\sqrt{7}}$ **f.** $\sqrt{10}^{\sqrt{2}}$ **g.** $(3^{\sqrt{5}})(3^{-\sqrt{5}})$ **h.** $4^{3\sqrt{2}} \div 4^{2\sqrt{2}}$

3. For each given pair of numbers, use a calculator to determine which number is larger.

a. $5^{\sqrt{2}}, 5^{1.4}$ **b.** $3^{\sqrt{2}}, 2^{\sqrt{3}}$ **c.** $3^{\pi}, \pi^3$ **d.** $5^{\sqrt{3}}, 3^{\sqrt{5}}$

4. In general, for any real numbers a, x, and y, the following property holds.

If $a>1$ and $x<y$, then $a^x<a^y$.

Use a calculator to verify that this property holds for the given values of a, x, and y.

a. $a = 1.62;\ x = 1.3;\ y = 1.4$ **b.** $a = 7.35;\ x = 0.6;\ y = 0.7$
c. $a = 4.03;\ x = -0.7;\ y = -0.6$ **d.** $a = 1.93;\ x = 1.4;\ y = 2$

C **5. a.** Make a table of values for $(1.08)^x$, where $x = 0, 1, 2, \ldots, 10$.
b. Graph the function $y = (1.08)^x$, using the table of values from part **a**.
c. From the graph in part **b**, estimate the value of y when the value of x is 1.5.
d. Use a calculator to evaluate $(1.08)^{1.5}$.
e. Use the graph from part **b** to find the value of n such that $(1.08)^n = 1.41$.

6. A certain plant grows 8% taller each week. Its height can be predicted using the following formula.

$H = h(1.08)^t$, where h is the height of the plant at the first measurement,
t is the time, in weeks, after the first measurement, and
H is the plant's height after t weeks.

Using the graph from exercise 5, find the number of weeks it would take for a plant that measures 10 cm to reach each given height. (Round answers to the nearest tenth.)

a. 12 cm **b.** 15 cm **c.** 18 cm **d.** 20 cm

7. Plans for a proposed rocket include having it attain a velocity of $[100(1.08)^t - 100]$ m/s in space, where t is the number of seconds after firing. Use the graph from exercise 5 to estimate the time it would take the rocket to reach each given velocity. (Round answers to the nearest tenth of a second.)

a. 100 m/s **b.** 200 m/s **c.** 300 m/s

2-3 Exponential Equations

A power that contains a variable in the exponent is called an **exponential expression.** Properties of exponents can be applied to solve equations involving exponents, or **exponential equations**. One special property holds for equations involving powers that have the same base.

> For $m, n \in \mathbf{R}$, $a > 0$, and $a \neq 1$,
> $a^m = a^n$ if, and only if, $m = n$.

Note that the phrase "if, and only if," means that the statement is "reversible".
For the property above, "$a^m = a^n$ if, and only if, $m = n$" means "$a^m = a^n$ if $m = n$, and $m = n$ if $a^m = a^n$".

EXAMPLE 1: **a.** Solve $4^{n-8} = 2^7$.

Rewrite the equation so that the bases are the same.	$4^{n-8} = 2^7$ $(2^2)^{n-8} = 2^7$
Simplify the exponents.	$2^{2n-16} = 2^7$
Since the bases are the same, the exponents are equal.	$2n - 16 = 7$ $2n = 23$
Solve for n.	$n = \frac{23}{2}$ or 11.5

b. Solve $4^{x+2} = 8^3$.

$4^{x+2} = 8^3$	
$(2^2)^{x+2} = (2^3)^3$	Rewrite so that the bases are the same.
$2^{2x+4} = 2^9$	Simplify exponents.
$2x + 4 = 9$	The exponents are equal.
$2x = 5$	
$x = \frac{5}{2}$ or 2.5	

Another property holds for equations involving powers with different bases, yet having the same exponent.

> For $m, n \in \mathbf{R}$, $a, b > 0$, and $m \neq 0$,
> $a^m = b^m$ if, and only if, $a = b$ when m is odd, and
> $a^m = b^m$ if, and only if, $a = \pm b$ when m is even.

Notice that if $m = 0$ then $a^0 = b^0$ for all a and b.

EXAMPLE 2: Solve $[(5x)^2]^2 = (2x + 3)^4$.

First, rewrite the equation so that exponents are the same.

$$((5x)^2)^2 = (2x + 3)^4$$
$$(5x)^4 = (2x + 3)^4$$

Since exponents are the same and even, the bases are either equal or equal with opposite signs.

$$5x = \pm(2x + 3)$$

$$5x = 2x + 3 \qquad 5x = -(2x + 3)$$
$$3x = 3 \qquad 7x = -3$$

There are two solutions.

$$x = 1 \qquad x = -\frac{3}{7}$$

Sometimes, it may be necessary to use a combination of different properties of exponents when solving exponential equations.

EXAMPLE 3: Solve $(x - 5)^{\frac{2}{3}} = \left(\frac{1}{27}\right)^{-\frac{1}{9}}$.

You can eliminate fractions in exponents by cubing both sides of the equation.

$$(x - 5)^{\frac{2}{3}} = \left(\frac{1}{27}\right)^{-\frac{1}{9}}$$
$$\left[(x - 5)^{\frac{2}{3}}\right]^3 = \left[\left(\frac{1}{27}\right)^{-\frac{1}{9}}\right]^3$$

Simplify exponents.

$$(x - 5)^2 = \left(\frac{1}{27}\right)^{-\frac{1}{3}} \qquad \left(\frac{1}{27}\right) = 27^{\frac{1}{3}}$$

There are two solutions.

$$(x - 5)^2 = 3$$
$$x - 5 = \sqrt{3} \text{ or } x - 5 = -\sqrt{3}$$
$$x = 5 + \sqrt{3} \text{ or } x = 5 - \sqrt{3}$$

EXERCISE 2-3

A **1.** Solve for x.

a. $2^x = 2$ **b.** $3^x = 27$ **c.** $2^x = 16$ **d.** $2^x = \frac{1}{4}$

e. $3^x = \frac{1}{9}$ **f.** $2^x = \frac{1}{16}$ **g.** $5^x = \frac{1}{125}$ **h.** $5^x = \sqrt{125}$

i. $7^x = 7\sqrt{7}$ **j.** $2^x = 8^3$ **k.** $5^{x+4} = 25$ **l.** $3^{2+x} = 81$

2. Solve each equation. There may be more than one solution for each equation.

a. $(x + 2)^4 = 5^4$ **b.** $(y - 1)^3 = 4^3$ **c.** $(x - 3)^5 = 1$ **d.** $(y + 2)^2 = 1$

3. Rewrite each equation without fractional exponents by raising each side of the equation to the same power.

a. $x^{\frac{2}{3}} = 8$ **b.** $y^{-\frac{3}{2}} = 8$ **c.** $z^{\frac{3}{4}} = 27$

d. $x^{-\frac{3}{4}} = 8$ **e.** $y^{\frac{5}{3}} = 32$ **f.** $z^{-\frac{3}{2}} = 216$

B 4. Solve for x.

a. $3^x = \sqrt{27}$ b. $9^{1+x} = 3$ c. $9^{x-7} = 27$ d. $\left(\frac{1}{4}\right)^{x+4} = 8$

e. $9^{1-x} = 27$ f. $8^{2x-1} = 2$ g. $64^{x-2} = 16^{4x}$ h. $3^{5-x} = \frac{1}{3}$

i. $2^{3x+4} = 0.25$ j. $49^{x-1} = 7\sqrt{7}$ k. $121^{x-2} = 11\sqrt{11}$ l. $10^{x-4} = 100^{4-x}$

5. Solve each equation.

a. $(2x + 1)^4 = (3x - 5)^4$ b. $(2x - 1)^5 = (x + 1)^5$ c. $(5x + 2)^4 = [(4x)^2]^2$

d. $\sqrt{6x - 3} = (2x - 5)^{\frac{1}{2}}$ e. $\sqrt[3]{7x - 3} = (5x + 7)^{\frac{1}{3}}$ f. $(9x^2)^2 = (2x + 9)^4$

6. A radioactive substance decays according to the formula

$A = A_0\left(\frac{1}{2}\right)^{\frac{t}{h}}$, where A_0 is the initial mass of the substance,

A is the mass remaining after time t, and
h is the half-life of the substance given in the same units as that of time. (Half-life is the time it takes for a substance to lose half of its radioactivity.)

a. The half-life of a radioactive substance is 4.0 h. How much of a 240 g sample of the substance remains after 12 h?
b. Cobalt-58 has a half-life of 9.0 h. How many grams of a 256 g cobalt sample remain after 31.5 h?
c. Iodine-131 has a half-life of 8 d. How much of a 200.0 g sample of iodine remains after 20 d?
d. The half-life of a radioactive substance is 12 d. How much of a 500 g sample of the radioactive substance remains after 40 h? after 1000 h?

7. A laboratory received 200 g of radioactive radon and 16 d later 12.5 g of the radioactive material remained. What is the half-life of the radon?

C 8. Solve for x. Find a common factor first.

a. $3^{x+1} + 3^x = 324$ b. $4^{x+1} + 4^x = 160$ c. $2^{x+2} + 2^x = 320$ d. $2^{x+2} - 2^x = 96$

9. Solve for x.

a. $\dfrac{3^{x^2}}{3^x} = 9^3$ b. $\dfrac{2^{x^2}}{(2^x)^2} = 8$ c. $\sqrt{\dfrac{9^{x+3}}{27^x}} = 81$

10. Solve.

a. $4^{2x} - 8(4)^x + 16 = 0$ b. $3^{2x} - 26(3)^x - 27 = 0$

c. $5^{2x} - 26(5)^x + 25 = 0$ d. $2^{2x-1} - 3(2^{x-1}) + 1 = 0$

e. $2^{\frac{2x}{3}+1} - 3(2^{\frac{x}{3}}) - 20 = 0$ f. $4^x - 9^x = 0$

Application

Radiocarbon Dating

In 1960, Willard F. Libby, an American scientist, received a Nobel prize for discovering an ingenious method of dating archaeological relics. The method involves measuring the amount of radioactive carbon in the relic.

A carbon atom is represented by C-12. A radioactive carbon atom is represented by C-14. For every trillion C-12 atoms in organic matter, there is one C-14 atom. Plants initially absorb carbon, including C-14, through respiration. From the plants, C-14 is passed along the food chain to higher organisms, including humans.

Thus, every living organism contains (and has contained) the same ratio of C-14 to C-12. Once an organism dies, though, it can no longer absorb carbon compounds. Consequently, the C-14 in an organism is not replenished and the number of C-14 atoms begins to decrease as a result of radioactive decay.

A measurement of the ratio of C-14 to C-12 in the remains of an organism is sufficient information to determine when the organism died, since the rate at which C-14 decays is known. The radioactivity of C-14 decreases at a rate proportional to the amount present, so that after 5700 a, the amount of radioactive carbon has decreased by one-half. This 5700 a period is called the *half-life* of C-14.

An exponential equation that can be used to determine the ratio of C-14 to C-12 in a fossil after t years is given below.

$M = M_0(2)^{\frac{-t}{5700}}$, where M is the ratio of C-14 to C-12 that remains t years after the organism dies, and M_0 is the ratio of C-14 to C-12 in the organism when it died.

1. What percent of C-14 remains 17 100 a after a living organism dies?
2. A paleontologist determines that a fossil is about 45 000 a old. What percent of the original C-14 would a fossil this old contain?
3. A human bone found in England contained about 90% of the C-14 found in a similar bone in a living person. Could the bone have belonged to a Druid, a Roman soldier, or a person who lived during the time of William the Conqueror? (Use a calculator to devise a method for finding an approximate value of x that satisfies the equation $2^x = 0.9$.)
4. For a fossil from a certain animal, suppose that $M = \frac{1}{10} M_0$. About how long ago did the animal die?

2-4 Exponential Functions

In 1987, the Earth's population reached five billion people and continues to increase at a rate of approximately 1.2%/a. The population of the Earth in $(1987 + n)$ years can be predicted using the equation $P = 5 \times 10^9 (1.012)^n$. An equation such as this defines an **exponential function.**

> Any function defined by an equation of the form
> $f(x) = a^x$, where $a > 0$, and $a \neq 1$
> is an **exponential function** with base a.

Notice that the base a is restricted to positive numbers. If a were zero or negative, then the function f would be undefined for some values. For example, consider the following situations.

If $a = 0$ and $x = -1$, then $a^x = 0^{-1}$ or $\frac{1}{0}$, which is undefined.

If $a = -1$ and $x = \frac{1}{2}$, then $a^x = (-1)^{\frac{1}{2}}$ or $\sqrt{-1}$, which is not a real number.

EXAMPLE 1: Determine which of the given equations defines an exponential function.

a. $y = 2^x$ — This equation defines an exponential function, since it is in the form $f(x) = a^x$ and $a > 0$, $a \neq 1$. The base of the function is 2.

b. $y = \left(\frac{1}{2}\right)^x$ — This equation defines an exponential function with base $\frac{1}{2}$.

c. $y = x^2$ — This does not define an exponential function because the exponent does not contain a variable and the base is a variable.

d. $y = 1^x$ — This does not define an exponential function because the base is 1.

Some important properties of exponential functions can be depicted by graphing the functions.

EXAMPLE 2: On the same set of axes, graph the function defined by each given equation.

$f(x) = 5^x$, $g(x) = 3^x$, $h(x) = 2^x$, $k(x) = \left(\frac{1}{2}\right)^x$, $l(x) = \left(\frac{1}{3}\right)^x$

Make a table of values for $-4 \le x \le 4$.

x	-4	-3	-2	-1	0	1	2	3	4
$f(x) = 5^x$	$\frac{1}{625}$	$\frac{1}{125}$	$\frac{1}{25}$	$\frac{1}{5}$	1	5	25	125	625
$g(x) = 3^x$	$\frac{1}{81}$	$\frac{1}{27}$	$\frac{1}{9}$	$\frac{1}{3}$	1	3	9	27	81
$h(x) = 2^x$	$\frac{1}{16}$	$\frac{1}{8}$	$\frac{1}{4}$	$\frac{1}{2}$	1	2	4	8	16
$k(x) = \left(\frac{1}{2}\right)^x$	16	8	4	2	1	$\frac{1}{2}$	$\frac{1}{4}$	$\frac{1}{8}$	$\frac{1}{16}$
$l(x) = \left(\frac{1}{3}\right)^x$	81	27	9	3	1	$\frac{1}{3}$	$\frac{1}{9}$	$\frac{1}{27}$	$\frac{1}{81}$

These are the values of each function for $-4 \le x \le 4$.

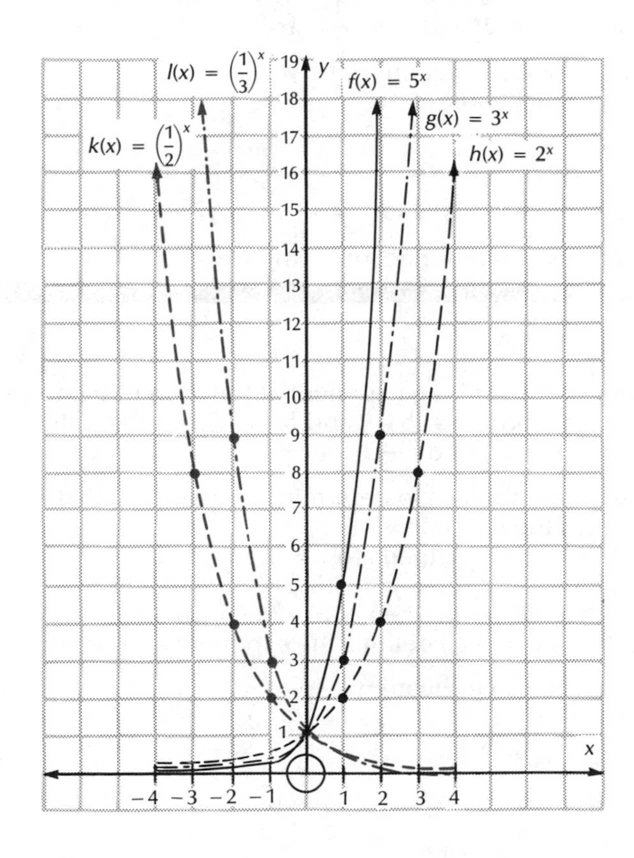

By examining the table of values and the graph of each function, you can identify the following properties of exponential functions that are defined by $y = a^x$.

- The graph of each exponential function passes through the point (0, 1). That is, $a^x = 1$ when $x = 0$.
- The domain of x is the set of real numbers. Each function is defined for all real values of x.
- The range of each function is the set of positive real numbers. That is, $a^x > 0$ for $a > 0$ and $x \in \mathbf{R}$.

The graphs in Example 2 also suggest the following are properties of exponential functions for $a > 1$ and for $0 < a < 1$.

$a>1$	$0<a<1$
• If $x>0$, then $a^x>1$. • If $x<0$, then $0<a^x<1$. • As x increases, a^x increases. • As x approaches $-\infty$, a^x approaches 0^+.	• If $x>0$, then $0<a^x<1$. • If $x<0$, then $a^x>1$. • As x increases, a^x approaches 0^+. • As x decreases, a^x increases.

Notice that the graphs of $y = 2^x$ and $y = \left(\frac{1}{2}\right)^x$ are images of one another under reflection in the y-axis. The y-axis is the line of reflection.

In general, the graphs of $y = a^x$ and $y = \left(\frac{1}{a}\right)^x$, or $y = a^{-x}$, are images of one another under reflection in the y-axis.

EXAMPLE 3: Suppose that f is an exponential function in the form $y = a(b^x)$, where $a, b \in \mathbf{R}$ and $b > 0$. Given that $f(0) = 3$ and $f(2) = 12$, find $f(-3)$.

Use known values to determine an equation that defines the function.

Since $f(0) = 3$, then $a(b^0) = 3$, or $a = 3$.
Since $a = 3$, then $y = 3(b^x)$.
Since $f(2) = 12$, then $3(b^2) = 12$, or $b = 2$. Since $b > 0$, then $b = 2$.
Thus, $y = 3(2^x)$ defines the exponential function.

Now you can evaluate $f(-3)$.

$$f(-3) = 3(2^{-3})$$
$$= 3\left(\frac{1}{8}\right)$$
$$= \frac{3}{8}$$

EXERCISE 2-4

A **1.** Which of the given equations defines an exponential function? Give reasons for your answer.

a. $y = 3^x$ **b.** $y = -2(3^x)$ **c.** $y = 5(3^{-x})$

d. $A = 100(2)^{-\frac{t}{h}}$ **e.** $L = 2.72(A)^{\frac{2}{5}}$ **f.** $I = 50(3)^{-6d}$

g. $P = 75(2)^{-\frac{7}{200}}$ **h.** $V = 10(-2.7)^{-2t}$ **i.** $R = 1.2(A)^{\frac{1}{3}}$

2. Graph $x = 2^y$ for $-3<y<3$.

a. At what point does the graph intersect the x-axis?
b. As x increases, what happens to the value of y?
c. As x decreases, what happens to the value of y?
d. As x becomes very small, what value does y approach?
e. For what values of y is x negative?
f. For what values of y is x positive?

B **3.** Find an equation of the exponential function defined by $f(x) = a(b^x)$, given each pair of conditions.

a. $b = \frac{3}{4}, f(1) = 4$ **b.** $f(0) = \frac{1}{3}, f(2) = 12$

c. $f(1) = 9, f(3) = 225$ **d.** $f\left(\frac{1}{2}\right) = 32, f\left(-\frac{1}{2}\right) = 2$

e. $f(0) = 1, f(3) = 1000$ **f.** $f(0) = \frac{1}{2}, f(-1) = \frac{1}{10}$

4. If f is an exponential function with base a, show that $f(x) \times f(y) = f(x + y)$.

5. Given that $f(x) = 3^x$, evaluate each expression.

a. $f(x + 1) \div f(x)$ **b.** $f(x + 2) \div f(x - 2)$

6. **a.** Graph the function defined by $y = 3^x$ and by $y = 3^{-x}$.
b. How are the graphs in part **a** related?

7. **a.** Given that $f(x) = 3^x$, show that $f(x + 1) - f(x) = 2(3^x)$.
b. Given that $f(x) = a(b^x)$, find $f(x + a) - f(x)$.

8. **a.** Evaluate $3^{1.5}$ without using a calculator, given that $3^{0.5} = 1.732$.
b. Evaluate $3^{-1.5}$ without using a calculator, given that $3^{-0.5} = 0.577$.

9. a. Graph the function defined by $y = (0.62)^x$, using the table of values given below.

x	-3	-2	-1.5	-1	0	0.5	1	1.5	2	3
$(0.62)^x$	4.20	2.60	2.05	1.61	1.00	0.79	0.62	0.49	0.38	0.24

b. Use the graph in part **a** to evaluate each of the following.

i. $(0.62)^{-0.4}$ **ii.** $(0.62)^{-0.8}$
iii. $(0.62)^{-1.2}$ **iv.** $(0.62)^{-1.6}$

c. Use the results from part **b** to verify each of the following.

i. $(0.62)^{-0.4} \times (0.62)^{-0.8} = (0.62)^{-1.2}$
ii. $(0.62)^{-1.2} \div (0.62)^{-0.4} = (0.62)^{-0.8}$
iii. $[(0.62)^{-0.4}]^3 = (0.62)^{-1.2}$
iv. $\sqrt[4]{(0.62)^{-1.6}} = (0.62)^{-0.4}$

d. Use the graph in part **a** to solve each equation for x.

i. $(0.62)^x = 0.90$ **ii.** $(0.62)^x = 1.4$
iii. $(0.62)^x = 2.5$ **iv.** $(0.62)^x = 2.8$

10. a. Graph $y = 3^x$ and $y = 3^{x+1}$ for $-2 \leq x \leq 4$.

b. Find points having y-coordinate $\frac{1}{3}$ on each graph in part **a** and join the points with a line segment.

c. Repeat part **b** for points with y-coordinates 1 and 3.

d. Verify that one graph is the image of the other under a horizontal translation of 1 unit.

e. Find points having x-coordinate -2 on each graph and join the points with a line segment.

f. Repeat part **e** for points with x-coordinates 1 and 3.

g. Verify that one graph is the image of the other under a vertical stretch of factor 3.

C 11. a. For $f(x) = 2^x$, graph the functions defined by $y = f(x)$, $y = f(x + 2)$, and $y = f(x - 3)$.

b. Describe the translation that maps each of the following.

i. the graph of $y = f(x)$ onto the graph of $y = f(x + 2)$
ii. the graph of $y = f(x)$ onto the graph of $y = f(x - 3)$

12. Show that if the point (2, 8) lies on the graph of f, where $f(x) = b^x$, then $f(-3) = \frac{\sqrt{2}}{32}$.

13. If $\left(3, \frac{8}{27}\right)$ is a point on the graph of the exponential function f, where $f(x) = b^x$, find $f(2)$.

14. Solve for x: $\frac{4^x}{3^{x+1}} = \frac{9}{64}$.

15. If $f(x) = 5^{2x+1}$, show that $f(x + 1) - 5f(x)$ is divisible by 100 if x is a non-negative number.

Application

"Music is a hidden exercise in arithmetic, of a mind unconscious of dealing in numbers." Leibniz

In a piano, there are many strings of fixed length, each of which emits a sound of definite frequency. Ideally, each string is set into vibration by striking a key on the piano keyboard. The piano keyboard is organized into groups of 12 keys, each producing a specific sound by striking a stretched string. The keys in each group of 12 are denoted A, A#, B, C, C#, D, D#, E, F, F#, G, and G#.

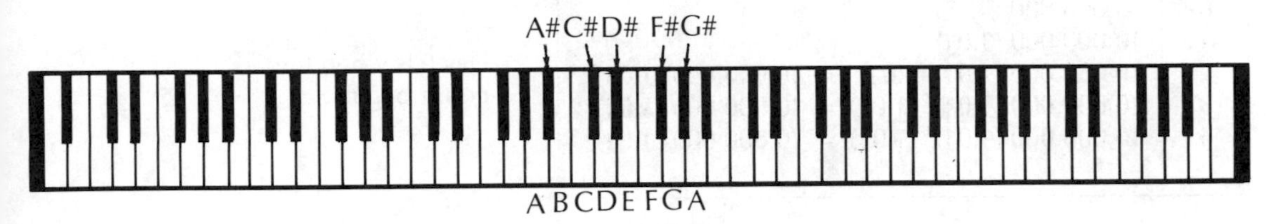

One key, called A4 or "A below middle C", vibrates at a frequency of 220 Hz. A5 is an *octave* higher and has a frequency of 440 Hz. Pianos are usually tuned so that the ratio of frequencies of consecutive notes is constant. For example, the ratio of the frequencies of middle C to C# is the same as the ratio of frequencies of D to D#, and of F# to G, and so on. If this constant ratio is r and the progression from a frequency of 220 Hz (A4) occurs in 12 steps, then the situation depicted in the following table occurs.

A4	A#	B	C	C#	. . .	A5
220	$220r$	$220r^2$	$220r^3$	$220r^4$	. . .	$220r^{12} = 440$

Thus, $r^{12} = 2$ and $r = \sqrt[12]{2}$.

On a piano, each note has a frequency $\sqrt[12]{2}$ times the previous note.

1. Find the frequencies of all the piano keys from A4 to A5.

2. Number the keys (notes) as follows:
   A3: -12, A4: 0, A5: 12, A6: 24, A7: 36.
   Draw a graph relating key number and frequency.

3. Does the graph represent a function? Explain.

4. Is the graph exponential? Give reasons.

5. Find an equation relating a note to its frequency.

2-5 Growth and Decay

Exponential equations can provide a useful model for representing situations that involve growth of a single population. For example, suppose a population of 10 000 000 amoeba in a pond increases each day. Approximately 8% of the amoeba divide into two amoeba, while about 7% are eaten by other inhabitants of the pond. Therefore, the amoeba population grows at a rate of about 1%/d. Each day, the pond contains 101% of the previous day's population.The number of amoeba in the pond each day is shown in the table below.

Day	Population
0	10 000 000
1	10 000 000 (1.01)
2	10 000 000 (1.01) (1.01) $=$ 10 000 000 $(1.01)^2$
3	10 000 000 $(1.01)^2$ (1.01) $=$ 10 000 000 $(1.01)^3$
4	10 000 000 $(1.01)^3$ (1.01) $=$ 10 000 000 $(1.01)^4$
...	...

Day 0 is when the count begins.

The table below depicts a pattern of growth, where P_0 is the initial population.

Notice that P_0 increases at a rate of 1%/d.

Day	Population
0	P_0
1	$P_0(1.01)$
2	$P_0(1.01)(1.01) = P_0(1.01)^2$
3	$P_0(1.01)^2(1.01) = P_0(1.01)^3$
4	$P_0(1.01)^3(1.01) = P_0(1.01)^4$
...	...

The pattern that emerges from the table leads to a general formula for determining the population after n days.

That is,

$P_n = P_0(1.01)^n$, where P_0 is the initial population (that is, $n = 0$), and P_n is the population after n days.

The **growth factor** is the base of the exponential. In this situation, the growth factor is 1.01.

In general, for a growth of i% per period, the growth factor is $(1 + i)$ and the formula for the population after n periods is $P_n = P_0(1 + i)^n$.

EXAMPLE 1: \$100 is invested for 7 a at an interest rate of 5%/a, compounded annually. Determine an exponential equation that can be applied to find the accumulated amount, A, of the money. Then find the value of A.

Since money accumulates as it earns interest, the situation is identical to population growth, where the population increases at a particular rate. Use the formula $P_n = P_0(1 + i)^n$.

In this case,

P_7 is the amount of money accumulated after 7 a, or the accumulated amount, A.

P_0 is the initial amount of money, or \$100.

The rate of growth, i, is 5%, or 0.05.

Each period is one year.

The exponential equation is determined by substituting known values into the formula for population growth.

$$\begin{aligned} P_n &= P_0(1 + i)^n \\ A &= 100(1 + 0.05)^7 \\ A &= 100(1.05)^7 \\ &\doteq 100(1.407\,100) \\ &= 140.71 \end{aligned}$$

$P_7 = A$

(to the nearest hundredth)

At a rate of 5%/a, \$100 will accumulate to \$140.71 in 7 a.

If money is compounded semiannually, then the number of compounding periods per year is twice the number of years. Thus, if \$100 is invested for n years at 5%/a, compounded semiannually, the accumulated amount can be determined by the following formula.

$$A = 100\left(1 + \frac{0.05}{2}\right)^{2n}$$

number of periods ($2n$)

interest per period ($\frac{0.05}{2}$)

Similarly, if money is compounded b times per year, the accumulated amount of \$100 in n years at 5% interest is determined by the following formula.

$$A = 100\left(1 + \frac{0.05}{b}\right)^{nb}$$

number of periods (nb)

interest per period ($\frac{0.05}{b}$)

Exponential equations like these can be used to determine the accumulated amount of a given investment.

EXAMPLE 2: If \$100 is invested for 5 a at a rate of 10%/a, compounded quarterly, what is the accumulated amount?

Use the formula $A = P_0(1 + i)^n$. Substitute known values into the equation.

The number of periods n is 5×4 or 20.
The interest rate $i = \frac{0.10}{4}$ or 0.025.

The original amount P_0 is \$100.

$$
\begin{aligned}
A &= 100\left(1 + \frac{0.10}{4}\right)^{20} \\
&= 100(1.025)^{20} \\
&\doteq 100(1.638\ 61) \\
&= 163.39 \quad \text{(to the nearest hundredth)}
\end{aligned}
$$

The accumulated amount of \$100 in 5 a, at an interest rate of 10%/a, compounded quarterly, is \$163.39.

EXAMPLE 3: Canada's population increases annually due to births and new immigrants. The population also decreases due to migrations to other countries and deaths. The overall effect of the increases and decreases is a 1.25% annual population increase. If Canada's population was 25 000 000 in 1986, what would be the expected population in 2036, assuming the increase continues at the same rate?

Use the formula for population growth,

$$P_n = P_0(1 + i)^n.$$

The time period from 1986 to 2036 is 50 a, so $n = 50$.
The growth factor, i, is 1.25%.
The initial population, P_0, is 25 000 000.

Substitute known values into the formula.

$$
\begin{aligned}
P_{50} &= 25\ 000\ 000\,(1.0125)^{50} \\
&\doteq 25\ 000\ 000\,(1.861\ 022\ 3) \\
&= 46\ 526\ 000 \quad \text{(to the nearest thousand)}
\end{aligned}
$$

By the year 2036, Canada's population is expected to be 46 526 000.

EXERCISE 2-5

A 1. If a population of 1 000 000 people increases to 1 000 000 $(1.019)^{40}$ in 40 a, what is the annual increase in population expressed as a percent per year?

2. An investment of \$200 accumulates to an amount represented by 200 $(1.06)^{20}$.

   a. Suggest a period during which the money accumulates and an interest rate that might result in this amount.
   b. Explain why \$200, earning 12%/a interest, compounded semiannually for 10 a, would give a solution to part **a**.
   c. Determine two other possible solutions to part **a**.

3. Find an expression for the accumulated amount of each given investment.

   a. \$450 for 8 a at 7%/a
   b. \$900 for 12 a at 8%/a
   c. \$1200 for 6 a at 10%/a
   d. \$800 for 10.5 a at 12%/a, compounded semiannually
   e. \$2100 for 7 a at 9%/a, compounded semiannually
   f. \$1000 for 6 a at 10%/a, compounded quarterly
   g. \$1500 for $3\frac{1}{4}$ a at 8%/a, compounded semiannually

4. **a.** How does the value of 2^t increase as t increases by 1?
   b. How does the value of 2^t increase as t decreases by 1?
   c. How does the value of 2^{-t} increase as t increases by 1?

5. A mathematical model that describes the activity of a radioactive isotope is given by the following formula.

   $N = N_0\left(\frac{1}{2}\right)^{\frac{t}{4}}$, where N is the amount of radioactive isotopes at time t (days), and N_0 is the amount of radioactive isotopes when $t = 0$.

   a. Use the formula to show that the amount of radioactive isotopes decreases to half the initial amount in 4 d.
   b. What fraction of the original amount of isotopes remains at the end of each time period?

   i. 8 d **ii.** 12 d **iii.** 20 d

B 6. Use the information given in Example 3 of this lesson to estimate Canada's population in the year 2000 and the year 2050, assuming that the annual population increase remains constant.

7. Suppose that the population of a certain country is growing at a rate of 3.2%/a. If the population was 12 000 000 in 1975, what is the expected population in 1995?

8. A grocery store's prices increase by 1% each month for one year. If a loaf of bread costs $1.40 at the beginning of the year, what would it cost at the end of the year?

9. If $2000 is invested in a bond that pays 9%/a interest, compounded semiannually, what amount would the bond be worth in 5 a?

10. What would be the value of $2500 in 10.5 a if it is invested at an interest rate of 12%/a, compounded semiannually?

11. Which is the better investment: 10%/a interest, compounded annually, or 9%/a interest, compounded monthly?

12. Manhattan Island was purchased in 1626 for goods worth about $24. If the $24 paid for the island had been invested at 8%/a interest, what would the $24 be worth in 1988?

13. A piece of paper is torn in half and one piece is placed on top of the other, as shown at the right. These two pieces are then torn in half and placed on top of each other to form four pieces. This process is repeated 50 times. If each piece of paper is 0.008 cm thick, would the resulting pile reach the sun, which is 150×10^6 km from Earth?

14. A radioactive isotope reduces in mass by 50% every 4 d. How many grams of a 640 g sample of the isotope remain after 20 d?

15. A certain population of birds, P, is increasing at an estimated rate of 2% every decade. That is, they are multiplying by a factor of 1.02 every decade. While checking data, an ornithologist shows that there could be an error of 3%, or 0.03. Would it make any difference in the long run if the factor was overestimated by 0.03 or underestimated by 0.03? Explain.

C 16. Atmospheric pressure can be represented by the exponential equation

$P = 100\left(\frac{1}{2}\right)^{\frac{h}{5.2}}$, where h is the elevation above sea level in kilometres and P is the atmospheric pressure in kilopascals (kPa).

At an altitude higher than 3 km, humans are in danger of "blacking out" and require additional oxygen, unless they are in a pressurized environment. Determine the atmospheric pressure at this altitude, to the nearest kilopascal.

Application

The Record Mile

The history of the record times for the fastest mile run shows times ranging from 4 min 36.5 s in 1865 to the latest record of 3 min 46.31 s achieved by Steve Cram of England in 1985. The record time is being decreased gradually and a question frequently asked is "what are the human limits?" It is obvious that the record cannot decrease indefinitely. Writing in *Scientific American* (June, 1976), three researchers, Henry Ryder, Harry Carr, and Paul Herget, concluded that the current running records are well below physiological limits and that performance limits are chiefly psychological. They claim that records, in events other than sprints, are set not by running faster than anyone has before, but rather, by running at present sprint speeds over a longer period of time. For example, a runner maintaining a pace of 200 m in 19.5 s (the world's record in 1986) for a full mile would achieve the ultimate record for the mile. (1 mile = 1.609 344 km). This ultimate speed is calculated to be 2 min 36.9 s for the mile.

A curve that fits the model that includes past records and the ultimate record is the learning curve, so named by Clark Hull (1844–1952), who used it in his learning theories. The following model was obtained using the known data.

$$S = 615.38\,[1 - 10^{-0.001\,177(y - 1554)}],$$

where S is the expected record running speed in metres per minute and y is the year in which the record is achieved.

Thus, for the year 2000, the expected record for the mile can be found using the model and substituting 2000 for y.

$$\begin{aligned} S &= 615.38\,[1 - 10^{-0.001\,177(2000 - 1554)}] \\ &\doteq 431.6 \end{aligned}$$

This speed of 431.6 m/min converts to 3.67 min/mile, or 3 min 43.7 s, for a mile. The record for the mile in the year 2000 is expected to be 3 min 43.7 s.

Find the expected record time for the mile for the year 2050.

2-6 The Number e

There are many situations that involve continuous growth or at least growth that is continuous for some periods of time. Banks, for example, offer interest rates that are compounded annually, semiannually, quarterly, monthly, and even daily. Some banks have even offered *continuously* compounded interest. To understand continuously compounded interest, consider the following situation.

Suppose \$1 is invested for 1 a at an interest rate of 8%/a. The rate can be compounded in a variety of different ways, as shown in the table below. Recall that the accumulated amount of a given investment is determined by the following formula.

$$A = \left(1 + \frac{i}{b}\right)^{b}$$

(b ← number of periods; $\frac{i}{b}$ ← interest per period)

Interest Period	Interest	Number of Periods	Accumulated Amount	
annually	8%	1	1.08	= 1.08
semiannually	4%	2	$(1.04)^2$	= 1.0816
quarterly	2%	4	$(1.02)^4$	= 1.082 43
monthly	$\frac{8}{12}$%	12	$\left(1 + \frac{0.08}{12}\right)^{12}$	= 1.082 999 5
daily	$\frac{8}{365}$%	365	$\left(1 + \frac{0.08}{365}\right)^{365}$	= 1.083 277 5
k times per year	$\frac{8}{k}$%	k	$\left(1 + \frac{0.08}{k}\right)^{k}$	= ?

The accumulated amount of the last entry in the table is not obvious. Consider the situation where the number of interest periods per year continues to increase. From the table, if \$1 is invested at 8%/a, compounded k times per year, then the accumulated amount of the investment is given by the formula

$A = \left(1 + \frac{0.08}{k}\right)^{k}$. The equation can be rewritten as follows.

$$A = \left(1 + \frac{0.08}{k}\right)^{k} = \left[1 + \left(\frac{1}{\frac{k}{0.08}}\right)\right]^{\left(\frac{k}{0.08}\right)0.08}$$

$$= \left[\left(1 + \frac{1}{n}\right)^{n}\right]^{0.08}, \quad \text{where } n = \frac{k}{0.08}$$

Thus, as k becomes very large, so does n.

Now consider what happens to the value of $\left(1 + \frac{1}{n}\right)^{n}$ as n becomes very large.

To investigate, try increasingly large values of n, as shown in the table at the right. As n increases, the value of $\left(1 + \frac{1}{n}\right)^{n}$ seems to approach a particular number. In fact, it approaches a special irrational number called **e**.

n	A
100	2.704 813 8
1000	2.716 923 9
10 000	2.718 145 9
100 000	2.718 268 2
1 000 000	2.718 280 4

The Swiss mathematician Leonard Euler (1707–1783) proved that this unique number e exists and that its decimal approximation is as follows.

$e = 2.718\ 281\ 824\ 590\ldots$

$\doteq 2.718$ (to the nearest thousandth)

Thus, a bank offering 8%/a interest, compounded continuously, would have to pay $(2.718)^{0.08}$ for \$1 invested for 1 a. But $(2.718)^{0.08} = 1.083\ 278$. One would expect that interest compounded continuously would result in an accumulated amount far greater than the accumulated amount that results from interest compounded annually. Actually, the equivalent interest rate the bank pays for continuously compounded interest is less than 8.5%!

EXAMPLE: At 100° C, hot water cools in a room according to a formula called Newton's Law of Cooling, which is given below.

$T = a + A\,e^{-0.04t}$, where a is the room temperature in degrees Celsius,

A is the difference in temperature of the water and the temperature of the room at the start ($t = 0$), and T is the temperature (Celsius) t minutes after the temperature measurements start.

If the room temperature is 20° C, what will the temperature of 100° C water be after cooling for 18 min in the room?

Substitute known values into the formula.

$$T = a + A\,e^{-0.04t} \qquad a = 20,\ A = 80,\ t = 18$$

$$\therefore T = 20 + 80(e^{(-0.04)\times 18})$$

$$= 20 + 80(e^{-0.72}) \qquad \text{(Use the } \boxed{e^x} \text{ key on a calculator).}$$

$$= 20 + 38.9$$

$$= 58.9$$

The water temperature is 58.9° C after 18 min.

The base of an exponential expression can often be changed. For example, the formula for radioactive decay, $A = A_0\left(\frac{1}{2}\right)^{\frac{t}{h}}$, can be changed and simplified for particular cases. If the half-life, h, of radioactive material is 4 a, the formula can be rewritten as follows.

$$A = A_0\left(\frac{1}{2}\right)^{\frac{t}{4}} = A_0(2^{-1})^{\frac{t}{4}}$$

$$= A_0\left(2^{\frac{1}{4}}\right)^{-t} = A_0(1.189)^{-t} \qquad 2^{\frac{1}{4}} = 1.189$$

$$= A_0(0.841)^{t} \qquad 1.189^{-1} = 0.841$$

The half-life of 4 a has been "incorporated" into the base and the exponent involves only t.

The number e frequently appears as a base in formulas involving growth and decay. This base can be changed to base 2 by noting that $2^{1.44} = 2.71$, or e. Thus, an exponential such as $e^{-0.3t}$ becomes $(2^{1.44})^{-0.3t}$, or $2^{-0.432t}$.

EXERCISE 2-6

A 1. A calculator with an $\boxed{e^x}$ key can be used to evaluate $e^{0.78}$, as shown below.

$\boxed{0.78}$ $\boxed{e^x}$ $\boxed{=}$ 2.1814722

Evaluate each of the following using a calculator.

a. $e^{1.3}$ **b.** $e^{0.25}$ **c.** $e^{2.3}$ **d.** $e^{-1.5}$ **e.** $e^{\frac{1}{3}}$ **f.** $e^{-\frac{1}{3}}$

2. **a.** Make a table of values for e^x for $x = -3.0, -2.5, -2.0 \ldots, 0, \ldots 1.5, \ldots, 2.5, 3.0$.
   b. Graph the function defined by $y = e^x$ for $-3<x<3$.
   c. From the graph in part **b**, estimate the values of $e^{-1.2}$, $e^{2.7}$, and $e^{1.5}$. Check your results using a calculator.

3. **a.** Sketch the graphs of $y = 2^x$, $y = 3^x$, and $y = e^x$ on the same axes.
   b. What point is common to all three graphs?
   c. Sketch the graph of $y = e^{-x}$.

B 4. Show that P dollars invested for t years and compounded continuously at r%/a will accumulate to $Pe^{\frac{rt}{100}}$ dollars.

5. **a.** Evaluate $\left(1 - \frac{1}{n}\right)^n$ for $n = 1000$ and 1 000 000.
   b. Compare the result from part **a** with a decimal approximation of e^{-1}.

6. Given that $3^{0.63} = 2$, $2^{1.58} = 3$, $3^{1.47} = 5$, $2^{2.22} = 5$, $e^{0.69} = 2$, and $2^{1.44} = e$, change each given exponential as indicated.

   a. $3^{0.7x}$ to base 2 **b.** $e^{\left(-\frac{7}{4}\right)t}$ to base 2 **c.** $2^{0.54x}$ to base e

7. Suppose coffee temperature is 80° C when poured into a cup and the room temperature is 20° C. Use the formula for Newton's Law of Cooling, $T = a + Ae^{-0.04t}$, to answer each part. (See the Example in this lesson.)
   a. Find the temperature of the coffee 5, 10, 15, and 20 min after pouring.
   b. How long, to the nearest minute, must a person wait before sipping a cup of coffee that is poured at at temperature of 80° C if the sipping temperature of coffee is 50° C?

C 8. The famous arch in St. Louis, Missouri has the shape of a curve called a *catenary*, which has an equation of the form $y = 2(e^{\frac{x}{4}} + e^{-\frac{x}{4}})$. Graph the catenary.

Application

Asking questions can often lead to a deeper understanding of a subject. Two interesting questions related to exponents are given below.

When does $x^y = y^x$?
If there are solutions, what is the graph of the solution set?

First, note that any ordered pair (a, a) would satisfy the equation and such ordered pairs lie on the line $y = x$. For example, the ordered pairs (1, 1), (2, 2), (3, 3) etc. would all satisfy the equation and each lies on the line $y = x$.

One might suspect that this is the solution, but there is more. For example, (4, 2) and (2, 4) also satisfy the equation. Answering the following questions will help you find enough points to graph $x^y = y^x$.

1. Show that if a point (a, b) satisfies the equation, so does (b, a).

2. Show that $\left(\frac{9}{4}, \frac{27}{8}\right)$ and $\left(3^{\frac{1}{2}}, 3^{\frac{3}{2}}\right)$ satisfy the equation.

3. Martin Gardner, a well-known mathematician and author, claims that when $x > y$ and n is a positive integer,
   $x = \left(1 + \frac{1}{n}\right)^{n+1}, y = \left(1 + \frac{1}{n}\right)^{n}$ give positive rational number solutions.
   Show that such ordered pairs, (x, y), satisfy the equation $x^y = y^x$.

4. Use the Martin Gardner equations from question 3 to find the points that correspond to $n = 1, 2, 3, 4$, and 5. Verify that the points do satisfy the equation $x^y = y^x$.

5. Do values of n such as $\frac{1}{2}, \frac{1}{3}, \frac{1}{4}$, and $\frac{1}{5}$ in the Martin Gardner equations give solutions of the equation?

6. Trying $n = -\frac{1}{4}$ may help you determine why Martin Gardner excluded fractions in his equations.

7. A high-school teacher and his students showed that for $n > 0$ and $n \neq 1$,
   $x = n^{\left(\frac{1}{n-1}\right)}, y = n^{\left(\frac{n}{n-1}\right)}$ result in solutions of the equations.
   Show that such ordered pairs, (x, y), satisfy $x^y = y^x$.

8. Find solutions, (x, y), that correspond to $n = 2, 3, 4, \frac{1}{2}, \frac{1}{3}$.

9. From the solutions you have found, draw the graph defined by $x^y = y^x$.

Review

1. Evaluate each of the following without using a calculator.

   a. $36^{\frac{3}{2}}$ b. $81^{-\frac{3}{2}}$ c. $32^{0.2}$ d. $\left(\frac{1}{16}\right)^{-\frac{3}{2}}$ e. $\sqrt[4]{256}$

2. Solve for x.

   a. $8^x = \frac{1}{16}$ b. $49^x = 7$ c. $27^{2x-1} = 9$
   d. $3^{4-x} = 9^{x-1}$ e. $\sqrt[3]{32} = 2^x$ f. $36^{x-2} = 6\sqrt{6}$

3. Use a calculator to evaluate each of the following.

   a. $(0.62)^{1.7}$ b. $(1.52)^{0.93}$ c. $40(1.05)^9$ d. $0.33(1.64)^{-6.3}$ e. $\sqrt[4]{12.1}$

4. Evaluate.

   a. $17^{\frac{2}{3}}$ b. $(5.62)^{-\frac{2}{3}}$ c. $\sqrt[3]{2}$ d. $2^{\sqrt{3}+1}$ e. $(1.63)^{-\sqrt{3}}$

5. Solve each equation.

   a. $2^x = \frac{1}{16}$ b. $3^x = 27$ c. $e^3 = e^x$ d. $\left(\frac{1}{8}\right)^x = 8$ e. $3^{x-2} = 9$

6. If $f(x) = 6(2^x)$, evaluate each expression.

   a. $f(x + 3) \div f(x)$ b. $f(x + 5) \div f(x)$

7. On the same axes, graph the function defined by $y = x^3$ and by $y = 3$. Find the point(s) of intersection of the two graphs.

8. Find an equation of an exponential function defined by $f(x) = a(b^x)$, given each of the following.

   a. $b = \frac{2}{3}$, $f(1) = 6$ b. $f(0) = 3$, $f(2) = 48$

9. Graph the function defined by $y = 2^x$.
   a. From the graph, find $2^{0.43}$.
   b. Use the value from part **a** to evaluate $2^{5.43}$.

10. If $f(x) = 10^{2x}$, show that $f(x + 1) - f(x)$ is divisible by 99, where x is an integer and $x > 0$.

11. Cobalt- 58 has a half-life of 9.0 h. How many grams of 1 kg supply remain after 40.5 h?

12. Princess Mary Hospital, a cancer treatment centre, maintains a supply of 150.0 g gold-198 (Au-198) at all times. Au-198 has a half-life of 2.7 d. Deliveries of the radioactive material are made every Monday. What should each Monday's delivery be in order to maintain an adequate supply of Au-198 at all times?

13. Suppose that the number of words typed per minute by a beginning typist is given by the equation

$$N(t) = 100 - 100(3.2)^{-0.5t},$$

where $N(t)$ is the number of words typed per minute after t weeks of practice. Find each of the following.

a. $N(0)$ **b.** $N(2)$ **c.** $N(5)$ **d.** $N(10)$

14. The value of a milling machine depreciates 10% each year. Find the depreciated value of a \$150 000 machine after 5 a.

15. If the population of a country with 40 000 000 people is increasing at a rate of 3.1%/a, what is the expected population of that country in 12 a?

16. If a \$1000 savings bond pays interest at a rate of $9\frac{1}{2}$%/a, compounded annually, how much is it worth when it reaches maturity in 8 a?

17. If \$5000 is invested in a bond paying interest at a rate of 8%/a, compounded semiannually, how much is it worth in 10 a?

18. Radioactive substances decay over time and decay can be modelled using an exponential function defined by

$A = A_0\left(\frac{1}{2}\right)^{\frac{t}{h}}$, where A_0 is the original mass of radioactive material,
A is the mass of the material after time t, and
h is the time for the mass to decrease by one half (the half-life of the material).

a. The half-life of a radioactive isotope is 8 d. If 1600 g of the isotope are measured now, how many grams are left after 2 d, 4 d, and 20 d?

b. Drug X enters the blood stream and gradually, dilutes decreasing exponentially with a half-life of 2.5 d. If the initial amount of drug administered to a patient is 75 mg, what amount of drug is still in the blood stream after 30 d?

c. Radioactive iodine is used to determine if people have a thyroid deficiency. The iodine, when injected into a person, is absorbed by a healthy thyroid gland. If radioactive iodine has a half-life of 8.1 d, how much iodine should be present in a healthy thyroid 10 d after an injection of 125 mg ?

19. Some scientists speculate that there were equal amounts of uranium-235 and uranium-238 when the Earth was formed. Uranium-235 decays faster than uranium-238, and today they appear in the Earth's crust in the ratio 1:139. If the half-life of uranium-235 is 7.13×10^8 a and the half-life of uranium-238 is 4.51×10^9 a, estimate the age of the Earth.

Test

1. Evaluate each of the following without using a calculator.

   a. $9^{2.5}$ b. $(0.125)^{-\frac{2}{3}}$ c. $\left(6\frac{1}{4}\right)^{-0.5}$ d. $\sqrt[4]{81}$

2. Solve for x.

   a. $25^x = 125$ b. $4^{x-3} = 8$ c. $9^{-(x-5)} = 81^{4x}$

3. Use a calculator to evaluate each of the following.

   a. $(96.2)^{0.05}$ b. $72(0.75)^{12}$ c. $13(1.03)^{-4}$ d. $\sqrt[5]{0.65}$

4. Evaluate each of the following.

   a. $19.6^{\frac{2}{9}}$ b. $(0.15)^{-\frac{3}{7}}$ c. $(0.97)^{\sqrt{2}}$ d. $(\sqrt{0.651})^{1-\sqrt{3}}$

5. Solve for x.

   a. $\left(\frac{1}{e}\right)^4 = e^x$ b. $4^x = 32$ c. $25^x = 125$ d. $4^{-2x} = \frac{1}{16}$

6. On the same axes, graph the function defined by $y = x^4$ and by $y = 3$. Find the point(s) of intersection of the two graphs.

7. Find an equation of an exponential function defined by $f(x) = a(b^x)$ for each given pair of conditions.

   a. $f(1) = 10, f(2) = 5$ b. $f\left(\frac{1}{2}\right) = 18, f\left(-\frac{1}{2}\right) = 2$

8. Iodine-131 has a half-life of 8 d. A laboratory receives a 1.5 kg supply on Monday. How many grams remain after 20 d?

9. Radon-222 has a half-life of 3.8 d. How many grams of radon-222 are needed to maintain a minimum of 7.0 g supply of the radioactive isotope over a period of 14 d?

10. A golf ball loses some of its resiliency each time it is hit. The distance it travels decreases by 0.005% after each normal hit. How far will it travel after being hit the 1000th time, if a normal hit would send a new ball 200 m?

11. If \$4000 is invested in a bond paying an interest rate of 10%/a, compounded semiannually, to what amount does the investment accumulate in 6 a?

Cumulative Review

1. Which of the following graphs represent functions?

a. 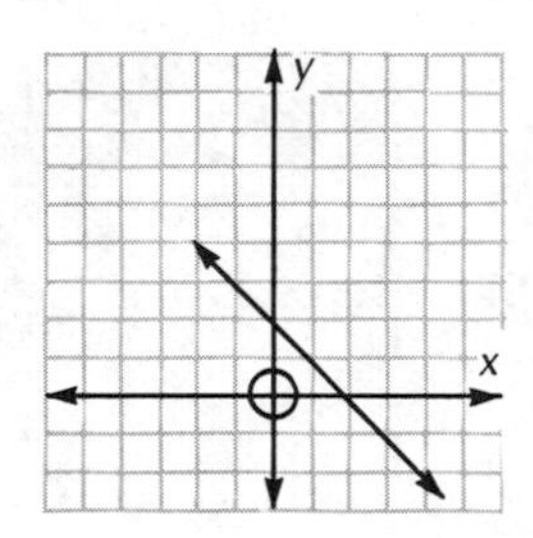

b. 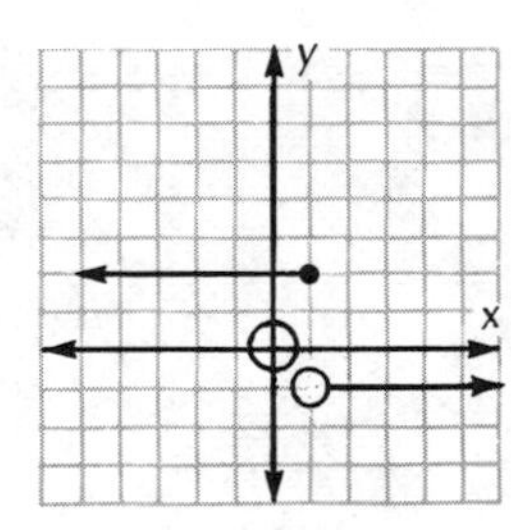

c. 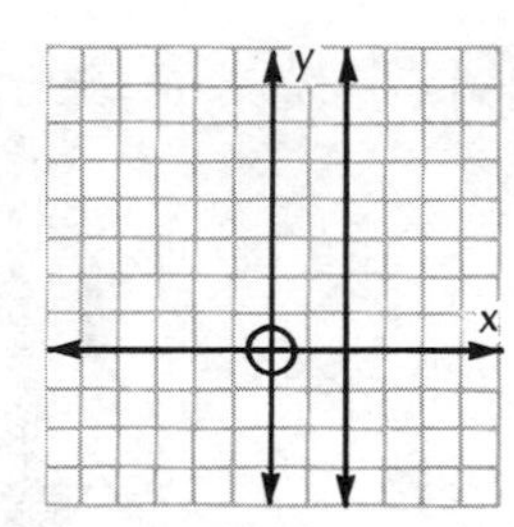

2. Graph each function using the interval $-4 \leq x \leq 3$.

a. $f = \{(x,y) \mid y = x^2\}$
b. $f = \{(x,y) \mid y = x^2 + 2\}$
c. $f = \{(x,y) \mid y = (x - 1)^2\}$
d. $f = \{(x,y) \mid y = (x - 2)^2 + 3\}$

3. Copy each graph of f and g. Then graph $f + g$.

a. 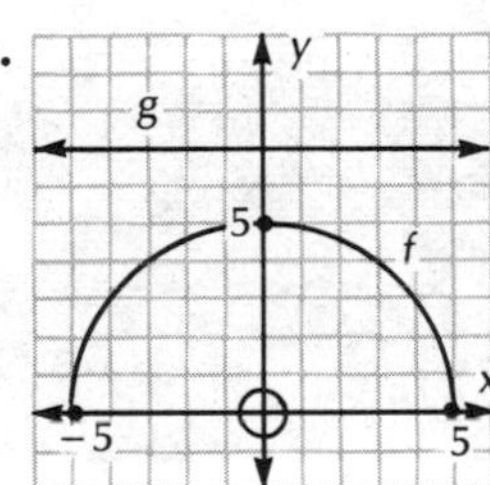

f: $x^2 + y^2 = 25$
g: $y = 7$

b. 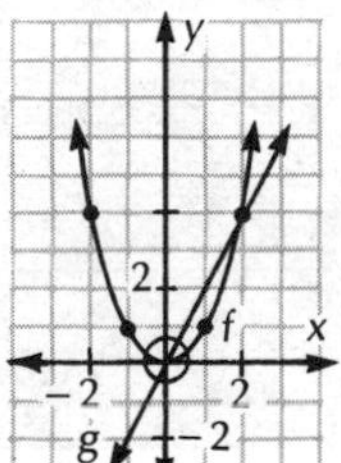

f: $y = x^2$
g: $y = 2x$

4. Given that $f{:}x \to \frac{1}{x}$ and g: $x \to x^2 - 9$, answer each of the following.

a. Find a defining equation of $f \circ g$.
b. Graph $f \circ g$.
c. Find equations of the vertical asymptotes of the graph of $f \circ g$.

5. Use transformations to describe how the graph of each given function may be obtained from the graph of $y = f(x)$.

a. $y = f(x) - 3$
b. $y = f(x) + 5$
c. $y = 2f(x)$
d. $y = f(2x)$
e. $\frac{1}{3}y = 2f(x)$
f. $y = f(x - 2)$
g. $y = -f(x)$
h. $y = f^{-1}(x)$
i. $y = \left(\frac{1}{2}\right) f(x)$

3 Logarithms

3-1 The Logarithmic Function

A new gas field is located in the Atlantic Ocean off the coast of the Maritimes. Determining how long resources can be utilized is a critical issue in deciding whether an investment is economical. For example, suppose that for each year, 12% of the available gas is extracted from the field. When 10% of the original resources are left, it will no longer be economical to extract gas. For how many years can gas be extracted economically?

Problems of this type were encountered in Unit 2. Each year, the available resources are reduced by a factor of 12%. That is, 88%, or 0.88, of the resources available at the beginning of a year remain at the end of the year. In n years, the resources will be reduced by a factor of $(0.88)^n$ of the original amount. When this factor becomes 10%, or 0.1, the resources will be considered depleted. The number of years, n, can be found by solving the exponential equation $(0.88)^n = 0.1$. **Logarithms** and **logarithmic functions**, which are closely related to exponential functions, can be used to solve such equations.

The inverse of an exponential function is also a function. For example, $y = 2^x$ defines an exponential function whose graph is shown below. As seen in Unit 1, the graph of the inverse of a function is obtained by reflecting the graph of the function in the line $y = x$. Since the equation of the inverse is obtained by interchanging x and y in the original equation, the function defined by $y = 2^x$ has an inverse defined by $x = 2^y$.

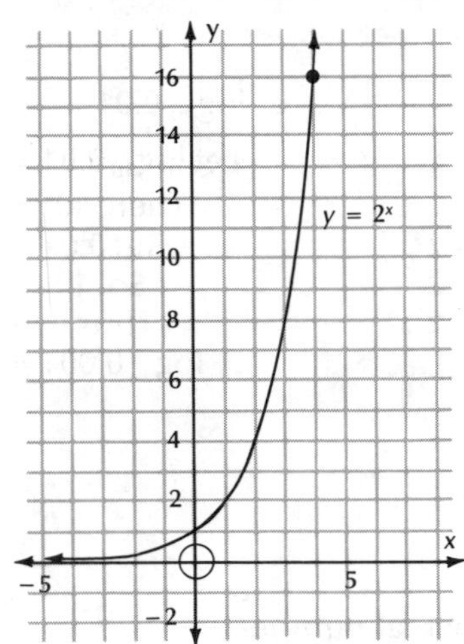

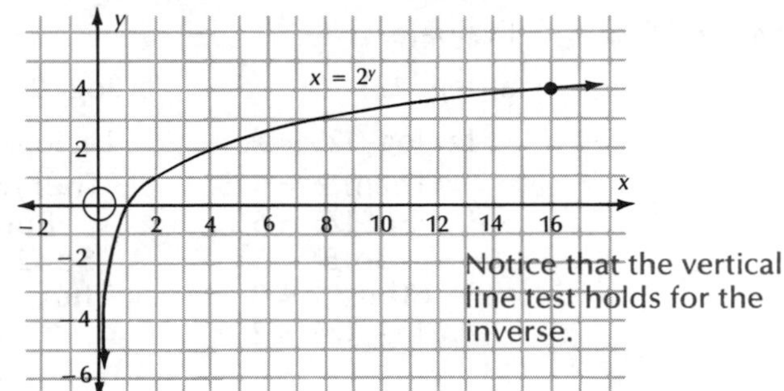

Notice that the vertical line test holds for the inverse.

The inverse of an exponential function is called a **logarithmic function**. The defining equation, $x = 2^y$, of the inverse function can be written as $y = \log_2 x$ and is read "y equals the **logarithm** of x to the base 2".

> In general, a logarithmic function, $y = \log_a x$, is defined as follows. If a and N are positive real numbers and $a \neq 1$, then
>
> $$\underbrace{y = \log_a N}_{\text{logarithmic form}} \text{ if, and only if, } \underbrace{a^y = N}_{\text{exponential form}}.$$

EXAMPLE 1: Express each equation in logarithmic form.

a. $2^5 = 32$ $\quad\therefore \log_2 32 = 5$

b. $6^{-2} = \frac{1}{36}$ $\quad\therefore \log_6 \frac{1}{36} = 2$

c. $\sqrt{49} = 7$ $\quad\therefore \log_{49} 7 = \frac{1}{2}$

The above graph of $y = \log_2 x$ indicates that every positive number, x, has a unique logarithm to the base 2. This leads to the following property.

> If $\log_a M = \log_a N$, then $M = N$.

Since $a^1 = a$ and $a^0 = 1$, then the following properties of logarithms hold.

> $\log_a a = 1$, and $\log_a 1 = 0$.

It is helpful to think of a logarithm as an exponent.

$\log_a x$ means "the exponent to which a must be raised to give x".

Thus, $\log_3 9$ is the exponent to which 3 must be raised to give 9.
Since $3^2 = 9$, then $\log_3 9 = 2$.

EXAMPLE 2: Evaluate.

a. $\log_5 125$

Let $\log_5 125 = x$.
Then, $5^x = 125$.
But $125 = 5^3$.
So, $5^x = 5^3$.
Thus, $x = 3$.
$\therefore \log_5 125 = 3$

b. $\log_8 2$

Let $\log_8 2 = x$.
Then, $8^x = 2$.
But $8 = 2^3$.
So, $(2^3)^x = 2$.
Thus, $2^{3x} = 2^1$.
$3x = 1$
$x = \frac{1}{3}$
$\therefore \log_8 2 = \frac{1}{3}$

c. $\log_{10} 0.01$

Let $\log_{10} 0.01 = x$.
Then, $10^x = 0.01$.
But $0.01 = 10^{-2}$.
So, $10^x = 10^{-2}$.
Thus, $x = -2$.
$\therefore \log_{10} 0.001 = -2$

From Example 2, it seems that logarithms may have any real number values. Is it possible to find the value of the logarithm of a negative number?

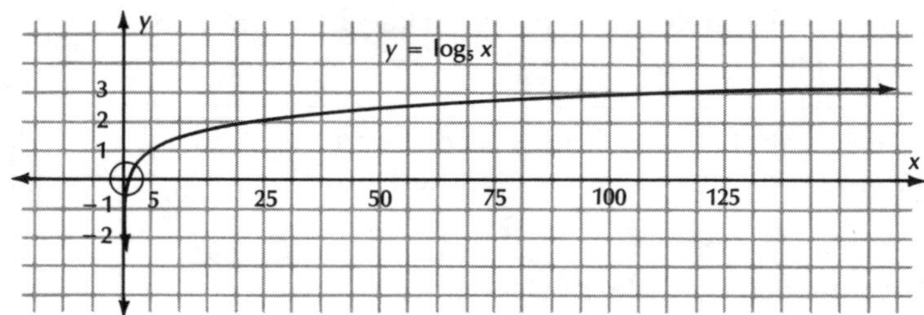

Consider $\log_5 (-25)$.
To evaluate $\log_5 (-25)$, let $\log_5 (-25) = x$.
Then $5^x = -25$.
However, the exponential 5^x is positive for all values of x.
Therefore, $\log_5(-25)$ is undefined.

Logarithms of negative numbers and zero are not defined. The domain of the logarithmic function defined by $y = \log_5 x$ is the set of positive real numbers, as is illustrated in the graph, and the range is the set of all reals.

EXAMPLE 3: Solve.

a. $\log_7 x = 2$
$7^2 = x$
$\therefore x = 49$

b. $\log_x 81 = 4$
$x^4 = 81$
$x^4 = 3^4$
$\therefore x = 3$

c. $\log_2 32 = x$
$2^x = 32$
$2^x = 2^5$
$\therefore x = 5$

EXERCISE 3-1

A **1.** Rewrite in logarithmic form.

a. $2^5 = 32$ **b.** $3^2 = 9$ **c.** $5^5 = 3125$ **d.** $7^2 = 49$

e. $16^{\frac{1}{2}} = 4$ **f.** $125^{\frac{1}{3}} = 5$ **g.** $36^{0.5} = 6$ **h.** $25^{1.5} = 125$

i. $a^b = c$ **j.** $2^x = 5$ **k.** $a^0 = 1$ **l.** $1.5^y = 0.3$

2. Rewrite in exponential form.

a. $\log_2 16 = 4$ **b.** $\log_5 125 = 3$ **c.** $\log_3 81 = 4$ **d.** $\log_7 1 = 0$

e. $\log_6 \sqrt{6} = \frac{1}{2}$ **f.** $\log_5 5\sqrt{5} = 1.5$ **g.** $\log_6 36\sqrt{6} = 2.5$ **h.** $\log_4 \sqrt{2} = 0.25$

3. Evaluate.

a. $\log_3 27$ **b.** $\log_3 1$ **c.** $\log_3 3$ **d.** $\log_2 8$

e. $\log_{10} 100$ **f.** $\log_2 \left(\frac{1}{2}\right)$ **g.** $\log_2 \left(\frac{1}{8}\right)$ **h.** $\log_{10} 0.001$

i. $\log_3 3^{-2}$ **j.** $\log_2 2^x$ **k.** $\log_3 \sqrt{3}$ **l.** $\log_a a^x$

4. Evaluate

a. $5 \log_3 9$ **b.** $3 \log_2 1$ **c.** $7 \log_5 125$ **d.** $3 \log_7 49$

e. $a^{\log_a x}$ **f.** $7 \log_7 \left(\frac{1}{7}\right)$ **g.** $9 \log_3 \left(\frac{1}{27}\right)$ **h.** $15 \log_2 1$

5. Solve.

a. $\log_x 27 = 3$ **b.** $\log_x \sqrt[3]{25} = 5$ **c.** $\log_x 8 = \frac{3}{4}$

d. $\log_x 16 = -2$ **e.** $\log_x \left(\frac{1}{10}\right) = 0.1$ **f.** $\log_x 3 = 2$

g. $\log_x 25 = \frac{2}{3}$ **h.** $\log_x \left(\frac{49}{16}\right) = -\frac{2}{3}$

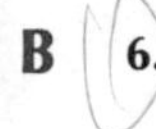

B **6.** **a.** On the same axes, graph each given function over the intervals $-5 < x < 30$ and $-5 < y < 30$.
i. $y = 2^x$ **ii.** $y = 3^x$ **iii.** $y = 4^x$

b. On the same graph, sketch the graph of each inverse function from part **a.** Write a defining equation of each inverse function.

c. What point do all the graphs defined by equations of the form $y = a^x$ have in common?

d. What point do all the graphs defined by equations of the form $y = \log_a x$ have in common?

7. **a.** Make a table of values for the function defined by $y = \log_2 x$ for $x = \frac{1}{4}, \frac{1}{2}, 1, 2, 4, 8, 16$.

b. Graph the function defined by $y = \log_2 x$.

c. Use the graph in part **b** to find approximate values of $\log_2 3$, $\log_2 5$, and $\log_2 15$.

8. Evaluate.

a. $\log_{\frac{1}{3}} 27$
b. $\log_5 \sqrt[3]{25}$
c. $\log_3 \sqrt[5]{9}$
d. $\log_{27} \sqrt{3}$
e. $\log_2 \left(\sqrt[3]{\frac{1}{4}}\right)$
f. $\log_{10} \left(\frac{1}{\sqrt{1000}}\right)$
g. $\log_{\frac{1}{3}} 9\sqrt{27}$
h. $\log_2 \sqrt{0.125}$

9. Solve.

a. $\log_3 27 = x$
b. $\log_3 \left(\frac{1}{27}\right) = y$
c. $\log_8 32 = x$
d. $\log_7 x = -$
e. $\log_2 \left(\frac{1}{16}\right) = y$
f. $\log_4 b = -2$
g. $\log_2 x = 2.5$
h. $\log_9 y = -$
i. $\log_a 4 = -2$
j. $\log_x 81 = -4$
k. $\log_a 32 = 2.5$
l. $\log_y 81 = 0.$
m. $\log_a 5 = -\frac{1}{2}$
n. $\log_x 7 = 1$
o. $\log_b 1 = 0$
p. $\log_3 x = 3$
q. $\log_2 (x + 4) = 5$
r. $\log_2 (x + 1) = 3$
s. $\log_3 (x - 3) = 3$
t. $5 \log_2 (x -$

10. Solve each equation.

a. $\log_5 125 - \log_5 5 = \log_5 x$
b. $\log_2 16 - \log_2 8 = \log_2 y$
c. $\log_3 9 + \log_3 27 = \log_3 x$
d. $\log_4 64 + \log_4 64 = \log_4 x$

11. Solve.

a. $\log_2 (x^2 - x) = \log_2 12$
b. $\log_5 (2x - 3) = 2$
c. $\log_3 (x^2 + 12) = \log_3 7x$

C 12. a. Evaluate.

i. $\log_3 9$ and $\log_9 3$
ii. $\log_5 125$ and $\log_{125} 5$

b. Prove that $\log_b a = \frac{1}{\log_a b}$.

13. Solve each system of equations.

a. $2^{x+y} = 32$
$2^{x-y} = 8$

b. $2^{x+y} = 16$
$2^{x-y} = 1$

c. $3^{x+y} = 81$
$5^{x-y} = 125$

14. Evaluate.

a. $2 \log_2 16$
b. $10 \log_{10} 100$

15. a. Graph the functions defined by $y = \log_3 x$ and by $y = \log_{\frac{1}{3}} x$.

b. Describe how the graphs in part **a** are related.

16. Solve.

a. $\log_7 (\log_4 x) = 0$
b. $\log_5 [\log_2 (\log_3 x)] = 0$

17. a. Is $\log_2 27$ greater than 3? greater than 4? greater than 5?

b. Use a calculator to find $\log_2 27$, correct to two decimal places.

Historical Note

In the sixteenth and seventeenth century, discovering relationships, such as the relationship developed by Kepler for planetary motion around the sun, could involve computation that would absorb a scientist for a lifetime. The invention of logarithms shortened the work of astronomers so much that the great mathematician Laplace once claimed that their lives were effectively doubled. It is questionable whether much of today's technology, or the mathematics associated with it, could have been developed without logarithms.

The Scottish mathematician John Napier (1550–1617) is credited with the discovery of logarithms. His genius can only be surmised because exponents, and in particular, the properties of exponents, were unknown during his lifetime.

Napier lived at a time when algebra was in its infancy, and so he approached problems involving logarithms geometrically. Napier used a base other than 10, but after much work, he and a fellow mathematician, Henry Briggs, together worked out some changes that led to present-day logarithms. Quickly recognized as a valuable invention, logarithmic tables were calculated for thousands of numbers, and the values were calculated to many decimal places. Tables such as these were used extensively for calculations in middle-school algebra until about a decade ago, and are sometimes still used for computation.

Today, calculators and computers are preferred for computational tasks that were formerly solved with a slide rule, a tool used to calculate logarithms and logarithmic tables.

Logarithms and exponential functions have become increasingly important. They can be used to model situations involving growth and decay in such diverse areas as the intensity of sound, the Richter scale for measuring earthquakes, the pH scale for measuring acidity of a substance, the behavior of radioactive materials, the population growth of countries, and the world of finance, to name only a few.

3-2 Properties of Logarithms: Multiplication and Divisi

Properties of logarithms are similar to properties of exponents. In fact, exponent properties can be used to prove properties of logarithms.

EXAMPLE 1: **a.** Prove that $\log_a MN = \log_a M + \log_a N$.

Let $\log_a M = x$ and $\log_a N = y$, where $M, N, a > 0, a \neq 1$.

Then, $M = a^x$ and $N = a^y$ — This is the definition of a logarithm.

$MN = a^x a^y$ — Use the Product Rule for exponents.

$MN = a^{x+y}$

$\log_a MN = \log_a a^{x+y}$

$\log_a MN = x + y$ — Definition of logarithm

$\therefore \log_a MN = \log_a M + \log_a N$ — Substitution

b. Prove that $\log_a \frac{M}{N} = \log_a M - \log_a N$

Let $\log_a M = x$ and $\log_a N = y$, where $M, N, a > 0, a \neq 1$.

Then, $M = a^x$, and $N = a^y$. — Definition of a logarithm

$\frac{M}{N} = \frac{a^x}{a^y}$

$\frac{M}{N} = a^{x-y}$ — Quotient Rule for exponents

$\log_a \frac{M}{N} = x - y$ — Definition of logarithm

$\therefore \log_a \frac{M}{N} = \log_a M - \log_a N$ — Substitution

> In general, for $M, N, a > 0$ and $a \neq 1$,
>
> $\log_a MN = \log_a M + \log_a N$ and $\log_a \left(\frac{M}{N}\right) = \log_a M - \log_a N$.

EXAMPLE 2: Show that $\log_2 (4 \times 16) = \log_2 4 + \log_2 16$.

Evaluate both sides of the equation.

L.S.

$\log_2 (4 \times 16) = \log_2 64$

$= 6$ — $2^6 = 64$

R.S.

$\log_2 4 + \log_2 16 = 2 + 4$

$= 6$ — $4 = 2^2$, $16 = 2^4$

$\therefore \log_2 (4 \times 16) = \log_2 4 + \log_2 16$

A calculator with a $\boxed{\log}$ key can be used to find the logarithm of a number to the base 10. For example, you can use the following keystrokes to find $\log_{10} 175$.

$\boxed{175}$ $\boxed{\log}$ 2.243 038

Thus, $\log_{10} 175 = 2.243\,038$. That is, $10^{2.243\,038} = 175$.

EXAMPLE 3: Use a calculator to verify that $\log_{10}\left(\frac{42}{5}\right) = \log_{10} 42 - \log_{10} 5$.

L.S.

$\boxed{42}$ $\boxed{\div}$ $\boxed{5}$ $\boxed{=}$ $\boxed{\log}$ 0.924 2792

R.S.

$\boxed{42}$ $\boxed{\log}$ $\boxed{-}$ $\boxed{5}$ $\boxed{\log}$ $\boxed{=}$ 0.924 2792

Since the $\boxed{\log}$ key on a calculator is a base 10 key, it will be used often for calculations. Whenever a logarithm is written without a base, the base is understood to be 10.
For example, $\log_{10} x$ can be written as $\log x$.

EXAMPLE 4: Solve.

a.
$$\begin{aligned} \log(x+1) + \log(x-2) &= 1 \\ \log(x+1)(x-2) &= 1 \\ (x+1)(x-2) &= 10 \\ x^2 - x - 2 &= 10 \\ x^2 - x - 12 &= 0 \\ \therefore x = 4 \text{ or } x &= -3 \end{aligned}$$

b.
$$\begin{aligned} \log_3 8x - \log_3(x-2) &= 2 \\ \log_3\left(\frac{8x}{x-2}\right) &= 2 \\ \frac{8x}{x-2} &= 3^2 \\ 8x &= 9x - 18 \\ \therefore x &= 18 \end{aligned}$$

When solving logarithmic equations, be sure to check your results for inadmissible solutions.
Consider part **a** of Example 4.

When $x = -3$,
$\log(x+1) = \log(-2)$,
and $\log(x-2) = \log(-5)$.
Both $\log(-2)$ and $\log(-5)$ are undefined, so $x = -3$ is an inadmissible solution.

When $x = 4$,
$\log(x+1) = \log 5$,
and $\log(x-1) = \log 2$.
These values are defined.

Thus, for part **a**, the solution is $x = 4$

Consider part **b** of Example 4.
When $x = 18$, $\log_3 8x = \log_3 144$ and $\log_3(x-2) = \log_3 16$.
Both values are defined.
Thus, the solution for part **b** is $x = 18$.

When using a calculator to evaluate logarithms, give answers correct to three decimal places, unless otherwise specified.

EXERCISE 3-2

A 1. Express as a sum of logarithms.

a. $\log(145 \times 192)$
b. $\log_3(1792 \times 853)$
c. $\log_4(1.56 \times 0.359)$
d. $\log_5(70.52 \times 8953)$
e. $\log_2(17 \times 19 \times 152)$
f. $\log_3(192 \times 273 \times 584)$

2. Express as a logarithm of a product.

a. $\log 7 + \log 5$
b. $\log_5 92 + \log_5 63$
c. $\log_9 78 + \log_9 952$
d. $\log_6 9751 + \log_6 1.567$
e. $\log_2 5 + \log_2 7 + \log_2 10$
f. $\log_3 82 + \log_3 91 + \log_3 77$

3. Express as a difference of logarithms.

a. $\log_5\left(\frac{10}{7}\right)$
b. $\log_2\left(\frac{56}{83}\right)$
c. $\log_7\left(\frac{873}{942}\right)$
d. $\log\left(\frac{0.72}{1.56}\right)$
e. $\log\left(\frac{1}{10}\right)$
f. $\log\left(\frac{a}{b}\right)$

4. Express as a logarithm of a quotient.

a. $\log 17 - \log 95$
b. $\log_3 60 - \log_3 20$
c. $\log_4 872 - \log_4 2.37$
d. $\log_2 673 - \log_2 985$
e. $\log 0.015 - \log 0.7$
f. $\log_5 190 - \log_5 23$

5. Solve for x.

a. $\log_7(2x - 1) = \log_7 5$
b. $\log_2(x + 1) = \log_2 5$
c. $\log_3(2x - 1) = \log_3(x + 5)$
d. $\log_2(x^2 - 12) = \log_2 x$
e. $\log(x^2 - 5) = \log 4$
f. $\log x + \log(x - 2) = \log 3$

B 6. Use a calculator to verify each of the following.

a. $\log(42 \times 73) = \log 42 + \log 73$
b. $\log(1.56 \times 0.32) = \log 1.56 + \log 0.32$
c. $\log\left(\frac{723}{561}\right) = \log 723 - \log 561$
d. $\log\left(\frac{54}{83}\right) = \log 54 - \log 83$

7. Express as a single logarithm.

a. $\log_3 2 + \log_3 7$
b. $\log_2 12 - \log_2 3$
c. $\log 2 + \log 3 + \log 4$
d. $\log_7 2 + \log_7 15 - \log_7 6$
e. $\log_7 64 + \log_7 2 - \log_7 14$
f. $\log_5 7 + \log_5 3 - \log_5 2$

8. Evaluate.

a. $\log 25 + \log 4$
b. $\log_7 14 + \log_7 3.5$
c. $\log_3 54 + \log_3 0.5$
d. $\log_6 9 + \log_6 4$
e. $\log_4 24 + \log_4\left(\frac{1}{3}\right)$
f. $\log_5 100 + \log_5\left(\frac{1}{4}\right)$
g. $\log_5 100 - \log_5 4$
h. $\log_3 54 - \log_3 2$
i. $\log_2 48 - \log_2 3$
j. $\log_6 12 - \log_6\left(\frac{1}{3}\right)$
k. $\log_4 32 - \log_4 0.5$
l. $\log_{\frac{1}{2}} 72 - \log_{\frac{1}{2}} 9$

9. Solve for x.

a. $\log_2 x = 2\log_2 7 + \log_2 3$
b. $\log_5 x = 3\log_5 4 + \log_5 2$
c. $\log_3 x = 2\log_3 10 - \log_3 25$
d. $\log_9 x = 2\log_9 25 - 3\log_9 5$
e. $\log_2 x + \log_2 11 = \log_2 99$
f. $\log x + \log 13 = \log 91$

10. Verify.

a. $\log 3 + \log \left(\frac{1}{3}\right) = 0$

b. $\log \left(\frac{1}{5}\right) = -\log 5$

c. $\log 4 + \log 4 + \log 4 = \log 4^3$

d. $\log 5^4 = 4 \log 5$

11. Show that $\log \frac{2}{1.08} \neq \frac{\log 2}{\log 1.08}$.

12. Graph the functions defined by $y = \log x$ and by $y = \log 2x$.

a. Show that the graph of $y = \log 2x$ is a translation image of the graph of $y = \log x$.

b. Describe the translation obtained in part **a.**

13. Show that the graphs defined by $y = \log_3 x$, $y = \log_4 x$, and $y = \log_5 x$ all have a point in common.

C 14. Solve each equation.

a. $\log_5 (x + 1) + \log_5 3 = 2$

b. $\log_3 (2x + 1) + \log_3 5 = 3$

c. $\log_3 (x - 2) + \log_3 x = 1$

d. $\log (x - 9) + \log x = 1$

e. $\log_6 x - \log_6 (x - 1) = 1$

f. $\log_5 (x - 1) + \log_5 (x + 3) = \log_5 (x - 5)$

g. $\log x + \log (x - 5) = \log (2x - 12)$

h. $\log_4 x - \log_2 3 = 2$

15. The astronomer Johannes Kepler (1571–1630) determined that the time, T, in days, for a planet to revolve around the sun and the average distance, d, in millions of kilometres, of the planet from the sun are related. The relation is defined by the equation

$$\log T = \frac{3}{2} \log d - 0.7.$$

a. Earth is about 150 000 000 km from the Sun. Verify that Kepler's equation gives a good approximation of the time it takes the Earth to revolve around the Sun (a period of revolution).

b. In Kepler's time, only six planets were known. Find the average distance of the remaining five planets from the Sun, given the time, T, for each to revolve around the Sun.

i. Mercury, 0.24 a ii. Venus, 0.61 a iii. Mars, 1.88a

iv. Jupiter, 11.86 a v. Saturn, 29.4 a

c. The outermost and smallest planet is Pluto. Percival Lowell predicted its existence by calculating irregularities in the orbits of Uranus and Neptune. In 1930, Pluto was discovered precisely where Lowell predicted it would be. Find the period of revolution of each of the three outermost planets, given its distance, in millions of kilometres, from the sun.

i. Uranus, 2854 ii. Neptune, 4473 iii. Pluto, 5880

16. If $\left(\frac{1}{2}\right)^{a+b} = 16$ and $\log_{a-b} 8 = -3$, find the value of a and of b.

3-3 Properties of Logarithms: Powers and Roots

There is a direct relationship between properties of powers and roots for exponents and properties of powers and roots for logarithms.

Since $(a^x)^n = a^{xn}$, then $\log_a (a^x)^n = \log_a a^{xn}$ — Take $\log_a$ of both sides.

$= nx.$ — Note that xn is the same as nx.

Let $a^x = M$. Then $\log_a M = x$. — Substitute into $\log_a (a^x)^n = nx$.

Thus, $\log_a M^n = n \log_a M$.

> In general, if $a, x > 0$, $a \neq 1$, $n \in \boldsymbol{R}$, then
> $\log_a x^n = n \log_a x$.

EXAMPLE 1:

a. $\log_3 10^{4.2} = 4.2 \log_3 10$ **b.** $\log 5^x = x \log 5$

c. $7.1 \log_2 3 = \log_2 3^{7.1}$ **d.** $x \log 9 = \log 9^x$

EXAMPLE 2: Express $\log_3 \sqrt[5]{36}$ in terms of $\log_3 6$.

$$\begin{aligned}\log_3 \sqrt[5]{36} &= \log_3 (36)^{\frac{1}{5}} \\ &= \log_3 (6^2)^{\frac{1}{5}} \\ &= \log_3 6^{\frac{2}{5}} \\ &= \tfrac{2}{5} \log_3 6\end{aligned}$$

EXAMPLE 3: Simplify.

a. $2 \log_6 3 + \frac{1}{2} \log_6 16$

$$\begin{aligned}&= \log_6 3^2 + \log_6 16^{\frac{1}{2}} \\ &= \log_6 9 + \log_6 4 \\ &= \log_6 36 \\ &= 2\end{aligned}$$

b. $\log x^5 + 2 \log \dfrac{1}{x} - 3 \log x$

$$\begin{aligned}&= \log x^5 + \log \frac{1}{x^2} - \log x^3 \\ &= \log \left[(x^5)\left(\frac{1}{x^2}\right) \div x^3 \right] \\ &= \log 1 \\ &= 0\end{aligned}$$

EXAMPLE 4: Given that $\log_8 2 = 0.333\ 33$ and $\log_8 3 = 0.528\ 32$, use the properties of logarithms to find $\log_8 12$ and $\log_8 36$.

$$\begin{aligned}\log_8 12 &= \log_8 (4 \times 3)\\ &= \log_8 2^2 + \log_8 3\\ &= 2\log_8 2 + \log_8 3\\ &= 2(0.333\ 33) + (0.528\ 32)\\ &\doteq 1.195\end{aligned}$$

$$\begin{aligned}\log_8 36 &= \log_8 (4 \times 9)\\ &= \log_8 (2^2 \times 3^2)\\ &= \log_8 2^2 + \log_8 3^2\\ &= 2\log_8 2 + 2\log_8 3\\ &= 2(0.333\ 33) + 2(0.528\ 32)\\ &\doteq 1.723\end{aligned}$$

EXERCISE 3-3

A **1.** Express as the product of a number and a logarithm.

a. $\log_3 7^2$ **b.** $\log_3 10^3$ **c.** $\log_7 2^{-4}$ **d.** $\log_{13} 12^{-4}$

e. $\log_2 \sqrt{10}$ **f.** $\log_4 5^{\frac{1}{2}}$ **g.** $\log_2 7^{0.5}$ **h.** $\log_3 5^{-0.1}$

i. $\log_7 10^{-3}$ **j.** $\log 2^{\frac{2}{3}}$ **k.** $\log 5^{0.2}$ **l.** $\log \pi^2$

2. Express as the logarithm of a power.

a. $5 \log 2$ **b.** $2 \log_2 7$ **c.** $\frac{1}{2} \log_3 10$ **d.** $\frac{3}{4} \log_5 6$

e. $-2 \log 8$ **f.** $-\log_2 7.5$ **g.** $-\frac{1}{2} \log_3 5$ **h.** $-\frac{2}{3} \log_4 7$

3. Express as the product of a number and a logarithm. Note that $x > 0$.

a. $\log x^5$ **b.** $\log \sqrt{x}$ **c.** $\log x^2y$ **d.** $\log \sqrt[4]{x^3}$ **e.** $\log (x^2y^3)$

f. $\log \left(\frac{1}{x}\right)$ **g.** $\log x\sqrt{x}$ **h.** $\sqrt[3]{xy}$ **i.** $\log x\sqrt{y}$ **j.** $\log \sqrt{xy^2}$

4. Solve for x, where $x > 0$.

a. $\log_3 x = 2 \log_3 5$ **b.** $\log_4 x = 3 \log_4 5$ **c.** $\log x = 4 \log 1$

d. $\log_5 x = \frac{2}{3} \log_5 8$ **e.** $\log_7 x = 3 \log_7 4$ **f.** $3 \log x = 6 \log 5$

B **5.** Determine if each equation is true or false.

a. $\log 5^{-2} = -2 \log 5$ **b.** $\log 4 = \frac{2}{3} \log 8$ **c.** $\log 27 = \frac{3}{4} \log 81$

d. $\frac{1}{3}\log 11 = \log \left(\frac{11}{3}\right)$ **e.** $\log 5 = \frac{1}{2} \log 10$ **f.** $\log 2 - \log \sqrt{2} = \log \sqrt{2}$

6. By taking the logarithm of both sides to the base 10, express each equation as a logarithmic equation involving sums or differences of logarithms.

a. $A = 4pr^2$ **b.** $V = \frac{4}{3}pr^3$ **c.** $T = 2\pi\sqrt{\frac{l}{g}}$ **d.** $PV^{1.4} = C$

7. Simplify. Note that $x > 0$.

a. $2 \log 5 + 2 \log 2$
b. $\frac{1}{2} \log_2 16 - \frac{1}{3} \log_2 8$
c. $\log 2 + 2 \log 3 - \log 18$
d. $\log_4 2 - \log_4 4 - \log_4 \left(\frac{1}{8}\right)$
e. $\log x^3 + \log \left(\frac{1}{x}\right) - 2 \log x$
f. $\log x^4 - 3 \log x + \log \frac{1}{x}$
g. $3 \log 5 \sqrt{50} - \log_5 2\sqrt{2}$
h. $\log_7 \sqrt[3]{28} - \frac{1}{3} \log_7 4$
i. $\log \sqrt{1000} - \log \sqrt[3]{100}$
j. $\log_2 \sqrt{36} - \log_2 \sqrt{72}$
k. $\log x^{\frac{1}{2}} + \log y^{\frac{1}{2}} - \frac{1}{2} \log xy$
l. $\log_2 \sqrt{6} - \frac{1}{2} \log_2 3$

8. Given that $\log_6 2 = 0.386\ 85$, $\log_6 3 = 0.613\ 15$, and $\log_6 5 = 0.898\ 24$, use the properties of logarithms to evaluate each of the following.

a. $\log_6 18$
b. $\log_6 20$
c. $\log_6 30$
d. $\log_6 \left(\frac{3}{2}\right)$
e. $\log_6 \left(\frac{5}{2}\right)$
f. $\log_6 \left(\frac{1}{5}\right)$
g. $\log_6 9$
h. $\log_6 300$
i. $\log_6 5000$
j. $\log_6 50$
k. $\log_6 \left(\frac{9}{4}\right)$
l. $\log_6 (0.5)$

9. Solve each equation for x.

a. $\log_3 x = \frac{1}{2} \log_3 16 + \frac{3}{4} \log_3 625$
b. $\log_2 x = \log_2 \sqrt{3} + \frac{1}{2} \log_2 3$
c. $\log_5 x = 2 \log_5 12 + \log_5 3$
d. $\log 250 - \log 2 = 3 \log x$
e. $\log_3 (x - 1) = -2$
f. $\log_3 (2x - 1) = 3$
g. $\log_2 (x - 2) + \log_2 (x) = \log_2 8$
h. $\log (2x + 1) + \log (x - 1) = \log 9$
i. $\log (x + 1) + \log (x - 2) = 1$
j. $\log_2 (x - 2) + \log_2 x = 3$

C 10. Consider the functions defined by $y = \log x$ and by $y = \log (x - 2)$.

a. Find the value of x for each when $y = 1$ and when $y = 0$.
b. Use the information from part **a** to sketch the graphs of $y = \log x$ and $y = \log (x - 2)$.
c. How are the two graphs in part **b** related?

11. Consider the functions defined by $y = \log x$ and by $y = \log \sqrt{x}$.

a. Find the value of x for each equation when $y = 1$ and when $y = 0$.
b. Use the information from part **a** to sketch the graph of each function.
c. How are the two graphs in part **b** related?

12. Describe how the graph of each equation is related to the graph of $y = \log x$.

a. $y = \log x^3$
b. $y = \log (x - 3)$
c. $y = \log \sqrt{x - 3}$
d. $y = \log \left(\frac{1}{x - 3}\right)$

13. Prove that $\log_2 3$ is an irrational number using an indirect proof. Let $\log_2 3 = \frac{a}{b}$ where $a, b \in \mathbf{Z}$, and $b \neq 0$.

14. Solve $(0.5)^x \leq 40$ for x.

Review

1. Rewrite in logarithmic form.

a. $3^5 = 243$ **b.** $5^8 = 390\ 625$ **c.** $(0.5)^4 = 0.0625$

d. $16^{\frac{3}{4}} = 8$ **e.** $4^{-\frac{1}{2}} = 0.5$ **f.** $x^{-3} = \frac{1}{x^3}$

g. $x^{\frac{1}{3}} = \sqrt[3]{x}$ **h.** $x^a = y$ **i.** $3^{x+2} = 0.81$

2. Rewrite in exponential form.

a. $\log_5 13 = x$ **b.** $\log_6 3 = x$ **c.** $\log_8 x = -2$ **d.** $\log_3 25 = x$

e. $\log_5 x = -3$ **f.** $\log_x 12 = 4$ **g.** $\log_x 20 = 10$ **h.** $\log_x 0.5 = -2$

3. Evaluate.

a. $\log_4 64$ **b.** $\log_2 16$ **c.** $\log_3 3^{-5}$ **d.** $\log_3 1$

e. $\log_8 \sqrt{8}$ **f.** $\log_2 \sqrt{8}$ **g.** $\log_2 \sqrt[3]{16}$ **h.** $\log 10^{-1.2}$

4. Explain why $\log_2(-4)$ is undefined.

5. Express as a sum or a difference.

a. $\log_2 (17 \times 15)$ **b.** $\log_3 (0.3 \times 0.5)$ **c.** $\log_4 \left(\frac{15}{7}\right)$ **d.** $\log_3 \left(\frac{26}{27}\right)$

e. $\log (11 \times 13 \times 17)$ **f.** $\log x^2y$ **g.** $\log \sqrt{xy}$ **h.** $\log \sqrt[3]{x^2}$

6. Express each as a single logarithm.

a. $\log_2 9 + \log_2 3$ **b.** $\log_7 25 + \log_7 10$ **c.** $\log_3 10 - \log_3 2$ **d.** $\log 75 - \log 5$

e. $\log_2 30x - \log_2 5$ **f.** $\log_5 48x + \log_5 3$ **g.** $\log_3 \sqrt{x} + \log_3 \sqrt[3]{x}$ **h.** $\log (a^2 - 1) - \log (a + 1)$

7. Solve for x.

a. $\log x = \log 5$ **b.** $\log x^2 = 4$ **c.** $\log x + 2 \log x = 6$

d. $\log x^2 + \log x = 9$ **e.** $\log_5 x = 3 \log_5 4$ **f.** $\log_7 x = \log_7 3$

g. $2 \log_3 x = \log_3 5$ **h.** $2 \log_3 x = \log_3 121$ **i.** $\log x + \log x^2 = 12$

j. $\log x + \log 2x = \log 50$ **k.** $\log x + \log 3x = \log 48$ **l.** $2 \log x + 2 \log 8 = 5 \log 4$

8. Use a calculator to evaluate each of the following.

a. $\log 25$ **b.** $\log 179$ **c.** $\log 2151$ **d.** $\log 0.51$ **e.** $\log 0.0023$

9. Evaluate without using a calculator.

a. $\log_2 24 - \log_2 3$ **b.** $\log_3 54 - \log_3 2$ **c.** $\log 4 + \log 25$

d. $\log 75 - \log 3 + \log 4$ **e.** $\log 1200 - \log 4 - \log 3$ **f.** $\log 75 + \log 4 - \log 3$

10. Use a calculator to solve for x, correct to 3 decimal places.

a. $5x = \log 2$ **b.** $(2x)\log 5 = \log 20$ **c.** $2x^2 - x \log 3 = 0$

11. Find $\log 400$, given that $\log 2 = 0.3010$.

3-4 Exponential Equations: Changing Bases

Exponential equations such as $4^{x-2} = 8$ and $25^{2x} = 5\sqrt{5}$ can be solved by expressing each side as a power with the same base.

To solve an equation like $2^t = 5$, the properties of logarithms can be used. In particular, the property that states that if $M = N$, then $\log_a M = \log_a N$, can be utilized.

$$4^{-2} = 8$$
$$(2^2)^{x-2} = 2^3$$
$$2^{2x-4} = 2^3$$
$$2x - 4 = 3$$
$$x = \frac{7}{2}$$

$$25^{2x} = \sqrt{5}$$
$$(5^2)^{2x} = 5(5^{\frac{1}{2}})$$
$$5^{4x} = 5^{\frac{3}{2}}$$
$$4x = \frac{3}{2}$$
$$x = \frac{3}{8}$$

$$2^t = 5$$
$$\log 2^t = \log 5 \qquad \text{Take the logarithm of each side of the equation.}$$
$$t \log 2 = \text{lot}\, 5$$
$$t = \frac{\log 5}{\log 2} \qquad \text{Use a calculator.}$$

[5] [log] [÷] [2] [log] [=] 2.321 928

$\therefore\ t \doteq 2.322.$

This technique can be used to change from one base to another.

EXAMPLE 1: Express 2 as a power with base 10.

Let $2 = 10^x$.
Take the logarithm of each side.

$$\log 2 = x \log 10$$
$$\log 2 = x \qquad \log 10 = 1$$
$$0.301\,029\,9 = x$$
$$\log 2 = 0.301\,029\,9$$
$$\therefore\ 2 \doteq 10^{0.301} \qquad \text{(correct to 3 decimal places)}$$

EXAMPLE 2: Find the value of $\log_3 25$.

Let $\log_3 25 = n$.
Then $3^n = 25$.
Take the logarithm of each side.

$$n \log 3 = \log 25$$
$$n = \frac{\log 25}{\log 3}$$
$$n = 2.929\,947$$

[25] [log] [÷] [3] [log] [=] 2.929 947

$$\therefore\ \log_3 25 \doteq 2.930$$

EXAMPLE 3: Express $A = 3^{0.5t}$ as an exponential equation with base 10.

Let $3 = 10^x$.

$\log 3 = x \log 10$ — Take the $\log_{10}$ of both sides.

$\log 3 = x$ — $\log 10 = 1$

$0.477 \doteq x$ — $\log 3 = 0.477\ 121\ 2$

$\therefore 3 = 10^{0.477}$

So $A = 3^{0.5t}$ can be written as

$A = (10^{0.477})^{0.5t}$, or $A = 10^{0.239t}$.

Note the following alternate solution.

$3^{0.5t} = (3^{0.5})^t$

Let $3^{0.5} = 10^x$

$0.5 \log 3 = x$ — Take the $\log_{10}$ of both sides.

$\therefore x \doteq 0.238\ 56$

$\therefore (3^{0.5})^t \doteq (10^{0.239})^t$, or $10^{0.239t}$

EXAMPLE 4: Solve $5^{3.2} = \log 10^x$ for x.

Take the logarithm of each side.

$3.2 \log 5 = x \log 10$ — Use a calculator.

$3.2 \log 5 = x$ — [3.2] [×] [5] [log] [=] 2.236 704

$\therefore x \doteq 3.495$

EXAMPLE 5: Solve $5^{t-1} = 3.92$ for t.

Take the logarithm of each side.

$$(t - 1)\log 5 = \log 3.92$$

$$t = \frac{\log 3.92}{\log 5} + 1$$

$$t = 1.848\ 800\ 4$$

$$t \doteq 1.849$$

EXAMPLE 6: Solve $\log x = 0.2423$ for x.

To solve this equation, use the [INV] and [log] keys on a calculator.

[0.2423] [INV] [log] 1.747 028 5

or [10] [y^x] [0.2423] [=] 1.747 028 5

$\therefore x \doteq 1.747$

EXERCISE 3-4

A

1. Express in logarithmic form.

a. $4^x = 50$ **b.** $8^x = 70$ **c.** $3^x = 70$ **d.** $2^x = 5^{x+2}$
e. $7^{x+5} = 4^x$ **f.** $2^{x+3} = 5^{x-1}$ **g.** $5^x = 3^{x+2}$ **h.** $x^y = y^x$

2. Use a calculator to solve each equation for x.

a. $\log x = 1.57$ **b.** $\log x = 0.013$ **c.** $\log x = -3.52$ **d.** $\log x = 5.73$

3. Express as a power with base 10.

a. 2.5 **b.** 19.3 **c.** 0.234 **d.** 0.0075 **e.** $\frac{1}{3}$

4. Solve using a calculator.

a. $5^x = 200$ **b.** $9^x = 100$ **c.** $2^x = 35$ **d.** $11^x = 0.99$
e. $(1.5)^x = 2$ **f.** $(1.08)^x = 2$ **g.** $(0.88)^x = 0.1$ **h.** $7^{x+3} = 5$
i. $10^{x-1} = 27.2$ **j.** $10^{x-3} = 35.4$ **k.** $2^{x+1} = 3^{x-1}$ **l.** $4^{2x} = 5^{2x-1}$

B

5. Express in exponential form. Then solve for x.

a. $x = \log_5 7$ **b.** $x = \log_3 12$ **c.** $x = \log_6 13.2$
d. $\log_x 1.25 = 4.7$ **e.** $\log_x 0.57 = 3.2$ **f.** $\log_x 0.25 = 0.75$

6. Evaluate.

a. $\log_2 76$ **b.** $\log_5 105$ **c.** $\log_3 5.6$ **d.** $\log_6 7.32$
e. $\log_4 0.32$ **f.** $\log_3 0.0015$ **g.** $\log_2 53.2$ **h.** $\log_{4.1} 6$

7. Express as a power with base 10.

a. 2^5 **b.** 3^{12} **c.** $18.6^{3.2}$ **d.** $20^{0.014}$
e. 2^{-3} **f.** $3^{-0.26}$ **g.** $\sqrt{8}$ **h.** $\sqrt[3]{15}$

8. Express each formula as an exponential equation with base 10.

a. $A = (1.05)^{5.57}$ **b.** $T = 20 + 80(2.7)^{-0.03t}$ **c.** $N = N_0\left(\frac{1}{2}\right)^{\frac{t}{h}}$

C

9. Solve for x.

a. $(5)^{2x} - 3(5)^x + 2 = 0$ **b.** $(7)^{2x+2} - (7)^{x+2} - 6(7)^2 = 0$
c. $3^{2x} - 3^x - 6 = 0$ **d.** $(4)^{4x} - 13(4)^{2x} + 36 = 0$

10. Prove that $a^{\log b} = b^{\log a}$.

11. If $\log_a 3 = \log_b 27$, show that $a^3 = b$.

12. Solve $4 \log_x 2 + \log_2 x = 5$.

13. Solve the equation $x^x = \pi$. Use a calculator to find the solution, correct to three decimal places.

Application

Finding Equations for Experimental Data

When compiling data from experiments, researchers sometimes determine that the data satisfies an exponential equation. One method used to find such an equation is to graph the data and change the scale on the axes so that the graph is a straight line.

Consider the exponential formula $y = b(a^x)$, where a and b are constants.
Taking the logarithm of both sides gives
$\log y = \log b + x \log a$.
Replacing $\log y$ by Y, $\log b$ by C, and $\log a$ by m, gives $Y = mX + C$, which is the equation of a straight line.
The y-intercept is C, or $\log b$, and the slope is m, or $\log a$.
Semi-logarithmic graph paper is used to graph this equation. This type of graph paper has a uniform x-axis and a logarithmic scale along the y-axis.

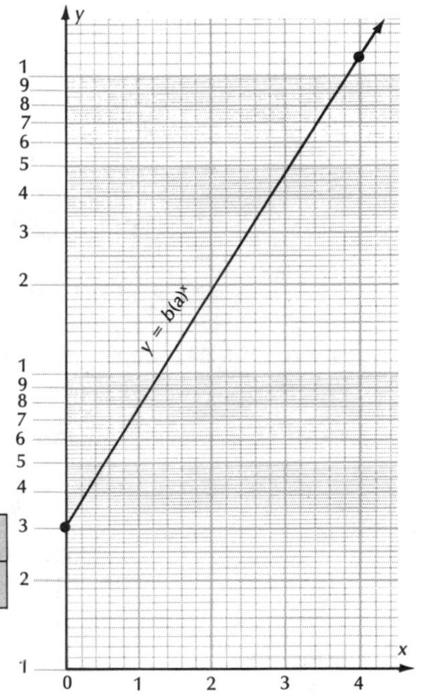

EXAMPLE: Show that the data in the given table satisfies an exponential equation of the form $y = b(a^x)$.

x	0	1	2	3	4
y	3	7.5	18.75	46.8	117.18

- First, graph the data using semi-logarithmic graph paper.
- Draw a straight line of "best fit" through the points.
- Find the y-intercept. Record the point $(0, \log 3)$
- Find another point on the line, like $(4, \log 117.18)$
- Find the slope of the line.

$$\frac{\log 117.18 - \log 3}{4 - 0} = \frac{\log 39.06}{4} = 0.3979$$

$$\therefore \log a = 0.3979$$
$$a = 2.4997 \doteq 2.5$$

- Use the y-intercept to find b.

$$\log b = \log 3$$
$$\therefore b = 3$$

Thus, an exponential equation that the data satisfies is $y = 3(2.5^x)$.

Find an exponential equation that satisfies the data in the given table.

x	0	1	2	3	4
y	2.5	17.5	122.5	857.5	6002.5

3-5 Applying Logarithms

There is evidence of growth and decay all around you. Plants grow and decay, populations increase and decrease, and radioactive elements decay. The accumulated amount, A, of an investment can be thought of as growth. Investment problems often involve the formula $A = A_0(1 + i)^n$.

A_0 is the amount of the original investment.
n is the number of periods.
i is the interest rate.

EXAMPLE 1: What amount will \$100 accumulate to if it is invested for 10 periods at an interest rate of 8% per period?

$$A = A_0(1 + i)^n$$

$A_0 = 100$, $i = 0.08$, $n = 10$.

$$A = 100(1 + 0.08)^{10}$$

Substitute known values.

$$\doteq 215.89$$

The accumulated amount is \$215.89.

Logarithms can be used to solve investment problems.

EXAMPLE 2: How long will it take for \$100 to accumulate to \$300 if it is invested at an interest rate of 8%/a?

$A = 300$, $A_0 = 100$, $i = 0.08$. Find n to the nearest year.

$$A = A_0(1 + i)^n$$
$$300 = 100(1 + 0.08)^n$$
$$3 = (1.08)^n$$

Take the logarithm of both sides.

$$\log 3 = n \log(1.08)$$
$$n = \frac{\log 3}{\log(1.08)}$$

Use a calculator.

$$n = \doteq 14.275$$

It will take about 14 a for the investment to accumulate to \$300.

EXAMPLE 3: Correct to one decimal place, what interest rate applies if \$100 accumulates to \$250 in 25 a?

$A = 250$, $A_0 = 100$, $n = 25$. Find i.

$$A = A_0(1 + i)^n$$
$$250 = 100(1 + i)^{25}$$
$$2.5 = (1 + i)^{25}$$
$$\log 2.5 = 25 \log(1 + i)$$
$$\log(1 + i) = \frac{\log 2.5}{25}$$

[2.5] [log] [÷] [25] [=]

$$\log(1 + i) \doteq 0.015\,917\,6$$

$1 + i = 10^{0.015\,917\,6}$

$$1 + i = 1.037\,331\,5$$
$$i = 0.037\,331\,5$$

The interest rate is about 3.7%.

EXAMPLE 4: Dry cleaners use a cleaning fluid that is purified by evaporation and condensation after each cleaning cycle. Every time the fluid is purified, 2% of the fluid is lost.

a. An equipment manufacturer claims that after 20 cycles, about two thirds of the fluid remains. Can this be verified by calculation?

Use the formula $A = A_0(1 + i)^n$.

The decay factor is 2%, or 0.02.
Thus, after each purification, (1 − 0.02), or 0.98, of the fluid remains.
After n purifications, the initial amount, A_0, becomes

$$A_0(0.098)^n = A_n.$$

After 20 cycles, the original amount will decrease to $(0.98)^{20}$, or 0.667 607 9.

Since $\frac{2}{3} \doteq 0.667$, the manufacturer's claim is correct.

b. If the fluid has to be "topped up" when one-half the original amount remains, after how many cycles should the cleaning fluid be "topped up"?

Find n such that $(0.98)^n = 0.5$

$$\begin{aligned} n \log(0.98) &= \log 0.5 \\ n &= \log 0.5 \div \log 0.98 \\ n &\doteq 34.31 \end{aligned}$$

$A_0 = 1, A_n = 0.5$
Take the logarithm of both sides of the equation.

The fluid should be "topped up" after 34 cycles.

c. A manufacturer has developed a new process for which two thirds of the cleaning fluid remains after 40 cycles. What percentage of fluid is lost after each cycle?

If the percentage lost each time is i, then

$$(1 - i)^{40} = \frac{2}{3}.$$

$$\begin{aligned} 40 \log(1 - i) &= \log\left(\frac{2}{3}\right) \\ 1 - i &= 0.9899 \\ i &= 0.0101 \end{aligned}$$

$A_0 = 1, A_n = \frac{2}{3}$
Take the logarithm of both sides.

[2] [÷] [3] [=] [log] [÷] [40] [=] [INV] [log] 0.989 914 5

The loss of fluid is about 1.0% per cycle.

EXERCISE 3-5

A 1. The accumulated amount of an investment is $950(1.075)^{12}$ dollars.

a. For how many interest periods did the amount accumulate?
b. What was the principal?
c. What was the rate of interest?

B 2. One-hundred dollars invested today at 5% per annum will be worth $\$100(1.05)^t$ in t years. In how many years will the money accumulate to $200?

3. A population is growing at a rate of 2.5%/a. That is, in t years, the population, P, increases to $P(1.025)^t$. How many years will it take for the population to double?

4. An insurance company promises to pay $350 after 20 a for every $100 invested. What rate of interest is the company paying?

5. A wound heals according to the formula
$$A = 80(10^{-0.023t}),$$
where A is the area of the wound, in cm^2, after t days.

a. What is the area of the initial wound?
b. What is the area of the wound after 5 d of healing?
c. In how many days will 80% of the wound be healed?

6. A new disinfectant spray is expected to kill 50% of the known germs in a room, but for health reasons it can only be used once a day. Between spraying, the germs increase by 25%. How many consecutive days of spraying are required to reduce the germs in the room to 10% of the original amount?

7. In a BBC documentary, it was stated that the surface detail of stonework in Venice is disappearing at the rate of 6%/a due to air pollution. How much of the "original" surface detail on an outdoor statue remains after 20 a?

8. Solid waste production is a major factor in the problem of disposal. It is estimated that in a certain country, production of waste is multiplied by 1.5 every 12 a.

a. Show that the formula
$$P = A(1.5)^{\frac{t}{2}}$$
could be used as a mathematical model for the production of waste.

b. In 1950, the production of waste was 100 million tonnes. Calculate the waste production in 1960, 1970, 1980, and 1990 using the model.

9. Blue jeans fade when washed due to loss of blue dye originally contained in the fabric. Suppose each washing removes about 2.5% of the dye from the fabric.
   a. What percentage of the dye remains in the fabric after 12 washings?
   b. How many washings are required to give jeans a well worn look? (For a well-worn look, the jeans should contain, at most, 30% of the original dye.)

10. Radioactive carbon-14 has a half-life of 5700 a. When an organism dies, the amount of carbon-14 present decays exponentially. By measuring the radioactivity, R, of the remains of a fossilized organism and comparing it with the radioactivity, R_0, of a living organism, archaeologists can give the approximate time of death of the organism using the formula

$$R = R_0\left(\frac{1}{2}\right)^{\frac{t}{5700}}.$$

   a. The radioactivity of carbon-14 in a present day living person is found to be ten times that of the mummy of an Egyptian king. How old is the mummy?
   b. An antique dealer sold a piece of wood purported to come from a chariot used by Caesar in ancient Rome. Archaeologists measured the radioactivity of the wood, compared it to a piece of new wood, and found that $R = 0.9R_0$. Was the dealer's claim true?

C 11. There is strong evidence that the Inuit left the mainland many years ago and settled in the Aleutian Islands. It is estimated that the Aleuts and Inuit have about 25% of their languages in common. Archaeologists estimate that after 1000 a, 20% of the words in a language are lost or replaced. Estimate how many years ago the Aleuts left the mainland.

12. Gas, released under pressure through a small opening, is cooled as it expands. Suppose that the gas temperature decreases by 20% each time gas passes through a small opening. If a cooled gas is passed through a small opening repeatedly, how many times must the gas be passed through the opening to reduce its temperature from 300° K to 100° K?

13. The normal height, h cm, and normal mass, m kg, of a calf at two stages of growth are given in the following chart.

Stage	Height (cm)	Mass (kg)
Weaning	98.7	208.2
Yearling	105.3	251.3

Suppose that calves grow according to the formula $m = x(h^y)$, where x and y are constants.

   a. Find the value of x and of y.
   b. Find the mass, m, given that $h = 110$ cm.

3-6 The Natural Logarithm

The number e is used as a base for logarithms in calculus and statistics to facilitate calculations. A logarithm to the base e is called a **natural logarithm, ln.**

ln x means $\log_e x$ ln 6 means $\log_e 6$

Recall that $e \doteq 2.718$.

A calculator can be used to evaluate natural logarithms.

To evaluate ln 5, enter [5] [ln] or [5] [ln x].

ln 5 $\doteq$ 1.609 437 9

EXAMPLE 1: Solve $18.2^{5.6} = e^x$, correct to two decimal places.

Take the natural logarithm of both sides.

$$(18.2)^{5.6} = e^x$$
$$5.6 \ln 18.2 = x \ln e$$
$$5.6 \ln 18.2 = x$$
$$x \doteq 16.25$$

$\ln e = \log_e e = 1$

[5.6] [×] [18.2] [ln] [=] 16.247 96

Notice that in Example 1, the base was changed from 18.2 to e. That is, $(18.2)^{5.6} = e^{16.25}$.

EXAMPLE 2: Change the exponential equation $y = 7(2^{0.23t})$ to an equivalent exponential equation with base e.

Find m and n such that

$$7 = e^m \quad \text{and} \quad 2 = e^n.$$
$$\ln 7 = m \ln e \qquad \ln 2 = \ln e$$
$$m = \ln 7 \qquad n = \ln 2$$
$$m \doteq 1.946 \quad \text{and} \quad n \doteq 0.693$$

Take the natural logarithm of both sides. Use a calculator.

Substitute known values into the original equation.

$$y = 7(2^{0.23t})$$
$$= e^{1.946} \times (e^{0.693})^{0.23t}$$
$$= e^{1.946} \times e^{0.159t}$$
$$= e^{0.159t + 1.946}$$

$7 = e^m$ or $e^{1.946}$

$2 = e^n$ or $e^{0.693}$

Therefore, the required equation is $y = e^{0.159t + 1.946}$.

EXAMPLE 3: Solve $\ln x = 1.532$, correct to three decimal places.

Use the [INV] [ln] keys on a calculator.

[1.532] [INV] [ln] 4.627 422 4

$\therefore x \doteq 4.627$

EXERCISE 3-6

A

1. Express as a natural logarithm.

   a. $3^x = 20$ b. $1.5^t = 8.2$ c. $e^t = 13$ d. $(0.72)^x = 9$

2. Evaluate each of the following using a calculator.

   a. $\ln 50$ b. $\ln 100$ c. $\ln 2$ d. $\ln 0.56$

3. Use a calculator to solve each equation.

   a. $\ln x = 0.045$ b. $\ln x = -0.15$ c. $e^x = 3$ d. $e^x = 0.56$

4. Evaluate where possible.

   a. $\ln e^3$ b. $\ln e$ c. $\ln 1$ d. $\ln\left(\frac{1}{e^3}\right)$
   e. $\ln 0$ f. $e^{\ln 2}$ g. $e^{\ln 5}$ h. $\ln e^{-2}$

5. Express as a single logarithm.

   a. $\ln 12 - \ln 4 + \ln 5$ b. $\frac{1}{2}\ln 9 - \ln 18$ c. $3\ln 2 - \frac{3}{2}\ln 16$
   d. $\ln 5 + 3$ e. $\frac{1}{2}\ln 16 - 3$ f. $5 - \ln 2$

6. Solve each equation. Give each answer in terms of ln.

   a. $e^x = 3$ b. $e^{2x} = 3$ c. $e^{x-2} = 5$ d. $e^{-x} = 3$
   e. $e^{2-x} = 3$ f. $e^{5-x} = 2$ g. $e^{3-x} = e^{2x}$ h. $e^{2x-2} = e$

B

7. Express each formula as an exponential equation with base e.

   a. $A = (1.56)^{2.1t}$ b. $V = V_0(1.6)^{-0.02t}$ c. $T = 20 + 80(2)^{-0.15t}$

8. Change each equation to an equivalent exponential equation with base e.

   a. $y = 50(2^x)$ b. $y = (1.05)^x$ c. $y = 780\left(\frac{1}{2}\right)^x$

9. The population of Canada can be estimated using the formula $N = 18.2e^{0.0145(t-1961)}$, where 18.2 million was the population in 1961 and N is the number of people, in millions, in year t. In what year is the population of Canada expected to be 30 million?

10. The intensity, I_0, of light from a car's headlights is reduced to I after passing through d metres of fog according to the formula
    $I = I_0e^{-0.14d}$.
    For what distance will the intensity be reduced to 0.01 of its original value?

11. The atmospheric pressure, P, at height h kilometres is given by the formula

$P = P_0e^{-kh}$.

The pressure at sea levels, P_0, is 101.3 kPa.

a. If $P = 89$ kPa when $h = 1$, find the value of k.
b. Calculate the pressure at a height of 2 km.

12. At 100°C, hot water cools in a room with temperature 20° C according to the formula

$T = 20 + 80e^{-0.03t}$, where T is the temperature t minutes after cooling begins.

How long will it take for the water to cool to 40° C in the room?

13. The speed, V, in kilometres per hour, of a boat travelling through water, t seconds after the engine is shut off, is given by

$V = V_0e^{-0.02t}$, where V_0 is the speed when the engine is shut off.

If a boat is moving at 8 km/h when the engine is shut off, how long will it take for the boat to reduce speed to 2 km/h? to 0.5 km/h?

14. When sunlight passes through water, it loses intensity as it penetrates to greater depths according to the formula

$I = I_0e^{-kd}$, where I_0 is the intensity of light at the surface of the water and I is the intensity, d metres below the surface. Suppose that $I = 0.3012\, I_0$ at a depth of 100 m.

a. Find the value of k.
b. Find the depth at which the intensity is decreased to 1% of the surface intensity.

C 15. When gamma-rays are passed through a heavy material, the rays are absorbed. The intensity, I, of the rays after absorption is given by the equation

$I = I_0e^{-kd}$, where I_0 is the intensity of the rays without a barrier, d is the thickness of the material (in centimetres), and k is a constant, determined by the material used.

If gamma rays are sent through a heavy material that is 7 cm thick, the intensity is reduced to $\frac{1}{8}$, or 0.125, of its original value.

a. Find the value of k, correct to four decimal places.
b. What thickness of heavy material is needed to reduce the intensity of the rays to 2% of the original intensity?

16. Solve.

a. $e^{2x} - e^x - 6 = 0$

b. $e^{4x} - 13e^{2x} + 36 = 0$

17. The life expectancy T, in years, of a natural resource such as oil, is the time it takes to use all the resource. If the rate of consumption remains constant, then life expectancy is given by

$T = \frac{1}{r}\ln\left(\frac{rR}{C} + 1\right)$, where C is the current consumption, r is the current growth rate of consumption, and R is the size of the resource (oil reserves).

Suppose that the world consumption of oil is growing at a rate of 6%/a and current consumption is 16 million barrels/d, or 5.8×10^9 barrels/a. Find the life expectancy of the world's oil supply, given each estimate of the size of the reserves.

a. $R = 1691 \times 10^9$ barrels (crude oil only)
b. $R = 1881 \times 10^9$ barrels (crude oil plus shale oil)

Application

The Richter Scale

An earthquake occurs when the stress or strain between continent-sized crustal plates that are locked together becomes too great. The land masses can snap apart, slide over one another, or slip sideways past each other. In any case, an earthquake occurs at the Earth's surface.

Seismologists use the Richter scale to measure the intensity of an earthquake. The Richter scale was revised in 1979 so that seismologists could estimate the energy released by an earthquake. The Richter magnitude, R, of an earthquake is defined by the formula

$R = 0.67 \log (0.01\,E) + 1.46$, where E is the energy in megaJoules (mJ).

For example, the energy released by an earthquake that measures 6.1 on the Richter scale can be determined as follows.

$$R = 0.67 \log (0.01E) + 1.46$$
$$6.1 = 0.67 \log (0.01E) + 1.46$$
$$\log (0.01E) = 6.925\,373\,1 \qquad (6.1 - 1.46) \div 0.67 = 6.925\,373\,1$$
$$0.01E = 10^{6.925\,373\,1}$$
$$\doteq 8\,421\,183$$
$$E \doteq 8.4 \times 10^6 \text{ mJ}$$

1. In 1906, the earthquake that devastated San Francisco, California registered 7.9 on the revised Richter scale. The highest recorded earthquake on the Richter scale measured 8.6. How many times as great as the 1906 San Francisco earthquake was the energy released by the most intense earthquake?
2. By what factor is the energy of an earthquake increased if the Richter magnitude is increased by each factor?

   a. 1 **b.** 2 **c.** 3

Review

1. Evaluate.

   a. $\log_3 3^{-2}$ b. $\log_2 \left(\frac{1}{8}\right)$ c. $\log_2 8^4$ d. $\log_2 \sqrt{2}$ e. $\log_2 \sqrt[5]{12}$

2. a. Graph the function, f, defined by $f(x) = 3^x$ for $-3 \le x \le 3$.
   b. Graph f^{-1} on the same axes as part **a**.
   c. State the defining equation of f^{-1}.

3. Rewrite in an equivalent logarithmic form.

   a. $3^4 = 81$ b. $(0.5)^3 = \frac{1}{8}$ c. $4^{1.5} = 8$ d. $16^{-2} = \frac{1}{256}$

4. Rewrite in an equivalent exponential form.

   a. $\log_3 243 = 5$ b. $\log_5 \sqrt{5} = 0.5$ c. $\log_{32} \left(\frac{1}{8}\right) = -\frac{3}{5}$ d. $\log_2 2\sqrt{2} = 1.5$

5. Solve.

   a. $\log 1000 = x$ b. $\log_{11} x = 2$ c. $\log_y 32 = \frac{5}{3}$ d. $\log_x 9 = 1$
   e. $\log_2 8 = x$ f. $\log_7 49 = y$ g. $\log_2 x = -2$ h. $\log_3 y = -1$
   i. $\log_x 64 = 2$ j. $\log_x 6 = 1$ k. $\log_3 (x + 2) = 4$ l. $\log_2 (x + 1) = 4$

6. Express as a sum or a difference of logarithms.

   a. $\log (17 \times 15)$ b. $\log_3 (17 \times 15 \times 13)$ c. $\log_2 \left(\frac{12}{5}\right)$ d. $\log \left(\frac{1}{5}\right)$

7. Rewrite as products of numbers and logarithms.

   a. $\log x^3$ b. $\log x^3y^4$ c. $\log \sqrt{xy}$ d. $\log \sqrt[3]{xy^2}$

8. Solve for x.

   a. $\log_3 x = 2 \log_3 7 + \log_3 4$ b. $\log_7 x = \log_7 35 - \log_7 5$

9. Express as a single logarithm, if possible, and evaluate.

   a. $\log 50 + \log 2$ b. $\log_6 72 - \log_6 2$
   c. $2 \log_6 3 + \log_6 10 = \frac{1}{2}\log_6 25$ d. $\log 40 + \log 25 - \log_a a^3$

10. If $\log_7 2 = 0.356\,21$, $\log_7 3 = 0.564\,58$, and $\log_7 5 = 0.827\,09$, use the properties of logarithms to evaluate each of the following without a calculator.

    a. $\log_7 6$ b. $\log_7 12$ c. $\log_7 200$
    d. $\log_7 1.5$ e. $\log_7 0.2$ f. $\log_7 12.5$

11. Use a calculator to solve each equation.

    a. $\log x = 2.62$ b. $\log x = -1.735$ c. $\log x = 0.372$ d. $5^x = 47.3$

12. Solve each equation.

a. $\log_3 x = \frac{1}{2}\log_3 25 - \log_3 100 + \log_3 40$ b. $\log z = \log \sqrt{5} + \log \sqrt{2}$

13. Change each equation to an equivalent exponential equation with base 10.

a. $y = 17.2(2^x)$ b. $y = (1.06)^t$ c. $y = 60(3^{0.4t})$

14. Evaluate.

a. $\log_2 17$ b. $\log_3 (0.1)$ c. $\log_2 (0.05)$ d. $\ln 20$ e. $\ln 0.2$

15. Find the number of years needed for each investment to accumulate to the given amount.

a. \$50 at 10%/a accumulates to \$75 b. \$100 at 9%/a accumulates to \$250

16. a. In 13 a, an investment of \$1000 accumulates to \$2400. What annual rate of interest does this investment yield?
b. A grandparent leaves a newborn baby \$2000 to be invested to yield \$6000 when the child is 20 years old. At what rate of interest should the money be invested to yield the required amount?

17. A new assembly-line worker will produce the same item N times per day according to the formula

$N = 80 - 60e^{-0.08t}$, where t is measured in days.

a. How many items does the worker produce on the first day?
b. How many items does the worker produce by the end of the tenth day?
c. For how many days must the worker repeat the task in order to produce 40 items each day?

18. For a period of its life, a tree grows according to the formula

$D = D_0e^{kt}$, where D is the diameter, in centimetres, of the tree t years after the beginning of the period.

After 2 a, the diameter of the tree is 15.62 cm. After 5 a, the diameter is 21.724 cm.
a. Find the value of D_0 and of k.
b. How many years will it take the tree to reach a diameter of 40 cm?

19. The brightness of an oscillating star increases by 12.5% every time it reverses position.

a. How many times brighter will the star be after 20 oscillations?
b. Another oscillating star increases in brightness 10 times in 10 oscillations. Find the percentage increase in brightness with each oscillation.

Test

Unit 3

1. Evaluate.

   a. $100^{\frac{3}{2}}$ b. $16^{0.75}$ c. $(0.008)^{-\frac{2}{3}}$ d. $(-0.125)^{-\frac{1}{3}}$

2. Sketch the graph of $y = \log_2 x$, where $\frac{1}{8} \leq x \leq 8$.

3. Evaluate.

   a. $\log_3 3^{0.5}$ b. $\log_2 32$ c. $7^{\log 5}$ d. $\log_3 \sqrt{3}$ e. $\log_5 \sqrt[2]{5^3}$

4. Rewrite in equivalent logarithmic form.

   a. $16^{0.5} = 4$ b. $2^{-1} = 0.5$ c. $10^{-3} = 0.001$ d. $81^{\frac{3}{4}} = 27$

5. Rewrite in equivalent exponential form.

   a. $\log_2 \left(\frac{1}{4}\right) = -2$ b. $\log_5 5 = 2$ c. $\log_9 \sqrt{3} = 0.25$ d. $\log 100 = 2$

6. Solve.

   a. $\log_x 125 = 3$ b. $\log x = 2$ c. $\log_8 16 = x$
   d. $\log_{16} x = 0.75$ e. $\log_a 7 = -1$ f. $\log_3 (x - 2) = 3$
   g. $\log_2 x = \log_2 10 + \log_2 25$ h. $\log_2 y = \frac{1}{3} \log_2 27 - \frac{1}{4} \log_2 16$

7. Change the equation $y = 0.37(2.3^{2.2t})$ to an equivalent equation with base 10.

8. Solve using a calculator.

   a. $\log x = -1.735$ b. $\log x = 0.001$ c. $10^x = 28.3$ d. $2^x = 31.9$

9. Evaluate.

   a. $\log_3 100$ b. $\log_6 105$ c. $\log_{4.1} 6$ d. $\log 0.015$

10. a. In 14 a, an investment of $10 000 accumulates to $27 500. What annual rate of interest does this investment yield?
    b. For each $100 invested, a trust company guarantees to pay $466 in 20 a. What rate of interest does such an investment return?

11. Each time the ribbon of a dot matrix printer is run through the printer, the quantity of ink in the ribbon decreases by 2%. The ribbon should be discarded when it contains 60% of the ink that a new ribbon contains. Find the number of times a ribbon can be run through the printer before a new ribbon is required.

12. The speed, V, of a chemical reaction increases with the temperature, t, at a constant rate of 10% and is given by the formula

    $V = 100(2.5)^{0.1t}$

    a. Find the speed of the reaction when $t = 0$
    b. Find the value of t when $V = 300$.

13. State the domain and then solve for x.

    a. $\log_5 (x + 2) = \log_5 (2x - 4)$ b. $\log (x + 1) + \log (x - 1) = 1$

Cumulative Review

1. Solve each equation.

   a. $2^x = 32$ b. $2^x = \frac{1}{8}$ c. $2^x = 4^3$ d. $9^{x-2} = 3^2$

2. Find an equation of an exponential function defined by $f(x) = a(b^x)$, given each of the following.

   a. $b = \frac{3}{4}$, $f(0) = 5$ b. $f(0) = 2$, $f(2) = 18$ (two answers)

3. Given that $f{:}x \to \frac{1}{x}$ for $-1 < x < 7$ and $g{:}x \to x - 3$ for $-1 < x < 7$, answer each of the following.

   a. Graph f and g.
   b. Graph $\frac{f}{g}$.
   c. Find a defining equation of $\frac{f}{g}$.
   d. Find the vertical asymptotes of the graph of $\frac{f}{g}$.

4. Copy the given graphs of f and g, and sketch the graphs of $f + g$ and $f - g$.

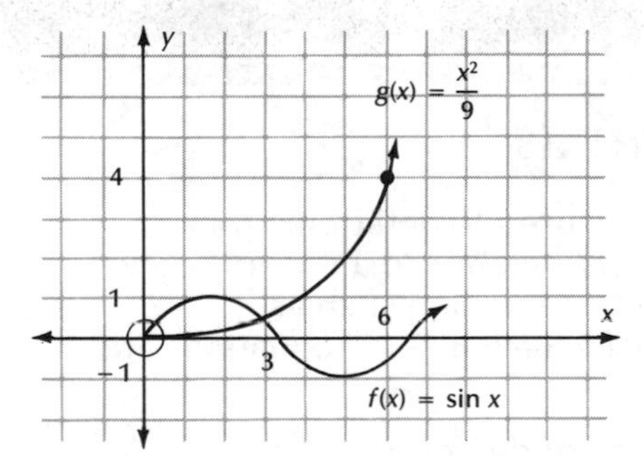

5. Solve and graph each inequality on a number line.

   a. $|x| > 3$ b. $|x| < 1$ c. $|x| \geq 2$
   d. $|x - 3| > 2$ e. $|x + 2| < 5$ f. $|3x + 6| > 0$

6. Solve.

   a. $|x - 2| = 5$ b. $|2 - x| + 3 = 5$ c. $8 - 2|x + 1| = 0$

7. Given that $g{:}x \to x^2$, answer each of the following.

   a. Graph g.
   b. Graph the inverse of g.
   c. Show that g^{-1} is a function if the domain of g is $\{x \mid x > 0\}$.
   d. Show that g^{-1} is a function if the domain of g is $\{x \mid x < 0\}$.

8. If $h{:}x \to |x|$, prove graphically that the inverse of h is not a function.

9. What amount will \$1000 accumulate to in 6 a if it is invested at 12%/a, compounded semiannually?

4 Polynomials and Factoring

4-1 Factoring Polynomials

The equation $d = 0.006v^2 + 0.03v + 2$ is used to determine the number of metres needed to bring an automobile to a full stop, given that the vehicle is travelling at v km/h. An equation such as $d = 0.006v^2 + 0.03v + 2$ is a **polynomial equation**. Such equations are often used in mathematics and science.

In general, a **polynomial** is an expression of the form

$a_nx^n + a_{n-1}x^{n-1} + \ldots + a_1x + a_0,$

where $n \in \boldsymbol{Z}$, and each coefficient $a_k \in \boldsymbol{R}$.

The **degree** of the polynomial is n, the greatest exponent. Further, $a_n \neq 0$.

A polynomial of the form $ax^2 + bx + c$, where $a, b, c \neq 0$, is a **quadratic trinomial.** A quadratic trinomial has degree 2 and contains a quadratic term, a linear term, and a constant term.

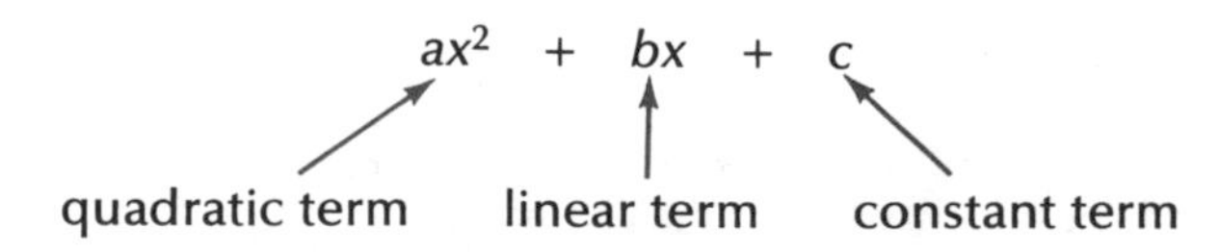

A polynomial is **factored** when it is expressed as the product of two or more polynomials of lesser degree.

EXAMPLE 1: **a.** Factor $3x^2 - 9x - 12$.

$$3x^2 - 9x - 12 = 3(x^2 - 3x - 4)$$
$$= 3(x - 4)(x + 1)$$

b. Factor $10mx^3 - 8m^2x^2 + 6m^3x$.

$$10mx^3 - 8m^2x^2 + 6m^3x$$
$$= 2mx(5x^2 - 4mx + 3m^2)$$

Some polynomials fit special patterns that make them easier to factor.

Difference of Squares: $a^2 - b^2 = (a + b)(a - b)$

Perfect Square Trinomials: $a^2 + 2ab + b^2 = (a + b)^2$
$a^2 - 2ab + b^2 = (a - b)^2$

EXAMPLE 2: Factor each polynomial.

a. $x^2 - 25 = (x + 5)(x - 5)$ Difference of squares
b. $9m^2 - 100n^4p^2 = (3m + 10n^2p)(3m - 10n^2p)$
c. $m^2 + 6m + 9 = (m + 3)^2$
d. $9x^2 - 30xy + 25y^2 = (3x - 5y)^2$ Perfect square trinomials

EXAMPLE 3: Factor by grouping. Then factor any special polynomials that result.

a. $ax^2 - ay^2 + 3x^2 - 3y^2$
$= a(x^2 - y^2) + 3(x^2 - y^2)$
$= (a + 3)(x^2 - y^2)$
$= (a + 3)(x + y)(x - y)$

b. $9x^2 - 12xy + 4y^2 - 16$
$= (9x^2 - 12xy + 4y^2) - 16$
$= (3x - 2y)^2 - 16$
$= [(3x - 2y) + 4][(3x - 2y) - 4]$
$= (3x - 2y + 4)(3x - 2y - 4)$

EXAMPLE 4: Factor $6x^2 + 7x - 5$.

If $6x^2 + 7x - 5$ is factorable, then the factors are binomials of the form $(rx + a)$ and $(sx + b)$, and
$(rx + a)(sx + b) = rsx^2 + (rb + sa)x + ab$,
where $rs = 6$, $rb + sa = 7$, and $ab = -5$.

Since r and s are factors of 6, the first terms of the factors must be one of the following pairs.

$$(x \quad)(6x \quad) \text{ or } (2x \quad)(3x \quad)$$

The coefficients, a and b, are factors of 5. Since $ab = -5$, then either a or b must be negative. The possible second terms of the binomial factors are as follows.

$$(\quad +1)(\quad -5) \text{ or } (\quad -1)(\quad +5)$$

The product of any combination of the above pairs will produce $6x^2$ as the quadratic term and -5 as the constant term. Make an organized list to find the combination that gives $7x$ as the linear term.

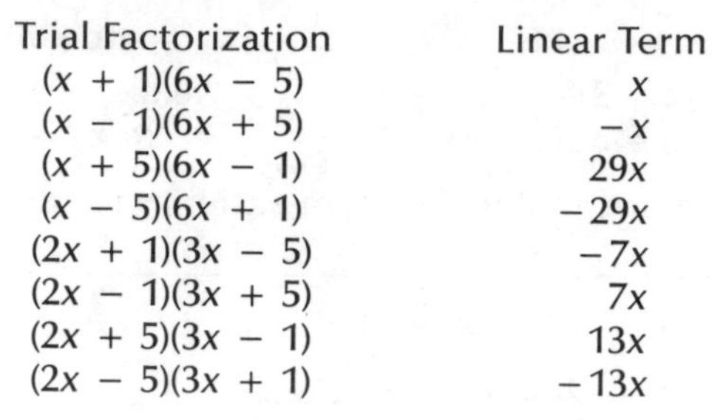

Trial Factorization	Linear Term
$(x + 1)(6x - 5)$	x
$(x - 1)(6x + 5)$	$-x$
$(x + 5)(6x - 1)$	$29x$
$(x - 5)(6x + 1)$	$-29x$
$(2x + 1)(3x - 5)$	$-7x$
$(2x - 1)(3x + 5)$	$7x$
$(2x + 5)(3x - 1)$	$13x$
$(2x - 5)(3x + 1)$	$-13x$

The trial factorization that gives $7x$ as the linear term is

$$6x^2 + 7x - 5 = (2x - 1)(3x + 5).$$

EXAMPLE 5: Factor $3x^2 + 11x + 6$.

The factors will be binomials of the form $(rx + a)$ and $(sx + b)$.

$$(rx + a)(sx + b) = rsx^2 + (rb + sa)x + ab,$$
where $rs = 3$, $rb + sa = 11$, and $ab = 6$.

Notice that the coefficient of the linear term, $rb + sa$, and the product of the coefficient of the quadratic term and the constant term, $rsab$, are related. Make an organized list of factors of the product of the coefficient of the quadratic term and the constant term, $rsab = (3)(6) = 18$, and look for a sum equal to the coefficient of the linear term.

Factors		Sum
1	18	19
2	9	11
3	6	9

Rewrite $3x^2 + 11x + 6$ with the middle term separated into the sum of factors and then factor by grouping.

$$\begin{aligned} 3x^2 + 11x + 6 &= 3x^2 + 9x + 2x + 6 \\ &= 3x(x + 3) + 2(x + 3) \\ &= (3x + 2)(x + 3) \end{aligned}$$

EXERCISE 4-1

A

1. For each equation, find the value of a and of b.

   a. $(x + 9)(ax + b) = 3x^2 + 34x + 63$
   b. $(ax + 5)(3x + b) = 6x^2 + 29x + 35$
   c. $(ax + 5)(bx + 7) = 12x^2 + 41x + 35$
   d. $(5x + a)(7x + b) = 35x^2 - 32x - 12$
   e. $(2x + a)(5x + b) = 10x^2 - 53x + 63$
   f. $(4x + a)(3x + b) = 12x^2 - x - 20$

2. Factor by grouping.

   a. $3x + 3y + ax + ay$
   b. $ax + bx - ay - by$
   c. $mr - ms + nr - ns$
   d. $px + 3qx + 2py + 6qy$
   e. $3ax + 3ay - by - bx + 2cx + 2cy$
   f. $3mx - 9x + my - 3y - 2m + 6$

3. Factor each polynomial.

a. $x^2 + 5x + 4$ b. $x^2 - 10x + 24$ c. $x^2 - x - 12$
d. $x^2 + x - 20$ e. $y^2 - 25z^2$ f. $m^2 + m + \frac{1}{4}$
g. $4x^2 - 9y^2$ h. $9a^2 - 1$ i. $2x^2 + 17x + 15$
j. $2x^2 + 5x + 3$ k. $5x^2 + 34x - 7$ l. $3x^2 + 22x + 24$

4. Remove a common factor and then factor any special trinomials that result.

a. $ax^2 + 3ax + 2a$ b. $2x^2 + 14x + 24$
c. $5x^2 + 20xy + 15y^2$ d. $3a^3b - 21a^2b^2 + 30ab^3$

B

5. Factor by grouping.

a. $ax^2 + 3ax + 2a + bx^2 + 3bx + 2b$ b. $my^2 + ny^2 + 5my + 5ny + 6m + 6n$
c. $a^2x + 6ay - 3ax + 20y - 10x - 2a^2y$ d. $x^2y + 6x - 4y + 8 - 2x^2 - 3xy$

6. Factor.

a. $6x^2 + 5x - 25$ b. $4x^2 - 12x + 9$ c. $9x^2 + 12x + 4$
d. $8x^2 - 18x + 9$ e. $12x^2 + 17x + 6$ f. $4x^2 - 21x - 18$
g. $4x^2 - 4x - 63$ h. $20x^2 + 37x + 15$ i. $15x^2 - 4x - 4$

7. Factor. (Each expression has a common factor.)

a. $12x^2 + 45x + 27$ b. $27r^6 - 12q^2r^2$
c. $4pq^2 + 17pq - 15p$ d. $50x^2 - 55x - 30$
e. $8m^2n^2 + 32m^2n + 30m^2$ f. $ab^3 - 16a^3b$
g. $60p^2q^2r + 130p^2qr + 60p^2r$ h. $10ax^2 - 21ax + 9a$
i. $100s^2r^2 - 210s^2r - 100s^2$ j. $50x^2y^2 - 40xy^3 + 8y^4$
k. $a^3 - 2a^2 + a$ l. $2x^3 + 12x^2 + 18x$
m. $2x^3 - 32x$ n. $5x^3 - 45x$

C

8. Factor. (Each expression has more than two factors.)

a. $x^4 - 1$ b. $s^8 - 1$ c. $b^4 - 2b^2 + 1$
d. $z^4 - 3z^2 - 4$ e. $8x^4 - 6x^2 - 27$ f. $625r^4 - 200r^2 + 16$

9. For what values of k, $k \in \mathbf{Z}$, is each polynomial factorable?

a. $x^2 + kx + 6$ b. $x^2 + kx - 8$ c. $2x^2 + kx + 3$
d. $3x^2 + kx + 4$ e. $6x^2 + kx - 10$ f. $3x^2 + 5x + k$

10. Factor each polynomial by first grouping to show a difference of squares.

a. $x^2 + 6x + 9 - y^2$ b. $a^2 - b^2 - 4b - 4$
c. $4m^2 + 1 - n^2 - 4m$ d. $9x^2 - y^2 + 12x + 4$
e. $x^2 - y^2 + 4x - 2y + 3$ f. $a^2 - b^2 + 6a - 10b - 16$
g. $9m^2 - 25p^2 + 12mn + 4n^2$ h. $4r^2 + 9s^2 - 4q^2 + 12rs$
i. $a^2 + 2ab + b^2 - c^2 - 2c - 1$ j. $-x^2 + y^2 + 6yz + 9z^2 + 4x - 4$

4-2 Solving Quadratic Equations

Many problems in science, economics, and the manufacturing industry require the solution of an equation that involves quadratic polynomials, or a **quadratic equation**. Solving such an equation involves finding the values that satisfy the equation, or finding the **roots** of the equation. Sometimes the roots of an equation can be found by factoring the polynomial and then applying the **zero product rule.**

The zero product rule states that if two factors have a product of zero, then one of the factors must be zero. That is, if $ab = 0$, then either $a = 0$, or $b = 0$, or both.

EXAMPLE 1: Solve each quadratic equation by factoring.

a. $3x^2 - 21 = 2x$

$$3x^2 - 21 = 2x$$
$$3x^2 - 2x - 21 = 0$$
$$(3x + 7)(x - 3) = 0$$
$$\therefore 3x + 7 = 0 \text{ or } x - 3 = 0$$

The solution set is $\left\{-\frac{7}{3}, 3\right\}$.

b. $5x^3 + 45x = -30x^2$

$$5x^3 + 45x = -30x^3$$
$$5x^3 + 30x^2 + 45x = 0$$
$$5x(x^2 + 6x + 9) = 0$$
$$5x(x + 3)^2 = 0$$
$$\therefore 5x = 0 \text{ or } x + 3 = 0$$

The solution set is $\{-3, 0\}$. Since the factor $(x + 3)$ appears twice, -3 is a **double root**.

Alternatives to solving quadratic equations by factoring are to **complete the square** or to use the **quadratic formula.**

EXAMPLE 2: Solve each quadratic equation by completing the square.

a. $3x^2 + 2x - 10 = 0$

Isolate the quadratic and linear terms.

$$3x^2 + 2x - 10 = 0$$
$$3x^2 + 2x = 10$$

Divide both sides by the coefficient of the quadratic term.

$$\frac{1}{3}(3x^2 + 2x) = \frac{1}{3}(10)$$

Obtain a trinomial on the left side by adding the square of half the coefficient of the linear term to both sides of the equation.

$$x^2 + \frac{2}{3}x = \frac{10}{3}$$
$$x^2 + \frac{2}{3}x + \frac{1}{9} = \frac{10}{3} + \frac{1}{9}$$

Factor the left side and solve the resulting equation.

$$\left(x + \frac{1}{3}\right)^2 = \frac{31}{9}$$
$$x + \frac{1}{3} = \pm\frac{\sqrt{31}}{3}$$

$$\therefore x = \frac{-1 + \sqrt{31}}{3} \quad \text{or} \quad x = \frac{-1 - \sqrt{31}}{3}$$

b. $ax^2 + bx + c = 0$

$$ax^2 + bx = -c$$ Isolate quadratic and linear terms.

$$\frac{1}{a}(ax^2 + bx) = \frac{1}{a}(-c)$$ Divide by $\frac{1}{a}$. Note that $a \neq 0$.

$$x^2 + \frac{b}{a}x = -\frac{c}{a}$$

$$x^2 + \frac{b}{a}x + \frac{b^2}{4a^2} = \frac{b^2}{4a^2} - \frac{c}{a}$$ Obtain a trinomial square.

$$\left(x + \frac{b}{2a}\right)^2 = \left(\frac{b^2 - 4ac}{4a^2}\right)$$ Factor and solve.

$$x + \frac{b}{2a} = \pm\sqrt{\frac{b^2 - 4ac}{4a^2}}$$

$$x + \frac{b}{2a} = \pm\frac{\sqrt{b^2 - 4ac}}{2a}$$

$$\therefore x = \frac{-b + \sqrt{b^2 - 4ac}}{2a} \quad \text{or} \quad x = \frac{-b - \sqrt{b^2 - 4ac}}{2a}$$

The Quadratic Formula

For a quadratic equation of the form $ax^2 + bx + c = 0$, where $a, b, c \in \mathbf{R}$ and $a \neq 0$, the roots of the equation are given by the formula

$$x = \frac{-b \pm \sqrt{b^2 - 4ac}}{2a}.$$

EXAMPLE 3: Use the quadratic formula to find the roots of each quadratic equation.

a. $2x^2 - x = 5$

$$x = \frac{-b \pm \sqrt{b^2 - 4ac}}{2a}$$

$$= \frac{-(-1) \pm \sqrt{1 - 4(2)(-5)}}{4}$$

$$= \frac{1 \pm \sqrt{41}}{4}$$

The roots are $x = \frac{1 + \sqrt{41}}{4}$ and $x = \frac{1 - \sqrt{41}}{4}$.

b. $3x^2 + 2x + 5 = 0$

$$x = \frac{-b \pm \sqrt{b^2 - 4ac}}{2a}$$

$$= \frac{-2 \pm \sqrt{4 - 4(3)(5)}}{6}$$

$$= \frac{-2 \pm \sqrt{-56}}{6}$$

The radicand is negative. Therefore, there are no real roots.

c. $4x^2 - 12x + 9 = 0$

$$x = \frac{-b \pm \sqrt{b^2 - 4ac}}{2a}$$

$$= \frac{12 \pm \sqrt{144 - 144}}{8}$$

$$= \frac{12 \pm \sqrt{0}}{8}$$

There is one root, that is, $x = \frac{3}{2}$.

Note that in a situation like part **b** of Example 3, where there are no real roots, the solution set is denoted by { } or $\varnothing$.

The expression $b^2 - 4ac$ is called the **discriminant**. The discriminant determines the character of the roots of a quadratic equation, $Q(x) = 0$, described as follows.

If $b^2 - 4ac > 0$, then $\sqrt{b^2 - 4ac}$ is defined and $Q(x)$ has two distinct real roots.
If $b^2 - 4ac < 0$, then $\sqrt{b^2 - 4ac}$ is not defined and $Q(x)$ has no real roots.
If $b^2 - 4ac = 0$, then $\sqrt{b^2 - 4ac} = 0$ and $Q(x)$ has one double root.

EXAMPLE 4: Use the discriminant to determine the character of the roots of each equation.

a. $3x^2 - 5x + 2 = 0$

$b^2 - 4ac$
$= (-5)^2 - 4(3)(2)$
$= 1$

Since the discriminant is positive, there are two distinct real roots.

b. $x^2 + x + 0.25 = 0$

$b^2 - 4ac$
$= (1)^2 - 4(1)(0.25)$
$= 0$

Since the discriminant is zero, there is one double root.

c. $2x^2 + 3 = x$

$b^2 - 4ac$
$= (-1)^2 - 4(2)(3)$
$= -23$

Since the discriminant is negative, there are no real roots.

EXERCISE 4-2

A 1. Find the roots of each equation by factoring.

a. $x^2 - 3x - 4 = 0$ **b.** $x^2 - 5x - 14 = 0$ **c.** $x^2 - 9 = 0$
d. $x^2 + 6 = 5x$ **e.** $3x^2 = 6x$ **f.** $(x - 1)(x + 5) = 3x + 1$
g. $(x - 4)(x + 2) = 7$ **h.** $2x^2 - x - 28 = 0$ **i.** $4x^2 + 9x - 28 = 0$

2. Find the roots of each equation by using the quadratic formula. Give the answers as radicals in simplest form.

a. $x^2 + 3x - 7 = 0$ **b.** $x^2 + 3x + 10 = 0$ **c.** $2x^2 - 3x + 1 = 0$
d. $3x^2 - 5x - 2 = 0$ **e.** $x - 3x^2 = 8$ **f.** $2x + 3x^2 = 7$
g. $7x - 5 = x^2$ **h.** $3x - 3x^2 = 4x + 2$ **i.** $x^2 - 3x + 2 = x - 2x^2 + 1$

3. Find the roots of each equation by completing the square.

a. $x^2 + 4x = 2$ **b.** $x^2 - 6x = 7$ **c.** $x^2 - 5x - 3 = 0$
d. $x^2 + x - 5 = 0$ **e.** $x^2 - 10x = 3$ **f.** $x^2 - 5 = 2x$
g. $2x^2 - 5x + 1 = 0$ **h.** $2x - x^2 = 1$ **i.** $3x^2 - x - 1 = 6$

B 4. Find the discriminant for each equation and determine if the equation has two distinct real roots, one double root, or no real roots.

a. $3x^2 - 3x + 2 = 0$ **b.** $x^2 + x - 5 = 0$
c. $x^2 - 5 = 3x$ **d.** $5x^2 = 3x + 1$
e. $1.5x^2 + 0.5x - 0.2 = 0$ **f.** $0.2x^2 + 0.4x + 1.2 = 0$
g. $3x^2 - x - 1 = x + 3$ **h.** $2x - 3x^2 + 5 = 8 - x$
i. $3.5x - x^2 = 1.5 - x$ **j.** $0.3x^2 - 3.2 = 0.8x + x^2$

5. A garden is 5 m longer than it is wide. The total area of the garden is 750 m². Write a quadratic equation and solve it by factoring to determine the length and width of the garden.

6. A right-angled triangle has dimensions as shown.

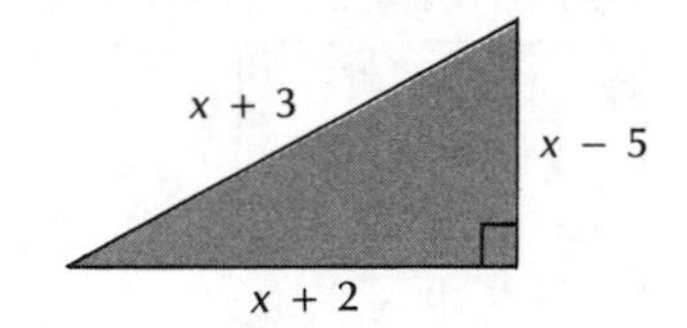

   a. Use the Pythagorean Theorem, $a^2 + b^2 = c^2$, to write a quadratic equation involving the lengths of the three sides.
   b. Solve the equation from part **a** to find the lengths of the sides.

7. Find three consecutive integers such that the product of the first and last is one less than five times the middle integer.

8. The Parson's lawn is a 25 m × 15 m rectangle. Jody mows a strip of uniform width around the lawn and leaves a patch of lawn that is 60% of the original area. What is the width of the strip?

9. A circular bushing with a thickness of 4 mm is pressed into a bearing. The area of the original hole in the bearing is reduced by one-third. Find the original inside diameter of the bearing.

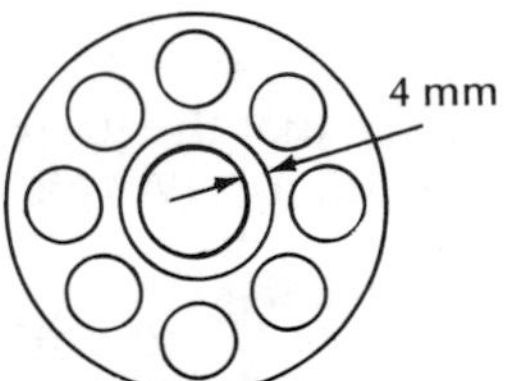

10. The Community Chest Charity Relay has two parts, an 18 km run and a 30 km canoe race. On the winning team, the canoeists travelled 8 km/h faster than the runner. The winning time was exactly 3 h. How fast did the runner travel?

Recall that $d = vt$.

11. A rectangular piece of tin is 10 cm longer than it is wide. It is made into a box with no lid by cutting 5 cm squares out of each corner and folding up the sides. The volume of the box is 1 L. What are the original dimensions of the piece of tin?

Note: 1 L = (10 cm)³

C 12. Solve each equation.

   a. $\frac{1}{x+3} + \frac{1}{x+1} = 1$
   b. $\frac{2}{x+1} + \frac{1}{x+1} = 3$
   c. $\frac{1}{x+3} + \frac{1}{x-3} = 1$
   d. $\frac{2}{x-1} - \frac{1}{x-1} = 3$
   e. $\frac{1}{x} + \frac{1}{x+1} = \frac{5}{6}$
   f. $\frac{3x}{x-3} - \frac{15}{5x-15} = \frac{21}{15}$

13. Find the roots of each equation.

   a. $(a - 1)^2 - 5(a - 1) + 4 = 0$
   b. $(b - 7)^2 - 4 = 0$
   c. $4[(x - 3)^2 - 3] = 13(x - 3)$
   d. $2[(x - 1)^2 - 9] = -2(x - 1)[(x - 1) - 3]$
   e. $6(x - 1)^2 - 5(x - 1)(x + 2) - 6(x + 2)^2 = 0$
   f. $9(x - 3)^2 - 16(x + 1)^2 = 0$

4-3 Zeros of a Polynomial and Factoring

A function defined by a polynomial equation $y = P(x)$ can be graphed by using a table of values. For example, the polynomial function defined by $P(x) = x^3 + 3x^2 - 6x - 8$ is graphed below from a table of values.

x	$P(x)$
-5	-28
-4	0
-3	10
-2	8
-1	0
0	-8
1	-10
2	0
3	28

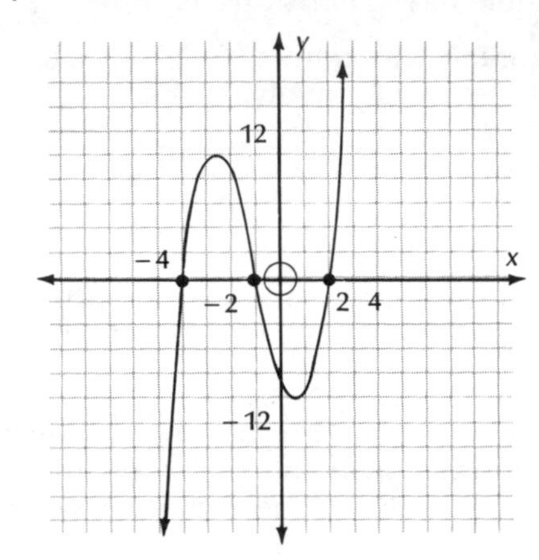

Notice that the graph of the polynomial function $P(x)$ crosses the x-axis at three points. When x is -4, -1, or 2, the value of $P(x)$ is 0. The numbers -4, -1, and 2 are the **zeros** of the polynomial.

Consider the graphs of the polynomial functions $f(x)$, $g(x)$, and $h(x)$, as shown below.

$f(x) = x^2 + x - 2$

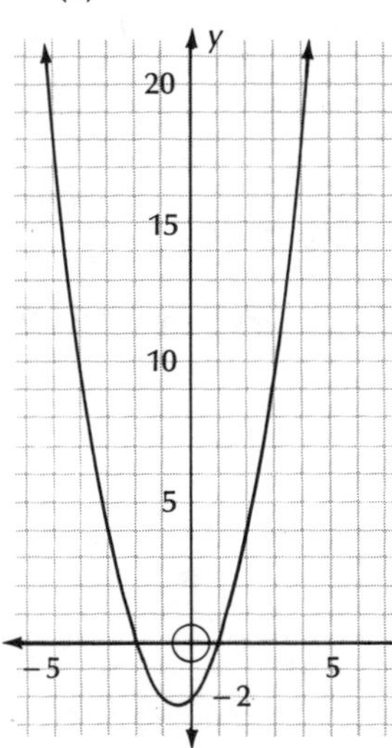

$g(x) = x^2 - 2x + 1$

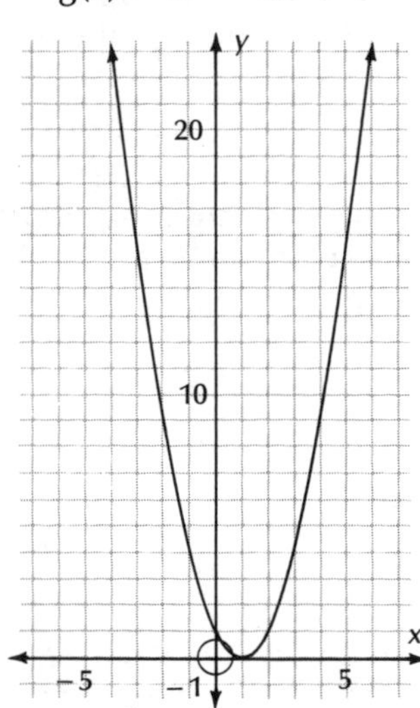

$h(x) = x^2 + x + 1$

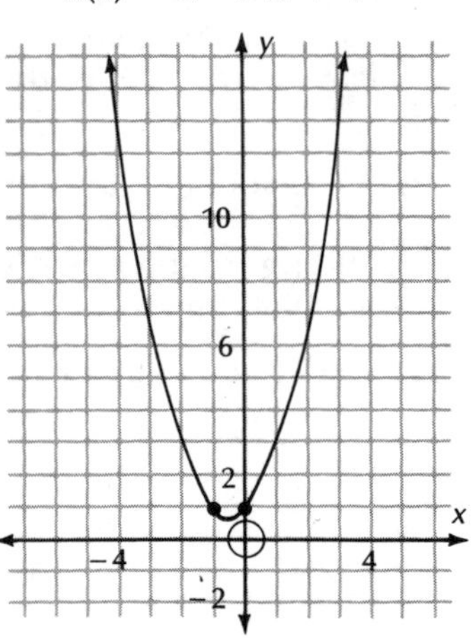

The above graphs show that a polynomial may have several zeros, one zero, or no zeros.

Recall that a polynomial is defined as

$P(x) = a_n x^n + a_{n-1}x^{n-1} + \ldots + a_1 x + a_0$, where $n \in \mathbf{Z}$ and $a_k \in \mathbf{R}$.

Consider $P(x) = x^3 + 3x^2 - 2x + 6$, where x is a negative number and the absolute value of x is large. The value of $P(x)$ will be large and negative since x^3 is negative when x is negative.

Similarly, if x is positive and has a large absolute value, then the value of $P(x)$ will be positive because x^3 is positive for any positive value of x.
This holds for all polynomials of odd degree.

Now consider $P(x) = x^4 + 2x^3 - 3x^2 - x + 1$.
The value of $P(x)$ is positive for any x with a large absolute value because x^4 is positive when x is positive and when x is negative.
This holds for all polynomials of even degree.

The value of $P(x) = a_nx^n + a_{n-1}x^{n-1} + \ldots + a_1x + a_0$ for x, where the absolute value of x is very large, is summarized in the table below.

x	$P(x)$ odd degree		$P(x)$ even degree	
	$a_n > 0$	$a_n < 0$	$a_n > 0$	$a_n < 0$
$x > 0$ and $\lvert x \rvert$ large	$P(x) > 0$	$P(x) < 0$	$P(x) > 0$	$P(x) < 0$
$x < 0$ and $\lvert x \rvert$ large	$P(x) < 0$	$P(x) > 0$	$P(x) > 0$	$P(x) < 0$

The graph of any polynomial is a continuous curve . If one point of a continuous curve lies above the x-axis and another lies below the x-axis, then the graph must cross the x-axis at some point between the two points.

Because the value of $P(x)$ changes from positive to negative when $P(x)$ is of odd degree, there must be at least one real number, x, for which $P(x) = 0$.

On the other hand, if the polynomial is of even degree, the polynomial might remain only positive or negative for all real numbers and $P(x)$ might not have a real zero.

This property of continuous curves suggests a method for approximating the zeros of a polynomial.

EXAMPLE 1: Approximate, to the nearest tenth, the zeros of $P(x) = x^3 - 5x^2 + x + 4$ between the values of -5 and 5.

Make a table of values for $P(x)$.

x	$P(x)$
−5	−251
−4	−144
−3	−71
−2	−26
−1	−3
0	4
1	1
2	−6
3	−11
4	−8
5	9

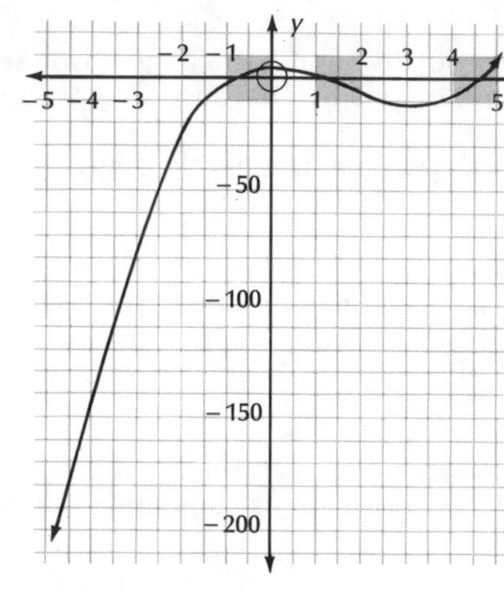

In each of the box intervals, the value P(x) changes from positive to negativ Therefore, the valu P(x) is 0 somewher within those interv

Evaluate $P(x)$ at values within the intervals.

x	$P(x)$	x	$P(x)$	x	$P(x)$
−1	−3	1	1	4	−8
−0.8	−0.512	1.1	0.381	4.5	−1.625
−0.7	+0.507	1.2	−0.272	4.6	0.136
−0.5	2.125				

The zeros of $P(x)$, to the nearest tenth, are -0.7, 1.2, and 4.6.

EXAMPLE 2: Sketch the graph of $P(x) = (x - 2)(x + 1)(x - 3)$ and state the parts of the domain over which $P(x)$ is positive.

$P(x)$ has zeros at 2, -1, and 3. Therefore, the graph of $P(x)$ crosses the x-axis at $(-1, 0)$, $(2, 0)$, and $(3, 0)$. Because $P(x)$ is of odd degree and $a_3 > 0$, then $P(x) < 0$ when $x < 0$ and $|x|$ is large. This indicates that the graph extends downward in quadrant III.

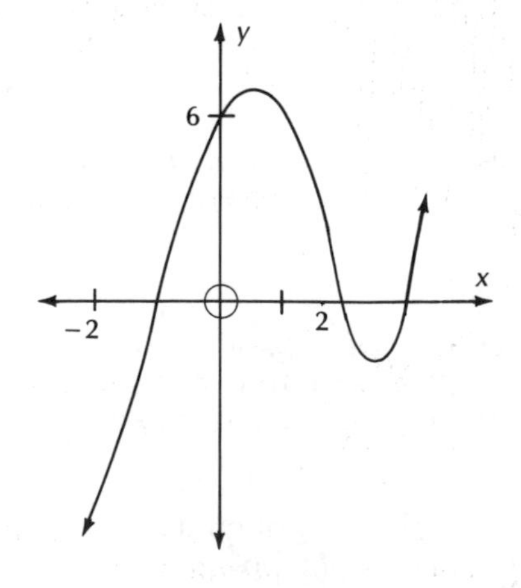

Similarly, $P(x) > 0$ when $x > 0$ and $|x|$ is large, and the graph extends upward to the right. Therefore, the graph must have the general shape as shown in the sketch at the right. This graph is not exact but it does show that $P(x)$ is positive in the intervals $-1 < x < 2$ and $x > 3$.

EXERCISE 4-3

A **1.** Examine the graph of each polynomial function and approximate the zeros of each polynomial.

a. $P(x) = x^2 + 2x - 2$

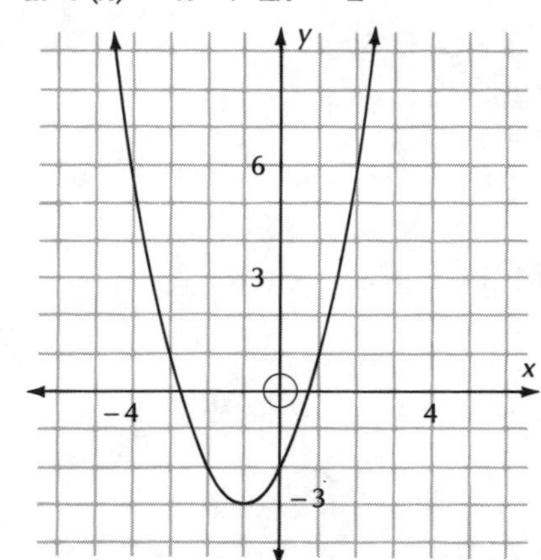

b. $P(x) = x^3 + 3x^2 - 2x - 5$

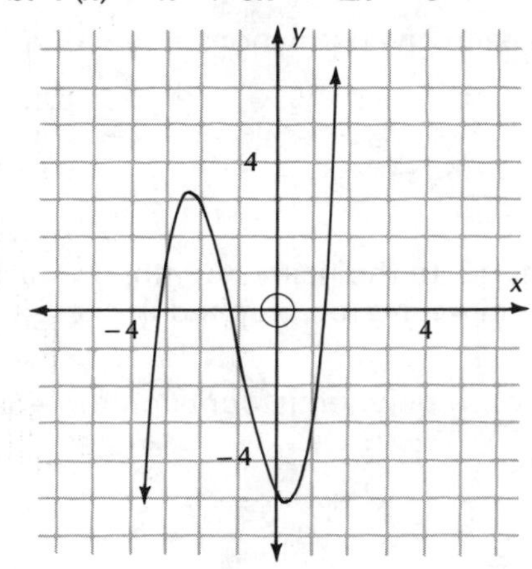

c. $P(x) = \frac{1}{2}x^3 - 3x^2 + 2x + 3$

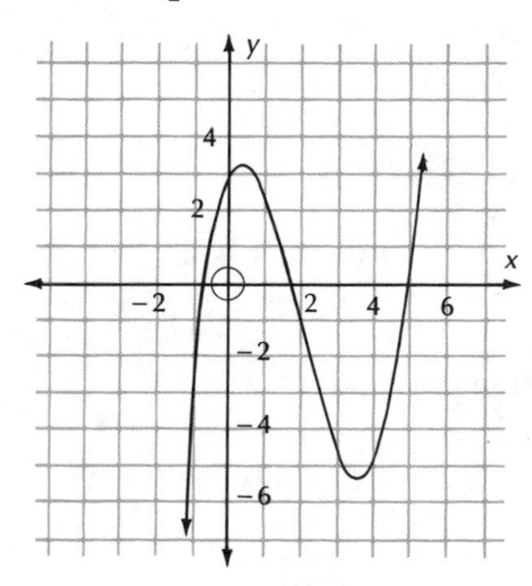

d. $P(x) = x^4 - x^3 - x^2 - x + 1$

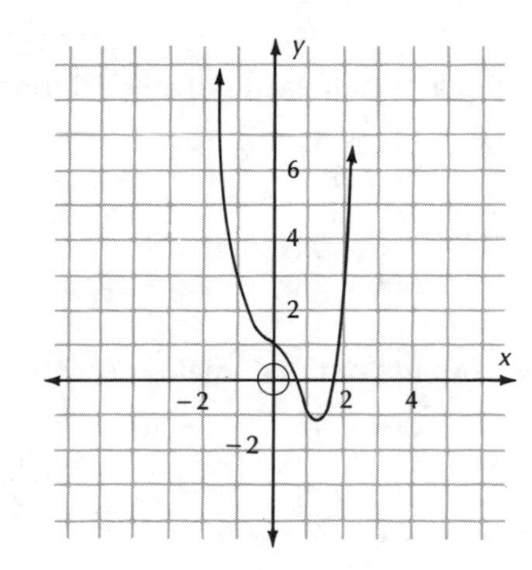

2. Evaluate each polynomial function for the given values.

a. $T(x) = x^3 - 3x^2 + x + 2$; $T(2)$, $T(-1)$, $T\left(\frac{1}{2}\right)$

b. $T(x) = -x^2 + 3x - 5$; $T(-5)$, $T(-3)$, $T(0)$

c. $R(x) = 2x^2 - 5x + 1$; $R(0)$, $R(-6)$, $R(1.5)$

d. $S(x) = \frac{1}{2}x^3 - 2x^2 + 3x + 2$; $S(-2)$, $S(5)$, $S(-0.2)$

e. $Q(x) = \frac{1}{2}x^2 - x + 5$; $Q(-1)$, $Q(-2)$, $Q(-2.5)$

f. $V(x) = x^3 - x^2 + x + 1$; $V(-1)$, $V(-1.1)$, $V(-1.2)$

3. Without graphing or evaluating, state which of the given polynomials must have at least one zero.

a. $x^2 - 2x + 5$
b. $x^2 - x + x^3 + 15$
c. $23x^2 - x^4 - 34x + 6x^3 + 26$
d. $3x^4 - x^3 + x^5 + x^2 - 10$

4. Graph each given polynomial function for $-3 \le x \le 3$.

a. $F(x) = x^2 - 3x - 5$
b. $G(x) = x^3 - 3x^2 + x - 1$
c. $H(x) = x^3 - 3x^2 + 3$
d. $K(x) = x^4 + 3x^3 - 2x^2 - 5x + 2$
e. $S(x) = -2x^2 - 3x + 5$
f. $T(x) = x^3 + 3x^2 - 4$

B 5. Determine, to the nearest tenth, the values of the zeros of each polynomial function graphed in exercise 1.

6. Graph each polynomial function for $-5 \le x \le 5$.

a. $F(x) = x^2 - 3x - 3$
b. $R(x) = x^3 - x + 3$
c. $T(x) = x^3 - x^2 + 3x - 1$
d. $G(x) = x^3 - 5x^2 + 2x + 6$
e. $L(x) = x^4 - x^3 - 3x^2 - x - 1$
f. $W(x) = -2x^3 - 3x^2 + 5x + 3$

7. Determine, to the nearest hundredth, the zeros of $F(x)$, $R(x)$, and $T(x)$ as given in exercise 6.

8. Sketch the graph of each polynomial function.

a. $y = (x - 5)(x + 1)$
b. $y = (x - 3)(x + 2)$
c. $y = x^2 - 3x + 2$
d. $y = x^2 + 7x + 12$
e. $y = x^2 - 8x + 16$
f. $y = 3x(x - 2)$
g. $y = (x - 3)(x + 3)(x - 1)$
h. $y = -(x - 5)(x - 1)(x + 4)$
i. $y = (x - 2)(x + 2)(x - 1)(x - 5)$
j. $y = -x(x - 6)(x - 2)(x + 3)$

9. Over what parts of the domain is each function positive?

a. $y = (x - 2)(x + 1)$
b. $y = -3x(x - 3)(x - 1)$
c. $y = x^2 + x - 6$
d. $y = -2x^3 + 8x^2 + 10x$
e. $y = 3(x - 5)(x + 5)$
f. $y = x(x - 2)(x + 3)$
g. $y = (x - 2)(x + 4)(x - 7)$
h. $y = x^3 - 6x^2 + 9x$

C 10. Sketch at least two possible graphs for each polynomial function, given that a, b, and c each represent a positive real number.

a. $F(x) = x^2 + ax + b$
b. $G(x) = -x^2 + ax + b$
c. $P(x) = x^3 + ax^2 + bx + c$
d. $Q(x) = -x^3 + ax^2 + bx + c$

11. Consider the polynomial $x^2 + ax + 1$.

a. What values of a will allow the polynomial exactly one zero?
b. What values of a will allow no zeros?
c. What values of a will allow two zeros?

Using the Calculator Evaluating Polynomials in Nested Form

Evaluating a polynomial with a non-programmable calculator can be a tedious process. For example, to evaluate $f(x) = x^3 - 3x^2 + 5x - 2$ for $x = 7$, you could use the following keystrokes.

[7] [y^x] [3] [−] [3] [×] [7] [y^x] [2] [+] [5] [×] [7] [−] [2] [=]

Using a non-scientific calculator, or one without a [y^x] key, evaluating a polynomial can involve even more keystrokes since the memory keys would likely be used.

However, if the polynomial is written in **nested** form, as shown below, the number of keystrokes is reduced.

$$x^3 - 3x^2 + 5x - 2 = x(x^2 - 3x + 5) - 2 = x[x(x - 3) + 5] - 2$$

Working from the inner brackets to the outer brackets and replacing x with 7, the keystrokes are as follows.

[7] [−] [3] [=] [×] [7] [+] [5] [=] [×] [7] [−] [2] [=]

To write a polynomial in nested form, apply the Distributive Property repeatedly until every variable has an exponent of 1. Use brackets as necessary. For example, consider the following.

$$\begin{aligned} &5x^4 + 2x^3 - 3x^2 + x - 5 \\ &= x(5x^3 + 2x^2 - 3x + 1) - 5 \\ &= x(x(5x^2 + 2x - 3) + 1) - 5 \\ &= x(x(x(5x + 2) - 3) + 1) - 5 \end{aligned}$$

$$\begin{aligned} &x^4 - 3x^2 + 2 \\ &= x(x^3 - 3x) + 2 \\ &= x(x(x^2 - 3) + 2 \\ &= x(x(x(x) - 3)) + 2 \end{aligned}$$

1. Write each polynomial in nested form.

a. $x^3 + 3x^2 - 5x - 6$

b. $7x^4 + 3x^3 - x^2 + 4x + 1$

c. $x^3 - x$

d. $5x^3 - 6x^2 + 8x - 9$

e. $x^5 + 3x^3 - 2x + 5$

f. $2x^3 - x + 6$

Nested notation is also preferred when polynomials are evaluated using a computer. The reason is that when a computer evaluates x^n, it does so by finding $\log x$ and then computing $10^{n \log x}$. In nested form, only multiplications, additions, and subtractions are performed. This makes evaluating $x^3 - 3x^2 + 5x - 2$ almost three times faster and also eliminates errors due to approximations when the logarithmic function is computed.

2. Evaluate the polynomial $5x^4 + 2x^3 - 3x^2 + x - 5$ for $1 \le x \le 100$ using a loop on a microcomputer. Time how long it takes to evaluate the polynomial when it is written in standard form and then how long it takes when written in nested form.

4-4 Introduction to Complex Numbers

The quadratic equation $x^2 + 1 = 0$ has no real solution because there is no real number, x, such that $x^2 = -1$. Similarly, there are many quadratic equations which, when solved using the quadratic formula, result in a negative discriminant and therefore have no real solution.

For all quadratic equations to have roots, the number system must be extended beyond the real numbers. A new number, $\boldsymbol{i}$, is defined below.

$$i^2 = -1 \text{ and } i = \sqrt{-1}$$

This new number, i, is called the **imaginary unit**, although it is as useful as any of the other numbers that you have studied so far. The term *imaginary* refers to the difficulty in the past in interpreting the uses of i. There are, in fact, many areas of science and technology that involve the application of this unit. When the set of real numbers is extended using i, the set of **complex numbers**, **C**, results.

The set of complex numbers is given as $\mathbf{C} = \{z \mid z = a + bi, a, b \in \boldsymbol{R}\}$.

If $b = 0$, then z is a real number. Therefore, the set of real numbers is a subset of the set of complex numbers.

If $a = 0$, then z is referred to as a *pure imaginary number*. The numbers $2i$, $-i$, and $i\sqrt{5}$ are pure imaginary numbers. The set of imaginary numbers is also a subset of the set of complex numbers.

Each number given below is a complex number.

$$3 + 2i, \quad 7, \quad 0.3i, \quad \frac{1 - 6i}{5}, \quad -3i$$

7 can be written as $7 + 0i$

$-3i$ can be written as $0 - 3i$.

Many familiar rules of algebra apply to complex numbers. However, care must be taken when working with radicals that have a negative radicand.

In general, $\sqrt{-n} = i\sqrt{n}$, for $n > 0$.

Note that a radical is considered to be simplified when the radicand contains no negative quantities and no square factors.

EXAMPLE 1: Simplify.

a. $\sqrt{-50}$
$= i\sqrt{50}$
$= i\sqrt{25}\sqrt{2}$
$= 5i\sqrt{2}$

b. $3\sqrt{-2} - \sqrt{-32}$
$= 3i\sqrt{2} - i\sqrt{32}$
$= 3i\sqrt{2} - 4i\sqrt{2}$
$= -i\sqrt{2}$

c. $\sqrt{-3}\sqrt{-27}$
$= (i\sqrt{3})(i\sqrt{27})$
$= i^2\sqrt{(3)(27)}$
$= i^2\sqrt{81}$
$= -1(9)$
$= -9$

In part **c** of Example 1, the product $\sqrt{-3}\sqrt{-27}$ *is not equal to* $\sqrt{-3 \times -27} = \sqrt{81}$, or 9, because the rule $\sqrt{a}\sqrt{b} = \sqrt{ab}$ does not hold if a and b are both negative.

Pairs of complex numbers can be added, subtracted, and multiplied in exactly the same way as pairs of binomials. Remember that $i^2 = -1$.

EXAMPLE 2: Simplify.

a. $(3 - 2i) - (5 + i)$
$= (3 - 5) + (-2i - i)$
$= -2 - 3i$

b. $(3 + i)(5 + 2i)$
$= 3(5) + 3(2i) + 5i + i(2i)$
$= 15 + 6i + 5i + 2i^2$
$= 15 + 11i + 2(-1)$
$= 13 + 11i$

c. $(2 + 5i)(2 - 5i)$
$= 2(2) + 2(-5i) + 5i(2) + 5i(-5i)$
$= 4 - 10i + 10i + 25$
$= 29$

$(5i)(-5i) = -25i^2$
$= 25$

Notice that in part **c** of Example 2, the product is a real number. The complex numbers $2 + 5i$ and $2 - 5i$ are **conjugates**. The product of conjugates is always a real number.

> In general, for a complex number $a + bi$,
> $a + bi$ and $a - bi$ are **conjugates.**
> The product of conjugates, $(a + bi)(a - bi) = a^2 + b^2$, is a real number.

EXAMPLE 3: Find the roots of each quadratic equation.

a. $x^2 + 3 = 0$
$x^2 = -3$
$x = \pm\sqrt{-3}$
$x = i\sqrt{3}$ or $x = -i\sqrt{3}$

The roots are $i\sqrt{3}$ and $-i\sqrt{3}$.

b. $x^2 - 4x + 5 = 0$ Use the quadratic formula.

$$x = \frac{-b \pm \sqrt{b^2 - 4ac}}{2a}$$

$$x = \frac{-(-4) \pm \sqrt{(-4)^2 - 4(1)(5)}}{2(1)}$$

$$x = \frac{4 \pm \sqrt{-4}}{2}$$

$$x = \frac{4 \pm 2i}{2}$$

$x = 2 + i$ or $2 - i$

The roots are $2 + i$ and $2 - i$.

EXERCISE 4-4

A

1. Simplify each radical.

a. $\sqrt{-36}$ **b.** $\sqrt{-100}$ **c.** $\sqrt{-45}$ **d.** $\sqrt{-60}$

e. $-\sqrt{-4}$ **f.** $\sqrt{-\frac{18}{2}}$ **g.** $\sqrt{-\frac{100}{5}}$ **h.** $\sqrt{(-3)^2}$

2. Simplify each sum and difference.

a. $(3 + 2i) + (7 + i)$ **b.** $(5 - 4i) + (3 + 2i)$ **c.** $(6 + 5i) - (2 + i)$
d. $(4 - 7i) + (3 + 6i)$ **e.** $(2 - i) - (3 - 5i)$ **f.** $4i - (1 + 3i)$

3. Find each product.

a. $(3 - 2i)(1 + i)$ **b.** $(2 - i)(2 + i)$ **c.** $3i(2 - 3i)$
d. $(4 + i)(2 + 5i)$ **e.** $(1 - 2i)(5 + i)$ **f.** $(3 - 4i)(1 + 7i)$

4. State the conjugate of each complex number.

a. $3 + 2i$ **b.** $2 - i$ **c.** $2i$ **d.** 8

B

5. Simplify each sum and difference.

a. $3\sqrt{-5} + \sqrt{-20}$ **b.** $2\sqrt{-8} + 3i\sqrt{2}$
c. $4i\sqrt{5} + \sqrt{-20}$ **d.** $\sqrt{28} - 3\sqrt{6} + \sqrt{-24} - \sqrt{7}$
e. $4\sqrt{3} + 2\sqrt{-80} + \sqrt{27} - 10\sqrt{-5}$ **f.** $6i\sqrt{2} - 2\sqrt{6} + \sqrt{-18} + \sqrt{150}$

6. Simplify.

a. $(\sqrt{-15})(\sqrt{6})$ **b.** $\sqrt{-2}\sqrt{-10}$ **c.** $i\sqrt{-6}$

d. $\sqrt{-\frac{9}{16}}$ **e.** $\left(\sqrt{-\frac{1}{3}}\right)\left(\sqrt{-\frac{1}{3}}\right)$ **f.** $\frac{\sqrt{-8}}{\sqrt{2}}$

g. $\frac{\sqrt{75}}{i\sqrt{3}}$ **h.** $\left(\sqrt{-\frac{15}{2}}\right)\left(\sqrt{-\frac{6}{5}}\right)$ **i.** $\sqrt{-3}\sqrt{-\frac{1}{3}}$

7. Find each product.

a. $(2 + i)(1 + 2i)(1 - i)$ **b.** $(3 - i)(1 - i)(1 + i)$ **c.** $(4 + i)(3 - i)(2 + i)$
d. $(5 + 2i)^2$ **e.** $(4 - 3i)^2$ **f.** $(1 + i)^2(3 + i)$
g. $(3 - i\sqrt{2})(\sqrt{2} + 2i)$ **h.** $(-1 + i\sqrt{3})^2$ **i.** $3i(i + 1)(i - 1)$

8. Determine the roots of each quadratic equation.

a. $x^2 + 9 = 0$ **b.** $x^2 + 18 = 0$ **c.** $3x^2 = 7$
d. $x^2 + 3x + 8 = 0$ **e.** $x^2 - 2x + 10 = 0$ **f.** $x^2 - 4x + 29 = 0$
g. $3x^2 = 5x - 2$ **h.** $3x^2 + 3 = 2x$ **i.** $5x = 3x^2 + 3$

9. Find the product of each complex number with its conjugate.

a. $3 - 4i$ **b.** $2 + i$ **c.** $1 - i$ **d.** $5 - 2i$
e. $6 + 2i$ **f.** -3 **g.** i **h.** $-5i$

10. Evaluate.

a. i^2 **b.** i^3 **c.** i^4 **d.** i^5
e. i^6 **f.** i^7 **g.** i^8 **h.** i^{17}
i. i^{34} **j.** i^{100} **k.** i^{101} **l.** i^{283}

11. The value of i^n equals $-i$. What can you conclude about n?

Application

Representing Complex Numbers by Graphing

A complex number, $a + bi$, can be represented as a **vector** in the **complex plane.**

A vector is represented by an arrow with its tail at the origin and its head at the point (a, b).

The numbers $z = (3 + 5i)$ and $t = (-4 - 2i)$ are graphed at the right.

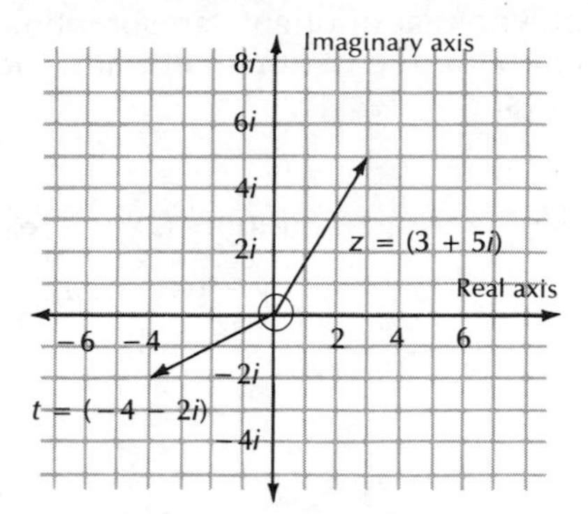

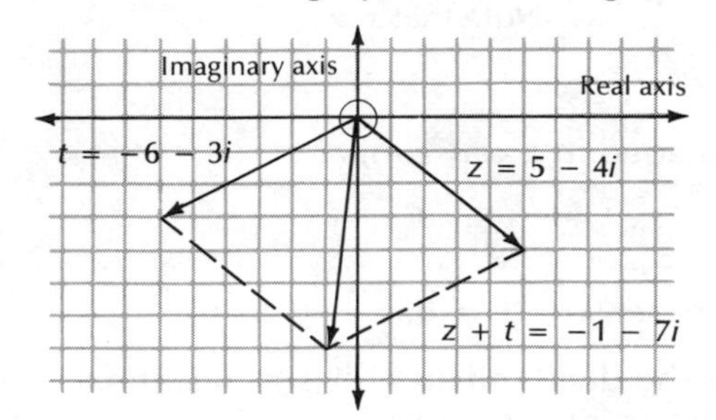

The sum of two complex numbers is shown by adding their vectors using the **Parallelogram Law.**

$z = 5 - 4i$
$t = -6 - 3i$
$z + t = -1 - 7i$

1. Graph each complex number in the complex plane.

   a. $3 - 2i$ **b.** $-5 + 4i$ **c.** $-6 - 3i$ **d.** $2i$ **e.** 5

2. Graph each sum and difference.

   a. $(2 + 5i) + (3 - 2i)$ **b.** $(2 - 6i) + (3 + i)$ **c.** $(4 - 3i) - (2 + 2i)$

3. Graph each given complex number with its conjugate. How are the graphs of a complex number and its conjugate related?

   a. $3 + 2i$ **b.** 5 **c.** $-3i$

4. The absolute value of a complex number is the length of its vector graphed in the complex plane. Use this definition and the Pythagorean Theorem to show that the absolute value of any complex number, $a + bi$, is equal to $\sqrt{a^2 + b^2}$.

5. Find the absolute value of each complex number.

   a. $2 - 3i$ **b.** $3 - i$ **c.** -5 **d.** i **e.** $-i$

6. Show that the absolute value of a complex number z, or $|z|$, is equal to $\sqrt{(z)(\bar{z})}$, where z and $\bar{z}$ are conjugates.

7. Graph each pair of complex numbers and their product in the complex plane.

   a. $(2 + 3i), (2 + i)$ **b.** $(3 + 2i), (1 + 3i)$ **c.** $(3 + 4i), (1 + i)$

8. Use a ruler and a protractor to find a relationship among the lengths of a complex product and the lengths of its factors, and the angles formed by the complex product and the angles formed by its factors.

4-5 Dividing Polynomials

A polynomial quotient can sometimes be simplified by factoring its numerator and denominator and then dividing through by common factors.

EXAMPLE 1: Simplify $(2x^2y - 6xy - 20y) \div (2x - 10)$.

$$\frac{2x^2y - 6xy - 20y}{2x - 10} = \frac{2y(x^2 - 3x - 10)}{2x - 10}$$

$$= \frac{2y(x - 5)(x + 2)}{2(x - 5)}$$ Note that $x \neq 5$.

$$= y(x + 2)$$

If a polynomial cannot be factored, it can still be divided in a way similar to long division in arithmetic.

EXAMPLE 2: Divide $x^2 + 6x^3 - 5$ by $2x - 1$, where $2x - 1 \neq 0$.

$$2x - 1 \overline{)6x^3 + x^2 + 0x - 5}$$

Write the dividend and divisor in *standard form*. That is, order the terms in decreasing degree, and insert zero coefficients for any missing terms.

$$\begin{array}{r} 3x^2 \phantom{{}+ x^2 + 0x - 5} \\ 2x - 1 \overline{)6x^3 + x^2 + 0x - 5} \\ \underline{6x^3 - 3x^2} \phantom{{}+ 0x - 5} \\ 4x^2 + 0x - 5 \end{array}$$

Divide the first term of the dividend by the first term of the divisor to obtain a partial quotient, $3x^2$. Multiply the partial quotient by the divisor and subtract the result from the dividend to obtain a remainder, which becomes the new dividend, $4x^2 + 0x - 5$.

$$\begin{array}{r} 3x^2 + 2x + 1 \\ 2x - 1 \overline{)6x^3 + x^2 + 0x - 5} \\ \underline{6x^3 - 3x^2} \phantom{{}+ 0x - 5} \\ 4x^2 + 0x \phantom{{}- 5} \\ \underline{4x^2 - 2x} \phantom{{}- 5} \\ 2x - 5 \\ \underline{2x - 1} \\ -4 \end{array}$$

Continue until the remainder is of lower degree than the divisor.

$$\therefore \frac{x^2 + 6x^3 - 5}{2x - 1} = 3x^2 + 2x + 1 - \frac{4}{2x - 1}.$$

The result of a division can also be written as a division statement $P(x) = D(x)\,Q(x) + R(x)$, where $P(x)$ is the dividend, $D(x)$ is the divisor, $Q(x)$ is the quotient, and $R(x)$ is the remainder.

For Example 2, the division statement is $x^2 + 6x^3 - 5 = (2x - 1)(3x^2 + 2x + 1) - 4$. Division can be checked by multiplying the divisor and quotient and then adding the remainder.

L.S. = Dividend
$= 6x^3 + x^2 - 5$

R.S. = (Divisor)(Quotient) + Remainder
$= (2x - 1)(3x^2 + 2x + 1) - 4$
$= 6x^3 + x^2 - 5$
= L.S. ✓

This is the check for Example 2.

The long division process can be applied to divisors other than binomials.

EXAMPLE 3: Divide $10x^4 + 11x^3 - 14x^2 - 7x + 5$ by $2x^2 + x - 3$. Give the answer as a division statement.

$$
\begin{array}{r}
5x^2 + 3x - 1 \\
2x^2 + x - 3 \overline{)\,10x^4 + 11x^3 - 14x^2 - 7x + 5} \\
\underline{10x^4 + 5x^3 - 15x^2} \\
6x^3 + x^2 - 7x \\
\underline{6x^3 + 3x^2 - 9x} \\
-2x^2 + 2x + 5 \\
\underline{-2x^2 - x + 3} \\
3x + 2
\end{array}
$$

$\therefore 10x^4 + 11x^3 - 14x^2 - 7x + 5 = (2x^2 + x - 3)(5x^2 + 3x - 1) + (3x + 2)$

EXERCISE 4-5

A **1.** Rewrite each polynomial in standard form, and insert a zero coefficient for any missing term.

a. $3x^2 - 5$
b. $2x^3 - 3x + x^2 + 1$
c. $2x + 5 - 3x^2 + x^3$
d. $2x^4 + 3x$
e. $x^3 - 4 + 3x$
f. $x^6 - 3x^3 + 4$

B **2.** Divide each polynomial using long division.

a. $(x^2 - 3x + 5) \div (x - 2)$
b. $(5x - 2x^2 + 3) \div (x + 3)$
c. $(3m^3 - 2m + 5 - m^2) \div (m + 2)$
d. $(7x^2 + 4x - 8 + 2x^3) \div (2x + 3)$
e. $(2x^4 - 6x^3 + 3x^2 - 10x + 3) \div (x - 3)$
f. $(11x - 5x^2 - 2x^3 + 10x^4 - 3) \div (5x - 1)$

3. Divide and give each answer as a division statement.

a. $(4x^2 - x - 6) \div (x + 4)$
b. $(4x^3 + 3x - 2) \div (x + 2)$
c. $(3x^3 - 7x^2 - 10x + 5) \div (3x - 1)$
d. $(2x + 3x^4 + 7) \div (x + 3)$
e. $(x^3 - x^5 + x - 1) \div (x - 1)$
f. $(x^4 - 1 + x) \div (x - 1)$

4. Find the remainder and quotient by long division.

a. $(6r^3 + 5r^2 - 6r + 3) \div (2r + 3)$
b. $(9x^3 - 9x^2 - 10x + 4) \div (3x - 1)$
c. $(6x^4 + 13x^3 - x^2 - 2x + 4) \div (2x^2 + x - 1)$
d. $(10t^6 - 3t^4 - 4t^3 + 5t^2 + 3t - 5) \div (2t^2 - 1)$

C **5.** Determine the value of k so that the first polynomial is exactly divisible by the second. That is, the remainder is zero.

a. $3x^3 + 11x^2 + kx + 15;\ x + 3$
b. $2x^3 - 3x^2 - 7x + k;\ 2x + 3$

4-6 Synthetic Divison

Synthetic division is a "shorthand" method for dividing a polynomial by a binomial, where the binomial is of the form $x - a$. For example, you can divide $3x^3 - 4x^2 + 2x - 5$ by $x - 2$ either by using long division or by using synthetic division since the divisor is of the form $x - a$. Notice that for synthetic division, only the coefficients of the terms of the polynomials are used.

Long Division

$$\begin{array}{r} 3x^2 + 2x + 6 \\ x - 2\overline{)3x^3 - 4x^2 + 2x - 5} \\ \underline{3x^3 - 6x^2 } \\ 2x^2 + 2x - 5 \\ \underline{2x^2 - 4x } \\ 6x - 5 \\ \underline{6x - 12} \\ 7 \end{array}$$

$\therefore 3x^3 - 4x^2 + 2x - 5$
$= (3x^2 + 2x + 6)(x - 2) + 7$

Synthetic Division

This is a. Coefficients of dividend

$$\begin{array}{r|rrrr} 2 & \boxed{3} & -4 & 2 & -5 \\ \hline & \boxed{3} & & & \end{array}$$

Bring down the first coefficient.

Now, multiply 3 by a, or 2, and add the result to the next coefficient of the dividend. Continue the process for each coefficient.

$$\begin{array}{r|rrrr} 2 & 3 & -4 & 2 & -5 \\ & & 6 & 4 & 12 \\ \hline & 3 & 2 & 6 & 7 \end{array}$$

Coefficients of quotient   Remainder

EXAMPLE: Divide, using synthetic division.

Note that $(x + 5) = [x - (-5)]$.

a. $(3x^3 + 13x^2 - 9x + 5) \div (x + 5)$

$$\begin{array}{r|rrrr} -5 & 3 & 13 & -9 & 5 \\ & & -15 & 10 & -5 \\ \hline & 3 & -2 & 1 & 0 \end{array}$$

$\therefore 3x^3 + 13x^2 - 9x + 5$
$= (x + 5)(3x^2 - 2x + 1)$

b. $(4x^2 - x^3 + 3) \div (x - 1)$

$$\begin{array}{r|rrrr} 1 & -1 & 4 & 0 & 3 \\ & & -1 & 3 & 3 \\ \hline & -1 & 3 & 3 & 6 \end{array}$$

Rearrange the dividend.

$\therefore 4x^2 - x^3 + 3$
$= (x - 1)(-x^2 + 3x + 3) + 6$

EXERCISE 4-6

A 1. Divide, using synthetic division, and give the answer as a division statement.

a. $(3x^2 - x + 2) \div (x - 3)$
b. $(5x^2 + x - 6) \div (x - 2)$
c. $(m^3 + 3m^2 - 5m - 2) \div (m - 2)$
d. $(3x^3 - 2x^2 + 5x - 1) \div (x + 4)$
e. $(2t^3 - t + 1) \div (t + 5)$
f. $(n - 3n^2 + n^3 + 5) \div (n - 2)$
g. $(p^4 - p^2 + 3) \div (p - 4)$
h. $(x - x^3 + 7) \div (x - 8)$
i. $(3n^2 + n^4 - 2) \div (n + 3)$
j. $(s^4 - s^2 + s + 6) \div (s + 2)$
k. $(2x^2 - 7x + 3) \div \left(x - \frac{1}{2}\right)$
l. $(4x^3 - 4x^2 - 9x + 3) \div \left(x - \frac{3}{2}\right)$
m. $(4x^3 - x^2 + 5x - 3) \div \left(x - \frac{3}{4}\right)$
n. $(4x^4 - 3x^2 + x - 1) \div \left(x - \frac{3}{2}\right)$

Review

1. Factor each polynomial.

   a. $3x^2 - 4x - 4$
   b. $2x^2 + 11x - 63$
   c. $4x^2 - 45x + 81$
   d. $12x^2 + 10x - 12$
   e. $4m^2x^2 - 25m^2x - 56m^2$
   f. $10x^2y + xy - 3y$
   g. $8p^2r - 10pqr - 3q^2r$
   h. $(a + 2)^2 + (a + 2) - 6$
   i. $7x^2 - 23x + 6$

2. Examine the graph of each polynomial function to estimate the zeros. Then approximate the value of the zeros to the nearest hundredth.

   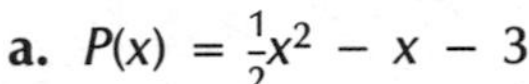
   a. $P(x) = \frac{1}{2}x^2 - x - 3$

   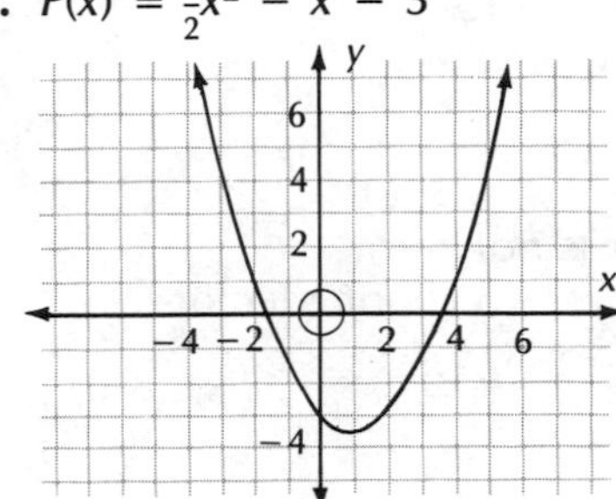

   b. $P(x) = 2x^2 - 5x - 4$

   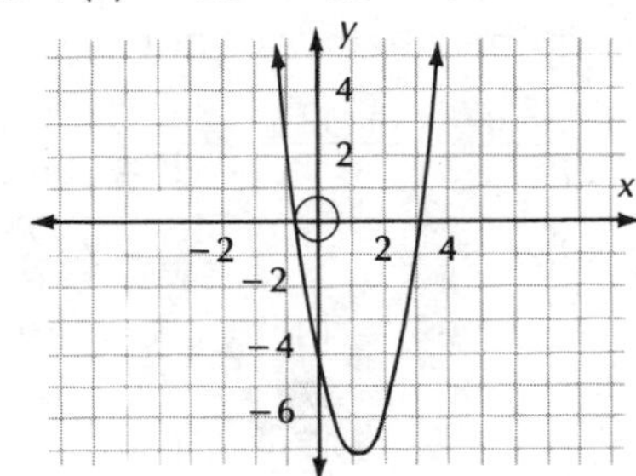

3. Graph each polynomial function for $-5 \le x \le 5$.

   a. $f(x) = x^2 - 4x + 1$
   b. $g(x) = x^3 - 3x^2 - x + 2$

4. Find the roots of each polynomial equation by factoring.

   a. $x^2 - 7x - 18 = 0$
   b. $12x^2 - 32x - 35 = 0$
   c. $6x^2 + 14x + 4 = 0$
   d. $x^4 - 5x^2 + 4 = 0$
   e. $(x - 1)(x + 9) = 8x$
   f. $(x + 3)(4x - 5) = x^2 - 9$

5. Find the roots of each polynomial equation by completing the square.

   a. $x^2 + 4x = 10$
   b. $2x^2 - 6x - 3 = 0$
   c. $x^2 - 3x = 5$

6. Find the roots of each polynomial equation by using the quadratic formula. Find all the complex roots.

   a. $x^2 - 5x + 1 = 0$
   b. $3x^2 - x - 7 = 0$
   c. $2x^2 + x + 5$
   d. $3x - 5x^2 + 2$
   e. $x^2 - 3x + 2 = x - 2x^2 + 1$
   f. $0.8x^2 + 0.25x = 1.2$

7. A rectangular room is 4 m longer than it is wide. The room has a hardwood strip, 2 m wide, along the perimeter of the room. A carpet overlaps the hardwood by 1 m and has a total area of 77 m². What are the dimensions of the room?

8. Simplify.

   a. $(3 - 2i) + (4 + 5i)$
   b. $(1 - 4i) - (2 - i)$
   c. $4i\sqrt{5} + \sqrt{-20}$
   d. $\sqrt{28} - 3\sqrt{-6} + \sqrt{-24} - \sqrt{7}$
   e. $3i\sqrt{5}\sqrt{-10}$
   f. $\sqrt{-12} \div i\sqrt{3}$
   g. $(2 - i)(5 + i)$
   h. $(2 - 3i)(2 + 3i)$
   i. $(1 - i)^2(i + 1)$

9. Divide using long division. Give each answer as a division statement.

   a. $(x^3 + 3x^2 - 4x - 12) \div (x + 2)$
   b. $(3x^3 - 4x^2 - 16x + 5) \div (x - 3)$
   c. $(x - 2x^3 + 3) \div (x - 1)$
   d. $(x^4 - 2x^3 + x - 2) \div (x^2 + x - 1)$

4-7 The Remainder Theorem and The Factor Theorem

In arithmetic, when a number is divided by one of its factors, the remainder is zero.

$72 \div 8 = 9$ with a remainder of 0. Therefore, 8 is a factor of 72 and $72 = 8 \times 9$.

Similarly, when a polynomial, $P(x)$, is divided by a binomial, $x - c$, the remainder is zero if, and only if, $x - c$ is a factor of $P(x)$.

$72 \div 5 = 14$ with a remainder of 2. Therefore, 5 is not a factor of 72 and $72 = 5 \times 14 + 2$.

EXAMPLE 1: $S(x) = x^3 + 3x^2 - x + 2$. Divide $S(x)$ by $x - 3$ to determine whether or not $x - 3$ is a factor of $S(x)$.

$$\begin{array}{r}
x^2 + 6x + 17 \\
x - 3\overline{)x^3 + 3x^2 - x + 2} \\
\underline{x^3 - 3x^2} \\
6x^2 - x \\
\underline{6x^2 - 18x} \\
17x + 2 \\
\underline{17x - 51} \\
53
\end{array}$$

When $x^3 - 3x^2 - x + 2$ is divided by $x - 3$, the remainder is not zero. Therefore, $x - 3$ is not a factor of $x^3 - 3x^2 - x + 2$.

Notice that for all x, $S(x) = (x - 3)(x^3 - 3x^2 - x + 2) + 53$.

Therefore, if $x = 3$, then

$$\begin{aligned}
S(3) &= (3 - 3)[3^3 - 3(3)^2 - 3 + 2] + 53 \\
&= (0)(27 - 27 + 3 + 2) + 53 \\
&= 53 \\
\therefore S(3) &= 53
\end{aligned}$$

A similar result holds for any polynomial, $P(x)$, divided by a binomial of the form $x - c$.

If $P(x)$ is divided by $x - c$, then

$$\begin{aligned}
P(x) &= (x - c)\,Q(x) + R. \\
\therefore P(c) &= (c - c)\,Q(c) + R \\
&= (0)\,Q(c) + R \\
&= R
\end{aligned}$$

$Q(x)$ is the quotient.
R is the remainder.
Note that the remainder is a real number.

> **The Remainder Theorem**
> If a polynomial, $P(x)$ is divided by $x - c$, the remainder is the value of $P(c)$.

If $x - c$ divides $P(x)$ evenly, then the remainder of $P(x) \div (x - c)$ is zero and hence $P(c) = 0$. This fact leads to the following theorem.

> **The Factor Theorem**
> $x - c$ is a factor of $P(x)$ if, and only if, $P(c) = 0$.

EXAMPLE 2: Show that $x - 2$ is a factor of $x^3 - 7x + 6$, and find two other factors of $x^3 - 7x + 6$. Then write $x^3 - 7x + 6$ in completely factored form.

$$\begin{array}{r} x^2 + 2x - 3 \\ x - 2\overline{)x^3 + 0x^2 - 7x + 6} \\ \underline{x^3 - 2x^2} \qquad\qquad \\ 2x^2 - 7x \qquad \\ \underline{2x^2 - 4x} \qquad \\ -3x + 6 \\ \underline{-3x + 6} \\ 0 \end{array}$$

Since the remainder is zero, $x - 2$ is a factor of $x^3 - 7x + 6$ and $x^3 - 7x + 6 = (x - 2)(x^2 + 2x - 3)$.

The remaining factors are determined by factoring the quotient.
$x^2 + 2x - 3 = (x + 3)(x - 1)$
Thus, $x + 3$ and $x - 1$ are two other factors.

$\therefore x^3 - 7x + 6 = (x - 2)(x + 3)(x - 1)$

EXAMPLE 3: Show that -2 is a root of $2x^3 + x^2 - 2x + 8 = 0$ and find two other roots of the equation.

For $x = -2$, $2x^3 + x^2 - 2x + 8$
$= 2(-8) + 4 - 2(-2) + 8$
$= 0.$

Thus, -2 is a root of the equation.

The division could also be done mentally or by polynomial division.

Since -2 is a root of $2x^3 + x^2 - 2x + 8 = 0$, then $x - (-2)$ is a factor. Divide $2x^3 + x^2 - 2x + 8 = 0$ by $x + 2$. Synthetic division is shown below.

$$\begin{array}{r|rrrr} -2 & 2 & 1 & -2 & 8 \\ & & -4 & 6 & -8 \\ \hline & 2 & -3 & 4 & 0 \end{array}$$

The remainder is zero.
Therefore, $P(-2) = 0$ and -2 is a root of $2x^3 + x^2 - 2x + 8 = 0$.

The synthetic division shows that
$2x^3 + x^2 - 2x + 8 = (x + 2)(2x^2 - 3x + 4)$.
To find the remaining roots, find the roots of $2x^2 - 3x + 4 = 0$.

Since $2x^2 - 3x + 4$ does not appear to factor easily, apply the quadratic formula.

$$\begin{aligned} x &= \frac{-b \pm \sqrt{b^2 - 4ac}}{2a} \\ &= \frac{-(-3) \pm \sqrt{(-3)^2 - 4(2)(4)}}{2(2)} \\ &= \frac{3 \pm \sqrt{-23}}{4} \\ &= \frac{3 + i\sqrt{23}}{4} \text{ or } \frac{3 - i\sqrt{23}}{4} \end{aligned}$$

Therefore, the roots of $2x^3 + x^2 - 2x + 8 = 0$ are -2, $\frac{3 + i\sqrt{23}}{4}$, and $\frac{3 - i\sqrt{23}}{4}$.

EXAMPLE 4: Give the complete factorization of $x^3 + 1$.

First, consider the equation $x^3 + 1 = 0$.
If $x^3 + 1 = 0$, then $x^3 = -1$.
Therefore, -1 is a root of $x^3 + 1 = 0$.
From this and the Factor Theorem, $x + 1$ is a factor of $x^3 + 1$.

Now divide $x^3 + 1$ by $x + 1$ to find another factor.

$$
\begin{array}{r}
x^2 - x + 1 \\
x + 1 \overline{)x^3 + 0x^2 + 0x + 1} \\
\underline{x^3 + x^2} \qquad\qquad \\
-x^2 + 0x + 1 \\
\underline{-x^2 - x} \qquad \\
x + 1 \\
\underline{x + 1} \\
0
\end{array}
$$

Therefore, the factorization is $x^3 + 1 = (x + 1)(x^2 - x + 1)$.

The factorizations of the general sums and differences of cubes can be derived in a similar way.

Sum of Cubes
$a^3 + b^3 = (a + b)(a^2 - ab + b^2)$

Difference of Cubes
$a^3 - b^3 = (a - b)(a^2 + ab + b^2)$

$y^3 + 27 = (y + 3)(y^2 - 3y + 9)$
$8m^3 + n^6 = (2m + n^2)(4m^2 - 2mn^2 + n^4)$

$m^3 - 64 = (m - 4)(m^2 + 4m + 16)$
$x^9 - 27y^3z^6 = (x^3 - 3yz^2)(x^6 + 3x^3yz^2 + 9y^2z^4)$

EXERCISE 4-7

A 1. Evaluate each polynomial for the given value of x.

a. $x^2 - 3x + 5;\ x = 2$
b. $3x^2 + x - 5;\ x = -3$
c. $2x^3 - x^2 - x - 1;\ x = -4$
d. $3x^3 + x^2 + 5x - 2;\ x = 4$
e. $4x^4 - 5x^3 + x^2 - x + 3;\ x = -2$
f. $x^5 - x^4 + x^3 - x^2 + x - 1;\ x = -1$

2. Determine whether the second polynomial is a factor of the first.

a. $x^3 + 2x^2 - 5x + 6;\ x - 2$
b. $2x^3 + 9x^2 + 7x - 6;\ x + 3$
c. $3x^3 + 5x^2 - 26x + 8;\ x - 4$
d. $2x^3 - 9x^2 + 13x - 6;\ x - 2$
e. $3x^4 - x^2 + 2x + 1;\ x - 3$
f. $4x^5 - 3x^2 + x - 2;\ x - 2$

3. One root of each polynomial equation is given. Find the remaining roots.

a. $x^2 - 3x + 2 = 0;\ 2$
b. $x^2 - 5x - 14 = 0;\ 7$
c. $x^3 - 4x^2 - x + 4 = 0;\ 4$
d. $2x^3 - 7x^2 + 7x - 2 = 0;\ 2$
e. $4x^3 - 4x^2 - x + 1 = 0;\ 1$
f. $x^3 - x^2 - 3x - 1 = 0;\ -1$

4. Factor completely.

a. $y^3 + 8$
b. $c^3 - 1000$
c. $8a^6 - b^3$
d. $r^6 + \frac{1}{125}$

B 5. A polynomial and its graph are given. Determine one zero from the graph and verify it using the Factor Theorem. Then find the other roots.

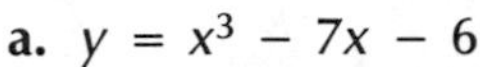

a. $y = x^3 - 7x - 6$

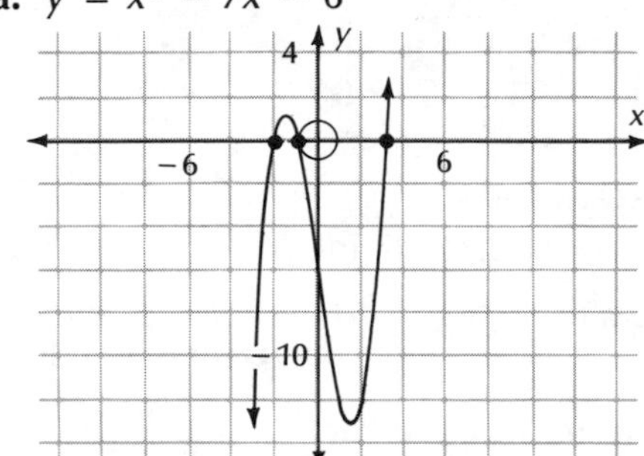

b. $y = x^3 - x^2 - 7x + 7$

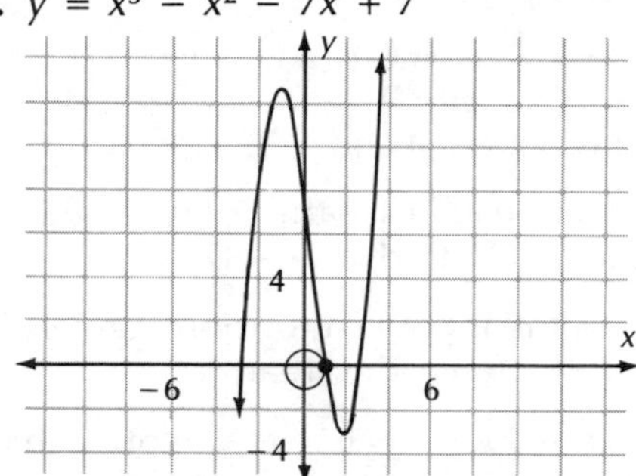

c. $y = 2x^3 + 4x^2 - 3x - 6$

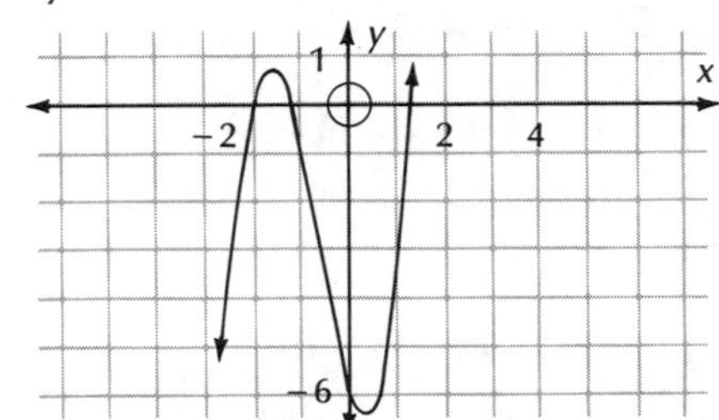

d. $y = x^3 - 5x^2 + 8x - 6$

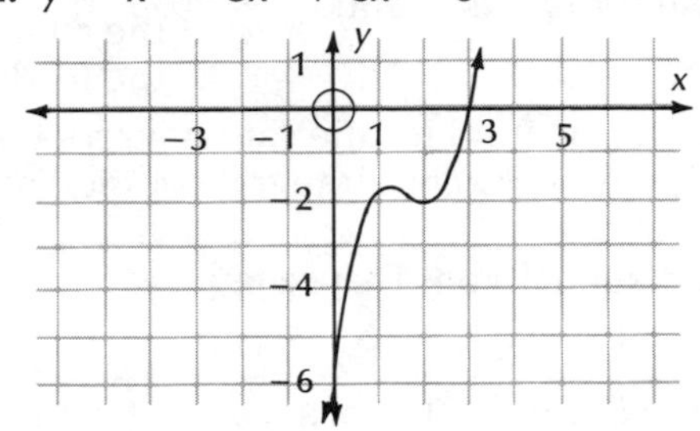

6. Determine whether the second polynomial is a factor of the first.

a. $x^5 - 1;\ x - 1$
b. $x^3 - 6x^2 - 4x - 15;\ x - 3$
c. $3x^2 - 2x - 5;\ x - 1$
d. $2x^3 - 16x^2 + 13x + 7;\ x - 7$
e. $x^4 - 5x^2 + 6;\ x - \sqrt{2}$
f. $2x^3 - x^2 - 7x + 6;\ x - 1.5$

7. One factor of each polynomial is given. Find the remaining factors and write the polynomial in completely factored form.

a. $6x^3 - 13x^2 - 13x + 30;\ x - 2$
b. $2x^3 + x^2 - 27x - 36;\ x + 3$
c. $x^4 + 3x^3 - x - 3;\ x + 3$
d. $12x^3 + 8x^2 - 3x - 2;\ 3x + 2$
e. $2x^4 + 3x^3 + 16x + 24;\ 2x + 3$
f. $8x^4 + 12x^3 - 18x^2 - 27x;\ 2x + 3$
g. $x^5 - 9x^3 + x^2 - 9;\ x^2 - 9$
h. $x^5 - 2x^4 + 6x^3 - 12x^2 + 9x - 18;\ x - 2$

8. Factor completely.

a. $x^6 - 1$
b. $64t^6 + s^6$
c. $y^6 - 2y^3 + 1$
d. $64x^6 + 16x^3 + 1$
e. $m^6 + 26m^3 - 27$
f. $8x^6 + 19x^3 - 27$

9. Each given polynomial equation has at least one integral root between 5 and −5. Use the Factor Theorem and the quadratic formula to determine three roots for each equation.

a. $2x^3 + 9x^2 - 20x - 12 = 0$
b. $x^3 - 2x^2 - 5x + 6 = 0$
c. $x^3 + 3x^2 - 6x - 18 = 0$
d. $2x^3 + x^2 - 5x + 2 = 0$
e. $6x^3 + 17x^2 - 4x - 3 = 0$
f. $2x^3 - x^2 - 2x + 1 = 0$

C 10. For each polynomial, determine the zeros and sketch the graph.

a. $x^3 + x^2 - 17x + 15$
b. $m^3 - 13m + 12$
c. $x^4 - 5x^2 + 4$
d. $x^4 - 13x^2 + 36$

4-8 Rational Roots of Polynomial Equations

In earlier lessons polynomial equations were solved by factoring, as shown below.

$x^2 - x - 12 = 0$
$(x - 4)(x + 3) = 0$
The roots are 4 and -3.

$x^3 - 2x^2 - 5x + 6 = 0$
$(x - 1)(x + 2)(x - 3) = 0$
The roots are 1, -2, and 3.

Notice that in each case the roots divide the constant term.

4 and -3 both divide -12.

1, -2, and 3 each divide 6.

There is a similar pattern for polynomials having a leading coefficient other than 1.

The *leading coefficient* is the coefficient of the first term.

$6x^2 + 7x - 3 = 0$
$(2x + 3)(3x - 1) = 0$
The roots are $-\frac{3}{2}$ and $\frac{1}{3}$.

Notice that the numerators of the roots, -3 and 1, are both factors of the constant term, 3. The denominators of the roots, 2 and 3, are factors of the leading coefficient, 6.

These patterns hold for the rational roots of any polynomial equation, $P(x) = 0$, where $P(x)$ has integral coefficients.

The Rational Root Theorem

Given that $P(x) = a_nx^n + a_{n-1}x^{n-1} + \ldots + a_1x + a_0$, if $P(x) = 0$ has a rational root of the form $\frac{p}{q}$, and $\frac{p}{q}$ is in lowest terms, then p must be a divisor of a_0 and q must be a divisor of a_n.

The theorem does not guarantee that every polynomial with integral coefficients has rational roots. It states that if a rational root exists, then in lowest terms, its numerator must divide the constant term and its denominator must divide the coefficient of the leading term.

EXAMPLE 1: List the possible rational roots, $\frac{p}{q}$, of $2x^3 - 5x^2 + 22x - 10 = 0$.

The leading coefficient is 2. Therefore, the possible values for the denominator, q, are the divisors of 2, or $\{\pm 1, \pm 2\}$.

The constant term, is 10. Therefore, the possible values for the numerator, p, are the divisors of 10, or $\{\pm 1, \pm 2, \pm 5, \pm 10\}$.

The possible rational roots of $2x^3 - 5x^2 + 22x - 10 = 0$ are $\left\{\pm 1, \pm \frac{1}{2}, \pm 2, \pm \frac{5}{2}, \pm 5, \pm 10\right\}$.

It is important to realize that these are *possible* rational roots. There may be *no* rational roots at all.

EXAMPLE 2: **a.** Factor $2x^3 - 9x^2 + 7x + 6 = 0$ to determine the roots.

First, determine the possible rational roots so that the Factor Theorem can be applied.

Possible numerator values are $\{\pm 1, \pm 2, \pm 3, \pm 6\}$.
Possible denominator values are $\{\pm 1, \pm 2\}$.
The possible rational roots are
$\left\{\pm 3, \pm 2, \pm 1, \pm 6, \pm \frac{3}{2}, \pm \frac{1}{2}\right\}$.

Then test the roots using either synthetic division or substitution.

$$\begin{array}{r|rrrr} 3 & 2 & -9 & 7 & 6 \\ & & 6 & -9 & -6 \\ \hline & 2 & -3 & -2 & 0 \end{array}$$

Since the remainder is zero, then $P(3) = 0$. Therefore, by the Factor Theorem, $x - 3$ is a factor.
$\therefore\ 2x^3 - 9x^2 + 7x + 6 = (x - 3)(2x^2 - 3x - 2)$

Now factor the quotient to determine the other roots.

$$2x^2 - 3x - 2 = 0$$
$$(2x + 1)(x - 2) = 0$$

The roots are 3, 2, and $-\frac{1}{2}$.

$$x = -\frac{1}{2} \text{ or } x = 2$$

b. Factor $3x^3 - 7x^2 + 8x - 2 = 0$ to determine the roots.

The possible rational roots are $\left\{\pm 2, \pm 1, \pm \frac{2}{3}, \pm \frac{1}{3}\right\}$. Test the roots.

$$\begin{array}{r|rrrr} 1 & 3 & -7 & 8 & -2 \\ & & 3 & -4 & 4 \\ \hline & 3 & -4 & 4 & 2 \end{array} \qquad \begin{array}{r|rrrr} \frac{1}{3} & 3 & -7 & 8 & -2 \\ & & 1 & -2 & 2 \\ \hline & 3 & -6 & 6 & 0 \end{array}$$

$P\left(\frac{1}{3}\right) = 0$, so $x - \frac{1}{3}$ is a factor of $3x^3 - 7x^2 + 8x - 2$.

$$\begin{aligned} \therefore\ 3x^3 - 7x^2 + 8x - 2 &= \left(x - \tfrac{1}{3}\right)(3x^2 - 6x + 6) \\ &= 3\left(x - \tfrac{1}{3}\right)(x^2 - 2x + 2) \\ &= (3x - 1)(x^2 - 2x + 2) \end{aligned}$$

Use the quadratic formula to determine the other roots.
$x^2 - 2x + 2 = 0$

$$x = \frac{-(-2) \pm \sqrt{(-2)^2 - 4(1)(2)}}{2(1)}$$

$$x = \frac{2 \pm \sqrt{-4}}{2}$$

The roots are $\frac{1}{3}$, $1 + i$, and $1 - i$.

If a root of a polynomial equation with integral coefficients is found to be in the form $\frac{p}{q}$, then not only is $x - \frac{p}{q}$ a factor of the polynomial, but $qx - p$ is also a factor.

In part **b** of Example 2, both $x - \frac{1}{3}$ and $3x - 1$ are factors of $3x^3 - 7x^2 + 8x - 2$.

EXERCISE 4-8

A

1. List the possible rational roots of each equation.

   a. $2x^2 - 3x + 2 = 0$
   b. $x^2 + 5x - 6 = 0$
   c. $3x^2 - 2x - 8 = 0$
   d. $5x^3 - 3x^2 - 2x + 2 = 0$
   e. $4x^3 + x - 6 = 0$
   f. $6x^4 - 3x^2 + 10 = 0$
   g. $x^4 + 3x^3 + 2x^2 - 8 = 0$
   h. $7x^3 + 3x^2 - 5x + 3 = 0$

2. Use the Rational Root Theorem to find the zeros of each polynomial.

   a. $x^3 - 2x^2 - 11x + 12$
   b. $x^3 + 5x^2 + 2x - 8$
   c. $x^3 + 4x^2 - 11x - 30$
   d. $x^3 + 4x^2 - 25x - 28$
   e. $3x^4 - 7x^3 - x^2 + 7x - 2$
   f. $2x^4 - 9x^3 - 14x^2 + 81x - 36$
   g. $3x^4 - x^3 - 29x^2 + 9x + 18$
   h. $2x^4 - x^3 - 11x^2 + 4x + 12$

B

3. Use the Rational Root Theorem and division to find the rational roots of each equation.

   a. $3x^2 - 8x - 16 = 0$
   b. $2x^2 - 3x + 1 = 0$
   c. $6x^2 - 19x + 15 = 0$
   d. $3x^3 + 13x^2 + 8x - 12 = 0$
   e. $4x^3 - 20x^2 - x + 5 = 0$
   f. $6x^3 + 11x^2 - 19x + 6 = 0$
   g. $4x^4 - x^3 - 28x^2 + 31x - 6 = 0$
   h. $9x^4 - 10x^2 + 1 = 0$

4. Each given equation has at least one rational root. Use the Rational Root Theorem to find one or two rational roots. Then apply the quadratic formula to determine the remaining roots.

   a. $x^3 + x^2 - 10x - 12 = 0$
   b. $x^3 - 5x - 2 = 0$
   c. $2x^3 - 5x^2 - 16x + 9 = 0$
   d. $12x^3 - 16x^2 + x + 1 = 0$
   e. $18x^3 - 33x^2 + 4x + 4 = 0$
   f. $x^4 - 8x^3 + 10x^2 + 16x - 3 = 0$
   g. $3x^4 - x^3 - 24x^2 + 17x - 3 = 0$
   h. $2x^4 - 19x^3 + 54x^2 - 57x + 18 = 0$

5. Factor completely.

   a. $x^3 - 3x^2 - 4x + 12$
   b. $6x^3 + 7x^2 - 9x + 2$
   c. $4x^3 + 3x^2 - 25x + 6$
   d. $12x^4 + 29x^3 + 4x^2 - 11x + 2$
   e. $10x^4 + 33x^3 + 3x^2 - 17x + 3$
   f. $4x^5 - 24x^4 + 43x^3 - 18x^2 - 11x + 6$
   g. $3x^4 + 5x^3 - 3x - 5$
   h. $x^5 - x^3 - 8x^2 + 8$

6. Consider the polynomial $P(x) = 3x^3 - 2x^2 + 3x - 2$.
   a. Describe the values of $P(x)$ for $x > 0$ and for $x < 0$.
   b. Does $P(x)$ have any zeros for $x < 0$?
   c. Construct two polynomials, one which cannot have zeros for $x < 0$, and the other which cannot have zeros for $x > 0$.

7. Use the Rational Root Theorem to determine whether the given graph could be the graph of the given equation.

a. $y = x^3 - 2x^2 - 5x + 6$

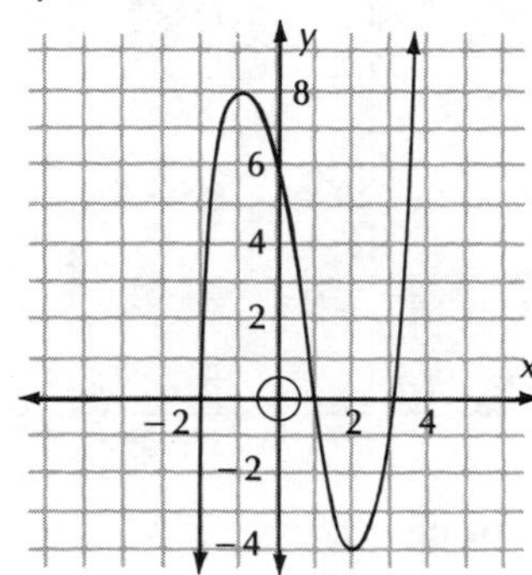

b. $y = 4x^3 - 8x^2 - 2x + 5$

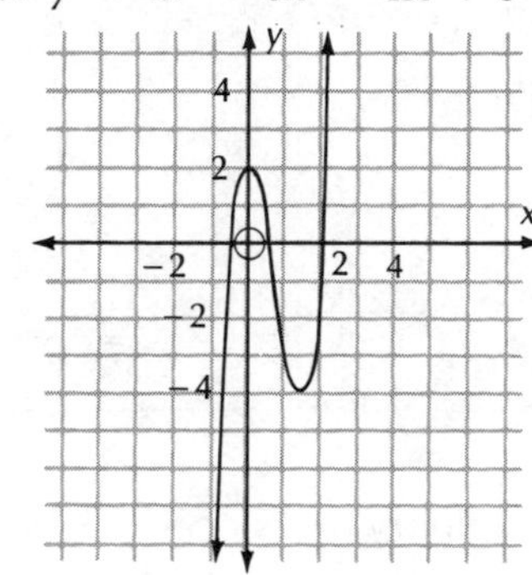

c. $y = x^3 - 3x^2 + 27x - 27$

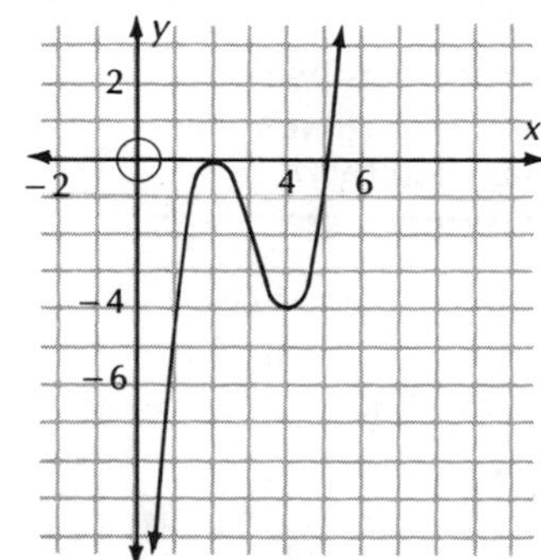

d. $y = x^3 - x^2 - 9x + 9$

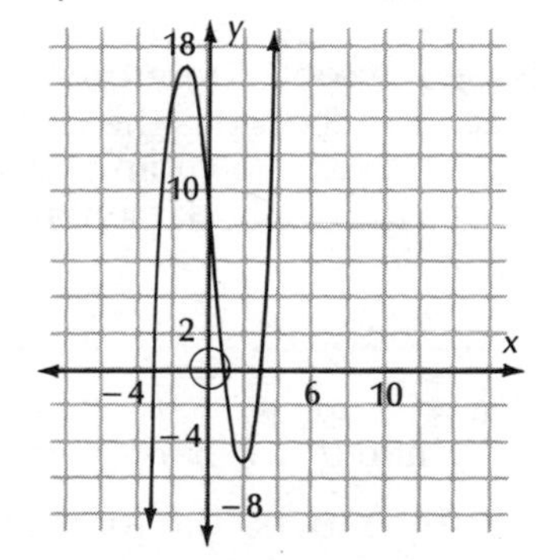

e. $y = 4x^3 - 9x^2 - 10x - 3$

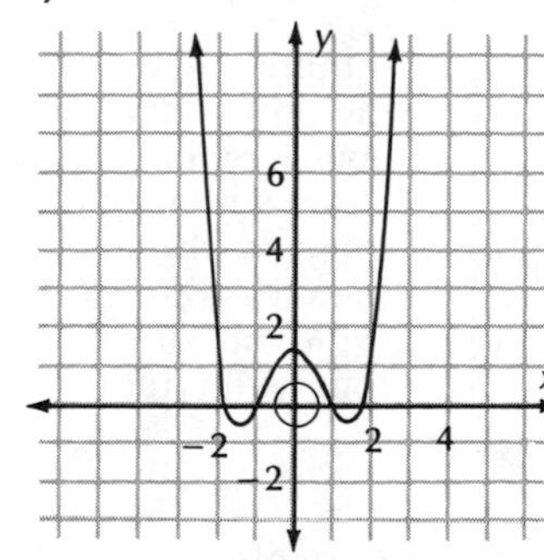

f. $y = x^3 - 5x^2 + 7x - 3$

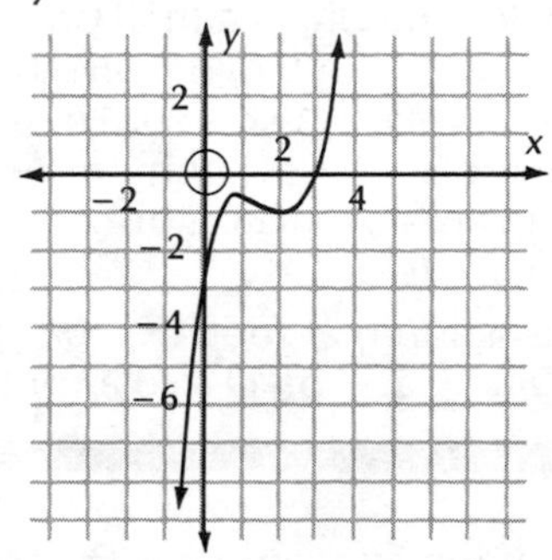

C 8. A **monic** polynomial is a polynomial whose highest degree term has a coefficient of 1. Given an integral monic polynomial, why must all of the rational roots be integers? Do all the roots have to be integers?

4-9 The Fundamental Theorem of Algebra

You may have noticed in previous examples and exercises that all quadratic, or second degree equations, have two roots; cubic, or third-degree equations have three roots, and so on.

Degree	Equation	Roots	Number of Roots
1	$5x - 7 = 0$	$\left\{\frac{7}{5}\right\}$	1
2	$2x^2 + x - 3 = 0$	$\left\{1, -\frac{3}{2}\right\}$	2
3	$3x^3 - 14x^2 + 23x - 10 = 0$	$\left\{\frac{2}{3}, 2 + i, 2 - i\right\}$	3
4	$x^4 + x^3 + 2x^2 + 4x - 8 = 0$	$\{1, -2, 2i, -2i\}$	4

Notice also that if imaginary roots occur, they occur in conjugate pairs.

In 1799, Karl Friedrich Gauss proved the **Fundamental Theorem of Algebra**. The theorem states that every polynomial equation that has real coefficients has at least one root. Therefore, because that root can be used to construct a factor that divides the original polynomial to give a quotient of lower degree, every polynomial of degree n has exactly n roots. The consequences of the Fundamental Theorem of Algebra are summarized below.

Given that $P(x) = a_n x^n + a_{n-1}x^{n-1} + \ldots + a_1 x + a_0$, where $a_k \in \boldsymbol{R}$, $a_n \neq 0$, and $0 \leq k \leq n$, then:

- $P(x) = 0$ has exactly n roots. The roots may be real or complex.
- A root may be counted more than once. For example, $x^2 + 2x + 1 = 0$ must have two roots, but $x^2 + 2x + 1 = (x + 1)(x + 1)$. Therefore, there are two roots, $x = -1$ and $x = -1$, which are equal. In general, roots of this nature are called **multiple roots**.
- *If* $P(x) = 0$ has a non-real root, $a + bi$, where $b \neq 0$, then its conjugate, $a - bi$, is also a root.

If there are two equal roots, then the root is called a **double root** or referred to as a root with **multiplicity** 2. If there are three equal roots, then the root is called a triple root or referred to as a root with multiplicity 3.

The consequences of the Fundamental Theorem of Algebra allow many different types of problems to be solved and enable deductions to be made about the roots of polynomial equations and the zeros of polynomial functions.

EXAMPLE 1: Construct the polynomial equation $S(x) = 0$ of lowest degree with integral coefficients having the given roots.

a. roots: $\frac{1}{2}, \frac{3}{5}$

If $S(x)$ has roots $\frac{1}{2}$ and $\frac{3}{5}$, then $2x - 1$ and $5x - 3$ are factors of $S(x)$.

$$\begin{aligned} S(x) &= (2x - 1)(5x - 3) \\ &= 10x^2 - 11x + 3 \end{aligned}$$

Therefore, the equation is $10x^2 - 11x + 3 = 0$

b. roots: $-1, 1 + i$

If $1 + i$ is a root, then $1 - i$ must also be a root because imaginary roots appear in conjugate pairs. Therefore, the polynomial equation must have three roots, $-1, 1 + i, 1 - i$, and three factors, $[x - (-1)]$, $[x - (1 + i)]$ and $[x - (1 - i)]$.

$$\begin{aligned} S(x) &= (x + 1)[x - (1 + i)][x - (1 - i)] \\ &= (x + 1)(x^2 - 2x + 2) \\ &= x^3 - x^2 + 2 \end{aligned}$$

Therefore, the equation is $x^3 - x^2 + 2 = 0$.

EXAMPLE 2: $T(x) = 0$ is a polynomial equation of degree 5 with real coefficients; -3 is a double root, and $3 + 2i$ is a non-real root. What can be stated about the other roots?

Since $T(x) = 0$ is of degree 5, it must have 5 roots. Three of the roots are given; -3, -3, and $3 + 2i$. Another root must be $3 - 2i$ since non-real roots always appear in conjugate pairs in polynomial equations with real coefficients. The fifth root must be a real number since non-real roots always appear in conjugate pairs. The information given places no restrictions on the fifth root — it could be any real number.

EXAMPLE 3: Given that one root of $x^4 - 4x^3 + 13x^2 - 18x - 10 = 0$ is $1 - 3i$, find the remaining roots.

Since $1 - 3i$ is a root, so is its conjugate, $1 + 3i$. Therefore, $[x - (1 - 3i)][x - (1 + 3i)]$, or $x^2 - 2x + 10$, is a factor.

$$\begin{array}{r|l} & x^2 - 2x - 1 \\ \hline x^2 - 2x + 10 & x^4 - 4x^3 + 13x^2 - 18x - 10 \\ & \underline{x^4 - 2x^3 + 10x^2} \\ & -2x^3 + 3x^2 - 18x \\ & \underline{-2x^3 + 4x^2 - 20x} \\ & -x^2 + 2x - 10 \\ & \underline{-x^2 + 2x - 10} \\ & 0 \end{array}$$

$\therefore x^4 - 4x^3 + 13x^2 - 18x - 10 = (x^2 - 2x + 10)(x^2 - 2x - 1)$

The quadratic formula can be used to determine that the roots of $x^2 - 2x - 1 = 0$ are $1 + \sqrt{2}$ and $1 - \sqrt{2}$. Therefore, the four roots of $x^4 - 4x^3 + 13x^2 - 18x - 10 = 0$ are $1 - 3i$, $1 + 3i$, $1 + \sqrt{2}$, and $1 - \sqrt{2}$.

The roots of $P(x) = 0$ are the zeros of the polynomial $P(x)$. Given that $P(x)$ has real coefficients and is of degree n, it has exactly n zeros. However, those zeros may not all be real; some of them will be conjugate pairs of non-reals. Some of the zeros may also be multiple zeros. Therefore, the graph of $y = P(x)$ will intersect (either cross or touch) the x-axis once for each **distinct** real root. Note that a multiple root is one distinct root.

EXAMPLE 4: Given that $F(x) = (x^2 - 1)(x + 1)$, sketch the graph of $y = F(x)$.

Complete the factorization. $F(x) = (x - 1)(x + 1)(x + 1)$ -1 is a double zero.
Therefore, $F(x)$ has two distinct zeros, 1 and -1.

Summarize the information about the zeros of the polynomial and its properties as $|x|$ becomes large.

x	$F(x)$
$x < 0$ $\|x\|$ is large	$F(x) < 0$ $\|F(x)\|$ is large
$x = -1$ $x = 0$ $x = 1$	$F(x) = 0$ $F(x) = -1$ $F(x) = 0$
$x > 0$ $\|x\|$ is large	$F(x) > 0$ $\|F(x)\|$ is large

The information in the table shows that the graph of $F(x)$ extends upward to the right as x becomes large and positive and the graph extends downward to the left when $x < 0$ and $|x|$ is large. Therefore, the graph crosses the x-axis an odd number of times. But since there are three zeros, the graph is tangent to the x-axis at $x = -1$.

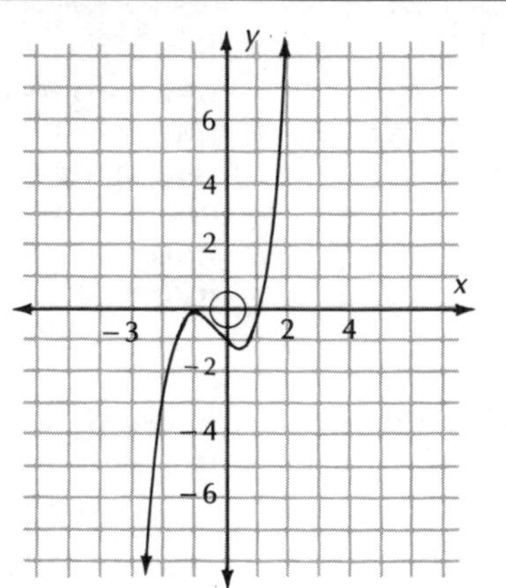

EXERCISE 4-9

A **1.** Determine the roots of each polynomial equation. If a root is a multiple root, then state its multiplicity.

a. $(x - 2)(x + 3)(x - i)(x + i) = 0$
b. $(3x - 2)(x - 1)(2x + 5) = 0$
c. $(x - 3)^2(x + 2)(x^2 - 5) = 0$
d. $x(x + 3)^2(x - 2)^3 = 0$
e. $x^3(x - 2)^2(x^2 + 4x + 4) = 0$
f. $[x - (3 + 4i)][x - (3 - 4i)](5x - 2)^2 = 0$

2. Find each product.

a. $[x + (1 + 2i)][x + (1 - 2i)]$
b. $[x - (3 - i)][x - (3 + i)]$
c. $[x - (2 - 3i)][x - (2 + 3i)]$
d. $[x + (5 + i)][x + (5 - i)]$
e. $(x - i)(x + i)(x - 3)$
f. $(x - 3i)(x + 3i)(2x - 1)$
g. $[2x - (1 + 3i)][2x - (1 - 3i)]$
h. $[2x - (3 - 4i)][2x - (3 + 4i)](3x - 2)$

3. For each equation, one root is given. Find the remaining roots.

a. $x^3 - 2x^2 - 5x + 6 = 0;\ 3$

b. $2x^3 - x^2 - 8x + 4 = 0;\ \frac{1}{2}$

c. $x^3 + x^2 - 5x - 5 = 0;\ \sqrt{5}$

d. $2x^3 - 8x^2 + 5x + 3 = 0;\ 3$

e. $2x^3 + 2x^2 - 3x + 2 = 0;\ -2$

f. $x^3 - 4x^2 + 6x - 4 = 0;\ 1 + i$

g. $x^3 - 6x^2 + 13x - 10 = 0;\ 2 - i$

h. $3x^3 - 8x^2 + 34x - 20 = 0;\ 1 + 3i$

B

4. For each given equation, show that the given number is a root with the indicated multiplicity. Then find the other roots.

a. $x^3 - 2x^2 - 15x + 36 = 0;\ 3$ - double

b. $x^4 - 6x^2 - 16 = 0;\ 2\sqrt{2}$

c. $2x^3 - 5x^2 + 12x - 5 = 0;\ 1 + 2i$

d. $x^4 + 3x^3 - 8x^2 - 15x + 15 = 0;\ \sqrt{5}$

e. $x^4 - 6x^3 + 22x^2 - 30x + 13 = 0;\ 1$ - double

f. $x^4 - 4x^3 + 14x^2 - 20x + 25 = 0;\ (1 + 2i)$ - double

g. $x^4 - 8x^3 + 27x^2 - 50x + 50 = 0;\ 3 - i$

h. $x^5 - 3x^4 - x^3 + 11x^2 - 12x + 4 = 0;\ 1$ - triple

5. For each graph, the degree of the associated equation is given. Give the real roots and their multiplicities, and state the number of imaginary roots.

a. degree 3

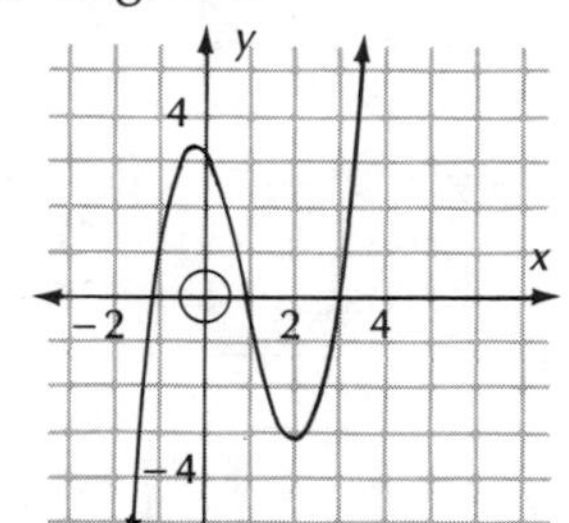

b. degree 3

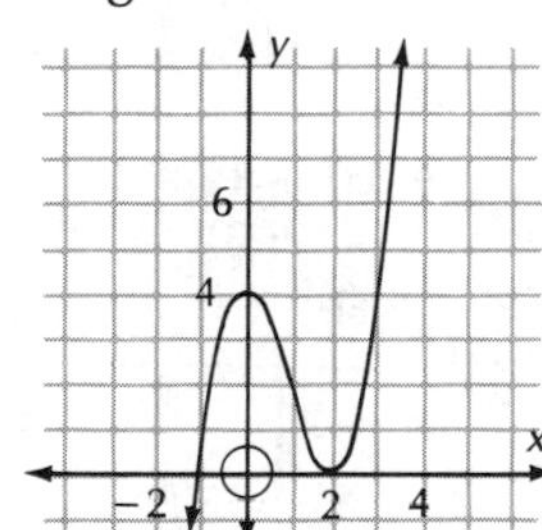

c. degree 4

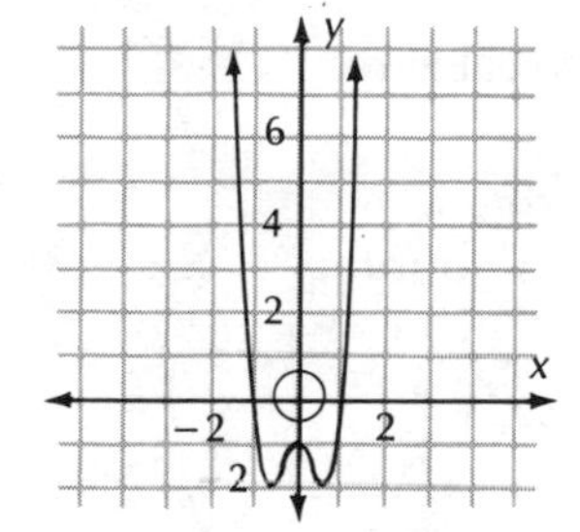

6. Find a polynomial equation having integral coefficients and the given characteristics.

a. quadratic (degree 2); roots: $3, -\frac{1}{2}$

b. cubic (degree 3); roots: 1-double, 3

c. cubic; roots: $\pm\sqrt{7}, -2$

d. quadratic; root: $1 - 2i$

e. cubic; roots: $3, 1 + i$

f. quartic (degree 4); roots: $1, -1, 2 + 3i$

g. quadratic; root: $1 - \sqrt{2}$

h. cubic; roots: $2 - \sqrt{3}, -\frac{1}{2}$

i. quintic (degree 5); roots: 1-double, $\frac{1}{2}$-double, 3

j. quintic; roots: $3 - i, i + 5, 1$

7. Graph each equation using the given information. Plot the x- and y-intercepts.

a. $y = x^3 + 3x^2 - 4$; zeros at 1 and -2-double

b. $y = x^3 + 3x^2 - 8x + 10$; zeros at $-5, 1 + i$

c. $y = x^4 - 8x^2 + 16$; zeros at 2-double and -2-double

d. $y = -x^2 - 9$; zero at $3i$

e. $y = x^5 - 2x^4 - 6x^3 - 6x^2 - 7x - 4$; zeros at -1-double, 4, i

4-10 Graphs of Polynomial Functions

Graphs of polynomial functions have characteristic shapes near their zeros depending on the nature of the zeros. Some polynomial functions are graphed below. The equations, their zeros, and the multiplicities of the zeros are given. Notice how the graphs are affected by the nature of the zeros.

Distinct real zeros

$y = x^2 - 2x - 3$
$= (x - 3)(x + 1)$
zeros: 3, −1

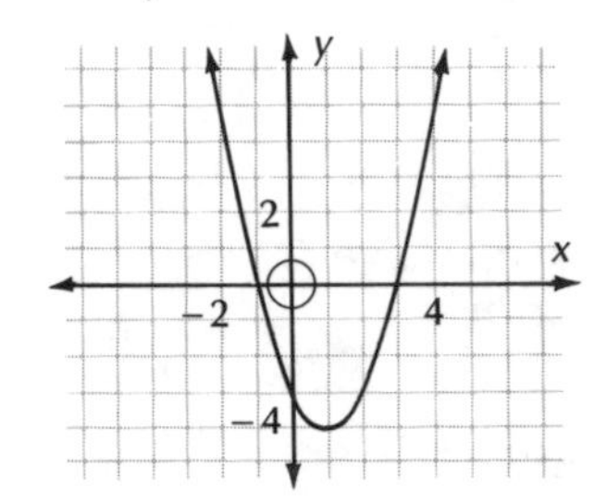

$y = x^3 + 2x^2 - 5x - 6$
$= (x + 1)(x - 2)(x + 3)$
zeros: −3, −1, 2

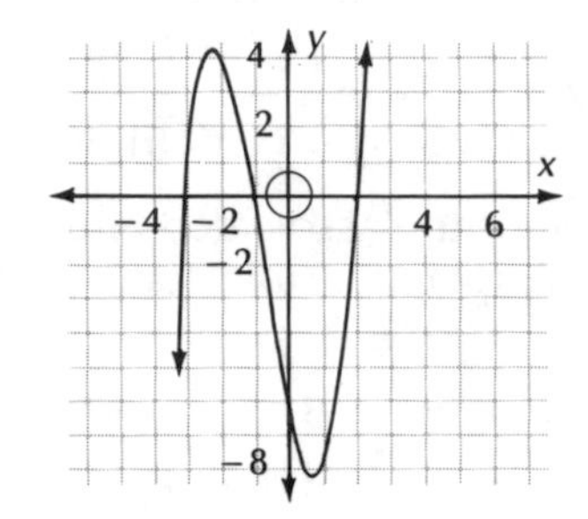

$y = x^4 - 5x^2 + 4$
$= (x + 1)(x - 1)(x + 2)(x - 2)$
zeros: −2, −1, 1, 2

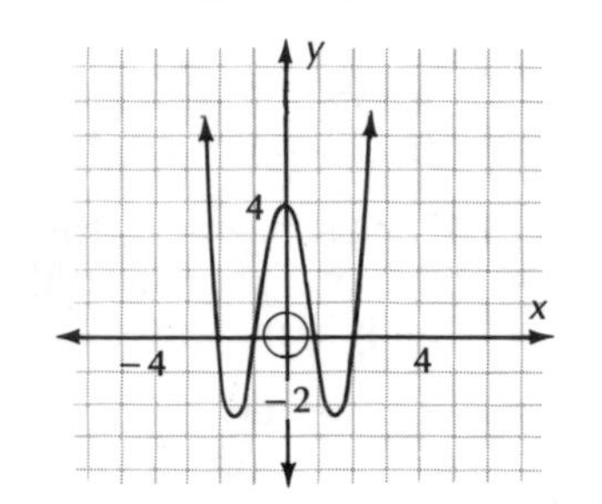

Multiple real zeros

$y = x^2 - 6x + 9$
$= (x - 3)(x - 3)$
zeros: −3-double

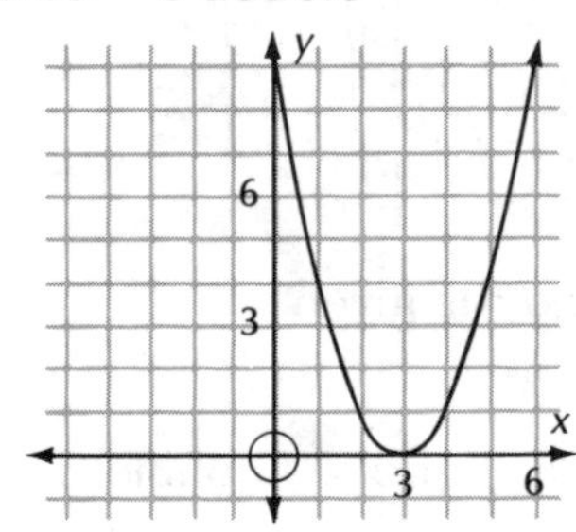

$y = x^3 - 3x^2 + 3x - 1$
$= (x - 1)(x - 1)(x - 1)$
zeros: 1-triple

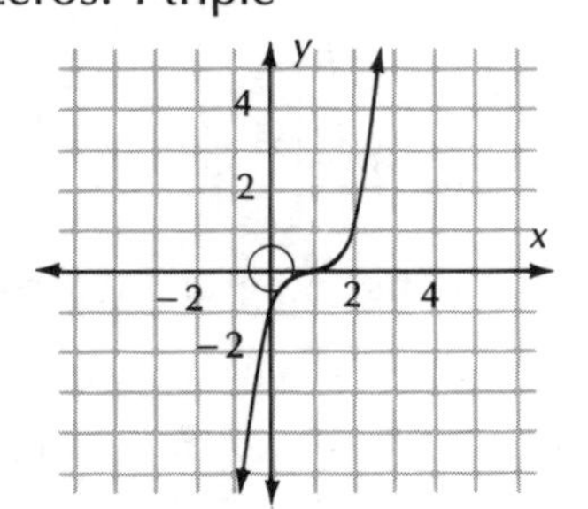

$y = x^5 + x^4 - 2x^3 - 2x^2 + x + 1$
$= (x + 1)^3(x - 1)^2$
zeros: −1-triple, 1-double

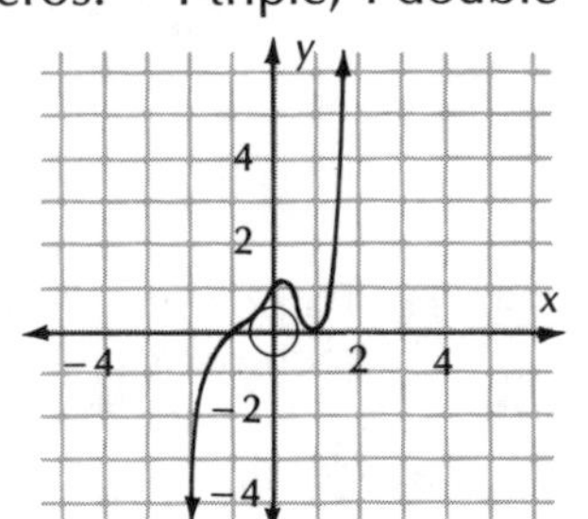

Imaginary zeros

$y = x^2 - 2x + 5$
$= [x - (1 + 2i)(x - (1 - 2i)]$
zeros: $1 + 2i$, $1 - 2i$

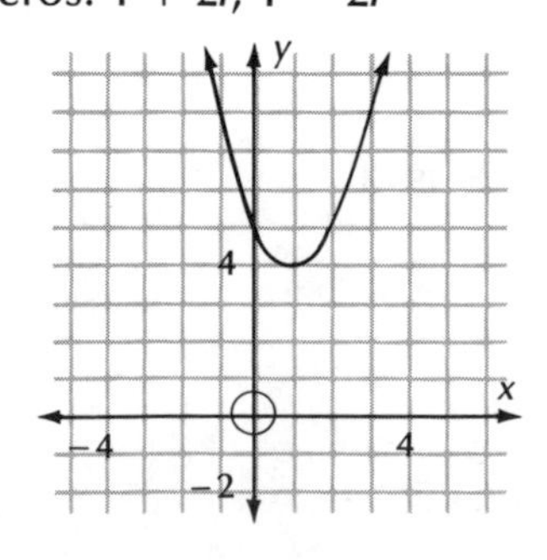

$y = x^3 - 3x^2 + x - 3$
$= (x^2 + 1)(x - 3)$
zeros: i, $-i$, 3

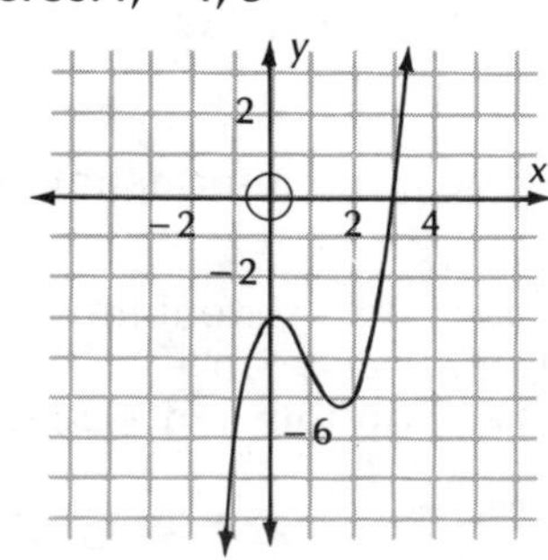

$y = x^4 - x^3 - x^2 - x - 2$
$= (x^2 + 1)(x - 2)(x + 1)$
zeros: i, i, −1, 2

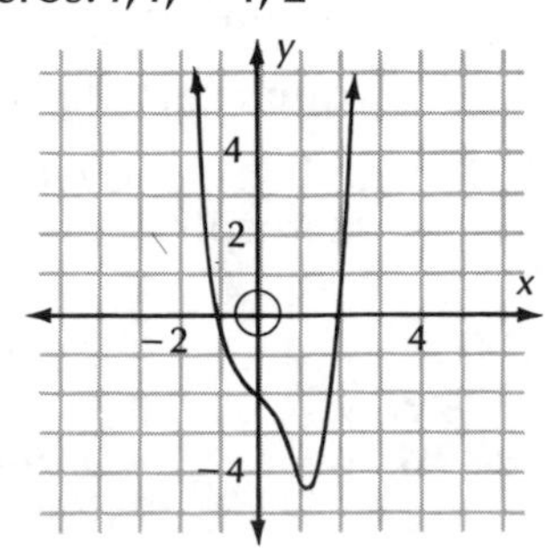

SUMMARY

Type of zero	Shape of the graph
Distinct real zero	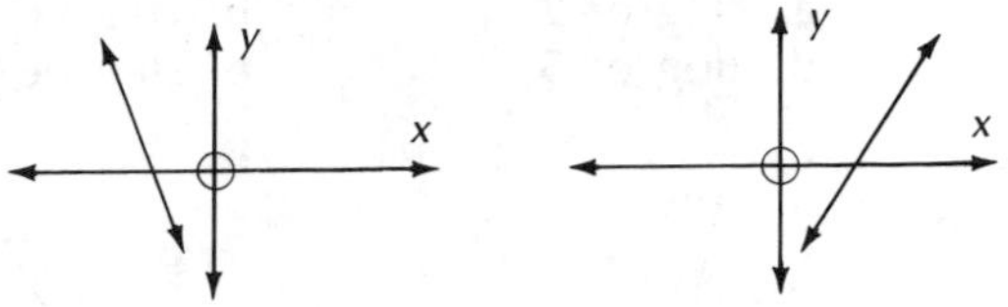
Zero of even multiplicity (zeros of multiplicity 2, 4, etc.)	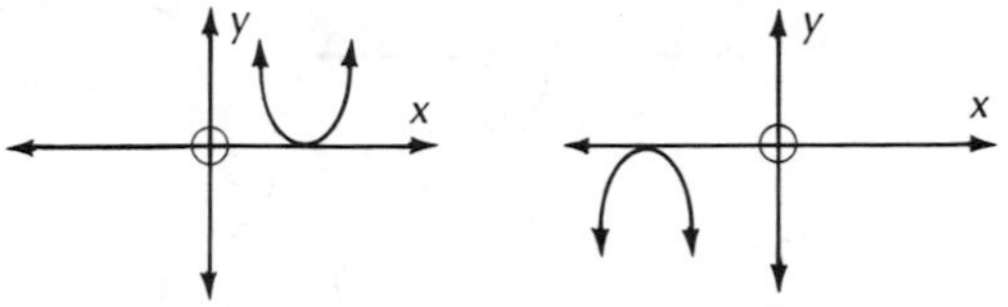
Zero of odd multiplicity (zeros of multiplicity 3, 5, etc.)	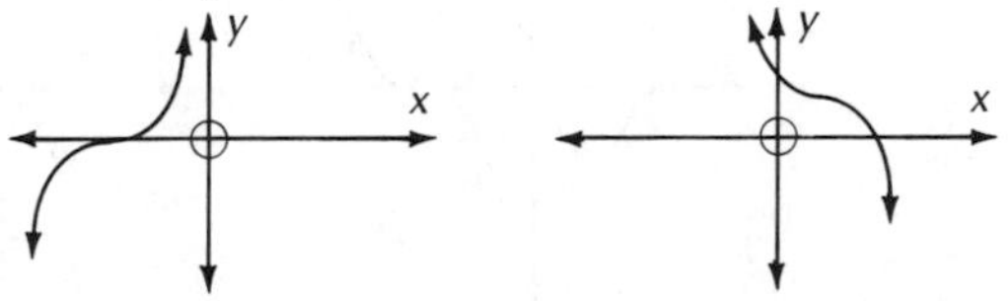
Imaginary zeros	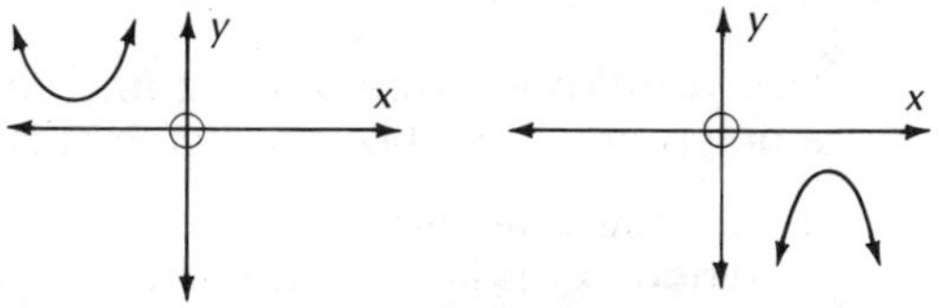

EXERCISE 4-10

A 1. Graph each equation to show that zeros of even and odd multiplicities follow the patterns given in this lesson.

a. $y = x^4$ **b.** $y = x^5$ **c.** $y = x^6$ **d.** $y = x^7$

2. Polynomial functions are sketched below. Which of the functions below have:

a. exactly three distinct real zeros and no imaginary zeros?
b. exactly one zero of even multiplicity and one other real zero?
c. exactly one pair of imaginary zeros and no real zeros?
d. a zero of odd multiplicity and some imaginary zeros?
e. zeros of two different multiplicities?
f. a zero of even multiplicity and some imaginary zeros?

i ii 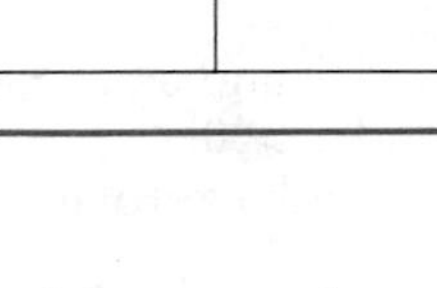 iii

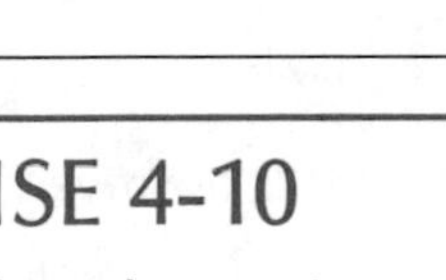

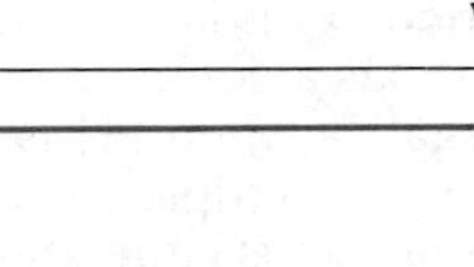

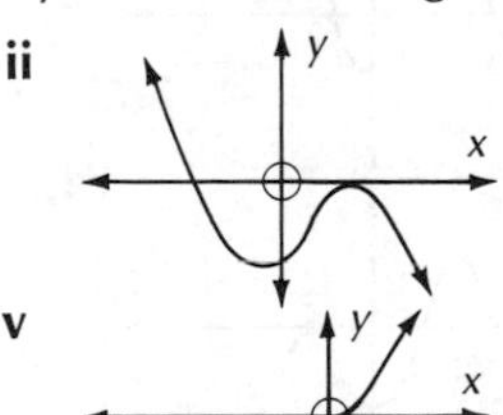

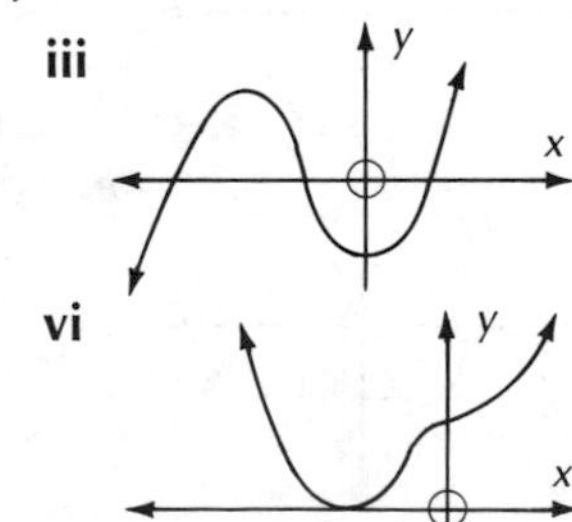

iv 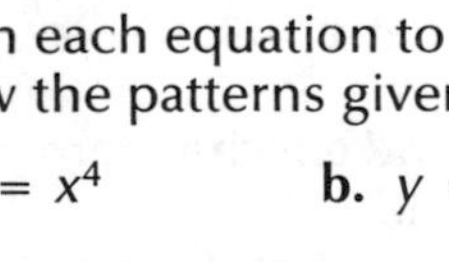 v 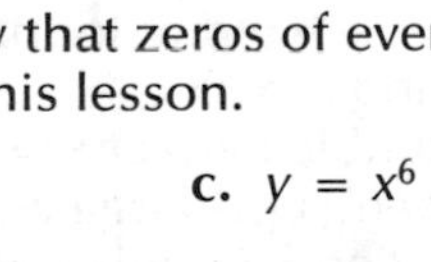 vi

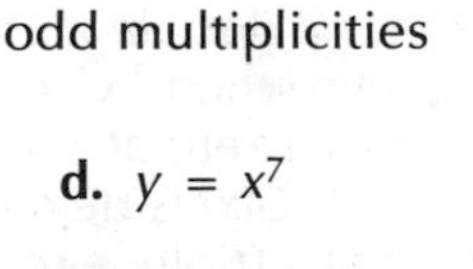

B 3. Which graph could possibly be the graph of a polynomial function with the given degree?

a. degree 2
b. degree 3
c. degree 4
d. degree 5
e. degree 6
f. degree 7

i

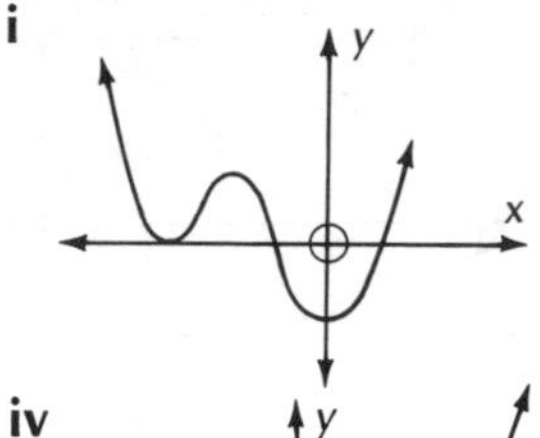

ii

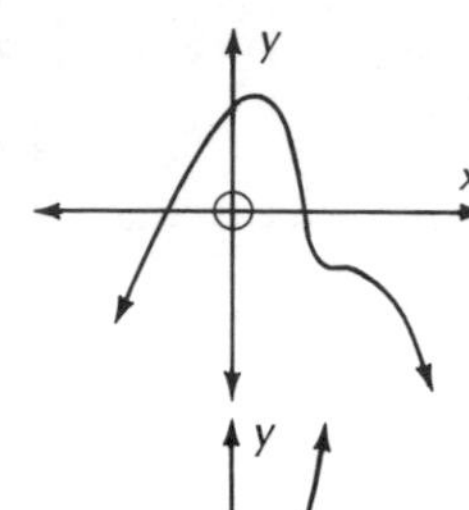

iii

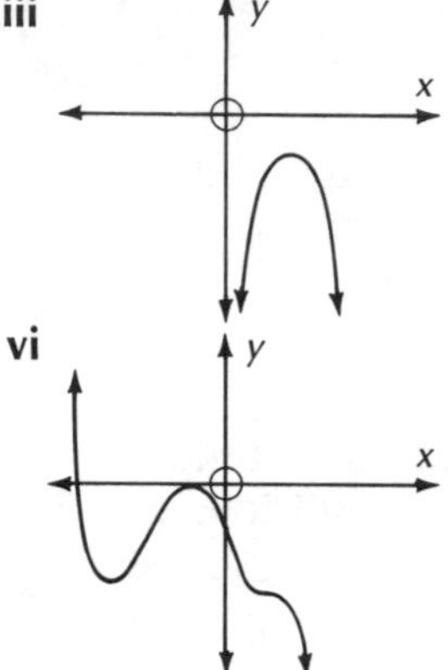

iv

v

vi

4. Use your knowledge of the appearance of the graph near the zeros of a polynomial function to sketch each graph.

a. $S(x)$ has real zeros at $x = 1$, $x = -2$, and $x = 4$. $S(x)$ is positive when $|x|$ is large and $x > 0$.
b. $T(x)$ has a double zero at $x = -3$ and a zero at $x = 2$. $T(x)$ is negative when $|x|$ is large and $x > 0$.
c. $Q(x)$ has a triple zero at $x = 3$ and a zero at $x = -2$. $Q(x)$ is positive when $|x|$ is large and $x > 0$.
d. $F(x)$ has a double zero at $x = -1$ and a double zero at $x = 3$. $F(x)$ is negative when $|x|$ is large and $x > 0$.
e. $G(x)$ has a zero at $x = 1$, a double zero at $x = -2$, and another zero at $x = 3$. $G(x)$ is negative when $|x|$ is large and $x > 0$.
f. $H(x)$ has a triple zero at $x = 3$ and a double zero at $x = -1$. $H(x)$ is positive when $|x|$ is large and $x > 0$.

5. Polynomial functions are graphed below. State the least number of zeros that each function might have and specify the type of zeros that they would be.

a.

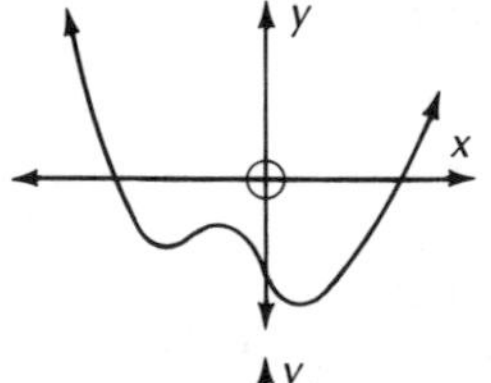

b.

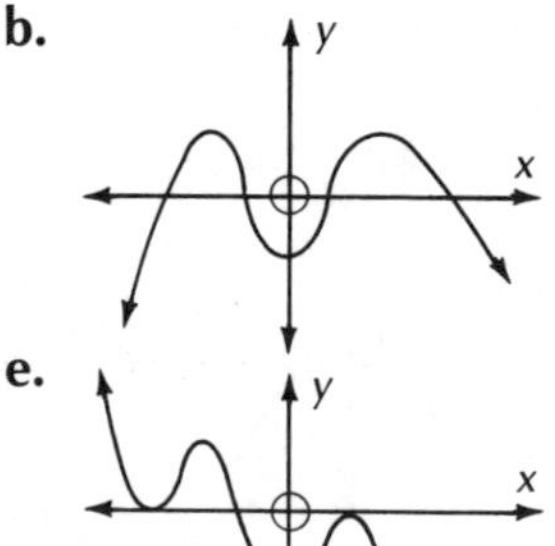

c.

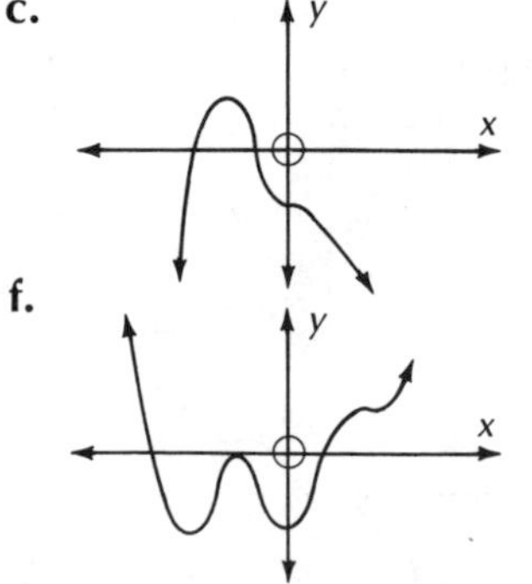

d.

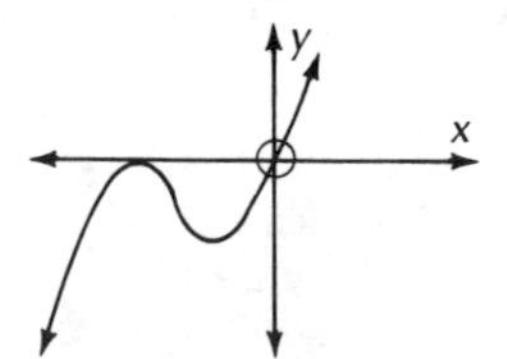

e.

f.

6. Factor each polynomial. Then sketch the graph using your knowledge of the property of the polynomial as $|x|$ becomes large and the shape of the graph near the zeros of the polynomial.

a. $x^3 - 5x^2 + 7x - 3$
b. $-x^3 - 3x^2 + 4x + 12$
c. $2x^3 - 5x^2 - 4x + 3$
d. $12x^3 + x^2 - 17x + 4$
e. $x^4 - 3x^3 - 2x^2 + 12x - 8$
f. $-x^4 - 2x^3 + 12x^2 - 14x + 5$
g. $4x^4 - 17x^2 + 4$
h. $3x^4 + 7x^3 + 3x^2 - 3x - 2$
i. $x^5 + 7x^4 + 10x^3 - 18x^2 - 27x + 27$
j. $x^5 + 2x^4 - 6x^3 - 8x^2 + 5x + 6$

EXTRA

Descartes' Rule of Signs

A polynomial of degree *n* must have *n* roots and any complex roots must appear as conjugate pairs. Descartes' Rule of Signs gives information about the number of real roots.

Descartes' Rule of Signs

Given that $P(x) = 0$ is a polynomial equation with real coefficients, then the number of positive real roots is either equal to the number of sign changes in the coefficients of $P(x)$ or is less than this number by a positive even integer.

The number of negative real roots is equal to the number of sign changes in the coefficients of $P(-x)$ or is less than this number by a positive even integer.

For example, consider $P(x) = x^4 + 2x^3 \overset{\downarrow}{-} 7x^2 \overset{\downarrow}{+} 3x \overset{\downarrow}{-} 2$. There are 3 sign changes. Therefore, there are either 3 positive roots or there is 3 − 2, or 1, positive root.

$$P(-x) = (-x)^4 + 2(-x)^3 - 7(-x)^2 + 3(-x) - 2$$
$$= x^4 - 2x^3 - 7x^2 - 3x - 2$$

There is only one sign change. Therefore, there is only one negative real root.

The information is summarized in the table at the right.

Number of positive roots	Number of negative roots	Number of imaginary roots	Total
3	1	0	4
1	1	2	4

From the information above, there must be at least one negative root. By the Rational Root Theorem, this root is −1 or −2. Once that root is located, you need not search for other negative roots.

Construct a table of roots, such as the one above, for each equation.

1. $x^3 + 4x^2 + x - 6 = 0$
2. $x^3 - 7x^2 + 14x - 8 = 0$
3. $2x^4 - 5x^3 + 11x^2 - 3x - 5 = 0$
4. $3x^3 - 11x^2 + 35x + 13 = 0$
5. $2x^5 - 5x^4 + 4x^3 + 3x^2 - 4x + 2 = 0$
6. $3x^5 - 8x^4 + 12x^3 + 2x^2 - 31x - 10 = 0$

4-11 Solving Radical Equations

Radical equations contain variables that appear in a radicand such as those shown below.

$\sqrt{m+5} = m + 2 \qquad \sqrt{x+8} - \sqrt{x-6} = 3 \qquad \sqrt{2y-1} = (y+2)\sqrt{y}$

These lead to polynomial equations that can be solved with previously learned techniques.

EXAMPLE 1: Solve each radical equation over the set of real numbers.

a.

$$\sqrt{m+5} + 3 = m + 2 \qquad \text{Isolate the radical.}$$
$$\sqrt{m+5} = m - 1$$
$$(\sqrt{m+5})^2 = (m-1)^2 \qquad \text{Square both sides.}$$
$$m + 5 = m^2 - 2m + 1$$
$$m^2 - 3m - 4 = 0 \qquad \text{Solve the resulting quadratic.}$$
$$(m-4)(m+1) = 0$$
$$m = 4 \text{ or } m = -1$$

Check the solutions.

For $m = 4$: L.S. $= \sqrt{4+5} + 3$
$= \sqrt{9} + 3$
$= 6$
R.S. $= 4 + 2 = 6$ ✓

For $m = -1$: L.S. $= \sqrt{-1+5} + 3$
$= \sqrt{4} + 3$
$= 5$
R.S. $= (-1) + 2 = 1$ L.S. $\neq$ R.S.

Therefore, 4 is a solution of the equation, but -1 is not. -1 is called an **extraneous root**. Squaring both sides of an equation often results in an extraneous root.

b. $\sqrt{x+9} - \sqrt{x-6} = 3$

$$\sqrt{x+9} = \sqrt{x-6} + 3$$
$$(\sqrt{x+9})^2 = (\sqrt{x-6} + 3)^2$$
$$x + 9 = x - 6 + 6\sqrt{x-6} + 9$$
$$6\sqrt{x-6} = 6$$
$$\sqrt{x-6} = 1$$
$$(\sqrt{x-6})^2 = 1^2$$
$$x - 6 = 1$$
$$x = 7$$

Check: L.S. $= \sqrt{7+9} - \sqrt{7-6}$
$= 3$
$=$ R.S. ✓

c. $\sqrt{3y+3} = (y-1)\sqrt{y}$

$$(\sqrt{3y+3})^2 = [(y-1)\sqrt{y}]^2$$
$$3y + 3 = y(y^2 - 2y + 1)$$
$$3y + 3 = y^3 - 2y^2 + y$$
$$y^3 - 2y^2 - 2y - 3 = 0$$

Check the possible rational roots, ± 3 and ± 1, to find that 3 is indeed a root. Therefore, $y - 3$ is a factor. Divide to find the other factor, $y^2 + y + 1$, and apply the quadratic formula to determine that the other roots are $\dfrac{-1 + i\sqrt{3}}{2}$ and $\dfrac{-1 - i\sqrt{3}}{2}$.

Since only real roots are desired here, the complex roots are discarded.

Check: L.S. $= \sqrt{3(3) + 3} = 2\sqrt{3}$
R.S. $= (3 - 1)\sqrt{3} = 2\sqrt{3}$ ✓

d. $\dfrac{1}{\sqrt{x-2}} = \dfrac{\sqrt{x-2}}{\sqrt{2x+4}}$

$\sqrt{2x+4} = (\sqrt{x-2})^2$

$\sqrt{2x+4} = x - 2$

$(\sqrt{2x+4})^2 = (x-2)^2$

$2x + 4 = x^2 - 4x + 4$

$x^2 - 6x = 0$

The possible solutions are 6 and 0.

Check 6: L.S. $= \dfrac{1}{\sqrt{6-2}} = \dfrac{1}{2}$

R.S. $= \dfrac{\sqrt{6-2}}{\sqrt{2(6)+4}} = \dfrac{1}{2}$

Check 0: L.S. $= \dfrac{1}{\sqrt{0-2}} = \dfrac{1}{2i}$

Using zero as a solution leads to non-real terms in the original equation. Therefore, 0 is discarded as a solution.
This equation has only one solution over the real numbers, that is 6.

EXERCISE 4-11

A 1. Solve each radical equation by inspection.

a. $\sqrt{x+1} = 3$ b. $3\sqrt{x} - 2 = 4$ c. $3\sqrt{2x+1} = 15$

d. $\sqrt{\dfrac{x}{3}} = 2$ e. $\sqrt{\dfrac{x}{2} + 1} = 3$ f. $\sqrt{3x^2+4} = 4$

2. Solve.

a. $\sqrt{3x+1} = x - 3$ b. $\sqrt{5x-1} - 1 = x$ c. $\sqrt{2t^2-2} - t = 1$

d. $\sqrt{b^2+9} = 2b - 3$ e. $\sqrt{x^2+3x-1} = x + 1$ f. $\sqrt{2n^2-n+4} - n = 2$

B 3. Solve over the set of real numbers.

a. $\sqrt{x+5} - \sqrt{x-3} = 2$ b. $\sqrt{5x+1} - \sqrt{x+1} = 2$

c. $\sqrt{3x+6} - \sqrt{x+6} = 2$ d. $3\sqrt{x-5} = \sqrt{3x-2} + 1$

e. $\sqrt{x^2+3x-2} - \sqrt{x^2-5} = 2$ f. $\sqrt{x^2+x+5} - \sqrt{x^2-3x} = 3$

4. Solve over the set of real numbers.

a. $\sqrt{x+1} = (x-1)\sqrt{x-2}$ b. $\sqrt{7x+1} = (x-2)\sqrt{x-1}$

c. $(x-3)\sqrt{x-1} = \sqrt{x^2-3x+6}$ d. $\sqrt{3x+2} = (x-4)\sqrt{x-1}$

e. $\sqrt{x^2+x+4} - \sqrt{x+1} = 2$ f. $\sqrt{x^2-x-2} = (x-2)\sqrt{x-3}$

5. Solve over the set of real numbers.

a. $\dfrac{1}{\sqrt{x+1}} = \dfrac{\sqrt{2x+3}}{2x}$ b. $\sqrt{x-2} - \dfrac{6}{\sqrt{x+3}} = 0$

c. $\dfrac{2}{\sqrt{x+6}} + \dfrac{1}{\sqrt{x-1}} = \dfrac{5}{2\sqrt{x-1}}$ d. $\dfrac{1}{\sqrt{3x+1}} + \dfrac{1}{\sqrt{x-1}} = \dfrac{\sqrt{x+4}}{\sqrt{3x+1}}$

C 6. Solve each continued radical.

a. $\sqrt{x + \sqrt{x + \sqrt{x + \ldots}}} = 2$ b. $\sqrt{x + \sqrt{x + \sqrt{x + \ldots}}} = 3$

c. $\sqrt{x + \sqrt{x + \sqrt{x + \ldots}}} = 4$ d. $\sqrt{x + \sqrt{x + \sqrt{x + \ldots}}} = n$

(Hint: To solve the equations, square both sides and subtract the original equation from the resulting equation.)

7. Use a procedure similar to that in exercise 6 to find the value of $\sqrt{1 + \sqrt{1 + \sqrt{1 + \ldots}}}$.

4-12 Solving Polynomial Inequalities

Polynomial inequalities are analyzed and solved using the techniques for solving polynomial equations.

EXAMPLE 1: If $S(x) = x^3 + 2x^2 - x - 2$, graph $S(x) \leq 0$ on a number line.

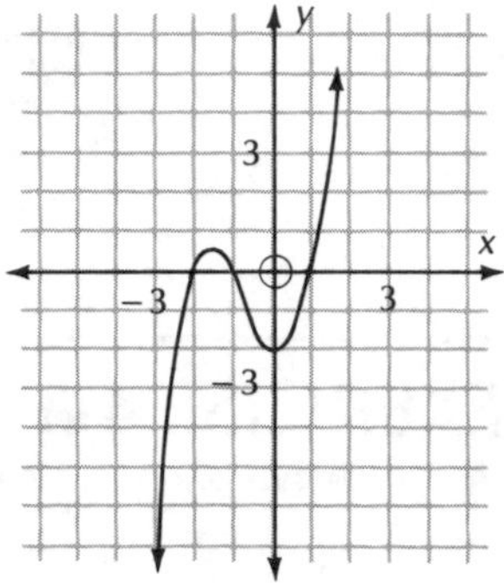

Sketch the graph of $y = S(x)$.

The Rational Root Theorem is used to list the possible rational zeros. The possible zeros are ± 1, and ± 2.

By substitution, -1, 1, and -2 are zeros.

From the graph of $y = S(x)$, $S(x) \leq 0$ if $x \leq -2$ and if $-1 \leq x \leq 1$. The solution of the inequality $S(x) \leq 0$ is graphed on a number line, as shown below.

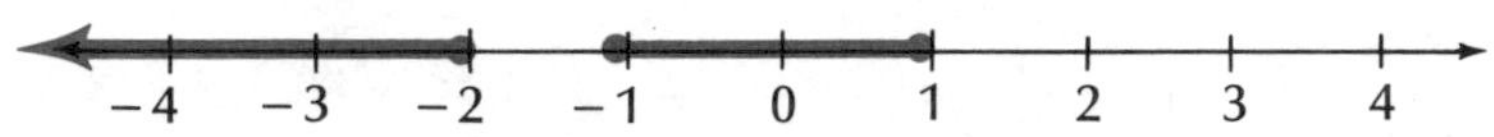

Sometimes it is necessary to use the quadratic formula to determine the intervals that satisfy the inequality. In addition, when multiple roots are involved, the intervals have to be drawn with care.

EXAMPLE 2: Solve and graph the solution set of each polynomial inequality on a number line.

a. $x^3 - 5x^2 + 6x - 2 < 0$

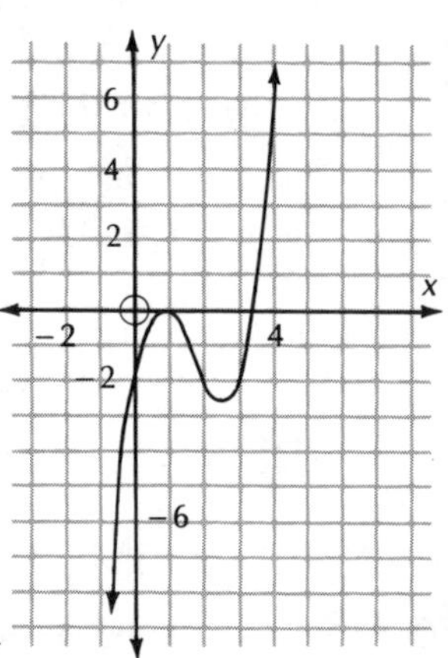

By substitution, 1 is a zero. The quadratic formula then gives $2 + \sqrt{2}$ and $2 - \sqrt{2}$ as the remaining zeros. Therefore, the zeros of the polynomial are 1, 0.59, and 3.41, correct to two decimal places. The graph of $y = x^3 - 5x^2 + 6x - 2$ is shown at the right and the solution of $x^3 - 5x^2 + 6x - 2 < 0$ is shown below.

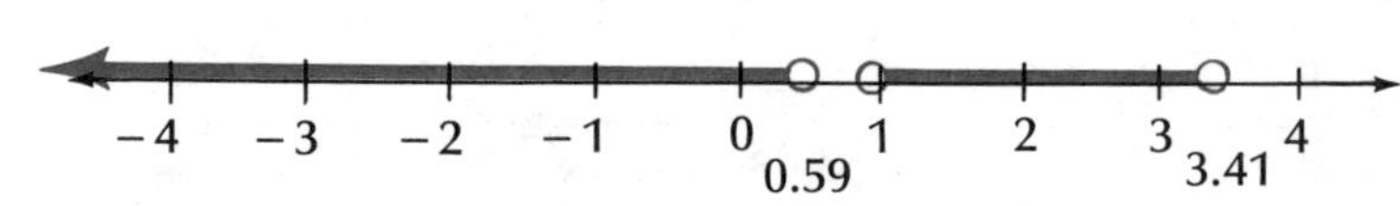

b. $2x^3 - 7x^2 + 4x + 4 > 0$

By substitution, the polynomial has one zero at $-\frac{1}{2}$ and a double zero at 2.

The graph of $y = 2x^3 - 7x^2 + 4x + 4$ is shown at the right and the solution of $2x^3 - 7x^2 + 4x + 4 > 0$ is given below.

Notice that the graph is tangent to the x-axis at the point (2, 0) and so 2 is not in the solution set of $2x^3 - 7x^2 + 4x + 4 > 0$.

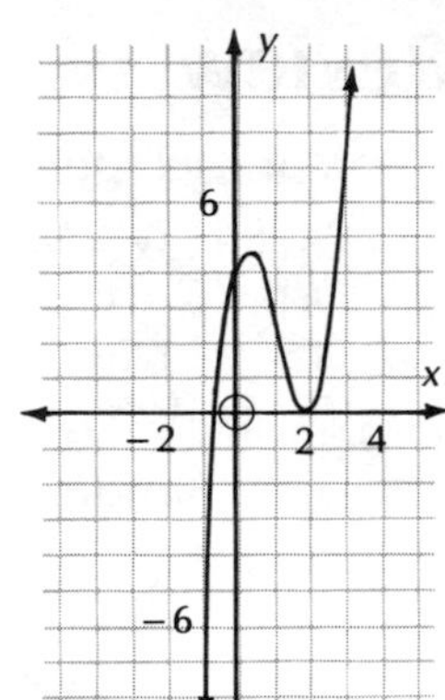

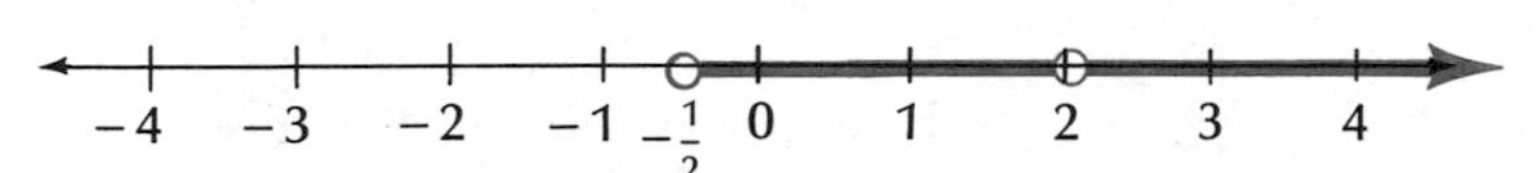

EXERCISE 4-12

A **1.** Given each graph, plot the given inequality on a number line.

a.

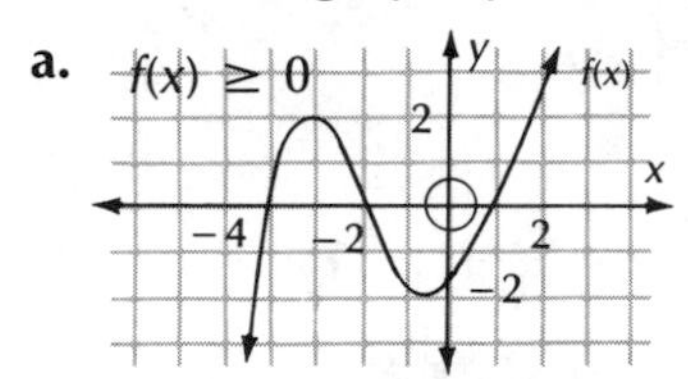

b.

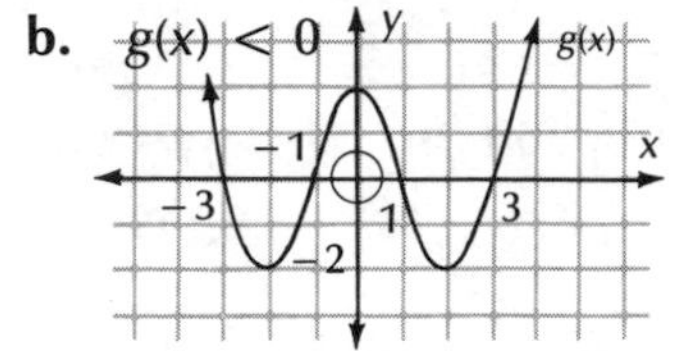

c.

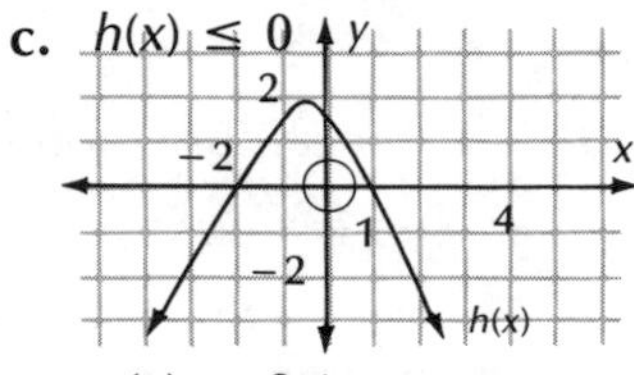

d.

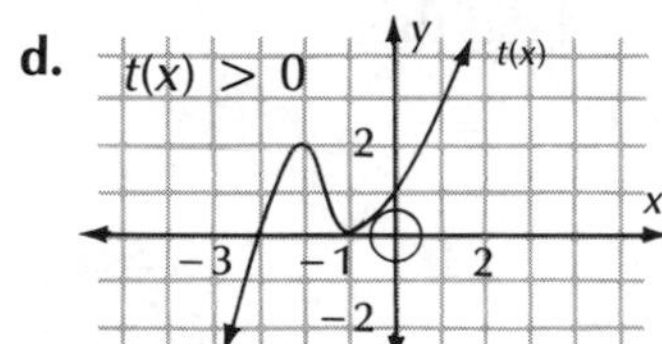

e.

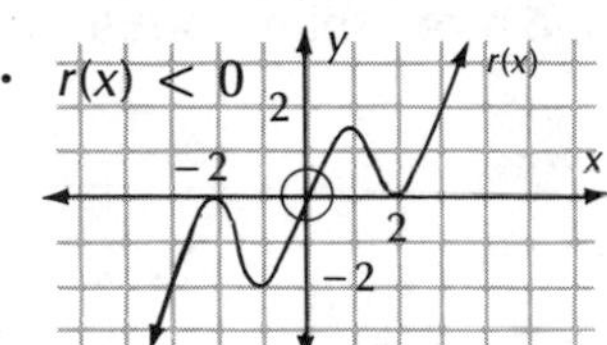

f.

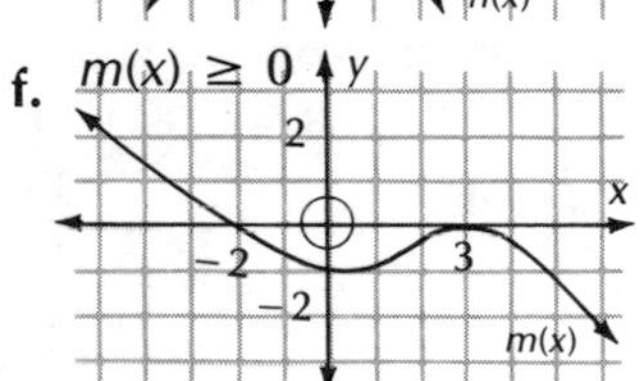

B **2.** Plot the given polynomial and then graph the required inequality on a number line.

a. $S(x) = x^3 - 3x^2 - x + 3;\ S(x) > 0$ **b.** $Q(x) = x^3 - x^2 - 8x + 12;\ Q(x) \geq 0$
c. $T(x) = x^4 - 5x^2 + 4;\ T(x) < 0$ **d.** $R(x) = x^4 - 2x^3 + x^2 + 2x - 2;\ R(x) > 0$

3. Graph each inequality by determining the zeros of the corresponding polynomial function and then testing the intervals.

a. $x^2 - 3x + 2 \leq 0$ **b.** $4x^2 - 4x - 15 > 0$
c. $3x^2 - 7x - 6 < 0$ **d.** $x^3 - 4x^2 + x + 6 \geq 0$
e. $4x^3 - 12x^2 - x + 3 \leq 0$ **f.** $2x^3 - 13x^2 + 24x - 9 > 0$
g. $2x^3 + 5x^2 - 11x + 4 \geq 0$ **h.** $3x^3 + 8x^2 - 15x + 4 < 0$
i. $x^4 - x^3 + x^2 + 9x - 10 > 0$ **j.** $2x^4 + 5x^3 - 12x^2 + x + 4 \leq 0$

4. Graph each inequality. Determine any irrational roots of the corresponding polynomial equation to the nearest tenth, and plot these on a number line.

a. $x^2 - 3 < 0$ **b.** $x^3 - 5x - 2 \geq 0$
c. $x^3 - 2x^2 - 7x + 2 > 0$ **d.** $x^4 - 2x^3 - 6x^2 + 8x + 8 \geq 0$
e. $x^4 - 5x^2 + 10x - 6 \leq 0$ **f.** $x^4 + 2x^3 - 4x^2 - 10x - 5 > 0$

Review

1. Factor each polynomial.

   a. $6x^2 + 5x - 4$
   b. $21x^3y^2 - 77x^2y^2 - 140xy^2$
   c. $81x^4 - 64$
   d. $18x^2 - 79xy - 9y^2$
   e. $8x^3 - 125y^6$
   f. $4(x - 3)^2(x + 1) + 5(x - 3)(x + 1) - 6(x + 1)$

2. Determine the zeros of each polynomial function, correct to the nearest hundredth.

   a. $P(x) = x^4 - 4x^2 - 5$

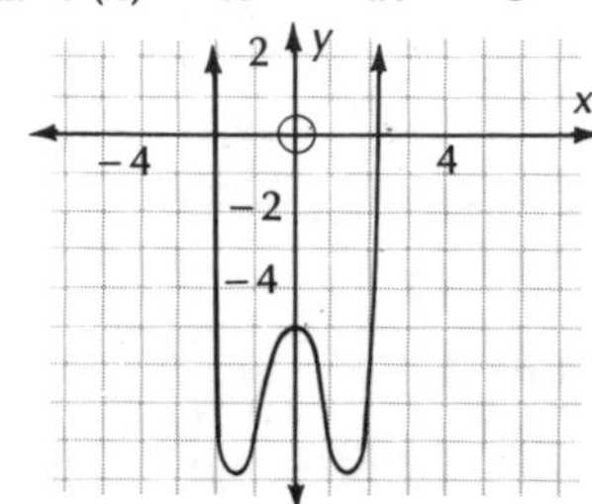

   b. $P(x) = \frac{1}{2}x^4 - x^3 - x^2 - x + 1$

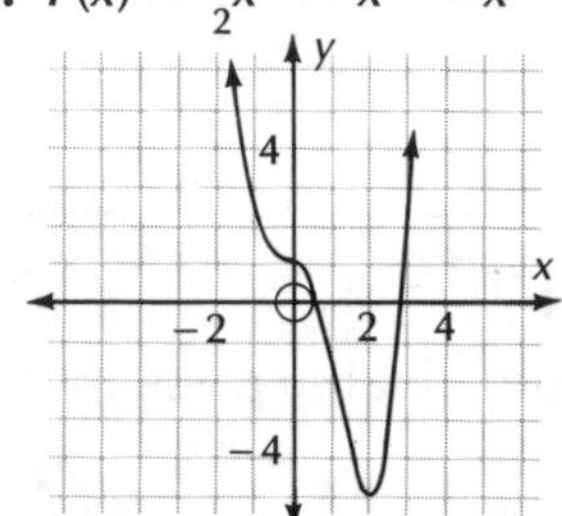

3. Graph each polynomial function for $-5 \leq x \leq 5$.

   a. $P(x) = -x^2 + x + 5$
   b. $P(x) = x^3 + x^2 - 4x - 4$

4. The length of a rectangular field is one less than double the width. The diagonal distance is one more than double the width. Find the perimeter of the field.

5. Simplify.

   a. $\sqrt{-49}$
   b. $\sqrt{(-4)^2}$
   c. $\sqrt{-5}\sqrt{-10}$
   d. $i\sqrt{-8}$
   e. $\dfrac{\sqrt{-24}}{-2}$
   f. $2\sqrt{-7} - \sqrt{-63}$
   g. $\sqrt{-12} + i\sqrt{5} - \sqrt{-20} + \sqrt{-27}$
   h. $(3 - 5i)(3 + 5i)$
   i. $(2 - i)^2(3 + i)$

6. Divide. Give answers in the form $P(x) = D(x)Q(x) + R(x)$.

   a. $(x^3 + x^2 - 2x - 1) \div (x + 1)$
   b. $(x^3 - 8x^2 + 21x - 20) \div (x - 4)$
   c. $(5x^3 - 2x^2 + 1) \div (x - 3)$
   d. $(x + x^3 - 4x^2 - 4) \div (x + 2)$
   e. $(x^3 - 3x^2 - x + 1) \div (x^2 - x + 1)$
   f. $(x^4 - 5x^3 + 15x^2 - 5x + 10) \div (x^2 + 1)$

7. Determine one zero of each of the polynomials graphed below and verify it. Then find the other roots.

   a. $y = x^3 + 3.5x^2 - 5x - 12$

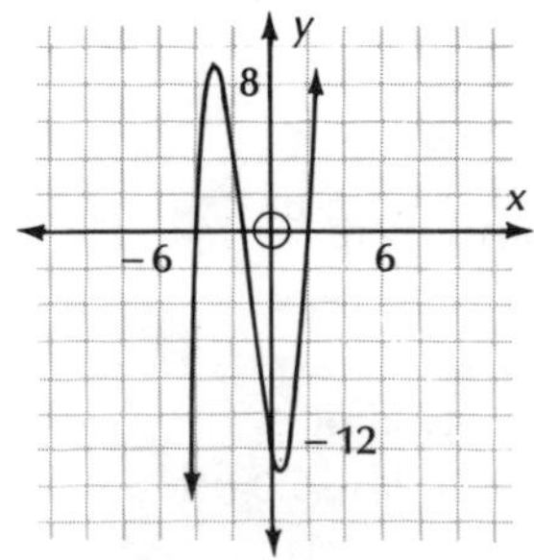

   b. $y = x^3 + 3x^2 - 2x - 6$

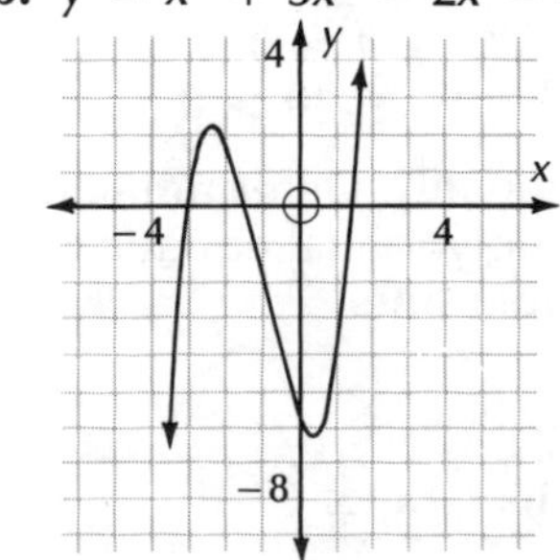

8. List the possible rational roots of each equation.

a. $x^2 - 3x - 10 = 0$
b. $x^2 + 7x - 8 = 0$
c. $2x^2 - 3x + 5 = 0$
d. $5x^2 - 7x - 10 = 0$
e. $x^3 - 4x + 12 = 0$
f. $2x^4 - x^2 + 6 = 0$
g. $4x^3 - 5x^2 + 2x + 6 = 0$
h. $6x^5 - 3x^3 - x + 1 = 0$

9. For each polynomial, show that the number that follows is a zero with the given multiplicity. Then find the remaining zeros.

a. $x^3 + 3x^2 - 2x - 6; -3$
b. $x^3 + 3x^2 - 9x + 5$; 1-double zero
c. $6x^3 - x^2 - 5x + 2; \frac{1}{2}$
d. $4x^3 - 19x^2 + 32x - 15; 2 + i$
e. $x^4 - 6x^3 + 17x^2 - 28x + 20$; 2-double zero

10. Determine the roots of each equation.

a. $x^2 - 3x - 4 = 0$
b. $3x^2 - 5x + 1 = 0$
c. $x^2 + 4x + 5 = 0$
d. $x^3 - 6x + 9 = 0$
e. $2x^3 + 7x^2 + 2x - 3 = 0$
f. $x^3 - 3x^2 + 2 = 0$
g. $x^3 - 3x^2 + 4x - 2 = 0$
h. $3x^3 - x^2 + 3x - 1 = 0$
i. $4x^3 - 11x^2 + 14x - 6 = 0$
j. $x^4 - 2x^3 + 4x^2 + 2x - 5 = 0$

11. Find a polynomial equation of least degree with integral coefficients that has the given characteristics.

a. roots 3 and -2
b. root $\frac{1}{2}$ and a double root at -1
c. root $1 - i$
d. roots -3 and $2 + i$
e. roots $\sqrt{2}$, $-\sqrt{2}$, and $2i$
f. roots $\frac{2}{3}, \frac{1}{5}$, and $3 + 2i$

12. Solve each radical equation over the set of real numbers.

a. $\sqrt{x + 5} = 3$
b. $\sqrt{2x + 1} + 1 = x$
c. $\sqrt{x^2 - x - 4} = \sqrt{3x + 1}$
d. $\sqrt{x^2 - x + 3} = \sqrt{x^2 - 5} + 1$
e. $\sqrt{x + 3} - \sqrt{x - 2} = 1$
f. $\sqrt{x^2 + 1} = (x - 2)\sqrt{x - 5}$
g. $\dfrac{1}{\sqrt{2x + 1}} = \dfrac{\sqrt{x}}{6}$
h. $\dfrac{1}{\sqrt{x - 1}} + \dfrac{1}{\sqrt{3x + 1}} = \dfrac{3}{\sqrt{3x + 1}}$

13. Use your knowledge of factoring and the shape of a graph near the zeros of a polynomial function to sketch the graph of each equation.

a. $y = x^3 + 2x^2 - 5x - 6$
b. $y = 6x^3 + x^2 - 31x + 10$
c. $y = 2x^4 + 11x^3 + 18x^2 + 4x - 8$
d. $y = x^4 - 8x^2 + 16$

14. Graph the solution set of each polynomial inequality on a number line. Plot any irrational roots, correct to the nearest tenth, and label them.

a. $x^2 - 2x - 3 > 0$
b. $x^2 - x + 3 \geq 0$
c. $2x^2 + x - 6 \geq 0$
d. $x^2 \leq x + 12$
e. $x^3 - 4x^2 + x + 6 < 0$
f. $x^4 - x^3 - 2x^2 + 6x - 4 > 0$

1. Factor completely.

   a. $5x^2 - 15x + 10$
   b. $12x^2 - 70xy - 12y^2$
   c. $x^4 - 4x^2 - 5$
   d. $9x^2y^2 - 3xy^2 - 12y^2$
   e. $x^6 - 1$
   f. $5(x + 2)(x - 3)^2 - 4(x + 2)(x - 3) - (x + 2)$

2. List the possible rational roots of $3x^2 - 3x^2 - x - 6 = 0$.

3. Find all the roots of each equation. Give irrational roots as radicals in simplest form.

   a. $x^3 - 3x - 2 = 0$
   b. $6x^3 - 17x^2 + 11x - 2 = 0$
   c. $12x^3 - 20x^2 + x + 3 = 0$
   d. $x^3 + x^2 - 14x - 8 = 0$
   e. $x^4 + 3x^3 + 3x^2 + 3x + 2 = 0$
   f. $3x^3 - 8x^2 + 8x - 5 = 0$

4. Graph the polynomial function $P(x) = x^3 + 3x^2 + 2x + 7$ for $-4 \le x \le 1$. Calculate any real zero, correct to the nearest hundredth.

5. Simplify.

   a. $\sqrt{-48}$
   b. $\sqrt{-20}\sqrt{-5}$
   c. $\sqrt{-28} - i\sqrt{2} + \sqrt{-7} - \sqrt{-8}$
   d. $(7 + 3i) - (2 - 5i)$
   e. $(2 - 3i)(2 + i)^2$
   f. i^5

6. Divide and give each answer in the form $P(x) = D(x)Q(x) + R(x)$.

   a. $(x^3 - 3x^2 - 13x + 10) \div (x - 5)$
   b. $(2x^3 - x^2 - 13x - 7) \div (2x + 1)$
   c. $(2x^4 - 7x^3 + 12x^2 - 8x + 5) \div (x^2 - 3x + 4)$

7. Given that $P(x) = \frac{1}{2}x^3 - 3x$ and $T(x) = x^3 + x^2 - 3x - 3$, graph $P(x)$ and $T(x)$ over the interval $-3 \le x \le 3$. Plot the inequalities $P(x) > 0$ and $T(x) \le 0$ on a number line. Plot any irrational zeros, correct to the nearest tenth, and label them.

8. Determine the polynomial equation of least degree with integral coefficients and having the given roots.

   a. -3 and 2
   b. $\frac{2}{3}$ and double root of 1
   c. 5 and $1 + 2i$
   d. -1, $3i$, and $1 - i$

9. a. If a factor of $P(x)$ is $3x - 2$, what is a root of $P(x) = 0$?
   b. If $P(-2) = 5$, what is the remainder of $P(x)$ after division by $x + 2$?

10. Solve each radical equation.

    a. $\sqrt{3x + 1} = x - 1$
    b. $\sqrt{x^2 + 3x - 1} - \sqrt{x^2 - x + 2} = 1$
    c. $(x - 2)\sqrt{x - 3} = 2\sqrt{3x + 4}$
    d. $\dfrac{2}{\sqrt{x + 4}} - \dfrac{1}{\sqrt{x - 1}} = \dfrac{1}{3\sqrt{x - 1}}$

Cumulative Review

1. State, with reasons, whether the graph represents a function. Give the domain and range of each.

a.

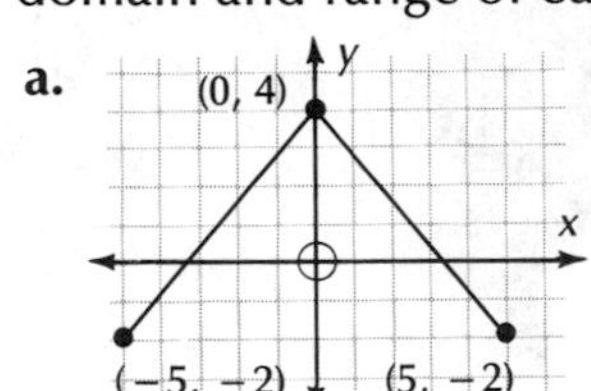

b.

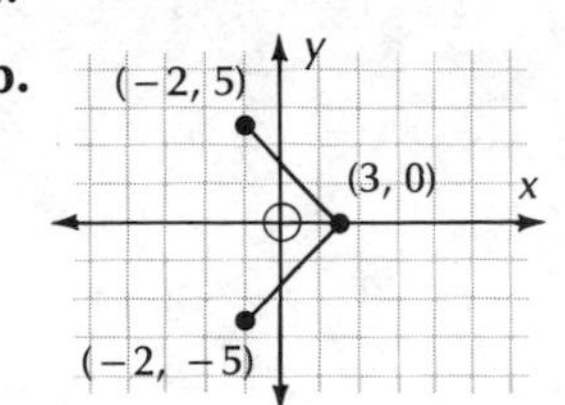

c.

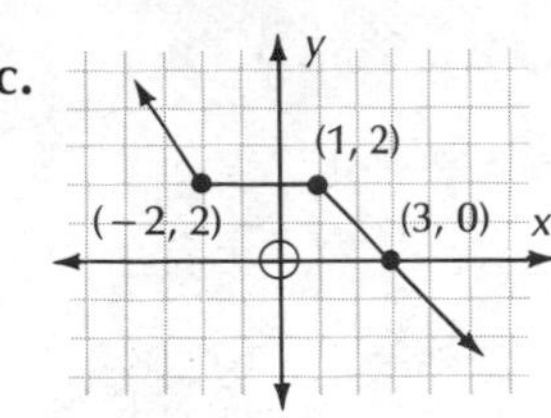

2. Solve.

   a. $9^{\frac{3}{2}} = x$ **b.** $\left(\frac{27}{64}\right)^{-\frac{4}{3}} = x$ **c.** $\left(8^{\frac{2}{3}} - 8^{\frac{1}{3}}\right)^3 = x$

   d. $2\sqrt{2} = 2^x$ **e.** $\sqrt{0.001} = 10^x$ **f.** $\left(9^{\frac{1}{2}}\right)\left(9^{\frac{1}{4}}\right) = 3x$

3. Evaluate.

   a. $\log_2 16$ **b.** $3 \log_9 1$ **c.** $\ln e^3$ **d.** $2^{\log_2 3}$

4. Solve each equation for x.

   a. $\log_3 (x - 2) = 2$ **b.** $\log_6 x = 0$ **c.** $\log_4 (4x) = 4$ **d.** $\log_3 (x - 2) = 4$

5. Find the length of time it will take \$1500, invested at a rate of 12%/a, compounded quarterly, to accumulate to \$2700.

6. Solve each exponential equation using a calculator.

   a. $10^x = 27.3$ **b.** $e^x = 3.5$ **c.** $e^{2x} = 3$ **d.** $e^{5-t} = 5$

7. **a.** Graph the function defined by $y = x^2$ and by $y = 2x$.
   b. Use the graph from part **a** to estimate the coordinates of the points of intersection of the two graphs.
   c. Use a calculator to find the coordinates, correct to three decimal places.

8. A satellite has a nuclear power supply. The power output is given by

   $P = 80(2.7)^{\frac{-t}{450}}$, where P is the power in watts and t, the time in days from the start of the mission.

   a. How much power is available at the start of the mission?
   b. How much power is available after 500 d?
   c. How long will it take for the power to drop to one-half of its original strength?

9. The decay of a radioactive substance can be modeled after the equation

   $A = A_0 2^{\frac{-t}{h}}$, where A_0 is the amount of radioactive substance present at time $t = 0$, A is the amount present at time t, and h is the half-life of the radiactive substance.

   A radioactive gas has a half-life of 4.2 d. How much of a 12 g sample remains at the end of 6.5 d?

5 Trigonometry and the Solution of Triangles

5-1 Trigonometric Functions

A ski tow has a cable that extends 1200 m up a hill. The angle of elevation from the horizontal to the top of the hill is 30°. To find the height of the hill, a similar triangle can be drawn having lengths of the sides as shown in the diagram. By equating the ratios of corresponding sides, the height is estimated to be 600 m.

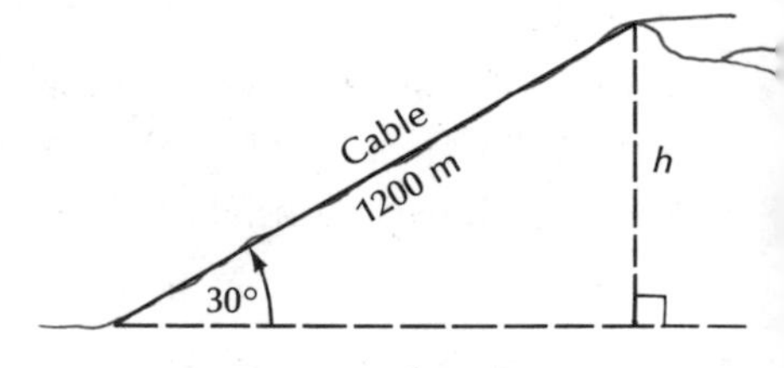

Surveyors, civil engineers, navigators, and astronomers often encounter problems involving the measurement of lengths of sides and angles of triangles. **Trigonometry** is the branch of mathematics that was developed to study and calculate angle measure and lengths of sides of triangles . Problems involving sound, light, electricity, and other wave motions rely on an understanding of *trigonometric functions*.

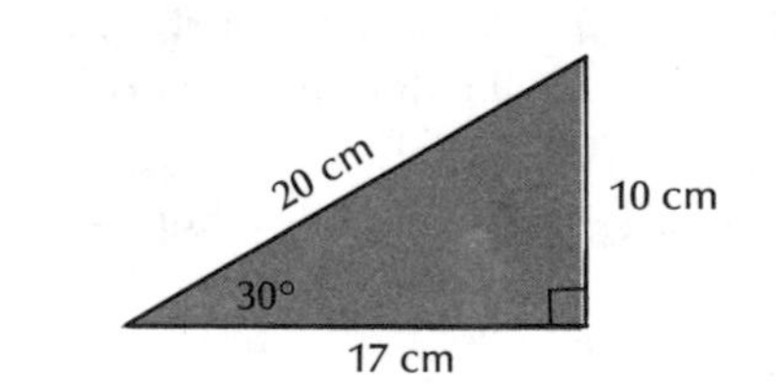

$$\frac{h}{1200} = \frac{10}{20}$$
$$h = 600 \text{ cm}$$

Greek letters are often used in mathematics to represent angles. Some letters that are commonly used are given below.

θ : Theta β : Beta: α : Alpha ϕ : Phi

In a right-angled triangle, the side opposite the right angle is called the **hypotenuse** (**HYP**). Once an angle, θ, is identified, the other two sides are identified as being **opposite** (**OPP**) or **adjacent** (**ADJ**) to the given angle θ. In this text, the sides will generally be referred to by their respective abbreviations.

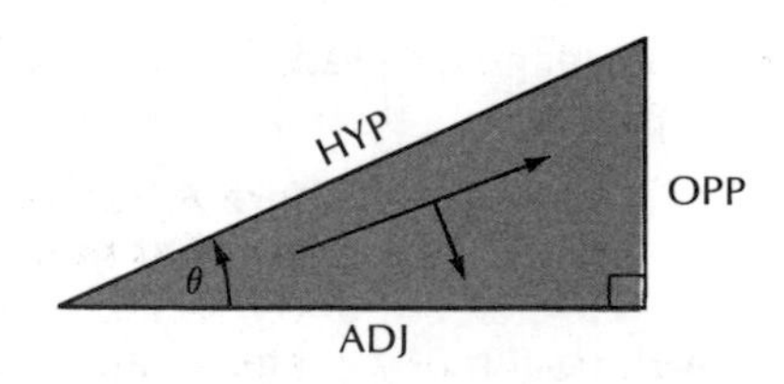

There are six **trigonometric functions** and their values are defined in terms of the lengths of the sides of a right-angled triangle. θ represents a given angle in a right-angled triangle.

Primary Functions	Reciprocal Functions
Sine $\sin\theta = \frac{\text{OPP}}{\text{HYP}}$	**Cosecant** $\csc\theta = \frac{\text{HYP}}{\text{OPP}}$
Cosine $\cos\theta = \frac{\text{ADJ}}{\text{HYP}}$	**Secant** $\sec\theta = \frac{\text{HYP}}{\text{ADJ}}$
Tangent $\tan\theta = \frac{\text{OPP}}{\text{ADJ}}$	**Cotangent** $\cot\theta = \frac{\text{ADJ}}{\text{OPP}}$

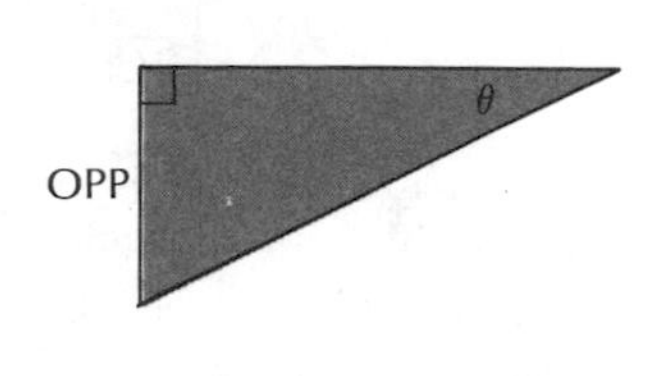

EXAMPLE 1: Find the value of the six trigonometric functions for each given right-angled triangle.

a.

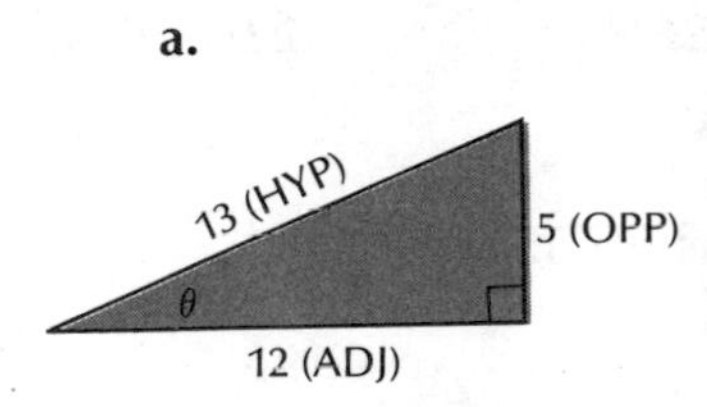

$\sin\theta = \frac{5}{13}$	$\csc\theta = \frac{13}{5}$
$\cos\theta = \frac{12}{13}$	$\sec\theta = \frac{13}{12}$
$\tan\theta = \frac{5}{12}$	$\cot\theta = \frac{12}{5}$

Notice the reciprocal pairs.

b.

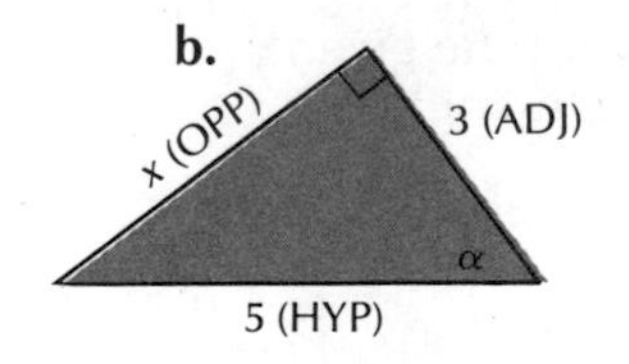

First, use the Pythagorean Theorem to find the value of x.

$5^2 = x^2 + 3^2$

$x^2 = 16$

$\therefore x = 4$

$\sin\alpha = \frac{4}{5}$; $\cos\alpha = \frac{3}{5}$; $\tan\alpha = \frac{4}{3}$

$\csc\alpha = \frac{5}{4}$; $\sec\alpha = \frac{5}{3}$; $\cot\alpha = \frac{3}{4}$

If the measure of an angle is known, then the value of the trigonometric functions can be found using a calculator.

EXAMPLE 2: Use a calculator to find the value of sin 57°, tan 57°, and csc 57°, correct to four decimal places.

Enter the given keystrokes to find each value.

[57] [sin] $\sin 57° \doteq 0.8387$

[57] [tan] $\tan 57° \doteq 1.5399$

[57] [sin] [$\frac{1}{x}$] $\csc 57° \doteq 1.1924$ $\csc 57° = \frac{1}{\sin 57°}$

If the value of a trigonometric function is known, then the measure of the corresponding angle can be found by using the inverse (INV) or second function (2nd Fn) key on a calculator.

EXAMPLE 3: **a.** If $\sin\theta = 0.6215$, find the measure of θ, correct to two decimal places.

Depending on your calculator, use one of the following series of keystrokes.

[0.6215] [2nd Fn] [sin] or [0.6215] [INV] [sin] or [0.6215] [ARC]

If $\sin\theta = 0.6215$, then $\theta \doteq 38.43°$.

b. If $\csc\theta = 1.8426$, find the measure of θ, correct to two decimal places.

[1.8426] [$\frac{1}{x}$] [INV] [sin] Recall that $\csc\theta = \frac{1}{\sin\theta}$.

$\therefore \theta \doteq 32.87°$

The values of the trigonometric functions depend only on the given acute angle θ of a right-angled triangle. Consider the right-angled triangles, as shown.

Notice that $\angle B = \angle Q = 90°$ and $\angle A = \angle P = \theta$.

For ΔABC, $\sin\theta = \frac{BC}{AC}$. For ΔPQR, $\sin\theta = \frac{QR}{PR}$.

Since the triangles are similar, $\frac{BC}{QR} = \frac{AC}{PR}$.

That is, $\frac{BC}{AC} = \frac{QR}{PR} = \sin\theta$.

Thus, $\sin\theta$ is independent of the size of the right-angled triangle, and depends only on the measure of the acute angle θ. Similar proofs establish that the same holds for $\cos\theta$ and $\tan\theta$.

EXERCISE 5-1

A 1. For the given triangle, find the value of all six trigonometric functions for θ and α. Express each answer as a fraction.

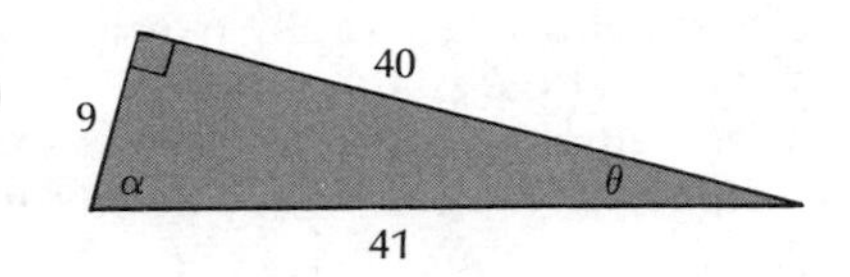

2. For each given triangle, first find the value of x. Then follow the instructions for exercise 1.

a.

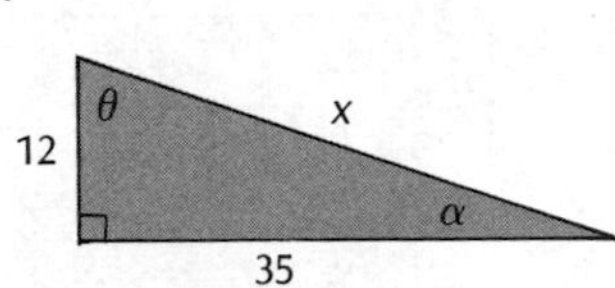

b.

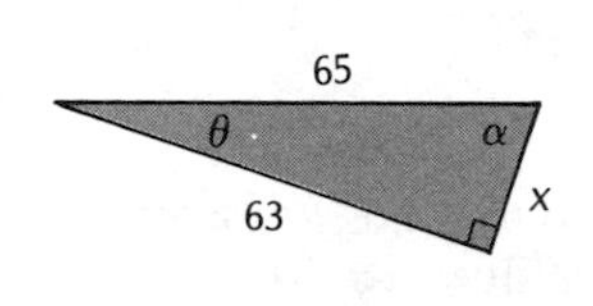

c.

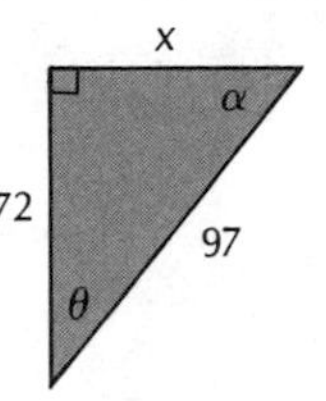

3. Name the three pairs of reciprocal trigonometric functions.

4. Use a calculator to evaluate each trigonometric function, correct to four decimal places.

a. $\sin 47°$	b. $\cos 63°$	c. $\tan 83°$	d. $\sec 28°$
e. $\csc 43.7°$	f. $\cot 28.3°$	g. $\tan 8.1°$	h. $\cos 4.83°$

5. Use a calculator to find the value of θ, correct to two decimal places. $(0° < \theta < 90°)$

a. $\sin \theta = 0.8276$	b. $\cos \theta = 0.4217$	c. $\tan \theta = 0.7364$	d. $\csc \theta = 1.0423$
e. $\sec \theta = 2.4163$	f. $\cot \theta = 1.0084$	g. $\sin \theta = \frac{3}{7}$	h. $\cos \theta = \frac{2}{3}$
i. $\tan \theta = \frac{5}{4}$	j. $\sec \theta = \frac{9}{7}$	k. $\csc \theta = \frac{11}{8}$	l. $\cot \theta = \frac{2}{5}$

B 6. If $\cos \theta = \frac{11}{61}$ and $0° < \theta < 90°$, find $\sin \theta$ and $\tan \theta$ *without* using a calculator. (Hint: sketch a right-angled triangle and use the Pythagorean Theorem.)

7. Without using a calculator, find the value of the "other" five trigonometric functions. $(0° < \theta < 90°)$

a. $\tan \theta = \frac{33}{56}$	b. $\sin \alpha = \frac{13}{85}$	c. $\cos \beta = \frac{5}{7}$

8. Given that $\cos \theta = 0.3187$, use a calculator to evaluate $\sin \theta$ and $\tan \theta$, correct to four decimal places. $(0° < \theta < 90°)$

9. Find the values of the "other" five trigonometric values, correct to four decimal places. $(0° < \theta < 90°)$

a. $\sin \theta = 0.8124$	b. $\cos \theta = 0.6291$	c. $\tan \theta = 1.0083$

C 10. Solve for θ, given that $0° < \theta < 90°$.

a. $\cos \theta = \frac{1}{2}$	b. $\tan \theta = \sqrt{3}$	c. $2 \cos \theta = \sqrt{3}$	d. $2 (\sin \theta)^2 = 1$
e. $\sqrt{3} \tan \theta = 1$	f. $3 \tan \theta = 4$	g. $4 \sin \theta = 3$	h. $5 \cos \theta = 2$

5-2 Trigonometric Identities

An *equation* is generally true for only some values of a variable. For example, the equation $2x + 3 = 7$ is true only if $x = 2$. An **identity** is true for *all* values of a variable. For example, $x^2 - 1 = (x - 1)(x + 1)$ is true for all values of x, and so it is an identity.

EXAMPLE 1: Determine if the given equation could be an identity.

a. $\sin \theta = \cos \theta$

Evaluate $\sin \theta$ and $\cos \theta$ for some values of θ.
Since $\sin \theta = \cos \theta$ is not true for all values of θ, it is not an identity.

θ	$\sin \theta$	$\cos \theta$
45°	0.7071	0.7071
60°	0.8660	0.5000
75°	0.9659	0.2588

b. $\cos \theta \tan \theta = \sin \theta$

The expression $\cos \theta \tan \theta$ represents the product of $\cos \theta$ with $\tan \theta$.
Try some values of θ in the equation.

θ	$\cos \theta$	$\tan \theta$	$\cos \theta \tan \theta$	$\sin \theta$
20°	0.9397	0.3640	0.3420	0.3420
45°	0.7071	1.0000	0.7071	0.7071
70°	0.3420	2.7475	0.9397	0.9397

It seems that $\cos \theta \tan \theta = \sin \theta$ could be an identity. However, a proof would be necessary to show that it is indeed an identity.

EXAMPLE 2: Use any right-angled triangle to prove that $\cos \theta \tan \theta = \sin \theta$ is an identity.

For ΔABC with sides a, b, and c, and angle θ,

$$\cos \theta = \frac{a}{b}, \tan \theta = \frac{c}{a}, \text{ and } \sin \theta = \frac{c}{b}.$$

Also, $\cos \theta \tan \theta = \left(\frac{a}{b}\right)\left(\frac{c}{a}\right) = \frac{c}{b}.$

$\therefore \cos \theta \tan \theta = \sin \theta$

Since this equation is true for any right-angled triangle, the equation is true for all values of θ, where $0° < \theta < 90°$.
Therefore, $\cos \theta \tan \theta = \sin \theta$ is an identity.

Notice that it is convention to label a triangle like the one given in Example 2. That is, label side a opposite $\angle A$, side b opposite $\angle B$, and side c opposite $\angle C$.

The following exercises will lead you to the discovery of several trigonometric identities.

EXERCISE 5-2

A 1. Use the given triangle to find each value.

a. $\sin\theta$, $\csc\theta$, and $\sin\theta\csc\theta$
b. $\cos\theta$, $\sec\theta$, and $\cos\theta\sec\theta$
c. $\tan\theta$, $\cot\theta$, and $\tan\theta\cot\theta$

2. **a.** Repeat exercise 1 using any right-angled $\triangle ABC$.

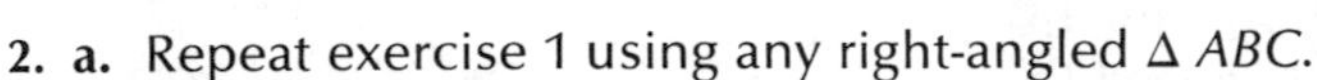

b. Complete each identity.

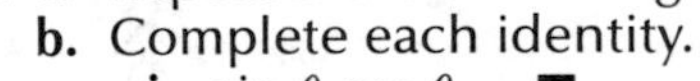

i. $\sin\theta\csc\theta = ■$
ii. $\cos\theta\sec\theta = ■$
iii. $\tan\theta\cot\theta = ■$

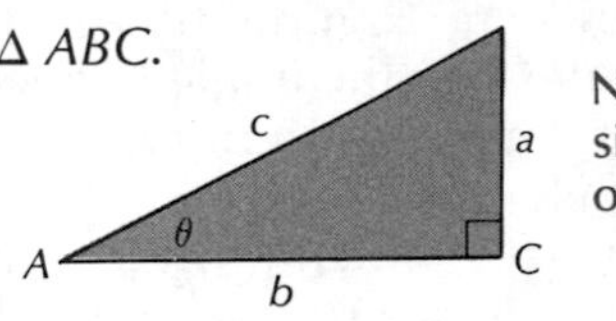

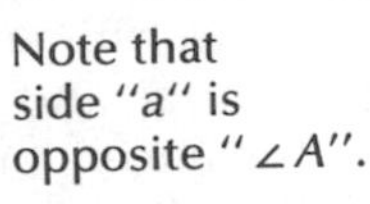

3. Use the given $\triangle RST$ to find each value.

a. $\dfrac{\sin\theta}{\cos\theta}$ **b.** $\tan\theta$ **c.** $\dfrac{\cos\theta}{\sin\theta}$ **d.** $\cot\theta$

4. Use the right-angled $\triangle ABC$ to find each value.

a. $\dfrac{\sin\theta}{\cos\theta}$ **b.** $\tan\theta$ **c.** $\dfrac{\cos\theta}{\sin\theta}$ **d.** $\cot\theta$

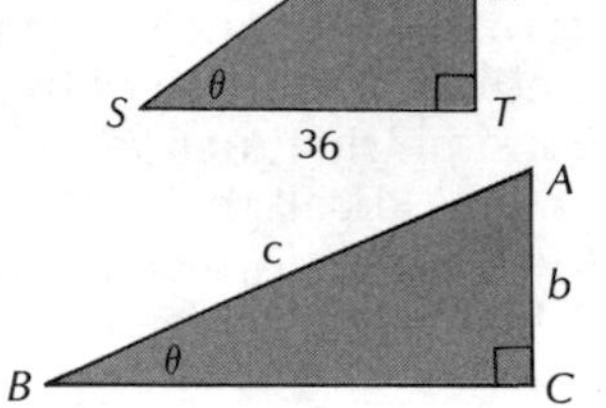

5. From the results of exercises 3 and 4, write $\tan\theta$ and $\cot\theta$ in terms of $\sin\theta$ and $\cos\theta$.

B 6. Use ΔABC to test and ΔPQR to prove that each equation is an identity. Note that a trigonometric value like $\sin^2\theta$ means $(\sin\theta)^2$.

a. $\sin^2\theta + \cos^2\theta = 1$
b. $\tan^2\theta + 1 = \sec^2\theta$
c. $\cot^2\theta + 1 = \csc^2\theta$

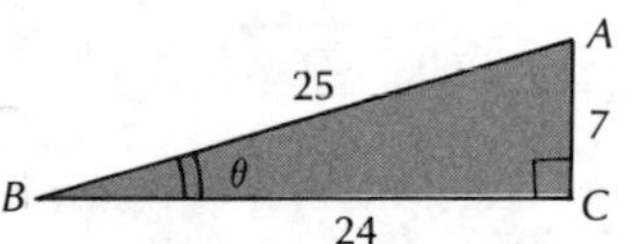

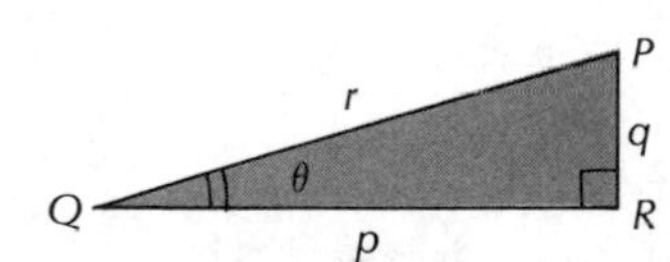

7. **a.** Copy and complete each table.

θ	$90° - \theta$	$\sin\theta$	$\cos(90° - \theta)$
10°	■	■	■
55°	■	■	■
63°	■	■	■
8.4°	■	■	■

θ	$90° - \theta$	$\cos\theta$	$\sin(90° - \theta)$
20°	■	■	■
35°	■	■	■
69°	■	■	■
12.8°	■	■	■

b. Write two identities that could possibly follow from part **a**.

C 8. Given that $\angle A = 45°$ and $\angle B = 30°$, use a calculator to determine which of the following are true.

a. $\sin(A + B) = \sin A\cos B + \cos A\sin B$
b. $\cos(2A) = \cos^2 A - \sin^2 A$
c. $\cos(A + B) = \cos A\cos B + \sin A\sin B$
d. $\sin(2A) = 2\sin A\cos A$
e. $\cos(A - B) = \cos A\cos B + \sin A\sin B$
f. $\tan(2B) = \dfrac{2\tan B}{1 - \tan^2 B}$
g. $\sin(A - B) = \cos A\sin B - \sin A\cos B$
h. $\tan\left(\dfrac{A}{2}\right) = \dfrac{\sin A}{1 + \cos A}$
i. $\sin(A + B) + \sin(A - B) = 2\sin A\cos B$
j. $\tan\left(\dfrac{A}{2}\right) = \dfrac{1 - \cos A}{\sin A}$
k. $\cos(A + B) - \cos(A - B) = 2\sin A\sin B$

5-3 Solving Right-Angled Triangles

Graham has been asked by his father to cut down a Ponderosa pine on their farm. It is standing 40 m from their home. Graham is concerned that when the tree is cut, it may hit the house. However, if he knows the height of the tree, then he can determine if it is safe to cut it down.

At a distance of 20 m from the base of the tree, Graham estimates that the angle between the horizontal and the line of sight to the top of the tree, or the **angle of elevation**, is 60°. He draws a sketch and notices that the tree, which grows vertically, represents one side of a right-angled triangle. Further, he knows the measure of one acute angle of the triangle and the length of the adjacent side. Determining the height of the tree, then, is the same as finding the length of the opposite side. A trigonometric function can be used to solve the problem. Recall that the value of the tangent function is the fraction formed by dividing the opposite side of a right-angled triangle by the adjacent side.

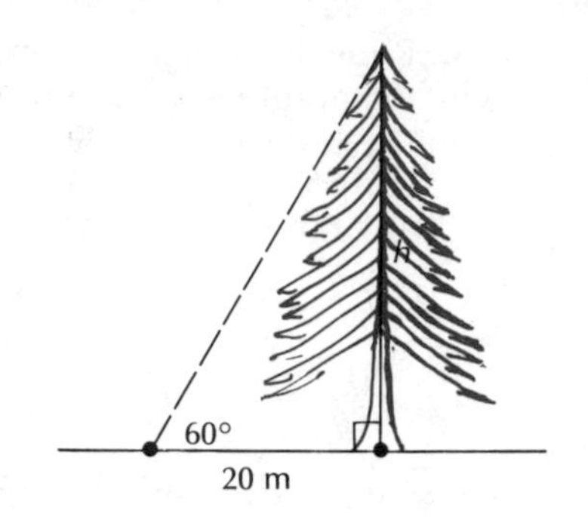

$$\tan\theta = \frac{\text{OPP}}{\text{ADJ}}$$

$$\tan 60° = \frac{h}{20}$$

h is the length of the opposite side, or the height of the tree.

$$h = 20 \tan 60°$$

$$\therefore h \doteq 35$$

Use these keystrokes on a calculator:

60 | tan | × | 20 | =

The height of the tree is about 35 m. Therefore, it will not hit the house if it is cut down.

When solving right-angled triangles, the first step is to determine which sides (opposite, adjacent, or hypotenuse) are given or required. This will help you decide which trigonometric function to use.

EXAMPLE 1: For each given triangle, find the value of x, correct to two decimal places.

a.

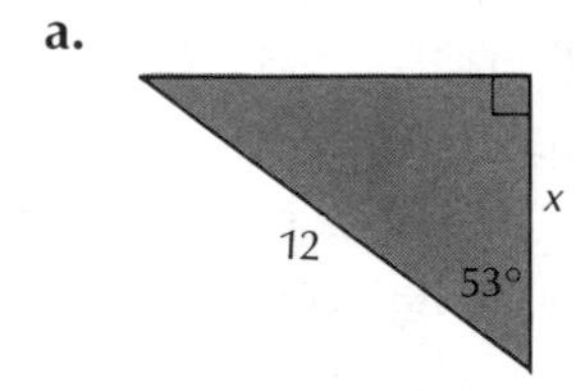

In addition to the right angle and the length of the hypotenuse, the measure of an acute angle is given. The length of the side adjacent to the acute angle is unknown. Therefore, use the cosine function.

$$\cos\theta = \frac{\text{ADJ}}{\text{HYP}}$$

$$\cos 53° = \frac{x}{12}$$

$$x = 12 \cos 53°$$

$$\therefore x \doteq 7.22$$

b.

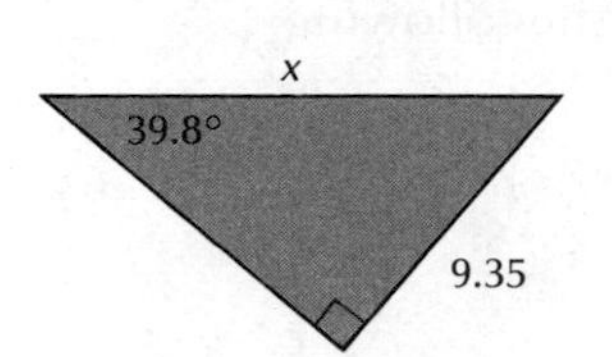

In addition to the right angle, the measure of an acute angle and the side opposite the acute angle are given. The length of the hypotenuse is unknown. Therefore, use the sine value.

$$\sin\theta = \frac{\text{OPP}}{\text{HYP}}$$

$$\sin 39.8^\circ = \frac{9.35}{x}$$

$$x \sin 39.8^\circ = 9.35$$

$$x = \frac{9.35}{\sin 39.8^\circ}$$

$$\therefore x \doteq 14.61$$

Use these keystrokes on a calculator:

[39.8] [sin] [1/x] [×] [9.35] [=]

EXAMPLE 2: For each given triangle, find the value of θ, correct to two decimal places.

a.

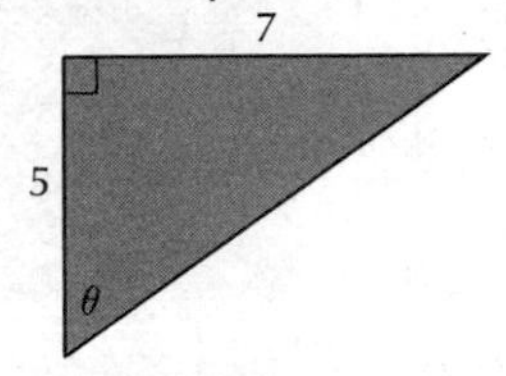

$\tan\theta = \frac{7}{5}$

$\tan\theta = 1.4$

$\therefore \theta \doteq 54.46^\circ$

b.

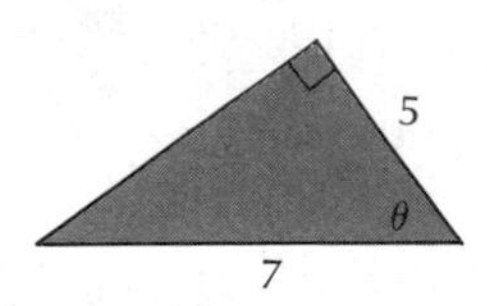

$\cos\theta = \frac{5}{7}$

$\cos\theta \doteq 0.7143$

$\therefore \theta \doteq 44.42^\circ$

EXAMPLE 3: For quadrilateral $ABCD$, $AD = 6.1$ cm, $DC = 7.3$ cm, $\angle DBC = 30^\circ$, and $\angle BAD = \angle BCD = 90^\circ$. Find the measure of $\angle ABD$, correct to two decimal places.

In ΔDBC, $\sin 30^\circ = \dfrac{7.3}{BD}$.

$$BD = \frac{7.3}{\sin 30^\circ}$$

$$BD \doteq 14.6$$

In ΔABD, $\sin\theta = \dfrac{AD}{BD}$.

$$\sin\theta = \frac{6.1}{14.6}$$

$$\sin\theta \doteq 0.4178$$

[0.4178] [INV] [sin] [=]

Therefore, $\angle ABD$, or θ, measures approximately 24.70°.

EXAMPLE 4: To calculate the height of a vertical cliff on the opposite side of a river, a surveyor makes the following measurements:

$CD = 23$ m, $\angle BDC = 90°$,
$\angle DCB = 38°$, and $\angle ADB = 47°$.

Find AB, the height of the cliff.

First find BD, the distance across the river.
In ΔBCD,

$$\tan 38° = \frac{BD}{CD}.$$
$$\tan 38° = \frac{BD}{23}$$
$$BD = 23 \tan 38°$$
$$\therefore BD \doteq 17.97$$

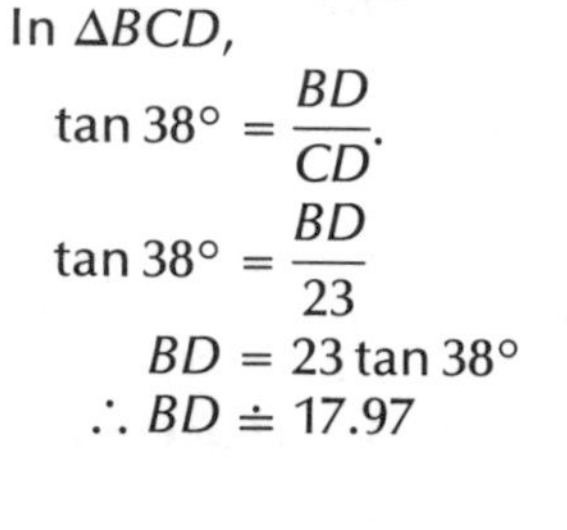

In ΔABD,

$$\tan 47° = \frac{AB}{BD}$$
$$\tan 47° = \frac{AB}{17.97}$$
$$AB = 17.97 \tan 47°$$
$$\therefore AB \doteq 19.27$$

The height of the cliff is about 19 m.

EXERCISE 5-3

Give all answers correct to two decimal places .

A 1. Find the value of x for each triangle.

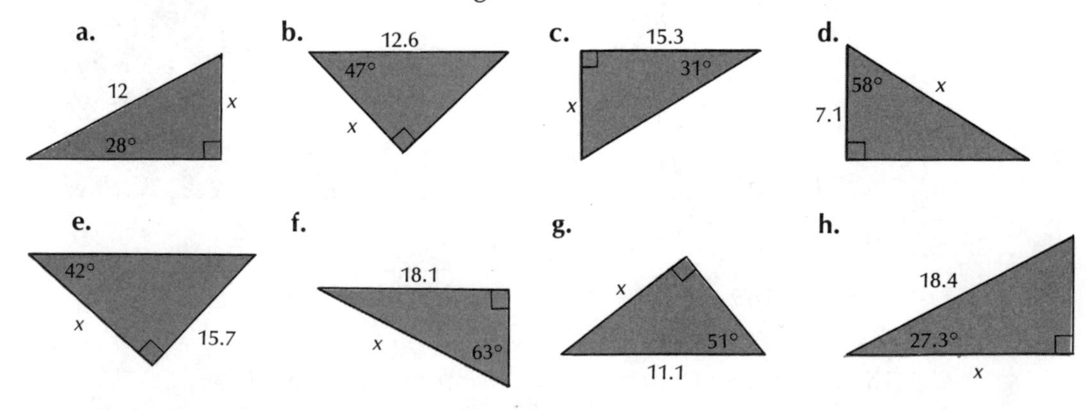

B 2. Find the value of θ for each triangle.

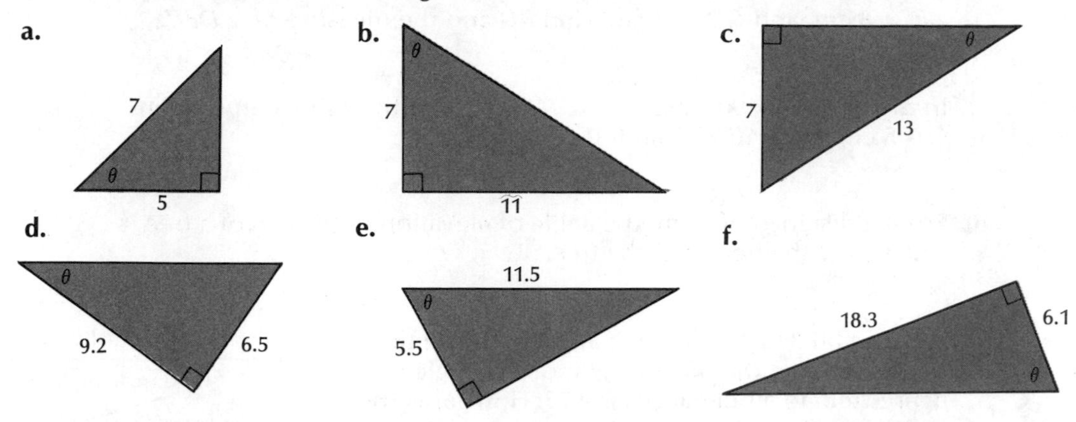

For exercises 3-6, recall the convention for labelling sides of a triangle .

3. In ΔABC, $\angle B = 90°$, $\angle A = 27.6°$, and $a = 12.7$. Find the length of side b.

4. In ΔPQR, $\angle P = 90°$, $p = 7.82$, and $q = 4.68$. Find the measure of $\angle PRQ$.

5. In ΔLMN, $\angle N = 90°$, $\angle M = 21.8°$, and $l = 19.13$. Find the length of side m.

6. In ΔDEF, $\angle E = 90°$, $d = 6.13$, and $f = 8.87$. Find the measure of $\angle DFE$.

7. Find the value of each variable.

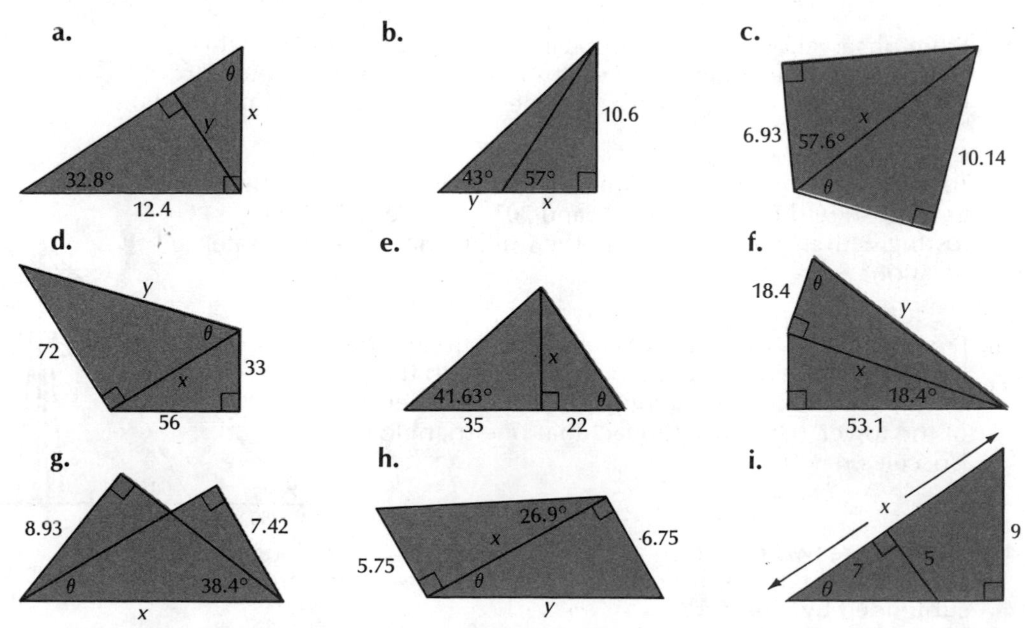

8. In quadrilateral $ABCD$, $\angle ABD = 90°$, $\angle BCD = 90°$, $\angle ADB = 37°$, $AB = 8$ cm, and $CD = 7$ cm. Find BD and the measure of $\angle DBC$.

9. In ΔABC, $\angle C = 90°$ and $\angle A = 71°$. The length of the altitude from C is 5 cm. Find AB, BC, and AC.

10. From a distance of 23 m, the angle of elevation to the top of a tree is 36.6°. Find the height of the tree.

11. From a cliff 34.2 m high, the angle between the horizontal and the line of sight, or the **angle of depression**, to a boat at sea is 4.7°. How far is the boat from the base of the cliff?

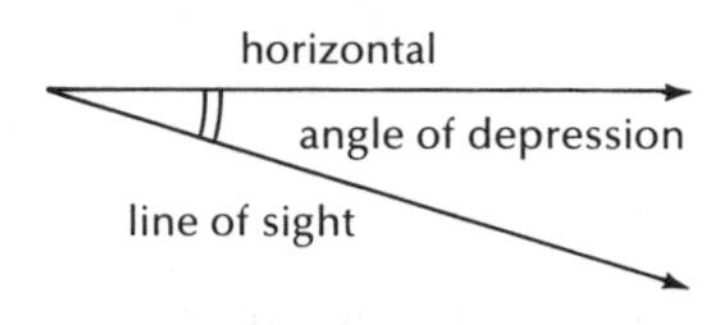

12. Two buildings are 38.2 m apart . From the top of the shorter building, the angle of elevation to the top of the taller building is 23.8°. The angle of depression to the base of the taller building is 41.4°. Find the height of each building.

13. A house has a width of 11.80 m. The roof forms an angle of 14° with the horizontal. The roof overhang is 0.60 m, as shown. Find the length of the rafters.

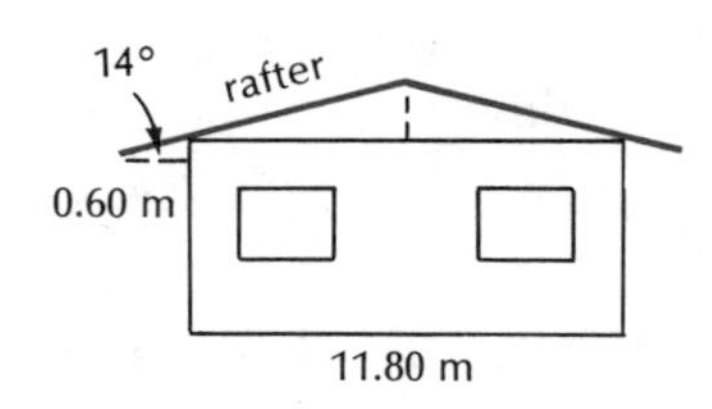

14. From observation points on opposite sides of a mountain that is 1482 m high, the angles of elevation to its peak are 48.1° and 37.6°. Find the length of a tunnel that connects the two observation points.

15. To be in a safe position, the angle θ that a ladder forms with the ground should be between 60° and 70°. A ladder 8.0 m long is resting with its base 2.6 m from the wall. Is the ladder in a safe position?

16. From a point A, the angle of elevation to the top of a tower is 45°. From a point B, 80 m closer to the tower, the angle of elevation is 60°. Find the height of the tower. (Hint: use the fact that one triangle is isosceles.)

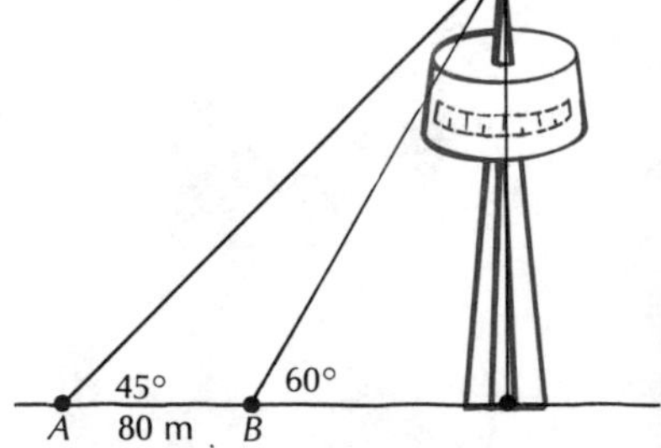

17. A and B are two points on a circle. Chord $\overline{AB}$ is 5.7 cm long and the radius of the circle is 6.1 cm. Find the measure of the central angle subtended by chord $\overline{AB}$.

18. A 32 m guy wire attached to the top of a tower is anchored 12 m from the base of the tower. A second guy wire from the centre of the tower is attached to the same anchor.

  a. How long is the second guy wire?
  b. What is the measure of the angle formed between the two wires?

C 19. A large box has a height of 108 cm and a bottom that measures 27 cm × 36 cm.

  a. Find the length of the longest rod that will just fit inside the box.
  b. Determine the measure of the angle the rod forms with the bottom of the box.

20. a. From a point 47 m north of a tower, the angle of elevation is 62°. Find the height of the tower.
  b. From a point due west of the same tower given in part **a**, the angle of elevation is 72°. How far is the point from the tower?
  c. Find the distance between the two observation points in parts **a** and **b**.
  d. What is the measure of the angle of elevation to the top of the tower from a point 53 m southeast of the tower?

21. From point A, 55 m south of a tower, the angle of elevation measures 67°. Find the height of the tower.

EXTRA

Area and Perimeter of Right-Angled Triangles

It is possible to find the area and perimeter of a right-angled triangle in terms of the hypotenuse, c, and the measure of one acute angle, $\angle A$.

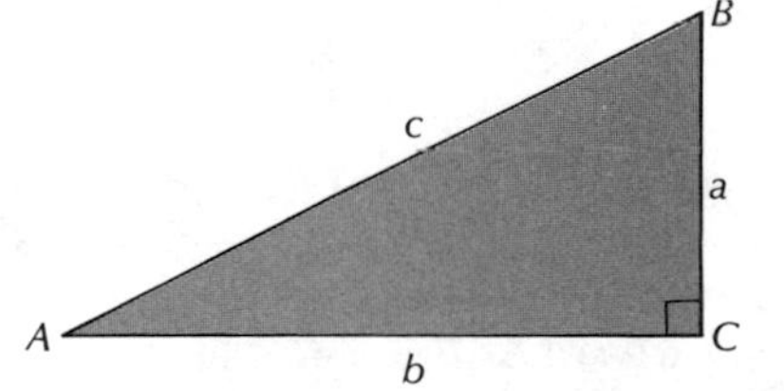

$\sin A = \frac{a}{c}$ or $a = c \sin A$

$\cos A = \frac{b}{c}$ or $b = c \cos A$

If the area of the triangle is K and the perimeter is P, then the following can be derived.

$K = \frac{1}{2}ab$ $\qquad$ $P = c + a + b$

$K = \frac{1}{2}(c \sin A)(c \cos A)$ $\qquad$ $P = c + c \sin A + c \cos A$ $\qquad$ Substitute known values.

$K = \frac{1}{2}c^2 \sin A \cos A$ $\qquad$ $P = c(1 + \sin A + \cos A)$

Find the area and perimeter of each triangle.

a.

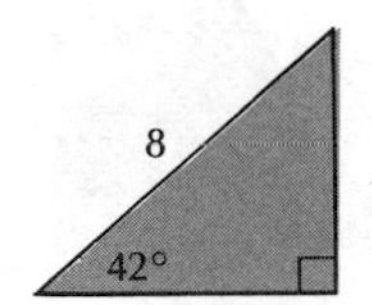

b.

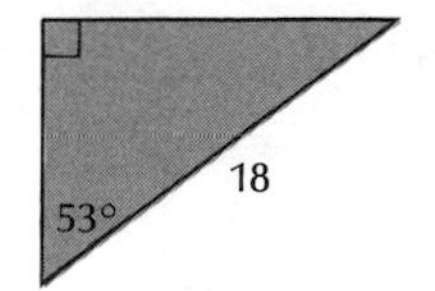

c.

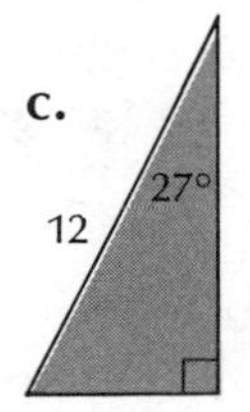

d.

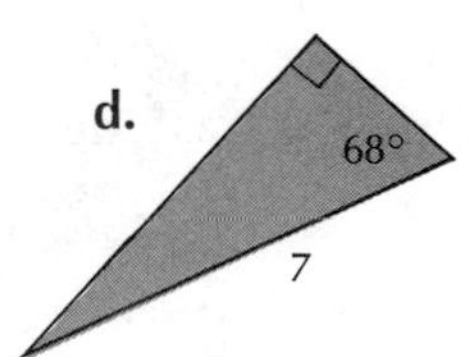

5-4 Finding the Area of a Polygon

Two roads intersect at an angle that measures 75°. A lot at the intersection has a frontage of 180 m on one road and 150 m on the other, as shown in the diagram at the right. The area of this triangular lot can be calculated if the length of one side of the triangle and the length of the altitude to it are known. The length of altitude H can be found using trigonometry.

In ΔPQS, $\sin 75° = \frac{H}{150}$.

$\therefore H = 150 \sin 75°$

$\therefore$ Area of $\Delta PQR = \frac{1}{2}$(base)(height)

$= \frac{1}{2}(180)(150 \sin 75°)$

$\doteq 13\ 040$

The area of the lot is approximately 13 040 m^2.

A formula for finding the area of a triangle can be determined using trigonometry. Consider ΔABC with altitude $\overline{BD}$, as shown. Notice that ΔADB is a right-angled triangle.

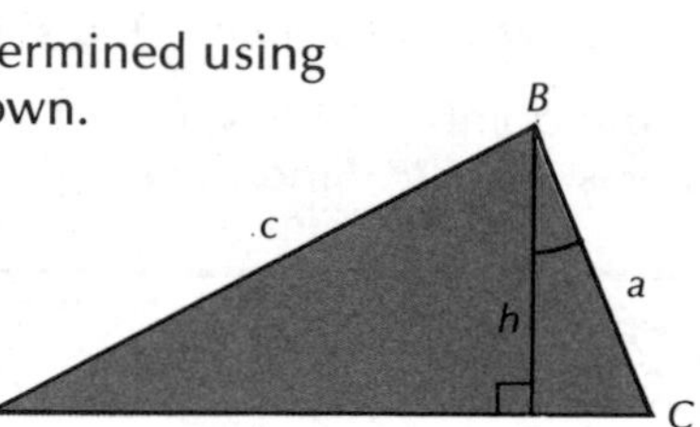

$\sin A = \frac{h}{c}$

$\therefore h = c \sin A$

Area of $\Delta ABC = \frac{1}{2}bh$

$= \frac{1}{2}(b)(c \sin A)$

b is the base.
h is the height.
$h = c \sin A$

From this, a general formula is obtained for finding the area of any ΔABC.

Area of $\Delta ABC = \frac{1}{2}bc \sin A$ $= \frac{1}{2}ac \sin B$ $= \frac{1}{2}ab \sin C$	In general, the area of any ΔABC is one half the product of any two sides, multiplied by the sine of the angle between them.

EXAMPLE 1: Find the area of ΔPQR, given that $p = 7.6$ cm, $q = 8.3$ cm, and $\angle R = 67.3°$.

Use the general formula for the area of a triangle, Area $= \frac{1}{2}ab \sin C$, where p and q are the known sides and $\angle R$ is the known angle.

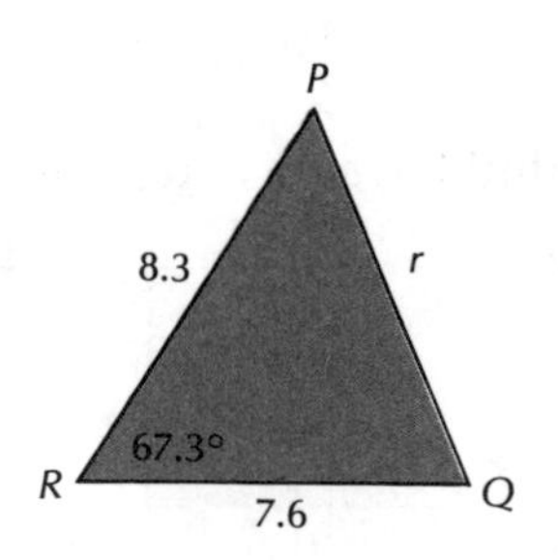

Area of $\Delta PQR = \frac{1}{2}(8.3)(7.6) \sin 67.3°$

$\doteq 29.10$

The area of ΔPQR is approximately 29.10 cm^2.

EXAMPLE 2: A regular pentagon is inscribed in a circle with radius 11.8 cm. Find the area of the pentagon.

If each vertex is joined to the centre of the circle, there will be five congruent triangles, each having a central angle that measures $\frac{360°}{5}$, or 72°.

First, determine the area of the shaded triangle.

$$\text{Area of triangle} = \frac{1}{2}(11.8)(11.8)\sin 72°$$

Then notice that the area of the pentagon is five times the area of the shaded triangle.

$$\begin{aligned}\text{Area of pentagon} &= 5\left[\tfrac{1}{2}(11.8)(11.8)\sin 72°\right] \\ &\doteq 331\end{aligned}$$

The area of the pentagon is approximately 331 cm^2.

A similar method can be used to find the area of a regular polygon with n sides, for $n > 4$, that is inscribed in a circle with radius r. In such a polygon, there are n triangles, each having an area represented by $\frac{1}{2}r^2 \sin\left(\frac{360°}{n}\right)$, where $n > 4$.

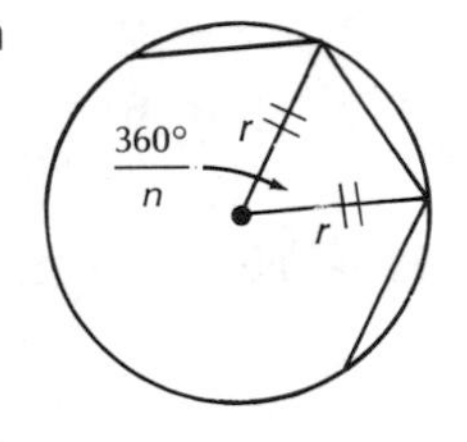

Therefore, the area of a regular polygon is given by the following formula.

> The area of a regular n-sided polygon that is inscribed in a circle with radius r is given by the formula
> Area $= \frac{1}{2}nr^2 \sin\left(\frac{360°}{n}\right)$, where $n > 4$.

EXAMPLE 3: A regular octagon having area 240 cm^2 is inscribed in a circle.
Find the length of the radius of the circle.

$$\begin{aligned}\text{Area of polygon} &= \frac{1}{2}nr^2\sin\left(\frac{360°}{n}\right) \\ 240 &= \frac{1}{2}(8)(r^2)\sin 45° \qquad \frac{360°}{8} = 45° \\ r^2 &= \frac{60}{\sin 45°} \\ r &\doteq 9.21\end{aligned}$$

The length of the radius of the circle is about 9.21 cm.

EXERCISE 5-4

Give all answers correct to two decimal places.

A 1. Find the area of each triangle.

a. 7.1 cm, 35.7°, 6.4 cm

b. 8.3 cm, 74°

c. 4.1 cm, 81°, 7.3 cm

2. Each polygon is inscribed in a circle with the given radius. Find the area of each regular inscribed polygon.

a.

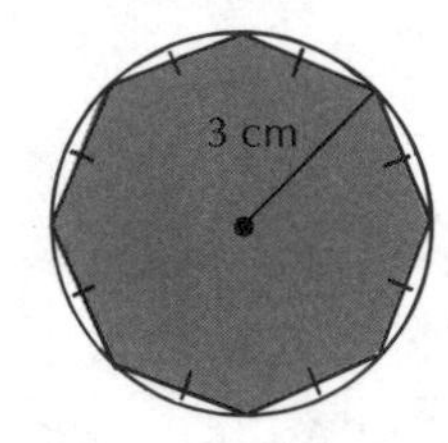

b.

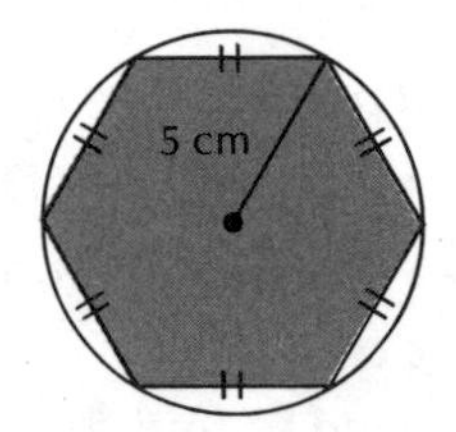

3. Find the area of a regular dodecagon (a 12-sided polygon) that is inscribed in a circle with radius 7 cm.

4. Find the area of each figure. (All lengths are given in centimetres.)

a.

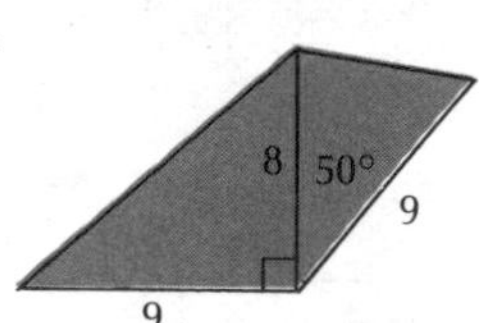

b.

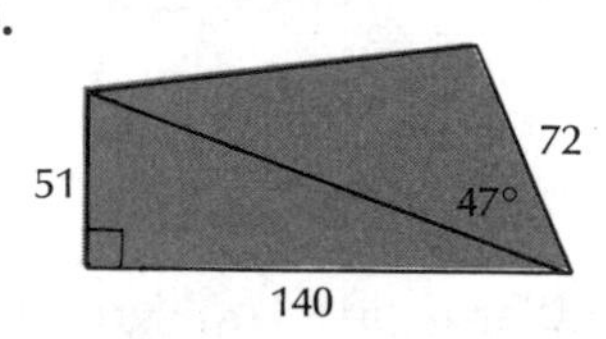

B 5. Find the area of each shaded region. (All lengths are given in centimetres.)

a.

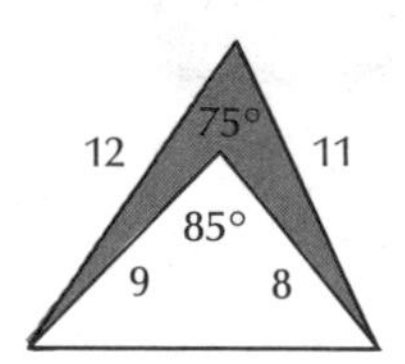

b.

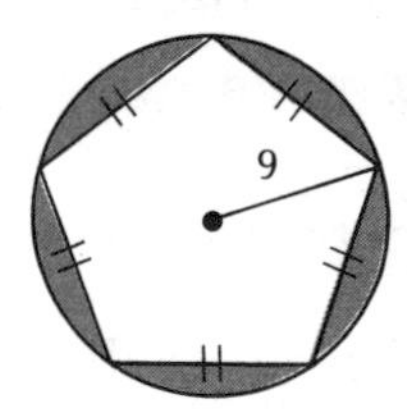

6. The area of a regular inscribed decagon is 150 cm^2. Find the radius of the circle.

7. The sides of a regular hexagon each measure 5.6 cm. Find the area of the hexagon.

8. **a.** Each side of a regular pentagon measures 5.6 cm. Find the area of the pentagon.
   b. If the pentagon in part **a** were inscribed in a circle, what would be the radius of the circle?

C 9. Each side of a hexagonal nut measures 11 mm. The hole in the middle of the nut has a diameter of 11 mm. Find the surface area of the top of the nut.

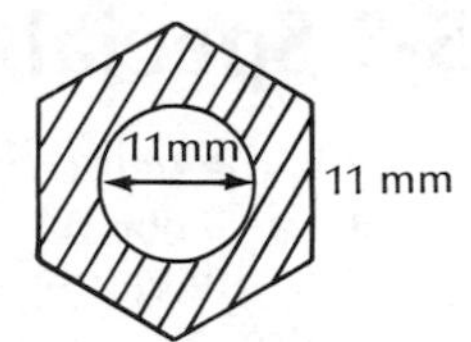

10. A hexagonal nut has a top with surface area 296 mm^2. If the hole in the middle has a diameter of 10 mm, find the length of a side of the nut.

11. A five storey building is to be constructed in the shape of a regular pentagon with an inner courtyard that is also in the shape of a regular pentagon. The exterior walls are to be 80 m long and the interior walls are to be 30 m long. Find the total floor area of the building.

80 m

30 m

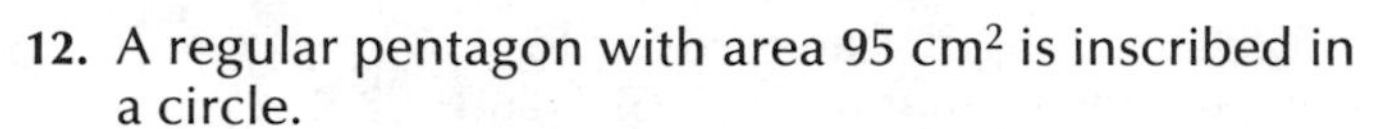

12. A regular pentagon with area 95 cm^2 is inscribed in a circle.

    a. Find the radius of the circle.
    b. Find the length of one side of the pentagon.

13. Quadrilateral $ABCD$ is inscribed in a circle with radius 5 cm, $\overline{BC}$ is a diameter of the circle, $DC = 6$ cm, and $AB = AD$. Find the area of quadrilateral $ABCD$.

Biography

Mary Fairfax Somerville (1780–1872)

Mary Fairfax Somerville grew up in the idyllic countryside of Scotland, which provided the perfect setting for a lonely young child who loved the country and the outdoors. Much of her youth was spent doing domestic chores and reading, although she did not readily take to academic subjects. In fact, her career in mathematics was sparked by an unusual incident.

While browsing through a magazine at a tea party, Somerville noticed some algebraic symbols that she did not understand. Curiosity and determination helped her obtain a copy of Euclid's *Elements* and, with little formal training, she began her exploration of mathematics.

In 1812, Somerville married a well-known surgeon who supported her continued interests in mathematics and astronomy. Her early work with trigonometry and conic sections laid the foundation for numerous contributions to astronomy. Somerville became known for her lectures on planetary and stellar motion, focussing on the work of the great French mathematician Laplace, who helped shape the field of mathematical analysis.

5-5 Special Triangles

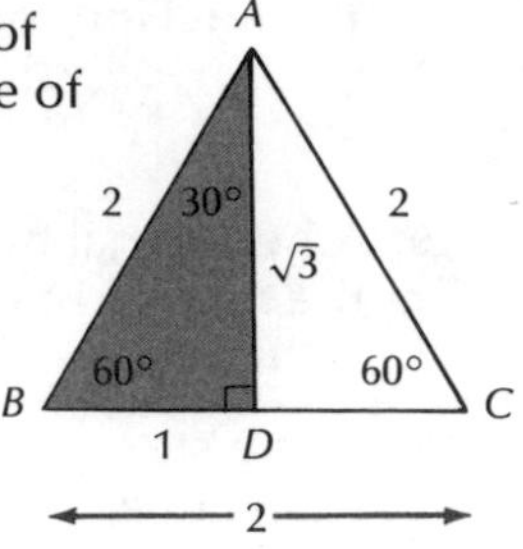

What is the value of sin 60°? A calculator will likely show the value of sin 60° as 0.866 025 4. However, this is an *approximation* of the value of sin 60°. The value of sin 60° can be determined without using a calculator.

Consider ΔABC, shown at the right. The triangle is equilateral with each side measuring 2 units. If $\angle BAC$ is bisected by $\overline{AD}$, then ΔABD is a **30°-60°-90° triangle** with $BD = 1$. The Pythagorean Theorem can be used to find the length of $\overline{AD}$.

$$AB^2 = BD^2 + AD^2$$
$$4 = 1 + AD^2$$
$$\therefore AD = \sqrt{3}$$

This 30°-60°-90° triangle with the indicated lengths can be used to evaluate the trigonometric functions for angles that measure 30° and 60°.

In general, the values are written as a fraction, in the form $\frac{a}{b}$, where $a, b \in \mathbf{R}$.

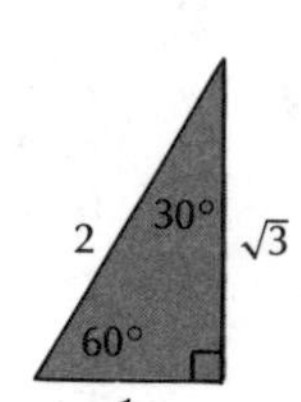

EXAMPLE 1: Use a 30°-60°-90° triangle to find each value, and write each value as a fraction.

a. $\sin 60° = \frac{\sqrt{3}}{2}$

b. $\tan 30° = \frac{1}{\sqrt{3}} = \frac{\sqrt{3}}{3}$

c. $\sin 30° + \tan 60° = \frac{1}{2} + \frac{\sqrt{3}}{1} = \frac{1 + 2\sqrt{3}}{2}$

EXAMPLE 2: For the given triangle, find the value of x, expressed as a fraction.

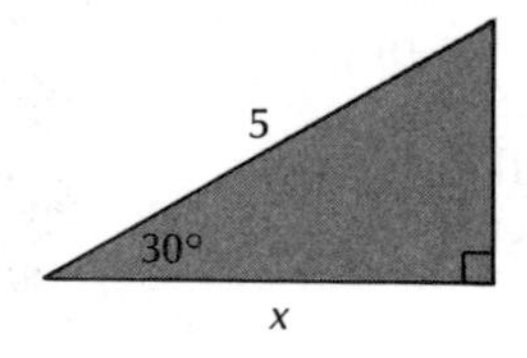

$$\cos 30° = \frac{x}{5}$$ Use the 30°-60°-90° triangle.

$$\frac{x}{5} = \frac{\sqrt{3}}{2}$$
$$x = \frac{5\sqrt{3}}{2}$$

Consider ΔPQR, as shown. ΔPQR is an isosceles right-angled triangle with $\angle P$ and $\angle Q$ each measuring 45° and its equal sides each measuring 1 unit.

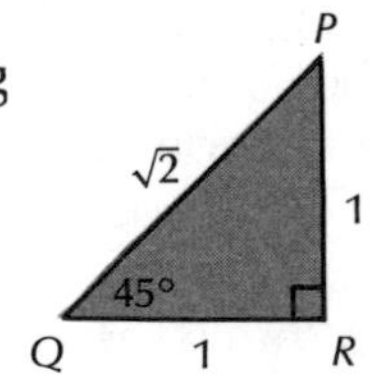

$$PQ^2 = QR^2 + PR^2$$
$$PQ^2 = 1^2 + 1^2$$
$$\therefore PQ = \sqrt{2}$$

This **45°-45°-90° triangle**, with the indicated lengths, can be used to find the values of the trigonometric functions for 45°. The values are written as a fraction, in the form $\frac{a}{b}$, where $a, b \in \mathbf{R}$.

EXAMPLE 3: Find each value, expressed as a fraction.

a. $\cos 45° = \frac{1}{\sqrt{2}} = \frac{\sqrt{2}}{2}$

b. $\cos^2 45° = (\cos 45°)^2 = \left(\frac{1}{\sqrt{2}}\right)^2 = \frac{1}{2}$

c. $\sin 45° \sin 60° = \left(\frac{1}{\sqrt{2}}\right)\left(\frac{\sqrt{3}}{2}\right) = \frac{\sqrt{6}}{4}$

EXAMPLE 4: For the given triangle, find the value of x, expressed as a fraction.

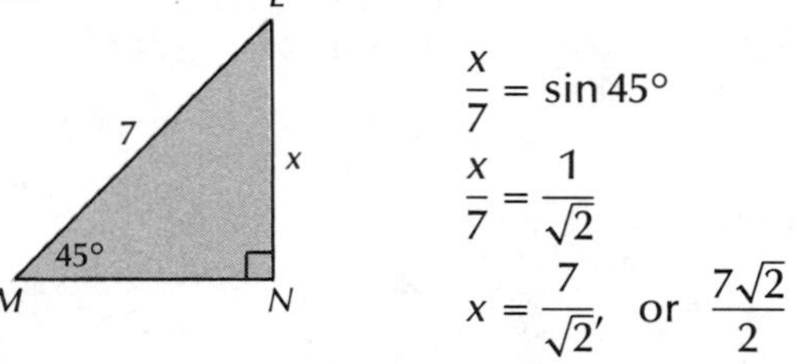

$$\frac{x}{7} = \sin 45°$$

$$\frac{x}{7} = \frac{1}{\sqrt{2}}$$

$$x = \frac{7}{\sqrt{2}}, \text{ or } \frac{7\sqrt{2}}{2}$$

SUMMARY

$\sin 60° = \frac{\sqrt{3}}{2}$ $\quad \sin 30° = \frac{1}{2}$ $\quad \sin 45° = \frac{1}{\sqrt{2}}$, or $\frac{\sqrt{2}}{2}$

$\cos 60° = \frac{1}{2}$ $\quad \cos 30° = \frac{\sqrt{3}}{2}$ $\quad \cos 45° = \frac{1}{\sqrt{2}}$, or $\frac{\sqrt{2}}{2}$

$\tan 60° = \sqrt{3}$ $\quad \tan 30° = \frac{1}{\sqrt{3}}$, or $\frac{\sqrt{3}}{3}$ $\quad \tan 45° = 1$

EXERCISE 5-5

Express each answer as a fraction.

A **1.** Find each value.

a. $\cos 30°$ **b.** $\tan 30°$ **c.** $\csc 45°$ **d.** $\sin 60°$
e. $\sec 30°$ **f.** $\cot 30°$ **g.** $\sin 45°$ **h.** $\tan 45°$

2. Find the value of θ, where $0° < \theta < 90°$.

a. $\sin \theta = \frac{1}{2}$ **b.** $\cos \theta = \frac{1}{\sqrt{2}}$ **c.** $\tan \theta = \frac{\sqrt{3}}{3}$

d. $\cos \theta = \frac{\sqrt{3}}{2}$ **e.** $\sec \theta = 2$ **f.** $\cot \theta = 1$

3. For each triangle, find the value of x.

a.

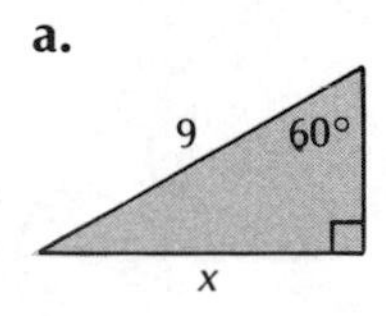

b.

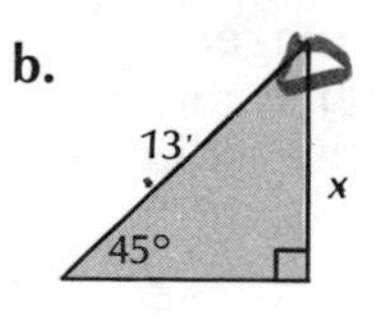

c.

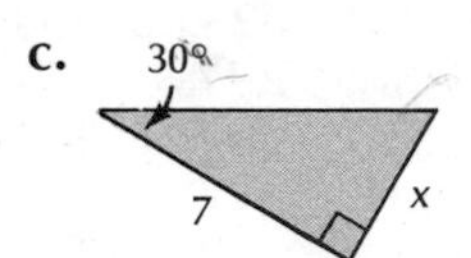

B d.

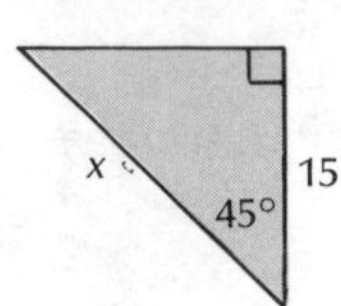

e.

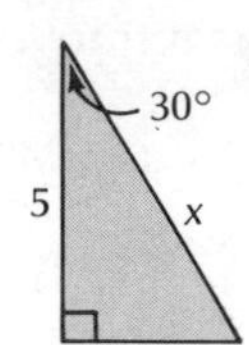

f.

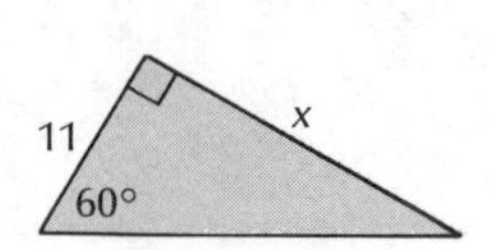

4. Evaluate each expression.

a. $\tan 60° \cos 45°$
b. $\cos 30° + \tan 60°$
c. $\sin^2 60°$
d. $\tan 45° - \tan 30°$
e. $\sec 60° \sec 45°$
f. $\sin^2 30° + \sin^2 60°$
g. $\sin^2 45° + \cos^2 45°$
h. $\sin 30° + \sin 60° + \sin 45°$
i. $\dfrac{\tan 30°}{\cos 45°}$
j. $\cos 30° + \cos 60° + \cos 45°$

5. For each triangle, find the value of x.

a.

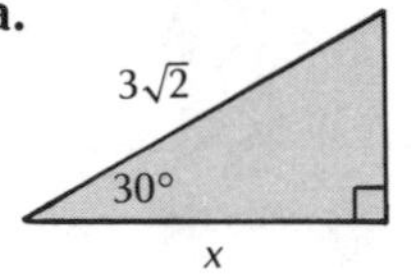

b.

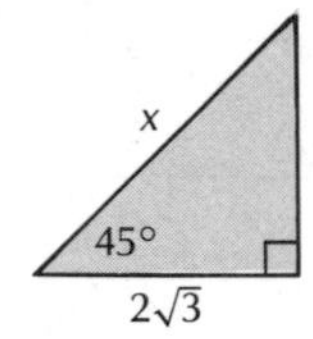

c.

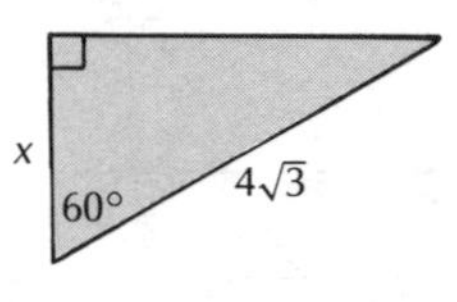

d.

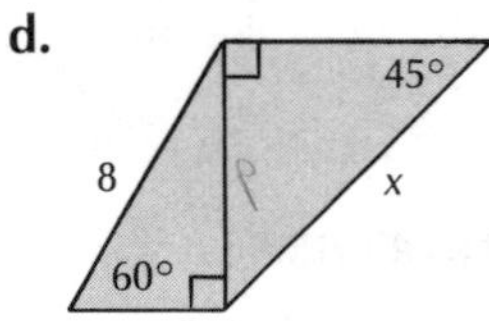

e.

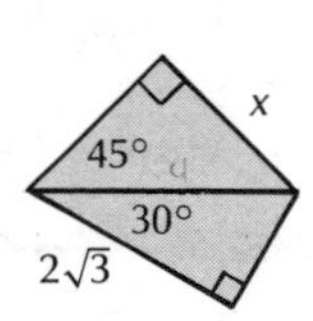

f.

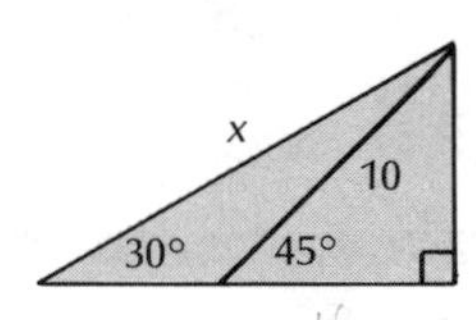

g.

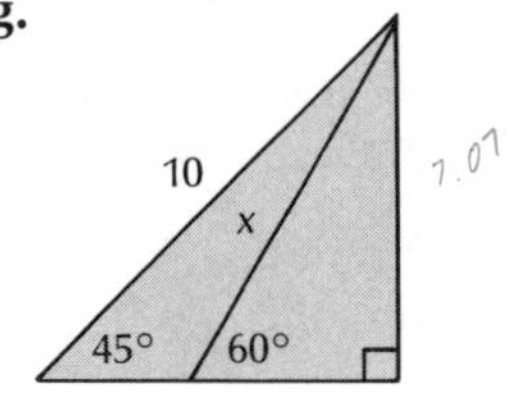

h.

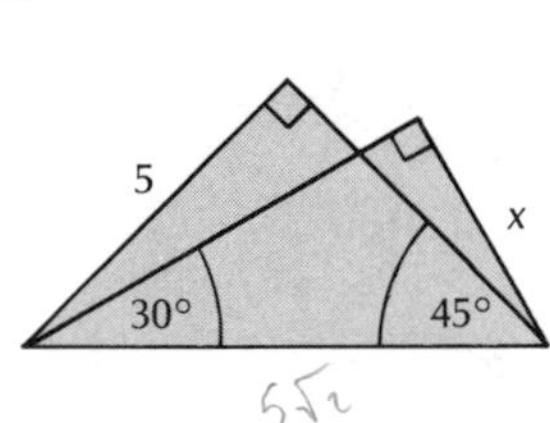

i.

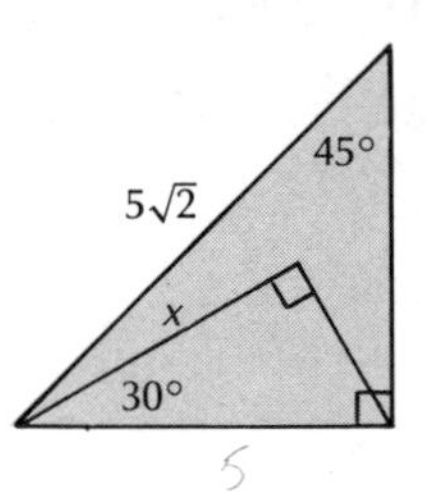

6. Find the area of a regular hexagon that is inscribed in a circle with radius 6 cm.

7. Find the area of a regular octagon that is inscribed in a circle with radius 7 cm.

C 8. A and B are the centres of two circles, as shown at the right, and $AB = 12$ cm. $\overline{PQ}$ is drawn tangent to both circles so that $\angle PAB = 45°$. Given that the radius of the larger circle is 10 cm, find the radius of the smaller circle.

Review

1. For the given triangle, find each value, expressed as a fraction.

   a. $\sin \alpha$ b. $\tan \theta$ c. $\cos \theta$
   d. $\sec \alpha$ e. $\cot \theta$ f. $\csc \alpha$

2. Given each trigonometric value, find the value of θ, where $0° < \theta < 90°$.

   a. $\cos \theta = 0.8765$ b. $\csc \theta = \frac{7}{5}$

3. Given that $\tan \theta = \frac{3}{2}$, where $0° < \theta < 90°$, find the value of $\sin \theta$ and $\cos \theta$, expressed as a fraction.

4. Given that $\sin \theta = 0.1864$, where $0° < \theta < 90°$, find the value of $\cos \theta$ and $\tan \theta$, correct to four decimal places.

5. Find the value of each unknown, correct to two decimal places.

   a.

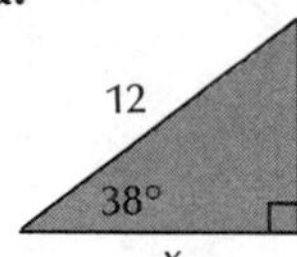

   b.

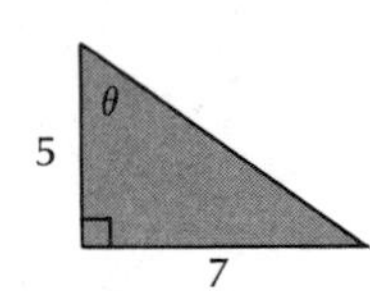

   c.

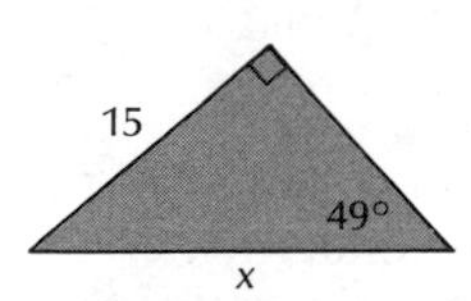

   d.

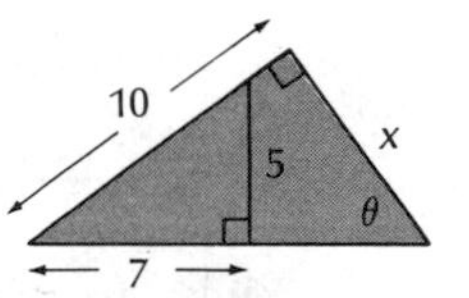

6. In ΔABC, $\angle A = 47.6°$, $BC = 7.68$ cm, and $\angle C = 90°$. Find AC.

7. In quadrilateral $PQRS$, $\angle PQS = 90°$, $\angle QSR = 90°$, $PQ = 8.11$ cm, $\angle PSQ = 31.8°$, and $SR = 4.19$ cm. Find QS and the size of $\angle SQR$.

8. From a point 60 m from the base of a building, the angle of elevation to the top of the building is 48°. From the same point, the angle of elevation to the top of a flagpole on the near side of the building is 51°. Find the height of the flagpole.

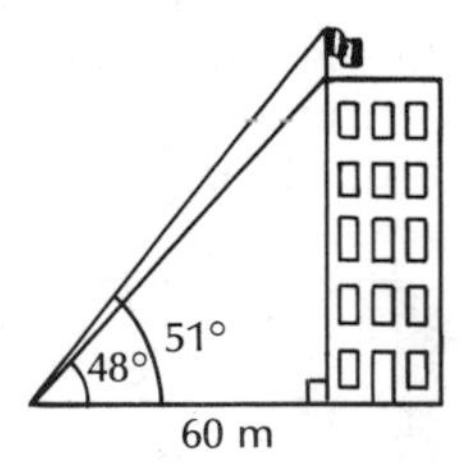

9. Find the area of each polygon, correct to two decimal places.

   a.

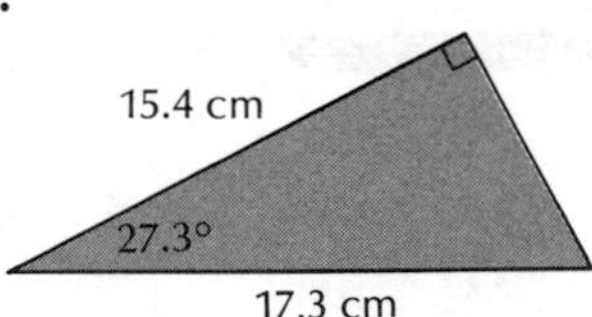

   b.

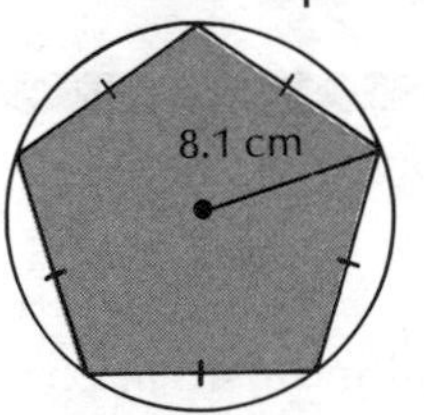

10. A regular dodecagon with area 140 cm^2 is inscribed in a circle. Find the radius of the circle.

11. Find each value, expressed as a fraction.

    a. $\sin 60° \tan 60°$ b. $\dfrac{\sin 30°}{\cos 30°}$ c. $\cos 30° - \sin 45°$

5-6 Angles in Standard Position

The trigonometry discussed in previous lessons has been limited to right-angled triangles and angles that measure less than 90°. An alternate way of defining the trigonometric functions is needed for more general cases, particularly situations involving obtuse angles.

For each set of axes at the right, the angle θ was generated by rotating the **initial ray**, on the positive x-axis, about the origin to the **terminal ray**. Rotating the initial ray counterclockwise results in a positive angle, whereas rotating the initial ray clockwise results in a negative angle. Each angle is in **standard position** since the vertex is at the origin and the initial ray lies on the positive x-axis.

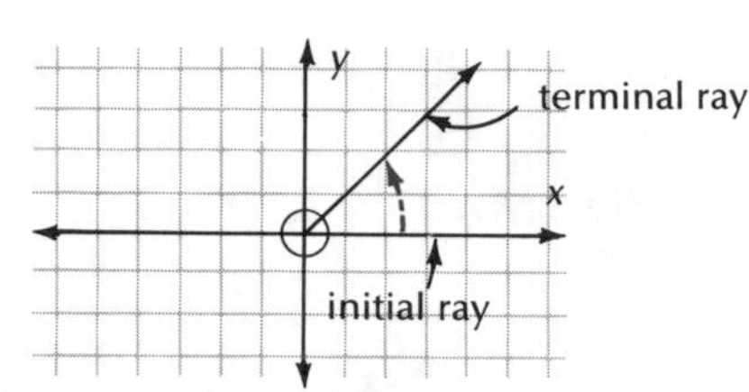

In the diagram at the right, the angle θ has been generated by rotating the terminal ray $\overline{OP}$ counterclockwise from the positive x-axis through the point $P(x, y)$. Notice that r is the radius of the circle formed by rotating the initial ray. The values of the trigonometric functions can now be defined in terms of the coordinates of $P(x, y)$ and the length of the terminal ray $\overline{OP}$. These values are given below. Note that $r > 0$.

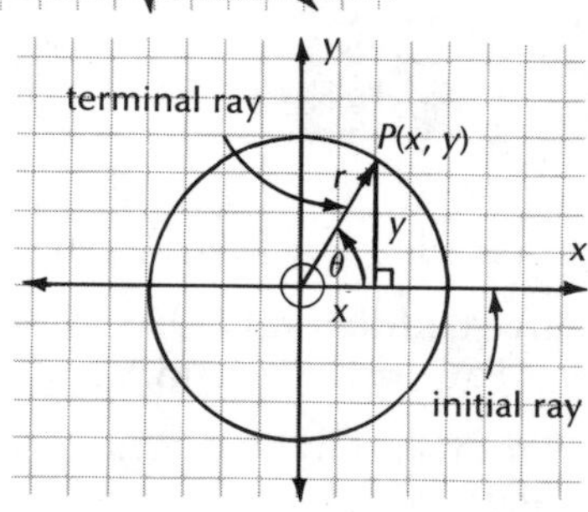

$\sin\theta = \dfrac{y}{r}$ $\cos\theta = \dfrac{x}{r}$ $\tan\theta = \dfrac{y}{x}$

$\csc\theta = \dfrac{r}{y}$ $\sec\theta = \dfrac{r}{x}$ $\cot\theta = \dfrac{x}{y}$

The above definitions can be used to evaluate the trigonometric functions for any angle θ.

EXAMPLE 1: Find the value of $\sin\theta$, $\cos\theta$, and $\tan\theta$ for each of the following.

a. $\sin\theta = \frac{4}{5}$

$\cos\theta = \frac{-3}{5} = -\frac{3}{5}$

$\tan\theta = \frac{4}{-3} = -\frac{4}{3}$

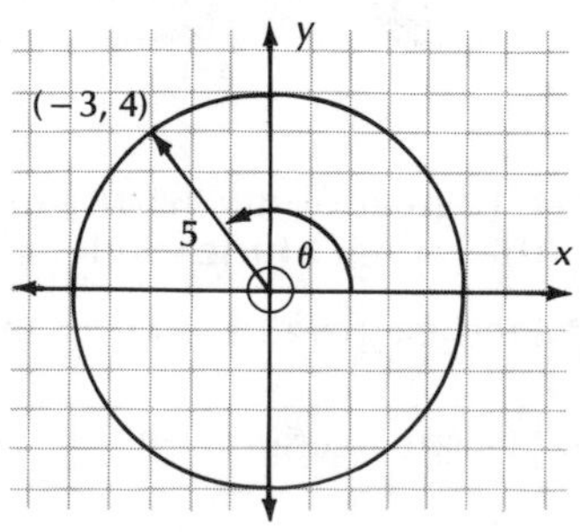

b.

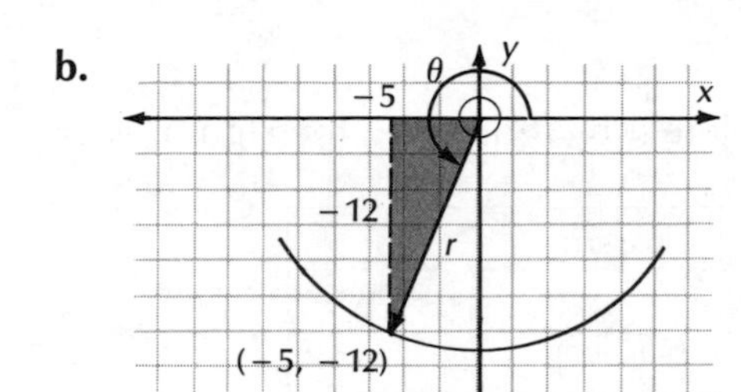

First, find the value of r.

$r^2 = x^2 + y^2$
$r^2 = 25 + 144$
$r^2 = 169$
$r = 13$

$\sin\theta = \frac{-12}{13} = -\frac{12}{13}$ $\quad \cos\theta = \frac{-5}{13} = -\frac{5}{13}$ $\quad \tan\theta = \frac{-12}{-5} = \frac{12}{5}$

EXAMPLE 2: Find the values of the six trigonometric functions for an angle in standard position whose terminal ray contains the point $A(9, -40)$.

Draw a graph that shows the angle in standard position and find the value of r.

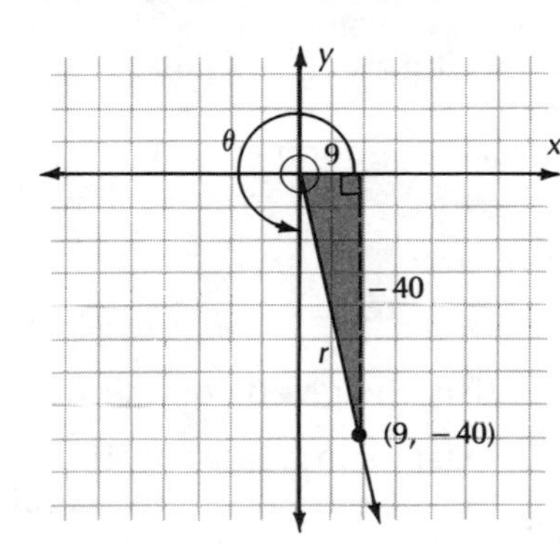

$r^2 = 9^2 + (-40)^2$
$r^2 = 1681$
$r = 41$

$\sin\theta = -\frac{40}{41}$ $\quad \csc\theta = -\frac{41}{40}$

$\cos\theta = \frac{9}{41}$ $\quad \sec\theta = \frac{41}{9}$

$\tan\theta = -\frac{40}{9}$ $\quad \cot\theta = -\frac{9}{40}$

EXAMPLE 3: The terminal ray of an angle θ lies in quadrant III. Given that $\sin\theta = \frac{-2}{3}$, find the value of $\cos\theta$ and $\tan\theta$.

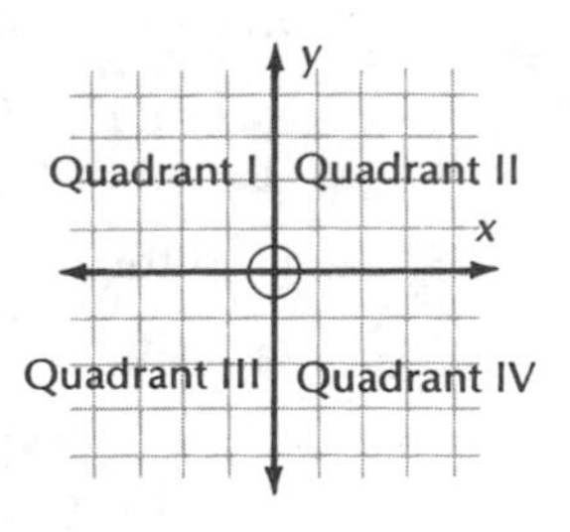

Since $\sin\theta = \frac{y}{r} = \frac{-2}{3}$, and the terminal ray lies in quadrant III, the terminal ray contains a point $P(x, -2)$ at a distance 3 units from the origin. That is, $r = 3$.

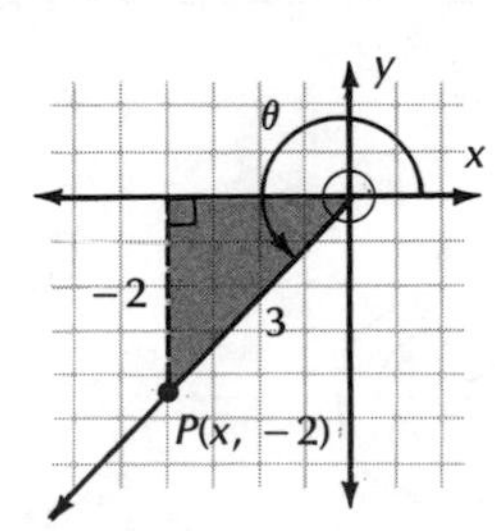

$x^2 + (-2)^2 = 3^2$
$x^2 + 4 = 9$
$x = -\sqrt{5}$ In quadrant III, $x < 0$.

$\therefore \cos\theta = \frac{-\sqrt{5}}{3}$ and $\tan\theta = \frac{-2}{-\sqrt{5}}$ or $\frac{2\sqrt{5}}{5}$.

EXERCISE 5-6

A 1. Copy the given table and complete it by indicating the sign of each expression.

	Quadrant			
	I	II	III	IV
x	+	−	−	+
y	■	■	■	■
r	■	■	■	■
$\sin\theta = \frac{y}{r}$	■	■	■	■
$\cos\theta = \frac{x}{r}$	■	■	■	■
$\tan\theta = \frac{y}{x}$	■	■	■	■

2. **a.** For each quadrant, use the results of exercise 1 to list the trigonometric functions that have a positive value.
   b. Interpret the given diagram. This is sometimes called the **cast rule**.
   c. In each quadrant, which of the reciprocal trigonometric functions are positive?

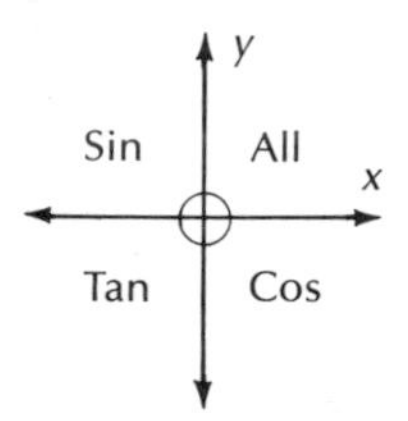

3. In which quadrant is the given condition true?

   a. $\cos\theta < 0$ **b.** $\tan\theta > 0$ **c.** $\sin\theta < 0$ **d.** $\sec\theta > 0$

4. Name the trigonometric functions that satisfy the given condition.

   a. positive in quadrant II
   b. negative in quadrant III
   c. positive in quadrant IV
   d. negative in quadrants II and III
   e. positive in quadrants I and II
   f. negative in quadrant III and positive in quadr

5. In which quadrant is the given condition satisfied?

   a. $\sin\theta > 0$ and $\cos\theta < 0$
   b. $\tan\theta < 0$ and $\cos\theta > 0$
   c. $\sin\theta < 0$ and $\cos\theta < 0$
   d. $\sec\theta > 0$ and $\sin\theta < 0$

B 6. Find the value of $\sin\theta$, $\cos\theta$, and $\tan\theta$ for each of the following.

a.

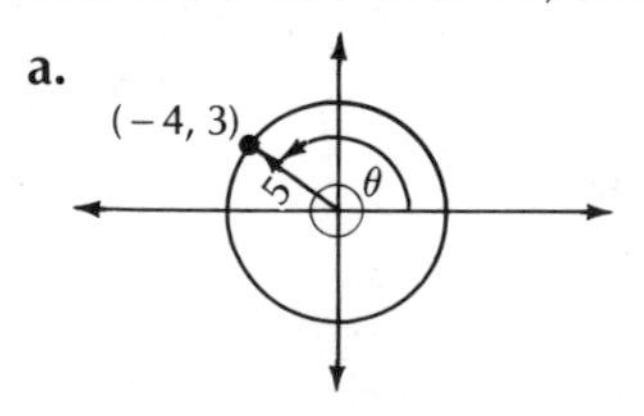

b.

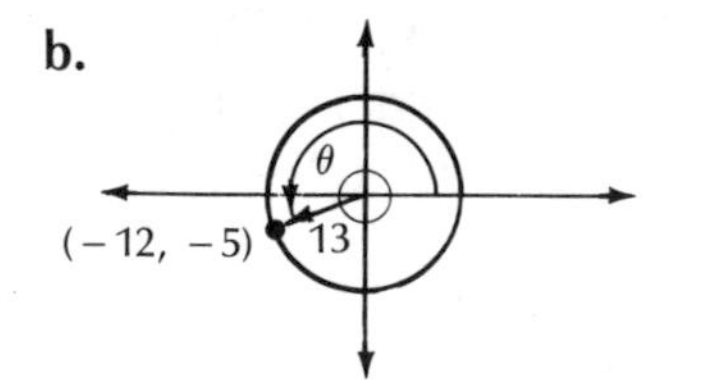

c.

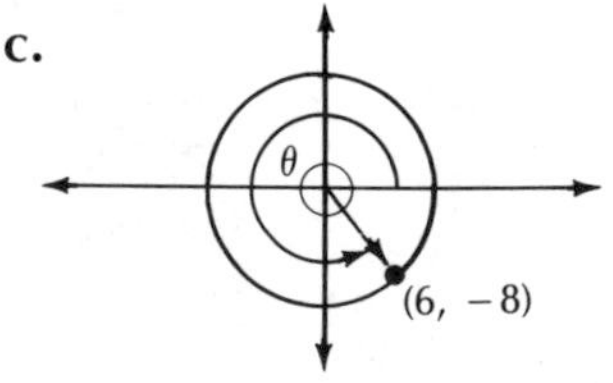

d.

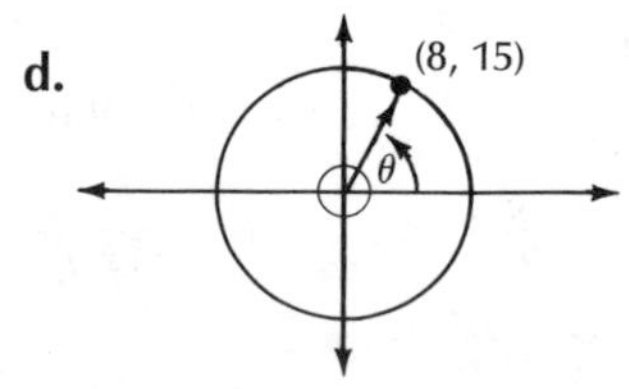

e.

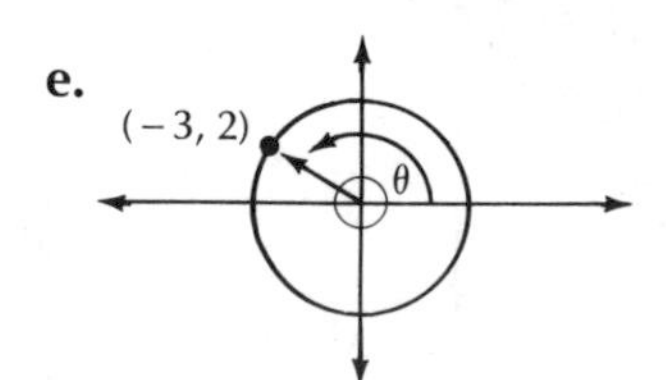

f.

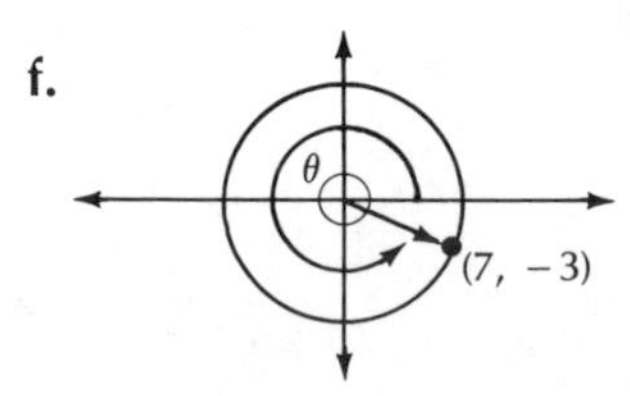

7. Evaluate the trigonometric functions for an angle in standard position that contains the given point.

   a. $A(9, 12)$ **b.** $B(-3, 5)$ **c.** $C(-4, -5)$ **d.** $D(1, -5)$

8. Copy and complete the given table for an angle in standard position.

Terminal Ray	$\sin \theta$	$\cos \theta$	$\tan \theta$
quadrant IV	$\frac{-3}{5}$	■	■
quadrant III	■	■	$\frac{4}{5}$
quadrant II	■	$\frac{-12}{13}$	■
quadrant III	$\frac{-3}{4}$	■	■
quadrant IV	■	$\frac{2}{5}$	■
quadrant II	■	■	$\frac{-3}{5}$

C 9. **a.** Given that $\sin \theta = \frac{-3}{5}$ and $\tan \theta < 0$, find $\cos \theta$ and $\tan \theta$.

   b. Given that $\cos \theta = \frac{4}{5}$ and $\sin \theta > 0$, find $\sin \theta$ and $\tan \theta$.

   c. Given that $\tan \theta = \frac{5}{12}$ and $\sin \theta < 0$, find $\cos \theta$ and $\csc \theta$.

   d. Given that $\cos \theta = \frac{2}{3}$ and $\sin \theta < 0$, find $\tan \theta$ and $\csc \theta$.

EXTRA

Using Trigonometry to Calculate π

The formula for the area of a circle is πr^2. For an inscribed regular polygon with n sides, the area is $\frac{1}{2} nr^2 \sin\left(\frac{360°}{n}\right)$.

The diagram at the right shows a regular 16-sided polygon inscribed in a circle. The diagram illustrates that the number of sides, n, increases as the area of the polygon approaches the area of the circle. Mathematicians say that the limiting value for the area of an "n"-sided regular polygon, as n becomes very large, is the area of the circle in which it is inscribed. This can be written symbolically as follows.

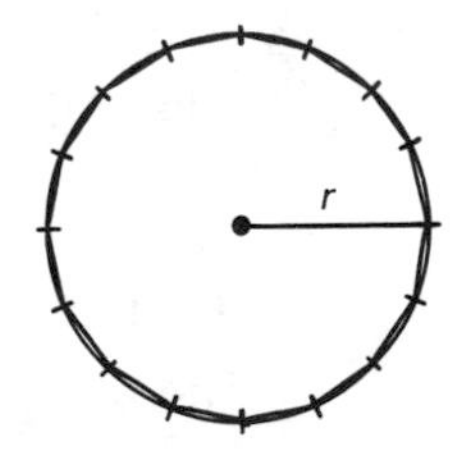

$$\lim_{n\to\infty} \left[\frac{1}{2} nr^2 \sin\left(\frac{360°}{n}\right)\right] = \pi r^2$$

$\lim_{n\to\infty}$ means the number of sides, n, increases without bound, or n becomes very large.

$$\lim_{n\to\infty} \left[\frac{1}{2} n \sin\left(\frac{360°}{n}\right)\right] = \pi$$

Divide both sides by r^2.

Evaluate $\frac{1}{2} n \sin\left(\frac{360°}{n}\right)$ for $n = 10, 100, 1000$ and compare your answers to $\pi = 3.141\,592\,654\ldots$.

5-7 Special Angles

In lesson 5-5, right-angled triangles with angles of 30°, 60°, and 45° were examined so that the values of the trigonometric functions could be determined without the use of a calculator. Can these triangles be used to find the values of the trigonometric functions in other quadrants?

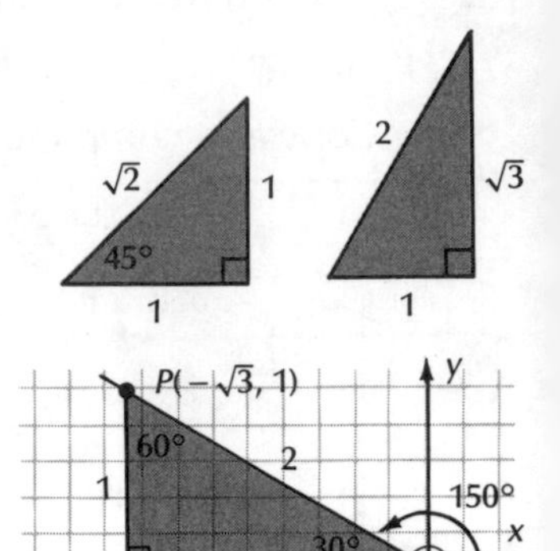

Consider an angle of 150° in standard position, as shown at the right. The acute angle between the terminal ray and the x-axis is called the **reference angle.** In this case, the terminal ray forms a reference angle of 30° with the negative x-axis. The coordinates of a point, P, on the terminal ray can be determined using a 30°-60°-90° triangle, as shown. The coordinates of P are $(-\sqrt{3}, 1)$ and $OP = r = 2$. From this, the trigonometric values for an angle of 150° can be determined.

$$\sin 150° = \frac{y}{r} = \frac{1}{2} \qquad \cos 150° = \frac{x}{r} = -\frac{\sqrt{3}}{2} \qquad \tan 150° = \frac{y}{x} = -\frac{1}{\sqrt{3}} \text{ or } -\frac{\sqrt{3}}{3}$$

$$\csc 150° = \frac{r}{y} = 2 \qquad \sec 150° = \frac{r}{x} = -\frac{2}{\sqrt{3}} \text{ or } \frac{-2\sqrt{3}}{3} \qquad \cot 150° = \frac{x}{y} = -\sqrt{3}$$

EXAMPLE 1:

a. Find the sine, cosine, and tangent of an angle of 315°, given that the angle is in standard position.

After rotating through 315°, the terminal ray will form a reference angle of 45° with the x-axis. To find one point on the terminal ray, use a 45°-45°-90° triangle, as shown. The terminal ray will contain the point $(1, -1)$.
Thus, $x = 1$, $y = -1$, and $r = \sqrt{2}$.

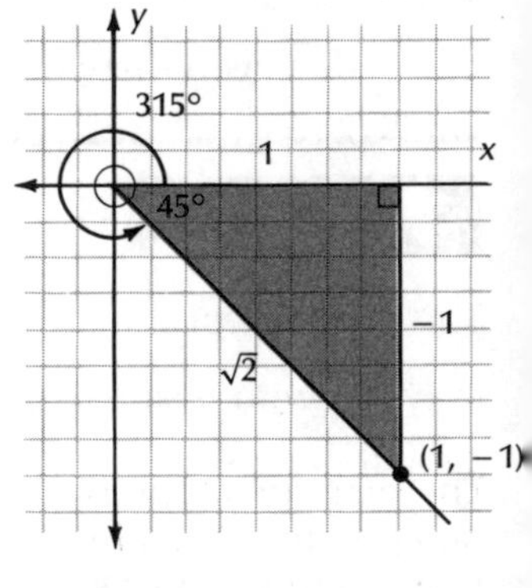

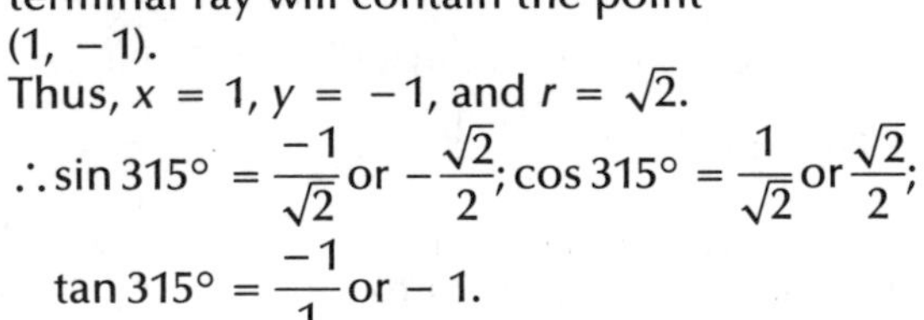

$$\therefore \sin 315° = \frac{-1}{\sqrt{2}} \text{ or } -\frac{\sqrt{2}}{2};\ \cos 315° = \frac{1}{\sqrt{2}} \text{ or } \frac{\sqrt{2}}{2};$$

$$\tan 315° = \frac{-1}{1} \text{ or } -1.$$

b. Find the sine, cosine, and tangent of an angle of 240°, given that the angle is in standard position.

The reference angle is 60° and the terminal ray contains the point $(-1, -\sqrt{3})$.
Thus, $x = -1$, $y = -\sqrt{3}$, and $r = 2$.

$$\therefore \sin 240° = -\frac{\sqrt{3}}{2};\quad \cos 240° = -\frac{1}{2};$$

$$\tan 240° = \frac{-\sqrt{3}}{-1} \text{ or } +\sqrt{3}$$

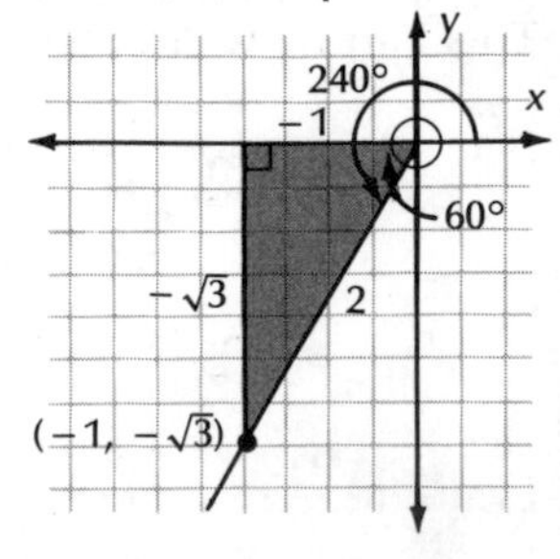

c. Find the sine, cosine, and tangent for an angle of $-225°$ in standard position.

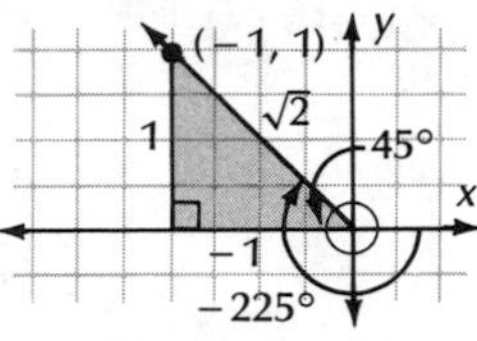

The negative sign indicates a clockwise rotation. Thus, the terminal ray is in quadrant II and the reference angle measures 45°.

$\therefore \sin(-225°) = \frac{1}{\sqrt{2}}$ or $\frac{\sqrt{2}}{2}$; $\cos(-225°) = -\frac{1}{\sqrt{2}}$ or $-\frac{\sqrt{2}}{2}$;
$\tan(-225°) = -1$

d. Find the sine, cosine, and tangent for an angle of 570° in standard position.

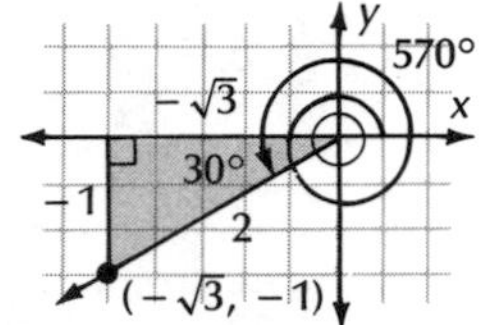

Since $570° = 360° + 210°$, the terminal ray makes one complete revolution and then comes to "rest" in quadrant III. An angle of 570° is **coterminal** with an angle of 210° because both angles have the same initial ray and the same terminal ray. Both angles produce a reference angle of 30° in the third quadrant.

$\therefore \sin 570° = -\frac{1}{2}$; $\cos 570° = -\frac{\sqrt{3}}{2}$; $\tan 570° = \frac{-1}{-\sqrt{3}}$ or $\frac{\sqrt{3}}{3}$

The values of the trigonometric functions can be related to a circle with centre O (0,0) and radius 1, which is called the **unit circle**. The values of the trigonometric functions are given below.

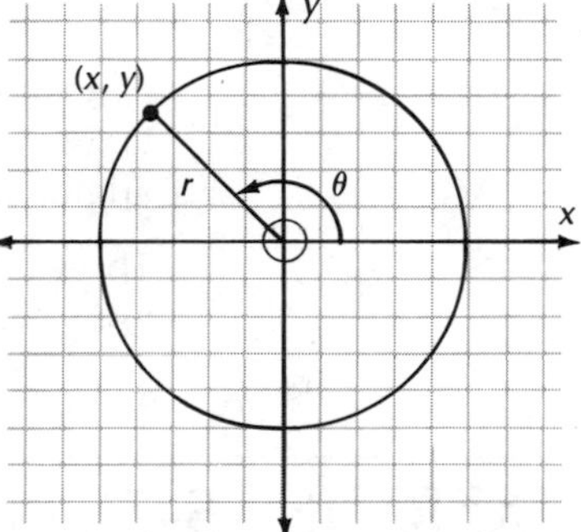

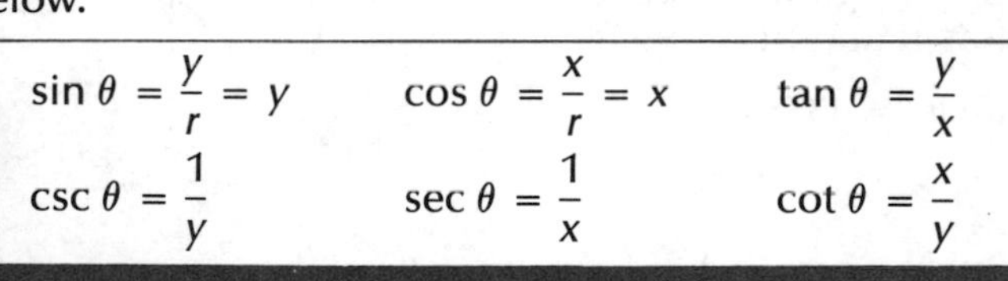

$\sin\theta = \frac{y}{r} = y$ $\quad \cos\theta = \frac{x}{r} = x$ $\quad \tan\theta = \frac{y}{x}$

$\csc\theta = \frac{1}{y}$ $\quad \sec\theta = \frac{1}{x}$ $\quad \cot\theta = \frac{x}{y}$

Angles of 0°, 90°, 180°, 270°, and 360° are called **quadrantal angles** and have a terminal ray on an axis that separates the quadrants.

EXAMPLE 2: Find the values of the trigonometric functions of 90°.

For an angle of 90° in standard position, $x = 0$, $y = 1$, and $r = 1$.

$\sin 90° = y = 1$ $\quad \cos 90° = x = 0$ $\quad \tan 90° = \frac{y}{x} = \frac{1}{0}$

This is undefined.

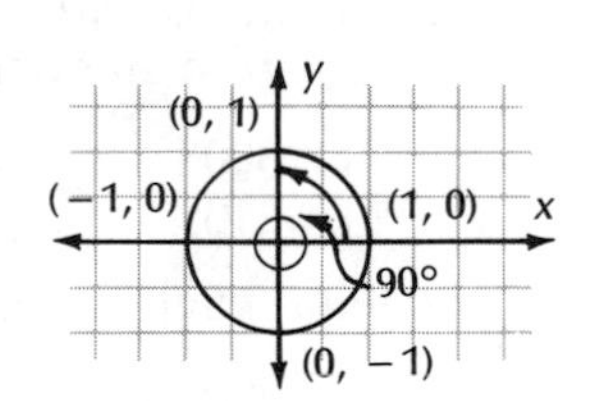

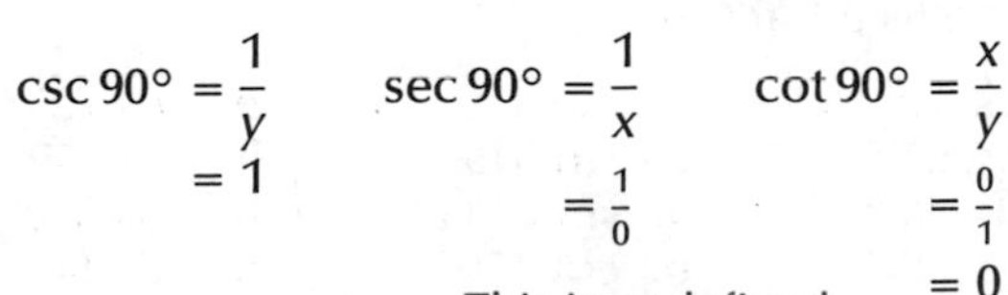

$\csc 90° = \frac{1}{y} = 1$ $\quad \sec 90° = \frac{1}{x} = \frac{1}{0}$ $\quad \cot 90° = \frac{x}{y} = \frac{0}{1} = 0$

This is undefined.

EXAMPLE 3: Write each trigonometric function in terms of its reference angle.

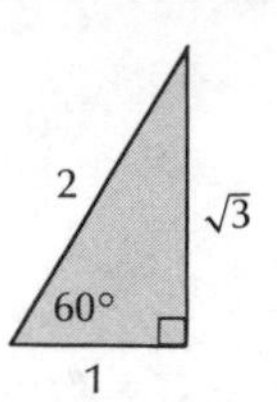

a. $\cos 135° = -\cos 45°$ The reference angle is 45°.

b. $\tan 240° = \tan 60°$ Cosine is negative in quadrant II.

EXAMPLE 4: a. Given that $\sin \theta = \frac{+\sqrt{3}}{2}$, find the value of θ, where $0° < \theta < 360°$.

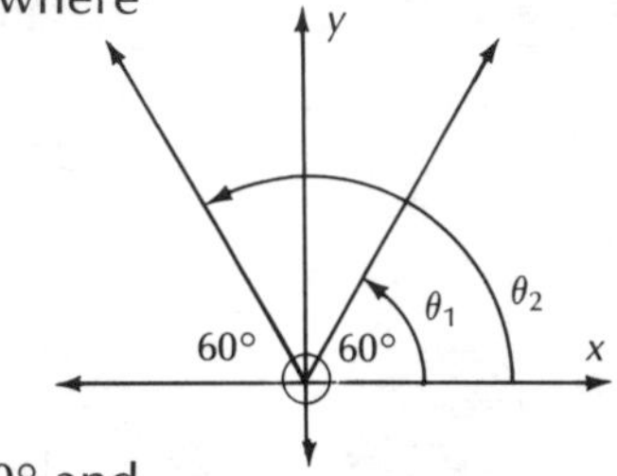

The reference angle is 60°.
The sine function is positive in quadrants I and II . Draw a diagram showing the reference angles of 60° in quadrants I and II.

From the diagram, the values of θ are $\theta_1 = 60°$ and $\theta_2 = 120°$.

b. Given that $\cos \theta = \frac{-1}{\sqrt{2}}$, find the value of θ, where $0° < \theta < 360°$.

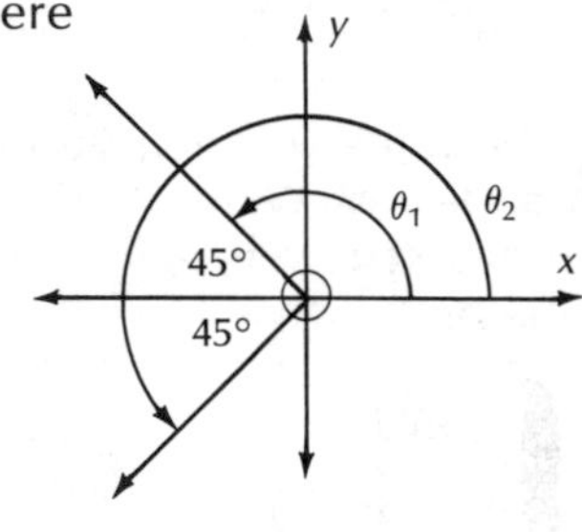

The reference angle is 45°.
Cosine is negative in quadrants II and III.
Draw a diagram showing the reference angles in quadrants II and III.

The values of θ are $\theta_1 = 135°$ and $\theta_2 = 225°$.

EXERCISE 5-7

A 1. Given each angle in standard position, state the measure of the reference angle.

a. 330°	b. 150°	c. 225°	d. 120°	e. 300°
f. 240°	g. 315°	h. 675°	i. −150°	j. 140°

2. Name the quadrant that contains the terminal ray of each angle, given in standard position.

a. 300°	b. 120°	c. 225°	d. 150°	e. 330°
f. 210°	g. −225°	h. 315°	i. 600°	j. 215°

3. Find each value, expressed as a fraction.

a. sin 30°	b. cos 45°	c. tan 120°	d. cos 225°
e. tan 300°	f. cos 150°	g. sin 315°	h. tan 210°
i. sin 240°	j. tan 690°	k. sin (−60°)	l. cos 300°
m. sec 210°	n. csc 225°	o. cot 150°	p. cot 240°

B 4. Evaluate each trigonometric function without using a calculator.

a. sin 210° b. cos 120° c. tan 225° d. cos 240°
e. sin 300° f. tan (−210°) g. sin 495° h. cos 330°
i. cot 150° j. sec 300° k. csc 240° l. sec 120°

5. Copy and complete the given table.

θ	$\sin\theta$	$\cos\theta$	$\tan\theta$	$\csc\theta$	$\sec\theta$	$\cot\theta$
0°	■	■	■	■	■	■
90°	■	■	■	■	■	■
180°	■	■	■	■	■	■
270°	■	■	■	■	■	■
360°	■	■	■	■	■	■

6. Evaluate.

a. sin −180° b. tan −270° c. cos −360° d. tan −180°
e. cos −450° f. sin 540° g. tan −450° h. sin 720°

7. For each given trigonometric value,
- state the reference angle,
- state the quadrants in which the terminal ray could lie, and
- find the values of θ, where $0° < \theta < 360°$.

a. $\sin\theta = \frac{-\sqrt{3}}{2}$ b. $\cos\theta = \frac{1}{2}$ c. $\tan\theta = \sqrt{3}$
d. $\cos\theta = \frac{\sqrt{3}}{2}$ e. $\tan\theta = -1$ f. $\cos\theta = \frac{-1}{\sqrt{2}}$
g. $\sin\theta = \frac{1}{2}$ h. $\sin\theta = \frac{-1}{\sqrt{2}}$ i. $\sec\theta = \sqrt{2}$

8. Find the value of θ, where $0° < \theta < 360°$.

a. $\cos\theta = 0$ b. $\sin\theta = 1$ c. $\tan\theta$ is undefined
d. $\tan\theta = 0$ e. $\sin\theta = 0$ f. $\csc\theta$ is undefined

C 9. Prove each of the following for any acute angle α.

a. $\sin(180° - \alpha) = \sin\alpha$ b. $\cos(180° - \alpha) = -\cos\alpha$ c. $\tan(180° - \alpha) = -\tan\alpha$

10. Find the value of θ, where $0° < \theta < 360°$.

a. $\sin\theta\,(2\cos\theta + 1) = 0$ b. $2\cos^2\theta - 1 = 0$
c. $\sin\theta\cos\theta - \sin\theta + \cos\theta - 1 = 0$ d. $2\sin^2\theta - 3\sin\theta + 1 = 0$
e. $\tan\theta\cos\theta + \cos\theta = 0$ f. $2\cos^2\theta + \cos\theta = 1$

5-8 Finding Trigonometric Functions of Any Angle

A calculator can be used to find the value of the trigonometric function of any angle, with the exception of some quadrantal angles.

EXAMPLE 1: Use a calculator to find the value of each trigonometric function, correct to four decimal places.

a. $\cos(-207°)$

[207] [−] [cos]

$\cos(-207°) = -0.8910$

b. $\tan 473°$

[473] [tan]

$\tan 473° = -2.3559$

c. $\sec 307°$

[307] [cos] [$\frac{1}{x}$]

$\sec 307° = 1.6616$

EXAMPLE 2: Write each trigonometric function in terms of its reference angle.

a. $\sin 147° = +\sin 33°$ — Sine is positive in quadrant II and the reference angle is 33°.

b. $\cos 207° = -\cos 27°$

c. $\tan 285° = -\tan 75°$

d. $\sin(-260°) = +\sin 80°$ — −260° lies in quadrant II.

If the value of a trigonometric function is known, then the size of the angle can be determined using a calculator and reference angles.

EXAMPLE 3: **a.** Given that $\sin\theta = 0.4540$, find the value of θ to the nearest degree, where $0° < \theta < 360°$.

Use a calculator to find the size of the reference angle.

[0.4540] [INV] [sin]

Thus, the size of the reference angle is 27°. Since the sine value is positive, θ is located in quadrant I or II.
Therefore, $\theta_1 = 27°$ and $\theta_2 = 153°$.

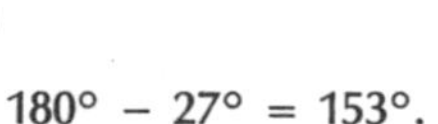

$180° - 27° = 153°$.

b. Given that $\tan\theta = -0.6356$, find the value of θ to the nearest degree, where $0° < \theta < 360°$.

The tangent value is negative, so the reference angle lies in quadrant II or IV.

[0.6356] [INV] [tan]

The size of the reference angle is 32.44°.
From the diagram,

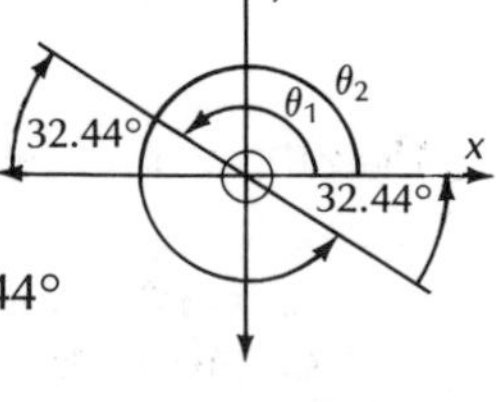

$\theta_1 = 180° - 32.44° = 147.56°$ and $\theta_2 = 360° - 32.44° = 327.56°$

EXAMPLE 4: Solve $12 \sin^2\theta + \sin\theta = 6$ for all values of θ, where $0° < \theta < 360°$.

$$12 \sin^2\theta + \sin\theta = 6$$
$$12 \sin^2\theta + \sin\theta - 6 = 0$$
$$(4\sin\theta + 3)(3\sin\theta - 2) = 0$$

Solve the equation for θ.

$4\sin\theta + 3 = 0$ or $3\sin\theta - 2 = 0$

$\sin\theta = -\frac{3}{4}$ or $\sin\theta = \frac{2}{3}$

The measure of the reference angle is 48.6°.
θ lies in quadrant III or IV.
$\therefore \theta = (180° + 48.6°) = 228.6°$
or $\theta = (360° - 48.6°) = 311.4°$

The measure of the reference angle is 42.1°.
θ lies in quadrant I or II.
$\therefore \theta = 42.1°$ or $\theta = (180° - 42.1°) = 137.9°$

EXERCISE 5-8

A

1. Use a calculator to evaluate each trigonometric function, correct to four decimal places.

   a. sin 147° **b.** cos 197° **c.** tan 305° **d.** sin 253°
   e. cos 481° **f.** tan (−107°) **g.** sec 231° **h.** cot 167°

2. State the size of the reference angle for each given angle measure.

   a. 219° **b.** 342° **c.** 126° **d.** 512°
   e. −195° **f.** 154° **g.** 563° **h.** 278°

3. Write each trigonometric function in terms of its reference angle.

   a. sin 207° **b.** cos 143° **c.** tan 303° **d.** sec 335°
   e. cos (−198°) **f.** tan 263° **g.** sin 784° **h.** cos 184°

B

4. Solve for θ, correct to two decimal places. $(0° < \theta < 360°)$

   a. $\sin\theta = 0.6190$ **b.** $\cos\theta = -0.8421$ **c.** $\tan\theta = 1.6283$
   d. $\cos\theta = 0.1403$ **e.** $\sin\theta = -0.0283$ **f.** $\tan\theta = -0.1205$
   g. $\sec\theta = 1.8214$ **h.** $\csc\theta = -1.0912$ **i.** $\cot\theta = -0.4271$
   j. $\csc\theta = 1.8423$ **k.** $\sec\theta = -3.1428$ **l.** $\cot\theta = 3.2416$

5. Solve for θ, correct to two decimal places. $(0° < \theta < 360°)$

   a. $(\sin\theta - 0.7)(\sin\theta + 0.3) = 0$ **b.** $(3\sin\theta - 2)(4\cos\theta + 1) = 0$
   c. $9\cos^2\theta - 4 = 0$ **d.** $4\sin^3\theta = 3\sin\theta$
   e. $2\cos^2\theta = \cos\theta + 1$ **f.** $15\sin^2\theta - \sin\theta - 2 = 0$

6. **a.** If $\tan\theta = 1.4207$ and $180° < \theta < 270°$, find the value of $\sin\theta$.
   b. If $\cos\theta = -0.6205$ and $90° < \theta < 180°$, find the value of $\sin\theta$.
   c. If $\sin\theta = 0.6247$ and $90° < \theta < 180°$, find the value of $\tan\theta$.

C

7. Solve for all values of θ, where $0° < \theta < 360°$.

   a. $2\sin^2\theta + 3\sin\theta + 1 = 0$ **b.** $\tan^2\theta = 11 + \sec\theta$
   c. $15\sin\theta\cos\theta + 9\cos\theta - 5\sin\theta = 3$

5-9 The Law of Sines

In lesson 5-4, three equivalent expressions for finding the area of a ΔABC were given as follows.

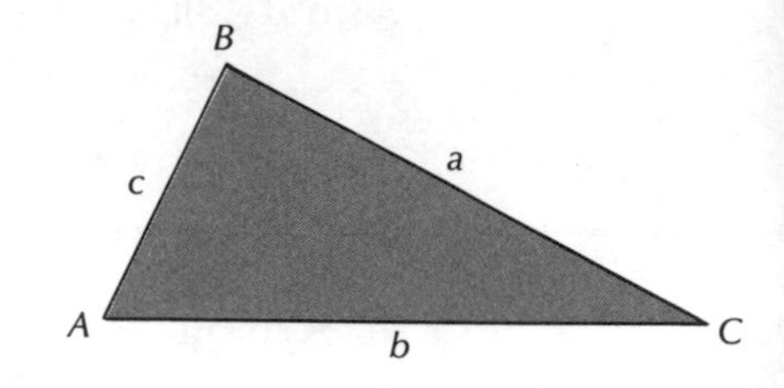

$$\text{Area} = \tfrac{1}{2}bc \sin A = \tfrac{1}{2}ac \sin B = \tfrac{1}{2}ab \sin C$$

Multiply each expression by 2 and divide by abc.

$$2\left(\frac{1\, bc \sin A}{2\, abc}\right) = 2\left(\frac{1\, ac \sin B}{2\, abc}\right) = 2\left(\frac{1\, ab \sin C}{2\, abc}\right)$$

Simplifying each expression results in the following relationship between the sides and angles of a triangle.

The Law of Sines

For any ΔABC, $\dfrac{\sin A}{a} = \dfrac{\sin B}{b} = \dfrac{\sin C}{c}$

In any ΔABC, the ratio of the sine of any angle to the length of the opposite side is a constant.

The Law of Sines can be used to solve triangles where the measure of two angles and one side are known. Note that a triangle is *solved* when the measures of all the sides and angles are known.

When the size of two angles and the length of one side of a triangle are known, the size of the third angle can be readily determined and the Law of Sines can be used to find the measures of the remaining two sides.

EXAMPLE 1: For the given triangle, find the value of x, correct to two decimal places.

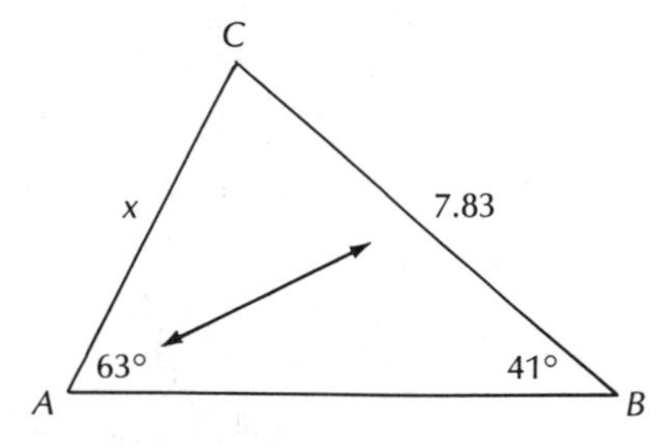

$$\frac{\sin A}{a} = \frac{\sin B}{b}$$

$$\frac{\sin 63°}{7.83} = \frac{\sin 41°}{x}$$

$$x \sin 63° = 7.83 \sin 41°$$

$$x = \frac{7.83 \sin 41°}{\sin 63°}$$

$$\therefore x \doteq 5.77$$

Be careful to use corresponding sides and angles.

[7.83] [×] [41] [sin] [÷] [63] [sin] [=]

EXAMPLE 2: Solve ΔABC, given that $\angle B = 28°$, $\angle C = 46°$, and $a = 11.41$ cm.

Use a diagram to show the given information.
The sum of the interior angles of a triangle is 180°.

$$\therefore \angle A + 28° + 46° = 180°$$
$$\angle A = 106°$$

Since the size of $\angle A$ is known, the Law of Sines can be used to find the length of the other two sides.

$$\frac{\sin A}{a} = \frac{\sin B}{b} = \frac{\sin C}{c}$$ ← These are the known values.

$$\frac{\sin A}{a} = \frac{\sin B}{b} \quad \text{and} \quad \frac{\sin A}{a} = \frac{\sin C}{c}$$

$$\frac{\sin 106°}{11.41} = \frac{\sin 28°}{b} \qquad \frac{\sin 106°}{11.41} = \frac{\sin 46°}{c}$$

$$b \doteq 5.57 \qquad c \doteq 8.54$$

Use the Law of Sines in conjunction with known values.

For this example, notice which values were given and which were determined.

$\left.\begin{array}{r} \angle B = 28° \\ \angle C = 46° \text{ cm} \\ a = 11.41 \text{ cm} \end{array}\right\}$ Given $\qquad \left.\begin{array}{r} \angle A = 106° \\ b = 5.57 \text{ cm} \\ c = 8.54 \text{ cm} \end{array}\right\}$ Determined

EXAMPLE 3: A guy wire is attached to the top of a tower and forms an angle of 43° with the ground. A second guy wire, attached to the top of the same tower, is anchored 20 m closer to the tower and forms and angle of 48° with the ground. Find the length of the second wire.

To use the Law of Sines, the size of ϕ must be known.

$$43° + \phi = 48°$$
$$\therefore \phi = 5°$$

The size of an exterior angle is equal to the sum of the sizes of the interior and non-adjacent angles.

$$\frac{\sin 5°}{20} = \frac{\sin 43°}{x}$$

Use the Law of Sines.

$$x \sin 5° = 20 \sin 43°$$
$$x \doteq 156.50$$

The second guy wire is approximately 156.50 m long.

EXERCISE 5-9

Give all answers correct to two decimal places.

A 1. Find the value of x.

a.

b.

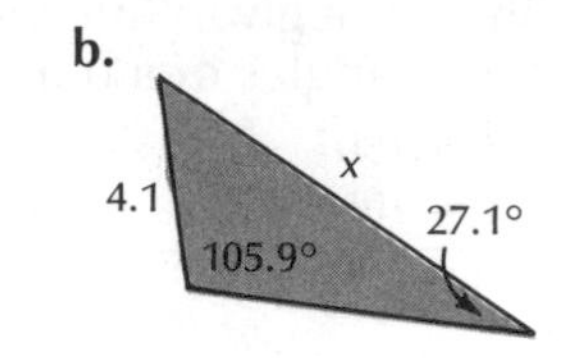

c.

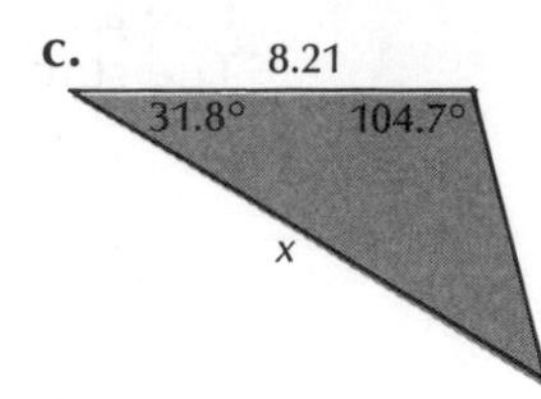

d.

e.

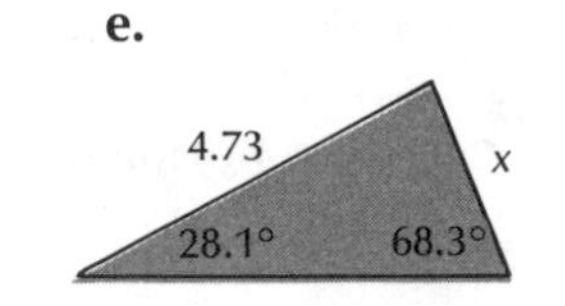

f.

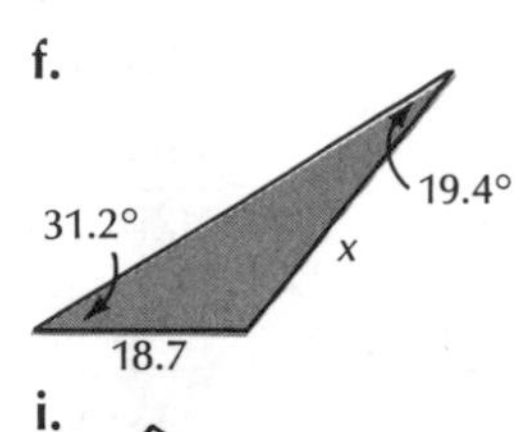

g.

h.

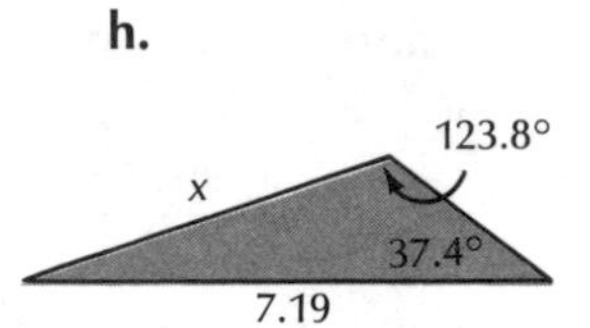

i.

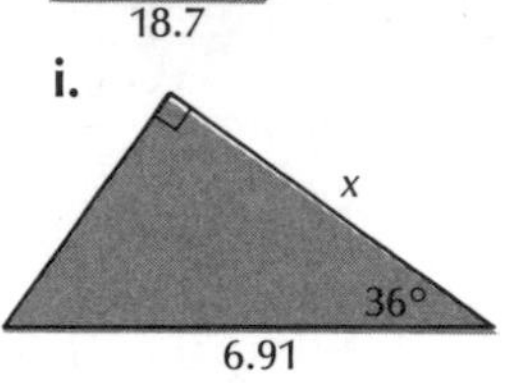

B 2. Find the value of x.

a.

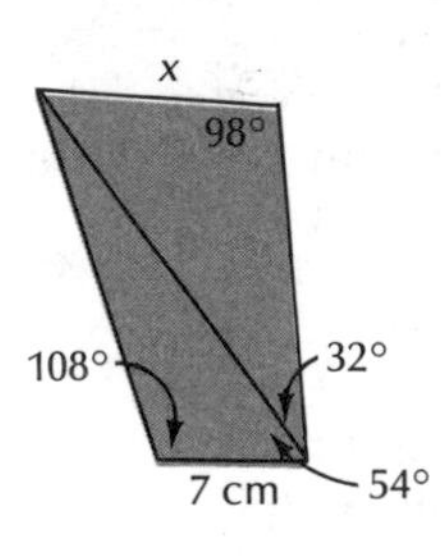

b.

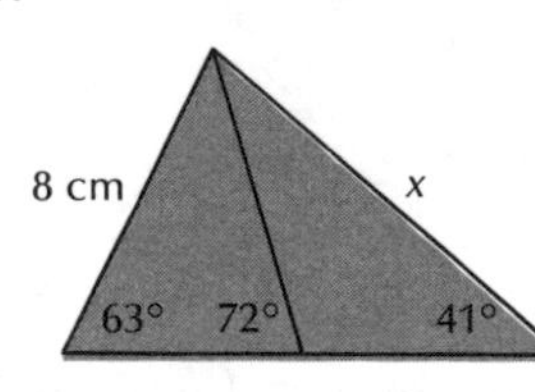

c.

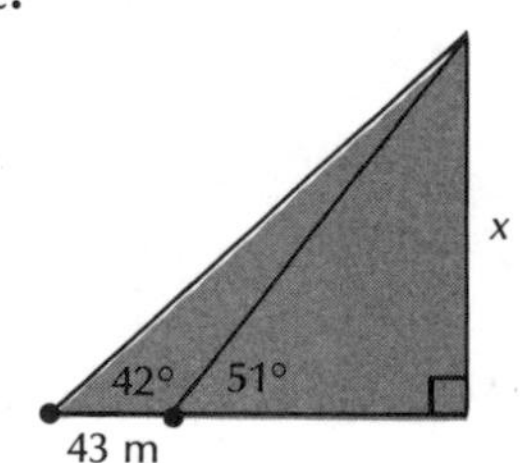

3. To find the distance AC across a small pond, a surveyor makes the following measurements.

$\angle CAB = 81.6°$, $AB = 63.4$ m, $\angle ABC = 47.2°$

Find the distance, AC, across the pond.

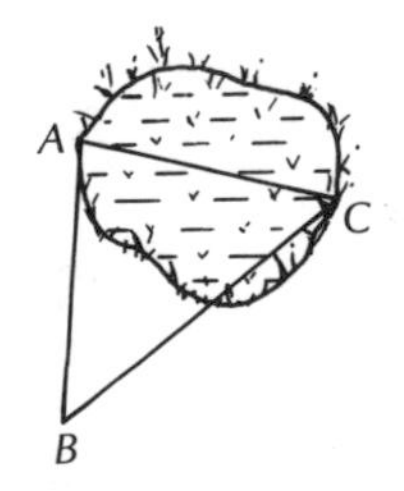

4. To find the height of a mountain, Susan measures the angle of elevation to be 17.6°. From a point 160 m closer to the mountain, she measures the angle of elevation as 18.8°. How high does she find the mountain to be?

5. ΔPQR is equilateral, with sides 7 cm long. The bisectors of $\angle Q$ and $\angle R$ intersect at A.

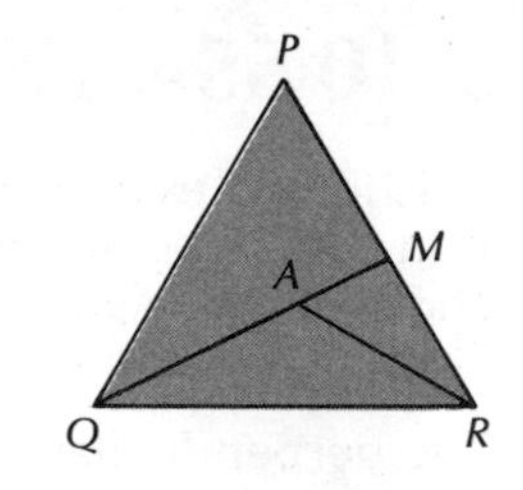

 a. Find QA.
 b. $\overline{QA}$ is extended to meet $\overline{PR}$ at M. Find the length of $\overline{QM}$.
 c. Find the ratio $\frac{QA}{QM}$.

6. Trees at points P and Q are separated by a deep canyon. To find the length of a bridge needed to join P and Q, a point A, 142 m from P, was selected. $\angle QPA$ and $\angle PQA$ were measured to be 51° and 61°, respectively. What is the distance between P and Q?

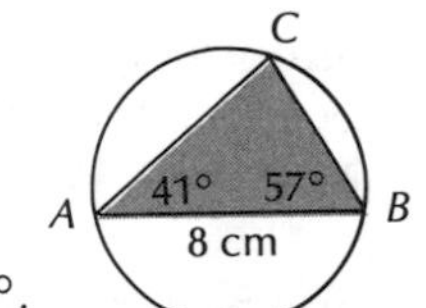

7. A telephone pole leans at an angle 8.3° away from the sun. When the angle of elevation of the sun is 23°, the length of the pole's shadow is 28 m. Find the length of the telephone pole.

8. A pendulum swings so that the angle between its extreme positions is 15.6° and the straight-line distance between the extreme positions of the end is 8.7 cm. Determine the length of the pendulum.

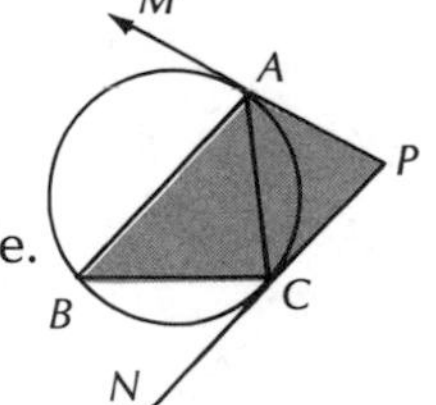

C 9. Chord $\overline{AB}$ subtends an inscribed $\angle ACB$. If $\angle ABC = 57°$ and $\angle BAC = 41°$, find the length of chords $\overline{BC}$ and $\overline{AC}$, given that $AB = 8$ cm.

10. $ABCD$ is an inscribed quadrilateral. $\angle ABD = 57°$, $\angle BAD = 70°$, $\angle DBC = 47°$, and $AD = 6$ cm. Find CD.

11. $\overline{PM}$ and $\overline{PN}$ are tangents to a circle at A and C, as shown. $\angle MAB = 75°$ and $\angle NCB = 45°$. If $AB = 8$ cm, find BC and AC.

12. A regular pentagon with diagonal 12 cm long is inscribed in a circle.
 a. Find the length of each side of the pentagon.
 b. Find the radius of the circle.

EXTRA

Alternate Proof of the Law of Sines

Case I
(ΔABC is acute)

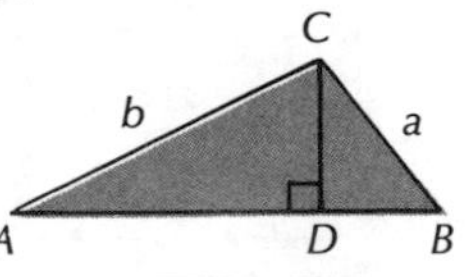

Case II
(ΔABC is obtuse)

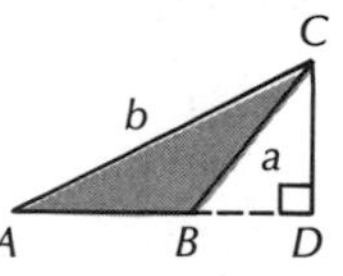

For each triangle above, $\overline{CD} \perp \overline{AB}$. Use each right-angled triangle to find an expression for CD in terms of $\angle A$ and b, and then in terms of $\angle B$ and a.

For each case, equate the two expressions to establish that $\frac{\sin A}{a} = \frac{\sin B}{b}$.

(Hint: use the results of exercise 9, lesson 5-7.)

5-10 SSA-The Ambiguous Case

This lesson examines triangles for which the lengths of two sides and the non-contained angle (SSA) are known. Consider, for example, ΔABC, shown at the right, with $AB = 8$ cm and $\angle B = 30°$. Several possibilities exist for different lengths of $\overline{AC}$.

The perpendicular distance, h, from A to $\overline{BC}$ is $8 \sin 30°$, or 4 cm.

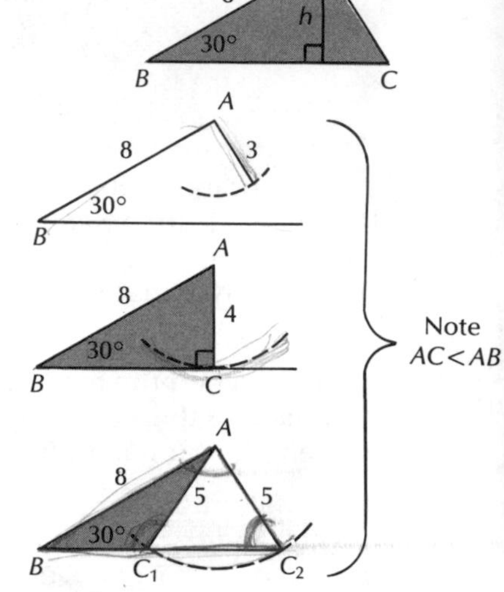

Suppose $AC = 3$ cm. In this situation, $\overline{AC}$ is too short to reach $\overline{BC}$, and so there is no triangle. Note that $AC < AB$.

Suppose $AC = 4$ cm. Then $\overline{AC}$ just reaches $\overline{BC}$, and there is one triangle, with $\angle ACB = 90°$.

Suppose $AC = 5$ cm. In this situation, there are two possible locations for C and thus, there are two triangles: ΔABC_1 and ΔABC_2.

Suppose $AC = 9$ cm. Then there is only one possible location for C and one triangle exists. Note that $AC > AB$.

This situation is called the **ambiguous case** because there may be two triangles, one triangle, or no triangles.

EXAMPLE 1: Find the value of θ, correct to two decimal places.

The side opposite the given angle is the longer of the two given sides ($7 > 5$), so there will be one solution.

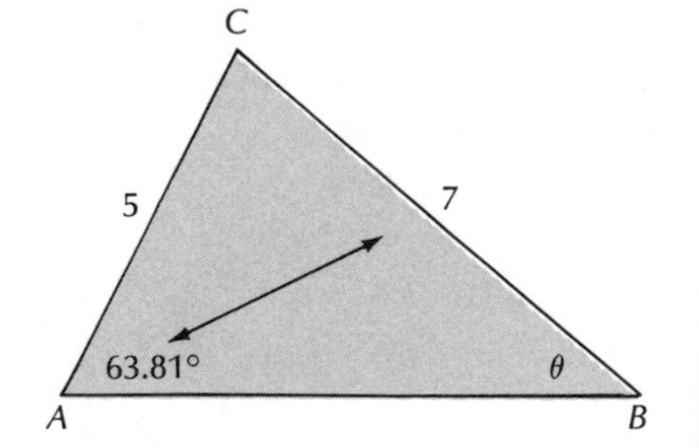

$$\frac{\sin A}{a} = \frac{\sin B}{b}$$

$$\frac{\sin 63.81°}{7} = \frac{\sin \theta}{5}$$

$$7 \sin \theta = 5 \sin 63.81°$$

$$\sin \theta = \frac{5 \sin 63.81°}{7}$$

$$\sin \theta \doteq 0.6409$$

$\theta \doteq 39.86°$ or $\theta \doteq 140.14°$

The second possibility, $\theta \doteq 140.14°$, is rejected because the sum of the interior angles of the triangle would be greater than 180°.

$\therefore \theta \doteq 39.86°$

EXAMPLE 2: For each given triangle, find the value of θ, correct to two decimal places.

a.

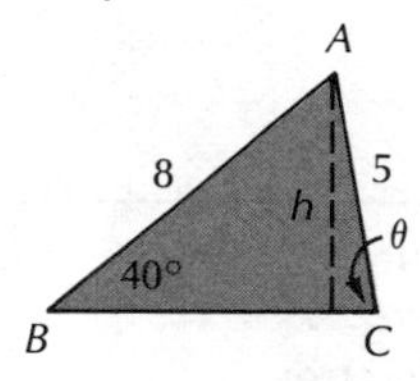

$$\frac{\sin 40°}{5} = \frac{\sin\theta}{8}$$
$$\sin\theta = \frac{8\sin 40°}{5}$$
$$\therefore \sin\theta \doteq 1.02$$

No solution is possible because $0 < \sin\theta < 1$.
In this case, $h = 8\sin 40°$ or approximately 5.1, and the triangle cannot be drawn.

b.

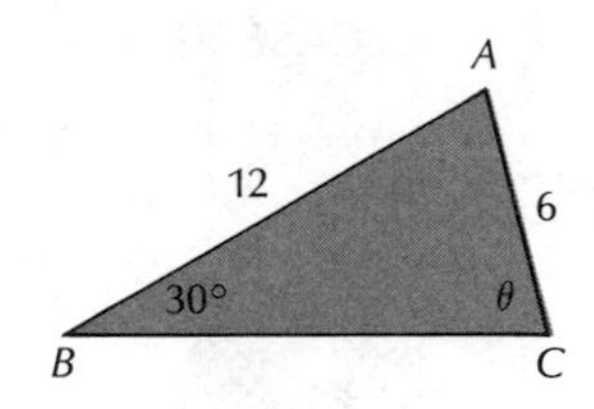

$$\frac{\sin 30°}{6} = \frac{\sin\theta}{12}$$
$$\sin\theta = \frac{12\sin 30°}{6}$$
$$= 1$$
$$\therefore \theta = 90°$$

EXAMPLE 3: **a.** For ΔABC, $AB = 8$ cm, $AC = 5$ cm, and $\angle ABC = 30°$. Find $\angle ACB$.

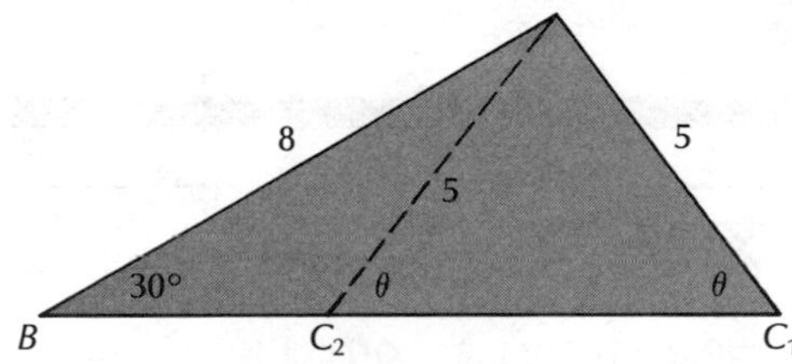

Use the Law of Sines.

$$\frac{\sin 30°}{5} = \frac{\sin\theta}{8}$$
$$\sin\theta = 0.8000$$

$\therefore \theta = 53.13°$ or $\theta = 126.87°$

$\therefore \angle AC_1B = 53.13°$ and $\angle AC_2B = 126.87°$

Recall that sine is positive in quadrants I and II.

Notice that ΔAC_1C_2 is isosceles. Thus, $\angle AC_2B$ will always be the supplement of $\angle AC_1B$.

b. Use the information from part **a** to find the size of $\angle BAC$.

Two triangles are possible, so there will be two answers.

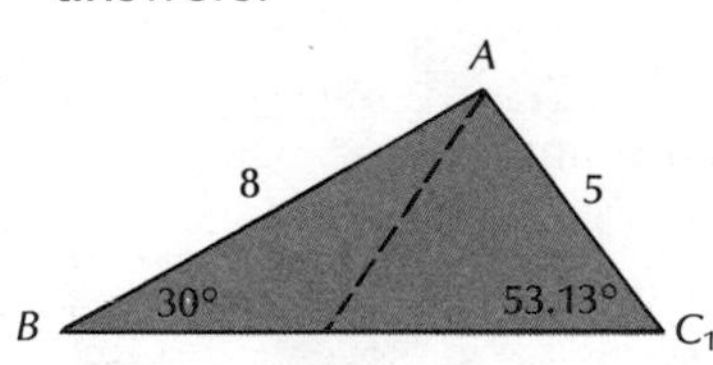

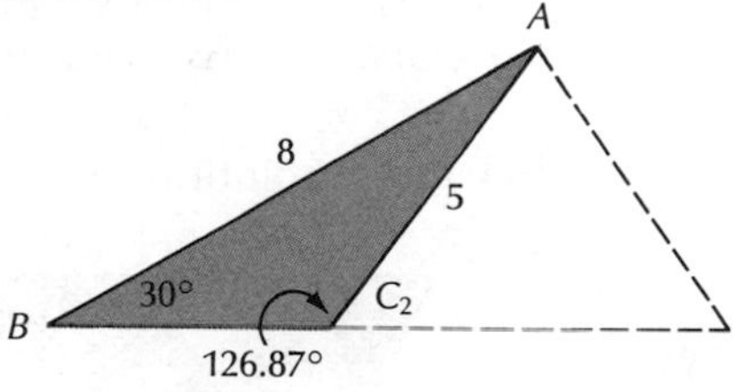

$\therefore BAC_1 = 180° - 30° - 53.13°$
$= 96.87°$

and

$\angle BAC_2 = 180° - 30° - 126.87°$
$= 23.13°$

c. Find BC.

$$\frac{\sin 53.13°}{8} = \frac{\sin 96.87°}{BC_1} \qquad \frac{\sin 126.87°}{8} = \frac{\sin 23.13°}{BC_2}$$

$$\therefore BC_1 = 9.93 \text{ cm} \qquad \therefore BC_2 = 3.93 \text{ cm}$$

In summary, when solving ΔABC where the length of two sides and the non-contained angle are known, the number of solutions depends on the length of the side opposite the given angle and how it compares to the altitude, $h = c \sin B$.

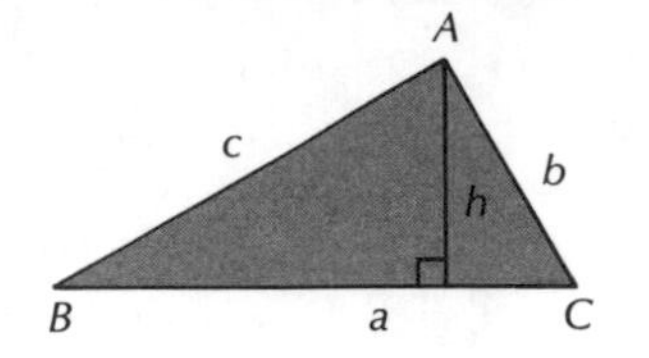

CASE I	CASE II	CASE III	CASE IV
$b < c \sin B$	$b = c \sin B$	$c \sin B < b < c$	$b \geq c$
No solution	One solution	Two solutions	One solution

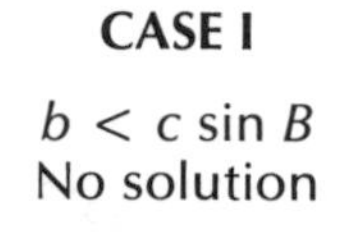
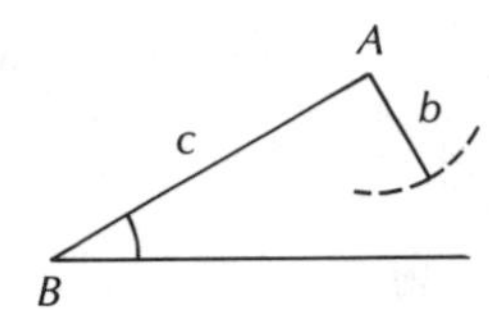

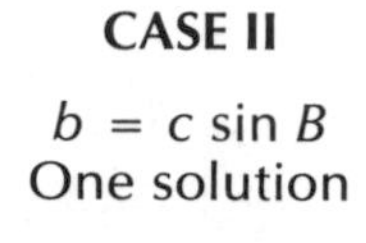
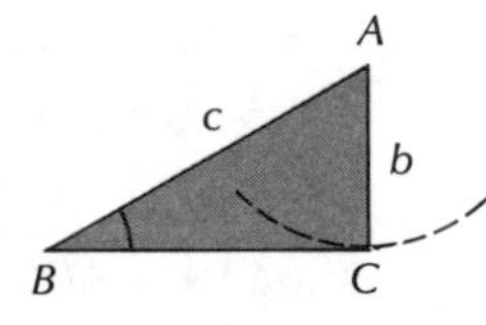

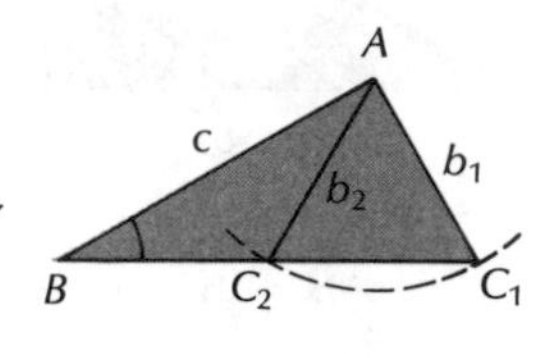

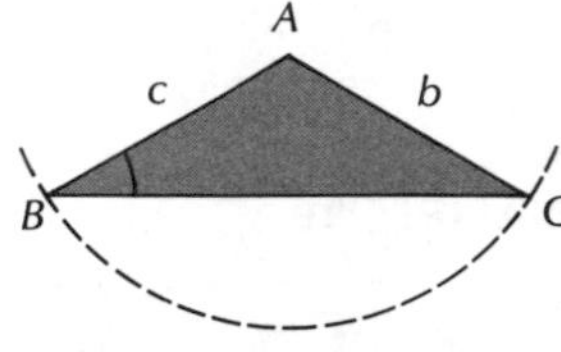

EXERCISE 5-10

Give each answer correct to two decimal places.

A 1. Use the triangle at the right to answer each part.

- **a.** For what value of x will there be no solution?
- **b.** For what value of x will there be one solution?
- **c.** For what value of x will there be two solutions?

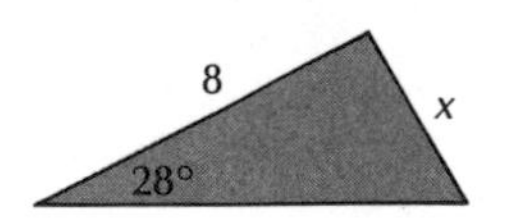

2. If there is one solution for ΔPQR, find the possible values of PR.

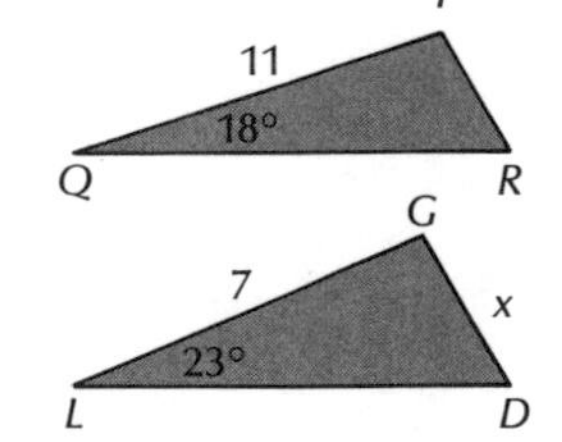

3. What restrictions on x will ensure that ΔGLD has two solutions?

4. How many solutions are there for each triangle?

a.

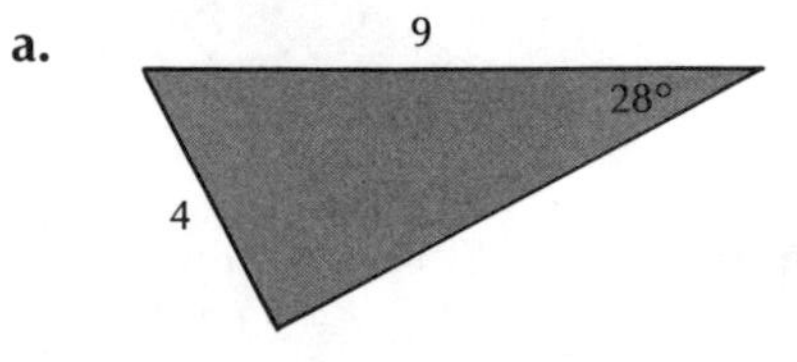

b.

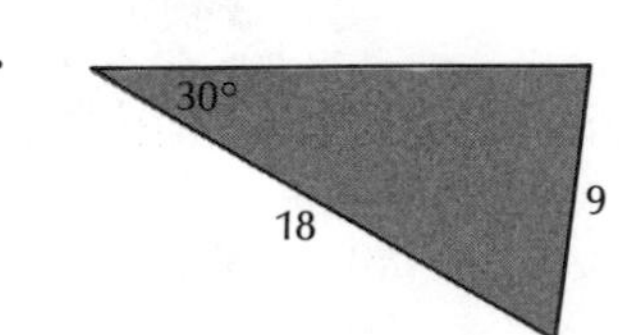

B 5. Solve for θ.

a.

b.

c.

d.

e.

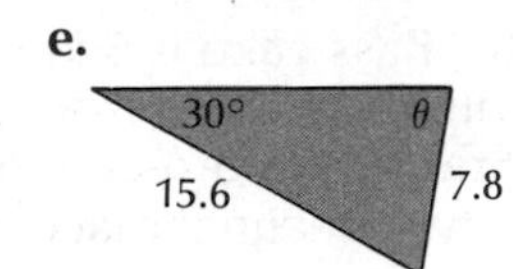

f.

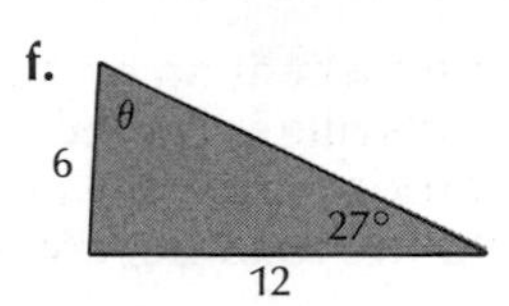

6. Find the measure of each unknown side and angle.

a.

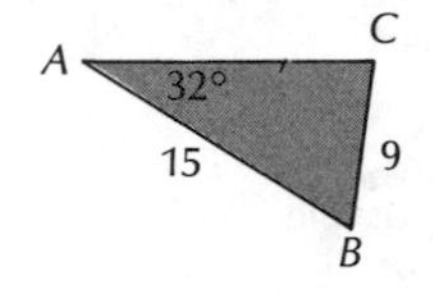

b.

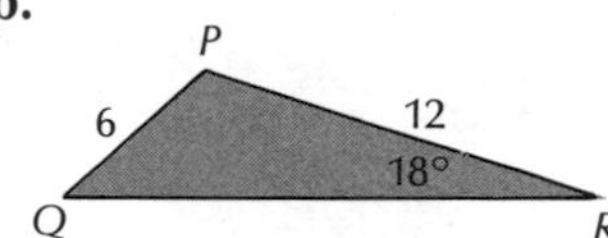

7. Find the value of θ.

a.

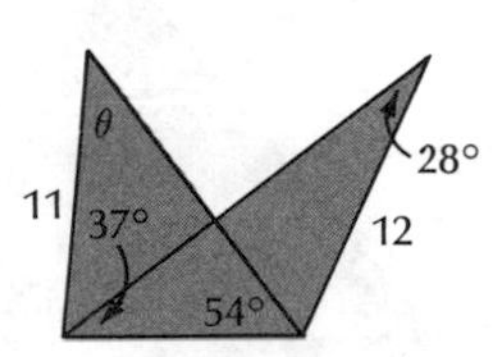

b.

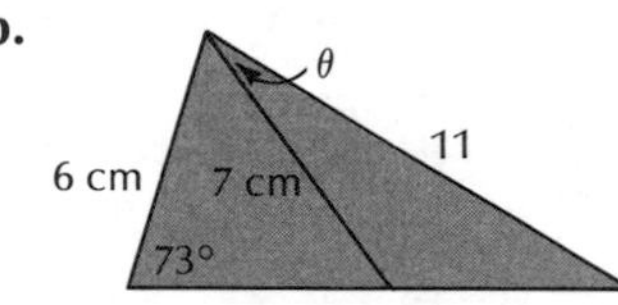

8. In ΔPQR, $PQ = 5$ cm, $QR = 7$ cm, and $\angle PQR = 37°$. Find the size of $\angle P$.

9. In quadrilateral $ABCD$, $\angle BCD = 90°$, $\angle BDC = 37°$, $\angle BDA = 37°$, $CD = 7$ cm, and $AB = 4$ cm. Find the size of $\angle BAD$.

C 10. On a par 3 hole, Amy's first shot was 157 m but sliced 27° to the right. She estimated that she was still 75 m from the pin. Find the straight-line distance from the tee to the pin.

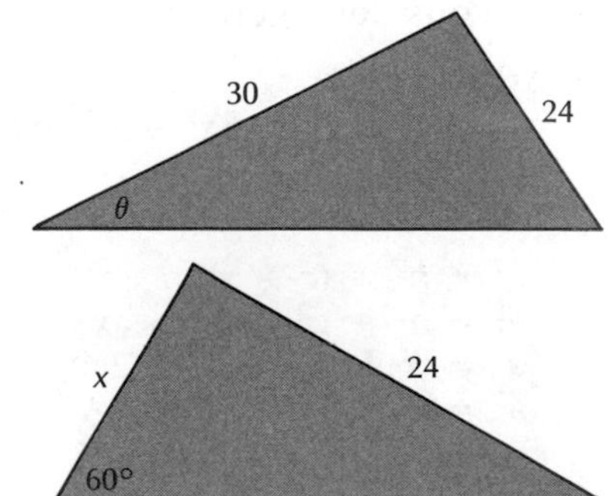

11. Use the triangle at the right to answer each part.

a. For what value of θ will there be one solution?
b. For what value of θ will there be two solutions?
c. For what value of θ will there be no solutions?

12. Use the triangle at the right to answer each part.

a. For what value of x will there be one solution?
b. For what value of x will there be two solutions?
c. For what value of x will there be no solutions?

5-11 The Law of Cosines

In order to use the Law of Sines, you need to know the size of an angle and the length of the side opposite that angle for a given triangle. Consider the following problem, where the length of two sides and the *contained angle* (SAS) are known.

Two highways intersect at an angle of 50°. Bass Lake is 5 km from the intersection. Steadsville is on the other highway, 7 km from the intersection. A proposed road will join Steadsville directly to Bass Lake. How long should the road be, correct to two decimal places?

Let ΔABC represent the situation.

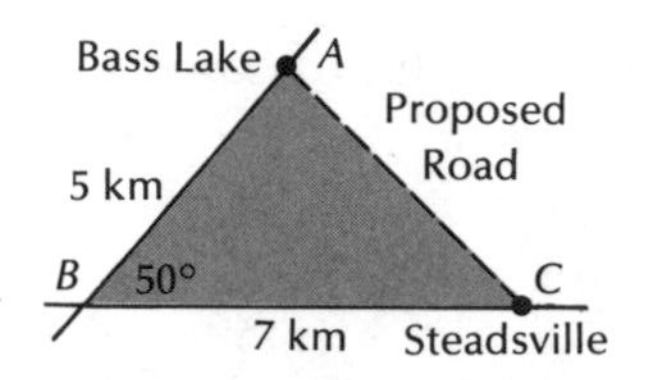

Draw $\overline{AD} \perp \overline{BC}$, with $AD = h$, $BD = x$, and $AC = d$.

In ΔABD,

$x = 5\cos 50°$ and $x^2 + h^2 = 25$. $\quad \cos 50° = \frac{x}{5}$

In ΔADC,

$$d^2 = h^2 + (7 - x)^2$$
$$d^2 = h^2 + 49 - 14x + x^2$$
$$d^2 = (x^2 + h^2) + 49 - 14x$$

Substitute known values into the equation.

$$\therefore d^2 = 25 + 49 - 14(5\cos 50°)$$
$$d^2 = 29.005$$
$$d = 5.39 \text{ km}$$

The proposed road should be 5.39 km long.

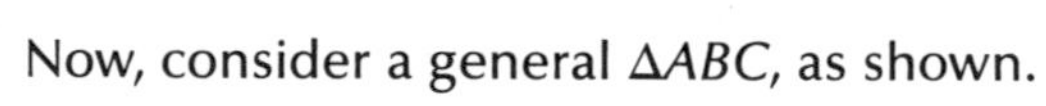

Now, consider a general ΔABC, as shown.

In ΔCAD,

$x = b\cos A$ and $x^2 + h^2 = b^2$.

In ΔCDB,

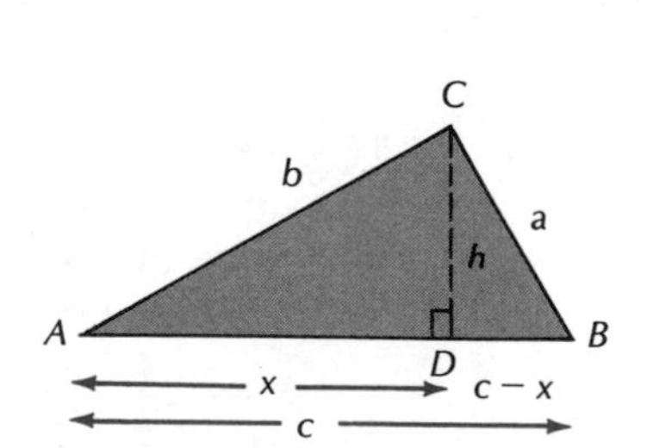

$$a^2 = h^2 + (c - x)^2$$
$$a^2 = h^2 + c^2 - 2cx + x^2 \qquad x^2 + h^2 = b^2 \text{ and } x = b\cos A$$
$$a^2 = (x + h)^2 + c^2 - 2cx$$
$$a^2 = b^2 + c^2 - 2bc\cos A$$

This relationship is called the **Law of Cosines** and is very useful for solving triangles where the measures of two sides and the contained angle (SAS) or the measures of three sides (SSS) are known.

> **Law of Cosines**
>
> For any ΔABC,
> $a^2 = b^2 + c^2 - 2bc \cos A$ or $b^2 = c^2 + a^2 - 2ca \cos B$
> or $c^2 = a^2 + b^2 - 2ab \cos C$.

EXAMPLE 1: For the given triangle, find the value of q, correct to two decimal places.

Since the measure of two sides and the contained angle are known, use the Law of Cosines.

$q^2 = p^2 + r^2 - 2pr \cos Q$

$q^2 = 9^2 + 8^2 - 2(9)(8) \cos 131°$ Be careful with the signs. $\cos 131° < 0$

$q^2 = 239.473$

$\therefore q \doteq 15.47$ cm

EXAMPLE 2: For the given triangle, find the value of θ, correct to two decimal places.

The length of three sides of the triangle are given, so the Law of Cosines can be used.

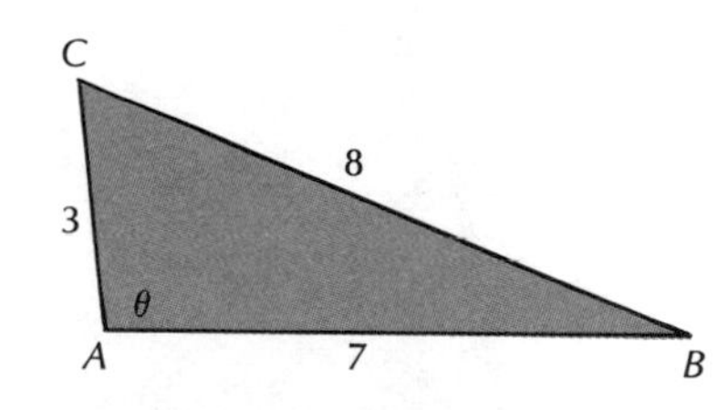

$a^2 = b^2 + c^2 - 2bc \cos A$

Note that these lie opposite each other.

$8^2 = 3^2 + 7^2 - 2(3)(7) \cos \theta$

$64 = 9 + 49 - 42 \cos \theta$

$6 = -42 \cos \theta$

$\cos \theta = -0.14286$

$\therefore \theta \doteq 98.21°$

Since cosine is negative, θ is in quadrant II or III, since θ is in ΔABC ($0° < \theta < 180°$).

EXAMPLE 3: The lens on Percy's camera has a 50° field of view. He plans to take a picture of the opening ceremonies at the Olympic Games. If he is sitting 80 m from one end of the field and 135 m from the other, will he be able to get the whole performance in his picture, given that the field is 100 m long?

Use the Law of Cosines.

$100^2 = 135^2 + 80^2 - 2(135)(80) \cos \theta$

$10\,000 = 18\,225 + 6400 - 21\,600 \cos \theta$

$-14\,625 = -21\,600 \cos \theta$

$\cos \theta = 0.677\,08$ θ is in quadrant I.

$\therefore \theta \doteq 47.38°$

Since his camera has a 50° field of view and he needs only 47.38°, he will get everything in the picture.

EXERCISE 5-11

Give all answers correct to two decimal places.

A 1. Find length of x or the size of θ, as indicated.

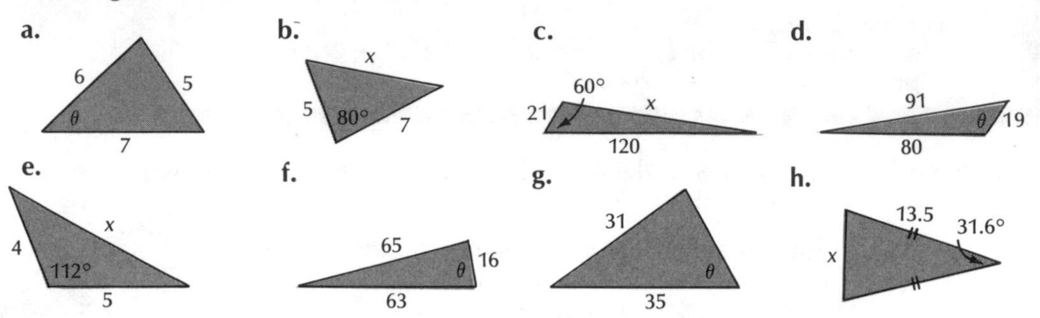

B 2. Find the length of x or the size of θ, as indicated.

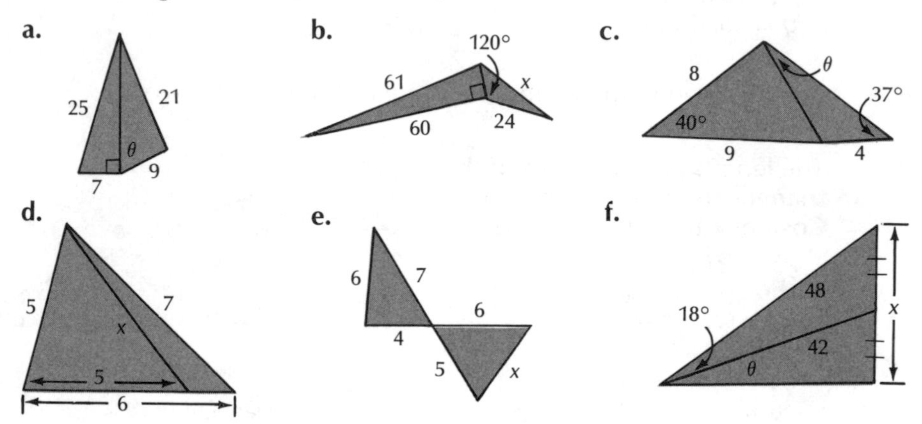

3. In ΔLMN, $LM = 20$ cm, $MN = 25$ cm, and $\angle LMN = 35°$. Find LN.

4. In ΔPLO, $PL = 15$ km, $LO = 30$ km, and $PO = 20$ km . Find $\angle LPO$.

5. In quadrilateral $XYZW$, $XY = 5$ cm, $YZ = 8$ cm, $ZW = 6$ cm, $XW = 7$ cm, and $\angle YXW = 108°$. Find $\angle YZW$.

6. A house is 11 m wide. The rafters on the south side of the house are 6 m long. In order to maximize the solar energy that may be collected, the rafters are inclined at an angle of 48°. How long are the rafters on the north side?

7. Terry drove a golf ball 215 m while playing a 410 m hole. She estimated that her ball landed 235 m from the pin. How many degrees to the left of the pin did Terry hook her shot?

8. Two guy wires from the top of a pole are 10 m and 7 m long and form an angle of 13.6°. If the wires are on the same side of the pole, how far apart are they anchored on the ground?

9. Two guy wires are anchored at the same point. The 15 m wire is attached to the top of the tower and the 12 m wire is attached to a point 6 m below the top of the tower. How far are the wires anchored from the base of the tower?

10. Two aircraft, one flying at 520 km/h and the other at 480 km/h, leave Edmonton International Airport at the same time. If the angle between their flight paths is 115°, how far apart will the planes be after 1.5 h?

C 11. A regular pentagon with sides 5 cm long is inscribed in a circle. Find the length of a diagonal.

12. Two roads intersect at an angle of 83°. A triangular lot at the corner has 240 m of frontage on one road and 120 m on the other. Find the length of the third side of the lot. (There are two answers).

13. Two chords of a circle form an angle of 37°, as shown. One chord is 8 cm long and the other is 5 cm long. Find the radius of the circle.

14. Prove the Law of Cosines for an obtuse-angled ΔABC. (Hint: you can refer to lesson 5-7, exercise **9b**.)

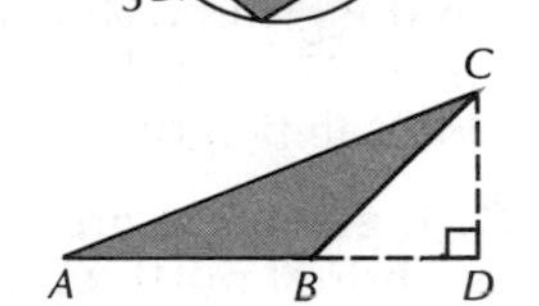

EXTRA

AAS Area Problem for a Triangle

To solve the SAS area problem for a triangle, the following formula was used.

$$\text{Area} = \frac{1}{2}bc \sin A \quad ①$$

The Law of Sines can be used as follows.

$$\frac{b}{\sin B} = \frac{c}{\sin C} \quad \text{or} \quad b = \frac{c \sin B}{\sin C} \quad ②$$

Note that c is opposite $\angle C$.

Substituting ② into ①

$$\text{Area} = \frac{1}{2}\frac{c^2 \sin A \sin B}{\sin C}$$

Find the area of each triangle.

a.

b.

c.

d.

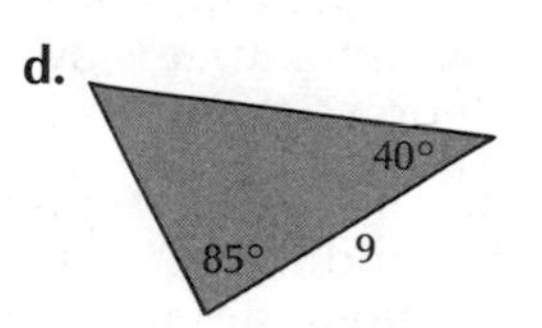

Problem Solving

Three Dimensional Problems

1. A rectangular box has measurements as shown in the diagram. $\overline{DF}$ is an iron rod that will just fit in the box. Find the size of the angle the rod forms with each of the following parts.

   a. the bottom of the box
   b. the end of the box
   c. the side of the box

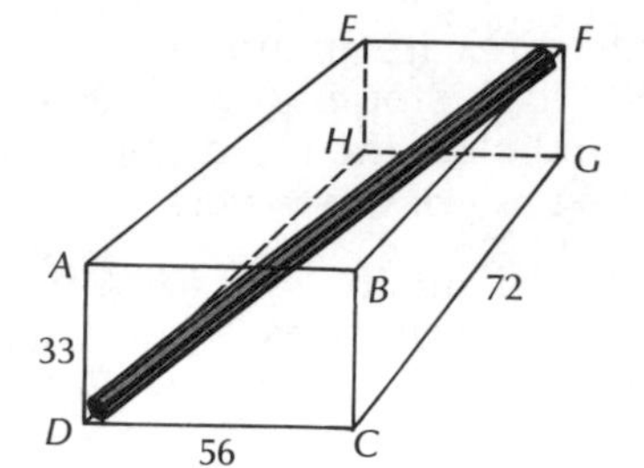

2. Using the information in question 1, find the measure of each angle.

   a. $\angle CDF$ **b.** $\angle ADF$ **c.** $\angle HDF$

3. A box has a bottom in the shape of a parallelogram. One side measures 17 cm, the other side measures 30 cm, and the size of the contained angle is 75°. If the box is 25 cm high, find the length of the longest rod that will fit in the box.

4. To find the height of an inaccessible tower at point C, ΔABC is laid out on the ground. It is found that $\angle BAC = 60°$, $\angle ABC = 40°$, and $AB = 37$ m. If the angle of elevation of the tower from point B is 53°, find the height of the tower.

5. Two guy wires are attached to the top of a 45 m tower. One wire is anchored north of the tower and forms an angle of 42° with the tower. The other wire is anchored southeast of the tower and forms an angle of 32° with the tower. Find the distance between the two anchors.

6. A garage is 8 m square and has a roof that comes to a peak, 1 m above the ceiling. The hip rafters extend from the corners of the garage to the peak. Neglecting any overhang, find the size of the angle between two consecutive hip rafters.

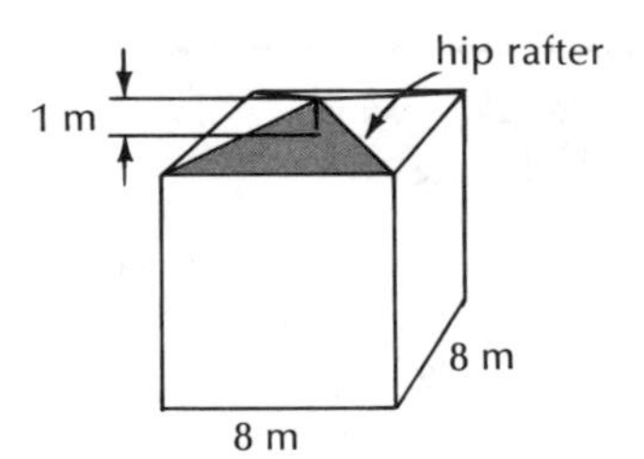

7. An aircraft left Mirabel Airport reached an elevation of 6 km, and travelled 5 km northeast before changing its heading and travelling 7 km further. It is now due north of the starting point, flying at an elevation of 6 km. Find the straight-line distance back to the airport.

8. From the top of a 1900 m mountain, the angle of depression to a cathedral that is due east of the mountain is 38°. The angle of depression to a bridge that is due north of the mountain is 42°.

   a. Find the straight-line distance from the cathedral to the bridge.
   b. Find the size of the angle between the lines of sight from the mountain top to the cathedral and the bridge.

Application

Polygons and π

Another formula that will generate π can be developed by considering the perimeter of an inscribed polygon. As the number of sides increases for the polygon, the perimeter of the polygon will approach the circumference of the circle, which is given by $C = 2\pi r$.

If the polygon has n sides, then

$$\theta = \frac{360°}{n} \quad \text{and} \quad \phi = \frac{180° - \left(\frac{360°}{n}\right)}{2}$$

$$= 90° - \frac{180°}{n}$$

From the Law of Sines,

$$\frac{x}{\sin\theta} = \frac{r}{\sin\phi} \quad \text{or} \quad \frac{x}{\sin\left(\frac{360°}{n}\right)} = \frac{r}{\sin\left[90° - \left(\frac{180°}{n}\right)\right]}$$

But $\sin(90° - \theta) = \cos\theta$.

$$\therefore \frac{x}{\sin\left(\frac{360°}{n}\right)} = \frac{r}{\cos\left(\frac{180°}{n}\right)} \qquad \therefore x = \frac{r\sin\left(\frac{360°}{n}\right)}{\cos\left(\frac{180°}{n}\right)}$$

Let P be the perimeter.
For an n-sided polygon,

$$P = nx = \frac{nr\sin\left(\frac{360°}{n}\right)}{\cos\left(\frac{180°}{n}\right)}.$$

As n increases without bound, the limiting value of the perimeter is the circumference of the circle.

$$\therefore 2\pi r = \lim_{n\to\infty}\left[\frac{nr\sin\left(\frac{360°}{n}\right)}{\cos\left(\frac{180°}{n}\right)}\right] \quad \text{and} \quad \pi = \lim_{n\to\infty}\left[\frac{n\sin\left(\frac{360°}{n}\right)}{2\cos\left(\frac{180°}{n}\right)}\right]$$

Evaluate $\dfrac{n\sin\left(\frac{360°}{n}\right)}{2\cos\left(\frac{180°}{n}\right)}$ for each given value of n, and compare the results to $\pi = 3.141\,592\,654\ldots.$

a. $n = 10$ *b.* $n = 100$ **c.** $n = 100$ **d.** $n = 10\,000$ **e.** $n = 100\,000$

Review

Give all answers correct to two decimal places, unless otherwise indicated.

1. For an angle in standard position, copy and complete the given table.

Terminal Ray	sin θ	cos θ	tan θ
quadrant II	$\frac{7}{25}$	■	■
quadrant IV	■	■	$-\frac{35}{12}$
quadrant III	$-\frac{56}{65}$	■	■
quadrant II	■	$-\frac{21}{29}$	■

2. Find each value, expressed as a fraction.

   a. sin 150° b. cos 315° c. tan 180° d. cos 210° e. tan 270°
   f. sin 180° g. sin 240° h. sin 90° i. tan 300° j. sin 45°

3. Solve for θ, where $0° < \theta < 360°$.

   a. $\cos\theta = 0.1987$ b. $\sin\theta = -0.8426$ c. $\tan\theta = 1.6814$
   d. $(\sin\theta + 0.6)(\tan\theta - 1.4) = 0$ e. $4\tan^2\theta - 9 = 0$ f. $15\sin^2\theta + \sin\theta - 2 = 0$

4. If $\sin\theta = -\frac{4}{7}$ and $\cos\theta > 0$, find $\tan\theta$, expressed as a fraction.

5. If $\cos\theta = -0.6843$ and $\sin\theta < 0$, find $\tan\theta$.

6. Find the value of x or θ, as indicated.

a.

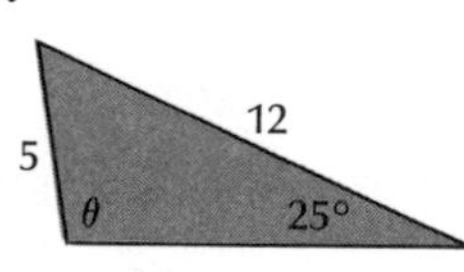

b.

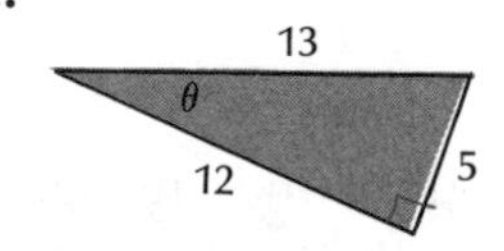

c.

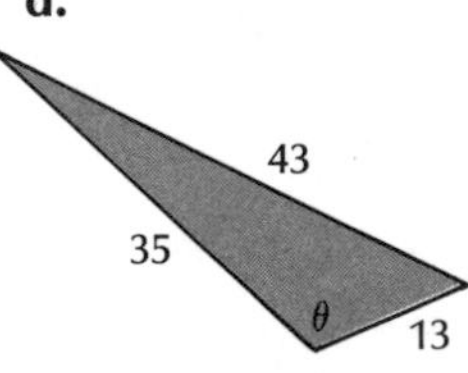

d.

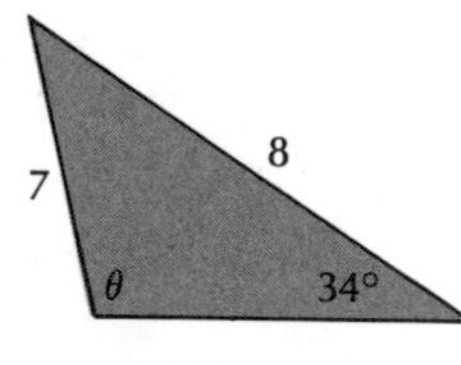

e.

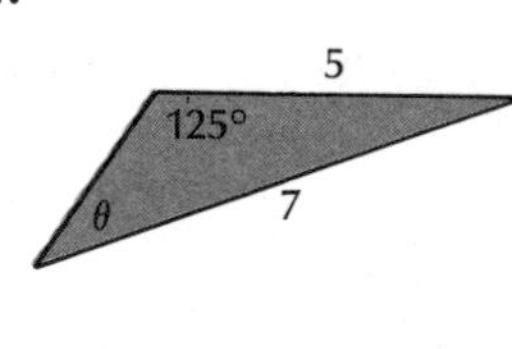

f.

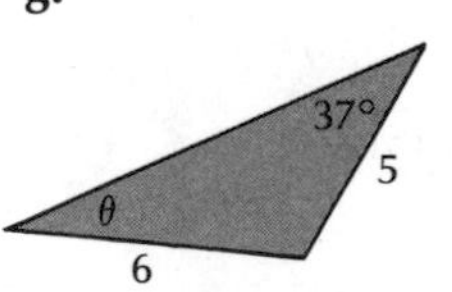

g.

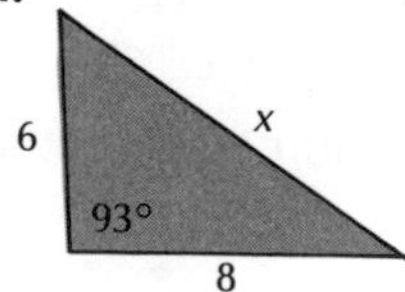

h.

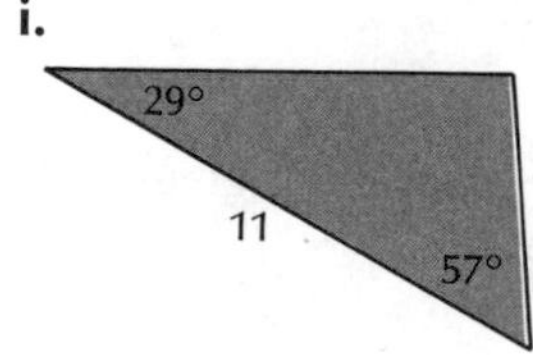

i.

7. For question 6, part c, solve for θ without using the Law of Cosines.

8. Find the measure of each unknown side and angle.

a.

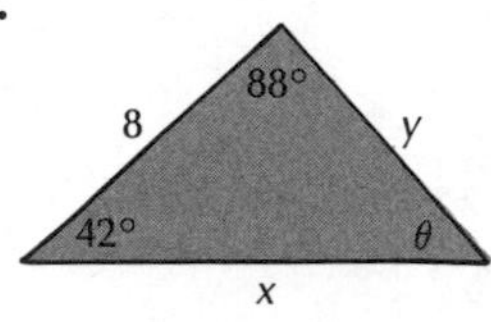

b.

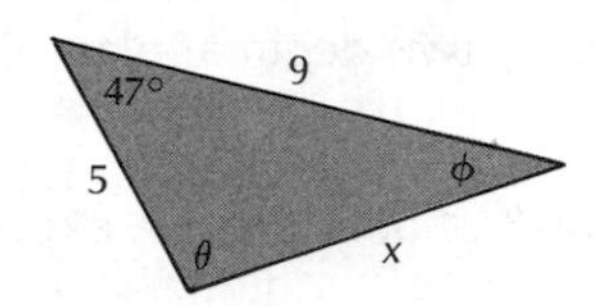

9. A parallelogram has sides that measure 6 cm and 7 cm. The longest diagonal is 11 cm long. Find the measure of the shortest diagonal.

10. Chord $\overline{AB}$ subtends an inscribed angle of 37° in a circle with centre O and radius 6 cm. Find the length of chord $\overline{AB}$.

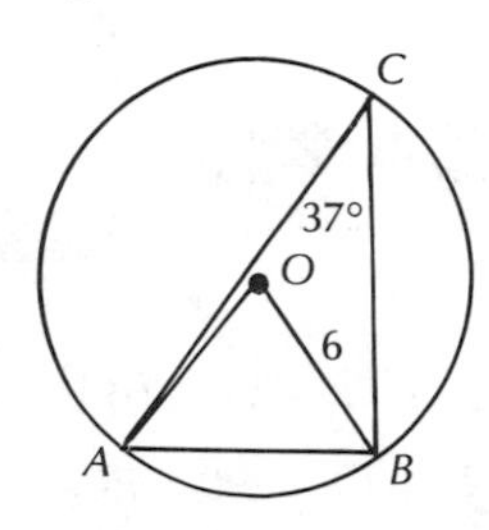

11. In quadrilateral $ABCD$, $AB = 7$ cm, $BC = 8$ cm, $\angle DAB = 108°$, $\angle ABD = 41°$, and $\angle DBC = 41°$. Find DC.

12. In quadrilateral $PQRS$, $QR = 5$, $RS = 7$, $PS = 7$, $\angle QPS = 121°$, and $\angle QRS = 132°$. Find the measure of $\angle PQS$.

13. A cliff has an angle of elevation of 43°. From a point 55 m closer to the cliff, the angle of elevation is 57°. Find the height of the cliff.

14. Two guy wires, 20 m and 15 m long, are attached to the top of a tower and form an angle of 18° between the wires. Determine the height of the tower.

15. Two observers, 5.7 km apart, spot an aircraft directly between them. For one observer, the angle of elevation is 48°. For the other observer, the angle of elevation is 57°. Find the altitude of the aircraft.

16. Ken walked 68 m up a hill that is inclined at an angle of 33° to the horizontal. His brother is standing 55 m from the base of the hill. Find the angle of depression from Ken to his brother.

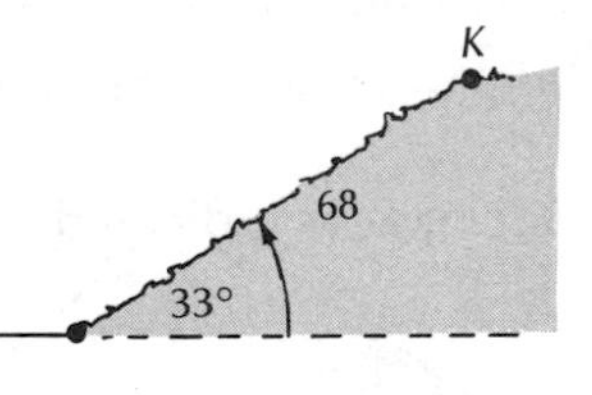

17. An aircraft left Pearson International Airport and travelled 8 km northwest, then changed its heading and travelled north 6 km further. It is now at an altitude of 7 km. Find the straight-line distance back to the airport.

18. Use the Law of Cosines to find the value of θ.

a. $2n + 1$ $n^2 + n + 1$ $n^2 + 2n$

b.

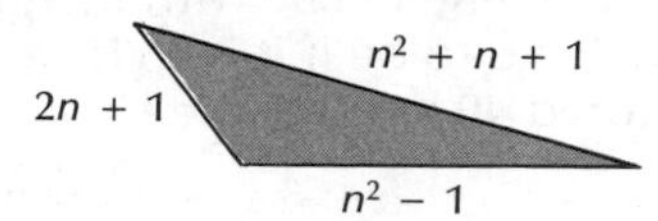

Test

Unit 5

Give all answers correct to two decimal places, unless otherwise indicated.

1. If $\tan\theta = -\frac{11}{60}$ and $\cos\theta \le 0$, find $\sin\theta$, expressed as a fraction.
2. If $\cos\theta = 0.2356$ and $\tan\theta \le 0$, find $\sin\theta$.
3. Find the value of θ or x, as indicated.

a.

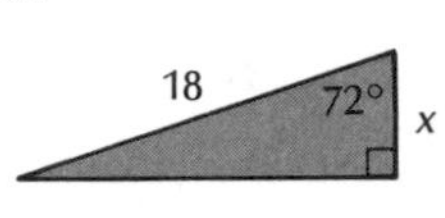

b.

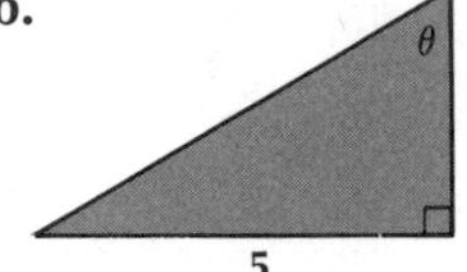

c.

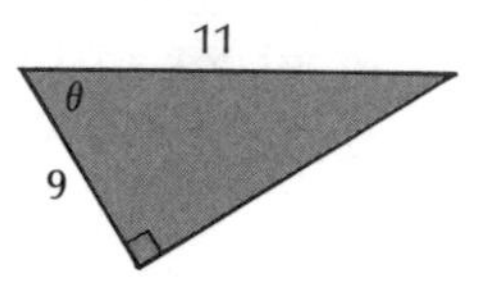

d.

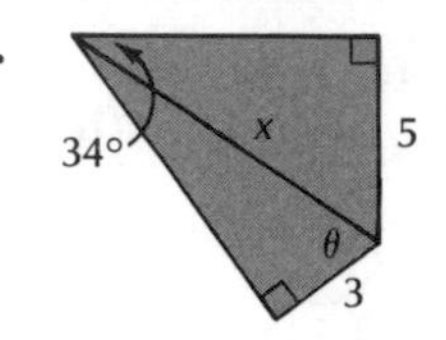

4. In ΔABC, $\angle C = 90°$, $BC = 17.4$ cm, and $\angle B = 38.2°$. Find AB.
5. In ΔPQR, $\angle Q = 90°$, $PQ = 3$ cm, and $RQ = 8$ cm. Find the size of $\angle P$.
6. Find the value of each shaded area.

a.

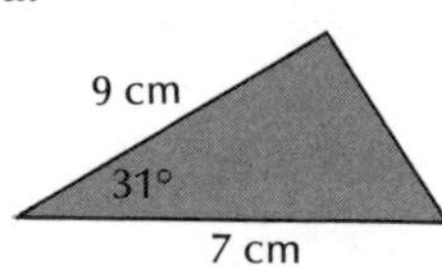

b.

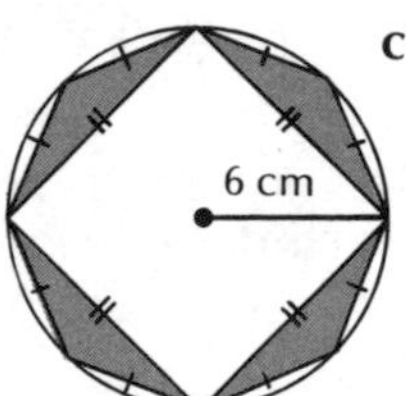

c.

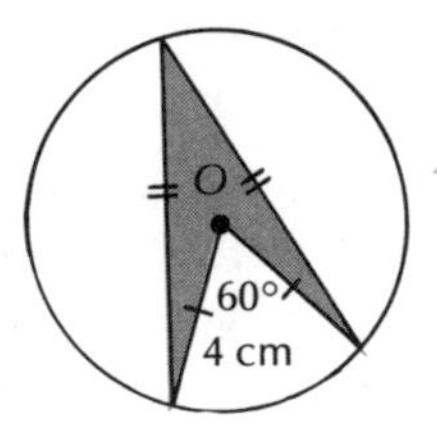

7. Find each value, expressed as a fraction.

   a. $\sin 300°$ **b.** $\cos 225°$ **c.** $\tan 150°$ **d.** $\sec 135°$ **e.** $\tan 240°$

8. Solve for θ, where $0° < \theta < 360°$.

   a. $\sin\theta = -0.1842$ **b.** $\tan\theta = 2.4716$ **c.** $(\sin\theta + 0.6)(\cos\theta - 0.2) = 0$

9. Solve for θ or x, as indicated.

a.

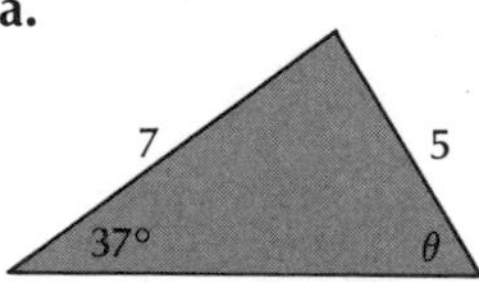

b.

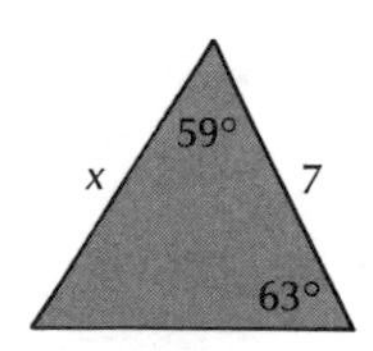

c.

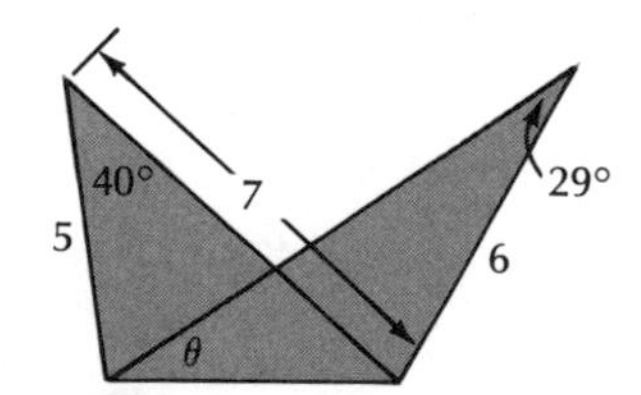

10. A guy wire attached to the top of a tower is anchored 50 m from its base and forms an angle of 68° with the ground. How long will a second guy wire have to be if it is to be attached half way up the tower and anchored 40 m from the base?

Cumulative Review

1. Factor each expression.

   a. $2y^2 + 7y + 5$
   b. $7a^2 - 4a - 11$
   c. $6 + 7y + 2y^2$
   d. $5x^3 + 11x^2 + 2x$
   e. $10x^3 - 15x^2 - 10x$
   f. $x^2 - 9$
   g. $a^2 + 2ab + b^2 - c^2$
   h. $1 - x^2 - 2xy - y^2$
   i. $x^4 - 16$

2. Find the quotient and remainder for each expression, and write the result in the form $D(x)\,Q(x) + R(x)$.

   a. $(x^3 - 5x + 5) \div (x + 2)$
   b. $(3x^3 - 2x^2 + x - 5) \div (x - 2)$

3. Find the value of k such that $2x^3 - x^2 + k + 6$ is divisible by $x + 1$.

4. Find a defining equation for the inverse of each given function.

   a. $f = \{(x, y) | y = 3x - 4\}$
   b. $g = \{(x, y) | y = x^3\}$
   c. $h = \{(x, y) | y = \sqrt{1 - x}\}$

5. Two functions, f and g, are defined by $y = x^2$ and $y = 2x - 3$, respectively.

   a. Graph f and g on the same axes.
   b. Use the graphs from part **a** to graph $f + g$ and $f - g$.
   c. Find a defining equation for $f + g$.

6. The population of the United Kingdom was estimated to be 56 000 000 in the middle of 1986. The population is increasing at an annual growth rate of 0.2%/a. Estimate the population of the United Kingdom in 2006 if the growth rate continues unchanged.

7. In how many years will $900 triple if invested at 8.5%/a, compounded annually?

8. A painting whose dimensions are 25 cm by 30 cm, is surrounded by a wooden picture frame. If the area of the frame is 268 cm^2, what is the width of the frame?

9. A ski slope is inclined at an angle of 23°. From a point 200 m from its base, the angle of elevation to the top of the mountain is 21°.

   a. Find the length of the ski slope.
   b. Find the vertical height of the mountain.

10. In ΔABC, $AB = 5$, $BC = 7$, and $AC = 6$. Find the length of the median from A.

6 Trigonometric Functions

6-1 Radian Measure

A variety of units can be used to measure angles. The **revolution** is a unit that is particularly useful in technology. For example, the speed of an engine might measure 2000 revolutions per minute (rev/min). Phonograph records have rotational frequencies of either 45 rev/min or $33\frac{1}{3}$ rev/min.

A unit that is very commonly used is the **degree** (°). The convention of using 360° to represent one complete revolution can be traced to the Babylonians, who used a number system based on 60. It has been conjectured that ancient Babylonian mathematicians noticed that six equilateral triangles could be drawn in a circle, as shown at the right. They subdivided each of the six central angles into 60 smaller parts, which they called *degrees.*

60°

More recently in mathematical history, a unit called the **radian** (**rad**) was introduced. Many formulas related to the circle can be readily expressed using radian measure. Other areas of mathematics, especially calculus, use radian measure extensively in theoretical and practical models involving angles and rotations.

An angle of 1 rad is related to a central angle of a circle, the radius of the circle, and the arc subtended by the central angle. A central angle of a circle has a measure of 1 rad if the length of the radius of the circle and the length of the arc subtended by the central angle are equal.

For the circle with centre C, shown at the right, if the length of minor arc AB is equal to AC, then $\angle ACB = 1$ rad. Notice that if the length of an arc measures 1.7 radii, the corresponding central angle measures 1.7 rad.

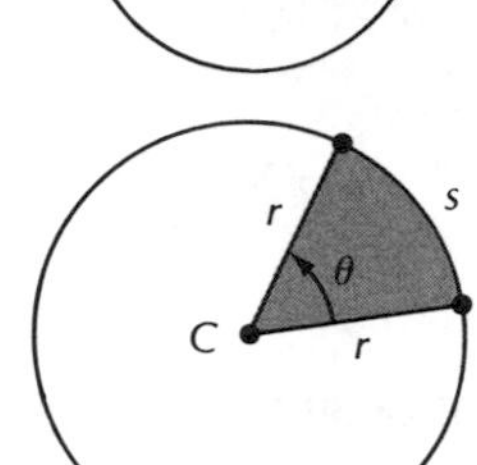

> For a circle with centre C, the measure of a central angle, θ, can be expressed in radians by dividing the arc length, s, by the radius, r.
>
> That is, $\theta = \frac{s}{r}$, where θ is expressed in radians.

EXAMPLE 1: Solve for each variable, correct to two decimal places.

a.

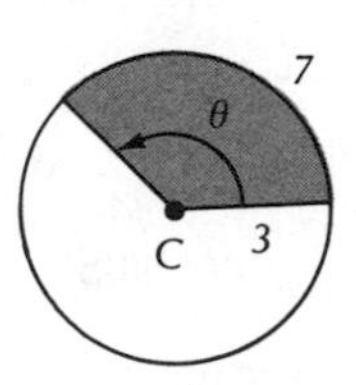

$$\theta = \frac{s}{r}$$

$$\theta = \frac{7}{3}$$

$$\theta = 2.33 \text{ rad}$$

b.

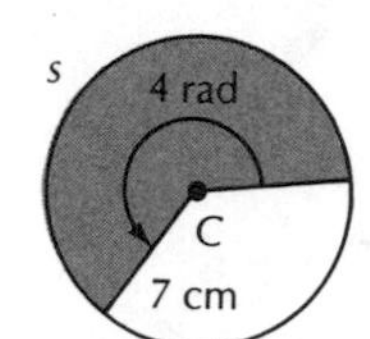

$$\theta = \frac{s}{r}$$

$$4 = \frac{s}{7}$$

$$s = 28.00 \text{ cm}$$

c.

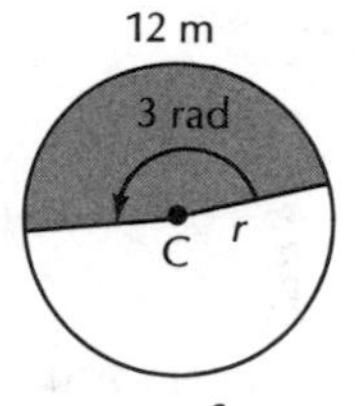

$$\theta = \frac{s}{r}$$

$$3 = \frac{12}{r}$$

$$r = 4.00 \text{ m}$$

To convert between the degree and radian measures of an angle, consider the angle that measures one revolution. For any central angle, θ, the formula $\theta = \frac{s}{r}$ can be used to find a relationship between degree and radian measure of an angle.

Notice that the arc length for one complete revolution is equal to the circumference of the circle.

$$\theta = \frac{s}{r}$$

For one revolution, $\theta = \frac{2\pi r}{r}$. $\qquad$ s is the circumference, or $2\pi r$.

$$\therefore \theta = 2\pi$$

Since 1 rev corresponds to 360°,
then $360° = 2\pi$ rad,
or $180° = \pi$ rad.

> The formula $180° = \pi$ rad is used to convert between degrees and radian measures.

EXAMPLE 2: Convert to radian measure.

a. $54°$

$$180° = \pi \text{ rad}$$
$$1° = \frac{\pi}{180°} \text{ rad}$$
$$54° = \frac{54\pi}{180°}$$
$$= \frac{3\pi}{10} \text{ rad}$$

b. $468°$

$$180° = \pi \text{ rad}$$
$$1° = \frac{\pi}{180°} \text{ rad}$$
$$468° = \frac{468\pi}{180°}$$
$$= \frac{13\pi}{5} \text{ rad}$$

EXAMPLE 3: Convert to degree measure.

a. $\frac{5\pi}{6}$ rad (or simply $\frac{5\pi}{6}$)

$$\pi \text{ rad} = 180°$$
$$\frac{5\pi}{6} \text{ rad} = \frac{5}{6}(180°)$$
$$= 150°$$

b. $\frac{9\pi}{4}$ When π is given as part of the angle measure, assume the unit is radians.

$$\pi \text{ rad} = 180°$$
$$\frac{9\pi}{4} \text{ rad} = \frac{9}{4}(180°)$$
$$= 405°$$

The area of a sector of a circle can be expressed in terms of the radius, r, and the central angle, θ, measured in radians.

EXAMPLE 4: Find the area of the shaded sector.

Notice that the area of the sector is a fraction of the circle. To determine what fraction the sector represents, write a ratio that compares the central angle to one complete revolution. Here the fraction is $\frac{3}{2\pi}$.

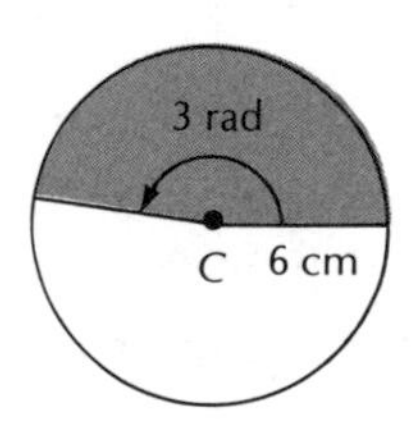

In general, the area of a circle is given by $A_C = \pi r^2$.

The area of the given sector is a fraction of the area of the circle.

$$A_s = \frac{3}{2\pi}(\pi r^2)$$
$$= \frac{3}{2\pi}(36\pi)$$
$$= 54 \text{ cm}^2$$

In general, the area of a sector with central angle θ is given by

$$A_s = \frac{\theta}{2\pi}(\pi r^2)$$
$$= \frac{1}{2}r^2\theta, \text{ or } A_s = \frac{1}{2}sr.$$

θ is given in radians.

EXAMPLE 5: Find the area of the shaded segment. The central angle is θ.

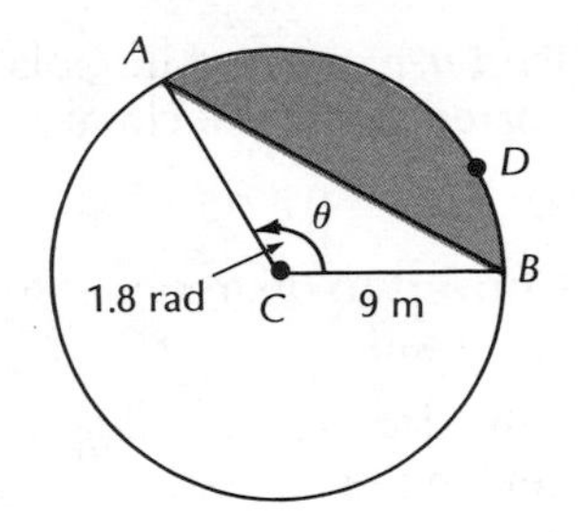

Area of sector $ABC = \frac{1}{2}r^2\theta$

Area of $\triangle ABC = \frac{1}{2}r^2\sin\theta$

The area of the segment is the difference between the sector area and the triangular area.

$\therefore$ Area of sector $ABD = \frac{1}{2}r^2\theta - \frac{1}{2}r^2\sin\theta$

$$\begin{aligned} \text{Area of sector } ABD &= \frac{1}{2}r^2(\theta - \sin\theta) \\ &= \frac{1}{2}(81)(1.8 - \sin 1.8) \\ &= \frac{1}{2}(81)(1.8 - 0.9738) \\ &\doteq 33.46 \end{aligned}$$

First press the DRG key, which appears on most calculators, to evaluate $\sin 1.8$ in radian mode.

The area of the segment is approximately 33.46 m^2.

EXERCISE 6-1

A **1.** Convert to radian measure. Express your answer in terms of π.

a. 30°	**b.** 60°	**c.** 90°	**d.** 135°	**e.** 210°
f. 300°	**g.** 450°	**h.** 36°	**i.** 220°	**j.** 288°
k. 126°	**l.** 132°	**m.** 420°	**n.** 504°	**o.** 324°

2. Convert to degree measure.

a. $\frac{\pi}{3}$	**b.** 2π	**c.** $\frac{3\pi}{2}$	**d.** $\frac{\pi}{4}$	**e.** $\frac{5\pi}{6}$
f. $\frac{\pi}{2}$	**g.** $\frac{\pi}{6}$	**h.** $\frac{7\pi}{9}$	**i.** $\frac{2\pi}{5}$	**j.** $\frac{3\pi}{10}$
k. $\frac{7\pi}{5}$	**l.** $\frac{13\pi}{9}$	**m.** $\frac{17\pi}{6}$	**n.** $\frac{13\pi}{4}$	**o.** $\frac{7\pi}{3}$

3. Use a calculator to evaluate each of the following, correct to four decimal places. (All angles are expressed in radians.)

a. $\sin 2.4$	**b.** $\cos 1.8$	**c.** $\tan 3.2$	**d.** $\sin 4.7$	**e.** $\cos 5.1$
f. $\sin\frac{2\pi}{3}$	**g.** $\cos\frac{7\pi}{6}$	**h.** $\tan\frac{7\pi}{4}$	**i.** $\sin\frac{3\pi}{10}$	**j.** $\cos\frac{5\pi}{9}$

4. Find θ, expressed in radians, for $0 < \theta < \frac{\pi}{2}$. Give each answer correct to two decimal places.

a. $\sin\theta = 0.8215$ b. $\cos\theta = 0.1537$ c. $\tan\theta = 1.2538$

B 5. Convert to degree measure, correct to two decimal places.
a. 1 rad b. 2 rad c. 3 rad

6. Solve for each variable, correct to two decimal places. (C is the centre of each circle.)

a.
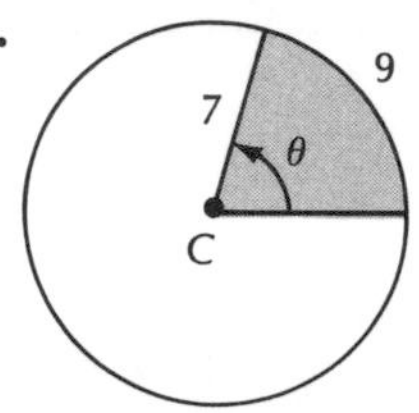

b.
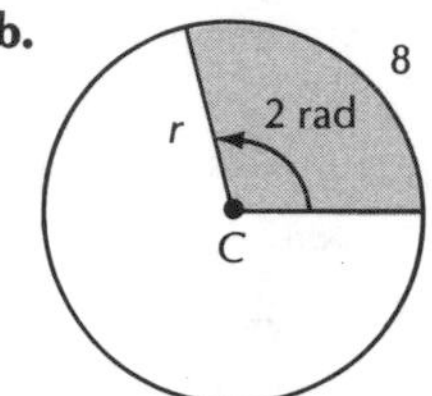

c.
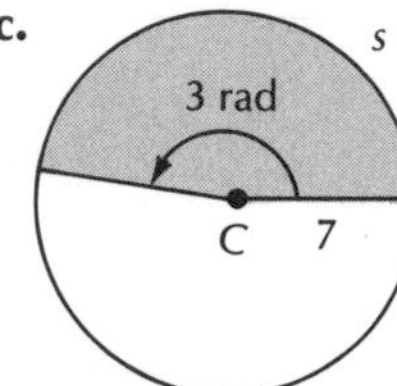

d.
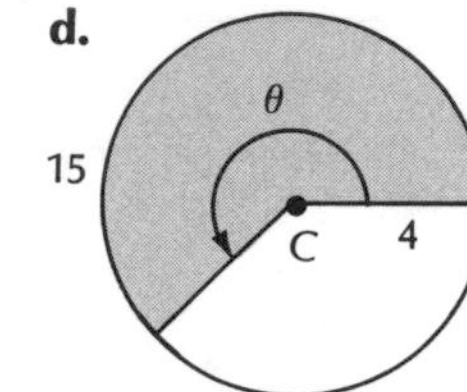

e.
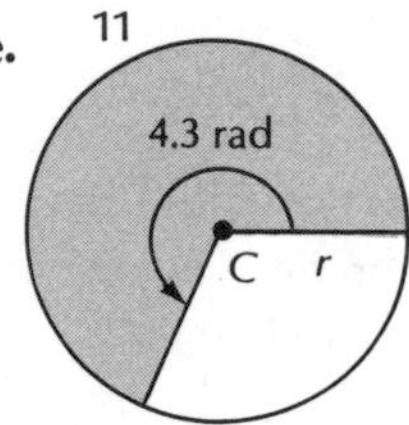

f.
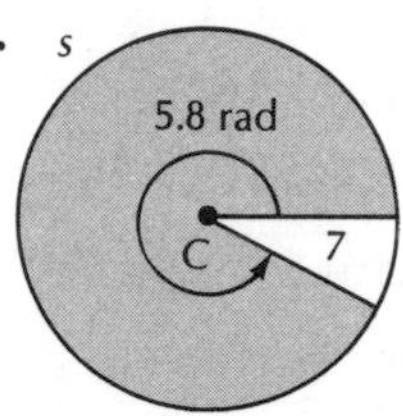

g.
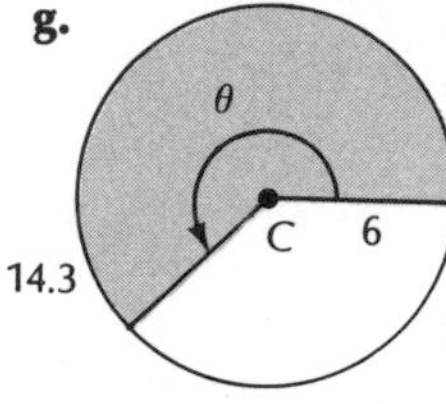

h.
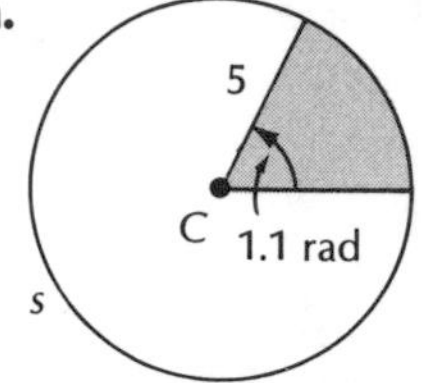

7. Find the area of each shaded figure, correct to two decimal places. (All angles are measured in radians.)

a.
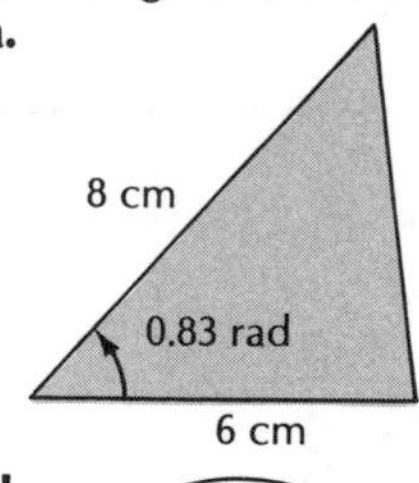

b.
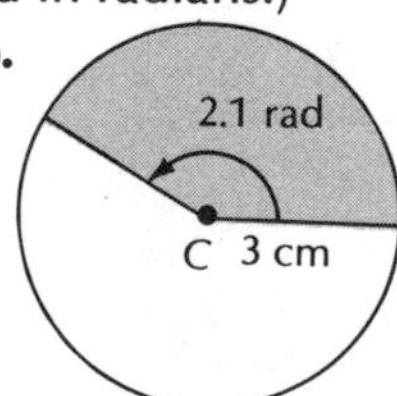

c.
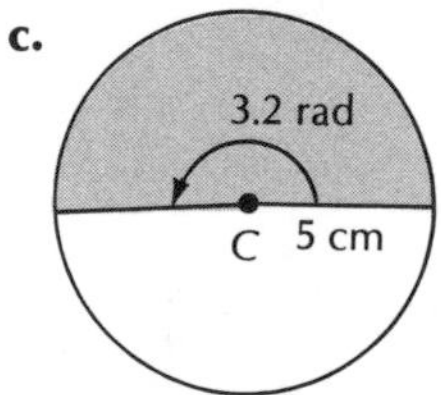

d.
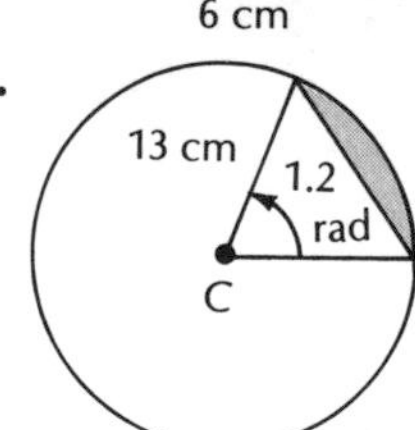

e.
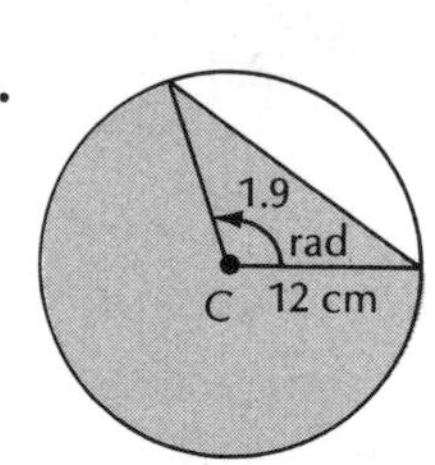

f.
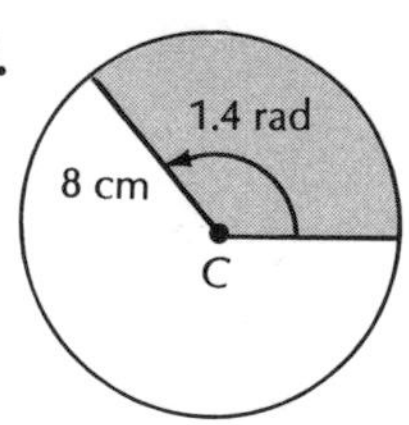

8. A pendulum that is 80 cm long swings through an arc 20 cm long.
   a. Express the angle through which the pendulum has swung in radians.
   b. Express the angle through which the pendulum has swung in degrees.

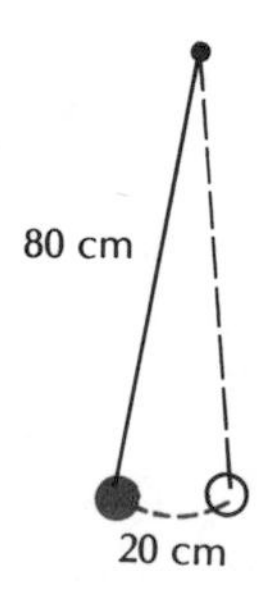

9. A bicycle has a tire with a diameter of 0.8 m. To the nearest revolution, how many revolutions does the tire complete in travelling a distance of 1 km?

10. In a circle with radius 4 cm, an arc subtends a central angle of 120°. Find the length of the arc.

11. In a circle with radius 21 cm, an arc subtends an inscribed angle of 30°. Find the length of the arc.

12. Find the distance between two cities that lie on the equator and that are 1° of longitude apart. Assume that the diameter of Earth is 12 740 km.

C 13. Find the area, correct to two decimal places, of each shaded region. (All angles are given in radians.)

a.

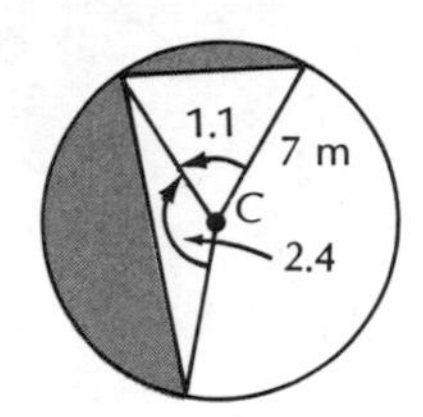

b.

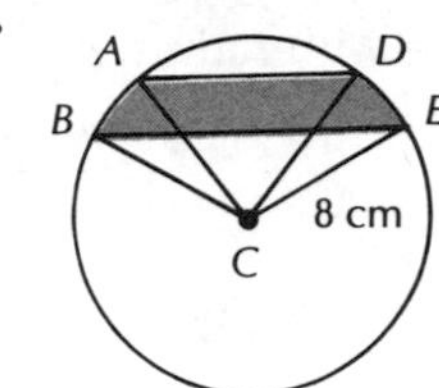

$\angle ACD = 1.3$ rad

$\angle BCE = 2.1$ rad

14. Find the distance between two cities that are separated by 1° of longitude if the cities are both 50° north of the equator. (Assume that the diameter of Earth is 12 740 km.)

EXTRA

Segment Definitions of Trigonometric Functions

The sine and cosine functions can be defined as the lengths of line segments in the unit circle. Consider the diagram at the right.

$\sin\theta = y$ $\qquad \cos\theta = x$

$= AB$ $\qquad = BC$

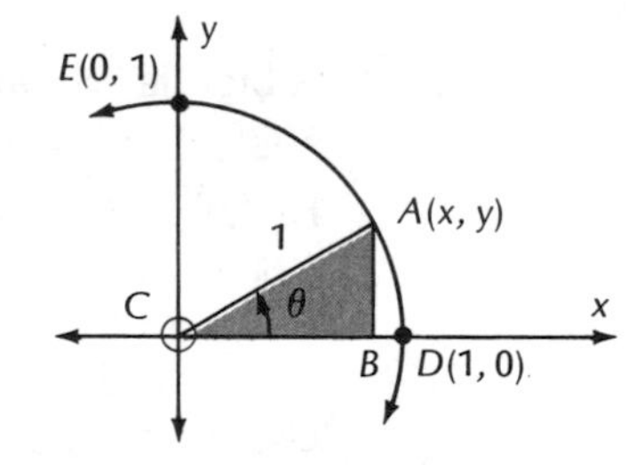

If tangents are drawn at D and E to intersect $\overline{CA}$ extended at F and G, respectively, then each of the other four trigonometric functions can be represented by the length of *one* of the resulting line segments.

Find each of the following.

a. $\tan\theta$ **b.** $\sec\theta$

c. $\csc\theta$ **d.** $\cot\theta$

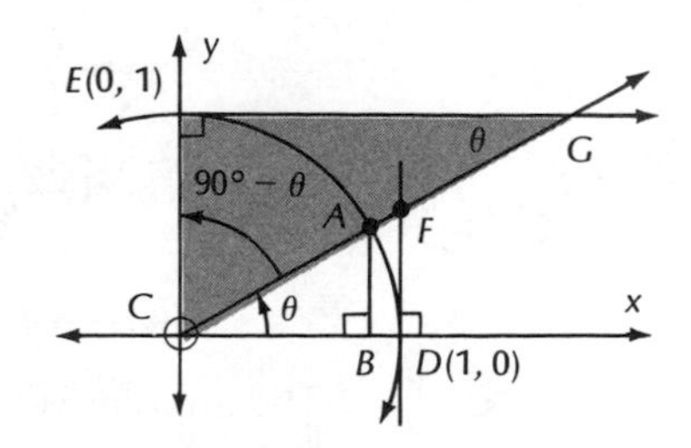

6-2 Angular Velocity

Linear velocity, v, is the rate of change of displacement, *s*, (or directed distance) with respect to time, *t*.

$$v = \frac{s}{t}$$

Radian measure of angles is particularly useful in solving problems that involve rotating objects, such as propellers and bicycle wheels. The rate of rotation of an object can be expressed as the rate at which an angle, θ, changes through time, *t*, and is called **angular velocity,** ω.

$$\omega = \frac{\theta}{t}$$

θ is the angle through which an object rotates in time *t*.

Using radian measure, $\theta = \frac{s}{r}$, where *s* is the arc length or the distance an object travels around a circle with radius, *r*.

$$\therefore \omega = \frac{s}{rt}$$

A relationship between linear velocity, *v*, and angular velocity, ω, can be obtained as follows.

Since $\theta = \frac{s}{r}$, then $s = r\theta$

Divide by *t*. $\frac{s}{t} = \frac{r\theta}{t}$ — Substitute $v = \frac{s}{t}$ and $\omega = \frac{\theta}{t}$.

$$\therefore v = \omega r$$

When using the preceding formulas, express angles in radian measure.

EXAMPLE 1: A bicycle wheel turns at a rate of 90 rev/min. Find the angular velocity, expressed in radians per second.

First, find θ, expressed in radians.

Since 1 rev = 2π rad
and $\theta = 90$ rev,
then $\theta = 180\pi$ rad.

Use the formula for angular velocity and substitute known values.

$$\omega = \frac{\theta}{t}$$

$$\omega = \frac{180\pi \text{ rad}}{60 \text{ s}}$$ $t = 1 \text{ min} = 60 \text{ s}$

$$\omega = 3\pi \text{ rad/s}$$

The angular velocity is 3π rad/s.

As a wheel rolls and completes one revolution without slipping, the centre of the wheel moves a distance of $2\pi r$, in a straight line.

$$CC' = 2\pi r$$
$$= AA'$$

This fact can be helpful in solving some problems that involve angular velocity.

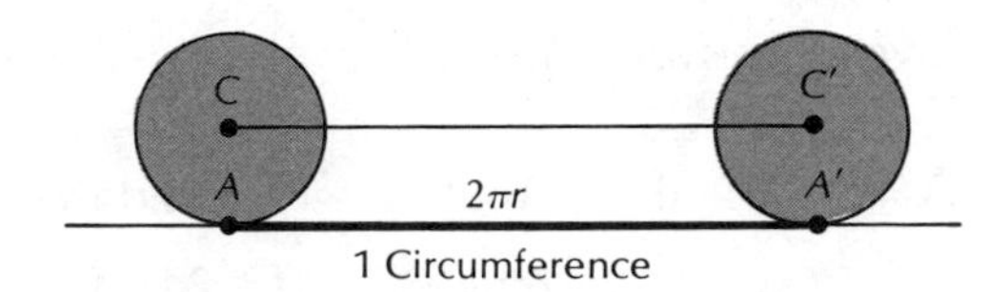

EXAMPLE 2: A van has tires that are 70 cm in diameter. As the van moves, the wheels turn at a rate of 4 rev/s. How far does the van travel in 10 s?

Solution I

$\omega = 4$ rev/s
$= 8\pi$ rad/s
$r = 35$ cm
$t = 10$ s

$\omega = \frac{s}{rt}$ Substitute known values.

$$8\pi = \frac{s}{(35)(10)}$$
$$s = 2800\pi$$
$$s \doteq 8796$$

Solution II

In 10 s, the wheel completes 40 revolutions. So, the distance the wheel travels is determined as follows.

$$40 \times 2\pi r = 40 \times 2 \times \pi \times 35$$
$$= 2800\pi$$
$$\doteq 8796$$

The van will travel about 8796 cm, or about 88 m, in 10 s.

EXAMPLE 3: The wheels of a car have a radius of 28 cm. Find the speed of the car, in kilometres per hour, when the wheels are turning with an angular velocity of 80 rad/s.

$$v = \omega r$$
$$= 80(28)$$
$$= 2240$$

The speed of the car is 2240 cm/s.

$$2240 \text{ cm/s} = \frac{2240 \times 3600}{100\,000} \text{ km/h}$$ 1 km = 100 000 cm, 1 h = 3600 s

$$= 80.64 \text{ km/h}$$

Therefore, the speed of the car is about 81 km/h.

EXERCISE 6-2

Give all answers correct to two decimal places.

A 1. Use the formula $\omega = \frac{\theta}{t}$ to find the value of the indicated variable.

a. If $\omega = 8$ rad/s and $t = 20$ s, find θ.
b. If $\omega = 4$ rad/s and $t = 1.2$ min, find θ.
c. If $\theta = 6$ rad and $t = 2.5$ s, find ω.
d. If $\theta = 5$ rad and $t = 0.6$ min, find ω.
e. If $\omega = 5\pi$ rad/s and $\theta = 7$ rad, find t.
f. If $\omega = 4\pi$ rad/s and $\theta = 12$ rad, find t.

2. Use the formula $\omega = \frac{s}{rt}$ to find the value of the indicated variable.

a. If $\omega = 5\pi$ rad/s, $r = 15$ cm, and $t = 13$ s, find s.
b. If $s = 75$ m, $r = 0.8$ m, and $t = 12$ s, find ω.
c. If $\omega = 2$ rad/s, $s = 15.8$ m, and $t = 5.1$ s, find r.
d. If $\omega = 4.1$ rad/s, $s = 32.4$ m, and $r = 0.7$ m, find t.
e. If $\omega = 4\pi$ rad/s, $r = 25$ cm, and $t = 0.6$ min, find s.
f. If $s = 40$ m, $r = 50$ cm, and $t = 18$ s, find ω.
g. If $\omega = 3$ rad/s, $s = 22.4$ m, and $t = 0.4$ min, find r.
h. If $\omega = 3.8$ rad/s, $s = 16.8$ m, and $r = 6.5$ cm, find t.

3. Use the formula $v = \omega r$ to find the value of the indicated variable.

a. If $\omega = 3\pi$ rad/min and $r = 1.6$ m, find v.
b. If $\omega = 5\pi$ rad/min and $r = 0.9$ m, find v
c. If $v = 28$ cm/s and $r = 2.1$ cm, find ω.
d. If $v = 35$ m/min and $r = 75$ cm, find ω.
e. If $\omega = 7.8$ rad/s and $v = 52$ cm/s, find r.
f. If $\omega = 86.2$ rad/min and $v = 88$ cm/s, fi

B 4. Find the time needed to generate an angle of 3 rad for a wheel that turns with an angular velocity of 2 rev/s.

5. Find the angle generated in 10 s by the arm of a windmill that is rotating with an angular velocity of 15 rev/min.

6. The wheels of a car have a radius of 32 cm and are turning with an angular velocity of 180 rev/min. Find the distance, in metres, travelled by the car in 17 s.

7. The wheels of a bicycle have a radius of 36 cm and are rotating with an angular velocity of 12 rad/s. Determine how much time the bicycle takes to travel 100 m.

8. A wheel has a diameter of 0.7 m. A point on the outer edge of the wheel is moving at 8.2 m/s. Find the angular velocity of the wheel.

9. The belt of a pulley is moving, without slipping, at 75 cm/s. Find the radius of the pulley if the angular velocity is 115 rev/min.

C 10. A cyclist pedals with an angular velocity of 1.2 rev/s. The pedals are attached to a drive gear with a radius of 7 cm.

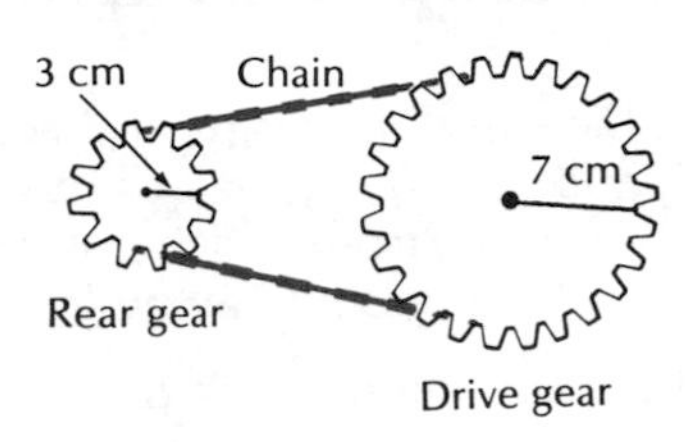

a. Find the angular velocity of the rear wheel if the chain is around a rear gear with a radius of 3 cm.

b. Find the velocity of the bike, in metres per second, if the rear wheel has a radius of 32 cm and is turning at the same rate as the rear gear.

11. A satellite is travelling in a circular orbit, 320 km above the surface of Earth. It takes 102 min to complete one revolution. Assuming that Earth's radius is 6370 km, find the linear velocity of the satellite.

12. Determine the linear velocity at the top of the C.N. Tower in Toronto, as Earth rotates on its axis. Assume that the latitude of Toronto is 44° N, the radius of Earth is 6370 km, and that the C.N. Tower is 553 m high.

13. An object attached to a string is spun in a circle. The tension on the string is called the **centripetal force**, F, and is given by the equation $F = \frac{mv^2}{r}$, where m is the mass of the object, v is its linear speed, and r is the radius of the circle.

a. If the mass and radius are held constant, how will the centripetal force change as the linear speed is doubled?

b. Write an equation for F in terms of angular velocity, ω.

EXTRA

Explorations in Space

Earth's orbit around the Sun is essentially circular and has a radius of 150 million kilometres. Earth completes 1 rev every 365 d.

1. Find the linear velocity, in kilometres per hour, of Earth as it orbits the Sun.

2. Earth rotates on its axis once every 24 h. Due to this rotation and assuming Earth is a sphere with radius 6370 km, answer the following.

a. Find the angular velocity of Earth, expressed in radians per hour.

b. Find the linear velocity of a point on the equator, expressed in kilometres per hour.

c. Find the linear velocity of the North Pole.

d. Find the linear velocity of Vancouver, which is 49° north of the equator.

Earth revolves on its axis in a *west to east* direction.

3. With reference to question 2 above, why do you suppose that satellites are launched in this direction whenever possible?

6-3 Graphs of the Trigonometric Functions

You have evaluated $\sin\theta$ and $\cos\theta$ for special angles such as 0°, 30°, 45°, 60°, 90°, and 120°. These values result in points that satisfy the equations $y = \sin\theta$ and $y = \cos\theta$, from which graphs of the sine and cosine functions can be drawn. More points can be found using a calculator.

Before plotting points, a *dynamic* picture of a point moving along the curve $y = \sin\theta$, can be obtained by considering a point moving around a unit circle. The *y*-value, *PB*, of a point *P* gives the value of $\sin\theta$, where $\angle POA = \theta°$.

As θ increases from 0° to 90°, *PB* or $\sin\theta$ increases from 0 to 1.
As θ increases from 90° to 180°, *PB* decreases from 1 to 0.
As θ increases from 180° to 270°, *PB* decreases from 0 to −1.
As θ increases from 270° to 360°, *PB* increases from −1 to 0.

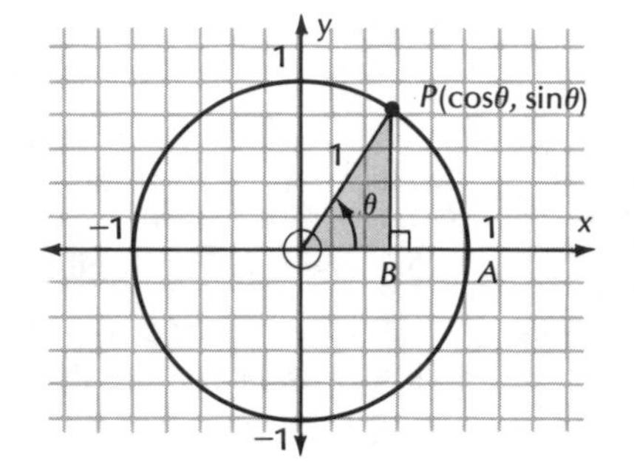

Thus, as *P* moves around the circle, the value of θ increases from 0° to 360°, whereas the value of *PB* fluctuates from 0 to 1, back down to 0, down to −1, and back to 0.

So, in one complete revolution, θ increases steadily, but *PB*, or $\sin\theta$, oscillates between 1 and −1.

Using the same dynamic picture, you can predict how the graph of $y = \sin\theta$ behaves as θ decreases from 0° to −360° to −720° to . . . , and increases from 360° to 720° to . . . .

Make a table of values to plot the curves point-by-point. For convenience, the measure of angle θ is shown both in degrees and in radians. The function values are correct to two decimal places.

θ	0°	30°	45°	60°	90°	120°	135°	150°	180°	225°	270°	315°	360°
θ	0	$\frac{\pi}{6}$	$\frac{\pi}{4}$	$\frac{\pi}{3}$	$\frac{\pi}{2}$	$\frac{2\pi}{3}$	$\frac{3\pi}{4}$	$\frac{5\pi}{6}$	π	$\frac{5\pi}{4}$	$\frac{3\pi}{2}$	$\frac{7\pi}{4}$	2π
$f(\theta) = \sin\theta$	0	0.50	0.71	0.87	1	0.87	0.71	0.50	0	−0.71	−1	−0.71	0
$g(\theta) = \cos\theta$	1	0.87	0.71	0.50	0	−0.50	−0.71	−0.87	−1	−0.71	0	0.71	1

This table of values includes angles for which $0 < \theta \leq 2\pi$. The trigonometric functions are defined for negative angles and for angles that exceed one revolution. The graphs repeat themselves in both directions and so are periodic.

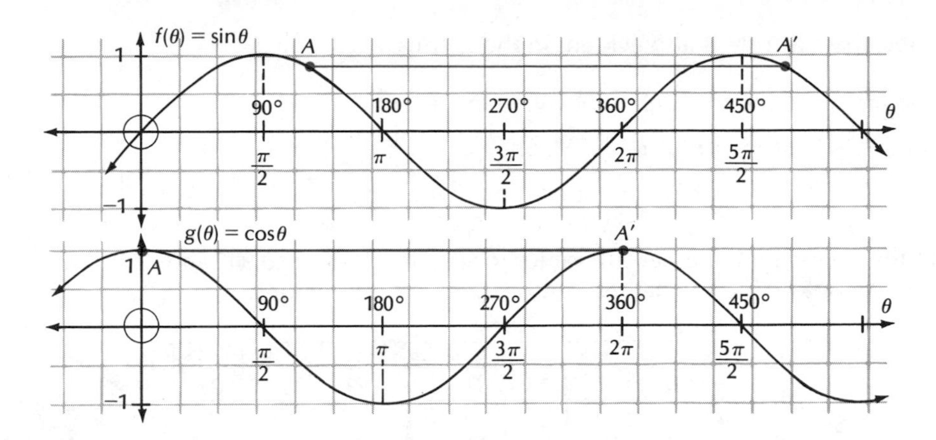

For each curve, A and A' are two points **in phase**. That is, they have the same relative position on the curve. The length of $\overline{AA'}$, the segment between successive points in phase, is the **period** of the function. The period for both the sine and cosine functions is 2π, or 360°.

The two graphs are continuous in both directions so that the sine and cosine functions are defined for all θ. Thus, the domain of each is $\{\theta | \theta \in \mathbf{R}\}$.

The curves oscillate between +1 and −1. Thus, the range of each function is given by $\{\sin\theta | -1 \le \sin\theta \le 1\}$ and $\{\cos\theta | -1 \le \cos\theta \le 1\}$, respectively.

EXAMPLE: A partial graph of the function defined by $y = g(x)$ is given. Find the period of g.

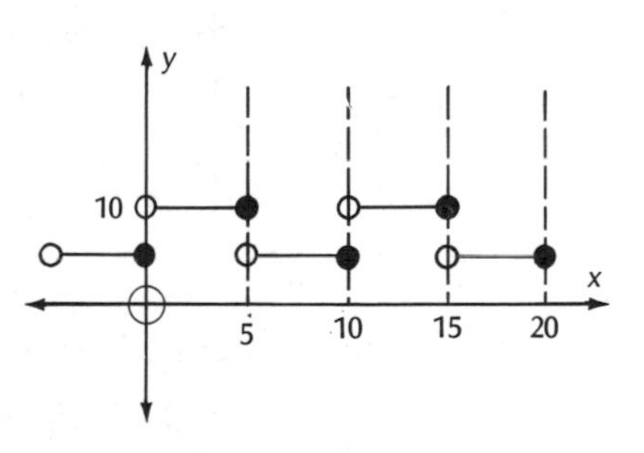

The period of g is 10 because the graph repeats every 10 units.

Notice that since the graph repeats every 10 units, $g(x) = g(x + 10)$.

So, for $x = 3$, $g(3) = g(13)$.
For $x = 13$, $g(13) = g(23)$.

Thus, $g(3) = g(13) = g(23) = g(33) = \cdots = g(10n + 3)$, for $n \in \mathbf{Z}$.

In general, a non-constant function, f, is **periodic** if $f(x) = f(x + p)$, where $p \neq 0$. If p is the smallest positive number for which $f(x) = f(x + p)$, then p is the period of f.

Notice that the graph of the sine function is above the θ-axis, between 0 and π, so that the function must be positive only in quadrants I and II. Similarly, for the cosine function, the curve is positive for $0 \le \theta \le \frac{\pi}{2}$ and $\frac{3\pi}{2} \le \theta \le 2\pi$, or in quadrants I and IV.

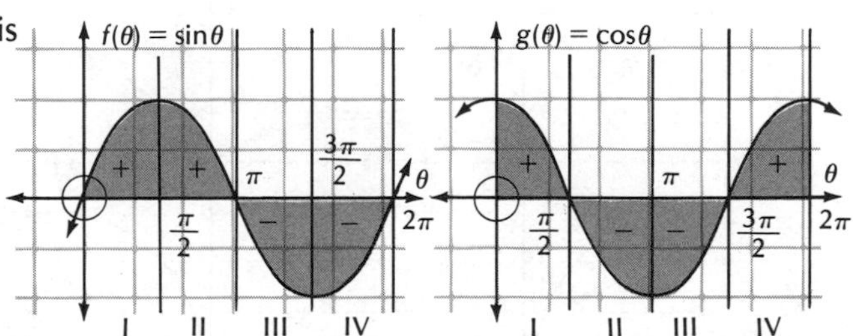

Thus, the cast rule is also evident in the graphs.

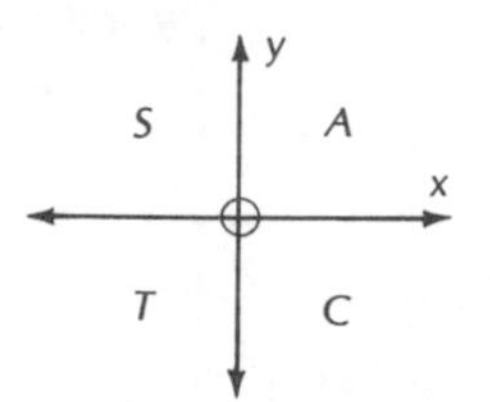

The tangent function, defined by $y = \tan\theta$, is not defined for $\theta = 90°$, or $\frac{\pi}{2}$ or for $\theta = 270°$, or $\frac{3\pi}{2}$.

In the following table, several values for θ that are close to 90° and 270°, are used to determine the nature of the curve in these regions.

θ	0°	45°	60°	72°	80°	85°	90°	95°	100°	108°	135°	180°	225°	260°	265°	27
θ	0	$\frac{\pi}{4}$	$\frac{\pi}{3}$	$\frac{2\pi}{5}$	$\frac{4\pi}{9}$	$\frac{17\pi}{36}$	$\frac{\pi}{2}$	$\frac{19\pi}{36}$	$\frac{5\pi}{9}$	$\frac{3\pi}{5}$	$\frac{3\pi}{4}$	π	$\frac{5\pi}{4}$	$\frac{13\pi}{9}$	$\frac{53\pi}{36}$	3 / 2
$h(\theta) = \tan\theta$	0	1.0	1.7	3.1	5.7	11.4	*	−11.4	−5.7	−3.1	−1.0	0	1.0	5.7	11.4	*

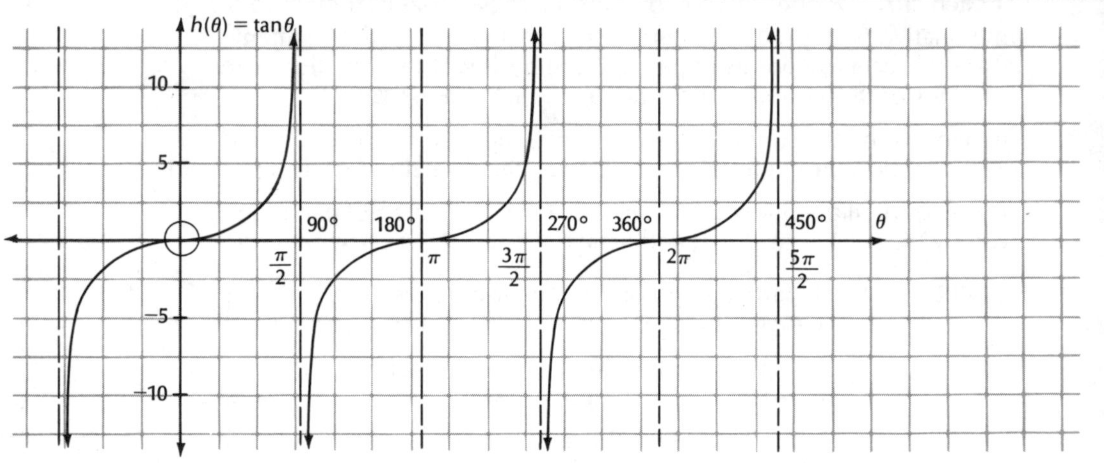

To graph $y = \csc\theta$, recall that $\csc\theta = \frac{1}{\sin\theta}$ and apply the techniques described in Unit 1. Because sine and cosecant are reciprocal functions, if $\sin\theta$ is small, then $\csc\theta$ is large.

For example, if $\sin\theta = \frac{1}{1000}$, then $\csc\theta = 1000$.

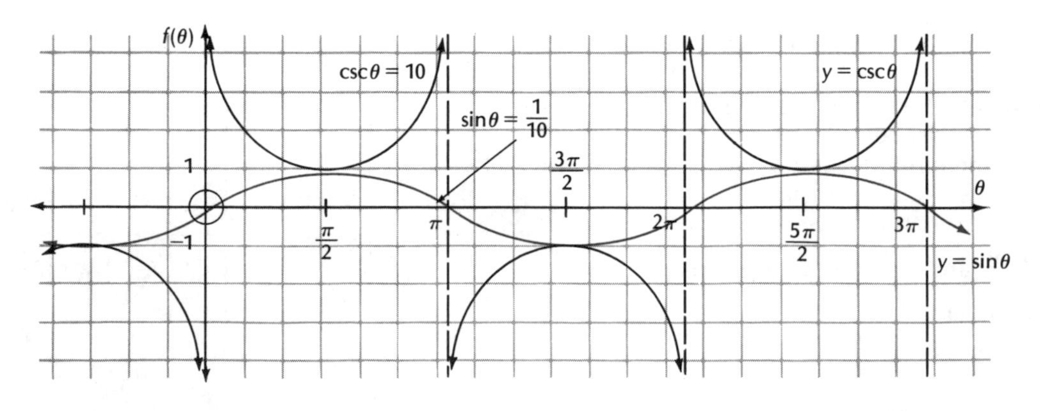

EXERCISE 6-3

A **1.** As θ increases, state the quadrants in which each situation occurs.

a. $\sin\theta$ decreases **b.** $\tan\theta$ increases
c. $\csc\theta$ decreases **d.** $\tan\theta$ is negative

2. Copy and complete the given table.

Function	Domain	Range	Period
sine	$\{\theta \mid \theta \in \mathbf{R}\}$	$\{\sin\theta \mid -1 \leq \sin\theta \leq 1\}$	2π
cosine	▬	▬	▬
tangent	▬	▬	▬
cosecant	▬	▬	▬

B **3.** **a.** Sketch the graph of each of the following for $\frac{-\pi}{2} \leq \theta \leq \frac{5\pi}{2}$.
i. $\cot\theta$ **ii.** $\sec\theta$

b. State the domain, range, and period of the corresponding functions for part **a**.

4. Solve for θ, where $0 < \theta \leq 2\pi$, using reference angles and the cast rule.
a. $\sin\theta = \frac{1}{2}$ **b.** $\tan\theta = -1$ **c.** $\sec\theta = -2$

5. Sketch the graph of each of the following, where $0 \leq \theta \leq 2\pi$.
a. $\sin\theta$ **b.** $\tan\theta$ **c.** $\csc\theta$

6. For each graph in exercise 5, locate any points where each of the following holds.
a. $\sin\theta = 1$ **b.** $\tan\theta = -1$ **c.** $\sec\theta = -2$

7. **a.** Sketch the graphs of $\sin\theta$ and $\cos\theta$ on the same set of axes.
b. Find θ, where $0 < \theta \leq 2\pi$ and where $\sin\theta = \cos\theta$.

8. A partial graph of a function, $g(x)$, is given.
a. Find the period of g.
b. Find $g(3)$ and prove that $g(3) = g(9)$.
c. Prove that $g(x) = g(x + 6n)$, where $n \in \mathbf{Z}$.

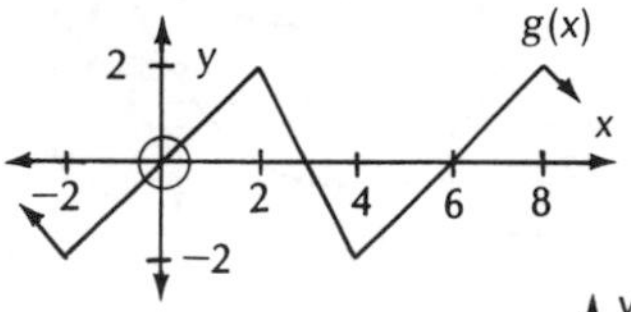

9. A partial graph of a function $k(x)$ is given.
a. Find the period of k.
b. Evaluate $k(3)$, $k(33)$, and $k(93)$.
c. Evaluate $k(104)$, $k(210)$, and $k(25)$.

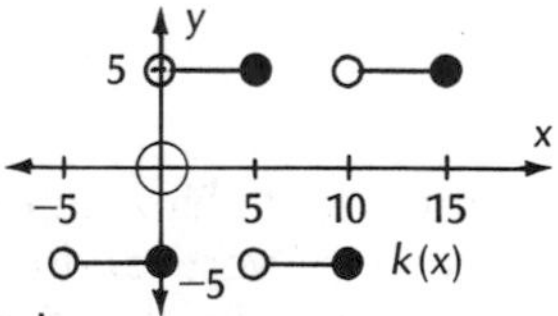

C **10.** **a.** Sketch the graph of $\sin\theta$, where $-2\pi \leq \theta \leq 4\pi$.
b. For any angle, θ, select a point on the graph. Locate a second point for an angle $(\theta + 2\pi)$. Compare the y-values at these two points.
c. Repeat part **b** for two other angles, α and β.
d. How do the values of $\sin\theta$ and $\sin(\theta + 2\pi)$ compare?

11. **a.** Sketch the graph of $\tan\theta$, where $\frac{-\pi}{2} \leq \theta \leq \frac{5\pi}{2}$.
b. Compare the y-values of two points for angles θ and $(\theta + \pi)$.
c. Compare the values of $\tan\theta$ and $\tan(\theta + \pi)$.

6-4 Amplitude and Period

Trigonometry can be applied in Physics to model rotating wheels, swinging pendulums, and even to analyse the sound produced by musical instruments. The sine and cosine functions are particularly useful in describing motions that repeat at regular time intervals. Solving problems involving **periodic motion** requires a knowledge of more general trigonometric functions.

EXAMPLE 1: Graph the functions defined by $f(x) = \cos x$ and $g(x) = 3\cos x$, where $0 \leq x \leq 3\pi$.

First, make a table of values.

x	0°	30°	60°	90°	120°	150°	180°	210°	240°	270°	300°	330°	360°	390°	420°	450°
$\cos x$	1	0.87	0.5	0	−0.5	−0.87	−1	−0.87	−0.5	0	0.5	0.87	1	0.87	0.5	0
$3\cos x$	3	2.60	1.5	0	−1.5	−2.60	−3	−2.60	−1.5	0	1.5	2.60	3	2.60	1.5	0

Then graph each function from the table of values.

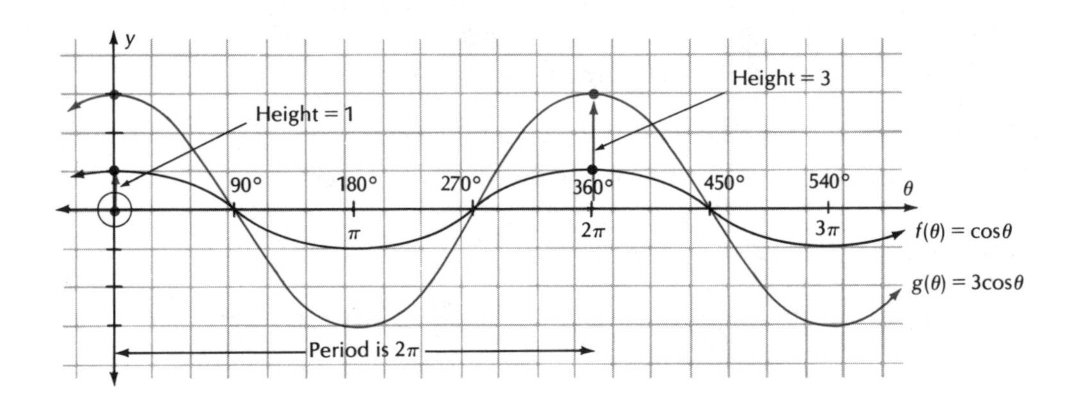

An important characteristic of a periodic function is the measure of "vertical rise and fall" of the graph. When a periodic function has a **maximum value, *M*,** and a **minimum value, *m*,** the **amplitude** of the function is defined as $\dfrac{M-m}{2}$.

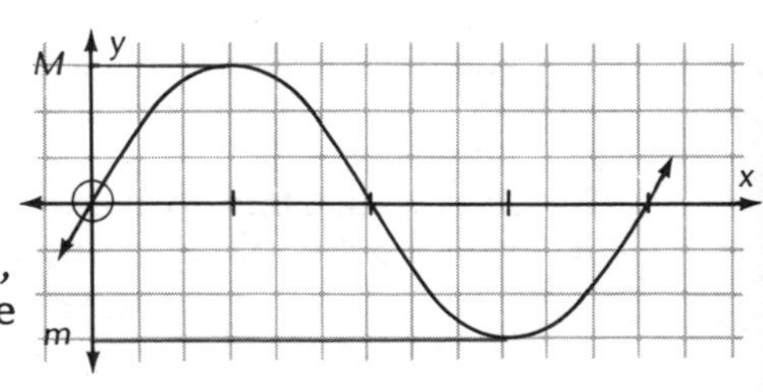

The period is 2π for both curves in Example 1. However, the amplitude for $g(x) = 3\cos x$ is 3, which is clearly three times the amplitude for $f(x) = \cos x$.

In general, the amplitude for $k\cos x$ and $k\sin x$ is $|k|$.

EXAMPLE 2: Graph the functions $y = \sin x$ and $y = \sin 2x$.

First make a table of values.

x	0°	30°	45°	60°	90°	135°	180°	225°	270°	315°	360°	405°	450°
$\sin x$	0	0.5	0.71	0.87	1	0.71	0	0.71	−1	−0.71	0	0.71	1
$\sin 2x$	0	0.87	1	0.87	0	−1	0	1	0	−1	0	1	0

Use the table of values to graph the functions.

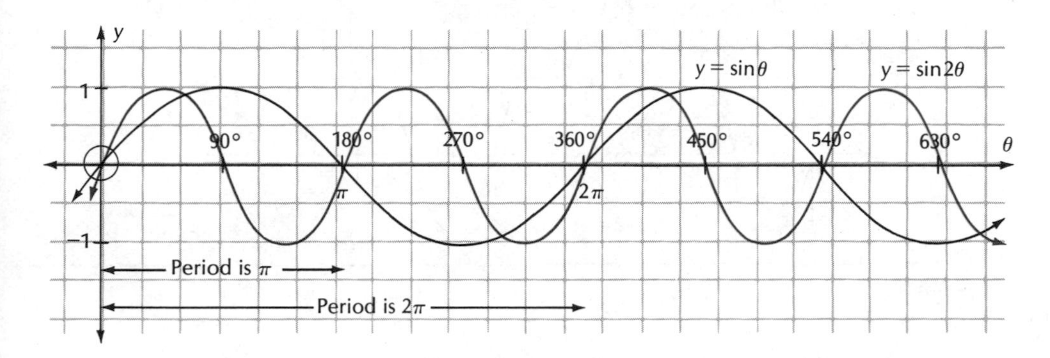

The amplitude for each curve is 1.
However, the period for $\sin x$ is 2π, or 360°.
the period for $\sin 2x$ is π, or 180°, and
the period for $\sin kx$ is $\frac{360°}{k}$, or $\frac{2\pi}{k}$.

EXAMPLE 3: Graph the function $s(x) = -\tan x$.

Recall that the graphs of $y = f(x)$ and $y = -f(x)$ are reflection images of each other in the x-axis. First sketch the graph of $y = \tan x$. Then sketch its reflection in the x-axis.

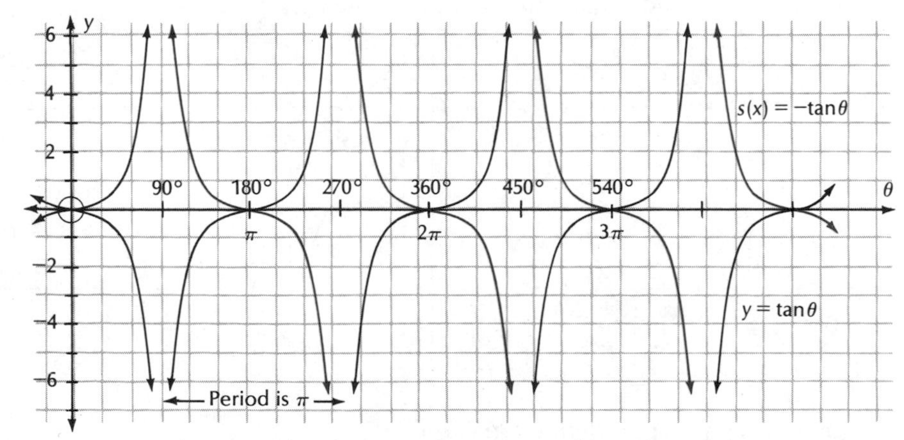

The period is the same for $\tan x$ and its mirror image, $-\tan x$.

EXAMPLE 4: **a.** Compare, in words, the graphs of $f(x) = \sin x$ and $h(x) = -2\sin 3x$.

The graph of $h(x) = -2\sin 3x$ is a reflection of the graph of $f(x) = \sin x$ in the x-axis, with the amplitude increased to 2 and the period shortened to $\frac{360°}{3} = 120°$, or $\frac{2\pi}{3}$.

b. Sketch the graph of $h(x) = -2\sin 3x$, where $0° \leq x \leq 360°$.

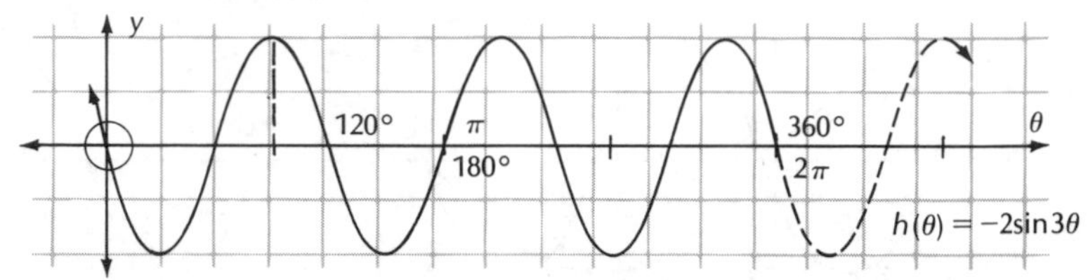

EXERCISE 6-4

A **1.** State the period and amplitude of the graph of each function.

a. $y = 2\sin\theta$ **b.** $y = \cos 4\theta$ **c.** $y = 3\sin 2\theta$

d. $y = \frac{1}{3}\cos 4\theta$ **e.** $y = -5\sin\frac{\theta}{4}$ **f.** $y = \frac{2}{3}\cos\frac{\theta}{3}$

2. Write a defining equation for each of the following.

a. a sine function reflected in the θ-axis **b.** a cosine function with period 120°

c. a sine function with amplitude $\frac{3}{4}$ **d.** a tangent function with period 720°

B **3.** Sketch the graph of each function, where $0° \leq x \leq 360°$.

a. $f(x) = 3\sin x$ **b.** $h(x) = -\cos x$ **c.** $m(x) = \cos 2x$

d. $n(x) = \frac{1}{2}\cos x$ **e.** $p(x) = \sin\frac{x}{2}$ **f.** $f(x) = -\sin x$

4. State an equation of the function that defines each given curve.

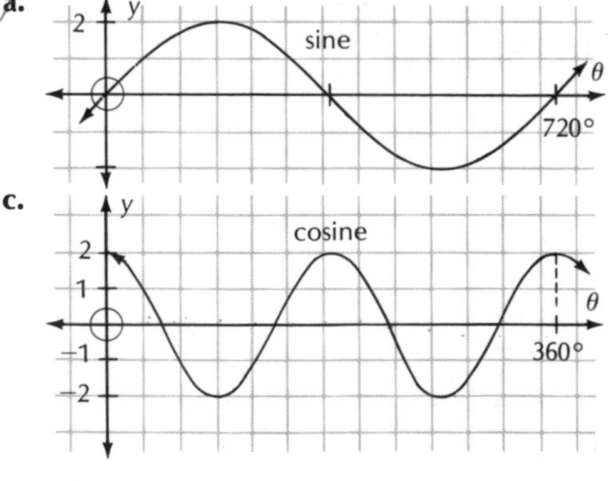

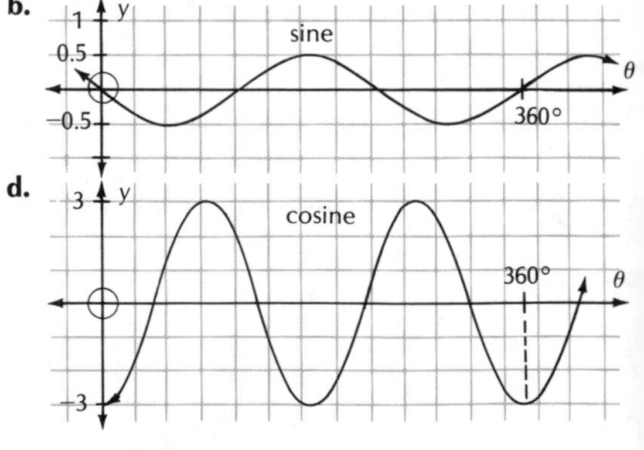

5. Sketch the graph of each function defined in exercise 2.

6. Sketch the graph of each function, where $0° \leq \theta \leq 360°$.

a. $y = -3\sin\theta$ **b.** $y = 2\cos 3\theta$ **c.** $y = -\tan 2\theta$

d. $y = 3\cos\frac{\theta}{2}$ **e.** $y = \tan\frac{\theta}{3}$ **f.** $y = -\frac{1}{4}\cos\frac{\theta}{2}$

g. $y = -\sin 3\theta$ **h.** $y = -2\sin 2\theta$ **i.** $y = 3\cos\frac{\theta}{4}$

C **7.** Sketch each function, where $0° \leq \theta \leq 360°$.

a. $y = 2\sin\frac{3\theta}{2}$ **b.** $y = -\cos\frac{2\theta}{3}$ **c.** $y = \tan\frac{3\theta}{4}$

d. $y = |\sin\theta|$ **e.** $y = 2|\cos\theta|$ **f.** $y = -2|\cos\theta|$

Application

Radio Transmissions

The sine curve is basic to the transmission of radio signals. The audio signal is mixed with a carrier signal to produce a total signal. All of the signals are sine curves, or waves.

For an **AM (amplitude modulation)** broadcast, the frequency of the audio signal remains constant, while the *amplitude* of the carrier signal is *modulated,* or adjusted, to produce the total signal.

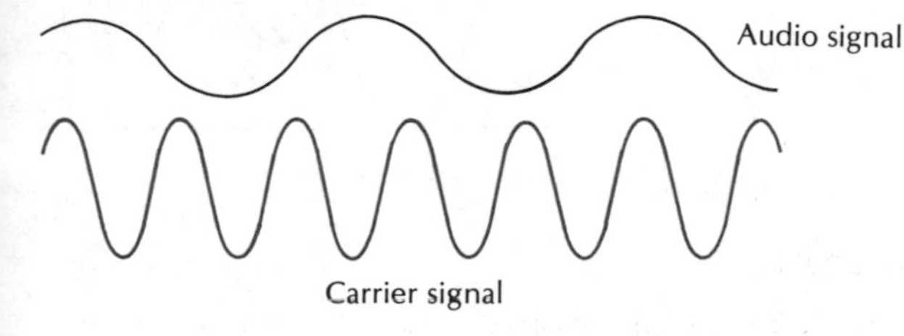

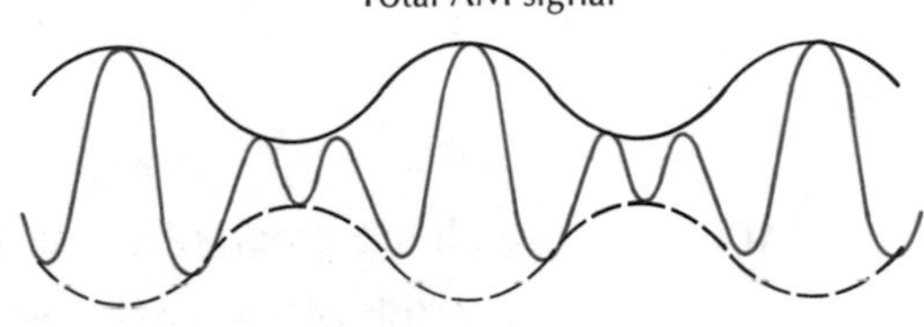

For an **FM (frequency modulation)** broadcast, the amplitude of the carrier signal remains constant, while the *frequency,* or period, of the audio signal is *modulated.*

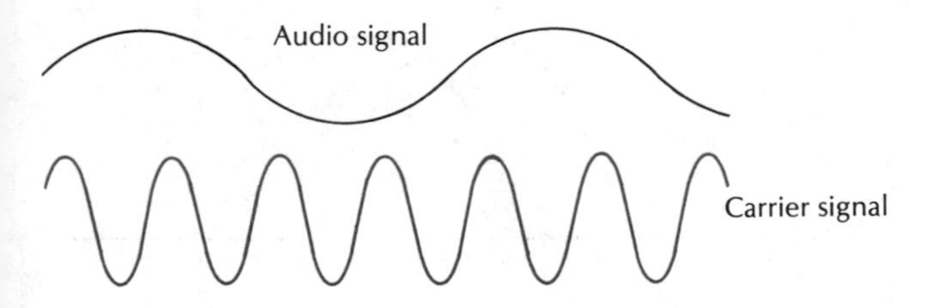

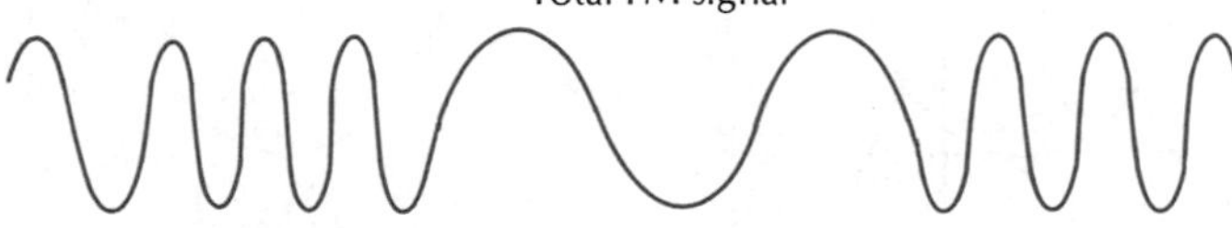

AM and FM radio stations have *carrier frequencies.*
Investigate the different carrier frequencies for various radio stations in your community. Generalize some differences between AM and FM broadcast signals, based on your findings.

6-5 Horizontal and Vertical Translations

As shown at the right, the graph of $y = (x - 3)^2$ is a horizontal translation of $y = x^2$, three units to the right. The graph of $y = x^2 + 2$ is a vertical translation of $y = x^2$, two units up.

The combined effect of these two translations on the graph of $y = x^2$ results in the graph of $y = (x - 3)^2 + 2$. Each point on the graph of $y = x^2$ is translated three units to the right and two units up.

In general, the graph of $y = f(x - a)$ is the image of the graph of $y = f(x)$, translated a units, parallel to the x-axis. Also, the graph of $y = f(x) + b$ is the image of the graph of $y = f(x)$, translated b units, parallel to the y-axis.

Concepts from transformation geometry can be applied to sketch the graphs of trigonometric functions.

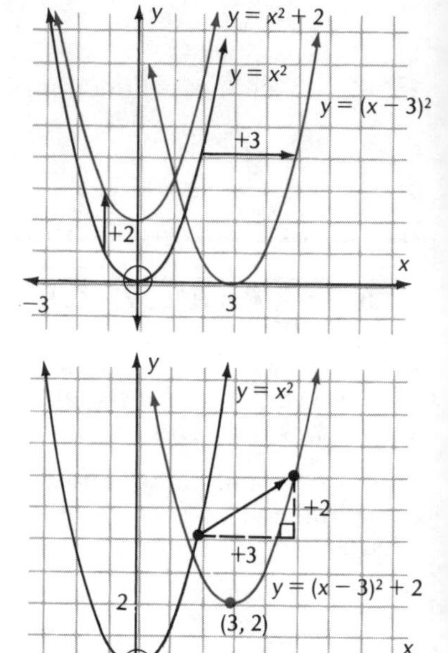

EXAMPLE 1: Sketch the graph of $y = \sin(x - 60°)$.

The graph of $y = \sin(x - 60°)$ is the image of $y = \sin x$, translated 60° to the right, parallel to the x-axis. Sketch the graph of $y = \sin x$. Then, find the image of each point on the curve, 60° to the right.

The x-axis is measured in degrees.

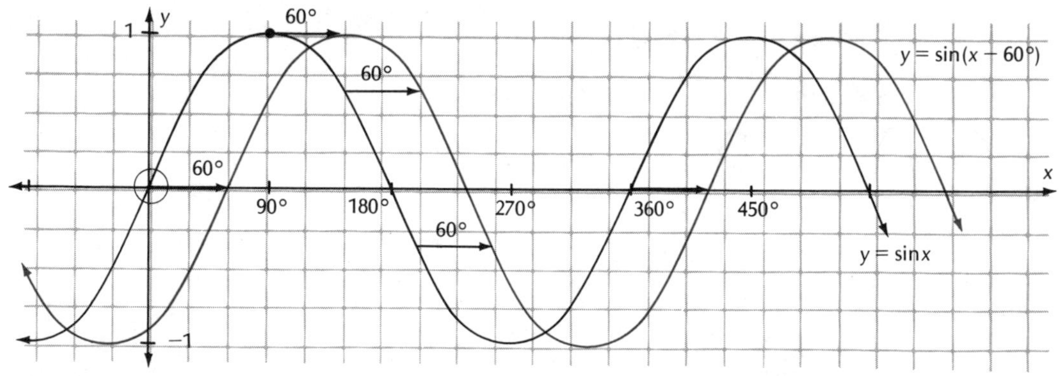

The function $y = \sin(x - 60°)$ can also be written as $y = \sin\left(x - \frac{\pi}{3}\right)$, where x is measured in radians. The horizontal translation of 60°, or $\frac{\pi}{3}$ rad, is called a **phase shift** of 60°, or $\frac{\pi}{3}$ rad.

EXAMPLE 2: Sketch the graph of $y = \cos x - 2$.

The graph of $y = \cos x - 2$ is the image of $y = \cos x$, translated 2 units down, parallel to the y-axis. First, sketch $y = \cos x$. Then find the image of each point of the curve, 2 units down.

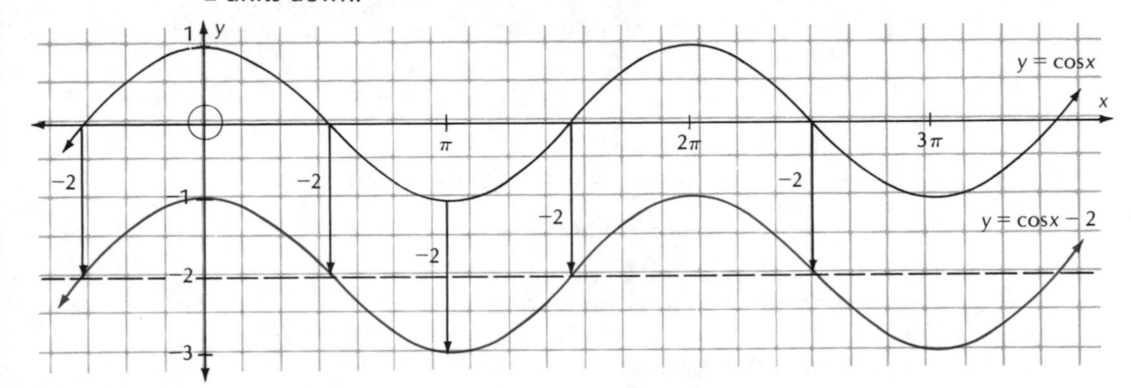

EXAMPLE 3:

a. Describe, in words, the transformations performed on the graph of $y = \sin\theta$ to obtain the graph of $y = -3\sin\left(\theta - \frac{\pi}{3}\right) + 2$.

$$y = -3\sin\left(\theta - \frac{\pi}{3}\right) + 2$$

- amplitude 3 → -3
- sine curve → sin
- phase shift, $\frac{\pi}{3}$ rad to the right → $\frac{\pi}{3}$
- vertical translation, 2 units up → $+2$

The graph is a sine curve, reflected in the θ-axis, with amplitude 3, a phase shift $\frac{\pi}{3}$ rad to the right, and a vertical translation 2 units up.

b. Sketch both curves given in part **a**.

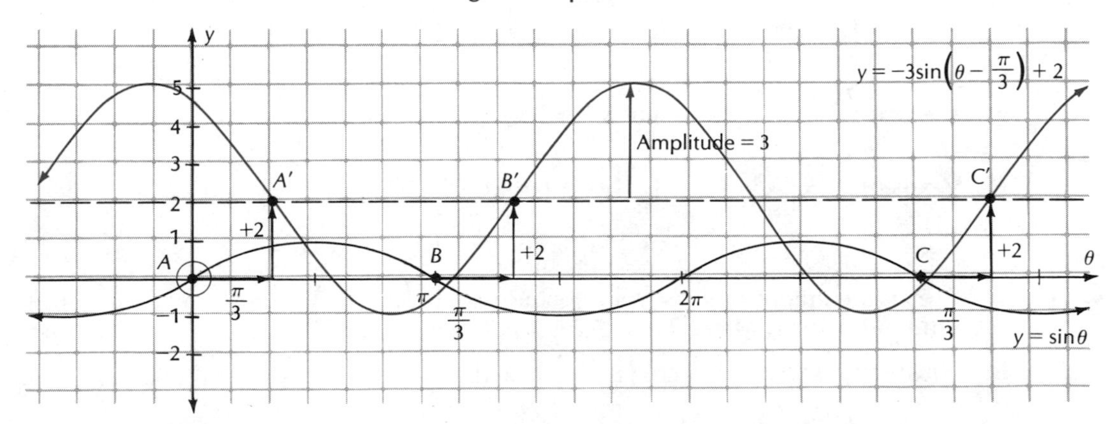

EXERCISE 6-5

A 1. A phase shift and/or vertical translation has been performed on the graph of each function. State the phase shift and/or vertical translation.

a. $y = \tan\left(\theta + \frac{\pi}{6}\right)$ **b.** $y = \cos(2\theta) - 3$ **c.** $y = \sin(\theta - 45°) + 1$

d. $y = 2\cos(\theta - \pi) - 3$ **e.** $y = 4 - \sin\left(\theta + \frac{\pi}{3}\right)$ **f.** $y = \cos(\theta + 30°) + \frac{1}{2}$

2. Write a defining equation for each function, as described.

a. a sine function with a phase shift of $\frac{\pi}{4}$
b. a cosine function, translated 2 units upward
c. a tangent function, translated 3 units downward with a phase shift of 90°
d. a sine function with amplitude 3 and a phase shift of $\frac{\pi}{6}$
e. a cosine function, reflected in the x-axis, with a vertical translation of +4 units
f. a sine function, reflected in the x-axis, with amplitude 3, a phase shift of $-\pi$, and a vertical translation of 2 units upward

B 3. Sketch the graph of each function, where $0° \leq x \leq 360°$.

a. $y = \sin\theta + 3$ **b.** $y = \cos(\theta + 45°)$ **c.** $y = \tan(\theta - 90°)$
d. $y = \sin(\theta + 30°) - 1$ **e.** $y = \cos(\theta - 60°) + 2$ **f.** $y = \sin(\theta + 90°) - 3$

4. Sketch the graph of each function described in exercise 2.

5. Sketch the graph of each function, where $0 \leq \theta \leq 2\pi$.

a. $y = -\sin(\theta + \pi)$ **b.** $y = 2\sin\theta - 2$

c. $y = -2\cos\left(\theta + \frac{\pi}{6}\right)$ **d.** $y = -2\sin\theta + 3$

e. $y = 3\cos\left(\theta + \frac{\pi}{6}\right) - 1$ **f.** $y = -\sin\left(\theta - \frac{\pi}{4}\right) + 1$

g. $y = -\cos\left(\theta + \frac{\pi}{3}\right) + 2$ **h.** $y = -3\cos\frac{\theta}{2}$

i. $y = 4\sin(2\theta) - 1$ **j.** $y = -\tan\left(\theta + \frac{\pi}{2}\right) + 1$

C 6. **a.** Sketch the graphs of $y = \sin(\theta + \pi)$ and $y = \cos\left(\theta + \frac{\pi}{2}\right)$ on the same set of axes, where $0 \leq \theta \leq 2\pi$.

b. Solve for θ: $\sin(\theta + \pi) = \cos\left(\theta + \frac{\pi}{2}\right)$, where $0 \leq \theta \leq 2\pi$.

7. By using reflections and horizontal translations, it is possible to define a given curve in several different ways.

   a. Using the sine function, write three different functions that define each curve.

i.

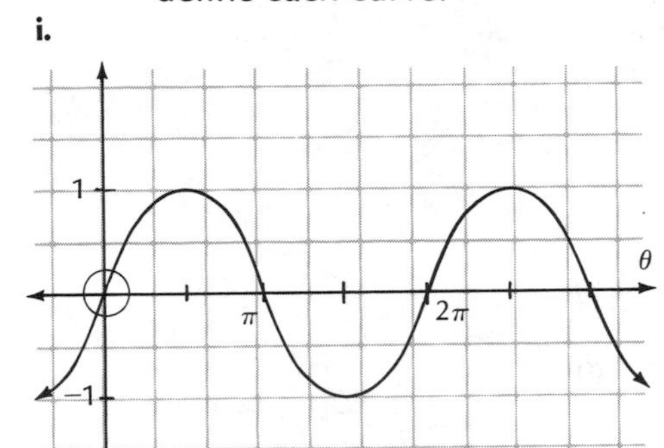

ii.

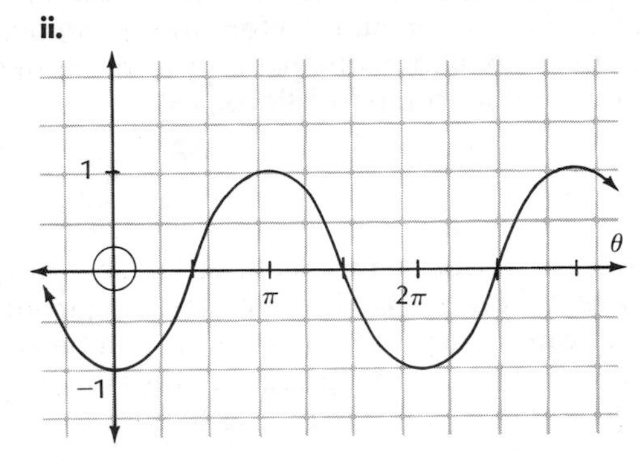

   b. For each curve given in part **a**, use the cosine function to write three different functions that define each curve.

8. The function defined by $y = \sin\left(2\theta + \frac{\pi}{2}\right) = \sin\left[2\left(\theta + \frac{\pi}{4}\right)\right]$ has a period of π and a phase shift of $\frac{\pi}{4}$. Sketch each function.

   a. $y = \sin\left(2\theta + \frac{\pi}{2}\right)$

   b. $y = 3\cos\left(2\theta - \frac{\pi}{3}\right)$

   c. $y = -\sin(3\theta + \pi) + 1$

   d. $y = -2\cos\left(2\theta - \frac{\pi}{2}\right) - 2$

Biography

Maria Gaetana Agnesi (1718–1799)

Perhaps Maria Agnesi was able to flourish as a mathematician because she was born in Milan, Italy during the Italian Renaissance, an era that encouraged men and women to expand horizons in a wide variety of fields. Agnesi was fluent in several languages by the age of nine and she developed a keen interest in diverse areas such as human perception, languages, and the work of Isaac Newton.

Although her father was a mathematician, Agnesi did not pursue mathematics until adulthood. In 1748, she published *Analytical Institutions,* a two-volume text on the work of Newton and Leibniz, another famous mathematician. Of particular interest is her work on a type of trigonometric function, called the *versed sine curve,* given by the equation $xy^2 = a^2(a - x)$. After her appointment to the University of Bologna as honorary lecturer, Agnesi continued to make contributions to mathematics, but spent her later years caring for the poor and the terminally ill.

6-6 Adding Ordinates

Not all periodic motions can be modelled as a simple sine or cosine function. Often, more complex motions can be modelled mathematically as the sum of two or more sine or cosine functions.

An oscilloscope is a device used in electronics to display a screen "image" of the wave resulting from several electronic sources. A microphone can be attached to an oscilloscope to pick up sound. The sound is then depicted in wave form on the screen.

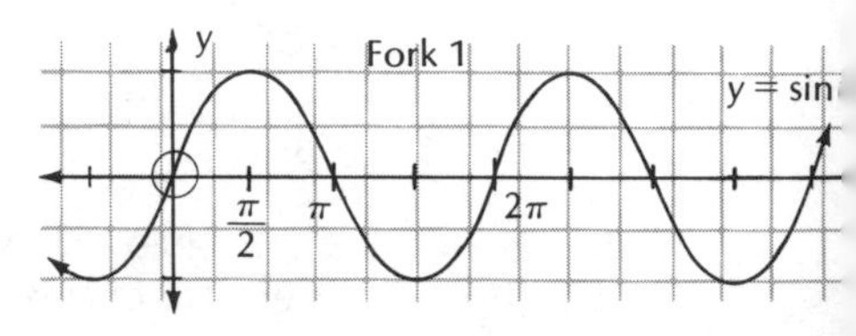

Consider the result of two tuning forks, with equal frequency, struck equally hard so that the loudness (amplitude) of each is the same. Now suppose that the second fork is struck slightly later than the first, so that it is $\frac{\pi}{2}$ rad, or 90° out of phase. What would the graph of the resulting sound look like if viewed on an oscilloscope?

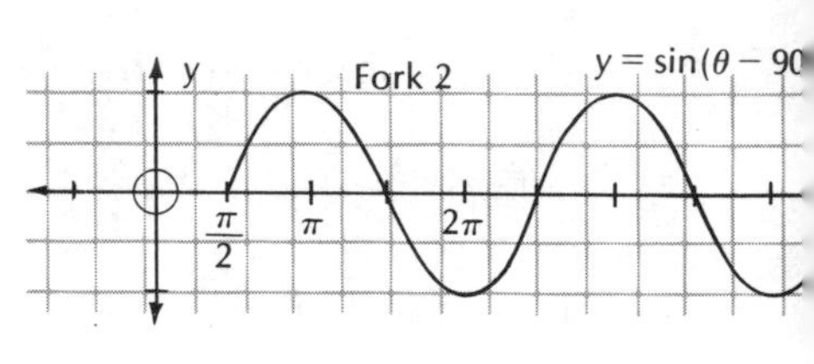

Start by graphing both curves on the same set of axes. Add corresponding ordinates of both curves to determine several points of the new curve. By joining the new points, a graph of the function $y = \sin\theta + \sin(\theta - \frac{\pi}{2})$ can be obtained. (Remember that y-values below the θ-axis are negative.)

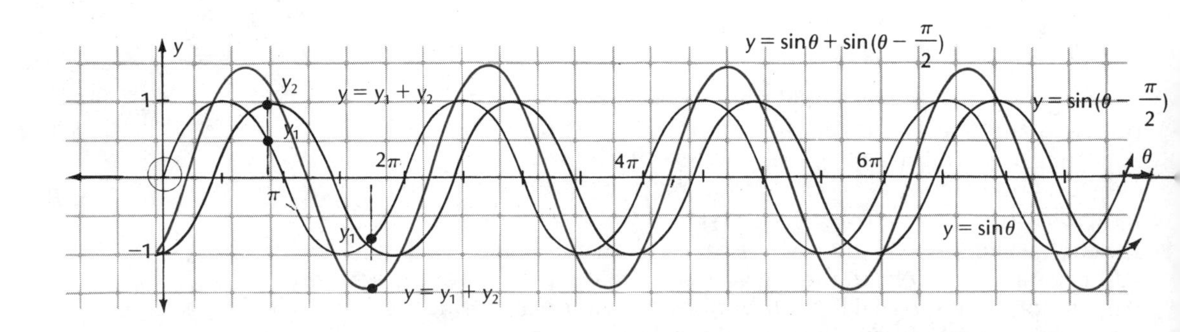

EXAMPLE: Sketch the graph of $y = \sin\theta + \sin 2\theta$, where $0 \leq \theta \leq 6\pi$.

First sketch the graphs of $y = \sin\theta$ and $y = \sin 2\theta$ on the same set of axes. Then add the ordinates to obtain points on the graph of $y = \sin\theta + \sin 2\theta$.

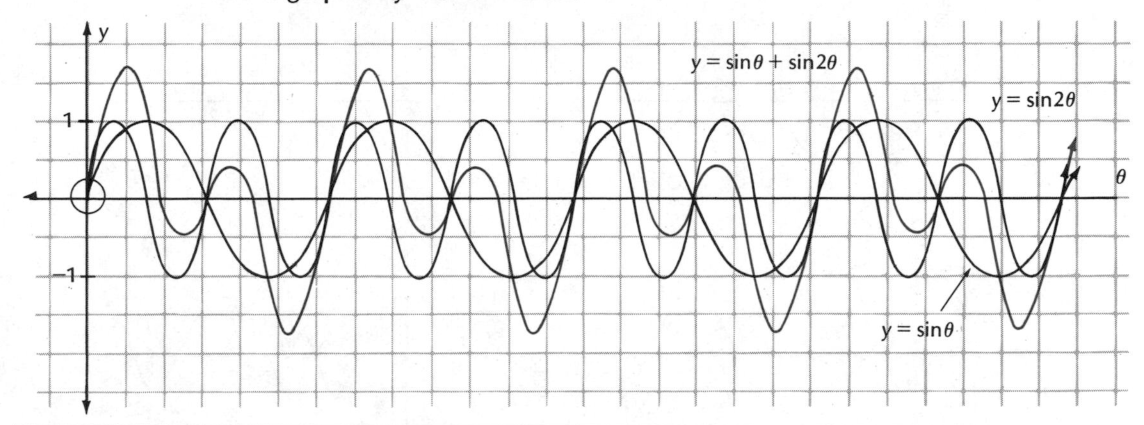

EXERCISE 6-6

A 1. Copy each graph. By adding ordinates, sketch the indicated function.

a. $y = \dfrac{x^2 + 1}{x} = x + \dfrac{1}{x}$

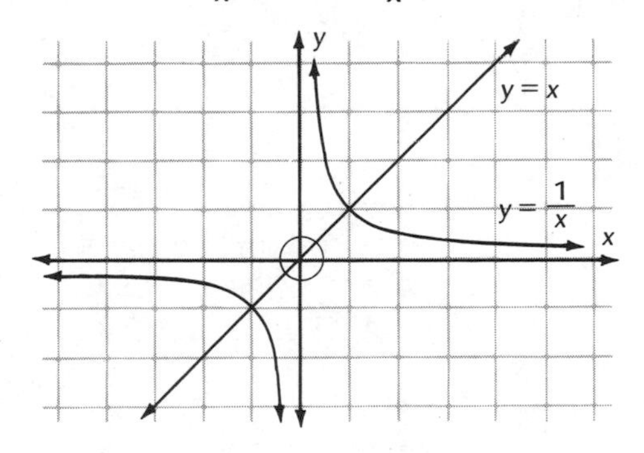

b. $y = \dfrac{x^2 - 1}{x} = x - \dfrac{1}{x}$

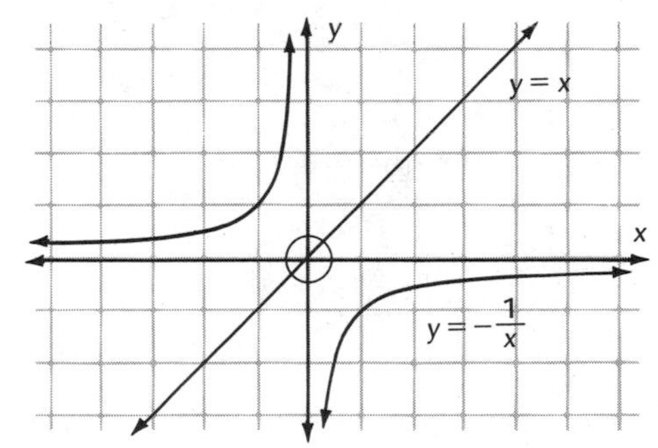

c. $y = x^3 - x$

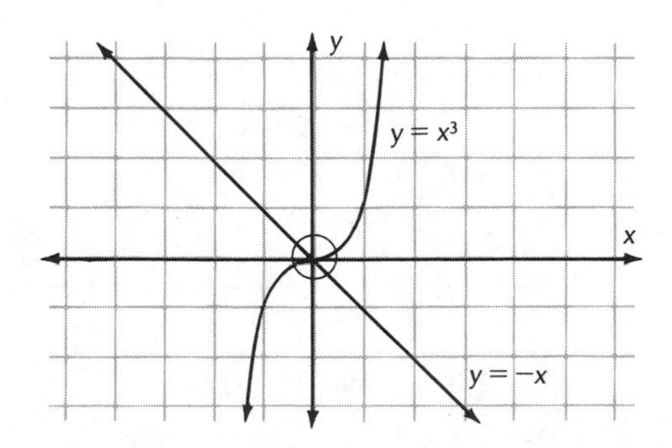

d. $y = \dfrac{x^3 + 1}{x} = x^2 + \dfrac{1}{x}$

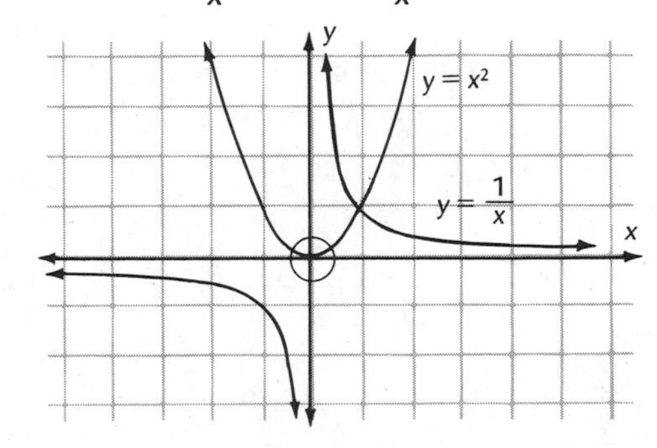

B **2.** Copy each graph. Then sketch the graph of the indicated function by adding ordinates.

a. $y = \sin\theta + \cos\theta$

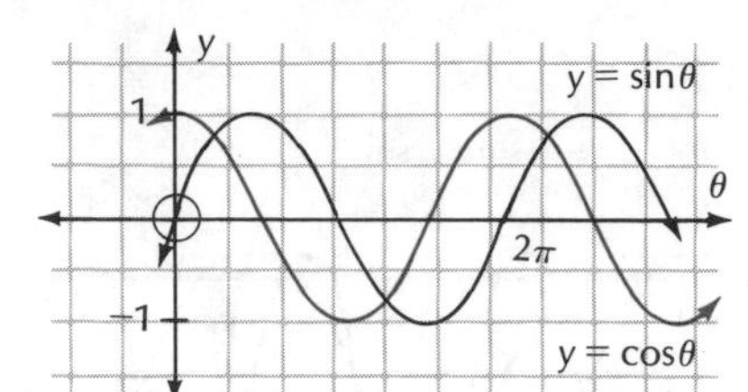

b. $y = \sin\theta - \cos\theta$

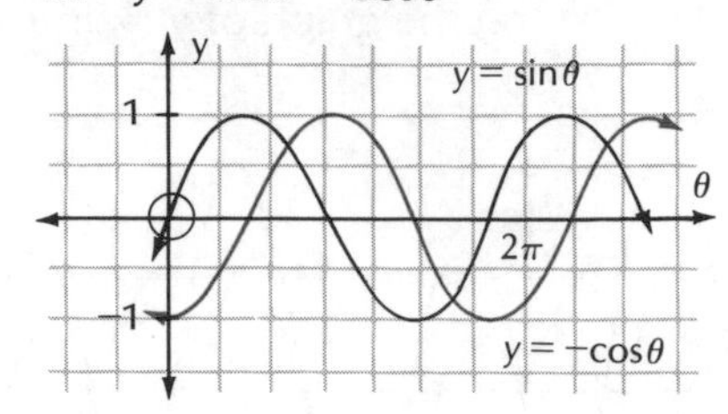

c. $y = 2\sin\theta + \cos\theta$

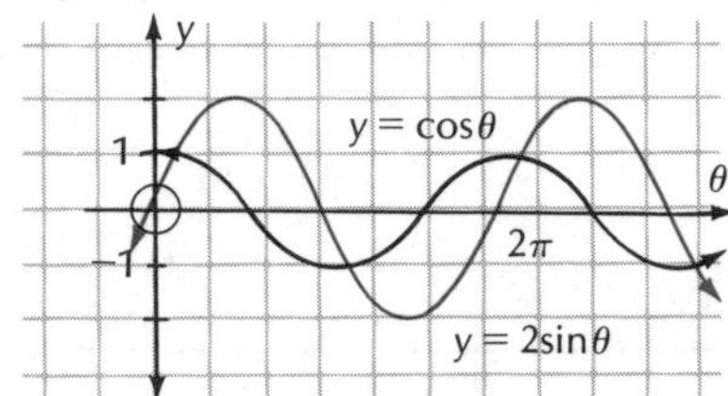

d. $y = \cos\theta - \sin\theta$

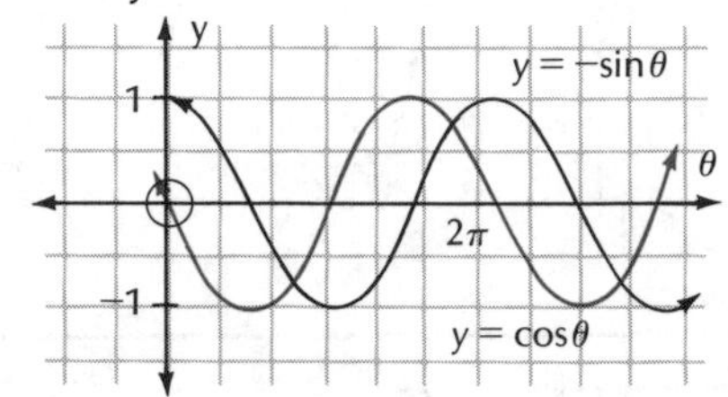

e. $y = \sin\theta + \cos 2\theta$

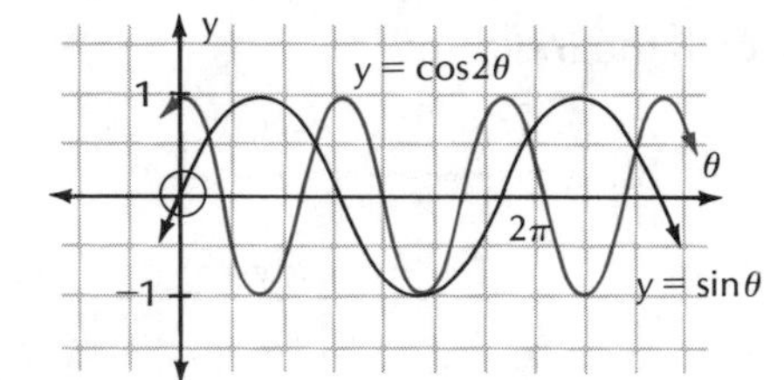

f. $y = \sin 2\theta + \cos\theta$

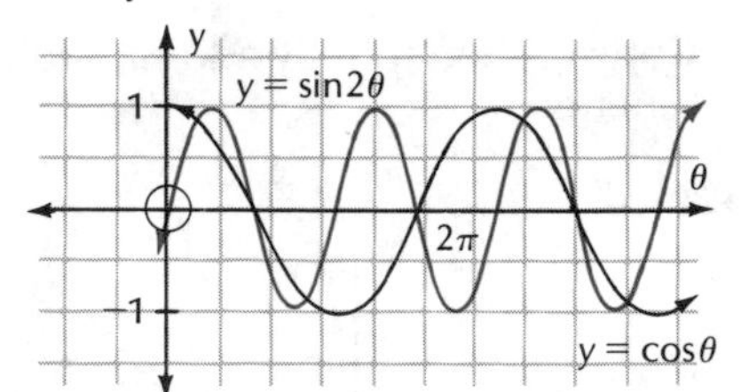

3. Sketch the graph of each function, where $0° \leq x \leq 360°$.

a. $y = 2\cos x + \sin x$

b. $y = 2\cos x - \sin x$

c. $y = \sin x - 2\cos x$

d. $y = \cos x - 2\sin x$

e. $y = \cos 2x - \sin x$

f. $y = \sin 2x - \cos x$

g. $y = \sin 2x - \sin x$

h. $y = \sin x - \sin 2x$

C **4.** Sketch the graph of each function, where $0° \leq x \leq 360°$.

a. $y = \sin x + |\cos x|$

b. $y = \sin x - |\cos x|$

c. $y = \cos x + |\sin 2x|$

d. $y = |\sin x| + |\cos x|$

5. Copy each graph. Then sketch the graph of the indicated function.

a. $y = \sin\theta + \sin 2\theta + \cos\theta$

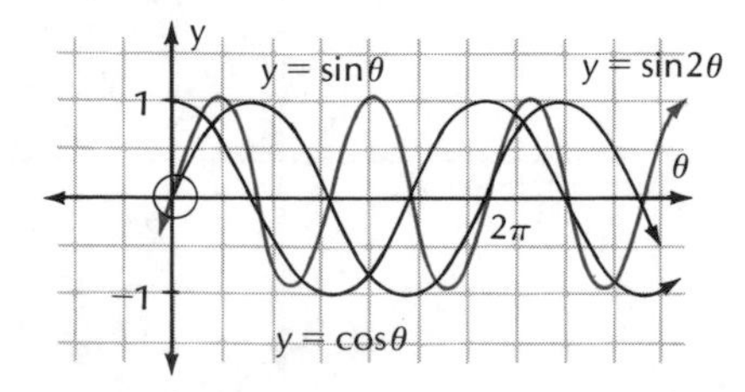

b. $y = \sin\theta + \sin 2\theta - \cos\theta$

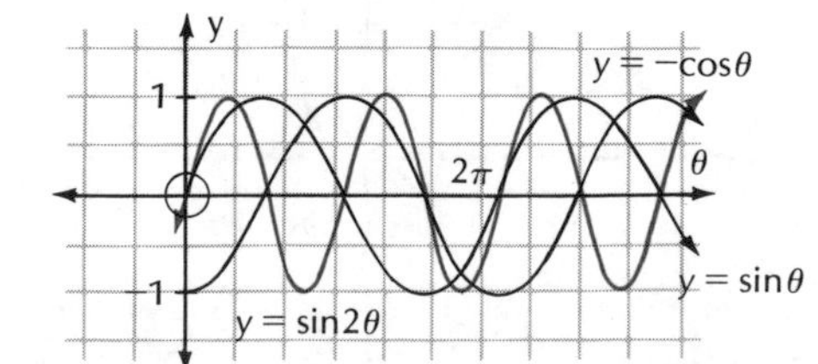

Review

1. Convert to radian measure.
   a. $200°$ b. $72°$ c. $126°$ d. $315°$

2. Convert to degree measure.
   a. $\frac{3\pi}{10}$ b. $\frac{11\pi}{9}$ c. $\frac{3\pi}{5}$ d. $\frac{7\pi}{6}$

3. Solve for the indicated variable.
   a.

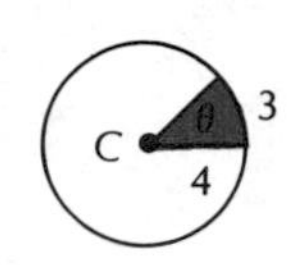

   b.

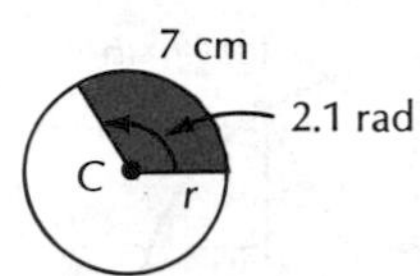

   c.

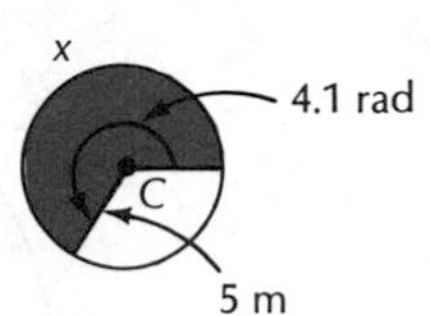

4. Find the area of each shaded region.
   a.

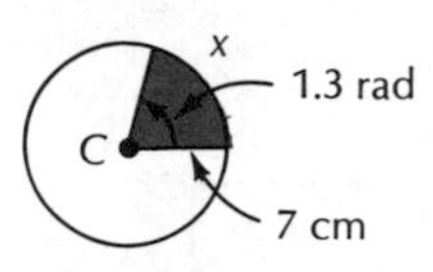

   b.

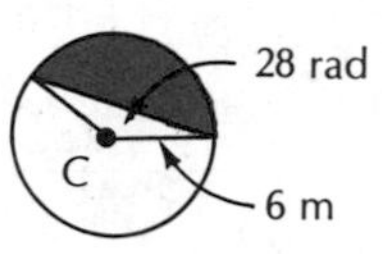

5. A bicycle tire is 0.72 m in diameter.
   a. Find the angle generated, in radians, if the wheel rolls 200 m.
   b. How many revolutions are completed in 1 km?

6. a. If $\omega = \frac{\theta}{t}$ with $\omega = 3\pi$ rad/s and $\theta = 5$ rad, find t.
   b. If $\omega = \frac{s}{rt}$ with $\omega = 3$ rad/s, $s = 19.2$ m, and $t = 4.8$ s, find r.
   c. If $v = \omega r$ with $v = 24$ m/s and $r = 0.45$ m, find ω.

7. Find the angle generated in 12 s by a wheel rotating with an angular velocity of 23 rev/min.

8. The belt of a pulley is moving, without slipping, at 58 cm/s when the angular velocity is 190 rev/min. Find the radius of the pulley.

9. State the domain and range of each of the following.
   a. $y = \cos\theta$ b. $y = \tan\theta$ c. $y = \csc\theta$

10. Describe, in words, the function defined by $y = -3\tan\left(\theta + \frac{\pi}{3}\right) + 1$.

11. Write a defining equation for each of the following.
    a. a sine function with amplitude 2, shifted $\frac{\pi}{3}$ rad to the left, and translated 3 units up
    b. a cotangent function, reflected in the θ-axis, shifted $\frac{2\pi}{3}$ rad to the right, and translated 2 units down

12. Sketch the graph of each function.
    a. $y = \cot\theta$ b. $y = \sec\theta$ c. $y = 2\sin\theta - 1$
    d. $y = -\sin\left(\theta + \frac{\pi}{6}\right)$ e. $y = -\cos 2\theta$ f. $y = \tan\left(\theta - \frac{\pi}{2}\right)$ g. $y = -\cos\theta + 2$

6-7 Simplifying Trigonometric Expressions

It is often useful to simplify mathematical expressions. Certain relationships between the trigonometric functions can be established to help simplify trigonometric expressions.

For a unit circle, or a circle with radius 1, the trigonometric functions can be defined as follows.

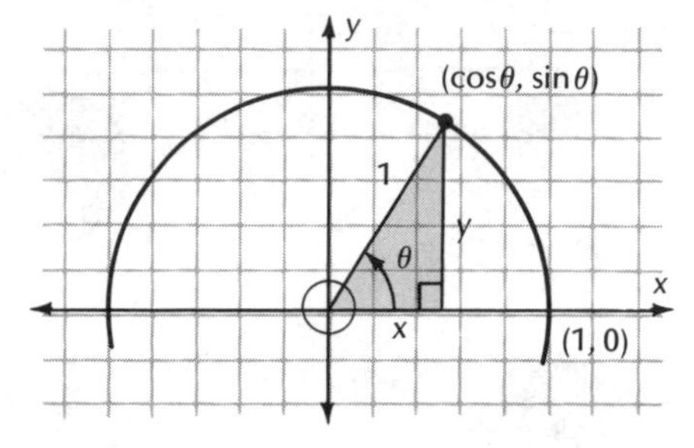

$$\sin\theta = y \qquad \cos\theta = x \qquad \tan\theta = \frac{y}{x}$$

$$\csc\theta = \frac{1}{y} \qquad \sec\theta = \frac{1}{x} \qquad \cot\theta = \frac{x}{y}$$

Notice that these functions are undefined if the denominators are zero.

Using the above definitions, the following relationships can be obtained directly. Since these relationships, which are expressed as equations, are true for all values of θ, they are identities. In particular, they are the **reciprocal identities**.

$$\csc\theta = \frac{1}{\sin\theta} \qquad \sec\theta = \frac{1}{\cos\theta} \qquad \cot\theta = \frac{1}{\tan\theta}$$

and $\sin\theta = \frac{1}{\csc\theta} \qquad \cos\theta = \frac{1}{\sec\theta} \qquad \tan\theta = \frac{1}{\cot\theta}$

The **quotient identities** also follow from the definition of the trigonometric functions.

$$\tan\theta = \frac{\sin\theta}{\cos\theta} \quad \text{and} \quad \cot\theta = \frac{\cos\theta}{\sin\theta}$$

$\tan\theta = \frac{y}{x} = \frac{\sin\theta}{\cos\theta}$

The three **Pythagorean identities** are obtained directly by applying the Pythagorean Theorem to this triangle.

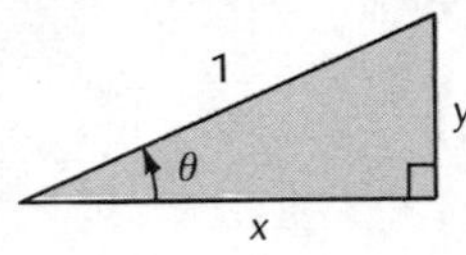

Since $y^2 + x^2 = 1$, then $\quad \sin^2\theta + \cos^2\theta = 1.$ ①

Divide both sides by $\cos^2\theta$. $\quad \dfrac{\sin^2\theta}{\cos^2\theta} + \dfrac{\cos^2\theta}{\cos^2\theta} = \dfrac{1}{\cos^2\theta}$

Apply known identities. $\quad \tan^2\theta + 1 = \sec^2\theta$ ②

Similarly, $\quad \cot^2\theta + 1 = \csc^2\theta$ — Divide both sides of ① by $\sin^2\theta$ and simplify.

$$\sin^2\theta + \cos^2\theta = 1 \qquad \tan^2\theta + 1 = \sec^2\theta \qquad \cot^2\theta + 1 = \csc^2\theta$$

All of these identities can be used to rewrite and simplify trigonometric expressions.

EXAMPLE 1: Write each expression using only sines and cosines.

a. $\cos\theta(\tan\theta + 1) = \cos\theta\left(\dfrac{\sin\theta}{\cos\theta} + 1\right)$ $\qquad \tan\theta = \dfrac{\sin\theta}{\cos\theta}$

$= \sin\theta + \cos\theta$

b. $\tan\theta + \cot\theta = \dfrac{\sin\theta}{\cos\theta} + \dfrac{\cos\theta}{\sin\theta}$ $\qquad$ Quotient identities

$= \dfrac{\sin^2\theta + \cos^2\theta}{\sin\theta\cos\theta}$ $\qquad$ Common denominator

$= \dfrac{1}{\sin\theta\cos\theta}$ $\qquad \sin^2\theta + \cos^2\theta = 1$

c. $\sec\theta + \tan\theta = \dfrac{1}{\cos\theta} + \dfrac{\sin\theta}{\cos\theta}$

$= \dfrac{1 + \sin\theta}{\cos\theta}$

d. $\sec\theta\cot\theta = \dfrac{1}{\cos\theta}\left(\dfrac{\cos\theta}{\sin\theta}\right)$

$= \dfrac{1}{\sin\theta}$

EXAMPLE 2: Simplify each expression.

a. $$\sec\theta\cot\theta = \left(\frac{1}{\cos\theta}\right)\left(\frac{\cos\theta}{\sin\theta}\right) = \frac{1}{\sin\theta} = \csc\theta$$

b. $$\frac{\sec\theta}{\csc\theta} = \frac{\frac{1}{\cos\theta}}{\frac{1}{\sin\theta}} = \left(\frac{1}{\cos\theta}\right)\left(\frac{\sin\theta}{1}\right) = \tan\theta$$

or

$$\frac{\sec\theta}{\csc\theta} = \frac{\frac{1}{x}}{\frac{1}{y}} = \left(\frac{1}{x}\right)\left(\frac{y}{1}\right) = \tan\theta$$

c. $$\frac{\sin^2\theta + \cos^2\theta}{\csc\theta} = \frac{1}{\csc\theta} = \sin\theta$$

or

$$\frac{\sin^2\theta + \cos^2\theta}{\csc\theta} = \frac{x^2 + y^2}{\frac{1}{y}} = \frac{1}{\frac{1}{y}} = y = \sin\theta$$

d. $$\cot\theta(\sec^2\theta - 1) = \cot\theta(\tan^2\theta) = \left(\frac{\cos\theta}{\sin\theta}\right)\left(\frac{\sin^2\theta}{\cos^2\theta}\right) = \frac{\sin\theta}{\cos\theta} = \tan\theta$$

$\tan^2\theta + 1 = \sec^2\theta$

e. $$\frac{1 - 2\sin\theta\cos\theta}{\sin\theta - \cos\theta} = \frac{\sin^2\theta - 2\sin\theta\cos\theta + \cos^2\theta}{\sin\theta - \cos\theta} = \frac{(\sin\theta - \cos\theta)^2}{\sin\theta - \cos\theta} = \sin\theta - \cos\theta$$

$\sin^2\theta + \cos^2\theta = 1$

The examples show that it is often useful to rewrite trigonometric expressions in terms of sines and cosines to make simplification easier. Be careful to observe the possible use of a Pythagorean identity whenever an expression is squared or a value of 1 is found in the expression.

EXERCISE 6-7

A **1.** Simplify each expression. Write each answer in terms of only sines and/or cosines.

a. $\dfrac{\cot\theta + 1}{\csc\theta}$ **b.** $\cos\theta(1 + \tan^2\theta)$ **c.** $\csc\theta\sin\theta - \sin^2\theta$

d. $\csc\theta - \cot\theta\cos\theta$ **e.** $\cot\theta + \dfrac{1}{\cot\theta}$ **f.** $\dfrac{1 + \tan^2\theta}{\tan^2\theta}$

g. $\dfrac{1 - \sin^2\theta}{\cot^2\theta}$ **h.** $\sec\theta(\cos\theta - \cot\theta)$ **i.** $\dfrac{\sin^4\theta - \cos^4\theta}{\sin\theta + \cos\theta}$

2. Simplify.

a. $\csc\theta\tan\theta$ **b.** $\dfrac{\tan^2\theta}{1 - \cos^2\theta}$ **c.** $\cot\theta\cos\theta + \sin\theta$

d. $\dfrac{1 + \tan^2\theta}{\tan^2\theta}$ **e.** $\sec\theta\cos\theta + \sec\theta\sin\theta$ **f.** $\cot^2\theta(1 - \cos^2\theta)$

g. $\sin\theta(\csc\theta - \sin\theta)$ **h.** $\dfrac{\sin^2\theta - \cos^2\theta}{\sin^2\theta - 2\sin\theta\cos\theta + \cos^2\theta}$ **i.** $\dfrac{\csc\theta}{\cot\theta} - \dfrac{\cot\theta}{\csc\theta}$

B **3.** Simplify. Write each answer in terms of only sines and/or cosines.

a. $\dfrac{1 - \cos^2\theta}{1 - \sec^2\theta}$ **b.** $(1 + \tan^2\theta)(1 - \cot^2\theta)$ **c.** $\dfrac{\sec\theta}{1 + \sec\theta} + \dfrac{\sec\theta}{1 - \sec\theta}$

d. $\sec\theta - \cos\theta$ **e.** $\dfrac{\sec\theta}{\cos\theta} - \dfrac{\tan\theta}{\cot\theta}$ **f.** $\dfrac{\sec\theta\sin\theta}{\cot\theta + \tan\theta}$

g. $\dfrac{\csc\theta + 1}{\csc\theta - 1} + \dfrac{\sin\theta + 1}{\sin\theta - 1}$ **h.** $\dfrac{\sin^2\theta}{1 - \cos\theta}$ **i.** $\dfrac{1 + \cot^2\theta}{1 + \tan^2\theta}$

4. Simplify.

a. $\dfrac{1}{1 + \cos\theta} + \dfrac{1}{1 - \cos\theta}$ **b.** $\dfrac{1 - 2\cos^2\theta - \sin^2\theta}{\sin^2\theta}$

c. $\cos^2\theta + \tan^2\theta + \sin^2\theta$ **d.** $\tan^2\theta\csc^2\theta - 1$

e. $\csc\theta - \cot\theta\cos\theta$ **f.** $\dfrac{\sec^2\theta}{1 - \sec^2\theta}$

g. $\dfrac{-\sin^2\theta}{1 - \cos\theta}$ **h.** $\sin\theta(\csc\theta - \sin\theta)\tan^2\theta$

i. $\dfrac{\sin^2\theta + 2\sin\theta\cos\theta + \cos^2\theta + 1}{1 + \sin\theta\cos\theta}$ **j.** $\dfrac{\dfrac{\sin\theta}{\csc\theta} + \dfrac{\cos\theta}{\sec\theta}}{\csc^2\theta - 1}$

C **5.** Simplify.

a. $\dfrac{\sin^2\theta + \sin\theta + \sin\theta\cos\theta + \cos\theta}{\sin\theta + \cos\theta}$ **b.** $\dfrac{\sec^2\theta - \tan^2\theta - \csc^2\theta}{\cos^2\theta}$

6. Write each of the six basic trigonometric functions in terms of $\sin\theta$.

6-8 Proving Trigonometric Identities

It is not always obvious that the left side (L.S.) of an identity equals the right side (R.S.). To prove a trigonometric identity, you must prove that the two sides are equal; you *do not know* that they are equal. As a result, both sides must be simplified independently.

EXAMPLE 1: Prove that $\tan\theta + \cot\theta = \sec\theta\csc\theta$.

Express each side of the equation in terms of sines and cosines. Then simplify.

$$\text{L.S.} = \tan\theta + \cot\theta$$
$$= \frac{\sin\theta}{\cos\theta} + \frac{\cos\theta}{\sin\theta}$$
$$= \frac{\sin^2\theta + \cos^2\theta}{\sin\theta\cos\theta}$$
$$= \frac{1}{\sin\theta\cos\theta}$$

$$\text{R.S.} = \sec\theta\csc\theta$$
$$= \left(\frac{1}{\cos\theta}\right)\left(\frac{1}{\sin\theta}\right)$$
$$= \frac{1}{\sin\theta\cos\theta} = \text{L.S.} \checkmark$$

$\sin^2\theta + \cos^2\theta = 1$

$\therefore \tan\theta + \cot\theta = \sec\theta\csc\theta$

In some situations, you can rewrite the more complex side of the equation so that it has the same format as the other side.

EXAMPLE 2: Prove that $\frac{1}{1+\sin\theta} + \frac{1}{1-\sin\theta} = \frac{2}{\cos^2\theta}$.

$$\text{L.S.} = \frac{1}{1+\sin\theta} + \frac{1}{1-\sin\theta}$$

Rewrite the L.S. so that it has the same format as the R.S.

$$= \frac{(1-\sin\theta) + (1+\sin\theta)}{(1+\sin\theta)(1-\sin\theta)}$$
$$= \frac{2}{1-\sin^2\theta}$$

$\sin^2\theta + \cos^2\theta = 1$

$$= \frac{2}{\cos^2\theta} = \text{R.S.} \checkmark$$

$1 - \sin^2\theta = \cos^2\theta$

$$\therefore \frac{1}{1+\sin\theta} + \frac{1}{1-\sin\theta} = \frac{2}{\cos^2\theta}$$

EXAMPLE 3: Prove that $\frac{\cos\theta}{1-\cos\theta} + \frac{\cos\theta}{1+\cos\theta} = 2\cot\theta\csc\theta$

$$\text{L.S.} = \frac{\cos\theta}{1-\cos\theta} + \frac{\cos\theta}{1+\cos\theta}$$
$$= \frac{2\cos\theta}{1-\cos^2\theta}$$
$$= \frac{2\cos\theta}{\sin^2\theta}$$

$$\text{R.S.} = 2\cot\theta\csc\theta$$
$$= \left(\frac{2\cos\theta}{\sin\theta}\right)\left(\frac{1}{\sin\theta}\right)$$
$$= \frac{2\cos\theta}{\sin^2\theta} = \text{L.S.} \checkmark$$

EXERCISE 6-8

A **1.** Prove each identity.

a. $\cos\theta\tan\theta = \sin\theta$

b. $\sin^2\theta + \sin^2\theta\cot^2\theta = 1$

c. $\cos^2\theta - \sin^2\theta = 2\cos^2\theta - 1$

d. $\sec^2\theta - 1 = \tan^2\theta$

e. $\dfrac{\sin^2\theta}{1 - \sin^2\theta} = \tan^2\theta$

f. $\dfrac{1}{\sec^2\theta} + \dfrac{1}{\csc^2\theta} = 1$

g. $\sin^4\theta - \cos^4\theta = \sin^2\theta - \cos^2\theta$

h. $(\cot\theta + 1)^2 = 2\cot\theta + \csc^2\theta$

i. $\tan\theta\sin\theta + \cos\theta = \sec\theta$

j. $(1 - \csc\theta)(1 + \csc\theta) = -\cot^2\theta$

k. $\dfrac{1 - \cos^2\theta}{1 - \sin^2\theta} = \dfrac{\tan\theta}{\cot\theta}$

l. $\dfrac{\cot\theta}{1 - \sin^2\theta} = \dfrac{\tan\theta}{1 - \cos^2\theta}$

m. $\dfrac{1}{\sec\theta} + \dfrac{\sin\theta}{\cot\theta} = \sec\theta$

n. $\sin\theta\tan\theta = \sec\theta - \cos\theta$

B **2.** Prove each identity.

a. $\dfrac{\sin\theta - 1}{\sec\theta} = \left(\dfrac{\cos\theta}{\csc\theta}\right) - \left(\dfrac{\sin\theta}{\tan\theta}\right)$

b. $\dfrac{1}{1 + \cos\theta} + \dfrac{1}{1 - \cos\theta} = \dfrac{2}{\sin^2\theta}$

c. $\dfrac{\sin\theta + 1}{\sin\theta - 1} + \dfrac{\csc\theta + 1}{\csc\theta - 1} = 0$

d. $\dfrac{\cot\theta + \cos\theta}{\cot\theta\cos\theta} = \dfrac{\cot\theta\cos\theta}{\cot\theta - \cos\theta}$

e. $\dfrac{\sin\theta + 1}{\sin\theta - 1} = \dfrac{1 + 2\csc\theta + \csc^2\theta}{1 - \csc^2\theta}$

f. $\dfrac{1 - \tan^2\theta}{1 - \cot^2\theta} = -\tan^2\theta$

g. $(1 - \sin\theta)(1 + \csc\theta) = \cot\theta\cos\theta$

h. $\cot^2\theta - \cos^2\theta = \cot^2\theta\cos^2\theta$

i. $\dfrac{\sin^2\theta + \cos^2\theta}{\sec\theta + \tan\theta} = \sec\theta - \tan\theta$

j. $\csc^2\theta - \sin^2\theta - \cot^2\theta = \cos^2\theta$

k. $(1 + \cos\theta)(\csc\theta - \cot\theta) = \sin\theta$

l. $\dfrac{\tan\theta}{\tan^2\theta - 1} = \dfrac{1}{\tan\theta - \cot\theta}$

m. $\dfrac{1 - 2\sin^2\theta}{\sin\theta\cos\theta} = \cot\theta - \tan\theta$

n. $\dfrac{\sec^2\theta - 1}{1 - \cos^2\theta} = \sec^2\theta$

C **3.** Substitute the unit circle definitions of the trigonometric functions (for example, $\sin\theta = y$) and use the Pythagorean relationship, $x^2 + y^2 = 1$, to prove each identity given in exercise 2.

4. Prove each identity.

a. $\dfrac{\sin\theta}{1 + \cos\theta} + \dfrac{1 + \cos\theta}{\sin\theta} = 2\csc\theta$

b. $\dfrac{\sin\theta}{1 + \cos\theta} + \cot\theta = \csc\theta$

c. $\dfrac{\cos\theta}{1 + \sin\theta} - 2\sec\theta = \dfrac{\cos\theta}{\sin\theta - 1}$

d. $\dfrac{1 - \tan^2\theta}{1 + \tan^2\theta} + 1 = 2\cos^2\theta$

e. $\dfrac{1 + \sin\theta}{1 - \sin\theta} = \dfrac{4\tan\theta}{\cos\theta} + \dfrac{1 - \sin\theta}{1 + \sin\theta}$

f. $\dfrac{1 - \tan^2\theta}{\tan\theta - \tan^2\theta} - \dfrac{1}{\tan\theta} = 1$

6-9 Solving Trigonometric Equations

Equations involving trigonometric expressions are called **trigonometric equations**. Finding the value of the variable is usually the same as finding the measure of the angle that satisfies the equation.

$\sin\theta = -\frac{1}{2}$ ← These are trigonometric equations.

$\sin\theta\cos\theta = \sin\theta$

EXAMPLE 1: Solve $\sin\theta = -\frac{1}{2}$, where $0° < \theta \leq 360°$.

Sine is negative in quadrants III and IV.

$\sin 30° = \frac{1}{2}$

The reference angle is 30°.

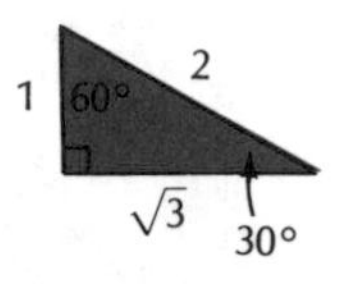

Solve the equation by graphing the curve.

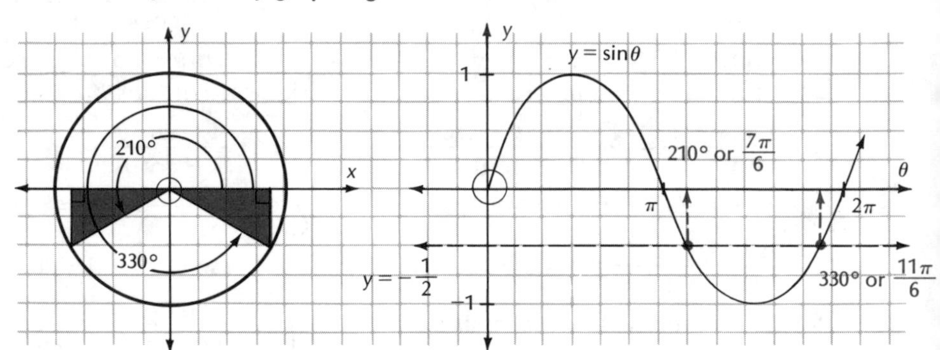

Therefore, the solution is $\theta = 210°$, $\theta = 330°$ or

$$\theta = \frac{7\pi}{6},\ \theta = \frac{11\pi}{6}.$$

As it is for solving quadratic equations, factoring can be an important tool for solving trigonometric equations.

EXAMPLE 2: Solve $\sin\theta\cos\theta = \sin\theta$, where $0° < \theta \leq 360°$.

$$\sin\theta\cos\theta = \sin\theta$$
$$\sin\theta\cos\theta - \sin\theta = 0$$
$$\therefore \sin\theta(\cos\theta - 1) = 0$$

$\sin\theta = 0$ or $\cos\theta = 1$

$\therefore \theta = 180°, 360°$ $\qquad \theta = 360°$

Therefore, $\theta = 180°, 360°$ or $\theta = \pi, 2\pi$.

EXAMPLE 3: Solve $3\sin^2\theta - 2 = 0$, where $0° < \theta \leq 360°$.

$$3\sin^2\theta - 2 = 0$$

$$\sin^2\theta = \frac{2}{3}$$ Solve for $\sin\theta$.

$$\sin\theta = \pm\sqrt{\frac{2}{3}}\text{, or } \sin\theta \doteq \pm 0.8165$$

The $\pm$ sign indicates that $\sin\theta$ can be in all four quadrants. If $\sin\theta = 0.8165$, then the reference angle is 54.74°. A diagram can be used to illustrate the four solutions.

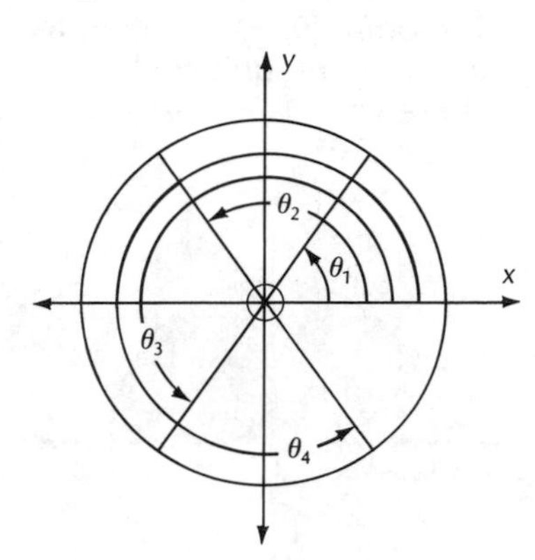

$\therefore \theta_1 = 54.74°$
$\theta_2 = 180° - 54.74° = 125.26°$
$\theta_3 = 180° + 54.74° = 234.74°$
$\theta_4 = 360° - 54.74° = 305.26°$

EXAMPLE 4: Solve $\cos 3\theta = \frac{1}{\sqrt{2}}$, where $0 < \theta \leq 2\pi$.

Since $0 < \theta \leq 2\pi$, then, for $\cos 3\theta$, first find all solutions such that $0 < 3\theta \leq 6\pi$. That is, find all the solutions in the first three revolutions.

For $\cos\alpha = \frac{1}{\sqrt{2}}$ the reference angle is 45° in quadrants I and IV.

Thus, $\alpha = \frac{\pi}{4}, \frac{7\pi}{4}, \frac{9\pi}{4}, \frac{15\pi}{4}, \frac{17\pi}{4}, \frac{23\pi}{4}$, where $0 < 3\theta \leq 6\pi$.

$\therefore 3\theta = \frac{\pi}{4}, \frac{7\pi}{4}, \frac{9\pi}{4}, \frac{15\pi}{4}, \frac{17\pi}{4}, \frac{23\pi}{4}$, where $0 < 3\theta \leq 6\pi$ $\qquad \alpha = 3\theta$

$\therefore \theta = \frac{\pi}{12}, \frac{7\pi}{12}, \frac{3\pi}{4}, \frac{5\pi}{4}, \frac{17\pi}{12}, \frac{23\pi}{12}$, where $0 < \theta \leq 2\pi$

Notice that the six solutions are all less than 2π, as required.

In Example 3, if the domain for θ had been given as $0° < \theta \leq 360°$, then the solutions would be expressed in degrees, as shown below.

$3\theta = 45°, 315°, 405°, 675°, 765°, 1035°$, where $0° < 3\theta \leq 1080°$
$\therefore \theta = 15°, 105°, 135°, 225°, 255°, 345°$, where $0° < \sin\theta \leq 360°$

In some situations, it may be necessary to use the identities developed in lesson 6-7.

EXAMPLE 5: Solve $\sin\theta + 1 - 2\cos^2\theta = 0$, where $0° < \theta \leq 360°$.

$$\sin\theta + 1 - 2\cos^2\theta = 0$$ Write the equation in terms of sine only.

$$\sin\theta + 1 - 2(1 - \sin^2\theta) = 0$$ $\sin^2\theta + \cos^2\theta = 1$

$$\sin\theta + 1 - 2 + 2\sin^2\theta = 0$$

$$2\sin^2\theta + \sin\theta - 1 = 0$$

$$(2\sin\theta - 1)(\sin\theta + 1) = 0$$ $2m^2 + m - 1 = (2m - 1)(m + 1)$

$\therefore \sin\theta = \frac{1}{2}$ or $\sin\theta = -1$

The reference angle is 30° in quadrants I and II.
$\therefore \theta_1 = 30°, \quad \theta_2 = 150°$

The point (0, −1) is the only point on the unit circle where y = −1.
$\therefore \theta_3 = 270°$

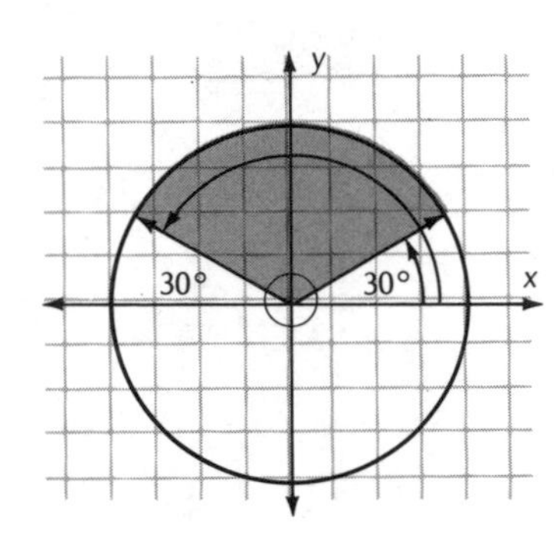

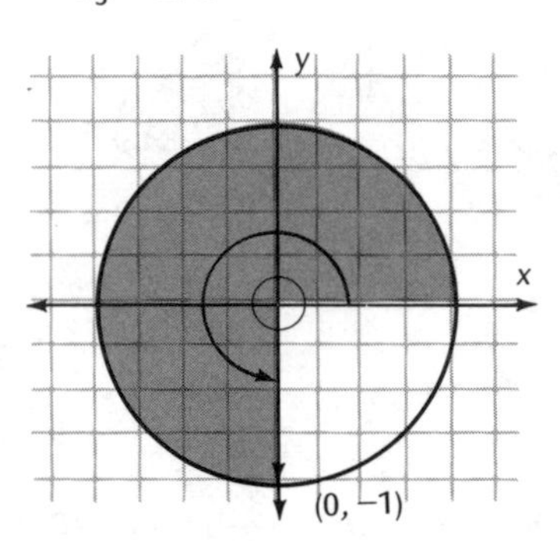

$\therefore \sin\theta = 30°, 150°, 270°$

EXERCISE 6-9

A **1.** Sketch the given function, where $0 \leq \theta \leq 2\pi$. Then solve the given trigonometric equation by graphing.

a. $y = \cos\theta$; $\cos\theta = -\frac{1}{2}$
b. $y = \tan\theta$; $\tan\theta = 1$
c. $y = \sin\theta$; $\sin\theta = -1$
d. $y = \cos 2\theta$; $\cos 2\theta = \frac{1}{2}$

2. Solve for θ, where $0 < \theta \leq 2\pi$.

a. $\sin\theta = \frac{-\sqrt{3}}{2}$
b. $\cos\theta = 0$
c. $\tan\theta = \sqrt{3}$
d. $\cos\theta = \frac{\sqrt{2}}{2}$
e. $\tan\theta$ is undefined
f. $\sin\theta = \frac{1}{2}$
g. $\tan\theta = 0$
h. $\sec\theta = \sqrt{2}$
i. $\csc\theta = \frac{2}{\sqrt{3}}$

3. Solve for θ, correct to two decimal places, where $0° < \theta \leq 360°$.

a. $\sin\theta = 0.4848$
b. $\cos\theta = -0.7309$
c. $\tan\theta = 1.6428$
d. $\sin\theta = -\frac{3}{4}$
e. $\cos\theta = \frac{2}{3}$
f. $\tan\theta = -\frac{1}{4}$

B **4.** Solve for θ, where $0 < \theta \leq 2\pi$.

a. $\sin\theta = \cos\theta$

b. $\sin\theta = -\cos\theta$

c. $\tan\theta = 2\sin\theta$

d. $2\sin\theta = \csc\theta$

e. $\sin\theta\tan\theta - \tan\theta = 0$

f. $2\sin^2\theta + \sin\theta = 0$

g. $2\cos^2\theta = 1$

h. $2\sin^2\theta - \sin\theta - 1 = 0$

i. $2\sin\theta\cos\theta = \cos\theta$

j. $4\cos^2\theta - 4\cos\theta + 1 = 0$

k. $\cos\theta(2\sin\theta - \sqrt{3})(\sin\theta + 1) = 0$

l. $\sin^3\theta - 2\sin^2\theta + \sin\theta = 0$

5. Solve for θ, correct to two decimal places, where $0° < \theta \leq 360°$.

a. $3\sin\theta - 2 = 0$

b. $3\sin\theta\cos\theta + \sin\theta = 0$

c. $3\sin^2\theta + 2\sin\theta = 0$

d. $12\cos^2\theta + \cos\theta - 1 = 0$

e. $5\cos^2\theta = 1$

f. $\sin\theta - 2\cos\theta = 0$

g. $3\sin\theta + \cos\theta = 0$

h. $3\sin\theta\cos\theta - 3\sin\theta + 2\cos\theta - 2 = 0$

i. $4\sec\theta + \csc\theta = 0$

j. $\sec\theta = 4\csc\theta$

6. Solve for θ, where $0 < \theta \leq 2\pi$.

a. $\tan 2\theta = \dfrac{-1}{\sqrt{3}}$

b. $\cos 2\theta = \dfrac{\sqrt{3}}{2}$

c. $\sin 3\theta = \dfrac{-\sqrt{2}}{2}$

d. $\tan\dfrac{\theta}{2} = 1$

7. Solve for θ, where $0 < \theta \leq 2\pi$.

a. $\sin\theta\cos 2\theta = \sin\theta$

b. $4\cos^2(2\theta) - 3 = 0$

c. $4\sin^2(3\theta) + 4\sin 3\theta + 1 = 0$

d. $2\sin 2\theta\cos 3\theta - \sqrt{3}\cos 3\theta = 0$

8. Solve for θ, where $0 < \theta \leq 2\pi$.

a. $4\cos^2\theta - 2\cos\theta - 2\sqrt{3}\cos\theta + \sqrt{3} = 0$

b. $2\sin\theta\tan\theta + \tan\theta - 2\sin\theta - 1 = 0$

c. $\sin\theta\cos\theta - \cos\theta + \sin\theta - 1 = 0$

d. $\sqrt{2}\cos\theta\tan\theta - \sqrt{6}\cos\theta + \tan\theta - \sqrt{3} = 0$

e. $1 - \sin\theta - 2\cos^2\theta = 0$

f. $2\cos^2\theta + \cos\theta + \tan^2\theta - \sec^2\theta = 0$

g. $\sin^2\theta + \cos^2\theta - \tan^2\theta + 2 = 0$

h. $\sin\theta\cos\theta - \sin\theta - \cos\theta + \sec^2\theta - \tan^2\theta = 0$

C **9.** Solve for θ, correct to two decimal places, where $0° < \theta \leq 360°$.

a. $4\sin^2\theta - 4\sin\theta - \cos^2\theta = 0$

b. $\sin^2\theta - \sin\theta\cos\theta - 12\cos^2\theta = 0$

c. $3\sin\theta\cos\theta + \cos^2\theta + 1 = 0$

6-10 Some Useful Trigonometric Relationships

On a unit circle a *positive* angle is measured in a *counterclockwise* direction while a *negative* angle is measured *clockwise*.

The diagram at the right shows two equal acute angles in standard position with measures of θ and $-\theta$, respectively.

Compare the values of sin, cos, and tan for θ and $-\theta$.

$$\sin\theta = y \quad \text{and} \quad \sin(-\theta) = -y$$
$$\cos\theta = x \quad \text{and} \quad \cos(-\theta) = x$$
$$\tan\theta = \frac{y}{x} \quad \text{and} \quad \tan(-\theta) = -\frac{y}{x}$$

Thus, $\sin(-\theta) = -\sin\theta$, $\cos(-\theta) = \cos\theta$, and $\tan(-\theta) = -\tan\theta$.

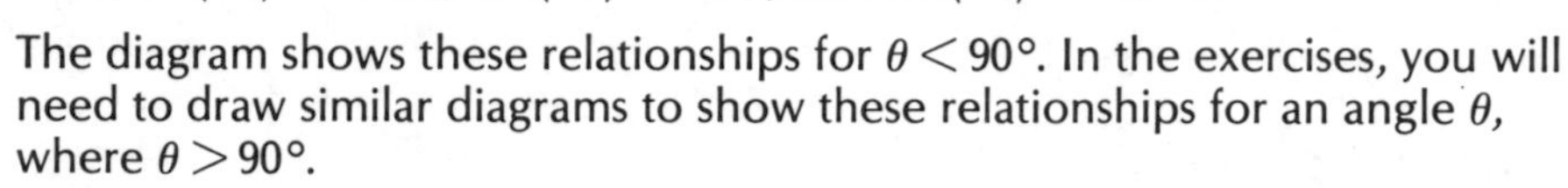

The diagram shows these relationships for $\theta < 90°$. In the exercises, you will need to draw similar diagrams to show these relationships for an angle θ, where $\theta > 90°$.

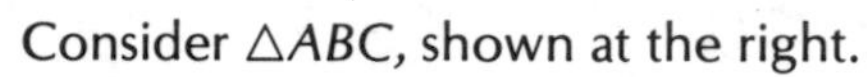

Consider $\triangle ABC$, shown at the right.

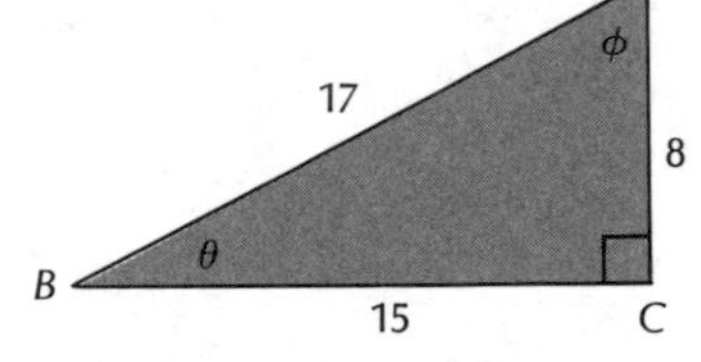

$$\sin\theta = \tfrac{8}{17} \text{ and } \cos\phi = \tfrac{8}{17}$$
$$\sin\phi = \tfrac{15}{17} \text{ and } \cos\theta = \tfrac{15}{17}$$

Notice that θ and ϕ are complementary angles, and that the sine of each angle is equal to the cosine of its complement. The cosine, cosecant, and cotangent functions are called the **complementary trigonometric functions**.

Complementary angles have a sum of 90°.

In general, for any right-angled triangle,

$$\sin\theta = \frac{b}{c} = \cos(90° - \theta) \text{ and } \cos\theta = \frac{a}{c} = \sin(90° - \theta);$$

$$\tan\theta = \frac{b}{a} = \cot(90° - \theta) \text{ and } \cot\theta = \frac{a}{b} = \tan(90° - \theta).$$

Expressing angles in radian measure gives the following relationships.

$$\sin\theta = \cos\left(\frac{\pi}{2} - \theta\right) \qquad \cos\theta = \sin\left(\frac{\pi}{2} - \theta\right)$$
$$\tan\theta = \cot\left(\frac{\pi}{2} - \theta\right) \qquad \cot\theta = \tan\left(\frac{\pi}{2} - \theta\right)$$
$$\sec\theta = \csc\left(\frac{\pi}{2} - \theta\right) \qquad \csc\theta = \sec\left(\frac{\pi}{2} - \theta\right)$$

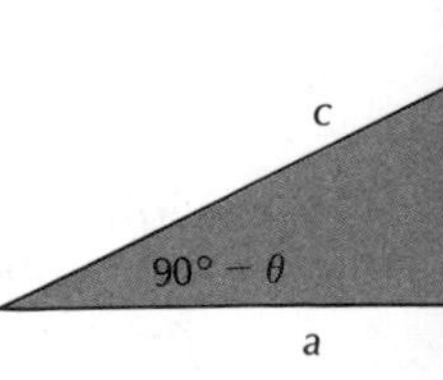

Again, these formulas are shown for θ, where $\theta < 90°$. However, the relationships for the complementary trigonometric functions are true for *all* values of θ.

For the diagram at the right, $\theta = 120°$. Does $\sin\theta = \cos(90° - \theta)$?

$$\begin{aligned}
\sin\theta &= \cos(90° - \theta) \\
\sin 120° &= \cos(90° - 120°) \\
&= \cos(-30°) \\
&= \cos 30°
\end{aligned}$$

Since L.S. $= \dfrac{\sqrt{3}}{2}$ and R.S. $= \dfrac{\sqrt{3}}{2}$, the formula is consistent.

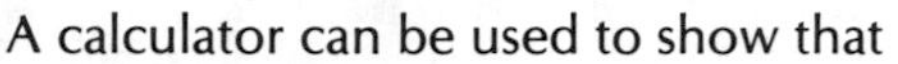

A calculator can be used to show that
$\sin 75° = \sin(45° + 30°) \neq \sin 45° + \sin 30°$.
So, in general, $\sin(A + B) \neq \sin A + \sin B$.
However, there is a relationship for $\sin(A + B)$ in terms of trigonometric functions of angles A and B.

In the diagram at the right, $\angle BOC = \theta$ and $\angle AOB = \phi$.
$\overline{AE}$ and $\overline{BC}$ are drawn perpendicular to the x-axis and $\overline{BD} \perp \overline{AE}$. Also, $\angle DAB = \theta$. (Why?)

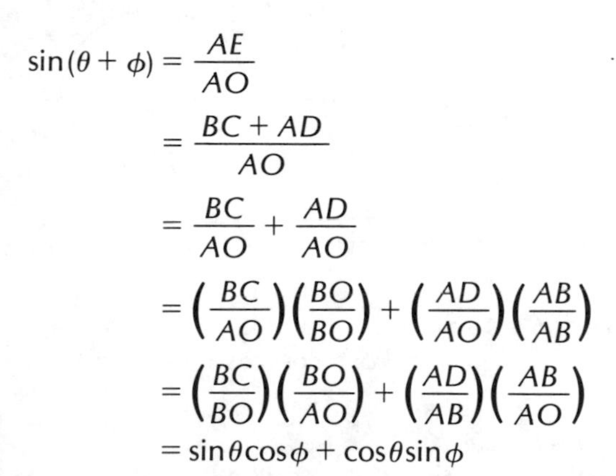

$$\begin{aligned}
\sin(\theta + \phi) &= \frac{AE}{AO} \\
&= \frac{BC + AD}{AO} \\
&= \frac{BC}{AO} + \frac{AD}{AO} \\
&= \left(\frac{BC}{AO}\right)\left(\frac{BO}{BO}\right) + \left(\frac{AD}{AO}\right)\left(\frac{AB}{AB}\right) \\
&= \left(\frac{BC}{BO}\right)\left(\frac{BO}{AO}\right) + \left(\frac{AD}{AB}\right)\left(\frac{AB}{AO}\right) \\
&= \sin\theta\cos\phi + \cos\theta\sin\phi
\end{aligned}$$

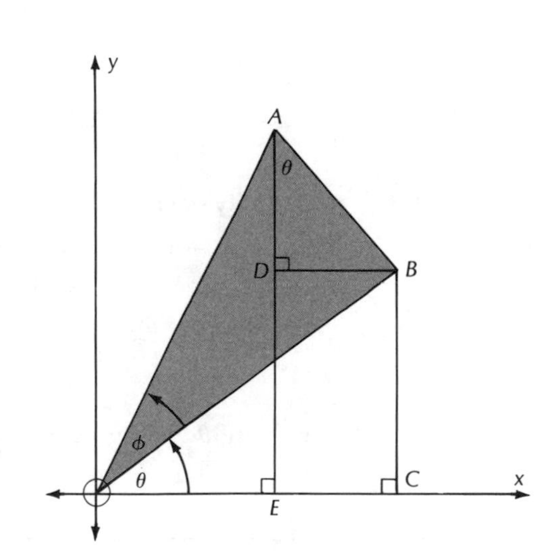

For angles θ and $-\phi$,

$$\begin{aligned}
\sin(\theta - \phi) &= \sin\theta\cos(-\phi) + \cos\theta\sin(-\phi) \\
&= \sin\theta\cos\phi - \cos\theta\sin\phi
\end{aligned}$$

Sum and Difference Formulas

$$\begin{aligned}
\sin(\theta + \phi) &= \sin\theta\cos\phi + \cos\theta\sin\phi \\
\sin(\theta - \phi) &= \sin\theta\cos\phi - \cos\theta\sin\phi \\
\cos(\theta + \phi) &= \cos\theta\cos\phi - \sin\theta\sin\phi \\
\cos(\theta - \phi) &= \cos\theta\cos\phi + \sin\theta\sin\phi
\end{aligned}$$

The development of $\cos(\theta + \phi)$ and of $\cos(\theta - \phi)$ is left to the exercises.

EXAMPLE 1: Evaluate each of the following. Express each answer in radical form.

a.
$$\begin{aligned}\sin 75^\circ &= \sin(30^\circ + 45^\circ)\\ &= \sin 30^\circ \cos 45^\circ + \cos 30^\circ \sin 45^\circ\\ &= \left(\frac{1}{2}\right)\left(\frac{1}{\sqrt{2}}\right) + \left(\frac{\sqrt{3}}{2}\right)\left(\frac{1}{\sqrt{2}}\right)\\ &= \frac{1+\sqrt{3}}{2\sqrt{2}}\\ &= \frac{\sqrt{2}+\sqrt{6}}{4}\end{aligned}$$

b.
$$\begin{aligned}\cos 165^\circ &= -\cos 15^\circ\\ &= -\cos(45^\circ - 30^\circ)\\ &= -(\cos 45^\circ \cos 30^\circ + \sin 45^\circ \sin 30^\circ)\\ &= -\left[\left(\frac{1}{\sqrt{2}}\right)\left(\frac{\sqrt{3}}{2}\right) + \left(\frac{1}{\sqrt{2}}\right)\left(\frac{1}{2}\right)\right]\\ &= \frac{-\sqrt{3}-1}{2\sqrt{2}}\\ &= \frac{-\sqrt{6}-\sqrt{2}}{4}\end{aligned}$$

$165^\circ = 180^\circ - 15^\circ$ is in Quadrant II.
The reference angle is 15°.

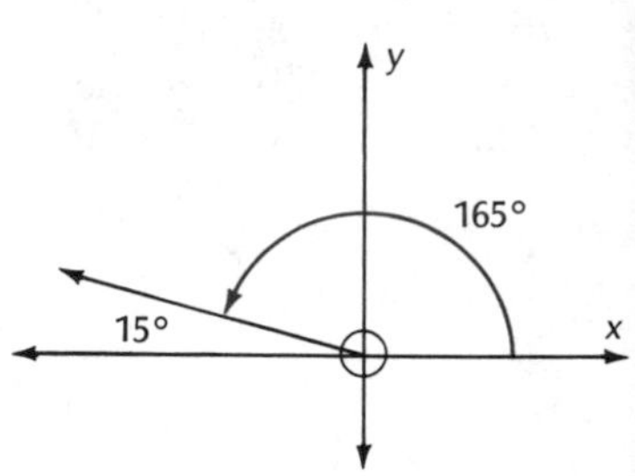

EXAMPLE 2: Simplify each of the following.

a.
$$\begin{aligned}\cos(-m-7) &= \cos[-(m+7)]\\ &= \cos(m+7)\end{aligned}$$
$\cos(-\theta) = \cos\theta$

b.
$$\begin{aligned}\cos(\pi - \theta) &= \cos\pi\cos\theta + \sin\pi\sin\theta\\ &= (-1)\cos\theta + (0)\sin\theta\\ &= -\cos\theta\end{aligned}$$
$\cos(\theta - \phi) = \cos\theta\cos\phi + \sin\theta\sin\phi$

c.
$$\begin{aligned}\sin 4\theta\cos 2\theta - \cos 4\theta \sin 2\theta &= \sin(4\theta - 2\theta)\\ &= \sin 2\theta\end{aligned}$$
$\sin\theta\cos\phi - \cos\theta\sin\phi = \sin(\theta - \phi)$

EXERCISE 6-10

A **1.** Use the complementary trigonometric relationships to write an equivalent expression for each of the following.

a. $\sin 47^\circ$ **b.** $\csc 31^\circ$ **c.** $\tan 62^\circ$
d. $\cos 81^\circ$ **e.** $\cos 18^\circ$ **f.** $\sec 43^\circ$

2. Express each of the following as a trigonometric value of a positive angle.

a. $\sin(-48^\circ)$ **b.** $\cos(-142^\circ)$ **c.** $\tan(-206^\circ)$

3. Expand.

a. $\sin(3\theta - \beta)$ **b.** $\cos(2\alpha + 3\beta)$ **c.** $\sin(-\alpha + \beta)$

B 4. Use the diagram at the right to simplify each of the following.

   a. $\sec(-\theta)$ b. $\csc(-\theta)$ c. $\cot(-\theta)$

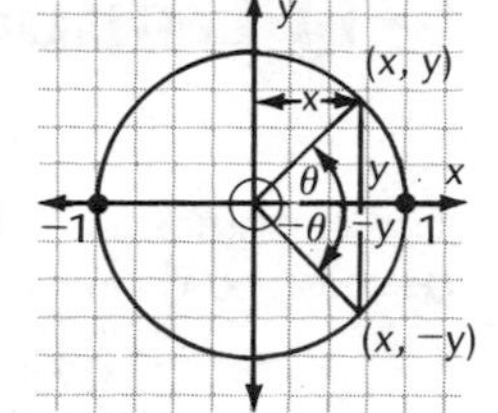

5. Use a diagram to show that the formulas for the complementary trigonometric functions, given in this lesson, are true in each given case.

   a. when $\frac{\pi}{2} < \theta < \pi$ b. when $\pi < \theta < \frac{3\pi}{2}$

6. From the diagram at the right, prove the expansion for each expression.

   a. $\cos(\theta + \phi)$ b. $\cos(\theta - \phi)$

7. Express each of the following in terms of θ only.

   a. $\cos(\theta - \pi)$ b. $\cos(90° + \theta)$
   c. $\sin(2\pi - \theta)$ d. $\cos(\theta - 2\pi)$
   e. $\sin(90° + \theta)$ f. $\sin\left(\theta - \frac{\pi}{2}\right)$

8. Use the relationships for complementary, positive, and negative angles to simplify each of the following.

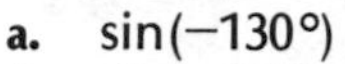

   a. $\sin(-130°)$ b. $\cos(-305°)$ c. $\cos(-220°)$
   d. $\sin(-195°)$ e. $\sin(-345°)$ f. $\cos(-105°)$

9. Find the value of each of the following. Express answers in radical form.

   a. $\cos 75°$ b. $\sin 15°$ c. $\cos 195°$
   d. $\sin 285°$ e. $\sin 195°$ f. $\cos 105°$

10. Simplify, using the sum and difference formulas.

   a. $\sin 2\theta \cos\beta - \cos 2\theta \sin\beta$ b. $\cos 4\theta \cos 6\theta + \sin 4\theta \sin 6\theta$
   c. $\sin 5\theta \sin 2\theta + \cos 5\theta \cos 2\theta$ d. $\cos 4\theta \sin\theta + \sin 4\theta \cos\theta$
   e. $\sin 5\theta \sin 3\theta - \cos 5\theta \cos 3\theta$ f. $\sin 2\theta \sin 7\theta - \cos 2\theta \cos 7\theta$

C 11. Evaluate each of the following. Express answers in radical form.

   a. $\sin(-195°)$ b. $\cos(-285°)$ c. $\cos(-105°)$

12. Prove each identity.

   a. $\frac{\cos(\theta - \phi)}{\cos(\theta + \phi)} = \frac{1 + \tan\theta\tan\phi}{1 - \tan\theta\tan\phi}$ b. $\frac{\sin(\theta - \phi)}{\sin(\theta + \phi)} = \frac{\tan\theta - \tan\phi}{\tan\theta + \tan\phi}$

13. Consider a circle with radius 1, as shown.

   a. Show that the coordinates of P are $(\cos B, \sin B)$.
   b. Show that the coordinates of Q are $(\cos A, \sin A)$.
   c. Find the coordinates of R and T.
   d. Explain why arc RT = arc PQ.
   e. Using the coordinates of P and Q, find PQ.
   f. Using the coordinates of R and T, find arc RT.
   g. Using $RT = PQ$, prove that $\sin(A - B) = \sin A \cos B - \cos A \sin B$

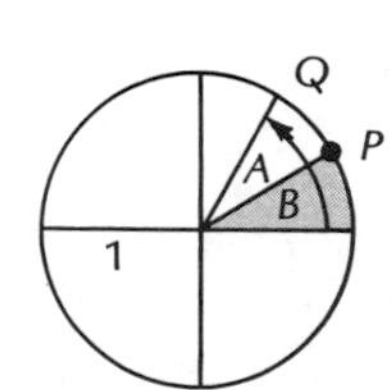

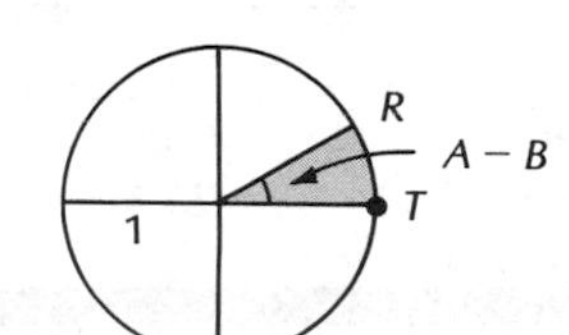

6-11 Double and Half-Angle Formulas

The formulas for $\sin 2\theta$ and $\cos 2\theta$, or the **double-angle formulas**, can be developed directly from the addition formulas.

$$\begin{aligned}\sin 2\theta &= \sin(\theta + \theta)\\ &= \sin\theta\cos\theta + \cos\theta\sin\theta\\ &= 2\sin\theta\cos\theta\end{aligned}$$

$$\begin{aligned}\cos 2\theta &= \cos(\theta + \theta)\\ &= \cos\theta\cos\theta - \sin\theta\sin\theta\\ &= \cos^2\theta - \sin^2\theta\end{aligned}$$

$\sin 2\theta = 2\sin\theta\cos\theta$ and $\cos 2\theta = \cos^2\theta - \sin^2\theta$

Two other formulas for $\cos 2\theta$ can be developed.

$$\begin{aligned}\cos 2\theta &= \cos^2\theta - \sin^2\theta\\ &= \cos^2\theta - (1 - \cos^2\theta)\\ &= 2\cos^2\theta - 1\end{aligned}$$

$$\begin{aligned}\cos 2\theta &= \cos^2\theta - \sin^2\theta\\ &= (1 - \sin^2\theta) - \sin^2\theta\\ &= 1 - 2\sin^2\theta\end{aligned}$$

$\cos 2\theta = 2\cos^2\theta - 1$ and $\cos 2\theta = 1 - 2\sin^2\theta$

The formulas for $\sin\frac{\theta}{2}$ and $\cos\frac{\theta}{2}$, or the **half-angle formulas**, are derived from the formulas for $\cos 2\theta$.

Since $\cos 2\theta = 1 - 2\sin^2\theta$,

then $\cos A = 1 - 2\sin^2\frac{A}{2}$.

$$2\sin^2\frac{A}{2} = 1 - \cos A$$

So, $\sin\frac{A}{2} = \pm\sqrt{\frac{1 - \cos A}{2}}$.

The half-angle formula for cosine is developed in a similar way by using $\cos 2\theta = 2\cos^2\theta - 1$.

$\sin\frac{A}{2} = \pm\sqrt{\frac{1 - \cos A}{2}}$ and $\cos\frac{A}{2} = \pm\sqrt{\frac{1 + \cos A}{2}}$

EXERCISE 6-11

A 1. If $\sin\theta = \frac{3}{5}$ and $\cos\theta = \frac{4}{5}$, evaluate each of the following.

a. $\sin 2\theta$ b. $\cos 2\theta$ c. $\sin\frac{\theta}{2}$ d. $\cos\frac{\theta}{2}$

2. Use the half-angle formulas to find the *exact* value for each of the following.

a. $\sin 15°$ b. $\cos 15°$ c. $\sin 22\frac{1}{2}°$ d. $\cos 22\frac{1}{2}°$

B 3. If $\sin\theta = \frac{21}{29}$, where $0 < \theta < \frac{\pi}{2}$, evaluate each of the following.

a. $\sin 2\theta$ b. $\cos 2\theta$ c. $\sin\frac{\theta}{2}$ d. $\cos\frac{\theta}{2}$

4. If $\tan\theta = \frac{-9}{40}$, where $\frac{\pi}{2} < \theta < \pi$, evaluate each of the following.

a. $\sin 2\theta$ b. $\cos 2\theta$ c. $\sin\frac{\theta}{2}$ d. $\cos\frac{\theta}{2}$

5. Use the half-angle formulas to find the exact value for each of the following.

a. $\cos 67.5°$ b. $\sin 112.5°$ c. $\sin 225°$

d. $\sin\frac{\pi}{12}$ e. $\sin\frac{3\pi}{8}$ f. $\cos\frac{7\pi}{12}$

C 6. If A and B are complementary angles, prove each of the following.

a. $\sin(A - B) = \cos 2B$ b. $\cos(A - B) = \sin 2A$

7. a. Write $\sin 3\theta$ in terms of $\sin\theta$. b. Write $\cos 3\theta$ in terms of $\cos\theta$.

8. Prove each identity.

a. $\dfrac{\cos 2\theta + 1}{\sin 2\theta} = \cot\theta$ b. $\dfrac{\sin 2\theta}{\sin\theta} - \dfrac{\cos 2\theta}{\cos\theta} = \dfrac{1}{\cos\theta}$

c. $\dfrac{\sin 2\theta}{\sin\theta} = 4\cos\theta - \dfrac{\cos 2\theta + 1}{\cos\theta}$ d. $\dfrac{1 + \tan^2\theta}{1 - \tan^2\theta} = \sec 2\theta$

e. $\sin^2\left(\dfrac{\theta}{2}\right) = \dfrac{\sin^2\theta}{2 + 2\cos\theta}$ f. $2\sec\theta\cos^2\left(\dfrac{\theta}{2}\right) = \sec\theta + 1$

g. $\csc 2\theta = 0.5\sec\theta\csc\theta$ h. $\sec 2\theta = \dfrac{\sec^2\theta}{2 - \sec^2\theta}$

9. From the formulas for $\sin\frac{\theta}{2}$ and $\cos\frac{\theta}{2}$ show that

$$\tan\left(\frac{\theta}{2}\right) = \pm\sqrt{\frac{1 - \cos\theta}{1 + \cos\theta}} = \pm\frac{\sin\theta}{1 + \cos\theta} = \pm\frac{1 - \cos\theta}{\sin\theta}.$$

10. Solve for θ, where $0 \leq \theta \leq 2\pi$.

a. $\cos 2\theta + \cos\theta = 0$ b. $\sin 2\theta + \sin\theta = 0$

Review

1. Copy and complete each table.

   a.

Degree Measure	60°		225°		126°		70°
Radian Measure	$\frac{\pi}{3}$	$\frac{5\pi}{6}$		$\frac{7\pi}{9}$		$\frac{3\pi}{5}$	

   b.

Degree Measure	80°	50°		162°		219°	
Radian Measure	1.40		1.35		3.47		8.13

2. Find the area of each shaded region.

   a.

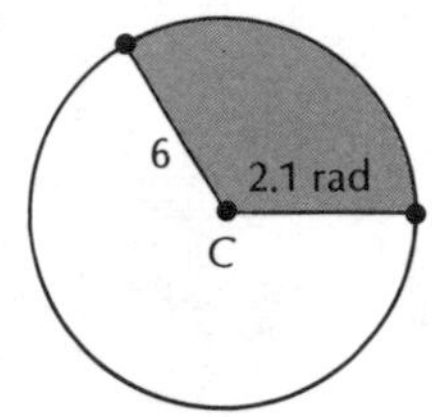

   b.

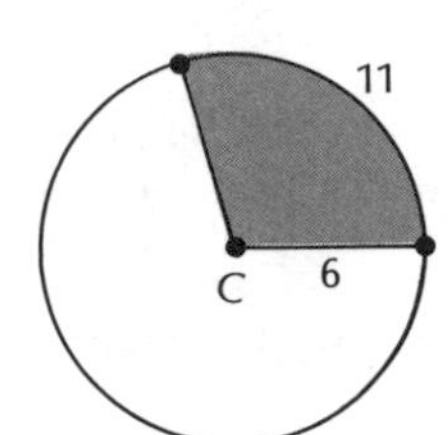

   c.

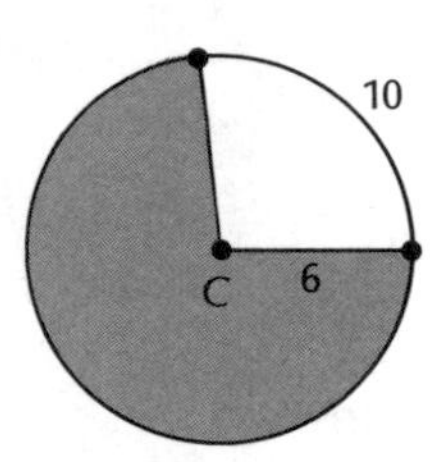

   d.

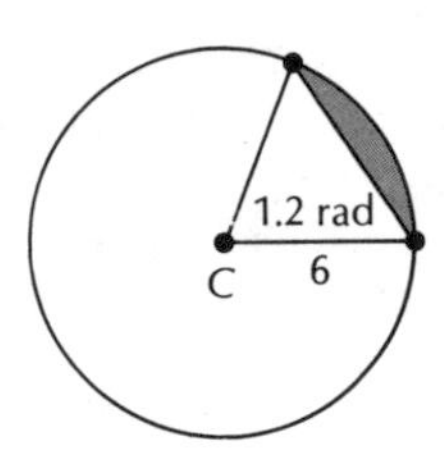

3. a. If $\omega = \frac{\theta}{t}$ with $\omega = \frac{5\pi}{6}$ rad/s and $\theta = 3$ rad, find the value of t.

   b. If $\omega = \frac{s}{rt}$ with $\omega = 2$ rad/s, $s = 15$ m, and $t = 3.2$ s, find the value of r.

   c. If $v = \omega r$ with $v = 18$ m/s and $\omega = \frac{2\pi}{3}$ rad/s, find the value of r.

4. Find the measure of the central angle generated in 75 s by a wheel with an angular velocity of $\frac{5\pi}{6}$ rad/s.

5. Find the velocity of the belt of a pulley that is moving, without slipping, at a speed of 2.6 m/s around a wheel with radius 8.5 cm.

6. State the domain and range of each function.

   a. $y = \sin\theta$ b. $y = \cot\theta$ c. $y = \sec\theta$

7. Sketch the graph of each function, where $0 \leq \theta \leq 2\pi$.

   a. $y = \sin 2\theta$ b. $y = -\cos\theta + 1$ c. $y = \tan\left(\theta + \frac{\pi}{2}\right)$

   d. $y = 2\sin\frac{\theta}{2}$ e. $y = -3\cos\theta - 2$ f. $y = -\frac{1}{2}\sin\left(\theta - \frac{\pi}{6}\right) - 1$

8. Sketch the graph of each function, where $0 \leq \theta \leq 2\pi$.
   a. $y = \sin x + \sin 2x$
   b. $y = \cos 2x - \cos x$

9. Rewrite each expression using sines and cosines only.
   a. $\dfrac{1}{1+\sin\theta} + \dfrac{1}{1-\sin\theta}$
   b. $\sec\theta + \tan\theta$
   c. $\dfrac{\cos^2\theta}{\sin\theta(1+\csc\theta)}$
   d. $\dfrac{1+\cos\theta}{\sin\theta+\tan\theta}$

10. Simplify.
   a. $\sin\theta\tan\theta + \cos\theta$
   b. $\cos\theta\sec^2\theta - \cos\theta\tan^2\theta$
   c. $\dfrac{\cos\theta+1}{\cos\theta} - \dfrac{\sin\theta+1}{\sin\theta}$
   d. $\dfrac{1}{\sec\theta - \tan\theta}$

11. Prove each identity.
   a. $\sec\theta + \tan\theta = \dfrac{\cos\theta}{1-\sin\theta}$
   b. $\dfrac{1-\tan^2\theta}{\cot^2\theta - 1} = \dfrac{1-\cos^2\theta}{\cos^2\theta}$
   c. $\dfrac{\sin\theta+\tan\theta}{1+\cos\theta} - \dfrac{1}{\cot\theta} = 0$
   d. $\dfrac{\cos^2\theta}{1+\sin\theta} = 1 - \sin\theta$

12. Solve for θ, where $0 < \theta < 2\pi$.
   a. $\sin\theta\cos\theta + \sin\theta = 0$
   b. $4\cos^2\theta = 1$
   c. $2\cos 2\theta + \sqrt{3} = 0$
   d. $2\cos^2\theta + \cos\theta = 1$

13. Solve for θ, where $0° < \theta \leq 360°$.
   a. $7\sin\theta\cos\theta = -\sin\theta$
   b. $12\sin^2\theta - 5\sin\theta - 2 = 0$
   c. $15\sin\theta\cos\theta + 10\sin\theta + 3\cos\theta + 2 = 0$
   d. $6\cos^2\theta + 6\cos\theta + \sin^2\theta = 0$

14. Find the exact value for each of the following.
   a. $\sin 225°$
   b. $\sin 345°$
   c. $\cos 165°$
   d. $\cos 285°$

15. Simplify.
   a. $\cos(-31°)$
   b. $\sin\left(\dfrac{\pi}{2} + \theta\right)$
   c. $\cos(2\pi - \theta)$
   d. $\sin(\theta - 2\pi)$
   e. $\sin\left(\theta - \dfrac{\pi}{2}\right)$
   f. $\cos\left(\dfrac{\pi}{2} - \theta\right)$
   g. $\sin 7\theta\cos 2\theta - \cos 7\theta\sin 2\theta$
   h. $\sin(-305°)$
   i. $\sin 6\theta\sin 2\theta - \cos 6\theta\cos 2\theta$
   j. $\cos(-100°)$

16. Use the half-angle formulas to find the exact value of each of the following.
   a. $\sin 67.5°$
   b. $\cos\dfrac{3\pi}{8}$
   c. $\sin\dfrac{7\pi}{12}$

17. If $\tan\theta = -\dfrac{15}{8}$, where $\dfrac{\pi}{2} < \theta < \pi$, evaluate each of the following.
   a. $\sin 2\theta$
   b. $\cos 2\theta$
   c. $\sin\dfrac{\theta}{2}$
   d. $\cos\dfrac{\theta}{2}$

18. Prove each identity.
   a. $\dfrac{\sin^2(2\theta)}{\sin^2\theta} = 4 - 4\sin^2\theta$
   b. $4\left(\sin\dfrac{\theta}{2}\right)\left(\cos\dfrac{\theta}{2}\right) = 2\sin\theta$

Test Unit 6

1. For each diagram, find the measure of θ in degrees and in radians.

   a.
   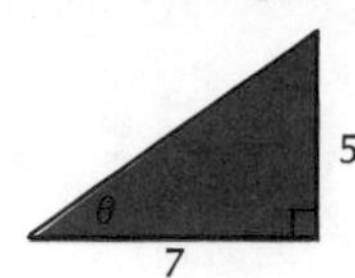

   b.
   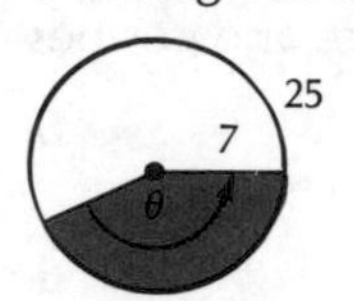

   c.
   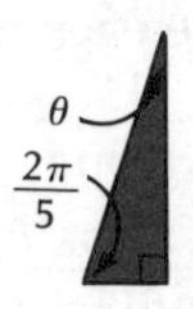

2. For part **b** of question 1, find the area of the major and minor sectors.

3. a. If $v = \omega r$ with $v = 15$ cm/s and $\omega = \frac{5\pi}{3}$ rad/s, find the value of r.

   b. If $\omega = \frac{\theta}{t}$ with $\omega = \frac{5\pi}{6}$ rad/s and $t = 2.3$ s, find the value of θ.

   c. If $\omega = \frac{s}{rt}$ with $s = 18$ cm, $r = 5$ cm, and $t = 15$ s, find the value of ω.

4. A bicycle has wheels with a diameter of 58 cm. The wheels are turning, without slipping, at a rate of 1.4 rev/s. Find the speed of the bicycle, in metres per second.

5. Sketch the graph of each function.

   a. $y = \frac{1}{2}\cos\theta$
   b. $y = -\sin 3\theta$
   c. $y = \tan\left(\theta - \frac{\pi}{4}\right)$
   d. $y = \sin 2\theta + 2\sin\theta$

6. Simplify, using $\sin\theta$ and $\cos\theta$ only.

   a. $\frac{1}{1 - \cos\theta} - \frac{1}{1 + \cos\theta}$
   b. $\tan\theta(\cos\theta + \cot\theta)$
   c. $\tan\theta + \cot\theta$
   d. $\sin 2\theta$

7. Prove each identity.

   a. $\sec^2\theta\csc^2\theta = \sec^2\theta + \csc^2\theta$
   b. $\frac{\sin\theta - 1}{\sin\theta + 1} = -\frac{\csc\theta - 1}{\csc\theta + 1}$
   c. $\cot^2\theta - \cot^2\theta\cos^2\theta = \cos^2\theta$
   d. $\frac{1 - \cos^2\theta}{\sec^2\theta - 1} = \cos^2\theta$

8. Solve for θ, where $0° < \theta \leq 360°$.

   a. $5\sin\theta\cos\theta - 3\cos\theta = 0$
   b. $7\sin\theta = 3\cos\theta$
   c. $5\sin^2\theta - 4\sin\theta - 1 = 0$
   d. $5\sin 2\theta = 4$

9. Simplify.

   a. $\cos\left(-\frac{2\pi}{3}\right)$
   b. $\sin\left(\frac{\pi}{2} - 3\theta\right)$
   c. $\cos(2\pi + 5\theta)$
   d. $\sin\left(\frac{\pi}{2} + 2\theta\right)$
   e. $\sin 7\theta\cos 3\theta - \cos 7\theta\sin 3\theta$

10. If $\sin\theta = \frac{5}{13}$, where $90° < \theta < 180°$, find the exact value for each of the following.

   a. $\sin 2\theta$
   b. $\cos 2\theta$
   c. $\sin\frac{\theta}{2}$
   d. $\cos\frac{\theta}{2}$

Cumulative Review

1. The graph of $y = 2x^2$ is translated 3 units to the left, parallel to the x-axis, and 5 units down, parallel to the y-axis. Find an equation of the image.

2. A function, f, is defined by $y = 3x + 4$.
   a. Graph the function.
   b. Find an equation of f^{-1}.
   c. Graph f^{-1}.

3. Evaluate, without using a calculator.
   a. $27^{\frac{2}{3}}$ **b.** $16^{0.25}$ **c.** $(6.25)^{-\frac{3}{2}}$ **d.** $\sqrt[4]{0.0016}$

4. What amount will \$1500 accumulate to if it is invested for 5 a at an interest rate of 8%/a, compounded annually?

5. **a.** Graph the function, f, defined by $f(x) = x^4$, where $-2 \leq x \leq 2$.
   b. Graph f^{-1} on the same axes used in part **a.**
   c. State a defining equation of f^{-1}.

6. Factor each polynomial.
   a. $2a^2 + 9a + 4$ **b.** $10x^2 + 3x - 4$ **c.** $10y^2 + 11y - 6$
   d. $5x^3 + 11x^2 + 2x$ **e.** $24 - 37a - 72a^2$ **f.** $3 + 11x - 4x^2$

7. Factor, using the Factor Theorem.
   a. $x^3 - 5x^2 + 2x + 8$ **b.** $y^3 + y^2 - 80y - 300$

8. A satellite is viewed from two points, A and B, that are 200 km apart. If the angles of elevation of the satellite are 28° and 35°, respectively, from the two points, find the height of the satellite if it is directly over the line joining the two points.

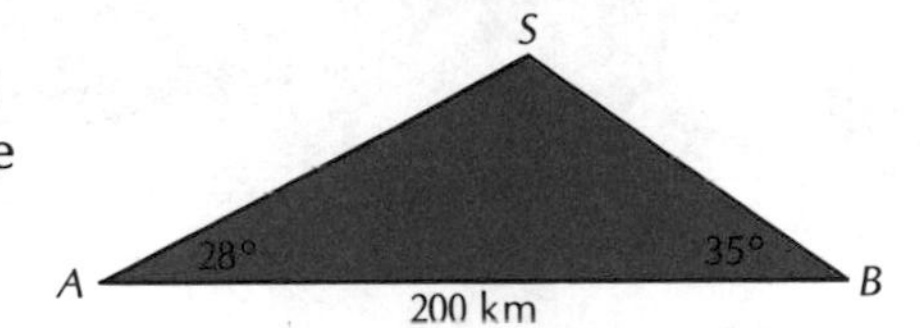

9. Solve $\triangle ABC$, if $a = 5$, $b = 7$, and $c = 11$.

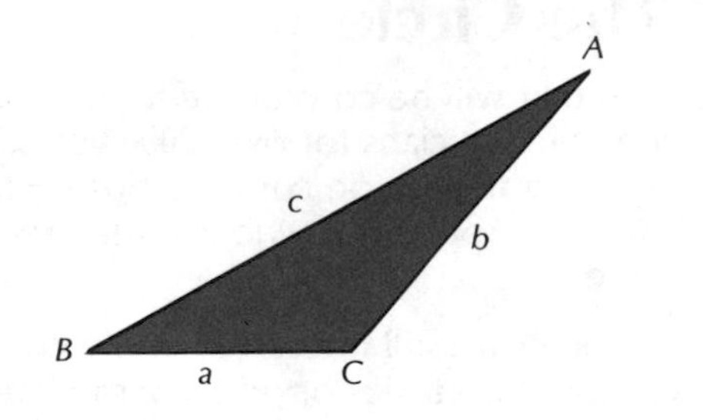

10. Find the value of each variable.
   a.

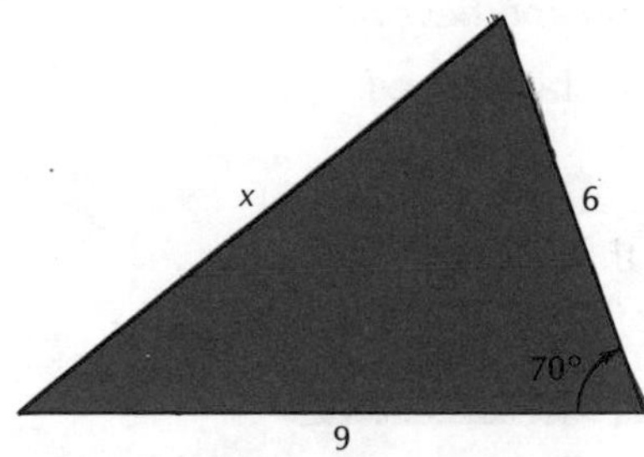

   b.

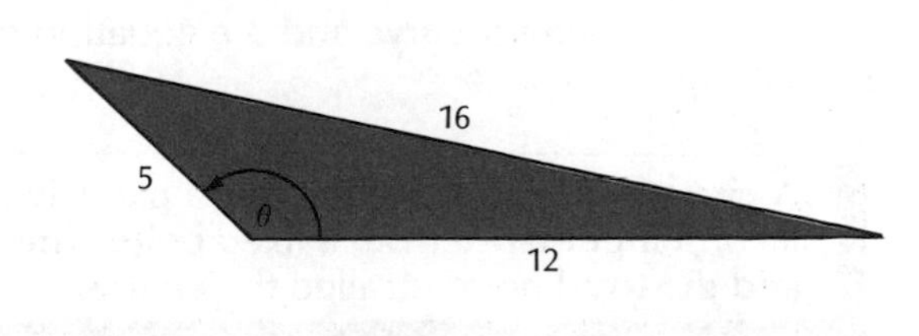

7 Second Degree Relations II

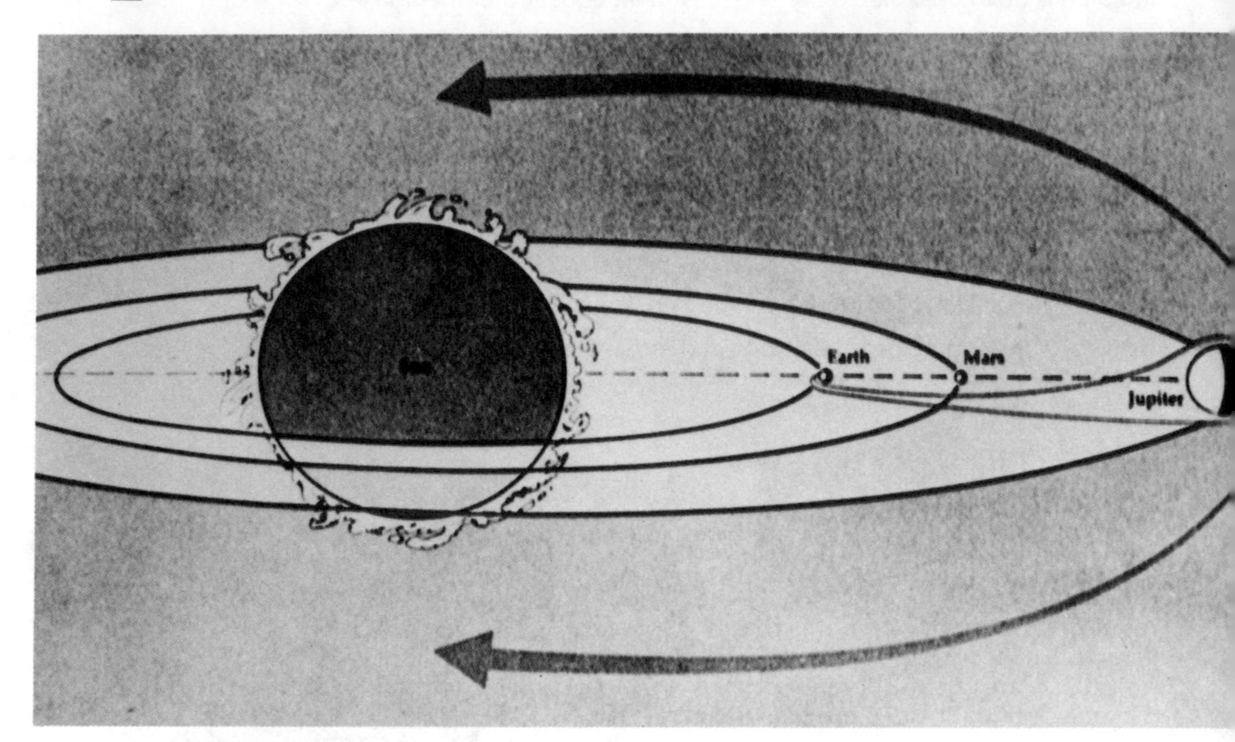

7-1 The Circle

The curves that will be considered in this and the following unit have been used by mathematicians for over 2000 years. In 200 B.C., Apollonius, a Greek, wrote a treatise on conic sections—the circle, parabola, ellipse, and hyperbola. It is Apollonius who is given credit for naming the last three of these curves.

Scientists today are still interested in the conic sections as these are the shapes of the trajectories or orbits of satellites under the effects of gravitation. The shape of the orbit depends mostly on the satellite's speed. Circular orbits are useful for telecommunications satellites, whereas parabolic orbits are used for sending spacecraft to the moon and beyond.

The circle is a familiar curve and the equation of a circle can be derived from its definition.

> A **circle** is the set of all points in a plane located such that each point is a constant distance from a fixed point. The distance is called the **radius** and the fixed point is called the **centre**.

EXAMPLE 1: Find an equation of the circle with centre C(2, −3) and radius 4.

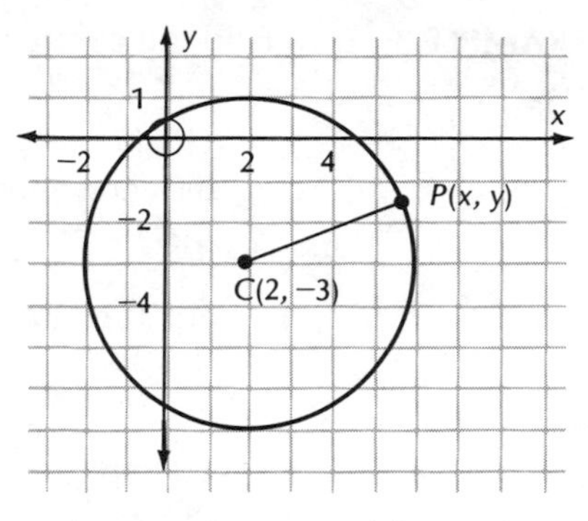

Let $P(x, y)$ be any point on the circle. Then $CP = 4$.

Recall that the distance, d, between two points (x_1, y_1) and (x_2, y_2) is given by

$$d = \sqrt{(x_2 - x_1)^2 + (y_2 - y_1)^2}.$$

So, the distance between P and C is

$$\sqrt{(x - 2)^2 + (y + 3)^2} = 4, \text{ or}$$

$$(x - 2)^2 + (y + 3)^2 = 16$$ This is an equation of the circle.

Notice that the equation states that the square of the distance between the point $P(x, y)$ and the centre $C(2, -3)$ is equal to the square of the radius.

A circle with centre $C(h, k)$ and radius r has a defining equation of the form $(x - h)^2 + (y - k)^2 = r^2$.

EXAMPLE 2: Find an equation of the circle with the given conditions.

a. centre $C(-3, 1)$ and tangent to the line $x - 2 = 0$

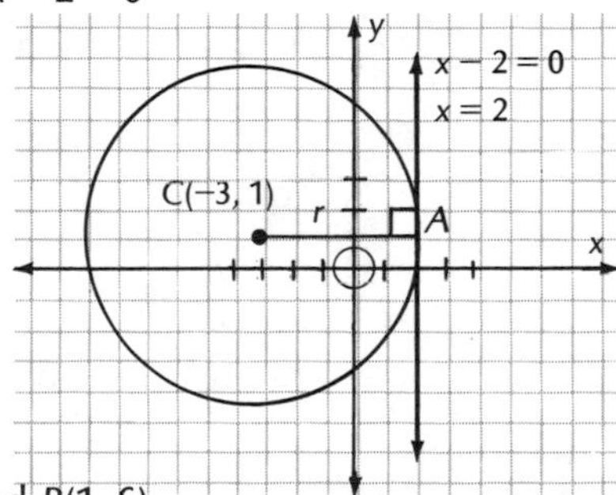

First locate the centre and draw the tangent line $x - 2 = 0$.

Then sketch a circle that touches the tangent line at A.
So, $\overline{CA}$ is a radius and $CA = 5$.
$\therefore r = 5$
Thus, $(x + 3)^2 + (y - 1)^2 = 25$ is an equation of the circle.

b. diameter $\overline{AB}$ with endpoints $A(-5, 4)$ and $B(1, 6)$

The centre of the circle is the midpoint of the diameter.

$$M\left(\frac{x_1 + x_2}{2}, \frac{y_1 + y_2}{2}\right)$$ Use the midpoint formula.

$$\therefore C\left(\frac{-5 + 1}{2}, \frac{4 + 6}{2}\right), \text{ or } C(-2, 5)$$

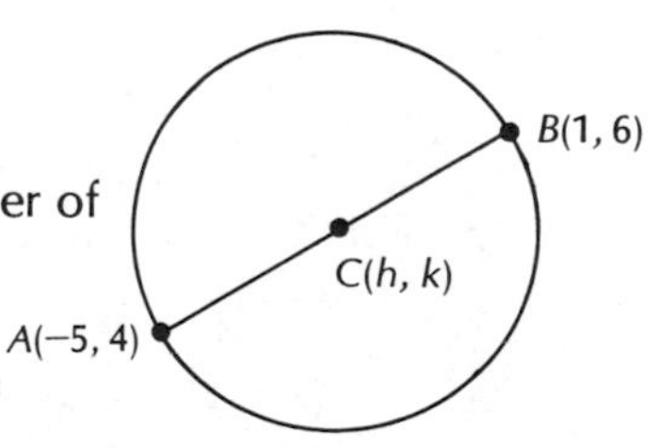

The radius is the distance from $C(-2, 5)$ to either of the points, A or B.

$$\therefore r = AC = \sqrt{(-2 + 5)^2 + (5 - 4)^2}$$
$$= \sqrt{10}$$

Hence, $(x + 2)^2 + (y - 5)^2 = 10$ is an equation of the circle.

EXAMPLE 3: Find the centre and the radius of the circle defined by each equation.

a. $(x - 1)^2 + (y + 5)^2 = 24$

The left side of the equation is the square of the distance between a fixed point $(1, -5)$ and a point $P(x, y)$. All such points, P, lie on a circle with centre $C(1, -5)$ and radius $r = \sqrt{24}$, or $2\sqrt{6}$. Thus, the equation defines a circle with centre $C(1, -5)$ and radius $r = 2\sqrt{6}$.

b. $(2x - 6)^2 + (2y + 10)^2 = 32$

To find the centre and the radius, rewrite the left side of the equation as the square of the distance between two points. Then simplify the equation so that it is in standard form.

$$[2(x - 3)]^2 + [2(y + 5)]^2 = 32$$
$$4(x - 3)^2 + 4(y + 5)^2 = 32$$
$$(x - 3)^2 + (y + 5)^2 = 8$$

Therefore, the centre is $C(3, -5)$ and the radius is $r = \sqrt{8}$, or $2\sqrt{2}$.

EXERCISE 7-1

A

1. Find the centre and the radius of the circle defined by each equation.

a. $(x - 1)^2 + (y + 4)^2 = 36$ **b.** $x^2 + (y - 2)^2 = 18$

c. $x^2 + y^2 = 50$ **d.** $\left(x - \frac{2}{3}\right)^2 + \left(y - \frac{1}{4}\right)^2 = \frac{32}{27}$

2. Find an equation of the circle with the given centre and radius.

a. $C(2, -5)$, $r = 3$ **b.** $C(-5, 0)$, $r = 3\sqrt{5}$

c. $C\left(\frac{2}{3}, -\frac{2}{3}\right)$, $r = \frac{2}{3}$ **d.** $C(0, 0)$, $r = \sqrt{5}$

B

3. Find the centre and radius of each circle.

a. $(2x - 8)^2 + (2y + 10)^2 = 36$ **b.** $(3x + 9)^2 + (3y - 12)^2 = 72$

c. $(3y + 5)^2 + (3x - 2)^2 = 25$ **d.** $16x^2 + (4y - 1)^2 = 16$

4. Find an equation of the circle with the given conditions.

a. centre $C(-2, 5)$ and contains the point $P(2, -1)$

b. $\overline{AB}$ is a diameter with endpoints $A(-5, 4)$ and $B(-9, 10)$

c. centre $C(5, -1)$ and contains the origin

d. centre on the x-axis and the x-intercepts are -2 and 10

5. Find an equation of the circle with centre $C(-2, 1)$ and tangent to the given line.

a. $x = 5$ **b.** $y + 3 = 0$ **c.** $2x - 5 = 0$

6. Find the domain and range of the relation defined by each equation.

a. $x^2 + y^2 = 36$ **b.** $x^2 + (y - 5)^2 = 9$

c. $(x - 3)^2 + (y + 4)^2 = 16$ **d.** $(x + 2)^2 + (y - 7)^2 = 25$

7. A circle with radius 4 is tangent to both axes. Find an equation of the circle. (There is more than one case.)

8. Sketch the curve defined by each equation.
 a. $y = +\sqrt{4 - x^2}$ b. $y = -\sqrt{4 - x^2}$
 c. $x = +\sqrt{4 - y^2}$ d. $y = +\sqrt{16 - (x - 3)^2}$

C

9. The diameter $\overline{AB}$ of a circle has endpoints $A(4, -6)$ and $B(6, 7)$. Find an equation of the circle.

10. A circle with centre on the y-axis and radius $\sqrt{29}$ contains the point $P(2, 3)$. Find the coordinates of the centre.

11. A circle contains the origin and has its centre on the line $x = y$. The radius of the circle is $\sqrt{32}$.
 a. Find the centre of the circle. b. Find an equation of the circle.

12. Describe the set of points that satisfies each equation.
 a. $(x^2 + y^2 - 4)(x^2 + y^2 - 25) = 0$ b. $x^3y + xy^3 - xy = 0$

13. Find an equation of the tangent to the given circle at the given point.
 a. $x^2 + y^2 = 25$ at $(-3, 4)$ b. $x^2 + y^2 = 13$ at $(2, -3)$
 c. $(x - 1)^2 + (y + 3)^2 = 25$ at $(4, 1)$ d. $(x + 3)^2 + (y - 7)^2 = 49$ at $(4, 7)$

14. Find the length of the tangent segment from the given point to the given circle.
 a. $x^2 + y^2 = 16$, $P(5, 7)$ b. $(x - 2)^2 + (y + 3)^2 = 25$, $P(-6, 4)$

15. The centre of a circle lies on the line $4x + y + 9 = 0$ and contains the points $A(-7, 2)$ and $B(3, -4)$. Find an equation of the circle.

EXTRA The Distance From a Point to a Line

The perpendicular distance from a point $P(x_1, y_1)$ to a given line $Ax + By + C = 0$, is given by the following formula.

$$d = \frac{|Ax_1 + By_1 + C|}{\sqrt{A^2 + B^2}}$$

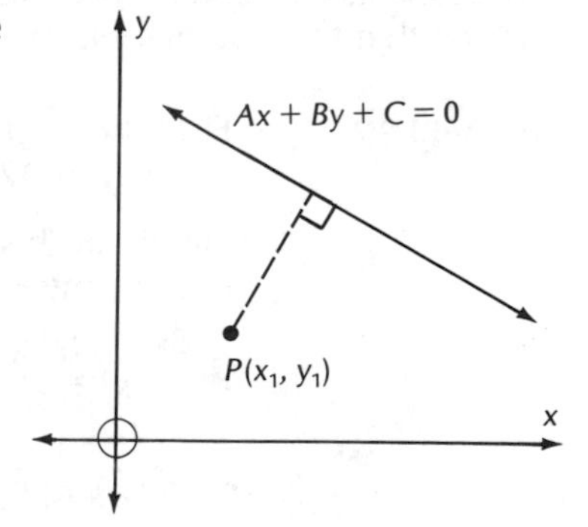

1. Find the distance from the given point to the given line.
 a. $P(3, 5)$ to the line $5x + y - 1 = 0$
 b. $P(2, -3)$ to the line $4x + 3y + 1 = 0$

2. Explain your answer to part **b** of question 1.

3. Find an equation of the circle with the given conditions.
 a. centre $C(2, 5)$ and tangent to the line $3x - y - 11 = 0$
 b. centre $C(3, -4)$ and tangent to the line $5x + 2y + 22 = 0$

7-2 The General Equation of a Circle

An equation of a circle is sometimes given in the form $x^2 + y^2 + Dx + Ey + F = 0$. An equation that reveals the centre and the radius of the circle can be obtained by completing the square.

EXAMPLE 1: Find the centre and the radius of the circle defined by $x^2 + y^2 + 8x - 4y - 2 = 0$.

$$(x^2 + 8x \quad) + (y^2 - 4y \quad) = 2 \qquad \text{Regroup the terms.}$$
$$(x^2 + 8x + 16) + (y^2 - 4y + 4) = 2 + 16 + 4 \qquad \text{Complete the square.}$$
$$(x + 4)^2 + (y - 2)^2 = 22$$

Therefore, the centre is $C(-4, 2)$ and the radius is $\sqrt{22}$.

Now, consider a circle in general, defined by $x^2 + y^2 + Dx + Ey + F = 0$. Complete the square to find the centre and the radius of the circle.

$$x^2 + y^2 + Dx + Ey + F = 0$$
$$(x^2 + Dx \quad) + (y^2 + Ey \quad) = -F$$
$$\left(x^2 + Dx + \frac{D^2}{4}\right) + \left(y^2 + Ey + \frac{E^2}{4}\right) = \frac{D^2}{4} + \frac{E^2}{4} - F$$
$$\left(x + \frac{D}{2}\right)^2 + \left(y + \frac{E}{2}\right)^2 = \frac{D^2 + E^2 - 4F}{4}$$

Thus, the centre is $C\left(-\frac{D}{2}, -\frac{E}{2}\right)$ and the radius is $\frac{1}{2}\sqrt{D^2 + E^2 - 4F}$.

> **The general equation of a circle** with centre C and radius r is
>
> $x^2 + y^2 + Dx + Ey + F = 0$, with
>
> centre $C\left(-\frac{D}{2}, -\frac{E}{2}\right)$, and radius $r = \frac{1}{2}\sqrt{D^2 + E^2 - 4F}$.

These equations can be used to find the centre and the radius of a circle. Notice that the coefficients of x^2 and y^2 are both 1.

EXAMPLE 2: Find the centre and the radius of the circle defined by $2x^2 + 2y^2 + 12x - 8y = 4$.

Divide both sides of the equation by 2 so that the coefficients of x^2 and y^2 become 1.

$$2x^2 + 2y^2 + 12x - 8y - 4 = 0$$
$$x^2 + y^2 + 6x - 4y - 2 = 0$$
$$x^2 + y^2 + Dx + Ey + F = 0$$
$$\therefore D = 6, E = -4, F = -2$$
$$C\left(-\frac{D}{2}, -\frac{E}{2}\right), \qquad r = \frac{1}{2}\sqrt{D^2 + E^2 - 4F}$$

$\therefore C\left(-\frac{6}{2}, -\frac{(-4)}{2}\right)$ $\qquad r = \frac{1}{2}\sqrt{36 + 16 + 8}$

$= (-3, 2)$ $\qquad = \frac{1}{2}\sqrt{60}$

$\qquad = \sqrt{15}$

Therefore, the centre is $C(-3, 2)$ and the radius is $\sqrt{15}$.

EXAMPLE 3: Find an equation of the circle with centre $C(1, -3)$ and radius 5.

Solution I

$$(x - 1)^2 + (y + 3)^2 = 25$$
$$\therefore x^2 - 2x + 1 + y^2 + 6y + 9 = 25$$
$$\therefore x^2 + y^2 - 2x + 6y - 15 = 0$$

Solution II

For $x^2 + y^2 + Dx + Ey + F = 0$,

$$-\frac{D}{2} = 1 \text{ and } -\frac{E}{2} = -3.$$

So, $D = -2$ and $E = 6$

$$\frac{1}{2}\sqrt{D^2 + E^2 - 4F} = 5$$
$$40 - 4F = 100$$
$$F = -15$$

Thus, an equation of the circle is $x^2 + y^2 - 2x + 6y - 15 = 0$.

EXAMPLE 4: Find an equation of the circle that contains the points $A(-2, 6)$, $B(5, 7)$, and $C(6, 0)$.

The equation is of the form $x^2 + y^2 + Dx + Ey + F = 0$.
Each point (x, y) on the curve must satisfy the equation.

$A(-2, 6) \rightarrow 4 + 36 - 2D + 6E + F = 0$ or $-2D + 6E + F = -40$ ①

$B(5, 7) \rightarrow 25 + 49 + 5D + 7E + F = 0$ or $5D + 7E + F = -74$ ②

$C(6, 0) \rightarrow 36 + 0 + 6D + 0E + F = 0$ or $6D + F = -36$ ③

Obtain a system of two equations in two unknowns by subtracting the equations ①, ②, and ③ in pairs.

① − ② $\quad -7D - E = 34$ ④
② − ③ $\quad -D + 7E = -38$ ⑤

This is the new system of equations.

$-49D - 7E = 238$ $\quad 7 \times$ ④
$-D + 7E = -38$ ⑤

Solve the new system of equations.

$$-50D = 200$$
$$D = -4$$

Substitute for D in ⑤. $\quad 4 + 7E = -38$

$$7E = -42$$
$$E = -6$$

Substitute for D in ③. $\quad -24 + F = -36$

$$F = -12$$

Therefore, an equation of the circle is $x^2 + y^2 - 4x - 6y - 12 = 0$.

EXERCISE 7-2

A **1.** Find an equation of the circle with the given centre and radius.

a. $C(3, -1), r = 7$ **b.** $C(0, -5), r = 5$

2. Find the centre and the radius of the circle defined by the given equation.

a. $x^2 + y^2 = 25$ **b.** $x^2 + y^2 = 36$

c. $x^2 + y^2 + 8x - 4y + 2 = 0$ **d.** $x^2 + y^2 - 2y - 4 = 0$

e. $x^2 + y^2 - 6x + 8y = 0$ **f.** $x^2 + y^2 - 4x + 6y + 13 = 0$

g. $x^2 + y^2 + 4x - 25 = 0$ **h.** $x^2 + y^2 - 6y = 16$

3. Describe the figure defined by part **f** of exercise 2.

B **4.** Find an equation of the circle with the given centre and radius.

a. $C(3, -5), r = \frac{5}{3}$ **b.** $C\left(-4, \frac{-2}{3}\right), r = 1$

c. $C\left(0, \frac{2}{5}\right), r = \frac{7}{5}$ **d.** $C\left(\frac{-3}{4}, \frac{1}{4}\right), r = \frac{1}{2}$

5. Find the centre and the radius of the circle defined by the given equation.

a. $2x^2 + 2y^2 + 20x - 16y + 4 = 0$ **b.** $3x^2 + 3y^2 - 12x - 18y = 9$

c. $12x - 2x^2 - 2y^2 + 4 = 0$ **d.** $3x^2 + 3y^2 + 24y - 12x = 0$

e. $2x^2 + 2y^2 - x + y - 5 = 0$ **f.** $2x^2 + 2y^2 + 5x - 3y - 1 = 0$

6. Find an equation of the circle that contains point P and has centre C.

a. $P(3, -4)$; $C(0, 0)$ **b.** $P(0, 0)$; $C(3, -4)$

c. $P(3, -4)$; $C(-2, 5)$ **d.** $P(-2, 1)$; $C(3, -2)$

7. Find an equation of the circle with the given conditions.

a. centre $C(-2, -3)$ and tangent to the line $x = 5$

b. centre $C(5, -1)$ and tangent to the line $y - 4 = 0$

8. Find an equation of the circle for which diameter $\overline{AB}$ has the given endpoints.

a. $A(0, 0), B(10, -4)$ **b.** $A(-3, 6), B(5, 8)$

9. Find the domain and range of the relation defined by each equation.

a. $x^2 + y^2 + 10x = 0$ **b.** $x^2 + y^2 - 6x + 4y + 4 = 0$

C **10.** Find an equation of the circle that contains the given points.

a. $P(0, 4), Q(9, 5), R(10, -4)$ **b.** $L(-4, 7), M(2, 3), N(-2, -3)$

11. A circle contains the points $P(9, 28)$, $Q(17, -16)$, and $R(-23, 4)$. Recall that, for any circle, the centre is on the perpendicular bisector of a chord.

a. Find an equation of the perpendicular bisector of $\overline{PR}$ and $\overline{QR}$.

b. Solve the system of equations from part **a** to determine the coordinates of the centre, C.

c. Find the length of $\overline{PC}$.

d. Determine an equation of the circle.

12. Find the length of the tangent segment from:

a. $A(7, 2)$ to the circle defined by $x^2 + y^2 = 16$.

b. $B(5, 4)$ to the circle defined by $x^2 + y^2 + 6x - 2y - 15 = 0$.

7-3 The Parabola in Standard Position

Parabolic reflectors are used as satellite dishes and in solar ovens. When the reflector is pointed at the source of incoming parallel rays (like a T.V. signal or even light from the Sun), all of the rays are reflected through a single point called the **focus**. Such a reflector is useful in concentrating very weak signals from distant satellites or generating extremely high temperatures at the focus if the reflector is pointed at the Sun.

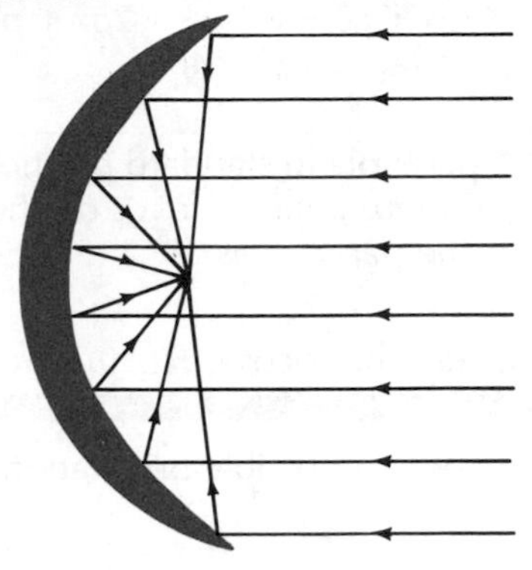

A **parabola** is the set of points in a plane located so that each point is equidistant from a fixed point and a fixed line. The fixed line is called the **directrix** and the fixed point is called the **focus**.

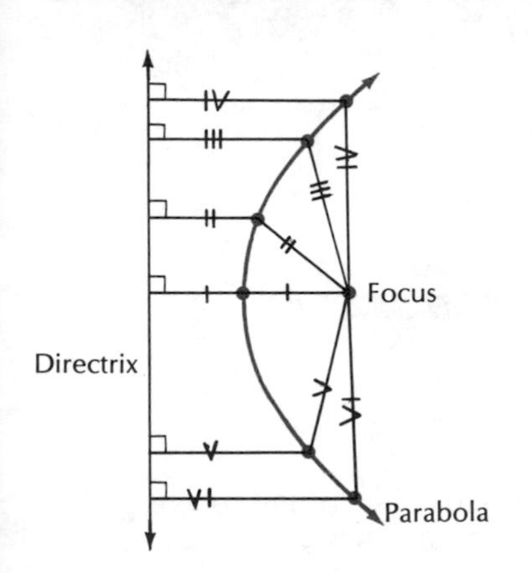

Note that the distance from a point on the parabola to the fixed line is the length of the perpendicular segment from the point to the line.

The line through the focus of a parabola and perpendicular to the directrix is the **axis of symmetry**, or simply the **axis**, of the parabola.

The point of intersection of a parabola with its axis is the **vertex**, ***V***, of the parabola.

A parabola is in **standard position** when its vertex is at the origin and its axis lies on a coordinate axis. An equation of a parabola in standard position can be derived from the definition, as shown below.

Consider a parabola with vertex $V(0, 0)$ and focus $F(p, 0)$. Since the vertex is a point on the parabola, it is equidistant from the focus and directrix. Therefore, the directrix is the line $x = -p$.

Here, if $P(x, y)$ is any point on the parabola, then $A(-p, y)$ lies on the directrix. Also, the distance between P and F is equal to the perpendicular distance between P and the directrix.

$\therefore PF = PA$

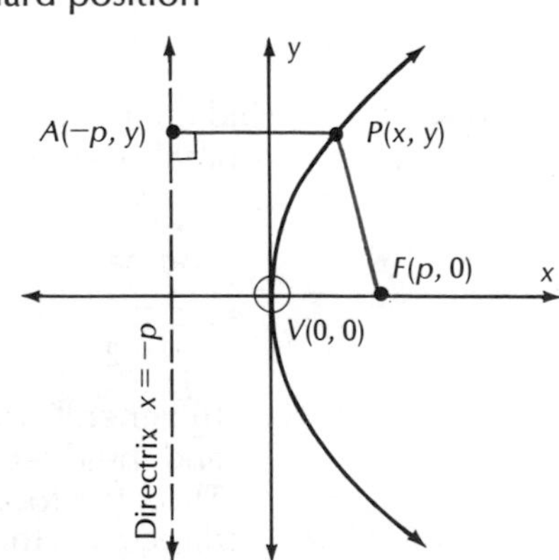

$$\sqrt{(x-p)^2+(y-0)^2}=\sqrt{(x+p)^2+(y-y)^2}$$ Apply the distance formula to find PF and PA.

$$x^2-2px+p^2+y^2=x^2+2px+p^2$$ Square both sides and expand.

$$\therefore y^2=4px$$ Simplify.

> A parabola in standard position, where the x-axis is the axis of symmetry, has its focus on the x-axis and vertex at (0, 0). An equation of the parabola is
>
> $y^2=4px,$
>
> where the focus is $F(p, 0)$, and the directrix is the line $x=-p$.

There are two possible orientations of the parabola defined by $y^2=4px$.

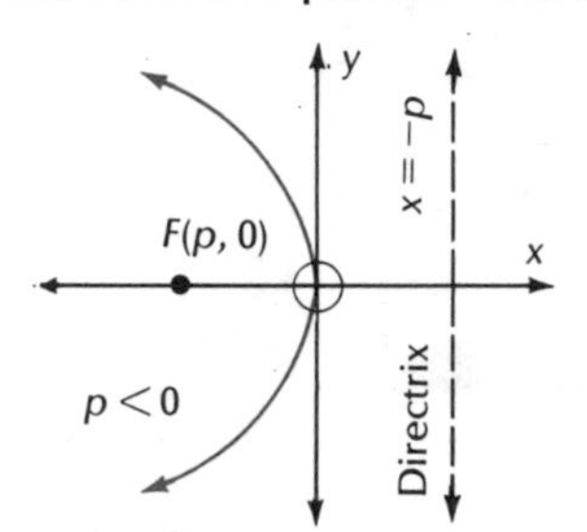

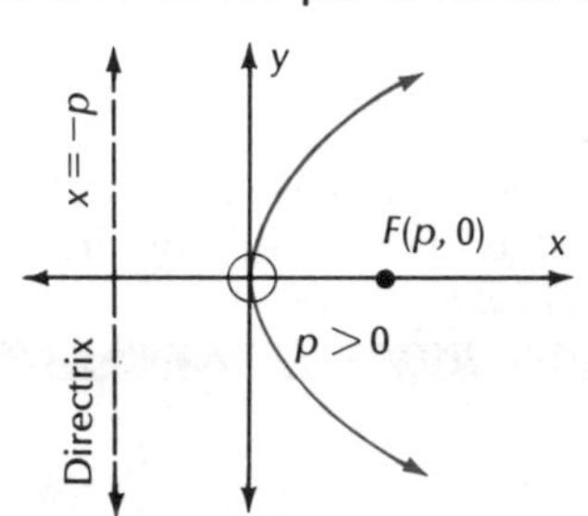

Notice that the parabola opens to the right when $p>0$.

> A parabola in standard position, where the y-axis is the axis of symmetry is defined by
>
> $x^2=4py,$
>
> where the focus is $F(0, p)$, and the directrix is the line $y=-p$.

Again, there are two possible orientations of the parabola $x^2=4py$.

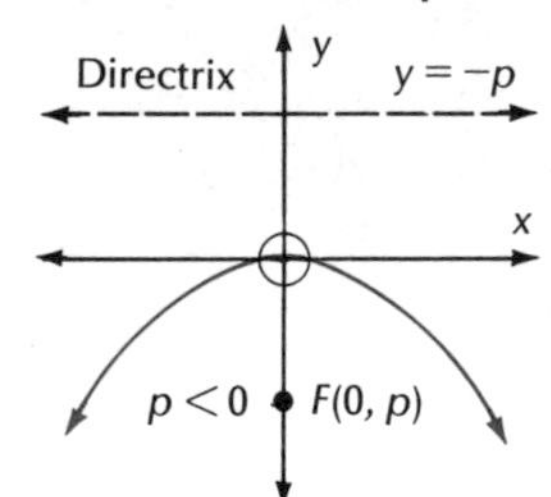

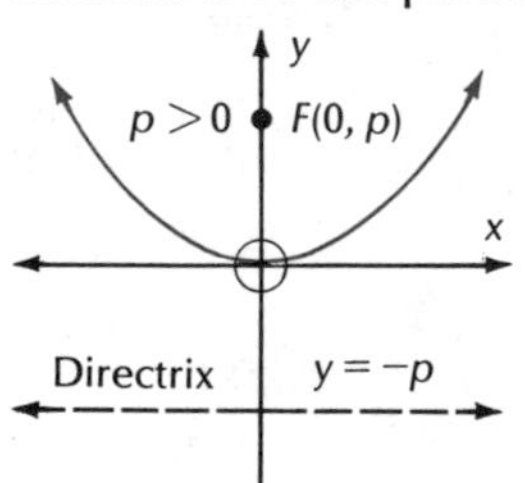

Notice that the parabola opens upward when $p>0$.

EXAMPLE 1: Find the focus and the directrix and then sketch the parabola defined by each equation.

a. $y^2=8x$

Compare $y^2=8x$ with $y^2=4px$.

$4p=8$

$\therefore p=2$

In general, the focus is $F(p, 0)$, and the directrix is the line $x=-p$. Thus, the focus is $F(2, 0)$, and the directrix is the line $x=-2$.

b. $x^2+10y=0$

Compare $x^2+10y=0$ with $x^2=4py$.

$4p=-10$

$\therefore p=\frac{-5}{2}$

Thus, the focus is $F\left(0, \frac{-5}{2}\right)$, and the directrix is the line $y=\frac{5}{2}$.

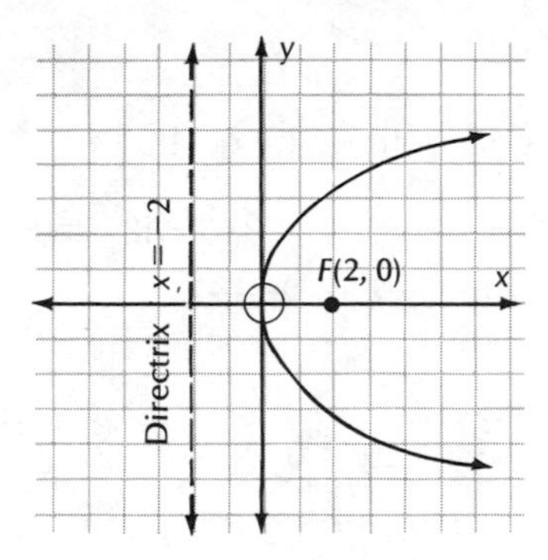

Notice that the parabola defined by $y^2 = +8x$ opens to the right.

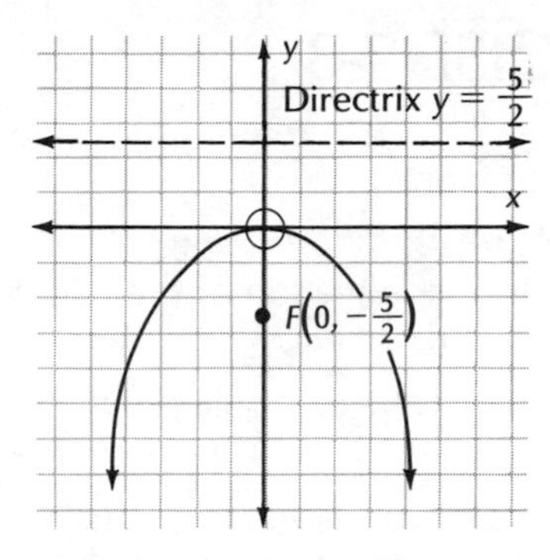

Notice that the parabola defined by $x^2 = -10y$ opens downward.

EXAMPLE 2: Find an equation of the parabola with vertex at the origin, given the following.

a. The focus is $F(0, -3)$.

Since the focus is on the y-axis and the vertex is at the origin, an equation of the parabola is of the form $x^2 = 4py$ with focus $F(0, p)$.
$\therefore p = -3$
Thus, an equation of the parabola is $x^2 = 4(-3)y$, or $x^2 = -12y$.

b. The directrix is the line $2x + 10 = 0$.

$\therefore x = -5$

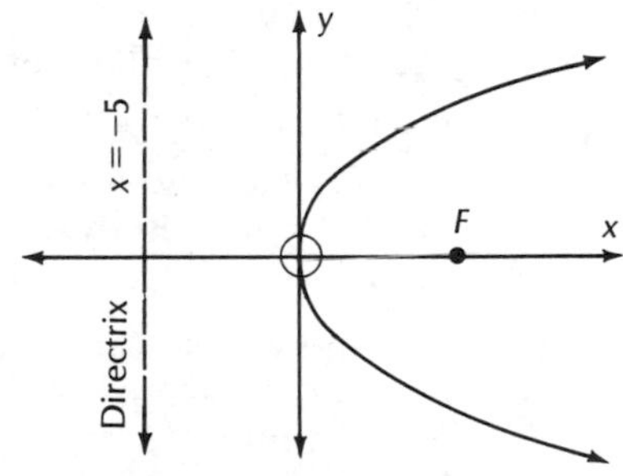

A parabola will always "wrap itself" around a focus, and so it cannot intersect a directrix. This parabola must open to the right.

An equation of the parabola is of the form $y^2 = 4px$ and the directrix is the line $x = -p$. For this parabola, $p = 5$. Thus, an equation of the parabola is $y^2 = 20x$.

c. The focus is on the y-axis and the parabola contains the point $P(-1, 6)$.

Since the focus is on the y-axis, an equation of the parabola is of the form $x^2 = 4py$.

Since $P(-1, 6)$ lies on the parabola,

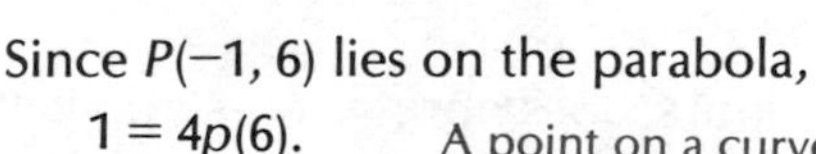

$1 = 4p(6)$.   A point on a curve satisfies the equation.

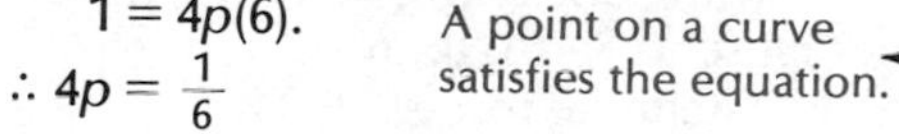

$\therefore 4p = \frac{1}{6}$

Therefore, an equation of the parabola is $x^2 = \frac{1}{6}y$, or $6x^2 - y = 0$.

EXERCISE 7-3

A **1.** Find the focus and directrix for the parabola defined by each equation.

a. $y^2 = 36x$ **b.** $x^2 + 24y = 0$ **c.** $3x^2 - 18y = 0$

2. Find an equation of the parabola with the given condition.

a. focus $F(0, -1)$ **b.** directrix $x + 7 = 0$ **c.** focus $F\left(\frac{2}{3}, 0\right)$

3. Sketch the parabola defined by each equation.

a. $x^2 = 15y$ **b.** $y^2 - 5x = 0$ **c.** $3x^2 + 8y = 0$ **d.** $2x = -y^2$

B **4.** Find an equation of the parabola in standard position given that $P(5, 2)$ lies on the curve and the focus is on the x-axis.

5. A parabola of the form $y^2 = 4px$ has its focus on the line $2x - 5y + 10 = 0$. Find an equation of the parabola.

6. A parabola of the form $x^2 = 4py$ has its focus on the line $2x - 5y + 10 = 0$. Find an equation of the parabola.

7. Find an equation of the parabola in standard position with a directrix of the form $y = -p$ if the parabola contains the point $Q(3, -4)$.

C **8.** Find an equation of the parabola in standard position that contains the point $A(-2, 6)$. (Consider both cases.)

9. Find an equation of the parabola in standard position that contains the points $P(1, -2\sqrt{5})$ and $Q(5, 10)$.

10. Find the length of the line segment that contains the focus, is perpendicular to the axis of symmetry, and has endpoints on the parabola defined by each equation.

a. $x^2 = 8y$ **b.** $y^2 = -24x$ **c.** $y^2 = 10x$

11. The line segment described in exercise 10 is called the **latus rectum**.

a. Sketch each parabola from exercise 10 and then sketch its latus rectum.

b. Predict a formula for the length of the latus rectum based on your results from exercise 10.

EXTRA

Parabolic Trajectories

Rock and metal fragments from space often enter Earth's atmosphere. They are seen as *meteors*, or shooting stars. If they are large enough to hit Earth's surface, then they are called *meteorites*.

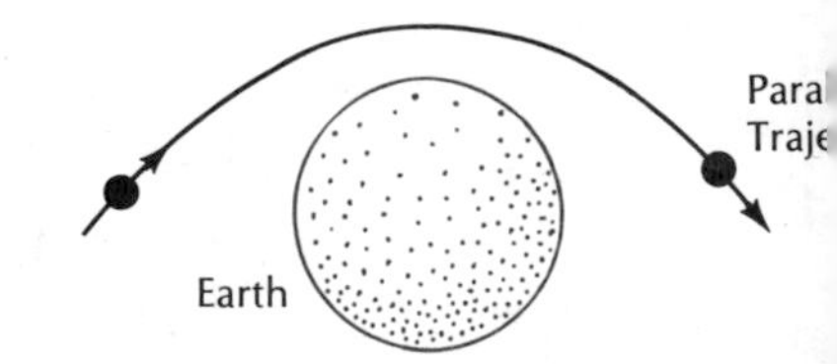

If an object, travelling at a speed of 11.2 km/s, does not enter the atmosphere and only comes close to Earth, then its trajectory will be "bent" by Earth's gravitational forces. It will continue to travel past Earth, never to return, on a path called a **parabolic trajectory**, with Earth's centre as its focus.

7-4 The Parabola: Axis Parallel to the x- or y-axis

In this lesson, the translation images of parabolas in standard position are considered.

EXAMPLE 1: **a.** A parabola defined by $x^2 = 4y$ is translated 2 units to the right, along the x-axis, and 3 units down, parallel to the y-axis. Find an equation of the translated parabola.

The translation is $(x, y) \rightarrow (x + 2, y - 3)$.
Replace x with $x - 2$ and replace y with $y + 3$ in the given equation of the parabola to obtain an equation of the translation image.

$$x^2 = 4y$$

$$(x - 2)^2 = 4(y + 3)$$ This is an equation of the translated parabola.

b. Graph the parabola and its translation image.

Use a table of values to graph the parabolas. Notice that each point (including the vertex) is translated +2 units along the x-axis and −3 units parallel to the y-axis.

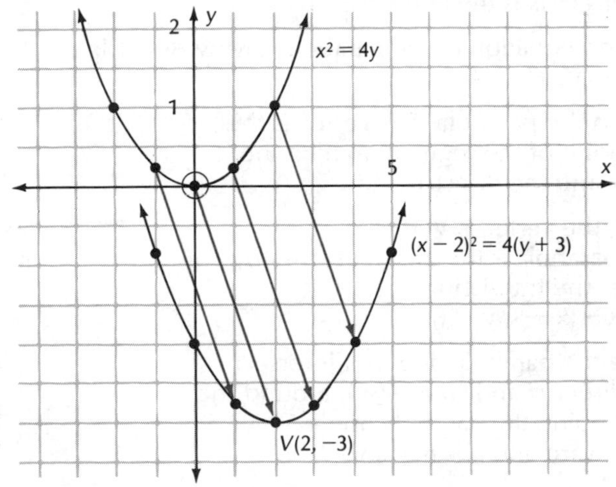

Notice how the vertex is obtained.

The preceding example suggests the following.

Under the translation $(x, y) \rightarrow (x + h, y + k)$, the image of $x^2 = 4py$ is $(x - h)^2 = 4p(y - k)$.

This image is a parabola with axis of symmetry parallel to the y-axis and with vertex $V(h, k)$.

The image of $y^2 = 4px$ is $(y - k)^2 = 4p(x - h)$, which is a parabola with axis of symmetry parallel to the x-axis and vertex $V(h, k)$.

The absolute value of p is the distance between the vertex and the focus. The absolute value of p can be used to find the focus once the vertex and axis of the parabola are known. The sign of p determines the direction in which the parabola opens.

EXAMPLE 2: Find the vertex, focus, and directrix of the parabola defined by $(y + 3)^2 = -8(x - 4)$.

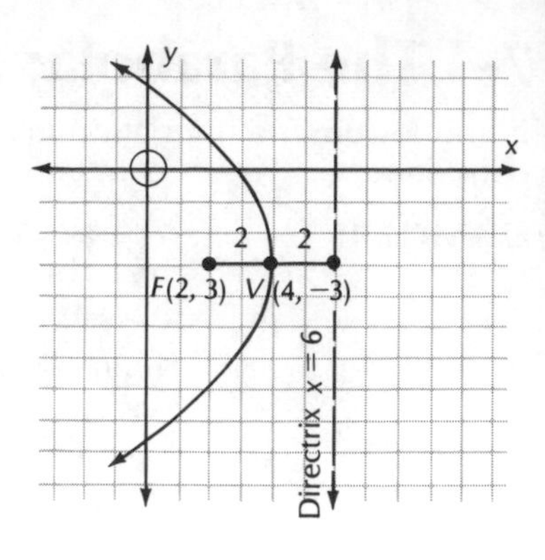

This parabola is the image of the parabola defined by $y^2 = -8x$ under the translation $(x, y) \rightarrow (x + 4, y - 3)$.

Since a parabola maps onto a *congruent* parabola under a translation, the vertex, focus, and directrix map onto a corresponding vertex, focus, and directrix of the image parabola. Compare the two equations and the mapping.

$$\begin{aligned}
y^2 = -8x &\rightarrow (y + 3)^2 = -8(x - 4) \\
(x, y) &\rightarrow (x + 4, y - 3) \\
V(0, 0) &\rightarrow V(4, -3) \\
F(-2, 0) &\rightarrow F(2, -3) \\
\text{directrix } x = 2 &\rightarrow \text{directrix } x = 6
\end{aligned}$$

Therefore, the vertex is $V(4, -3)$, the focus is $F(2, -3)$, and the directrix is the line $x = 6$.

EXAMPLE 3: Find an equation of the parabola having directrix $y = 2$ and focus $F(1, -4)$.

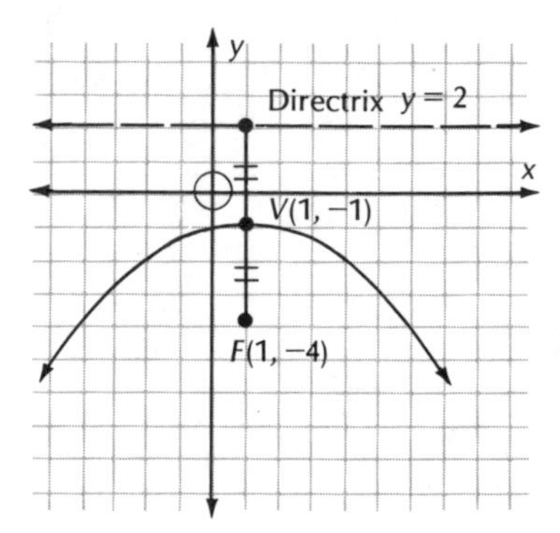

Sketch the parabola. The vertex is the midpoint of the segment joining the focus and the directrix.

Thus, the vertex is $V(1, -1)$.
The parabola is the image of $x^2 = 4py$ under the translation $(x, y) \rightarrow (x + 1, y - 1)$.

Since the parabola does not intersect the directrix and wraps itself around the focal point, the parabola opens downward and p is negative.

Since $VF = 3$, then $p = -3$.

Therefore, an equation of the parabola is $(x - 1)^2 = -12(y + 1)$.

EXERCISE 7-4

A 1. Sketch the parabola defined by the given equation.

a. $(x - 1)^2 = 16(y + 3)$ **b.** $(y - 2)^2 = -16(x - 5)$
c. $(x + 4)^2 = -12(y - 1)$ **d.** $(y + 6)^2 = 8(x - 1)$

2. Find the vertex, focus, and directrix of each parabola defined in exercise 1.

3. Find an equation of the axis of symmetry for each parabola defined in exercise 1.

4. Find the vertex for a parabola with the given properties.
   a. focus $F(2, -4)$; directrix $x = 6$
   b. focus $F(0, -8)$; directrix $y = 2$
   c. focus $F(-3, 5)$; directrix $x + 1 = 0$
   d. focus $F(-8, 2)$; directrix $y + 2 = 0$

B

5. Find an equation of the parabola with the given conditions.
   a. $V(-3, 5)$; directrix $x - 4 = 0$
   b. $V(4, -2)$; directrix $y + 6 = 0$
   c. $F(0, -3)$; $V(4, -3)$
   d. $F(3, 4)$; $V(3, -2)$
   e. $F(5, -1)$; directrix $x + 1 = 0$
   f. $F(1, -5)$; directrix $y + 1 = 0$

6. Find an equation of the parabola with focus $F(1, 0)$ and vertex at the point of intersection of the x-axis and the line $3x - 5y + 15 = 0$.

7. Find an equation of the parabola with directrix $y = 3$ and vertex at the point of intersection of the line $3x - 5y - 15 = 0$ and the y-axis.

8. A parabola has focus $F(-5, 2)$ and the directrix has an x-intercept of -1. Determine an equation of the parabola.

9. A parabola has focus $F(4, 3)$ and the directrix has a y-intercept of -1. Determine an equation of the parabola.

C

10. Find an equation of the parabola with the given conditions.
    a. $F(3, -2)$; directrix $x = 10$
    b. $F(4, 3)$; directrix $y - 10 = 0$
    c. $V(-5, -2)$; directrix $2x + 1 = 0$
    d. $V(3, -2)$; directrix $2y - 5 = 0$

11. A parabola that opens upward has vertex $V(2, -3)$ and contains the point $P(12, 2)$. Find an equation of the parabola.

12. A parabola that opens to the left has vertex $V(-2, -1)$ and contains the point $P(-6, 7)$. Find an equation of the parabola.

13. Find the vertex, focus, and directrix for the parabola defined by the given equation. Sketch each parabola.
    a. $x^2 - 4x - 10y - 26 = 0$
    b. $y^2 + 6x + 6y + 15 = 0$
    c. $x^2 + 8x + 5y + 11 = 0$
    d. $y^2 - 3x + 10y + 40 = 0$

EXTRA

Locus of Points

The **locus of points** is the set of points that satisfies a given condition. Finding the locus of points means finding an equation that defines the set of points satisfying the given condition.

Describe and sketch the locus of points.

a. Each point is equidistant from $A(-3, 4)$ and $B(6, -1)$.
b. The distance from $A(-3, 5)$ is twice the distance from $B(2, 4)$.
c. The distance from $A(3, 0)$ is twice the distance to the line $x = -3$.
d. The distance to the line $x = -3$ is twice the distance to the point $A(3, 0)$.

Review

1. Find the centre and the radius of the circle defined by the given equation.
   a. $(x-3)^2 + (y+2)^2 = 28$ b. $(2x-6)^2 + (2y+8)^2 = 36$
   c. $x^2 + y^2 - 8x + 10y - 6 = 0$ d. $3x^2 + 3y^2 - 18y - 15 = 0$

2. Find an equation of the circle with the given conditions.
   a. centre $C(4, -2)$ and contains $P(3, 4)$
   b. centre $C(5, 1)$ and tangent to the line $y + 4 = 0$
   c. $\overline{AB}$ is a diameter with endpoints $A(5, -2)$ and $B(9, 10)$

3. Find the centre and radius of the circle defined by each equation by completing the square.
   a. $x^2 + y^2 - 2x + 6y + 6 = 0$ b. $x^2 + y^2 - 6x = 0$

4. Find an equation of the circle with centre $C(2, -3)$ and the given property.
   a. circumference 10π b. area 36π

5. Find an equation of the circle that contains the points $P(6, 3)$, $Q(4, -5)$, and $R(9, -2)$.

6. Find the vertex, focus, and directrix for the parabola defined by the given equation.
   a. $x^2 = -10y$ b. $(x-3)^2 - 8(y+2) = 0$ c. $(y+4)^2 = 12x$

7. Find an equation of the parabola with the given conditions.
   a. $V(0, 0)$; $F(0, -6)$ b. $V(0, 0)$; directrix $x + 3 = 0$
   c. $V(2, -5)$; $F(2, -1)$ d. $V(3, 5)$; directrix $y + 1 = 0$
   e. $F(0, 3)$; $V(0, -1)$ f. $F(4, -2)$; directrix $x = -2$

8. The equation of a parabola is of the form $x^2 = 4py$ and the focus is on the line $2x - 3y + 12 = 0$. Determine an equation of the parabola. Then sketch the parabola.

9. A parabola has focus $F(0, 4)$ and its vertex is the y-intercept of the line $5x + 2y + 10 = 0$. Determine an equation of the parabola. Then sketch the parabola.

10. A parabola has its vertex at the origin, contains the point $A(-1, 5)$, and opens to the left. Find an equation of the parabola. Then sketch the parabola.

11. Find the vertex, focus, and directrix for the parabola defined by the given equation. Sketch the parabola.
    a. $y^2 - 5x - 10y = 0$ b. $x^2 + 6x - 16y + 25 = 0$

12. Find an equation of the tangent to the curve defined by each equation at the point $A(6, 2)$.
    a. $x^2 + y^2 = 40$ b. $(x-3)^2 + (y+1)^2 = 18$

13. Find the length of the tangent segment from $B(8, -2)$ to the circle defined by the given equation.
    a. $x^2 + y^2 = 36$ b. $(x+2)^2 + (y-1)^2 = 25$

7-5 The Ellipse in Standard Position

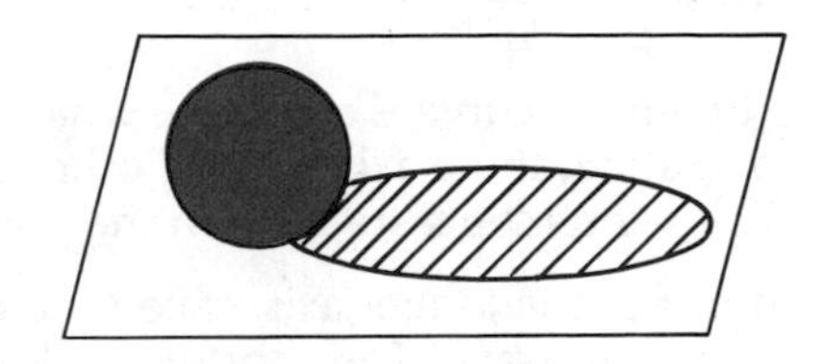

A ball rests on a table. On a sunny day the shadow cast by the ball is an elongated oval which becomes longer as the Sun sets. The section of the sphere that intercepts the Sun's rays is a circle and the shadow is, in effect, the shadow of this circle. A horizontal chord of the circle maps onto a chord of equal length in the shadow. Thus, the shadow is the image of the circle under a stretch in one direction only. The shape of this shadow is called an **ellipse**.

This same situation can be modelled mathematically by considering the image of a circle under a one-way stretch transformation. For example, consider the image of the circle defined by $x^2 + y^2 = 25$ under a one-way stretch described by $(x, y) \rightarrow (2x, y)$. This is a stretch transformation that doubles the x-coordinate of each point on the original curve while the y-coordinate remains unchanged. To find an equation of the image, replace x with $\frac{x}{2}$ in the equation of the circle, $x^2 + y^2 = 25$.

$$x^2 + y^2 = 25$$

$$\left(\frac{x}{2}\right)^2 + y^2 = 25$$

$$\therefore x^2 + 4y^2 = 100, \text{ or } \frac{x^2}{100} + \frac{y^2}{25} = 1$$

Notice that the denominators are the squares of the x- and y-intercepts. The graph of $x^2 + y^2 = 25$, the circle, and $\frac{x^2}{100} + \frac{y^2}{25} = 1$, its image, or the ellipse, are shown below.

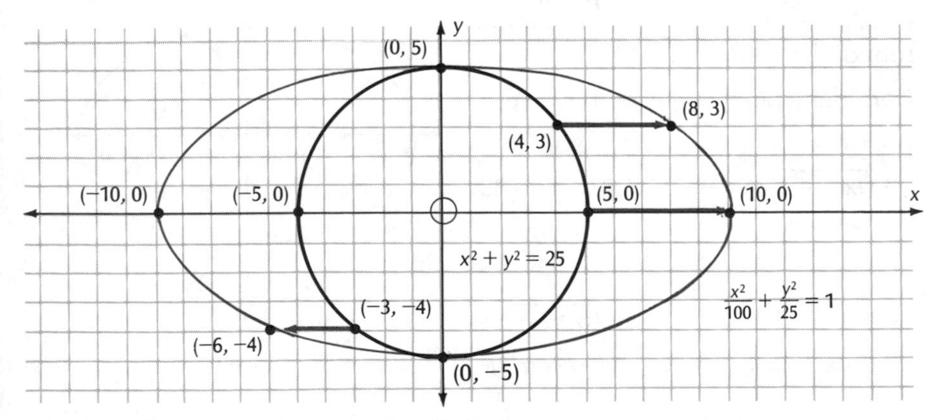

Consider the image of the graph of $x^2 + y^2 = 1$ under a two-way stretch described by $(x, y) \rightarrow (5x, 3y)$.

$$x^2 + y^2 = 1 \rightarrow \left(\frac{x}{5}\right)^2 + \left(\frac{y}{3}\right)^2 = 1$$

$$\text{or } \frac{x^2}{25} + \frac{y^2}{9} = 1$$

In general, the image of the circle $x^2 + y^2 = 1$ under a two-way stretch transformation $(x, y) \rightarrow (px, qy)$ has an equation of the form $\frac{x^2}{p^2} + \frac{y^2}{q^2} = 1$.

The image curve is an ellipse which has two axes of symmetry, one along the x-axis and the other along the y-axis.
The x-intercepts are $\pm p$ and the y-intercepts are $\pm q$.

If $p > q$, the longer axis, called the **major axis** of the ellipse, lies along the x-axis. The shorter axis, called the **minor axis** of the ellipse, lies along the y-axis.

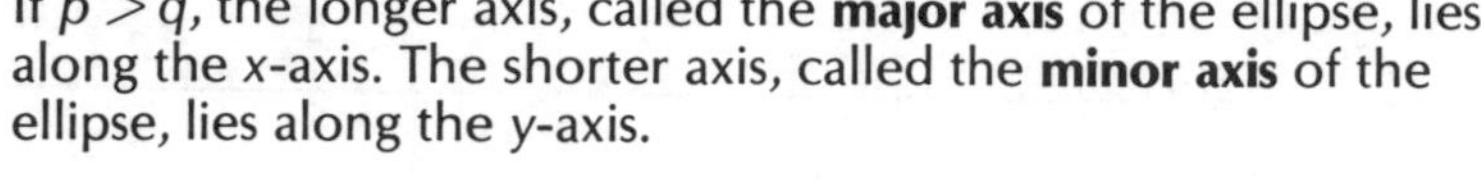

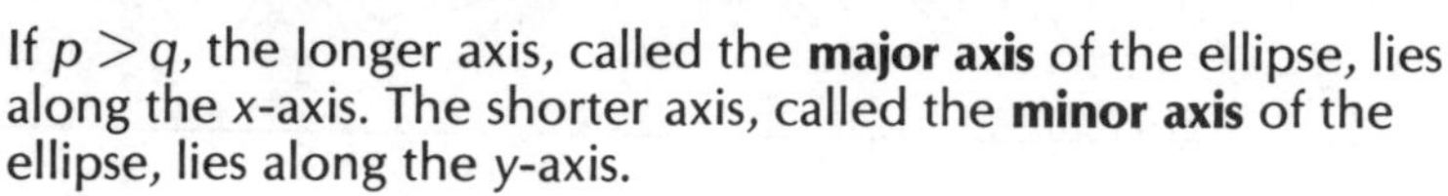

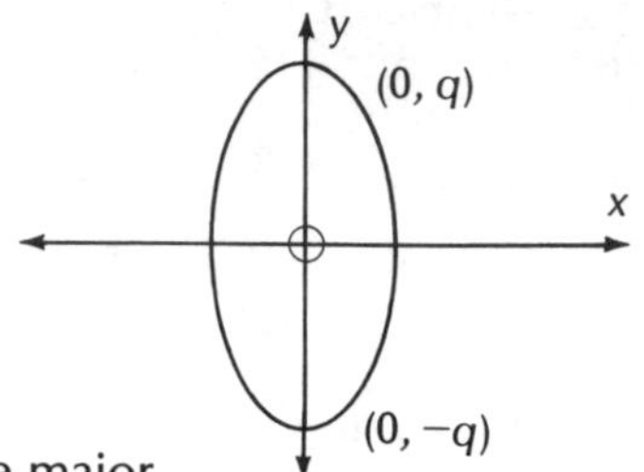

If $p < q$, the major axis lies along the y-axis and the minor axis lies along the x-axis.

The **vertices** of an ellipse are the endpoints of the major axis.

The **centre** of the ellipse is at (0, 0), the point of intersection of the major and minor axes.

An important property of an ellipse can also be used to find its equation and provide insights into further properties of the ellipse.

An ellipse can be described as a set of all points in a plane, located so that the sum of the distances from any point P to two fixed points is a constant. The fixed points F_1 and F_2 are called the **focal points**, or simply the **foci**. A line segment joining a point on the ellipse to a focus is called a **focal radius**.

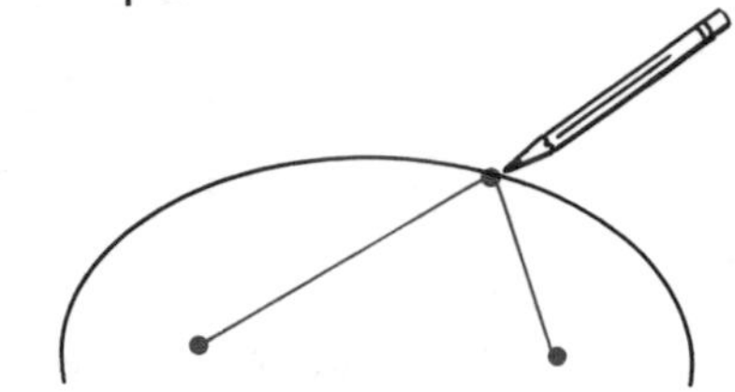

EXAMPLE 1: Find an equation of the ellipse with focal points $F_1(4, 0)$ and $F_2(-4, 0)$ if the sum of the focal radii is 10.

Consider a point $P(x, y)$ on the ellipse.

$PF_1 + PF_2 = 10$

$\therefore \sqrt{(x+4)^2 + y^2} + \sqrt{(x-4)^2 + y^2} = 10$

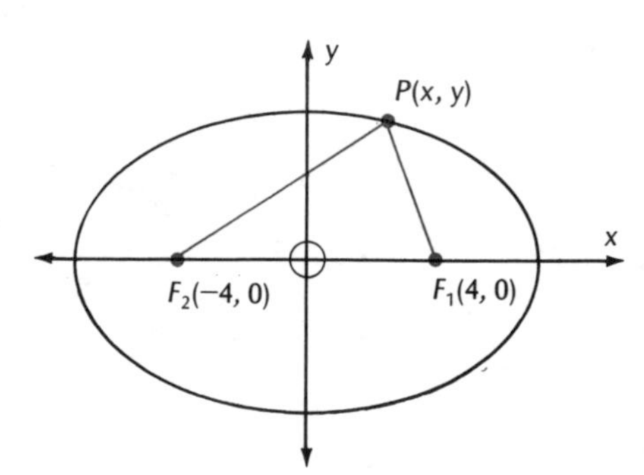

$$\left(\sqrt{(x+4)^2 + y^2}\right)^2 = \left(10 - \sqrt{(x-4)^2 + y^2}\right)^2 \qquad \text{Square both sides.}$$

$$x^2 + 8x + 16 + y^2 = 100 - 20\sqrt{(x-4)^2 + y^2} + x^2 - 8x + 16 + y^2$$

$$16x - 100 = -20\sqrt{x^2 - 8x + 16 + y^2}$$

$$4x - 25 = -5\sqrt{x^2 - 8x + 16 + y^2} \qquad \text{Divide by 4.}$$

$$16x^2 - 200x + 625 = 25(x^2 - 8x + 16 + y^2) \qquad \text{Square both sides.}$$

$$\therefore 9x^2 + 25y^2 = 225, \text{ or } \frac{x^2}{25} + \frac{y^2}{9} = 1 \qquad \text{This is an equation of the ellipse.}$$

Notice that the equation of the ellipse in Example 1 is the same as the one obtained by finding an equation of the image of the circle defined by $x^2 + y^2 = 1$ under the two-way stretch $(x, y) \rightarrow (5x, 3y)$.

Observe the following for the ellipse defined by $\frac{x^2}{25} + \frac{y^2}{9} = 1$.

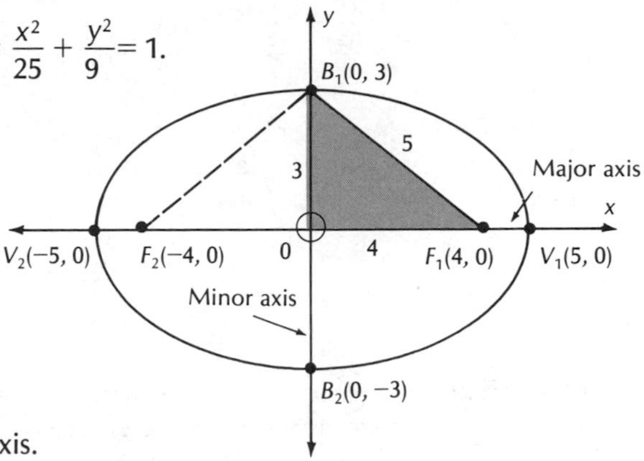

The graph is shown at the right.
The x-intercepts are ± 5 and the y-intercepts are ± 3.

There are two axes of symmetry.
The major axis is 10 units long.
The minor axis is 6 units long.

The vertices of the ellipse are the endpoints of the major axis, $V_1(5, 0)$ and $V_2(-5, 0)$.

The foci, $F_1(4, 0)$ and $F_2(-4, 0)$, lie on the major axis.

Notice also that B_1F_1 is equal to the **semi-major axis**, or half the major axis. So, the length of the major axis is the constant sum for the ellipse.

An ellipse with axes on the coordinate axes is in **standard position.**

There are two cases to consider for an ellipse in standard position.

Case 1. An ellipse with foci $F_1(c, 0)$ and $F_2(-c, 0)$ on the x-axis

$$\frac{x^2}{a^2} + \frac{y^2}{b^2} = 1, a > b$$

The length of the major axis is $2a$.
The length of the minor axis is $2b$.

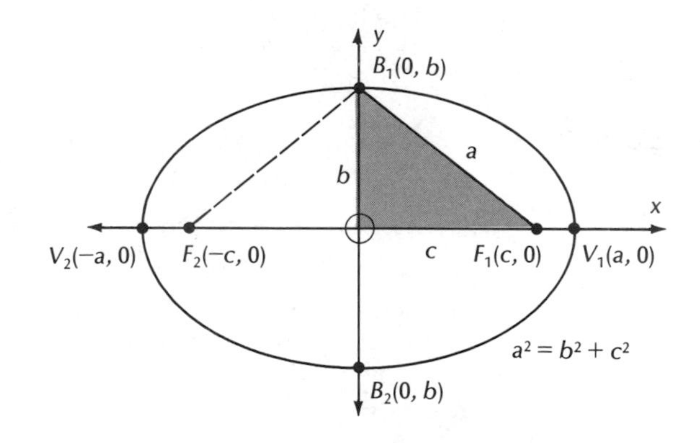

The right-angled $\triangle F_1OB_1$, along with the Pythagorean Theorem, gives a useful relationship among the sides a, b, and c.

$$b^2 + c^2 = a^2$$

From this relationship, the coordinates of the foci can readily be found when the values of a and b are known.

Case 2. An ellipse with foci $F_1(0, c)$ and $F_2(0, -c)$ on the y-axis

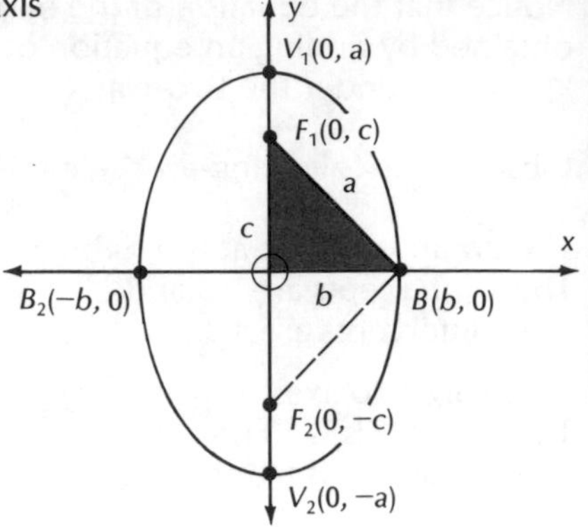

$$\frac{x^2}{b^2} + \frac{y^2}{a^2} = 1, a > b$$

The greater intercept is always a, so the coordinates of the vertices are always associated with the value of a.

EXAMPLE 2: Find the vertices, foci, and lengths of the major axis and minor axis for the ellipse defined by

$$\frac{x^2}{36} + \frac{y^2}{16} = 1.$$

The larger number is the denominator of x^2, so the major axis and foci are on the x-axis. That is $a = 6$, and $b = 4$.

$a^2 = b^2 + c^2$ Use the Pythagorean Theorem.
$36 = 16 + c^2$ Substitute known values.
$c^2 = 20$
$\therefore c = 2\sqrt{5}$

The vertices lie on the x-axis and are $V_1(6, 0)$ and $V_2(-6, 0)$.

The foci are $F_1(2\sqrt{5}, 0)$ and $F_2(-2\sqrt{5}, 0)$.

The length of the major axis is $2a$, or 12.
The length of the minor axis is $2b$, or 8.
The constant sum is $2a$, or 12.

EXAMPLE 3: Find an equation of the ellipse with centre at the origin, $V_1(0, 8)$, and $F_1(0, 6)$.

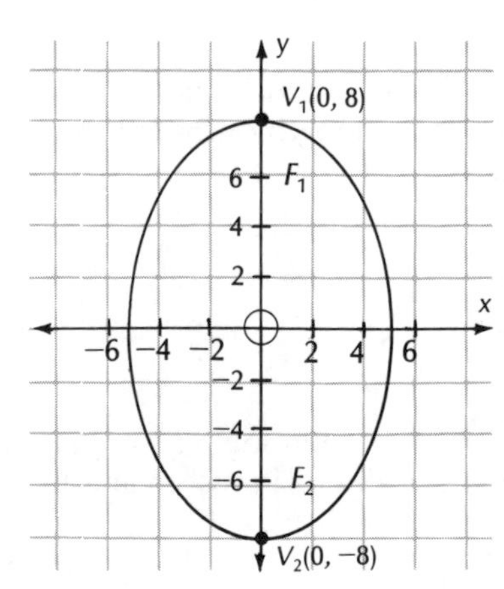

Since one focus and a vertex lie on the y-axis, the major axis lies on the y-axis.

The centre is (0, 0).
An equation of the ellipse is of the form

$$\frac{x^2}{b^2} + \frac{y^2}{a^2} = 1.$$

Since $OV_1 = 8$, then $a = 8$.
Since $OF_1 = 6$, then $c = 6$.
$a^2 = b^2 + c^2$
$64 = b^2 + 36$
$b^2 = 28$

Thus, an equation of the ellipse is $\frac{x^2}{28} + \frac{y^2}{64} = 1.$

EXAMPLE 4: Find an equation of the ellipse in standard position that contains the points $A(4, 4)$ and $B(2, 2\sqrt{10})$.

It is not clear whether the ellipse has foci on the x-axis or the y-axis. In either case, the ellipse can be represented by

$$\frac{x^2}{m} + \frac{y^2}{n} = 1.$$ Substitute known values to obtain a system of equations.

$$\frac{16}{m} + \frac{16}{n} = 1 \quad ①$$ $A(4, 4)$ is on the ellipse.

$$\frac{4}{m} + \frac{40}{n} = 1 \quad ②$$ $B(2, 2\sqrt{10})$ is on the ellipse.

$$\frac{144}{n} = 3, \text{ or } n = 48$$ Multiply ② × 4 and subtract ①

$$\therefore \frac{16}{m} + \frac{16}{48} = 1$$ Substitute for n in ①.

$$\therefore \frac{16}{m} + \frac{1}{3} = 1, \text{ or } \frac{16}{m} = \frac{2}{3}$$

$$\therefore m = 24$$

An equation of the ellipse is $\frac{x^2}{24} + \frac{y^2}{48} = 1$ and the foci are on the y-axis.

EXERCISE 7-5

A

1. For the ellipse defined by each equation, along which axis does the major axis lie?

   a. $\frac{x^2}{16} + \frac{y^2}{25} = 1$ **b.** $9x^2 + 49y^2 = 441$ **c.** $\frac{4x^2}{25} + \frac{y^2}{16} = 1$

2. Find the vertices of the ellipse defined by each equation.

   a. $\frac{x^2}{36} + \frac{y^2}{16} = 1$ **b.** $16y^2 + 9x^2 = 144$ **c.** $9x^2 + 4y^2 = 1$

3. Find the foci of the ellipse defined by each equation.

   a. $\frac{x^2}{16} + \frac{y^2}{36} = 1$ **b.** $20x^2 + 80y^2 = 160$ **c.** $\frac{x^2}{4} + \frac{y^2}{8} = 1$

4. For the ellipse defined by each equation, find the coordinates of the endpoints of the minor axis.

   a. $\frac{x^2}{4} + \frac{y^2}{36} = 1$ **b.** $4x^2 + 25y^2 = 1$ **c.** $25x^2 + 9y^2 = 225$

5. Using the vertices and the endpoints of the minor axis, sketch the ellipse defined by each equation.

   a. $\frac{x^2}{49} + \frac{y^2}{36} = 1$ **b.** $\frac{x^2}{25} + \frac{y^2}{64} = 1$ **c.** $9x^2 + 4y^2 = 1$
   d. $9x^2 + 4y^2 = 36$ **e.** $9x^2 + 4y^2 = 25$ **f.** $9y^2 + 16x^2 = 144$

B 6. Find an equation of the ellipse with the given conditions.

a. $F(0, 3)$; $V(0, 7)$

b. $F(-4, 0)$; major axis is 12 units long

c. $V(0, -8)$; minor axis is 8 units long

d. x-intercepts ± 6; y-intercepts ± 5

e. $F(-4, 0)$; y-intercepts ± 8

f. $F(6, 0)$; constant sum is 18

7. Find an equation of the image of the circle defined by $x^2 + y^2 = 25$ under each given transformation. Graph the circle and the image curve in each case.

a. $(x, y) \to \left(\frac{x}{3}, y\right)$

b. $(x, y) \to \left(x, \frac{y}{4}\right)$

c. $(x, y) \to \left(\frac{x}{2}, 3y\right)$

d. $(x, y) \to \left(\frac{4x}{5}, \frac{3y}{5}\right)$

8. a. Find an equation of the image of the circle defined by $x^2 + y^2 = 100$ under the stretch transformation $(x, y) \to \left(x, \frac{4y}{5}\right)$.

b. Sketch the circle and its image from part **a**.

c. Find an equation of the ellipse consisting of the set of all points, the sum of whose distances from $F_1(6, 0)$ and $F_2(-6, 0)$ is 20.

d. How are the ellipses in parts **a** and **c** related?

9. Find an equation of the ellipse with foci on the x-axis, major axis 12 units long and minor axis 8 units long.

10. Find an equation of the ellipse, in standard position, that has an x-intercept and a y-intercept that coincide with those for the line $8x - 3y + 24 = 0$.

11. Find an equation of the ellipse with centre at the origin, $V(0, 6\sqrt{2})$, and that contains the point $P(4, 6)$.

12. Find an equation of the ellipse, in standard position, with $V(-8, 0)$ and a focus on the line $4x - 5y - 20 = 0$.

13. Find an equation of the ellipse, in standard position, which contains $P(0, 3)$, if one focus is $F(-5, 0)$.

14. Find the domain and range of each relation.

a. $\frac{x^2}{16} + \frac{y^2}{49} = 1$

b. $4x^2 + 9y^2 = 1$

c. $\frac{9x^2}{4} + \frac{9y^2}{16} = 1$

15. Show that the image of the ellipse defined by $x^2 + 16y^2 = 64$ under the stretch transformation $(x, y) \to \left(\frac{x}{4}, y\right)$, is a circle.

16. Find a stretch transformation that maps the ellipse defined by $x^2 + 16y^2 = 64$ onto the circle defined by $x^2 + y^2 = 64$.

17. Find a stretch transformation that maps the ellipse defined by $\frac{x^2}{a^2} + \frac{y^2}{b^2} = 1$ onto the circle defined by $x^2 + y^2 = r^2$.

C **18.** Find an equation of the ellipse that contains each pair of points.

a. $P(6, 6), Q(2, 2\sqrt{15})$ **b.** $S(2, 3), T(1, \sqrt{15})$

19. The latus rectum of an ellipse is a focal chord, perpendicular to the major axis. Find the length of the latus rectum for the ellipse defined by each equation.

a. $\frac{x^2}{4} + \frac{y^2}{36} = 1$ **b.** $\frac{x^2}{49} + \frac{y^2}{14} = 1$

20. An ellipse with foci on the x-axis is tangent to each of the circles defined by $x^2 + y^2 = 16$ and $x^2 + y^2 = 100$ at two points. Find an equation of the ellipse.

21. Use the constant sum definition of an ellipse to develop an equation of the ellipse, in standard position, with foci on the x-axis. (See Example 1 of this lesson.) Assume the foci are at $(\pm c, 0)$ and the constant sum is $2a$. Recall that $a^2 = b^2 + c^2$ (or $b^2 = a^2 - c^2$).

22. **a.** Draw a large circle and any diameter.
b. Put a pin at a point P anywhere on the diameter.
c. Use a set square to draw a chord, $\overline{AB}$, such that $\overline{AB} \perp \overline{AP}$.
d. Draw at least 20 such chords.
e. What curve do the chords outline?

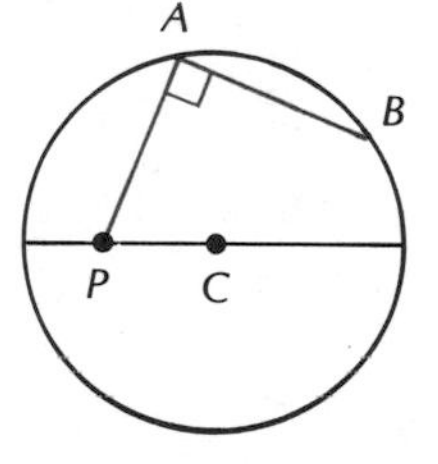

EXTRA

Elliptical Orbits

For many scientific satellites, a circular orbit would not be practical. When studying Earth's magnetic field or the Van Allen radiation belts, measurements are needed over a wide range of altitudes above Earth's surface—not at a constant altitude, as would be used with a circular orbit.

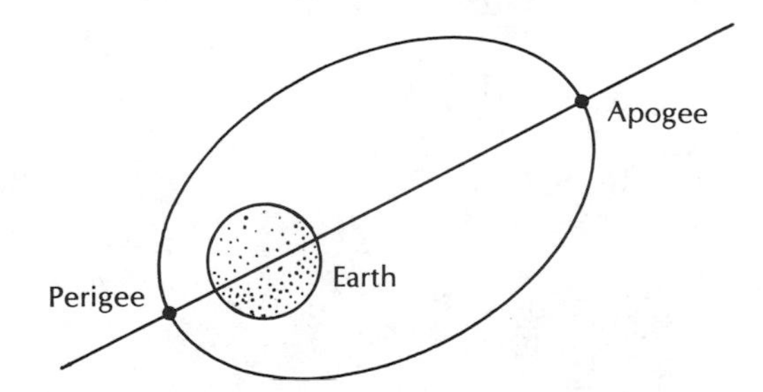

With an elliptical orbit, Earth is located at one focus. The closest point of approach of the satellite called the **perigee**, and the point furthest from Earth is called the **apogee**.

7-6 The Ellipse: Axis Parallel to the x- or y-axis

A translation can map an ellipse, in standard position, onto an image ellipse whose centre is not at the origin. Such a translation maps the ellipse onto a congruent image ellipse, and preserves all the properties of the ellipse, including the lengths of the major and minor axes.

EXAMPLE 1: Find the centre, vertices, foci, and the endpoints of the minor axis for the ellipse defined by

$$\frac{(x-3)^2}{25} + \frac{(y+2)^2}{16} = 1.$$

This ellipse is the image of the ellipse defined by $\frac{x^2}{25} + \frac{y^2}{16} = 1$ under the translation $(x, y) \rightarrow (x+3, y-2)$. Each point is translated 3 units right and 2 units down.

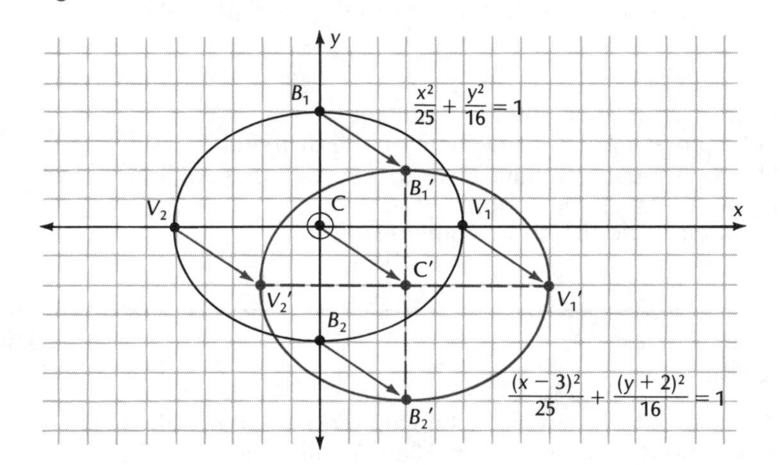

$$\frac{x^2}{25} + \frac{y^2}{16} = 1 \rightarrow \frac{(x-3)^2}{25} + \frac{(y+2)^2}{16} = 1$$ Compare the equations.

$$(x, y) \rightarrow (x+3, y-2)$$

$$C(0, 0) \rightarrow C'(3, -2)$$ The centre is $C'(3, -2)$.

$$V_1(5, 0),\ V_2(-5, 0) \rightarrow V_1'(8, -2),\ V_2'(-2, -2)$$ These are the vertices.

$$a^2 = b^2 + c^2$$
$$25 = 16 + c^2$$
$$\therefore c = 3$$

$$F_1(3, 0),\ F_2(-3, 0) \rightarrow F_1'(6, -2),\ F_2'(0, -2)$$ Foci

$$B_1(0, 4),\ B_2(0, -4) \rightarrow B_1'(3, 2),\ B_2'(3, -6)$$ Endpoints of the minor axis

Under a translation, $(x, y) \to (x + h, y + k)$, the image of an ellipse in standard position can have one of the following forms.

Major Axis Parallel to the x-axis	**Major Axis Parallel to the y-axis**
$\frac{(x-h)^2}{a^2} + \frac{(y-k)^2}{b^2} = 1$	$\frac{(x-h)^2}{b^2} + \frac{(y-k)^2}{a^2} = 1$

EXAMPLE 2: Find an equation of the ellipse given $V_1(4, 4)$, $V_2(4, -8)$, and $F_1(4, 2)$.

Sketch the ellipse.
Since V_1, V_2, and F_1 are on a line parallel to the y-axis, and the vertices are the endpoints of the major axis, the major axis is parallel to the y-axis.

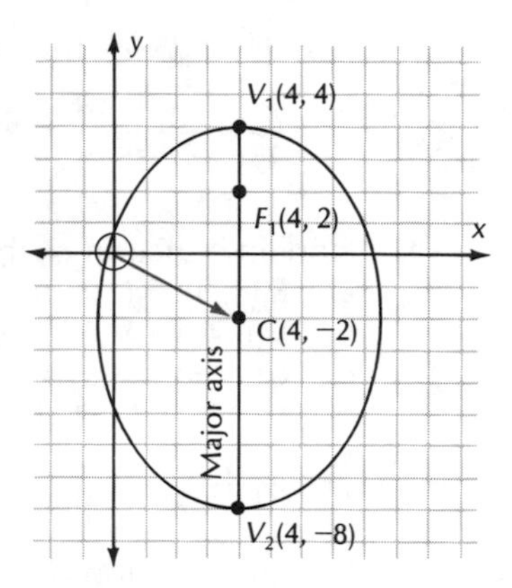

Therefore, the ellipse is the image of the ellipse defined by

$$\frac{x^2}{b^2} + \frac{y^2}{a^2} = 1.$$

The centre is $C(4, -2)$, the midpoint of the major axis.

Since the translation maps $(0, 0)$ onto $(4, -2)$, then the translation is given by $(x, y) \to (x + 4, y - 2)$.

Thus, an equation of the image ellipse is of the form

$$\frac{(x-4)^2}{b^2} + \frac{(y+2)^2}{a^2} = 1.$$

The distance from the centre to a vertex is a, or 6 and the distance from the centre to a focus is c, or 4.

$a^2 = b^2 + c^2$ Use the Pythagorean Theorem.
$36 = b^2 + 16$
$b^2 = 20$

Therefore, $\frac{(x-4)^2}{20} + \frac{(y+2)^2}{36} = 1$ is an equation of the ellipse.

EXERCISE 7-6

A **1.** Find the centre, foci, vertices, and endpoints of the minor axis for the ellipse defined by each equation.

a. $\frac{(x+3)^2}{9} + \frac{(y-2)^2}{25} = 1$ **b.** $\frac{(x-4)^2}{25} + \frac{(y+3)^2}{16} = 1$

c. $\frac{(x+4)^2}{64} + \frac{(y+2)^2}{100} = 1$ **d.** $\frac{(x-1)^2}{100} + \frac{(y+4)^2}{16} = 1$

2. Use the vertices and endpoints of the minor axis to sketch each ellipse defined in exercise 1.

B **3.** Find the foci for the ellipse defined by each equation.

a. $\frac{x^2}{25} + \frac{(y+3)^2}{36} = 1$ **b.** $\frac{(x-4)^2}{25} + \frac{(y+1)^2}{4} = 1$

4. Find an equation of the ellipse with the given conditions.

a. $F_1(8, 3)$, $F_2(-2, 3)$, and $V_1(9, 3)$
b. $V_1(-4, 6)$, $V_2(-4, -2)$, and $F_1(-4, 5)$
c. $C(2, -3)$, $V_2(2, 3)$, and $F_1(2, 2)$
d. $C(-4, 1)$, $F(-1, 1)$, and the constant sum is 10
e. $C(3, 4)$, $a = 6$, $b = 3$, and the major axis is parallel to the x-axis.
f. $C(-2, 5)$, $a = 8$, $b = 2$, and the major axis is parallel to the y-axis.

C **5.** Find an equation of the ellipse with the given conditions.

a. $V_1(-5, -5)$, $V_2(7, -5)$, and a focus on the line $2x - y + 3 = 0$
b. $F_1(2, -10)$, $F_2(2, -2)$, and a vertex on the line $3x - y - 5 = 0$

6. Find an equation of the ellipse with its major axis parallel to the x-axis, $C(3, -5)$, a vertex on the line $x + y - 3 = 0$, and a focus on the line $5x - y - 5 = 0$.

7. Find an equation of the ellipse with $V_1(1, 5)$, $F_1(1, 3)$, and constant sum 16.

8. Find an equation of the ellipse with $V_1(6, 2)$, $F_2(-6, 2)$, and constant sum 14.

9. Find an equation of the image, in standard position, of the ellipse defined by each equation.

a. $4x^2 + 9y^2 + 8x - 36y - 104 = 0$
b. $9x^2 + 4y^2 - 90x + 16y + 205 = 0$

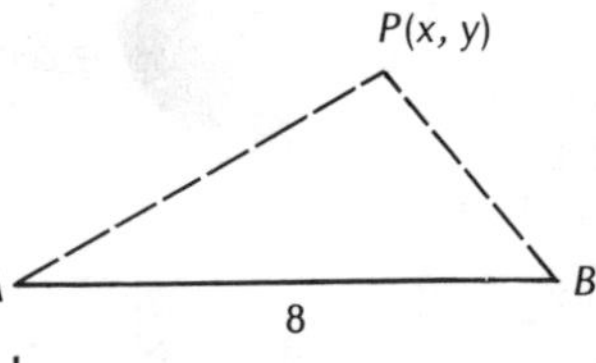

10. The base, $\overline{AB}$, of a triangle with vertex P, is 8 units long.
The midpoint of $\overline{AB}$ is the origin.
The product of the slopes of $\overline{PA}$ and $\overline{PB}$ is $-\frac{9}{16}$.
Find an equation that defines the set of points to which P belongs.

7-7 Applying Second Degree Relations

EXAMPLE: A stadium is 230 m long with sides 15 m high. It is covered by a roof in the shape of an elliptical profile. If the maximum height at the centre of the stadium is 45 m, measured from the ground, find an equation that defines the curvature of the roof.

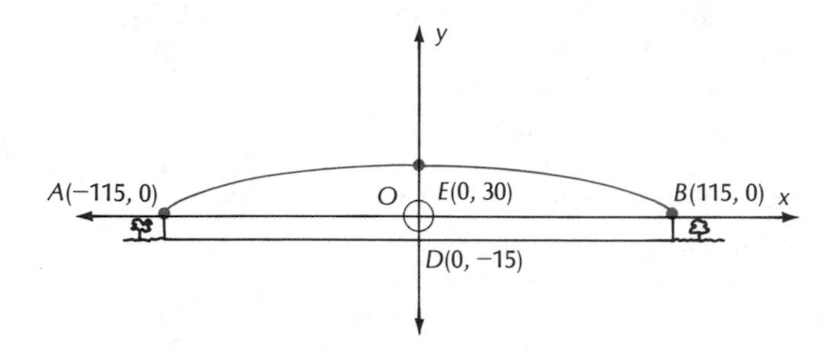

In the diagram, the x-axis and y-axis are positioned so that the ellipse has its centre at the origin.

Since the stadium is 230 m long, $AB = 230$ and $OB = 115$. So, the coordinates of A and B are $A(-115, 0)$ and $B(115, 0)$. Since the stadium rises 45 m above ground level, $ED = 45$, but with $OD = 15$ (the height of the walls). Then $OE = 30$ and the coordinates of E are $E(0, 30)$.

The ellipse is of the form $\frac{x^2}{a^2} + \frac{y^2}{b^2} = 1$, with $a = 115$ and $b = 30$.

Therefore, an equation of the ellipse is $\frac{x^2}{13\,225} + \frac{y^2}{900} = 1$.

EXERCISE 7-7

A

1. A tunnel opening is in the shape of an inverted parabola. If the tunnel has a maximum width of 18 m and a maximum height of 9 m, find an equation that defines the shape of the opening.

2. A parabolic reflector is designed so that a bulb is located at the focus. When in place, the bulb's filament is 1.5 cm from the back of the reflector. If the reflector opens to the right, find an equation that defines the shape of the reflector.

3. The foci of an elliptical racetrack are 300 m apart. If the infield is 400 m long, find the length of the widest part of the infield surrounded by the track.

4. Find an equation that defines the shape of the ellipse in exercise 3.

B 5. A roadway is 22 m wide. A tunnel is designed so that its opening is elliptical with a maximum width of 26 m. If the foci are located at the edge of the roadway, how high is the tunnel at the edge of the road?

6. A roadway, including paved shoulders, is 20 m wide. So that water will run off the roadway, it is paved in the shape of a parabola with a drop of 0.1 m between the centre and the outside edge of the shoulder.
   a. Find an equation that defines the shape of the roadway.
   b. Find the length of the vertical drop from the centre to the near edge of the shoulder, 9 m from the centre line.

7. The cross-section of a searchlight is parabolic in shape with the focus 5 cm from the back of the reflector. If the glass cover is 3 cm from the focus, find the length of a diameter of the glass.

8. A satellite travels in an elliptical orbit around Earth with the centre of Earth as one focus. Find an equation of the elliptical orbit if its closest point to Earth (perigee) is 650 km and its furthest point from Earth (apogee) is 1650 km. The radius of Earth is 6350 km.

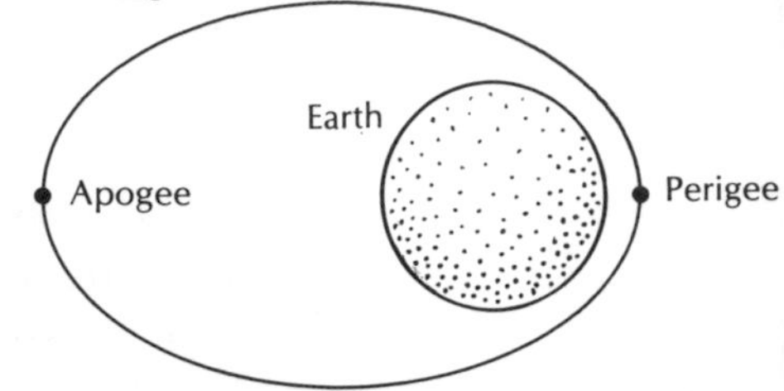

9. Earth travels around the Sun in an elliptical orbit with the Sun at one focus. The major axis of Earth's orbit around the Sun measures 300 million kilometres. The orbit is elliptical, and the furthest distance from Earth to the Sun is 152 million kilometres.
   a. Find an equation that defines Earth's orbit.
   b. Find the length of the minor axis.

C 10. A ball is thrown on a parabolic path that reaches a maximum height of 16 m. The ball just clears a 7 m spruce tree that is 7 m from where the ball is thrown. Find the horizontal distance the ball has traveled when it hits the ground. (There are 2 answers.)

11. An aircraft is flying in a clockwise circular path around an airport at constant speed. At 12:00 noon, the plane is 35 km east and 12 km north of the airport.
   a. Choose suitable axes, draw a diagram, and find an equation that defines the flight path.
   b. How far north or south of the airport will the plane be when it is 15 km west of the airport?
   c. If the plane is cruising at 250 km/h, what is its position at 12:15 P.M.?

12. Phyllis lives 12 km due north of her sister Marion. Their sister Sharon lives 4 km east of Phyllis and Marion, as shown in the diagram. There are two perpendicular roads from Sharon's house to each of her sisters' homes.
   a. Find an equation of a circle that contains the homes of the three sisters.
   b. Find the distance from Sharon's home to each of her sister's homes.

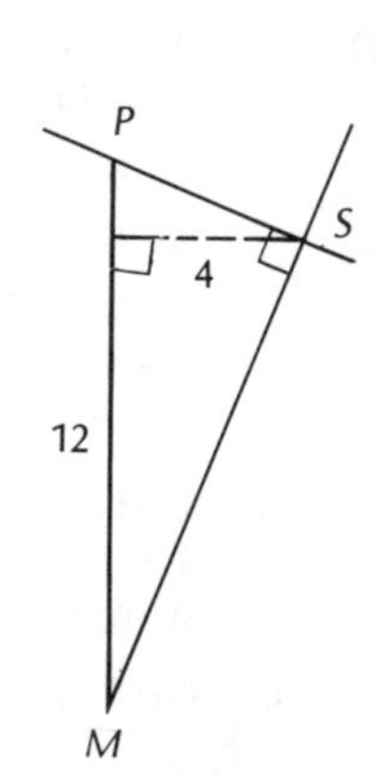

Application

Making Tracks

A 440 m track is constructed with a rectangular central area and semi-circular ends. Use a calculator to answer each question.

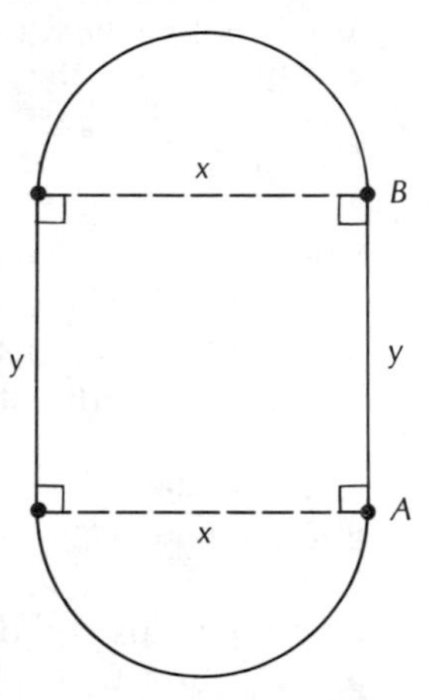

1. If the central area is a square, find the length of the "straight" between A and B and find the total area of the infield.
2. If the "straights" are twice the width of the track, then how long is each straight?
3. If the width of the track is 50 m, then how long are the "straights"?
4. If the "straights" are 100 m long, then what is the width of the track?

EXTRA

Latus Rectum of an Ellipse

A **latus rectum** is a focal chord that is perpendicular to the axis of symmetry of an ellipse.
There are two such segments in an ellipse.

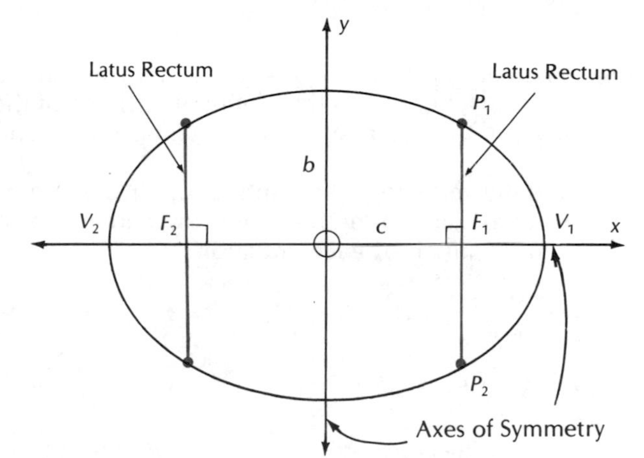

Consider an ellipse of the form
$$\frac{x^2}{a^2} + \frac{y^2}{b^2} = 1, \text{ where } a^2 = b^2 + c^2.$$

The ellipse shown at the right has foci F_1 and F_2 on the x-axis. Points P_1 and P_2 are located on the ellipse such that $\overline{P_1P_2}$ contains F_1 and is perpendicular to the axis of symmetry.

The x-coordinate of P_1 is c.

The length of the latus rectum is P_1P_2.

1. Find the y-coordinate of P_1 in terms of a and b.

   For the following questions, assume the ellipse is centred at the origin.

2. Find an equation of the ellipse with foci on the x-axis, a latus rectum 9 units long, and constant sum 16.
3. Find an equation of the ellipse with foci on the y-axis, a latus rectum $\frac{4}{3}$ units long, and minor axis 4 units long.

Review

1. Find the domain and range of each relation.
   a. $(x-4)^2+(y+1)^2=9$
   b. $x^2+y^2+4x+2y-11=0$
   c. $(y+2)^2=-8(x-1)$
   d. $x^2-6x-4y+5=0$
   e. $\frac{x^2}{9}+\frac{y^2}{4}=1$
   f. $4x^2+5y^2-40=0$

2. Find an equation of a circle with the given conditions.
   a. centre $C(-3, 5)$ and contains $P(3, -1)$
   b. centre $C(2, -4)$ and tangent to the line $y-3=0$
   c. diameter $\overline{AB}$ with endpoints $A(-6, 4)$ and $B(8, 10)$

3. Find the length of the tangent segment from $A(-8, 3)$ to the circle defined by $(x-2)^2+(y-1)^2=25$.

4. Find the focus and directrix of the parabola defined by each equation.
   a. $y^2+8x=0$
   b. $(x+3)^2=20(y-1)$
   c. $y^2=4x+8$

5. Find an equation of the parabola with the given conditions.
   a. $F(0, -6)$; $V(0, 0)$
   b. $F(0, 4)$; $V(0, -2)$
   c. $F(4, 0)$; directrix $x+2=0$
   d. $V(0, 0)$ and contains $P(-5, 2)$ (Two answers)

6. A parabolic arch has a height of 12 m. The width at the base is 32 m.
   a. Find an equation that defines the shape of the arch.
   b. Find the height of the arch 10 m from its centre.

7. Find the vertices, focal points, endpoints of the minor axis, length of the major axis, length of the minor axis, and the constant sum of the ellipse defined by each equation.
   a. $\frac{x^2}{64}+\frac{y^2}{36}=1$
   b. $\frac{x^2}{16}+\frac{y^2}{36}=1$
   c. $4x^2+9y^2=36$
   d. $\frac{(x-5)^2}{16}+\frac{(y+3)^2}{4}=1$
   e. $16x^2+144y^2=144$
   f. $\frac{(x+7)^2}{25}+\frac{(y+6)^2}{36}=1$

8. Sketch the ellipse defined by each equation using the endpoints of the minor axis and the vertices.
   a. $\frac{x^2}{4}+\frac{y^2}{36}=1$
   b. $4x^2+9y^2=1$
   c. $4x^2+9y^2=25$
   d. $\frac{(x-4)^2}{16}+(y+2)^2=1$

9. Find an equation of the image, in standard position, of the ellipse defined by each equation.
   a. $x^2+4y^2-6x-8y-3=0$
   b. $x^2+25y^2+4x+50y+4=0$

10. Find an equation of the ellipse with centre at the origin and the given conditions.
   a. $V(0, 8)$; $F(0, 4)$
   b. x-intercept -12; y-intercept 8
   c. $F(-3, 0)$; y-intercept 3
   d. $V(0, 9)$; minor axis 8 units long
   e. $V(0, 4\sqrt{3})$ and contains $P(1, -6)$
   f. $A(6, 1)$ and $B(2\sqrt{3}, \sqrt{3})$ are points on the ellipse

11. Find an equation of the ellipse with vertices $V_1(0, -3)$ and $V_2(8, -3)$, and a focus $F(1, -3)$.

12. Find an equation of the ellipse with its centre at the origin, a focus $F(0, -5)$, and a y-intercept on the line $8x + 2y = 16$.

13. Find an ellipse with vertices $V_1(-2, 6)$ and $V_2(-2, -4)$, and a focus on the line $2x + y = 0$.

14. A curling rink has straight walls that are 3 m high and an elliptical roof (profile) that rises to a height of 10 m above the ice surface. If the width of the building is 18 m, find an equation that defines the curvature of the roof.

15. A solar oven is 8 m wide and 3 m deep, with a parabolic cross-section. The crucible is placed at the focus to achieve a maximum temperature. Find the position of the crucible.

16. Find an equation of the image of the graph of $x^2 + y^2 = 100$ under each stretch transformation. Graph the circle and its image for each case.
   a. $(x, y) \rightarrow \left(\frac{x}{2}, y\right)$
   b. $(x, y) \rightarrow (x, 2y)$
   c. $(x, y) \rightarrow \left(\frac{x}{5}, 5y\right)$
   d. $(x, y) \rightarrow \left(\frac{2x}{5}, \frac{4y}{5}\right)$

17. a. Find an equation of the image of the circle defined by $x^2 + y^2 = 25$ under the stretch transformation $(x, y) \rightarrow \left(\frac{3x}{5}, y\right)$.
   b. Sketch the circle and its image from part **a**.
   c. Find an equation of an ellipse that defines the set of points $P(x, y)$, the sum of whose distances from $F_1(0, 4)$ and $F_2(0, -4)$ is 10.
   d. How are the ellipses in parts **a** and **c** related?

18. A parabolic reflector is used on the sidelines at televised football games to pick up the sound of the action on the field. The reflector has a diameter of 60 cm and a maximum depth of 12 cm.
   a. Find an equation that defines the parabolic shape of the reflector's profile.
   b. Find the desired position for the microphone if it is to be located at the focus.

Test Unit 7

1. Find the centre and the radius of the circle defined by each equation.
   a. $x^2 + (y - 3)^2 = 20$ **b.** $x^2 + y^2 - 14x + 6y + 9 = 0$

2. Find an equation of the circle with the given conditions.
   a. centre $C(5, -2)$ and contains $P(3, 2)$
   b. centre $C(3, 7)$ and tangent to the line $x + 5 = 0$
   c. centre on the line $x + y + 4 = 0$ and contains $D(7, -1)$ and $E(7, -7)$
   d. the positive x-axis and y-axis are tangents and the radius is 4

3. Find the focus and directrix for the parabola defined by each equation.
   a. $x^2 - 24y = 0$ **b.** $(y + 3)^2 = -28(x + 1)$ **c.** $x^2 - 4y + 12 = 0$

4. Find an equation of the parabola with the given conditions.
   a. $V(0, 0)$; $F(-4, 0)$
   b. $F(0, -7)$; directrix $y - 7 = 0$
   c. $F(-5, 4)$; directrix $x = -1$
   d. focus and vertex on the x-axis; contains $N(-5, 3)$; centre $C(0, 0)$

5. Find the foci and then, using the vertices and endpoints of the minor axis, sketch the ellipse defined by each equation.
   a. $\frac{x^2}{9} + \frac{y^2}{36} = 1$ **b.** $4x^2 + 9y^2 = 1$ **c.** $\frac{(x - 1)^2}{25} + \frac{(y + 2)^2}{4} = 1$

6. Find an equation of the image of the circle defined by $x^2 + y^2 = 36$ under the given stretch transformation.
   a. $(x, y) \to \left(\frac{x}{2}, y\right)$ **b.** $(x, y) \to \left(\frac{x}{3}, 3y\right)$ **c.** $(x, y) \to \left(x, \frac{y}{6}\right)$

7. Find the foci and vertices of the ellipse defined by $x^2 + 4y^2 + 8x - 8y + 16 = 0$. Then sketch the ellipse.

8. Find an equation of the ellipse with centre at the origin and the given conditions.
   a. $V(-6, 0)$ and $F(-5, 0)$
   b. x-intercept 3 and y-intercept 9
   c. $F(0, -5)$ and minor axis 8 units long
   d. $V(8, 0)$ and contains $P(4, -\sqrt{3})$

9. Find an equation of the ellipse with $F_1(-5, -2)$, $F_2(11, -2)$, and $V_1(13, -2)$.

10. Find an equation of the ellipse, with its centre at the origin, and which contains $J(2\sqrt{3}, 1)$ and $D(2, \sqrt{3})$.

11. A landscape gardener plans to make an elliptical feature garden 8 m long and 4 m wide. He plans to use two stakes, at points A and B, and then a cord, tied at A and B and pulled tight, to trace the ellipse.
   a. How far apart should A and B be located?
   b. How long should the cord be?

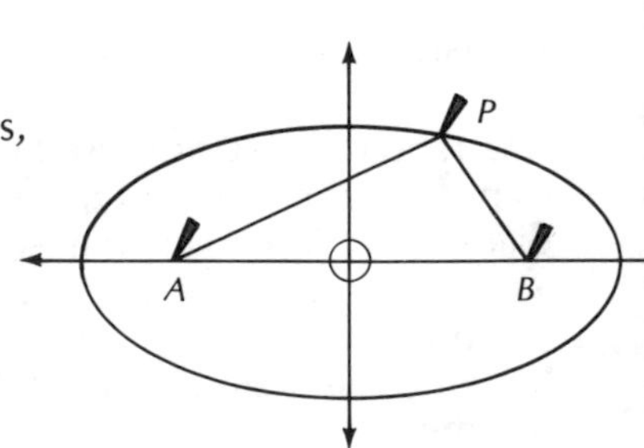

Cumulative Review

1. Given $f(x) = 3x + 4$ and $g(x) = x^2 + 1$, find the following.
   a. $f \circ g(2)$ **b.** $f \circ g(-3)$ **c.** $g \circ f(4)$ **d.** $g \circ f(-1)$

2. Solve.
   a. $5^x = \frac{1}{125}$ **b.** $1.5^x = 2.25$ **c.** $\left(\frac{1}{3}\right)^x = 9$ **d.** $2^{x-3} = 8$

3. Solve.
   a. $\log x = 1000$ **b.** $\log 2x = -4$ **c.** $\log 2(x + 1) = 5$

4. Solve each equation.
   a. $\log_3 x = 2\log_3 7 + \log_3 4$ **b.** $\log_2 54 - \log_2 x = \log_2 6$

5. Solve each equation, correct to 2 decimal places, using a calculator.
   a. $5^x = 2000$ **b.** $y^{\frac{1}{4}} = 10.6$ **c.** $7^{x-2} = 5072$

6. The annual population growth in a certain community is 5%/a of the population at the beginning of each year.
   a. Write a formula for the population t years from now.
   b. If the population of the community is 2000 and growth continues at the same rate, what will the population be in ten years?

7. Factor.
   a. $6x^2 - 5x - 6$ **b.** $t^2 + 14t + 49$ **c.** $4x^2 - 25$

8. Divide $3x^3 - 2x^2 + 7x - 5$ by $x + 3$. Give the answer in the form $P(x) = D(x)Q(x) + R(x)$.

9. Find the value of x, expressed as a fraction.

   a.

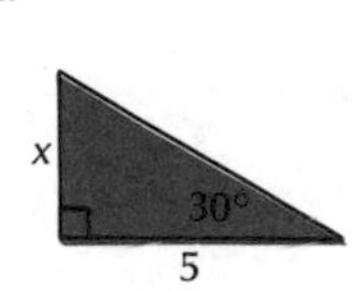

   b.

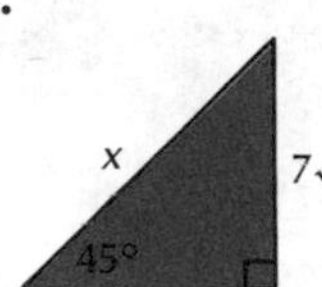

   c.

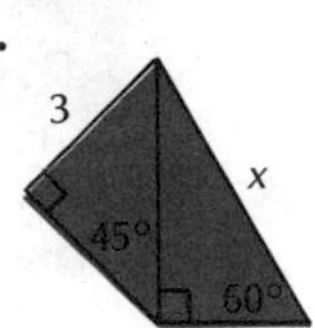

   d.

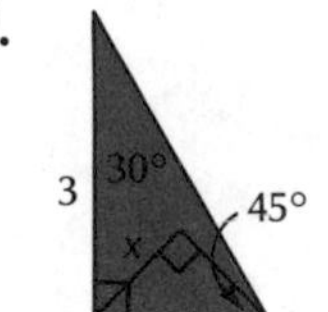

10. **a.** To find the distance across a small slough, Paul measures off a distance, AB, of 40 m, perpendicular to $\overline{AC}$. Find the distance, AC, across the slough.

    b. A tree growing at point C subtends an angle of 10.1° from A. Find the height of the tree.

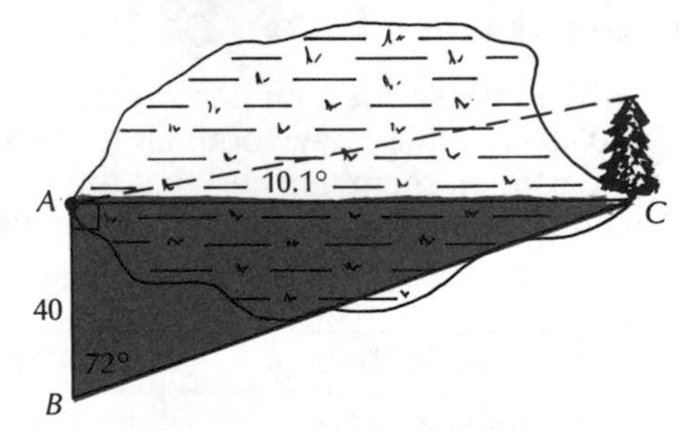

11. A rectangular field is 105 m wide and 240 m long. Find the angle between the longer side and the diagonal, to the nearest degree.

12. Prove that $\dfrac{\cos x}{1 + \sin x} + \dfrac{1 + \sin x}{\cos x} = 2\sec x$

8 Second Degree Relations II

8-1 The Hyperbola: An Introduction

The physical education department at Merivale High School has budgeted \$400 to purchase new footballs for next year's athletic program. The department members find that the more expensive the football, the fewer balls they can purchase, as shown in the table below.

Cost of one ball (c \$)	5	10	20	40	50	80	100
Number purchased (n)	80	40	20	10	8	5	4

Notice that as the value of one variable increases, the value of the other variable decreases. This is an example of an **inverse variation**. The variables in this situation are related by the equation

$$n = \frac{400}{c}, \text{ or } nc = 400.$$

The graph of this relation is shown at the right. In the context of purchasing footballs, n must be a whole number with $n, c > 0$. The resulting curve is one branch of a hyperbola.

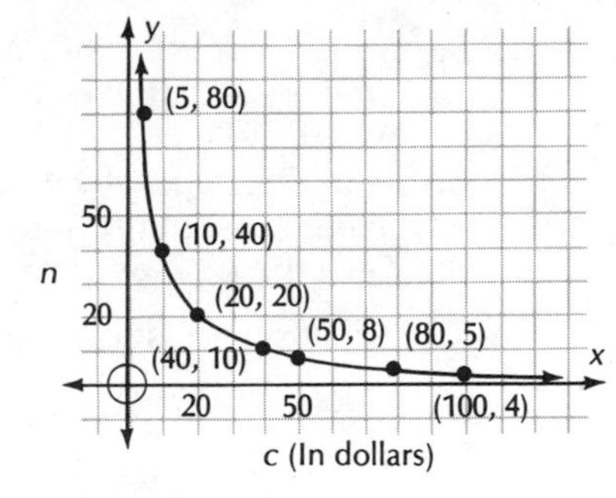

EXAMPLE 1: Suppose that x varies inversely as y and that $x = 4$ when $y = 3$.

a. Find the value of x when $y = 24$.
b. Find the value of y when $x = -6$.
c. Sketch the graph of the inverse variation.

For an inverse variation, the product of the variables is a constant, k.

$xy = k$
Since $x = 4$ when $y = 3$,
then $xy = 12$.

a. If $y = 24$, then $x(24) = 12$.
$$\therefore x = \frac{1}{2}$$

b. If $x = -6$, then $(-6)y = 12$.
$$\therefore y = -2$$

c. If this function is defined over the real numbers, then negative values are permissible. The resulting graph shows both branches of the hyperbola.

x	−12	−6	−4	−3	−2	−1	1	2	3	4	6	12
y	−1	−2	−3	−4	−6	−12	12	6	4	3	2	1

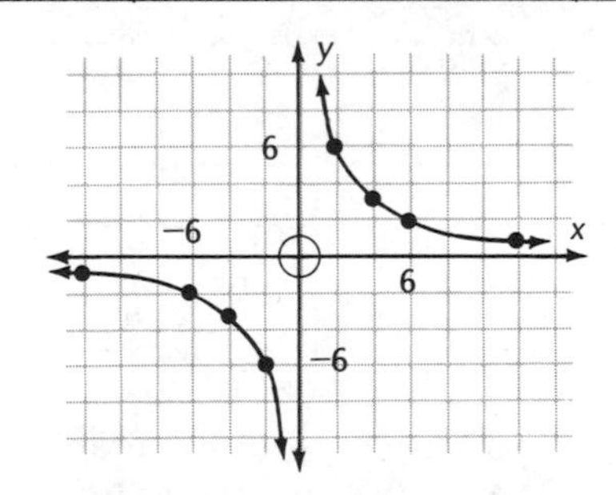

The graph of an inverse variation is a hyperbola.
Notice that the function in Example 1 is not defined for $x = 0$ or $y = 0$. The lines $x = 0$, or the y-axis, and $y = 0$, or the x-axis, are called the **asymptotes** of the hyperbola. For large, absolute values of either variable, the distance between the hyperbola and its asymptotes approaches zero.

EXAMPLE 2: Suppose that $x - 5$ varies inversely as $y + 2$.

a. Find an equation of the variation, given that $x = 2$ when $y = 4$.
b. Find the value of y when $x = 7$.
c. Sketch the graph of the inverse variation.
d. Give the equations of the asymptotes.

The variation equation is $(x - 5)(y + 2) = k$.

a. Since $x = 2$ when $y = 4$, then $(2 - 5)(4 + 2) = k$.

$$(-3)(6) = k$$
$$k = -18$$
$$\therefore (x - 5)(y + 2) = -18$$

b. When $x = 7$, $(7 - 5)(y + 2) = -18$

$$y + 2 = -9$$
$$\therefore y = -11$$

c. The curve defined by $(x - 5)(y + 2) = -18$ is the image of the graph of $xy = -18$ under the translation $(x, y) \rightarrow (x + 5, y - 2)$.

The curve defined by $xy = -18$ is a hyperbola in the second and fourth quadrants, since x and y have opposite signs.

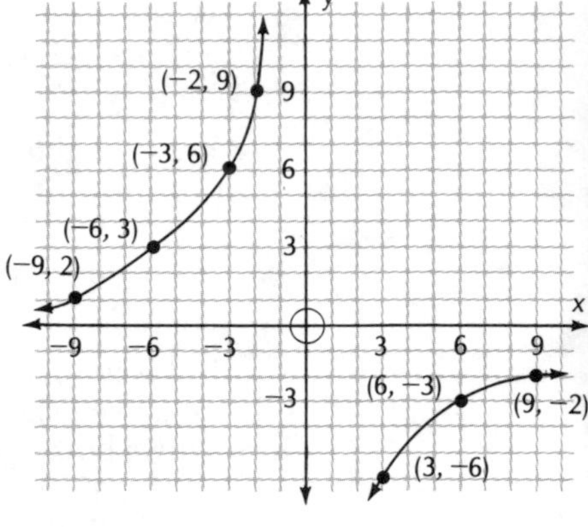

The required curve is the image of the graph of $xy = -18$, translated 5 units to the right and 2 units down.

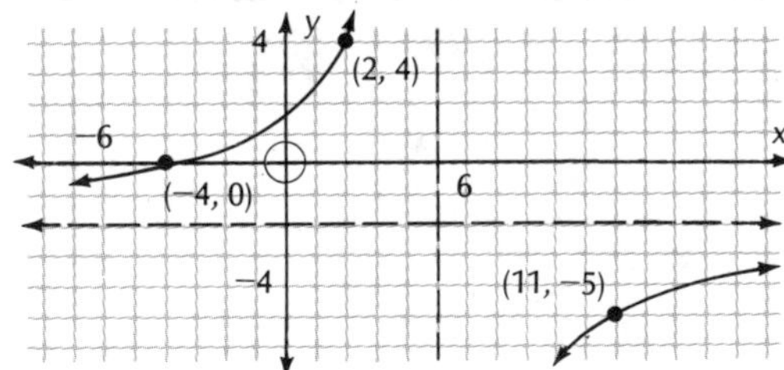

d. The equations of the asymptotes for the graph of $xy = -18$ are $x = 0$ and $y = 0$. The asymptotes for the graph of $(x - 5)(y + 2) = -18$ are the images of the graphs of $x = 0$ and $y = 0$ under the translation

$(x, y) \rightarrow (x + 5, y - 2)$.

Thus, the equations of the asymptotes are $x - 5 = 0$ and $y + 2 = 0$, or $x = 5$ and $y = -2$.

EXERCISE 8-1

A **1.** Suppose that P varies inversely as Q.

a. If $P = 8$ when $Q = 3$, find the value of P when $Q = -36$.
b. If $P = 4$ when $Q = -5$, find the value of Q when $P = 6$.
c. If $P = -7$ when $Q = -4$, find the value of Q when $P = -12$.

2. **a.** Sketch each inverse variation given in exercise 1.
b. Name the quadrants in which each graph from part **a** is located.

B **3.** Suppose that $M + 4$ varies inversely as $N - 3$.

a. If $M = 2$ when $N = -1$, find the value of M when $N = 11$.
b. If $M = 0$ when $N = 4$, find the value of N *when* $M = 4$.
c. If $M = -6$ when $N = -3$, find the value of N when $M = 4$.

4. **a.** Sketch each inverse variation given in exercise 3.
b. State the equations of the asymptotes for each graph in part **a**.

5. First write each given equation in the form $(x + a)(y + b) = k$. Then sketch the hyperbola defined by each equation and state the equations of its asymptotes.

a. $(x - 3)(y + 2) = 12$ **b.** $x + 5 = \dfrac{4}{y + 2}$

c. $y = \dfrac{-8}{x + 1}$ **d.** $y = \dfrac{16}{x + 3} + 5$

e. $x - 4 = \dfrac{1}{2(y + 3)}$ **f.** $y = \dfrac{-1}{3x - 9} + 2$

C **6.** In a **rectangular hyperbola**, the asymptotes are perpendicular to each other. Find an equation of a rectangular hyperbola having the x-axis and the y-axis as asymptotes and containing the given point.

a. $A(4, 2)$ **b.** $B(6, -3)$

7. Find an equation of a hyperbola having the given conditions.

a. asymptotes $x = 0$ and $y = 3$ and containing the point $C(-2, 1)$
b. asymptotes $x = -2$ and $y = 5$ and containing the point $D(-1, 3)$

8. Write each equation in the form $(x + a)(y + b) = k$. Then sketch the hyperbola defined by the equation and state the equations of the asymptotes.

a. $xy + 4x - 3y - 28 = 0$ **b.** $xy + 3x + 2y + 18 = 0$
c. $xy + 5x - 6 = 0$ **d.** $xy - 2y + 8 = 0$

9. The selling price, C, of a new car is partly constant due to dealer cost, F. A markup is added which varies inversely as the number of cars purchased, n. That is,

$$C = F + \frac{k}{n}, \text{ where } k \text{ is a constant.}$$

A taxi firm purchases 5 cars and pays \$18 400 for each car. If the firm had purchased only 4 cars, the cars would have cost \$18 500 each. How much would each car cost if 16 cars were purchased?

8-2 The Asymptotes of a Hyperbola

As seen in lesson 8-1, if the equations of the asymptotes of a hyperbola are $x - a = 0$ and $y - b = 0$, then the defining equation of the hyperbola is $(x - a)(y - b) = k$. The asymptotes of this hyperbola are always parallel to the x- and y-axes.

Now consider two *oblique* lines, defined by $x - y = 0$ and $x + y = 0$, and the corresponding equation $(x - y)(x + y) = k$, or $x^2 - y^2 = k$. Will the graph of an equation of this form be a hyperbola?

An *oblique* line is slanted.

EXAMPLE 1:

a. Graph $x - y = 0$ and $x + y = 0$.

The lines defined by $x - y = 0$ and $x + y = 0$ (that is, $y = x$ and $y = -x$) contain the origin and have slopes of 1 and -1, respectively.

b. Graph $(x - y)(x + y) = 16$, or $x^2 - y^2 = 16$.

To graph $x^2 - y^2 = 16$, use a table of values.
$y^2 = x^2 - 16$, or $y = \pm\sqrt{x^2 - 16}$

The values marked * are undefined in the reals.

x	y
−8	$\pm 4\sqrt{3}$
−5	±3
−4	0
−2	*
0	*
2	*
4	0
5	±3
8	$\pm 4\sqrt{3}$

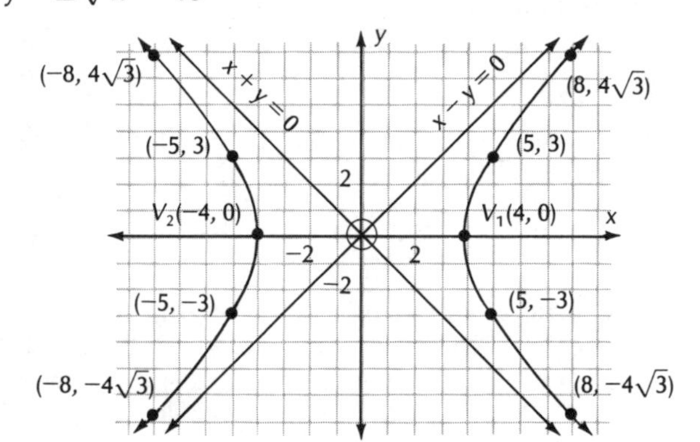

It appears that the graph of $x^2 - y^2 = 16$ is a hyperbola with two vertices, $V_1(4, 0)$ and $V_2(-4, 0)$. These points are useful in sketching a hyperbola because they indicate which axis the hyperbola intersects.

EXAMPLE 2: Show that $x - y = 0$ and $x + y = 0$ define the asymptotes for the hyperbola defined by $x^2 - y^2 = 16$.

A portion of the graph from Example 1 is shown at the right.

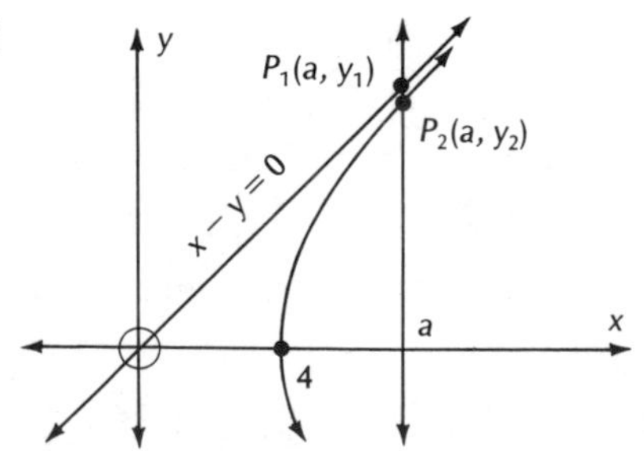

Consider some value for x, say a, where $a > 4$.

P_1 is on the line $x - y = 0$, or $y = x$.
$\therefore y_1 = a$

P_2 is on the curve defined by $x^2 - y^2 = 16$.

$\therefore y_2 = \sqrt{a^2 - 16}$

$y^2 = x^2 - 16$
$y = \sqrt{x^2 - 16}$ and $x = a$

For any $a > 4$, $a > \sqrt{a^2 - 16}$. So $y_1 > y_2$, and the point P_1 will always be above P_2 on the graph.

The distance between P_1 and P_2 is given by
$d = a - \sqrt{a^2 - 16}$.

On a calculator, you can show that as the value of a increases, the distance between P_1 and P_2 approaches zero.

This means that the hyperbola approaches the straight line $x - y = 0$, and that $x - y = 0$ is an asymptote of the hyperbola defined by $x^2 - y^2 = 16$. A similar calculation shows that $x + y = 0$ is the other asymptote.

EXAMPLE 3:

a. Find an equation of the hyperbola having asymptotes $x + 2y = 0$ and $x - 2y = 0$, and containing the point $A(-10, 4)$.

The hyperbola is of the form $(x + 2y)(x - 2y) = k$, or $x^2 - 4y^2 = k$.

$(-10, 4)$ is a point on the hyperbola.
$\therefore 100 - 4(16) = k$
$\therefore k = 36$

Substitute known values into $x^2 - 4y^2 = k$.

An equation of the hyperbola is $x^2 - 4y^2 = 36$.

b. Sketch the hyperbola.

The asymptotes defined by $x \pm 2y = 0$, or $y = \pm\frac{1}{2}x$, have slopes $+\frac{1}{2}$ and $-\frac{1}{2}$ and are sketched below.

If $x = 0$, then $-4y^2 = 36$, which has no solution. Thus, there are no y-intercepts.

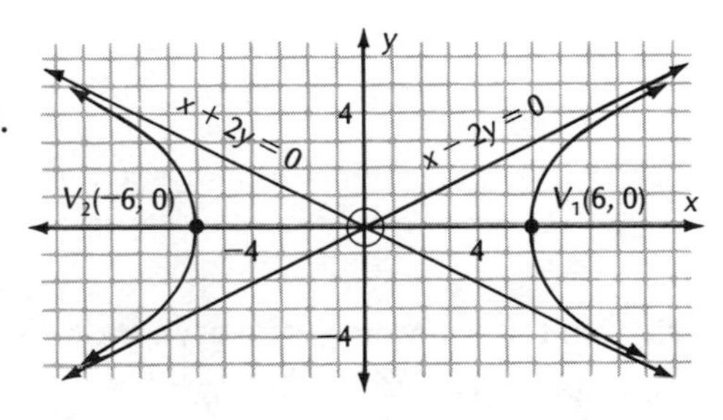

If $y = 0$, then $x^2 = 36$ and the x-intercepts are $+6$ and -6. Thus, the vertices are $V_1(6, 0)$ and $V_2(-6, 0)$. The hyperbola can now be sketched using the vertices and the asymptotes.

EXAMPLE 4: Sketch the hyperbola defined by $9x^2 - y^2 = -36$.

The hyperbola has no x-intercepts but it does have y-intercepts at +6 and −6. The vertices are $V_1(0, 6)$ and $V_2(0, -6)$.

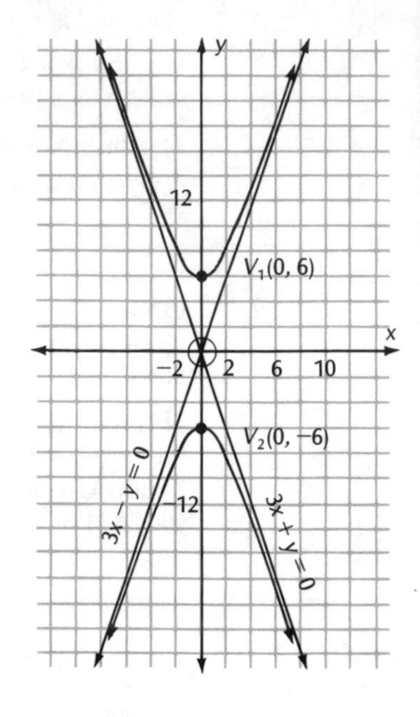

Factoring the left side of the equation reveals the asymptotes to be $3x - y = 0$ and $3x + y = 0$.

Thus, the asymptotes are two lines that contain the origin and have slopes of +3 and −3. The sketch of the hyperbola contains the vertices and approaches the asymptotes.

EXAMPLE 5: Find an equation of the image of the hyperbola defined by $x^2 - y^2 = 1$ under the stretch transformation $(x, y) \rightarrow (4x, 3y)$.

To find an equation of the image, substitute $\frac{x}{4}$ for x and $\frac{y}{3}$ for y in the original equation.

$$x^2 - y^2 = 1$$

$$\left(\frac{x}{4}\right)^2 - \left(\frac{y}{3}\right)^2 = 1$$

Therefore, an equation of the image is $\frac{x^2}{16} - \frac{y^2}{9} = 1$.

Notice that in Example 5, the asymptotes of $x^2 - y^2 = 1$ are $x - y = 0$ and $x + y = 0$. Under the stretch, $\frac{x}{4} - \frac{y}{3} = 0$

and $\frac{x}{4} + \frac{y}{3} = 0$ are the asymptotes.

EXERCISE 8-2

A **1.** Copy and complete the given table.

	Hyperbola	x-intercepts	y-intercepts	Vertices
a.	$x^2 - y^2 = 36$	■	■	■
b.	$x^2 - y^2 = -49$	■	■	■
c.	$y^2 - x^2 = -25$	■	■	■
d.	$4x^2 - 9y^2 = -36$	■	■	■
e.	$x^2 - 5y^2 = 20$	■	■	■
f.	$4x^2 - 16y^2 = -25$	■	■	■

2. State the slopes of each pair of lines.

a. $3x \pm y = 0$ **b.** $x \pm 5y = 0$ **c.** $2x \pm 7y = 0$

3. Write the equations of the asymptotes for each hyperbola.

a. $x^2 - y^2 = 36$ **b.** $16x^2 - y^2 = 400$ **c.** $x^2 - 4y^2 = -100$

d. $4x^2 - 25y^2 = 100$ **e.** $9y^2 - 4x^2 = 36$ **f.** $9x^2 - 4y^2 = -72$

B **4.** Sketch each hyperbola given in exercise 3 using the asymptotes.

5. Copy and complete the given table.

	Asymptotes	Point on Hyperbola	Equation of Hyperbola
a.	$x \pm y = 0$	$P(4, 1)$	■
b.	$x \pm y = 0$	$Q(-3, 7)$	■
c.	$2x \pm y = 0$	$R(5, -1)$	■
d.	$x \pm 3y = 0$	$S(-2, -5)$	■
e.	$3x \pm 5y = 0$	$T(5, 2)$	■

6. Find an equation of the hyperbola with the given conditions.

a. asymptotes $y = \pm\frac{3}{4}x$ and x-intercepts ± 5

b. asymptotes $y = \pm\frac{2}{3}x$ and y-intercepts ± 7

7. Find an equation of the image of the hyperbola defined by $x^2 - y^2 = 1$ under the given stretch.

a. $(x, y) \to (2x, 3y)$ **b.** $(x, y) \to \left(\frac{x}{3}, \frac{y}{4}\right)$

8. **a.** On separate sheets of paper, graph $x^2 - y^2 = 1$ and $xy = \frac{1}{2}$.

b. Place one sheet on top of the other and show that the graphs are congruent.

c. If the graphs of $x^2 - y^2 = 1$ and $xy = \frac{1}{2}$ are drawn on the same axes, what transformation would map one graph onto the other?

C **9.** $P_1(a, y_1)$ is a point on the line defined by $4x - 5y = 0$ and $P_2(a, y_2)$ is a point on the hyperbola defined by $16x^2 - 25y^2 = 400$.

a. Write the length $y_1 - y_2$ in terms of a.

b. Evaluate the length from part **a** for $a = 10$, $a = 20$, and $a = 100$, correct to two decimal places.

8-3 The Standard Equation of the Hyperbola

The Constant Difference Definition of the Hyperbola

A hyperbola is the set of points such that the difference in the distances to two fixed points is a constant. The fixed points are called the **foci** and the segments from a point on the hyperbola to a focus are called the **focal radii.**

This definition can be used to find an equation of a hyperbola.

EXAMPLE 1: Find an equation of the hyperbola with foci $F_1(6, 0)$ and $F_2(-6, 0)$ if the constant difference in the lengths of the focal radii is $6\sqrt{2}$.

Consider a point $P(x, y)$ on the hyperbola.

Since the constant difference in the lengths of the focal radii is $6\sqrt{2}$, then $PF_2 - PF_1 = 6\sqrt{2}$.

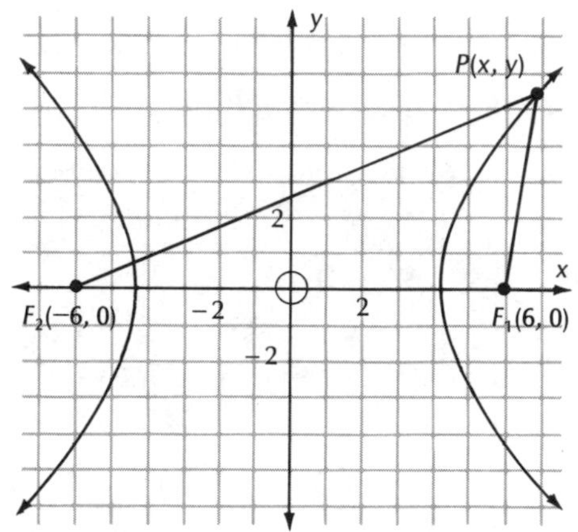

Use the distance formula, $d = \sqrt{(x_2 - x_1)^2 + (y_2 - y_1)^2}$.

$$\sqrt{(x + 6)^2 + y^2} - \sqrt{(x - 6)^2 + y^2} = 6\sqrt{2}$$

$$\left(\sqrt{(x + 6)^2 + y^2}\right)^2 = \left(6\sqrt{2} + \sqrt{(x - 6)^2 + y^2}\right)^2 \quad \text{Square both sides.}$$

$$x^2 + 12x + 36 + y^2 = 72 + 12\sqrt{2}\sqrt{(x - 6)^2 + y^2} + x^2 - 12x + 36 + y^2$$

$$24x - 72 = 12\sqrt{2}\sqrt{(x - 6)^2 + y^2}$$

$$(2x - 6)^2 = \left(\sqrt{2}\sqrt{(x - 6)^2 + y^2}\right)^2 \quad \text{Square both sides.}$$

$$4x^2 - 24x + 36 = 2(x^2 - 12x + 36 + y^2)$$

An equation of the hyperbola is $2x^2 - 2y^2 = 36$, or $x^2 - y^2 = 18$.

EXAMPLE 2: Find an equation of the hyperbola having vertices $V(\pm a, 0)$ and foci $F(\pm c, 0)$, where $c > a$.

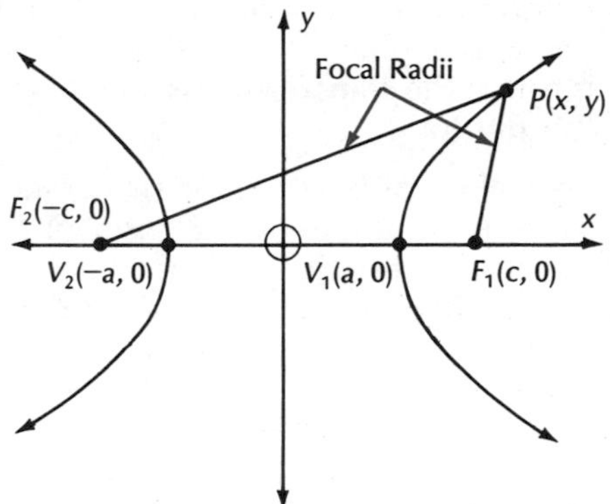

The constant difference can be found using any point on the hyperbola, say $V_1(a, 0)$.

$$\begin{aligned}\therefore \text{constant difference} &= F_2V_1 - F_1V_1 \\ &= F_2V_1 - F_2V_2 \\ &= V_2V_1 \\ &= 2a\end{aligned}$$

Now consider any point, $P(x, y)$, on the hyperbola.

$$|PF_2 - PF_1| = 2a$$

Use the distance formula.
$PF_2 = \sqrt{(x+c)^2 + y^2}$
$PF_1 = \sqrt{(x-c)^2 + y^2}$

$$\left|\sqrt{(x+c)^2+y^2} - \sqrt{(x-c)^2+y^2}\right| = 2a$$

$$\left(\sqrt{(x+c)^2+y^2}\right)^2 = \left(2a + \sqrt{(x-c)^2+y^2}\right)^2$$

$$x^2 + 2cx + c^2 + y^2 = 4a^2 + 4a\sqrt{(x-c)^2+y^2} + x^2 - 2cx + c^2 + y^2$$

$$(4cx - 4a^2)^2 = \left(4a\sqrt{(x-c)^2+y^2}\right)^2$$

$$c^2x^2 - 2a^2cx + a^4 = a^2(x^2 - 2cx + c^2 + y^2)$$

$$c^2x^2 - 2a^2cx + a^4 = a^2x^2 - 2a^2cx + a^2c^2 + a^2y^2$$

$$(c^2 - a^2)x^2 - a^2y^2 = a^2(c^2 - a^2)$$

But $c > a$ and $c^2 > a^2$.
$\therefore c^2 - a^2 > 0$

Let $c^2 - a^2 = b^2$.
$\therefore b^2x^2 - a^2y^2 = a^2b^2$ Divide both sides by a^2b^2.

Therefore, an equation of the hyperbola is $\dfrac{x^2}{a^2} - \dfrac{y^2}{b^2} = 1$.

> **The hyperbola with centre at the origin and foci on the x-axis** is given by
>
> $\dfrac{x^2}{a^2} - \dfrac{y^2}{b^2} = 1$, $F_1(c, 0)$, $F_2(-c, 0)$, where $a^2 + b^2 = c^2$.

The x-intercepts are $x = \pm a$ and they determine the coordinates of the vertices. The line segment joining the vertices is called the **transverse axis** and it is $2a$ units long.

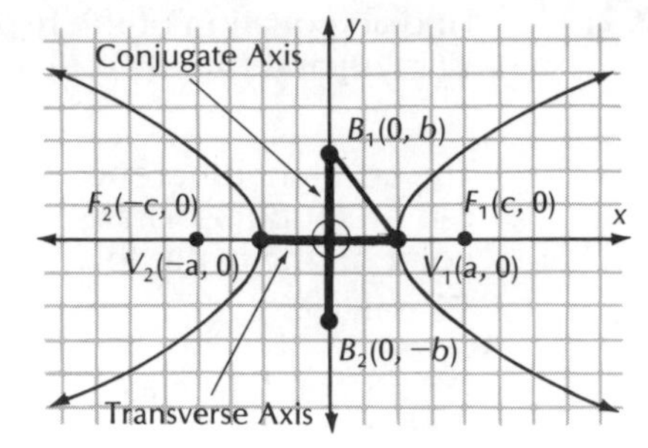

The values of b determine two points on the y-axis at the ends of a segment called the **conjugate axis**, which is $2b$ units long. Notice that $BV = \sqrt{a^2 + b^2} = c$.

The equation of the hyperbola with foci on the y-axis can be developed in a similar way.

> **The hyperbola with centre at the origin and foci on the y-axis** is given by
>
> $$\frac{y^2}{a^2} - \frac{x^2}{b^2} = 1, \quad F_1(0, c), F_2(0, -c), \text{ where } a^2 + b^2 = c^2.$$

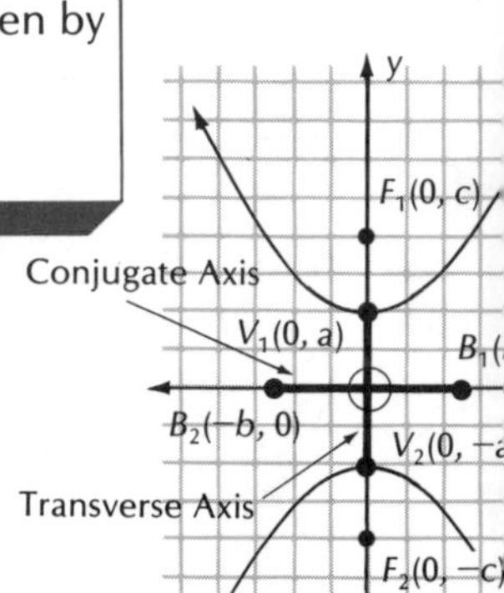

The intercepts are again associated with the value of a so that the vertices are $(0, \pm a)$ and the transverse axis is $2a$ units long.

Notice that the conjugate axis is again $2b$ units long, but it is along the x-axis.

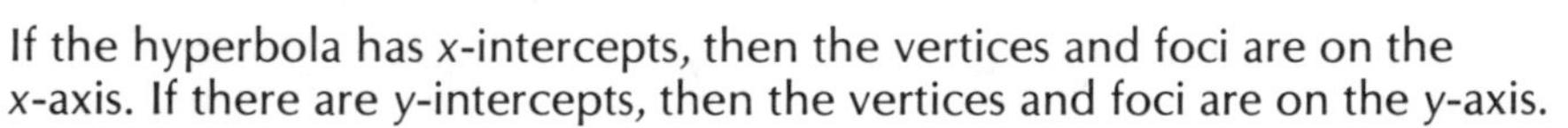

If the hyperbola has x-intercepts, then the vertices and foci are on the x-axis. If there are y-intercepts, then the vertices and foci are on the y-axis.

The transverse and conjugate axes are useful when sketching a hyperbola.

EXAMPLE 3: Sketch the graph of $\frac{x^2}{16} - \frac{y^2}{25} = 1$.

The x-intercepts, 4 and -4, determine the vertices, $(4, 0)$ and $(-4, 0)$. Therefore, $b = 5$ and the endpoints of the conjugate axis are $(0, 5)$ and $(0, -5)$.

Through endpoints of the transverse and conjugate axes, draw lines parallel to the conjugate and transverse axes, as shown. The

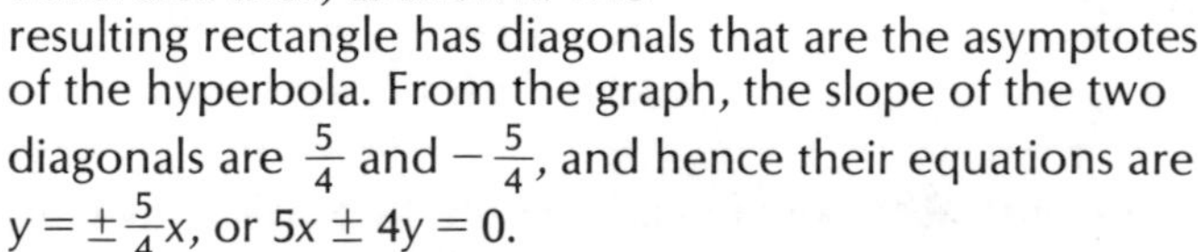

resulting rectangle has diagonals that are the asymptotes of the hyperbola. From the graph, the slope of the two diagonals are $\frac{5}{4}$ and $-\frac{5}{4}$, and hence their equations are $y = \pm\frac{5}{4}x$, or $5x \pm 4y = 0$.

Now that the vertices have been located and the asymptotes drawn, the hyperbola can be drawn through the vertices and approaching the asymptotes.

EXAMPLE 4: A hyperbola is defined by $16y^2 - 9x^2 = 144$.

a. Find the vertices, foci, length of transverse and conjugate axes, and the constant difference.

First, write the hyperbola in standard form.

$$\frac{y^2}{9} - \frac{x^2}{16} = 1$$

$a^2 = 9, b^2 = 16$

The y-intercepts are 3 and -3. So $a = 3, b = 4$, and the vertices are $V_1(0, 3)$ and $V_2(0, -3)$.

The transverse axis is $2a = 2(3)$, or 6 units long.

The constant difference is $2a$, or 6.

The conjugate axis is $2b = 2(4)$, or 8 units long.

For any hyperbola, $a^2 + b^2 = c^2$.
Thus, $9 + 16 = c^2$.
$\therefore c = 5$

The foci are on the y-axis at $F_1(0, 5)$ and $F_2(0, -5)$.

b. Sketch the hyperbola.

The transverse and conjugate axes and the associated rectangle are used to locate the asymptotes. The hyperbola is sketched through the vertices and approaching the asymptotes.

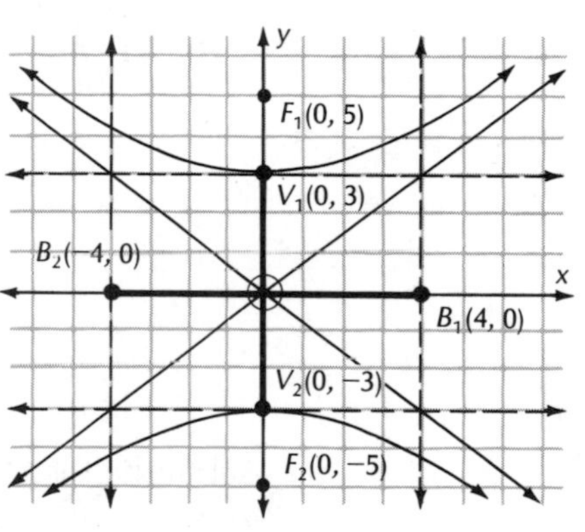

EXAMPLE 5: Find an equation of the hyperbola with centre (0, 0) and one foci at $F(-6, 0)$, given that the length of the conjugate axis is 10 units.

Since $F(-6, 0)$ is known, then $c = 6$ and the hyperbola has x-intercepts.

$$\therefore \frac{x^2}{a^2} - \frac{y^2}{b^2} = 1$$

The conjugate axis is $2b$, or 10 units long.
$\therefore b = 5$

For any hyperbola, $a^2 + b^2 = c^2$.
Thus, $a^2 + 25 = 36$.
$\therefore a^2 = 11$

Substitute $c = 6$ and $b = 5$.

Therefore, an equation of the hyperbola is $\frac{x^2}{11} - \frac{y^2}{25} = 1$.

EXAMPLE 6: Find an equation of the hyperbola with centre at the origin and containing the points $A(2\sqrt{5}, 1)$ and $B(-2\sqrt{7}, \sqrt{3})$.

There is not sufficient information to determine if the hyperbola is "horizontal" or "vertical". The hyperbola can then be represented by

$$\frac{x^2}{M} - \frac{y^2}{N} = 1.$$

Note: if the hyperbola has y-intercepts, then M and N will be negative.

Points on a curve must satisfy the equation of the curve.

$$\therefore A(2\sqrt{5}, 1) \rightarrow \frac{20}{M} - \frac{1}{N} = 1 \quad ①$$

$$B(-2\sqrt{7}, \sqrt{3}) \rightarrow \frac{28}{M} - \frac{3}{N} = 1 \quad ②$$

Solve for M by multiplying ① by 3 and then subtracting ②.

$$① \quad 3\left(\frac{20}{M} - \frac{1}{N}\right) = 3(1)$$

$$③ \quad \frac{60}{M} - \frac{3}{N} = 3$$

$$② \quad \frac{28}{M} - \frac{3}{N} = 1$$

$$\frac{32}{M} = 2$$

$$\therefore 2M = 32, \text{ or } M = 16.$$

Substitute for M in ①. Then solve for N.

$$\frac{20}{16} - \frac{1}{N} = 1$$

$$20N - 16 = 16N$$

$$4N = 16$$

$$N = 4$$

Therefore, an equation of the hyperbola is $\frac{x^2}{16} - \frac{y^2}{4} = 1.$

EXERCISE 8-3

Each hyperbola has its centre at the origin.

A 1. Does the hyperbola defined by the given equation have vertices and foci on the x-axis or the y-axis?

a. $\frac{x^2}{16} - \frac{y^2}{25} = 1$ **b.** $9x^2 - 16y^2 = -1$ **c.** $25y^2 - 4x^2 = 1$

2. Find the vertices for the hyperbola defined by each equation.

a. $\frac{x^2}{20} - \frac{y^2}{36} = 1$ b. $16y^2 - 4x^2 = -64$ c. $9x^2 - 25y^2 = -1$

3. Find the foci for the hyperbola defined by each equation.

a. $\frac{x^2}{36} - \frac{y^2}{4} = 1$ b. $4x^2 - 16y^2 = -64$ c. $x^2 - 4y^2 = 1$

4. Find the coordinates of the endpoints of the conjugate axis.

a. $\frac{x^2}{4} - \frac{y^2}{25} = -1$ b. $9x^2 - 16y^2 = 144$ c. $9x^2 - 36y^2 = 1$

5. Find the domain and range for each hyperbola defined in exercise 4.

B 6. Find an equation of the hyperbola with centre at (0, 0) and the given conditions.

a. $F_1(-7, 0)$ and $V_1(-5, 0)$
b. $F_1(0, 8)$ and transverse axis 8 units long
c. $V_1(8, 0)$ and conjugate axis 16 units long
d. x-intercepts ± 6 and $F_1(8, 0)$
e. $F_1(0, -3)$ and constant difference 2
f. y-intercepts ± 5 and conjugate axis 14 units long

7. Find the foci of a hyperbola having centre $C(0, 0)$, vertex $V_1(0, -4)$, and conjugate axis 6 units long.

8. Find the length of the conjugate axis for a hyperbola having centre $C(0, 0)$, vertex $V_1(-7, 0)$, and focus $F_1(8, 0)$.

9. Find an equation of a hyperbola with centre $C(0, 0)$ and the given conditions.

a. y-intercepts, conjugate axis 8 units long, and transverse axis 12 units long
b. $F_1(7, 0)$ and vertex on the line $8x - 5y - 40 = 0$
c. x-intercepts, conjugate axis 10 units long, and a focus on the line $3x - 8y - 24 = 0$
d. vertices on the y-axis, constant difference 18, and conjugate axis 18 units long
e. $V_1(0, 4)$ and containing the point $P(\sqrt{5}, 2\sqrt{5})$
f. $V_1(0, -8)$, given that the distance between the foci is 22 units

10. Find an equation of the image of the graph of $\frac{x^2}{16} - \frac{y^2}{25} = 1$ under the stretch transformation $(x, y) \rightarrow \left(\frac{5}{4}x, \frac{4}{5}y\right)$.

C 11. Find an equation of a hyperbola that contains the given points.

a. $A(3\sqrt{5}, 1), B(6\sqrt{2}, 2)$ b. $A(\sqrt{30}, 4), B(6, 3\sqrt{2})$

12. The **latus rectum** of a hyperbola is a focal chord parallel to the conjugate axis. Find the length of the latus rectum for the hyperbola defined by each equation.

a. $\frac{x^2}{20} - \frac{y^2}{36} = 1$ b. $\frac{x^2}{36} - \frac{y^2}{49} = 1$

8-4 The General Equation of the Hyperbola

Transformations can be used to shift the centre of a hyperbola from the origin to some other point. The length of the transverse axis remains $2a$ units and the length of the conjugate axis remains $2b$ units. The distance between the foci is $2c$.

EXAMPLE 1: **a.** Find the centre, vertices, foci, and endpoints of the conjugate axis for the hyperbola defined by

$$\frac{(x-2)^2}{9} - \frac{(y+1)^2}{16} = 1.$$

The hyperbola defined by $\frac{(x-2)^2}{9} - \frac{(y+1)^2}{16} = 1$ is the image of the graph of $\frac{x^2}{9} - \frac{y^2}{16} = 1$ under the transformation $(x, y) \rightarrow (x+2, y-1)$, which shifts the hyperbola 2 units to the right and 1 unit down.

equation of the hyperbola

$$\frac{x^2}{9} - \frac{y^2}{16} = 1 \qquad \frac{(x-2)^2}{9} - \frac{(y+1)^2}{16} = 1$$

$$(x, y) \rightarrow (x+2, y-1)$$

The centre is $C(0, 0)$.	The centre is $C'(2, -1)$.
The x-intercepts are 3 and -3, so the vertices are $V_1(3, 0)$ and $V_2(-3, 0)$.	The vertices are $V_1'(5, -1)$ and $V_2'(-1, -1)$.
$c^2 = a^2 + b^2$ $= 9 + 16$ $= 25$ $\therefore c = 5$ and $c = -5$ The foci are $F_1(5, 0)$ and $F_2(-5, 0)$.	The foci are $F_1'(7, -1)$ and $F_2'(-3, -1)$.
Since $b = 4$ and $b = -4$, the endpoints of the conjugate axis are $B_1(0, 4)$ and $B_2(0, -4)$.	The endpoints of the conjugate axis are $B_1'(2, 3)$ and $B_2'(2, -5)$.

b. Sketch the hyperbola defined in part **a.**

The hyperbola defined by $\frac{(x-2)^2}{9} - \frac{(y+1)^2}{16} = 1$ is sketched by first obtaining the asymptotes from the position of the transverse axis, $\overline{V_1'V_2'}$, and the conjugate axis, $\overline{B_1'B_2'}$.

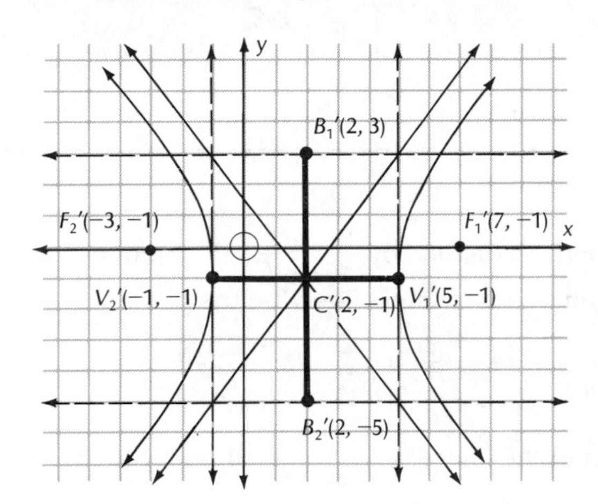

EXAMPLE 2: Find the equation of the hyperbola with vertices $V_1(2, 7)$ and $V_2(2, -1)$ and one focal point $F_1(2, 8)$.

The transverse axis extends between the vertices $V_1(2, 7)$ and $V_2(2, -1)$.
So, $2a = 8$, or $a = 4$.

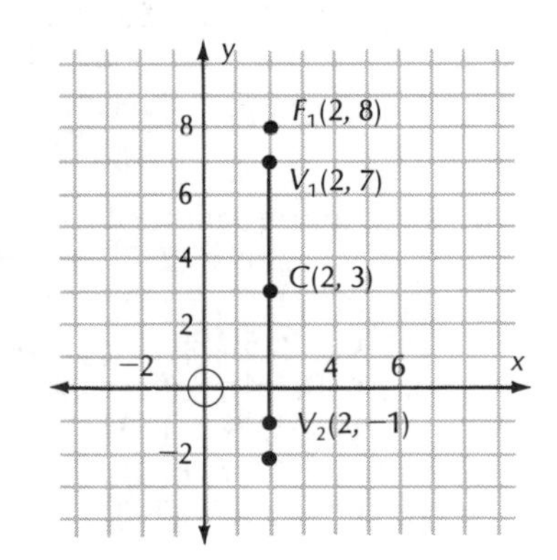

The centre is at the midpoint of the transverse axis. So the centre is $C(2, 3)$.

The distance from the centre $C(2, 3)$ to a focus $F_1(2, 8)$ is the value of c.
$\therefore c = 5$

For any hyperbola, $a^2 + b^2 = c^2$.
Thus, $16 + b^2 = 25$
and $b^2 = 9$.

The transverse axis is parallel to the y-axis, so the hyperbola is the image of the graph of $\frac{y^2}{16} - \frac{x^2}{9} = 1$ under the transformation $(x, y) \rightarrow (x + 2, y + 3)$.

The centre is $C(2, 3)$.

Therefore, an equation of the hyperbola is

$$\frac{(y-3)^2}{16} - \frac{(x-2)^2}{9} = 1.$$

The standard form for the equation of a hyperbola with centre $C(h, k)$ is given below.

Transverse Axis	Parallel to the x-axis	Parallel to the y-axis
Hyperbola	$\frac{(x-h)^2}{a^2} - \frac{(y-k)^2}{b^2} = 1$	$\frac{(y-k)^2}{a^2} - \frac{(x-h)^2}{b^2} = 1$

EXERCISE 8-4

A 1. The centre of the hyperbola defined by $\frac{x^2}{9} - \frac{y^2}{16} = 1$ is shifted according the the given transformation. Describe the transformation.

a. $(x, y) \rightarrow (x + 1, y - 2)$
b. $(x, y) \rightarrow (x - 2, y - 3)$
c. $(x, y) \rightarrow (x - 1, y + 3)$
d. $(x, y) \rightarrow (x + 2, y + 1)$

2. **a.** Write an equation of the image of $\frac{x^2}{9} - \frac{y^2}{16} = 1$ under each transformation given in exercise 1.
b. Determine the centre of each hyperbola derived in part **a**.

B 3. Find the centre, vertices, foci, and endpoints of the conjugate axis for the hyperbola defined by each equation.

a. $\frac{(x-1)^2}{16} - \frac{(y+3)^2}{9} = 1$
b. $\frac{(y-3)^2}{36} - \frac{(x+2)^2}{64} = 1$
c. $\frac{(x-2)^2}{4} - \frac{(y+1)^2}{16} = 1$
d. $\frac{(x+1)^2}{9} - \frac{(y+3)^2}{25} = -1$

4. Find an equation of the hyperbola with the given conditions.
a. $V_1(8, 2)$, $V_2(2, 2)$, and $F_2(0, 2)$
b. $F_1(-3, 5)$, $F_2(-3, -11)$, and $V_2(-3, -9)$
c. $C(-2, 6)$, $F_1(-6, 6)$, and $V_1(1, 6)$
d. $C(0, -4)$, $F_2(0, -10)$, and constant difference 10
e. $V_1(-1, 1)$, $F_1(-1, 4)$, and $C(-1, 2)$
f. $F_1(2, 1)$, $F_2(8, 1)$, and conjugate axis is 4 units long
g. $C(1, -4)$, $F_2(1, 1)$, and transverse axis is 8 units long

C 5. Determine an equation of the asymptotes to each hyperbola defined in exercise 4.

6. Find an equation of the hyperbola having the given conditions.
a. $F_1(-6, 4)$, $F_2(4, 4)$, and a vertex on the line $2x - y + 2 = 0$
b. $V_1(4, -10)$, $V_2(4, -2)$, and a focus on the line $x + y + 8 = 0$

7. Write an equation, in standard form, of each hyperbola. Then sketch the graph.
a. $9x^2 - 4y^2 - 72x - 16y + 92 = 0$
b. $9x^2 - y^2 - 54x + 6y + 81 = 0$

Review

1. Find the vertices, foci, and endpoints of the conjugate axis for the hyperbola defined by each equation.
   a. $\frac{x^2}{16} - \frac{y^2}{9} = 1$ b. $\frac{x^2}{49} - \frac{y^2}{81} = -1$ c. $4x^2 - 25y^2 = -100$

2. Find the equations of the asymptotes for each hyperbola.
   a. $\frac{x^2}{25} - \frac{y^2}{49} = -1$ b. $\frac{x^2}{16} - \frac{y^2}{4} = 1$ c. $\frac{25x^2}{49} - \frac{y^2}{4} = 1$

3. Find an equation of the hyperbola with centre at the origin and the given conditions.
   a. $V_1(0, 3)$ and $F_1(0, -7)$
   b. $F_1(4, 0)$ and conjugate axis is 6 units long
   c. $F_1(0, -5)$ and transverse axis is 6 units long
   d. $F(-6, 0)$ and constant difference 10

4. Find an equation of the hyperbola with centre at the origin, vertex $V_1(7, 0)$, and a focus on the line $2x - 9y + 18 = 0$.

5. Find an equation of a rectangular hyperbola with centre at the origin, focus $F_1(0, -12)$, and the length of the conjugate axis equal to the length of the transverse axis.

6. Find an equation of the hyperbola with centre at the origin, y-intercepts ± 4, and one focus $F_2(0, -5)$.

7. Find an equation of the hyperbola having centre at the origin and the given conditions.
   a. foci on the x-axis and the lengths of the transverse and conjugate axes are 8 units and 12 units, respectively
   b. the asymptotes are $x \pm 3y = 0$ and the hyperbola contains the point $A(-1, 2)$
   c. the asymptotes are $y = \pm \frac{2}{5}x$ and one vertex is $V_1(0, 4)$

8. Find the slopes of the asymptotes of a rectangular hyperbola with centre at the origin and transverse axis parallel to the y-axis.

9. Find the centre, vertices, foci, and endpoints of the conjugate axis of the hyperbola defined by each equation.
   a. $\frac{(x + 3)^2}{9} - \frac{(y + 1)^2}{16} = -1$ b. $\frac{(x - 2)^2}{64} - \frac{(y + 1)^2}{36} = 1$

10. Sketch the graph of each hyperbola defined in question 8.

11. Find an equation of the hyperbola with the given conditions.
    a. $V_1(-8, -3)$, $V_2(-2, -3)$ and $F_1(0, -3)$
    b. $F_1(-4, -9)$, $F_2(-4, -3)$ and $V_1(-4, -8)$

12. Write each equation in standard form.
    a. $25x^2 - 16y^2 - 50x - 96y + 281 = 0$
    b. $9x^2 - 4y^2 + 36x + 40y - 100 = 0$

8-5 Solving Systems of Equations by Graphing

Meteors, or shooting stars, are small particles of rock or metal that enter Earth's atmosphere. Sometimes, during its orbit around the Sun, Earth experiences meteor showers as it passes through bands of debris in space. In particular, Earth experiences two such meteor showers each year. The *orionides* occur in October and the *aquarides* occur in May as they follow an elliptical orbit around the Sun.

The diagram at the right shows Earth's orbit around the Sun as circular and the orbit of the band of debris as elliptical. The circle and the ellipse intersect in two points, showing that two intersecting curves can have more than one solution.

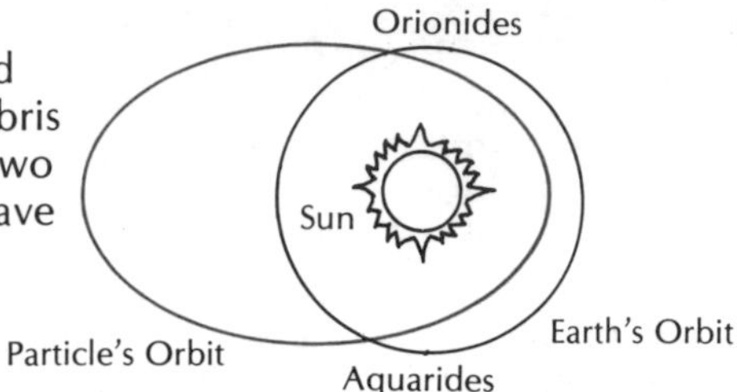

EXAMPLE 1: Find two integers such that the first integer is the square of the second and is also three more than twice the second.

Represent the situation algebraically by letting the first integer be y and the second integer be x.

$y = x^2$ — The first integer is the square of the second.

$y = 2x + 3$ — The first integer is three more than twice the second.

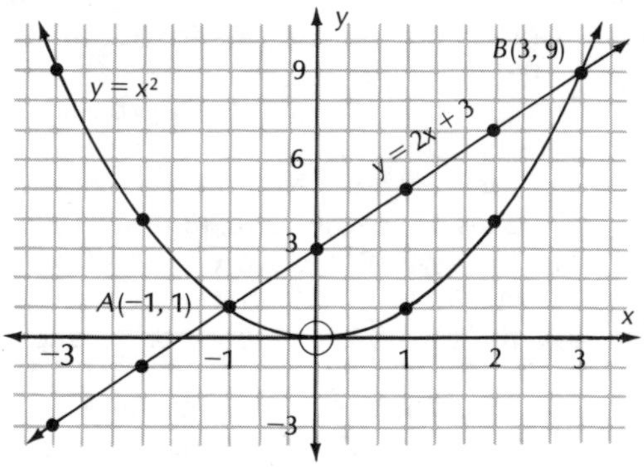

The two equations can then be graphed, with each representing all of the points satisfied by that particular equation. The graph is shown at the right.

The solution to the system of equations can be found using the coordinates of any points of intersection.

$(x, y) = (-1, 1)$
$(x, y) = (3, 9)$
The solutions are $(-1, 1)$ and $(3, 9)$.

The system of equations obtained in Example 1 is called a **linear-quadratic system** because it involves a linear equation and a quadratic equation. Such a system can have *one*, *two* or *no solutions* as the sketches that follow illustrate.

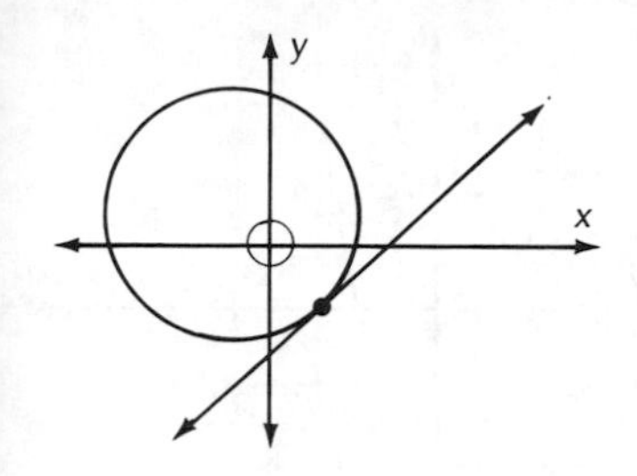

One Solution

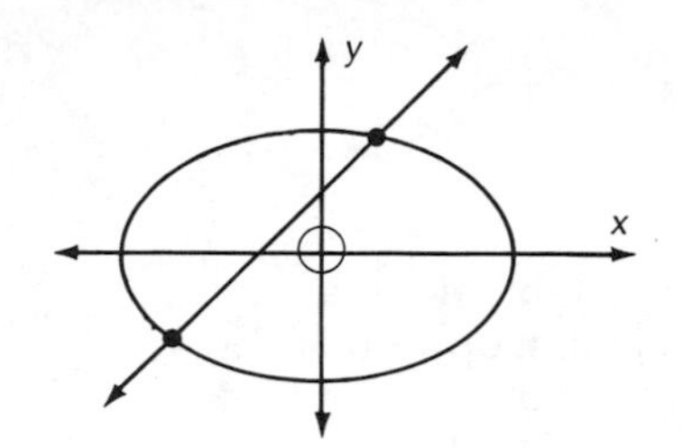

Two Solutions

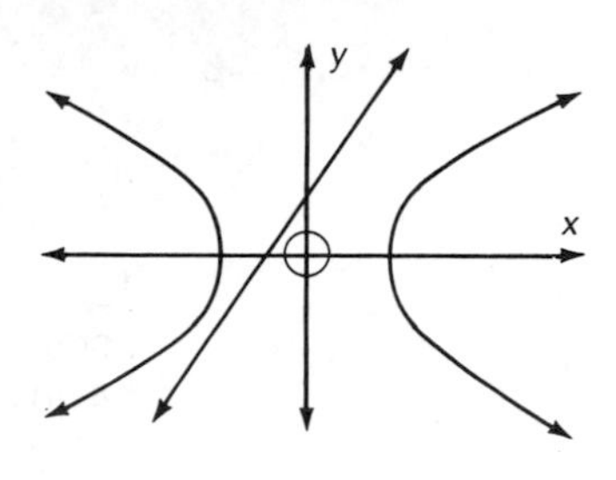

No Solution

For a **quadratic system**, or a system of two quadratic equations, there can be *one, two, three, four,* or *no solutions.*

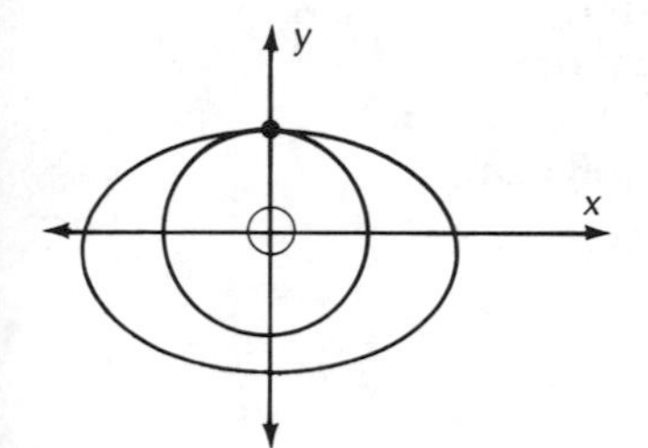

One Solution

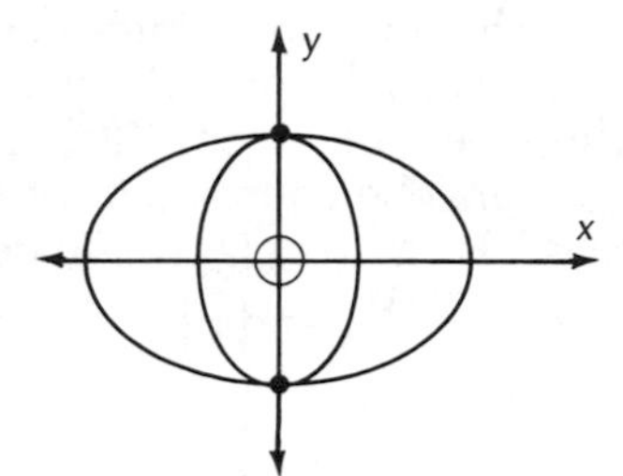

Two Solutions

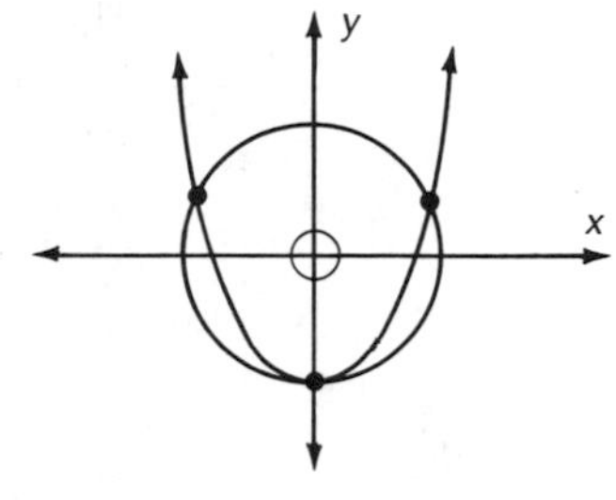

Three Solutions

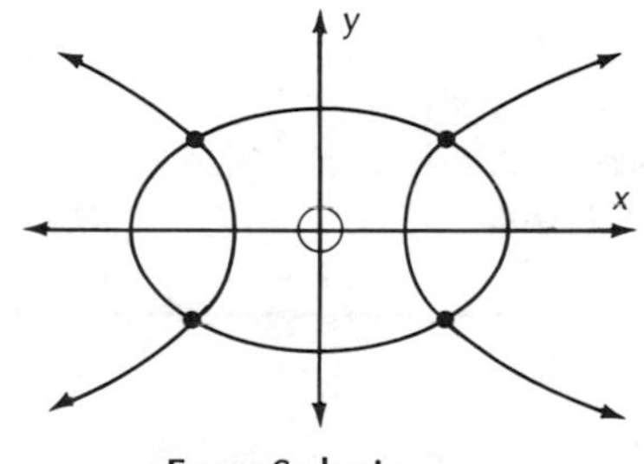

Four Solutions

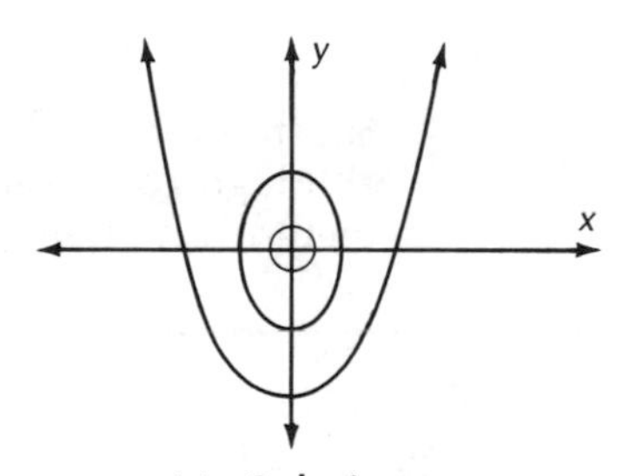

No Solution

Although one diagram has been shown to illustrate each possibility, the situations shown above are not unique.

EXAMPLE 2: Graph each system of equations and estimate the solution(s) to each.

a. $x^2 + y^2 = 25$
$x + 5 = 0$

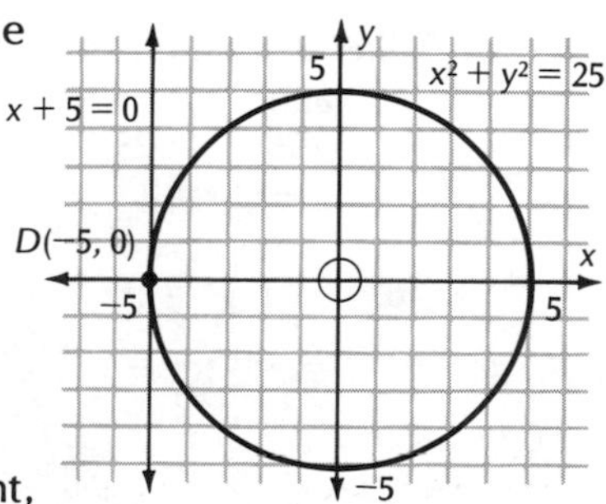

The first equation defines a circle with centre at the origin and radius 5. The second equation, $x = -5$, defines a line parallel to the y-axis.

There appears to be only one common point, $D(-5, 0)$. So the solution appears to be $x = -5$, $y = 0$. This solution can be verified by substitution.

b. 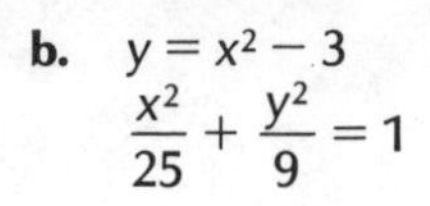

$$y = x^2 - 3$$
$$\frac{x^2}{25} + \frac{y^2}{9} = 1$$

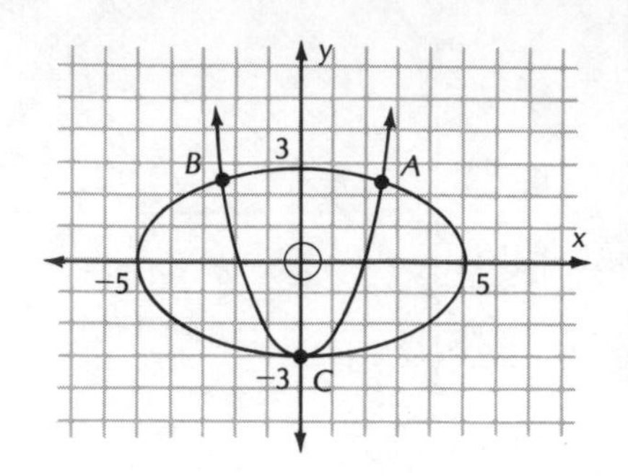

The first equation defines a parabola opening upward and having y-intercept −3. A table of values is used to determine other points. The second equation defines an ellipse with x-intercepts ±5 and y-intercepts ±3.

The graph shows three points of intersection and hence, there are three solutions. The two equations each have a y-intercept of −3. So, $C(0, -3)$ is one point of intersection. The coordinates of A and B can only be estimated. From the graph, the points A and B are estimated as $A\left(\frac{7}{3}, \frac{11}{4}\right)$ and $B\left(-\frac{7}{3}, \frac{11}{4}\right)$.

The solutions appear to be as follows.

$x = 0, y = -3 \qquad x = \frac{7}{3}, y = \frac{11}{4} \qquad x = -\frac{7}{3}, y = \frac{11}{4}$

Substitution would show that the last two solutions, although good estimates, are not correct. Algebraic methods are needed to find exact solutions.

EXERCISE 8-5

A **1.** Solve each system of equations by graphing.

a. $x + y = 12$, $x - y = 4$

b. $x - y + 4 = 0$, $x + y = 0$

c. $2x + y = 8$, $2x - y = 12$

d. $2x + 5y = 0$, $2y + 4 = 0$

2. Sketch each system of equations and state the number of solutions to each.

a. $x^2 + y^2 = 25$, $x - 2y = 0$

b. $y = x^2$, $y - 3 = 0$

c. $y = x^2 + 3$, $y = -x^2 - 3$

d. $x^2 + y^2 = 16$, $\frac{x^2}{25} + \frac{y^2}{16} = 1$

e. $y = -x^2 + 5$, $x^2 + y^2 = 25$

f. $x^2 + y^2 = 36$, $\frac{x^2}{9} - \frac{y^2}{25} = -1$

g. $\frac{x^2}{16} + \frac{y^2}{25} = 1$, $x - 5 = 0$

h. $\frac{x^2}{25} - \frac{y^2}{9} = 1$, $xy = 16$

i. $\frac{x^2}{9} - \frac{y^2}{36} = 1$, $2x - y = 0$

B **3.** Solve each system of equations by graphing.

a. $y = x^2 - 4$
$y = -x^2 + 4$

b. $xy = -36$
$x + y = 0$

c. $x^2 + y^2 = 36$
$\frac{x^2}{36} - \frac{y^2}{16} = 1$

d. $x = y^2 + 4$
$x^2 + y^2 = 16$

e. $x^2 + y^2 = 4$
$\frac{x^2}{16} + \frac{y^2}{25} = 1$

f. $x^2 + y^2 = 25$
$4x - 3y = 0$

g. $\frac{x^2}{49} + \frac{y^2}{16} = 1$
$\frac{x^2}{36} + \frac{y^2}{16} = 16$

h. $x^2 + y^2 = 25$
$xy = -12$

i. $\frac{x^2}{4} + \frac{y^2}{36} = 1$
$y = 3x^2 - 6$

4. Find two integers such that the sum of their squares is 25 and the second integer is five less than the square of the first.

5. Find two integers whose product is 12, given that the second integer is two more than twice the first integer.

6. Graph the given relations and estimate a solution to each system.

a. $xy = 6$
$x^2 - y^2 = 9$

b. $x^2 + y^2 = 25$
$x^2 - y^2 = 0$

c. $x^2 + y^2 = 25$
$y - 2x = 0$

C **7.** Factor each given quadratic relation to reveal two linear relations. Then graph the linear relations to determine which pairs are parallel and which intersect.

a. $(x - y)^2 - 16 = 0$

b. $36x^2 - (y + 3)^2 = 0$

c. $(x - 2y)^2 - 10(x - 2y) + 24 = 0$

d. $(5x - 7)^2 - y^2 = 0$

8. Graph each pair of relations on the same axes and solve for x and y.

a. $(x - y)^2 - 16 = 0$
$x + y = 0$

b. $36x^2 - (y + 3)^2 = 0$
$2x - y + 1 = 0$

c. $(x - 2y)^2 - 10(x - 2y) + 24 = 0$
$y = x - 3$

d. $(x + y)^2 - 25 = 0$
$x + y + 10 = 0$

9. Refer to the five diagrams of solutions to quadratic systems, shown in this lesson. Sketch as many other possibilities for each type of solution as you can.

8-6 Solving Linear-Quadratic Systems Algebraically

The length of a rectangular bungalow is 7 m longer than the width. Given that the floor area is 144 m², find the dimensions of the bungalow.

Let the width of the bungalow be x metres and the length be y metres.

$\therefore\ y = x + 7$ ① a linear equation

$xy = 144$ ② a quadratic equation

This system is a linear-quadratic system. An algebraic method can be used to find a solution.

From equation ①, $y = x + 7$.
Substitute for y in equation ②.

$$x(x + 7) = 144$$
$$x^2 + 7x - 144 = 0$$
$$(x + 16)(x - 9) = 0$$
$$\therefore x = -16 \text{ or } x = 9$$

The length and width of the bungalow must be positive.
Therefore, the solution is $x = 9$ and $y = 9 + 7$, or 16.

The dimensions of the bungalow are 9 m × 16 m.

EXAMPLE 1: Find the coordinates of the points of intersection of the graphs of $y - 3x = 0$ and $x^2 + y^2 = 70$.

$y - 3x = 0$ ①

$x^2 + y^2 = 70$ ②

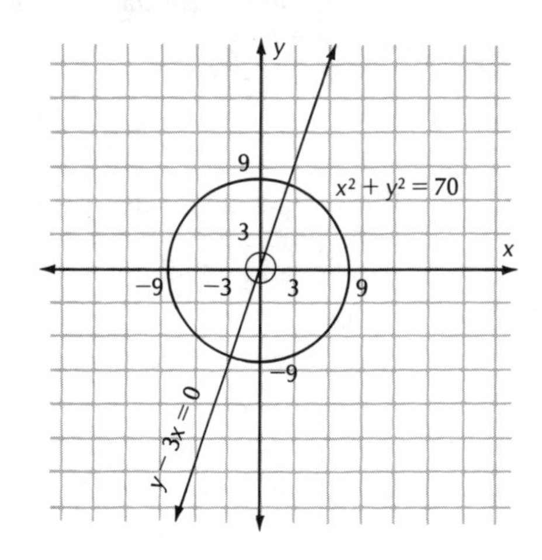

The first equation defines a straight line that contains the origin. So (0, 0) satisfies the equation.

The second equation defines a circle with radius $\sqrt{70}$ and centre on the origin.

So there are two points of intersection and, therefore, two solutions.

From ①, $y = 3x$.
Substitute for y in ②.

$$10x^2 = 70$$
$$x^2 = 7$$
$$x = \pm\sqrt{7}$$

Substitute in ①.

If $x = \sqrt{7}$, then $y - 3\sqrt{7} = 0$, or $y = 3\sqrt{7}$.

If $x = -\sqrt{7}$, then $y + 3\sqrt{7} = 0$, or $y = -3\sqrt{7}$.

The points of intersection are $(\sqrt{7}, 3\sqrt{7})$ and $(-\sqrt{7}, -3\sqrt{7})$.

EXAMPLE 2: Solve for x and y:
$$y - x + 5 = 0$$
$$x^2 + y^2 - 2x - 7 = 0.$$

$$y - x + 5 = 0 \quad ①$$
$$x^2 + y^2 - 2x - 7 = 0 \quad ②$$

The first equation defines a straight line with x-intercept 5 and y-intercept -5.

The second equation can be rewritten as $(x - 1)^2 + y^2 = 8$ to reveal that it defines a circle with centre $C(1, 0)$ and radius $\sqrt{8}$.

y
C
x
$\sqrt{8}$
-5

From ①, $y = x - 5$.
Substitute in ②.

$$x^2 + (x - 5)^2 - 2x - 7 = 0$$
$$x^2 + (x^2 - 10x + 25) - 2x - 7 = 0$$
$$2x^2 - 12x + 18 = 0$$
$$x^2 - 6x + 9 = 0$$
$$(x - 3)(x - 3) = 0$$
$$\therefore x = 3$$

If $x = 3$ then $y - 3 + 5 = 0$, or $y = -2$.
Thus, there is one point of intersection, $(3, -2)$.
Notice that here, the line is tangent to the circle.

EXAMPLE 3: **a.** Find any points of intersection for the graphs of $y - 2x = 0$ and $\frac{x^2}{16} - \frac{y^2}{25} = 1$.

$$y - 2x = 0 \quad ①$$
$$\frac{x^2}{16} - \frac{y^2}{25} = 1 \quad ②$$

From ①, $y = 2x$.
Substitute in ②.

$$\frac{x^2}{16} - \frac{4x^2}{25} = 1 \qquad y^2 = (2x)^2 = 4x^2$$
$$25x^2 - 64x^2 = 400$$
$$-39x^2 = 400$$
$$x^2 = -\frac{400}{39}$$

Since there is no real number, x, that satisfies this equation, there is no point of intersection for the line defined by $y - 2x = 0$ with the hyperbola defined by $\frac{x^2}{16} - \frac{y^2}{25} = 1$.

b. Graph $y - 2x = 0$ and $\frac{x^2}{16} - \frac{y^2}{25} = 1$ on the same set of axes to verify the solution to part **a.**

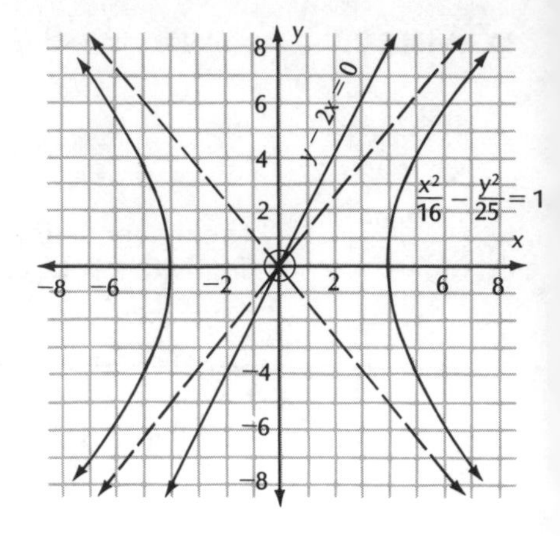

The first equation, $y - 2x = 0$, defines a line with slope $m = 2$ and y-intercept the origin.

The second equation, $\frac{x^2}{16} - \frac{y^2}{25} = 1$, defines a hyperbola with asymptotes $5x \pm 4y = 0$ and x-intercepts $+4$ and -4.

Since the line, $y - 2x = 0$, lies between the asymptotes of the hyperbola, intersecting them only at the origin, the line never intersects the hyperbola.

Therefore, there is no solution.

EXERCISE 8-6

A **1.** Find the coordinates of the points of intersection.

a. $x - 3 = 0$, $x^2 + y^2 = 36$ **b.** $y + 2 = 0$, $2x^2 + y^2 = 16$ **c.** $x + y = 0$, $xy = -12$

2. Solve for x and y.

a. $y - 2x = 0$, $xy = 8$ **b.** $y - 2 = 0$, $x^2 + 2y^2 = 16$ **c.** $x + 3 = 0$, $x^2 - y^2 = 0$

B **3.** Solve for x and y by graphing.

a. $y = x - 6$, $x^2 + y^2 = 26$ **b.** $2x^2 + y^2 = 18$, $y = x + 5$ **c.** $y = x - 2$, $y^2 = x - 2$

d. $x^2 - 2y^2 = 14$, $x = 2y - 2$ **e.** $y = x^2 - 4$, $2x + y + 5 = 0$ **f.** $x^2 - 4y^2 = 16$, $x + 2y = 0$

4. Solve for x and y.

a. $x^2 + y^2 + 2y - 3 = 0$, $y = x - 3$ **b.** $x^2 - 2y^2 + 2x + 5 = 0$, $x = y - 5$

c. $x^2 + 2y^2 - 2y = 21$, $y = 2x + 4$ **d.** $y = x^2 + 2x + 2$, $y = 4x + 1$

e. $xy + 2x - 16 = 0$, $x = y + 2$ **f.** $x^2 + y^2 - 3x = 10$, $x = 2y - 2$

5. A rectangular bungalow has a floor area of 128 m². If the perimeter is 48 m, find the dimensions of the bungalow.

6. Find two integers such that the second exceeds the first by two and twice the second exceeds the square of the first by one.

7. Two square gardens require 64 m of fencing to enclose them. If the total garden area is 130 m^2, find the dimensions of the gardens.

8. Two rectangular gardens each have a length 2 m longer than the width. The total garden area is 200 m^2 and the total perimeter is 80 m. Find the dimensions of the two gardens.

9. The hypotenuse of a right-angled triangle is 8 cm longer than the shorter side. If the perimeter is 30 cm, find the length of each side.

10. A lawn sprinkler sprays water in a circular region with a radius of 4 m. If it is placed 3 m from a fence, what length of fence will get wet?

11. The area of square $ABCD$ is 64 cm^2. Find the dimensions of squares A_1 and A_2, if the sum of their areas is 30 cm^2 less than the area of square $ABCD$.

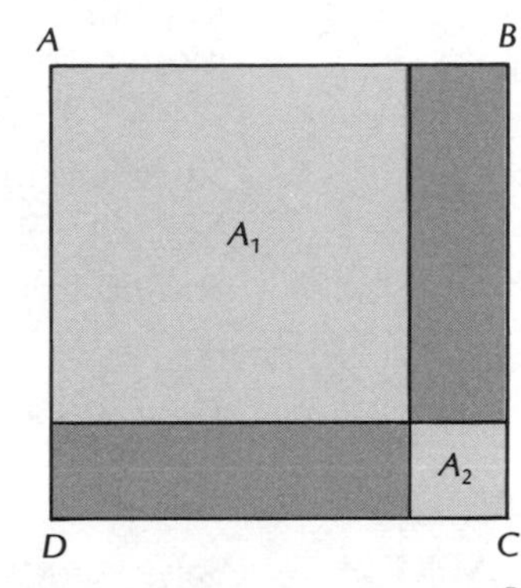

12. A rectangular plot of land $ABCD$, which is 20 m longer than it is wide, is to be fenced. $\overline{PQ}$ and $\overline{QR}$ are two partition fences so that $PQRD$ is a square region set aside for a warehouse. If the total length of fencing used is 480 m and the area of the square $PQRD$ is 4400 m^2 less than the area of the rectangle $ABCD$, find the dimensions of both the square and rectangular regions.

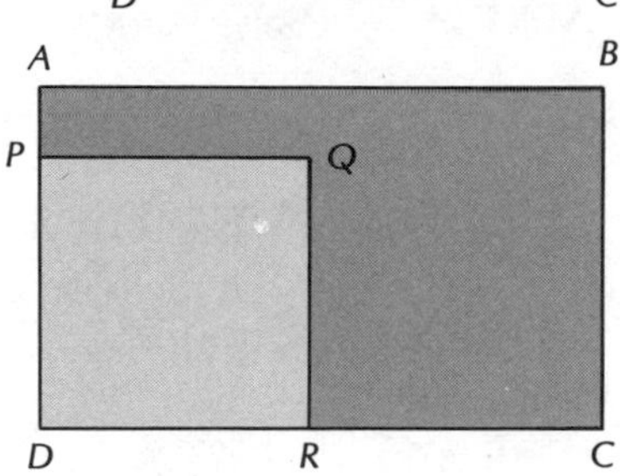

13. Find the coordinates of any points of intersection.

a. $x^2 + y^2 = 34$
$4x - y + 17 = 0$

b. $x^2 - 2x + 3y + 6 = 0$
$2x + 3y + 6 = 0$

c. $x^2 - y^2 + 2x - 3y - 11 = 0$
$2x - 3y - 3 = 0$

d. $xy = 36$
$4x - 3y + 6 = 0$

e. $4x^2 - 9y^2 = 144$
$2x - 3y + 12 = 0$

f. $y = x^2 + 3$
$2y = 5x + 3$

14. Solve algebraically.

a. $(x - y)^2 - 16 = 0$
$x + y = 0$

b. $36x^2 - (y + 3)^2 = 0$
$2x - y + 1 = 0$

c. $(x - 2y)^2 - 10(x - 2y) + 24 = 0$
$y = x - 3$

d. $(x + y)^2 - 25 = 0$
$x + y + 10 = 0$

8-7 Solving Quadratic Systems Algebraically

Algebraic methods used to solve linear-quadratic systems can also be used to solve quadratic systems.

EXAMPLE 1: Two square tapestries have a total surface area of 13 m². One tapestry is 5 m² larger than the other. Find the dimensions of each.

Let the width of one tapestry be x metres and the other be y metres.

Write equations that represent the given information.
$$x^2 + y^2 = 13 \quad ①$$
$$x^2 = y^2 + 5 \quad ②$$

Rewriting the system shows that it can be solved by elimination.
$$x^2 + y^2 = 13 \quad ①$$
$$x^2 - y^2 = 5 \quad ②$$
$$2x^2 = 18$$

Since length must be positive, $x = -3$ is an inadmissible root.
$$x^2 = 9$$
$$x = \pm 3$$

Substitute $x = 3$ in ①. $y = -2$ is an inadmissible root.
$$9 + y^2 = 13$$
$$y = \pm 2$$

Therefore, the dimensions of the tapestries are 2 m × 2 m and 3 m × 3 m.

EXAMPLE 2: Solve for x and y: $xy = -3$; $x^2 + y^2 = 10$.

Isolate y in the first equation.
$$y = \frac{-3}{x}$$

Substitute in the second equation.
$$x^2 + \frac{9}{x^2} = 10$$

Multiply by x^2 ($x \neq 0$).
$$x^4 + 9 = 10x^2$$

Solve for x.
$$x^4 - 10x^2 + 9 = 0$$
$$(x^2 - 9)(x^2 - 1) = 0$$
$$(x - 3)(x + 3)(x - 1)(x + 1) = 0$$
$$\therefore x = 3 \quad x = -3 \quad x = 1 \quad x = -1$$

Substitute for x in the first equation.
$$y = -1 \quad y = 1 \quad y = -3 \quad y = 3$$

Therefore, the solution is $(3, -1)$, $(-3, 1)$, $(1, -3)$, $(-1, 3)$.

EXERCISE 8-7

A 1. Find any points of intersection.

a. $x^2 + y^2 = 52$
$x^2 - y^2 = 20$

b. $9x^2 + 16y^2 = 144$
$9x^2 + 4y^2 = 36$

c. $y = x^2 - 4$
$y = x^2 + 4$

d. $y = x^2 - 8$
$y = -x^2 + 4$

e. $x^2 - 4y^2 = 4$
$4x^2 - y^2 = 16$

f. $4x^2 + y^2 = 50$
$x^2 - 2y^2 = 8$

B **2.** Solve for x and y.

a. $x^2 + y^2 = 25$
$y = x^2 - 5$

b. $xy = 15$
$x^2 + y^2 = 34$

c. $3x^2 + 2y^2 = 30$
$xy = 6$

d. $x^2 + y^2 = 20$
$y = x^2$

e. $x^2 - y^2 = -8$
$y = x^2 - 4$

f. $x = y^2 + 5$
$x = -y^2 + 13$

3. The hypotenuse of a right-angled triangle is $2\sqrt{5}$ cm long. If the area is 3 cm², find the length of the other two sides.

4. A square and a rectangular garden have equal widths. Given that the total surface area of the gardens is 234 m² and the rectangular garden is 72 m² larger than the square garden, find the dimensions of each garden.

5. Find two real numbers such that the sum of their squares is 36 and the difference of their squares is 4.

6. A backyard pool has an area of 50 m². If it were 1 m wider and 1 m shorter, the area would increase by 4 m². Find the original dimensions of the pool.

7. Mrs. Chamberlain bought some granola bars for $6.00 to hand out on Halloween. If each bar had cost 10¢ more, she would have received 3 fewer bars for $6.00. Find the original price of one granola bar.

8. On a return flight back east, an aircraft required 1 h less time to make a flight of 2600 km because its speed was 130 km/h faster, due to a jet stream. What was the speed of the return trip?

9. Keiji invested some money and received $72 simple interest in one year. Takashi invested $100 more than Keiji, but at an interest rate of 1% less than Keiji and still received $72 interest in one year. What amount did each invest?

10. A rectangular piece of sheet metal has an area of 4800 cm². Squares with sides 5 cm long are cut from the corners. The edges are then folded up to form a shallow pan with volume 17 500 cm³. Find the original dimensions of the sheet metal.

C **11.** Find the points of intersection for each system.

a. $x^2 - y^2 = 36$
$x^2 + y^2 + 6x = 0$

b. $y = (x - 3)^2 - 5$
$(x - 3)^2 + y^2 = 25$

c. $x^2 - 2y = 6$
$x^2 + y^2 - 4y = 21$

d. $y^2 - x + 4y + 9 = 0$
$y^2 + x + 4y - 9 = 0$

e. $(x - 3)y = 15$
$(x - 3)^2 + y^2 = 34$

f. $x^2 + y^2 = 34$
$x^2 + y^2 + 12y + 2 = 0$

g. $x^2 + y^2 + 4x = 12$
$4x^2 + 9y^2 + 16x = 128$

h. $y = (x - 4)^2$
$y^2 = 8(x - 4)$

12. Solve for x and y.

a. $(x + y)^2 - 9 = 0$
$x^2 + y^2 = 9$

b. $9x^2 - (y - 9)^2 = 0$
$y = -x^2 + 9$

Review

1. Solve for x and y.

   a. $2x + 5y + 4 = 0$
   $x + 3y + 1 = 0$

   b. $6x - 4y = 0$
   $4x + 8y = 8$

   c. $\frac{1}{3}x - \frac{1}{2}y = -4$
   $\frac{2}{3}x + \frac{1}{4}y = -3$

   d. $xy = -16$
   $x^2 + y^2 = 32$

   e. $2y = x^2 + 2$
   $y = x^2 - 4$

   f. $x^2 + y^2 = 100$
   $y^2 - 2x = 20$

2. First write each equation in the form $(x + a)(y + b) = k$. Then, sketch the hyperbola defined by each equation and state the equations of its asymptotes.

   a. $(x - 4)(y + 3) = 12$

   b. $x + 6 = \dfrac{3}{y + 4}$

   c. $y = \dfrac{-5}{x + 1}$

4. Determine the equations of the asymptotes for the hyperbola defined by each equation.

   a. $x^2 - y^2 = 16$

   b. $y^2 - 25x^2 = 64$

   c. $4x^2 - 16y^2 = 100$

5. Find an equation of the image of the hyperbola defined by $x^2 - y^2 = 1$ under the given stretch.

   a. $(x, y) \rightarrow (3x, 4y)$

   b. $(x, y) \rightarrow (2x, 5y)$

   c. $(x, y) \rightarrow \left(\frac{x}{2}, \frac{y}{4}\right)$

6. Find an equation of the hyperbola with foci $F_1(6, 0)$ and $F_2(-6, 0)$ if one vertex is on the line $2x - 5y - 10 = 0$.

7. Find an equation of the hyperbola with the given conditions.

   a. Foci are $F_2(0, -5)$, $F_1(0, 5)$; constant difference is 6.

   b. Foci are $F_1(3, 0)$, $F_2(-3, 0)$; constant difference is 4.

   c. Vertices are $V_1(-3, 0)$, $V_2(3, 0)$; focus is $F_1(-7, 0)$.

8. Determine the centre, vertices, foci, and endpoints of the conjugate axis for the hyperbola defined by each equation.

   a. $\dfrac{x^2}{16} - \dfrac{y^2}{9} = 1$

   b. $\dfrac{x^2}{49} - \dfrac{y^2}{81} = -1$

   c. $4x^2 - 25y^2 = -100$

   d. $\dfrac{(x + 1)^2}{4} - \dfrac{(y + 2)^2}{16} = 1$

   e. $\dfrac{(x + 3)^2}{64} - \dfrac{(y - 2)^2}{25} = 1$

   f. $\dfrac{(x + 3)^2}{36} - \dfrac{(y + 1)^2}{16} = -1$

9. Determine the asymptotes for each hyperbola defined in question 7.

10. Solve each system by graphing.

a. $3x + 4y = 0$
$x - 2y = -10$

b. $2x - y + 8 = 0$
$2x + y - 4 = 0$

c. $x^2 + y^2 = 25$
$x - y - 1 = 0$

d. $2x + y - 1 = 0$
$y = x^2 - 2$

e. $x^2 + y^2 = 36$
$9x^2 + 16y^2 = 144$

f. $xy = 20$
$x^2 - y^2 = 9$

11. Find the coordinates of any points of intersection.

a. $x - 2 = 0$
$x^2 + y^2 = 24$

b. $y + x^2 + 4 = 0$
$y + 6 = 0$

c. $x^2 + y^2 = 39$
$3x - 2y = 0$

d. $y = x^2 + 4$
$6x - y - 5 = 0$

e. $4x^2 - y^2 = -16$
$x + y = 0$

f. $xy = -20$
$2x + y - 6 = 0$

g. $y^2 + x - 5 = 0$
$x^2 + y^2 = 25$

h. $x^2 + y^2 = 40$
$x^2 - y^2 = 8$

i. $x^2 + y^2 = 16$
$x^2 + y + 4 = 0$

j. $9x^2 - 25y^2 = -225$
$x^2 + y^2 = 9$

k. $x^2 + y^2 = 49$
$x^2 + 4y^2 = 64$

l. $x = y^2 + 3$
$x = -y^2 + 11$

m. $2x^2 - y^2 - 2y - 5 = 0$
$x - y - 5 = 0$

n. $xy + 2y - 16 = 0$
$y - x - 2 = 0$

o. $2x^2 + 3y^2 = 30$
$xy = -6$

p. $y^2 - 2x + 2 = 0$
$y^2 - x - 4 = 0$

q. $x^2 + 4y^2 = 50$
$2x^2 - y^2 + 8 = 0$

r. $(y - 3)x = 15$
$(y - 3)^2 + x^2 = 34$

12. A picture frame has a perimeter of 56 cm and an area of 195 cm^2. Find the dimensions of the frame.

13. Two square gardens have dimensions such that the width of one is $\frac{2}{3}$ as long as the other. If the total garden area is 208 m^2, find the dimensions of each garden.

14. A right-angled triangle with hypotenuse 10 cm has an area of 20 cm^2. Find the dimensions of the triangle.

15. A baseball coach was given $320 to purchase baseballs. She found that this year, since the price of a ball increased by one dollar, she was able to purchase 16 fewer balls than last year. How many baseballs did she buy last year? this year?

16. Find two real numbers such that the sum of their squares is 25 and their product is -10.

17. Find two integers such that the sum of their squares is 25 and the square of the first number, decreased by 10, is twice the second number.

18. A jet can complete a 2400 km trip in 5 h less time than a light aircraft flying at a speed 500 km/h slower than the jet. Find the speed of each aircraft.

19. Two circles have a total surface area of 130π cm^2. If the area of the larger circle exceeds that of the smaller circle by 32π cm^2, find the radius of each circle.

Test Unit 8

1. $(P + 3)$ varies inversely as $(N - 2)$.

   a. If $P = 5$ when $N = 5$, find P when $N = 6$.
   b. If $P = 0$ when $N = 18$, find N when $P = 3$.

2. For question 1:
   a. sketch the graph of each inverse variation.
   b. state the equations of the asymptotes.

3. Find an equation of the hyperbola with asymptotes $x \pm 3y = 0$ and containing the point $A(3, 2)$. Sketch the hyperbola.

4. Find an equation of the hyperbola with asymptotes $2x \pm 5y = 0$, if the y-intercepts are ± 2.

5. Find the vertices, foci, length of the transverse and conjugate axes, and the constant difference for the hyperbola defined by each equation.
   a. $64x^2 - 4y^2 = 64$ b. $25x^2 - 9y^2 = -225$ c. $9x^2 - 4y^2 = 1$

6. Find an equation of the hyperbola with centre at the origin and the given conditions.
   a. $V(0, \pm 6)$ and $F(0, \pm 7)$
   b. $F(\pm 3, 0)$ and the transverse axis is 2 units long
   c. $V(\pm 4, 0)$ and containing the point $A(8, 2\sqrt{3})$
   d. $V(0, \pm 3)$ and the distance between the foci is 12 units

7. Find an equation of the hyperbola with the given conditions.

   a. $V_2(-8, 0)$, $F_2(-10, 0)$ and $V_1(-2, 0)$
   b. $V_1(-3, 5)$, $F_1(-3, 6)$ and $F_2(-3, -8)$

8. Find the centre, vertices, foci, and endpoints of the conjugate axis for the hyperbola defined by each equation.
   a. $\dfrac{(x - 5)^2}{9} - \dfrac{(y + 2)^2}{16} = 1$ b. $\dfrac{(x - 1)^2}{25} - \dfrac{(y + 3)^2}{144} = -1$

9. Sketch each hyperbola defined in question 8.

10. Solve each system by graphing.

    a. $x = y^2 + 3$, $\dfrac{x^2}{9} + \dfrac{y^2}{25} = 1$ b. $\dfrac{x^2}{25} - \dfrac{y^2}{4} = -1$, $2x + 5y = 0$ c. $x^2 + y^2 = 18$, $x - y = 0$

11. Solve each system algebraically.
    a. $y = x + 6$, $x^2 + y^2 = 26$ b. $x = y^2 - 4$, $x = -2y - 5$ c. $y = x + 2$, $xy + 2y = 16$

    d. $x^2 + y^2 = 49$, $4x^2 + y^2 = 64$ e. $x^2 + y^2 = 20$, $x = y^2$ f. $x^2 + y^2 = 100$, $x^2 - 2y = 20$

12. Fiona invests some money and receives \$48 in simple interest in one year. Connie invests \$200 more, but at an interest rate 2% less than Fiona does and still receives \$48 in simple interest. What amount did each invest?

Cumulative Review

1. Find the solution set of the inequality $|3x - 2| \geq 11$ and graph the solution on a number line.

2. Find an equation of an exponential function defined by $f(x) = a(b^x)$, given that $b = \frac{3}{4}$ and $f(1) = 3$.

3. A printing press depreciates 12% in value each year. Find the depreciated value of a $250 000 machine after 6 a.

4. Solve: $\log_7 x = \log_7 36 - \log_7 9$.

5. If $x + 4$ is a factor of $x^3 + 5x^2 + 2x - 8$, find the remaining factors.

6. The point $(-6, 8)$ is on the terminal ray of an angle θ in standard position.
   a. Find $\sin\theta$ and $\cos\theta$.
   b. Find θ to the nearest tenth degree.

7. Find the value of each variable given in the triangle at the right.

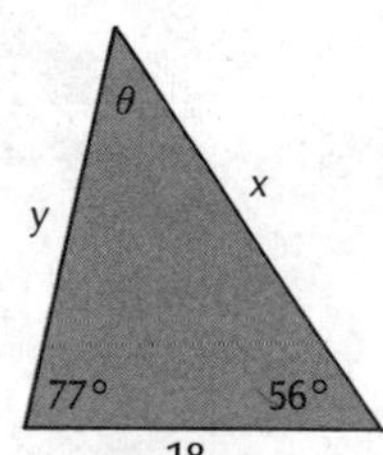

8. Convert the following to radian measure.
   a. 90° **b.** 315° **c.** 300° **d.** −72°

9. Convert the following to degree measure.
   a. $\frac{\pi}{3}$ rad **b.** $\frac{\pi}{4}$ rad **c.** $-\frac{3\pi}{5}$ rad **d.** $-\frac{7\pi}{12}$ rad

10. A function is defined by $y = 3\sin\frac{x}{3}$.
    a. Sketch the graph of the function.
    b. Find the period and amplitude of the function.

11. Express $\dfrac{1 + \tan^2 x}{\csc x \sec x}$ in terms of $\sin x$.

12. Find the centre and radius of the circle defined by $x^2 + y^2 - 4x - 6y - 3 = 0$.

9 Statistics

9-1 Measures of Central Tendency

The members of the Lions' baseball team scored the number of home runs as shown at the right during the season.

Home Runs by Individual Players
0, 1, 3, 1, 2, 4, 2, 1, 1, 0, 5, 1, 0, 1, 2

Statistics deals with the collection, analysis, interpretation, and presentation of data, like that in the Home Run chart.

One way of analysing data is to find *one* number that represents *all* of the numbers. This one number should be representative of a set of data by being a central value of the data.

Three different **measures of central tendency** are the *mean, median,* and *mode.*

1. The **mean**, called the "average" in everyday language and called the **arithmetic mean** by statisticians, is the sum of all the data values, divided by the number of values. The mean is represented by $\overline{x}$ (read "x bar").

$\bar{x} = \frac{\Sigma x}{n}$, where Σx means the sum of all the data and n is the total number of data points.

For the Home Run chart,

$$\bar{x} = \frac{0+1+3+1+2+4+2+1+1+0+5+1+0+1+2}{15}$$ Sum of data
There are 15 pieces of data.

$$= \frac{24}{15}$$
$$= 1.6$$

The mean number of home runs is 1.6.

The **frequency** is the number of times a value occurs in a set of data.

Organizing data in a table called a **frequency distribution** can make it easier to calculate the mean. The data for home runs are arranged in the frequency distribution shown at the right.

The total in the fx column is represented by Σfx, which is the total number of home runs scored.

The mean is $\bar{x} = \frac{\Sigma fx}{n} = \frac{24}{15}$, or 1.6.

Number of Home Runs x	Frequency f	Subtotal fx
0	3	0
1	6	6
2	3	6
3	1	3
4	1	4
5	1	5
Totals	$n = 15$	$\Sigma fx = 24$

2. The **mode** is the value that occurs most frequently.

   The mode of the home run results is 1 since it is the value with the highest frequency.
   Notice that if every number occurs only once, there is no mode. There might also be more than one mode if two or more values have the highest frequency.

3. The **median** is the value of the middle number when the data are arranged in numerical order.

   Since there are 15 players on the team, the middle value occurs at the eighth position.

   ↓
   0, 0, 0, 1, 1, 1, 1, 1, 1, 2, 2, 2, 3, 4, 5

   By adding another column to the frequency distribution, it can be easier to find the median. Since the median is in the eighth position, when the **cumulative frequency** is 8, $x = 1$.
   Notice that if there is an even number of data points, there will be two middle values. To find the median, find the mean of the two middle values.

Number of Home Runs x	Frequency f	Cumulative Frequency
0	3	3
1	6	9
2	3	12
3	1	13
4	1	14
5	1	15

EXAMPLE 1: The Leacock High School statistics class took a survey of Grade 2 students. They recorded the number of hours per week that the students spent watching television. Because of the large number of results, they recorded the results into groups of the same interval size, where each interval is 3 h.

The Number of Hours Per Week Spent Watching Television By Grade Two Students

Number of Hours	Tally	Frequency f	Cumulative Frequency	Midpoint of Interval (x)	Subtotal fx
0–2	II	2	2	1	2
3–5	IIII	4	6	4	16
6–8	~~IIII~~ III	8	14	7	56
9–11	IIII	4	18	10	40
12–14	~~IIII~~ ~~IIII~~	10	28	13	130
15–17	~~IIII~~ ~~IIII~~ II	12	40	16	192
18–20	~~IIII~~ III	8	48	19	152
21–23	~~IIII~~ ~~IIII~~ IIII	14	62	22	308
24–26	~~IIII~~ ~~IIII~~	10	72	25	250
27–29	~~IIII~~ III	8	80	28	224
		$n = 80$			$\Sigma fx = 1370$

Find the following.

a. mean **b.** median **c.** mode

Since the actual results are not given, the mean, median, and mode can only be estimated by using the midpoint of the interval.

a. $x = \frac{\Sigma fx}{n} = \frac{1370}{80}$, or 17.125

The *estimate* of the mean is 17.125 h.

b. The median occurs at the 40th and 41st positions if the data are ranked in order. From the Cumulative Frequency column, the 40th position occurs in the interval 15–17 and the 41st position occurs in the interval 18–20. You can *estimate* the median by averaging the midpoint of the two intervals.

Thus, the estimate of the median is $\frac{16 + 19}{2}$, or 17.5 h.

c. Since the interval 21–23 has the highest frequency, the mode is estimated as 22 h.

EXAMPLE 2: A student's grades in the laboratory, tests, and examination parts of a physics course were 78, 62, and 71, respectively. If the test is worth three times as much as the laboratory and the exam is worth six times as much as the laboratory, what is the student's average?

Because each part of the course is worth a different amount, each part is assigned a **weight**. The average is called the **weighted mean**, represented by $\overline{x}_w$.

Student's Grades x	Weight w	Subtotal xw
78	1	78
62	3	186
71	6	426
	$\Sigma w = 10$	$\Sigma xw = 690$

$$\overline{x}_w = \frac{\Sigma xw}{\Sigma w} = \frac{690}{10} = 69$$

The student's weighted mean grade is 69.

EXAMPLE 3: The T.O.Y.S. Corporation recorded the sales made by each of their salespersons during the year. The record for their top salesperson is shown. By using a *moving average*, seasonal or irregular patterns are down-played and the trends are easier to see. Find a three-month moving average for this person.

Month	Sales in Millions of $	3-Month Moving Average
Jan.	0.5	
Feb.	2.3	
Mar.	5.8	2.9
Apr.	3.0	3.7
May	7.9	5.6
June	8.9	6.6
July	9.8	8.9
Aug.	10.6	9.8
Sept.	5.4	8.6
Oct.	3.6	6.5
Nov.	2.1	3.7
Dec.	2.0	2.6

Find the mean for every three months.

To find the first moving average, find the mean for January, February, and March.

$$\overline{x} = \frac{0.5 + 2.3 + 5.8}{3} \doteq 2.9$$

The second moving average is found by calculating the mean for February, March, and April.

$$\overline{x} = \frac{2.3 + 5.8 + 3.0}{3} = 3.7$$

The salesperson's vacation in April lowered her sales that month but the effect is down-played in the moving average.

EXAMPLE 4: On the Lions' baseball team, what percentage of the players scored less than three home runs?

Home Runs by Individual Players
0, 1, 3, 1, 2,
4, 2, 1, 1, 0,
5, 1, 0, 1, 2

Since 12 players scored fewer than three home runs, then $\frac{12}{15} \times 100$, or 80% of the players scored fewer than 3 home runs.

Another way of expressing the result in Example 4 is to use **percentiles**, which divide data into 100 equal parts, with each part representing one percent of all values. Thus, the player with three home runs has a **percentile ranking** of 80. A person in the 80th percentile scored better than 80% of the players on the team.

EXERCISE 9-1

A **1.** **a.** For the 1987 Blue Jays' baseball team, find each statistic.

i. the mean number of runs
ii. the median number of runs
iii. the mean number of hits
iv. the median number of hits

b. Why is the mode not a good measure of central tendency to use for either hits or runs?

c. What is Barfield's percentile ranking for the number of runs?

d. What is Upshaw's percentile ranking for the number of hits?

Player	Runs	Hits
Thornton	5	1
Fernandez	90	186
Mulliniks	37	103
Bell	111	188
Moseby	106	167
Leach	26	55
Whitt	57	120
Fielder	30	47
Barfield	89	155
Lee	14	31
Beniquez	20	64
McGriff	58	73
Upshaw	68	125
Liriano	29	38
Gruber	50	80
Moore	15	23
Iorg	35	65
Sharperson	4	20
Ducey	12	9
DeWillis	2	3
Myers	1	1

2. Tom and Corinna flipped open a 450 page book and recorded the page number. They repeated this procedure 100 times. The results are shown in the given table.

Page Numbers	Frequency (f)
1–50	13
51–100	10
101–150	5
151–200	14
201–250	13
251–300	15
301–350	9
351–400	10
401–450	11

a. Make a table with the five columns indicated below.

(1) Page Numbers
(2) Frequency, (f)
(3) Cumulative Frequency
(4) Midpoint of the Interval, (x)
(5) Subtotal, (fx)

Include totals for columns (2) and (5).

b. Estimate the mean, median, and mode for this experiment.

B **3.** Fred's statistics teacher did not record one of his test marks. The teacher knows that the class mean for that test is 67.6. There are 15 students in the class and the other students received marks of 92, 37, 57, 88, 78, 68, 63, 58, 71, 83, 42, 51, 62, 85.

a. What is Fred's score?
b. What is the class median?
c. What is Fred's percentile rank?

4. Three companies, each employing five part-time students, pay annual salaries as indicated in the table at the right.
   a. For each company, find the following.
      i. the mean of the annual salaries
      ii. the median of the annual salaries
      iii. the mode of the annual salaries
   b. If each company was to advertise for new student employees, what measure of central tendency would each company probably use?

Company A	Company B	Company C
$1750	$900	$1200
$1000	$1200	$1250
$1200	$1200	$1300
$1000	$1100	$1000
$1050	$1050	$1000

5. A freight elevator is designed to carry a maximum load of 2000 kg. If it is loaded with 13 parcels that average 113.3 kg each, and 9 parcels that average 59.2 kg each, would the elevator be in danger of being overloaded?

6. In a mathematics class, the final exam is worth five times as much as a test and a test is worth three times as much as a quiz. A student received quiz marks of 70, 62, and 83, test marks of 79, 78, 82, 85, and 75, and a final exam mark of 73. Find the student's class average.

7. A restaurant owner keeps track of the number of hamburgers sold every week in his restaurant. The results are shown at the right. Find all of the four-week moving averages for the number of hamburger sales.

Week	Number of Hamburgers Sold
1	150
2	200
3	220
4	210
5	250
6	190
7	300
8	250
9	220
10	230

8. The results of 5 students out of 5000 who wrote a college entrance examination are given in the table below.

Name	Score on Exam	Percentile Rank
Husein	40	48
Sabina	50	63
Jonathan	60	72
Nicole	70	81
Jenny	80	92

   a. What percentage of the students scored as well as or higher than Sabina?
   b. What percentage of the students scored between 69 and 50, inclusive, on the exam?
   c. How many students received a score less than 70?
   d. How many students' scores were less than Jenny's?

9-2 Measures of Variation

While measures of central tendency are useful in analysing a distribution, sometimes only locating a central value may not be sufficient for analysis. It is sometimes useful to analyse how much the data varies.

Three cookie manufacturing companies claim to have an average of 15 chocolate chips per cookie. Tamir decided to test the manufacturers' claim by buying 5 cookies from each company and counting the number of chocolate chips in each cookie. He noticed that the mean for each company's cookies is 15 chocolate chips, as claimed, but the number of chocolate chips in each cookie varies from company to company.

	Company A	Company B	Company C
	15	13	3
	15	14	17
	15	15	17
	15	16	18
	15	17	20
Total	75	75	75

The *spread* of these distributions, or how much the data varies from a central value, can be analysed by considering three *measures of variation*.

1. Range

The **range** is the *difference* between the largest value and the smallest value.

Company A: $15 - 15 = 0$
Company B: $17 - 13 = 4$
Company C: $20 - 3 = 17$

The range is the simplest measure of variation but it is rarely used since *extreme values* in the distribution allow the range to become very large.

2. Deviation and Mean Deviation

Another way of looking at the spread of the data is to measure how much the amount of chocolate chips in each cookie deviates from the mean. Since the spread of the data is being measured, it is not important if a measurement is less than or greater than the mean. What is important is the *distance* from the mean. This can be determined by finding the *absolute value* of the deviation. By finding the average of the absolute values of the deviations, a measurement of the dispersion about the mean can be obtained.

This measurement is called the **mean deviation,** $\overline{M}$.

$$\overline{M} = \frac{\Sigma |d|}{n}$$

The distance from the mean is given as $d = x - \overline{x}$.

Company A			Company B			Company C		
x	d	$\|d\|$	x	d	$\|d\|$	x	d	$\|d\|$
15	0	0	13	−2	2	3	−12	12
15	0	0	14	−1	1	17	2	2
15	0	0	15	0	0	17	2	2
15	0	0	16	1	1	18	3	3
15	0	0	17	2	2	20	5	5
		$\Sigma \|d\| = 0$			$\Sigma \|d\| = 6$			$\Sigma \|d\| = 24$

The mean deviation for each company is given as follows.

Company A: $\overline{M} = \frac{0}{5}$ $= 0$

Company B: $\overline{M} = \frac{6}{5}$ $= 1.2$

Company C: $\overline{M} = \frac{24}{5}$ $= 4.8$

$n = 5$

Compared to the range, the mean deviation gives a more accurate indication of the spread of the data. Company C had an extreme range because one cookie had only 3 chocolate chips. This effect is down-played when the mean deviation is used.

3. Standard Deviation

The most commonly used measure of variation is the **standard deviation**.

Instead of finding the absolute value of the deviations, you determine the square of each deviation, which automatically makes each number positive. Then find the square root of the average of the squared deviations.

This measurement is the standard deviation, s.

$$s = \sqrt{\frac{\Sigma d^2}{n}}$$

$d = x - \overline{x}$

Company A			Company B			Company C		
x	d	d^2	x	d	d^2	x	d	d^2
15	0	0	13	−2	4	3	−12	144
15	0	0	14	−1	1	17	2	4
15	0	0	15	0	0	17	2	4
15	0	0	16	1	1	18	3	9
15	0	0	17	2	4	20	5	25
		$\Sigma d^2 = 0$			$\Sigma d^2 = 10$			$\Sigma d^2 = 186$

Notice that $m = 5$.

The standard deviation for each company is given as follows.

Company A: $s = \sqrt{\frac{0}{5}}$ $= 0$

Company B: $s = \sqrt{\frac{10}{5}}$ $= \sqrt{2}$ $\doteq 1.414$

Company C: $s = \sqrt{\frac{186}{5}}$ $= \sqrt{37.2}$ $\doteq 6.1$

The extreme value of 3 chocolate chips causes Company C to have the largest standard deviation but this extreme is down-played compared to the range.

As expected, Company A has a standard deviation value of zero since all of their cookies contained the mean number of chocolate chips.

Company B's data are clustered about the mean, and so Company B has a standard deviation that lies between Company A's and Company C's.

EXAMPLE 1: After receiving complaints about broken cookies, the quality control manager of More Chips Cookies selected one hundred boxes of More Chips cookies at random from local grocery stores. She opened each box and counted the number of broken cookies. The results are shown at the right. Determine a reasonable conclusion for the mean number of broken cookies per box and the standard deviation.

Number of Broken Cookies	Frequency f
0	1
1	4
2	10
3	12
4	14
5	15
6	13
7	12
8	11
9	6
10	2

Organize the data into a frequency distribution table. The formulas for mean deviation and standard deviation can then be changed to take the frequency into account.

$$\overline{M} = \frac{\Sigma f\,|d|}{n} \qquad s = \sqrt{\frac{\Sigma f d^2}{n}}$$

Adding some columns to the frequency distribution table makes these calculations easier.

Number of Broken Cookies	Frequency	Subtotal	Deviation				
x	f	fx	d	$\|d\|$	$f\|d\|$	d^2	fd^2
0	1	0	−5.15	5.15	5.15	26.52	26.5
1	4	4	−4.15	4.15	16.6	17.22	68.8
2	10	20	−3.15	3.15	31.5	9.92	99.2
3	12	36	−2.15	2.15	25.8	4.62	55.4
4	14	56	−1.15	1.15	16.1	1.32	18.4
5	15	75	−0.15	0.15	2.25	0.02	0.3
6	13	78	0.85	0.85	11.05	0.72	9.3
7	12	84	1.85	1.85	22.2	3.42	41.0
8	11	88	2.85	2.85	31.35	8.12	89.3
9	6	54	3.85	3.85	23.1	14.82	88.9
10	2	20	4.85	4.85	9.7	23.52	47.0
Totals	100	515			194.8		544.5

Mean: $\overline{x} = \frac{\Sigma fx}{n} = \frac{515}{100} = 5.15$

Range: $10 - 0 = 10$

Mean Deviation: $\overline{M} = \frac{\Sigma f\,|d|}{n} = \frac{194.8}{100} = 1.948$

Standard Deviation: $s = \sqrt{\frac{\Sigma fd^2}{n}} = \sqrt{\frac{544.5}{100}} \doteq 2.33$

The quality control manager of More Chips Cookie may conclude that each box of cookies contains an average of 5.15 broken cookies per box, with a standard deviation of 2.33 cookies.

EXAMPLE 2: For Example 1, what percent of the values lie between plus or minus one standard deviation from the mean?

$x = 5.15 \qquad x + s = 5.15 + 2.33 = 7.48$
$s = 2.33 \qquad x - s = 5.15 - 2.33 = 2.82$

Since the data are given in whole numbers, the number of boxes that contained between 3 and 7 broken cookies (the integer values between 2.82 and 7.48) must be calculated.

There were 12 + 14 + 15 + 13 + 12, or 66 boxes of broken cookies.

Therefore, $\frac{66}{100}$, or 66% of the boxes lie within plus or minus one standard deviation of the mean.

EXAMPLE 3: Each box of More Chips Cookies should have a mass of 300 g. Everyday, a sample of 10 boxes is checked. If the standard deviation exceeds 5.7 g, production must stop to check the machinery. Today's sample masses are shown at the right. Will production be stopped?

Number of grams
305, 317, 297, 301, 287 295, 303, 291, 306, 302

Solution:

x	d	d^2
305	4.6	21.16
317	16.6	275.56
297	−3.4	11.56
301	0.6	0.36
287	−13.4	179.56
295	−5.4	29.16
303	2.6	6.76
291	−9.4	88.36
306	5.6	31.36
302	1.6	2.56
3004		646.4

Calculate the mean and the standard deviation.

$n = 10$

$$\overline{x} = \frac{\Sigma x}{n} = \frac{3004}{10} = 300.4$$

$$s = \sqrt{\frac{\Sigma d^2}{n}} = \sqrt{\frac{646.4}{10}} \doteq 8.039$$

Even though the mean is very close to what it is supposed to be, production must stop until the machinery is corrected because the standard deviation of 8.039 g exceeds the limit of 5.7 g.

EXERCISE 9-2

A **1.** The table at the right shows the commission charged by six of Canada's discount brokerage firms if they sell 1000 shares at $10.00 per share. Find each of the following.

a. the mean
b. the range
c. the mean deviation
d. the standard deviation

Brokerage Firm	Commission
Disnat	$83
Gardiner	$119
Guardian	$83
Marathon	$70
Royal Bank	$80
T.D. Green Line	$65

2. The 1988 average annual salary for each professional sport is shown at the right. Find each of the following.
   a. the mean
   b. the range
   c. the mean deviation
   d. the standard deviation

Sport	Average Annual Salary (1988)
Baseball	$412 500
Basketball	$400 000
Football	$235 000
Hockey	$158 000

3. For a recent statistics test worth 20 points, Mrs. Warner compared the results from two classes, as shown in the table at the right.
   a. Find the range for each class.
   b. What do you notice about the ranges?
   c. Which class *appears* to have a greater distribution of marks?
   d. Find the mean for each class.
   e. Find the standard deviation for each class.

Class A	Class B
3	20
12	19
12	18
11	3
11	6
20	3

B 4. A recent survey of high-school students was conducted to determine how many hours per week students spent at part-time jobs. The results are given in the table at the right. Find each of the following.
   a. the mean
   b. the range
   c. the mean deviation
   d. the standard deviation

Number of Hours (x)	Frequency (f)
0	15
1	2
2	3
3	5
4	7
5	11
6	12
7	18
8	13
9	17

5. Two cities each have an average summer temperature of 21.3° C. City A has a standard deviation of 0.17° C and City B has a standard deviation of 3.21° C. Which city appears to have the more consistent temperature?

6. The coach of the school basketball team had three players each try 25 free throws every day during the week. The results are given below.

	Number of Successful Shots				
Player	Mon	Tues	Wed	Thurs	Fri
Becky	1	12	9	20	25
Helena	5	5	10	23	24
Marge	9	13	14	15	16

The coach needs to pick one player for the team. She feels that performance consistency, as well as a good average, is important.
   a. Find the mean for each player.
   b. Find the range for each player.
   c. Find the standard deviation for each player.
   d. Which player do you think the coach will select? Why?

9-3 Displaying Data

Data can be organized in many ways. You've already seen one way, the frequency distribution table. There are many other ways that data can be organized or displayed.

1. Graphs

a. Histogram

The frequency distribution table at the right gives the number of home runs hit by players on the Lions' baseball team.

Number of Home Runs	Frequency
0	3
1	6
2	3
3	1
4	1
5	1

This information can be displayed in a histogram, shown below.
Notice that there are no spaces between the bars.

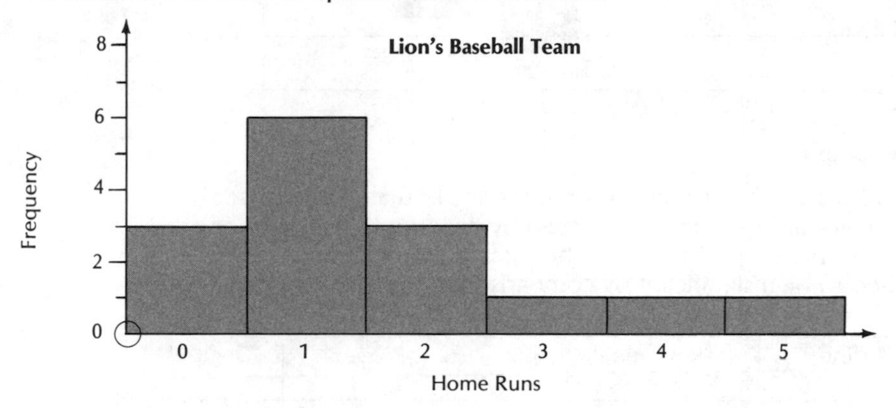

b. Frequency Polygon

A frequency polygon for the survey taken by the Leacock High School Statistics class, given in Example 1 of lesson 9-1, can be drawn using the midpoint of each interval. Plot the frequency associated with each midpoint and join the dots with straight lines.

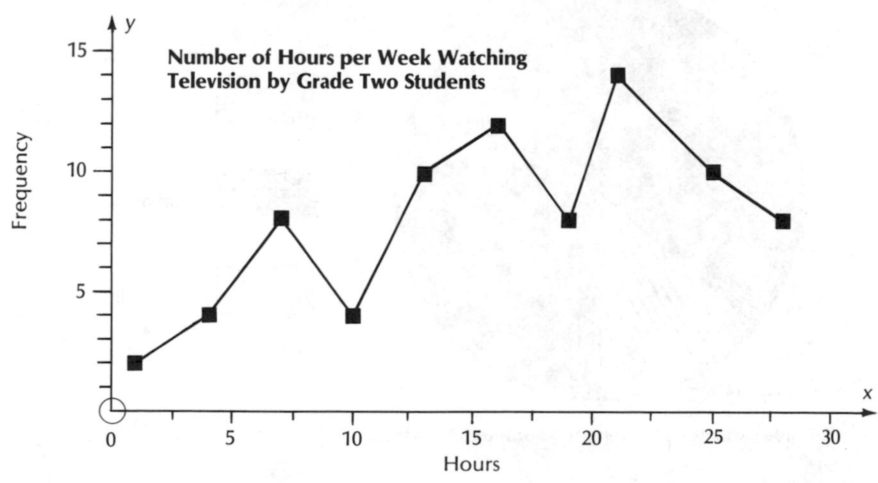

c. **Bar Graph**

A bar graph is used to display items in separate categories. This chart shows the growth ($) in Canada's exports between 1982 and 1986.

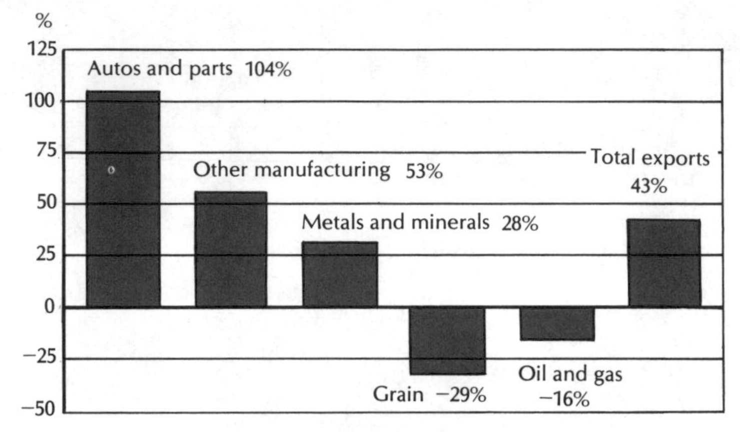

d. **Circle Graph**

The 1986 revenue passenger kilometres accumulated by Canada's three major airlines can be displayed by dividing the degrees of a circle into pie-shaped sections. The total for other airlines is assumed to be insignificant by comparison.

Airline	Revenue Passenger Kilometres (in billions)	Percent	Degrees
Air Canada	14.4	50%	180°
Canadian	10.5	36%	130°
Wardair	4.1	14%	50°
Totals	29	100%	360°

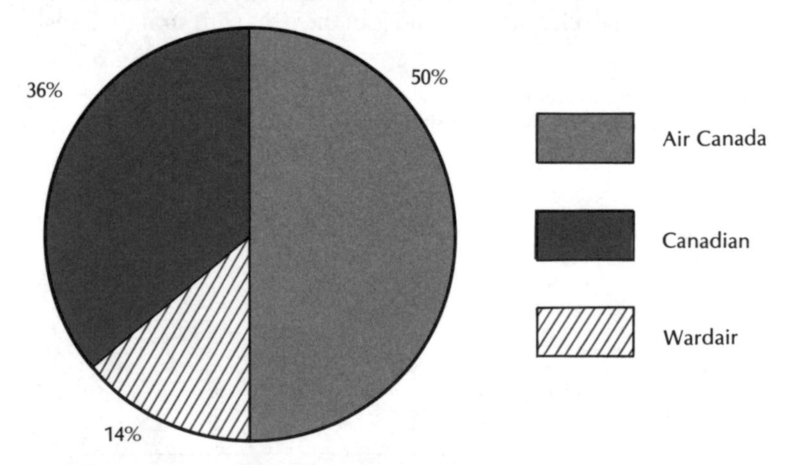

Canada's Revenue Passenger Kilometres by Airline

2. Stem and Leaf Plots

A stem and leaf plot is a way of organizing data into *groups*. Grouping data in a frequency distribution causes the actual data to be lost. A stem and leaf plot groups the data, keeps the actual data, and gives a quick version of a histogram, all at the same time.

Normally, the number of fielding errors made by American League Baseball Teams would be placed into the groups 100–109, 110–119, 120–129, 130–139, 140–149, and 150–159.

For the stem and leaf plot, these groups are kept. The first two digits are used as the stems and the third digits are used as the leaves.

American League—1986 Fielding Errors	
Team	Number of Errors
Toronto	100
California	107
Detroit	108
Chicago	117
Minnesota	118
Texas	122
Kansas City	123
New York	127
Boston	129
Baltimore	135
Oakland	135
Milwaukee	146
Seattle	156
Cleveland	157

Number of Errors 1986 American League	
Stem	Leaf
10	0, 7, 8
11	7, 8
12	2, 3, 7, 9
13	5, 5
14	6
15	6, 7

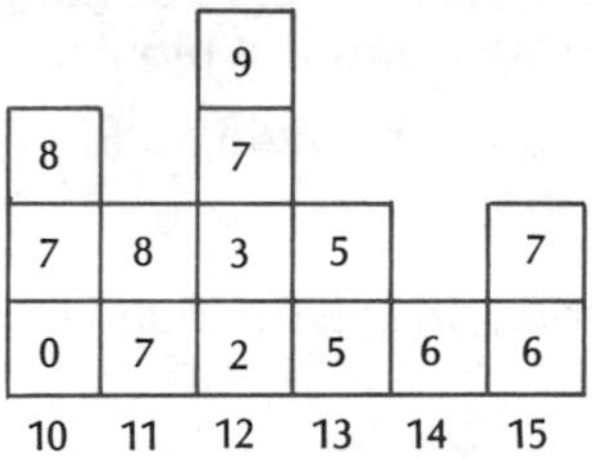

		9			
8		7			
7	8	3	5		7
0	7	2	5	6	6
10	11	12	13	14	15

This results in a grouped frequency distribution and no data is lost. Turning the stem and leaf plot on its side results in a histogram.

3. Box and Whisker Plot

The final grades of 60 students are recorded in a stem and leaf plot. To make calculations easier, the values in each leaf are arranged in order.

	Student Grades	
Stem	Leaf	Frequency
3	1, 3, 5, 7, 8	5
4	0, 0, 0, 3, 6, 8, 9	7
5	0, 0, 0, 0, 3, 5, 5, 6, 6, 7, 7	11
6	0, 1, 1, 1, 2, 2, 3, 3, 5, 5, 5, 5, 5, 6, 6, 7, 7, 9	18
7	0, 1, 2, 2, 2, 3, 4, 4, 6, 6, 7, 7, 8	13
8	2, 2, 8	3
9	0, 0, 5	3
		60

This data can be broken up into quarters with the **lower quartile score,** Q_L, occurring at the **25th percentile**, the **median score** occurring at the **50th percentile**, and the **upper quartile score,** Q_U, occurring at the **75th percentile**.

Rank n items in order as $x_1, x_2, x_3, \ldots, x_n$.

Q_L is found at the $\frac{1}{4}(n+1)^{\text{th}}$ position. — Q_L is the lower quartile score.

The median is found at the $\frac{1}{2}(n+1)^{\text{th}}$ position.

Q_U is found at the $\frac{3}{4}(n+1)^{\text{th}}$ position. — Q_U is the upper quartile score.

Since $\frac{1}{4}(61) = 15\frac{1}{4}$ position, Q_L occurs between x_{15} and x_{16}. — $(n+1) = (60+1)$

Since $x_{15} = 50$ and $x_{16} = 50$, then $Q_L = 50$.

Since $\frac{1}{2}(61) = 30\frac{1}{2}$ position, the median occurs between x_{30} and x_{31}.

Since $x_{30} = 63$ and $x_{31} = 63$, the median is 63.

Further, $\frac{3}{4}(61) = 47\frac{3}{4}$ position.
The upper quartile score occurs between x_{47} and x_{48}.
From the stem and leaf plot, $x_{47} = 73$ and $x_{48} = 74$.

Estimate Q_U by rounding off to the *nearest integer position below* Q_U.
Therefore, $Q_U = x_{47}$, or 73.

If necessary, Q_L can be found by rounding off to the *first integer position above* Q_L.

Student Grades	
Q_L	50
Median	63
Q_U	73

Now you can use this data to plot a **box and whisker plot**, which is one way of showing the centre and spread of a set of data.

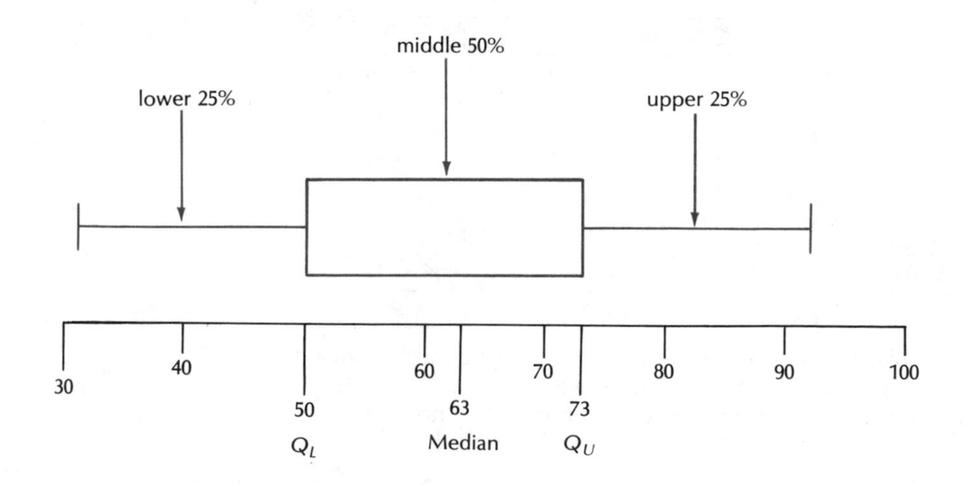

A *box* is drawn over the **interquartile range**, or the data between Q_L and Q_U. The whiskers are the 25% of the data below and the 25% of the data above the interquartile range.

Therefore, the interquartile range of the student's marks is 50–73. The box is the central region that contains half of the data.

EXERCISE 9-3

A **1.** Use the data from Example 1 of lesson 9-2 to answer each part.

a. Draw a histogram for this distribution.

b. Draw a frequency polygon for this distribution.

2. Using the data from exercise 1 of lesson 9-2, draw a bar graph.

3. Construct a circle graph to represent the data from exercise 2 of lesson 9-2.

4. An airline recorded the number of empty seats on a daily flight from Toronto to Montreal for 20 days. The results are shown at the right. Use a stem and leaf plot to organize the data.

Number of Empty Seats
5, 10, 15, 25, 16, 0, 30, 8, 31, 11, 3, 0, 18, 32, 11, 6, 22, 13, 31, 8

B **5.** Use the data from exercise 2 of lesson 9-1 to answer each part.

a. Draw a histogram for this distribution.

b. Draw a frequency polygon for this distribution.

6. Three thousand high-school students were asked "What is your favourite subject at school?" The results are shown below.

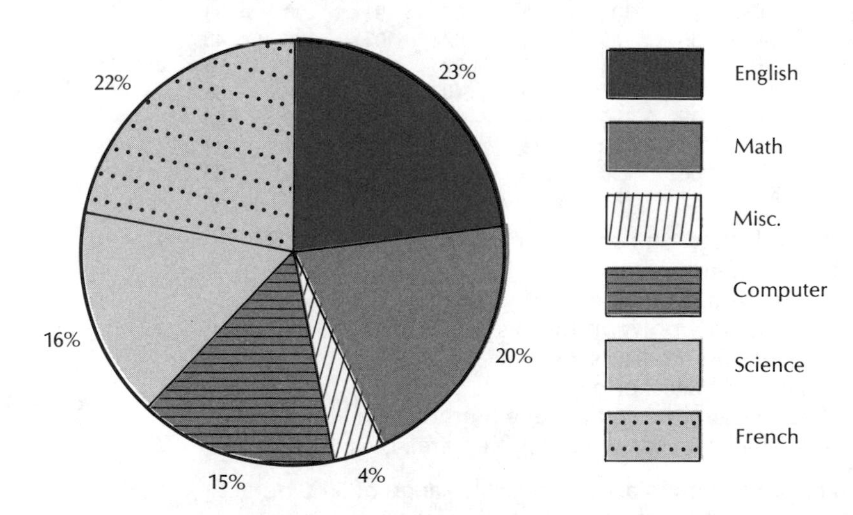

a. How many students preferred Math?

b. How many students preferred French?

c. How many students did not select English or French?

7. The histogram given below shows the number of kilograms lost by the participants at a weight-loss clinic.

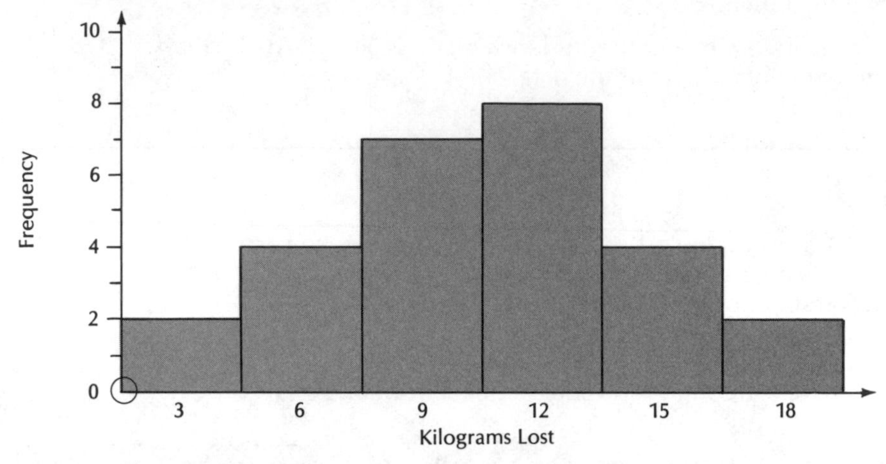

a. How many people lost between 6 kg and 18 kg, inclusive?
b. How many people attended the weight loss clinic?
c. What percentage of the people lost 9 kg or more?
d. What percentage lost less than 12 kg?

8. Concerned about the number of traffic accidents at a certain curve in a road, the local police recorded the speeds of the first 100 cars that passed along that area of road. The speeds, recorded in kilometres per hour, are given below.

103	98	87	109	62	90	92	87	63	65
91	82	73	105	78	80	83	89	62	78
62	37	61	93	106	76	87	91	90	93
54	46	54	86	75	94	97	101	100	49
111	39	86	82	74	74	82	65	92	98
49	49	82	96	97	90	40	85	86	68
72	58	83	56	96	87	81	99	79	86
85	62	83	83	60	83	71	77	81	89
87	76	83	86	50	75	91	72	76	90
89	80	85	97	82	76	81	73	75	88

a. Plot a stem and leaf graph using the numbers 3, 4, 5, 6, 7, 8, 9, 10, and 11 as the stems.
b. Construct a histogram for this distribution.
c. Construct a frequency polygon for this distribution.
d. Find Q_L, Q_U, and the median score.
e. Construct a box and whisker plot.
f. Using the box and whisker plot, make a prediction about the speed of 50% of all cars passing along that area of road.

C 9. Box and whisker plots contain an interquartile range of 50% but sometimes this range can be changed to a different percentage. Construct a 90% box and whisker plot for the data in exercise 8. (This means that 90% of the data will lie in the box with 5% in each whisker.)

Review

1. Students in a math class conducted an experiment by tossing 4 coins 50 times and counting the number of times "heads" occured for each toss. The results are shown at the right.

Number of Heads When Tossing 4 Coins
3, 2, 3, 0, 1, 2, 2, 4, 0, 1,
2, 2, 2, 3, 0, 1, 1, 2, 2, 2,
4, 3, 0, 1, 1, 2, 2, 2, 2, 2,
1, 4, 3, 2, 3, 2, 1, 2, 2, 2,
3, 2, 2, 2, 3, 3, 2, 2, 2, 2

   a. Make a frequency distribution for this data.
   b. Before trying this experiment, the class predicted the mean, median, and mode. What do you think they predicted?
   c. Calculate the mean, median, and mode for this distribution.
   d. Calculate the range, mean deviation, and standard deviation for this distribution.
   e. Draw a histogram for this distribution.
   f. Draw a circle graph for this distribution.
   g. Do the coins appear to be "fair coins"?

2. The number of absences for a certain class were recorded at the end of the year. The results are shown at the right.

Number of Absences				
3	5	2	6	10
0	12	7	21	0
8	16	13	11	2
1	1	3	8	5
12	25	0	0	1
8	3	4	11	5

   a. Make a stem and leaf plot using the numbers 0, 1, and 2 as the stems.
   b. Make a frequency distribution for this data.
   c. Draw a frequency polygon for this data.
   d. Using the frequency distribution, calculate the mean, median, and mode.
   e. Calculate the range, mean deviation, and standard deviation for this distribution.
   f. What is the percentile rank for a person who missed 16 classes?
   g. Find Q_L and Q_U.
   h. Construct a box and whisker plot for this distribution.

3. In 1986, the Blue Jays' six top hitters had batting averages of 0.310, 0.309, 0.309, 0.289, 0.281, and 0.268. Their corresponding times at bat were 687, 641, 246, 589, 424, and 239, respectively. Find their combined batting average.

4. In a certain town, the local natural gas company tracked the average amount of fuel used per household per month.

Month	Consumption (m³)
Jan.	725
Feb.	715
Mar.	637
Apr.	329
May	150
June	135
July	99
Aug.	85
Sept.	110
Oct.	357
Nov.	612
Dec.	717

   a. Find the three-month moving average.
   b. Draw a bar graph for the original data.
   c. On the same graph draw the bar graph for the three-month moving averages.
   d. How do the two graphs compare?

9-4 Scatter Diagrams

After a group of students completed a final exam, they were asked how many hours they had studied. These results were then compared with the final exam grades, and are shown at the right.

Number of Hours studied (x)	Grade on Exam (y)
8	62
5	43
10	79
13	85
10	70
5	55
18	92
15	90
2	35
9	75
4	68

One way of depicting this data is to use a **scatter diagram**.

A scatter diagram helps you to determine if there is a relationship between the number of hours studied and the final grade on the exam.

The scatter diagram is obtained by plotting all ordered pairs (x, y).

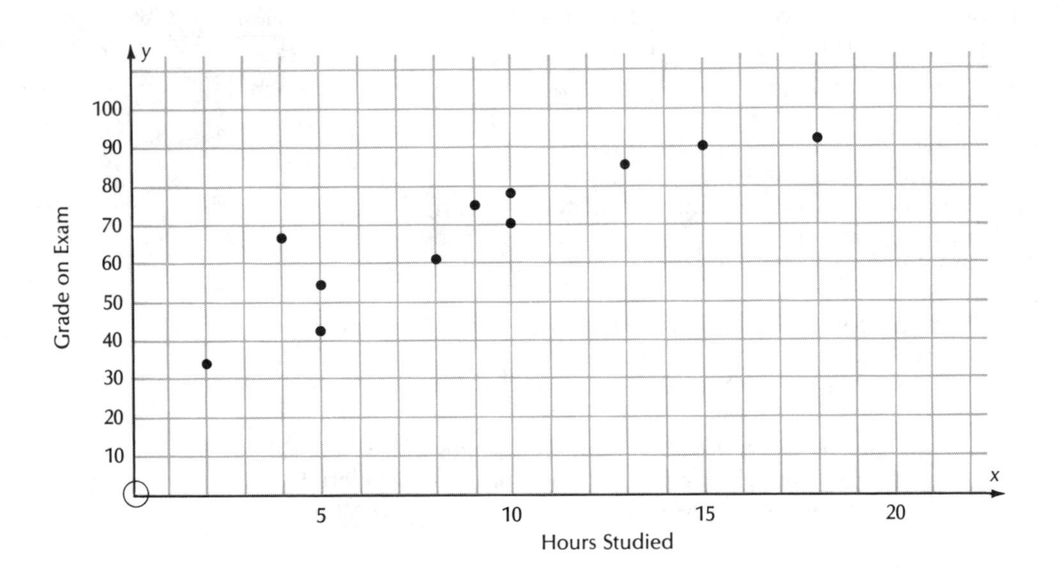

This scatter diagram suggests that the students who spent more time studying obtained a higher grade on the exam.

If there appears to be a relationship between two items, then there is said to be a **correlation** between the items.

In this case, there appears to be a **positive correlation** between the number of hours studied and the grade obtained on the final exam. The dots seem to be moving up as you look to the right along the graph. This means it appears that the greater the number of hours studied, the higher the grade on the exam.

EXERCISE 9-4

A **1.** The following report card marks were noted or 12 students in North Valley High School.

Student	Math	English	Music	Science
A	73	70	60	75
B	35	72	85	43
C	82	65	55	82
D	61	45	70	58
E	46	58	75	51
F	58	77	55	54
G	66	85	75	64
H	75	69	63	76
I	78	89	61	78
J	95	66	47	97
K	57	35	78	56
L	42	75	87	45

a. Make a scatter diagram, using Math as the x-axis and Science as the y-axis.
b. Make a scatter diagram, using Math as the x-axis and Music as the y-axis.
c. Make a scatter diagram, using Math as the x-axis and English as the y-axis.
d. What conclusions can you make by looking at your diagrams?
e. If a student has a grade of 85 in Math, estimate the student's Science grade.

B **2.** A toy manufacturer decided to test how long babies spent playing with the company's newest baby toy.

Age (in months)	Average Number of Minutes
6	1
7	2
8	3

a. Plot a scatter diagram, using age for the x-axis and number of minutes for the y-axis.
b. Draw a line through the points from part **a.**
c. Use this line to estimate how long a twelve-month old baby would play with this toy.
d. Find an equation of the line.
e. Use the line to calculate how long an 18 year-old would play with this toy. Why would this probably not be true?

3. A pen manufacturer believes that by increasing advertising funds they will increase sales. The manufacturer made comparisons, as shown at right.

Advertising Dollars (in $100 000)	Number of Pens Sold (in millions)
1	2
2	4
3	8
4	16
5	32

a. Plot a scatter diagram, using advertising dollars for the x-axis and number of pens sold for the y-axis.
b. Draw a smooth curve through these points.
c. Find an equation of this curve.
d. How many pens would be sold if $350 000 was spent on advertising?
e. What amount would the manufacturer have to spend on advertising to sell 10 million pens?

9-5 Types of Correlation

Joanne felt that a relationship might exist between the number of people in a family and how many television sets the family owned. She took a random sample of six families and obtained the following results.

Number of people in family	4	2	6	1	3	7
Number of TV sets	3	1	4	1	2	4

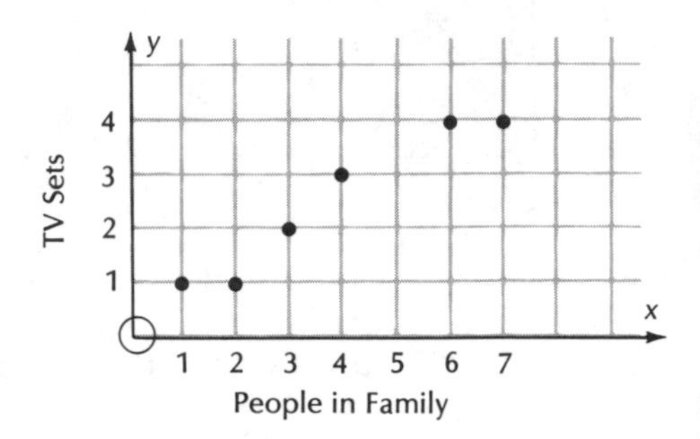

Joanne plotted the results on a scatter diagram, and she noticed that the results indicated a correlation.

In this case, the dots approximately form a straight line. This situation is called a **linear correlation.** Because the slope of this approximate line goes up to the right (that is, as the value of x increases, the value of y increases), there is a *positive correlation* between the number of people in a family and the number of television sets owned.

Joanne also decided to ask these families how many hours they spent per day watching television and how many hours they spent per day conversing as a family. She obtained the following results and plotted them on a scatter diagram.

Number of hours spent watching television	Number of hours spent in family conversation
3	1
5	0.5
1	2.5
2	2
4	0.75
3	1.5

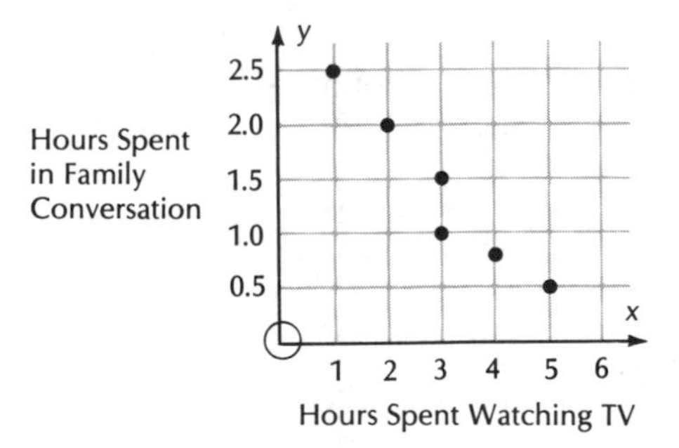

In this situation, an approximate straight line with a *negative* slope (that is, as x increases, y decreases) is formed. So, there is a *negative correlation* between the number of hours spent watching television per day and the number of hours spent in family conversation per day.

Joanne also asked these families how many cars they owned and compared this with the number of hours per day spent in family conversation. She obtained the following results and plotted them on a scatter diagram.

Number of hours spent in family conversation	Number of cars owned
1	1
0.5	2
2.5	3
2	1
0.75	3
1.5	2

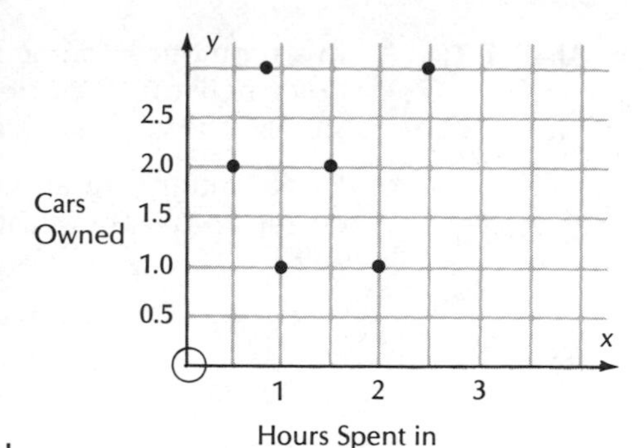

Because the only approximate line that can be formed here is a *horizontal line* (that is, a line with zero slope), there is *no* correlation between the number of hours spent in family conversation and the number of cars owned.

Not all relationships are linear, or follow a straight line. Joanne also asked 10 students how many hours they studied the night before an exam and compared this with the mark received on the exam. She obtained the following results.

Number of hours spent studying	Grade
0	32
1	40
1.5	47
2	61
2.5	75
3	78
4	80
5	71
8	60
9	52

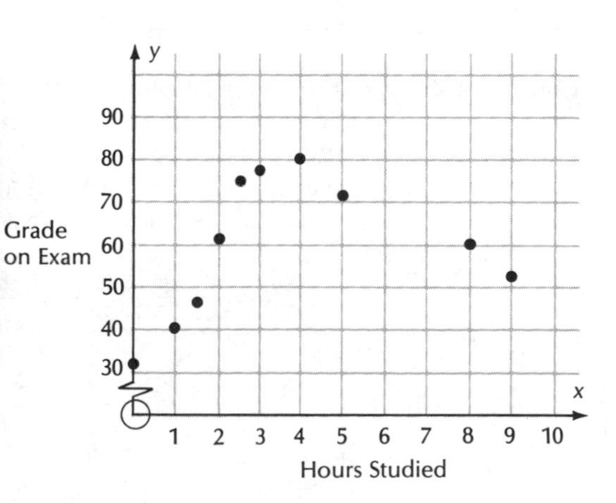

The scatter diagram for this data suggests a **curvilinear correlation**. In this situation, the dots approximate a parabola, which is a curved line. Why do you think this can happen when comparing the number of hours studied the night before an exam and the grade obtained?

Even though the scatter diagram might suggest a strong relationship between two items, there might not be such a relationship. For example, plotting the number of cars purchased annually with the annual sales of milk may show a strong positive correlation, but both variables depend on the size of the population that was surveyed. Here, a third variable produces the fallacy of thinking that there is a cause-effect relationship between the two items.

EXAMPLE 1: In a promotion to encourage people to buy a new car, a car dealership took a survey. The results are shown at the right.

Plot a scatter diagram to see what type of correlation, if any, exists.

Age of Car (in years)	Repairs during last year (in $100)
2	5
5	7.6
3	5.25
8	12
5	6.9
2	4.5
4	6.2

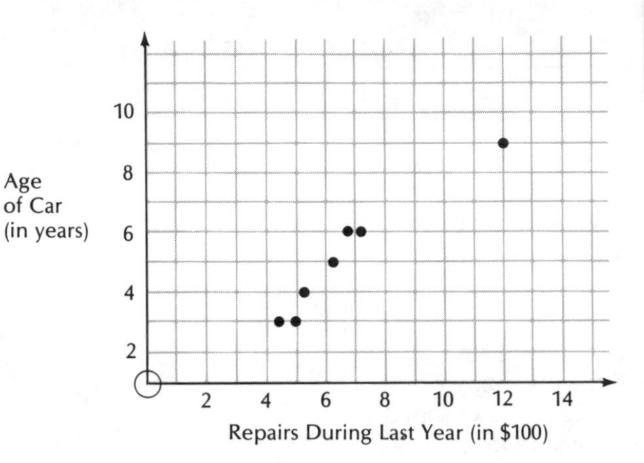

There appears to be a *positive correlation* between the age of the car and the amount spent on repairs.

EXAMPLE 2: The pricing policy for the Acme Widget Company is shown in the table at the right. Plot a scatter diagram to see what type of correlation, if any, exists.

Number of Widgets Purchased (in 1000s)	Price per Unit (in cents)
1	20
2	17
3	14
4	10
5	8

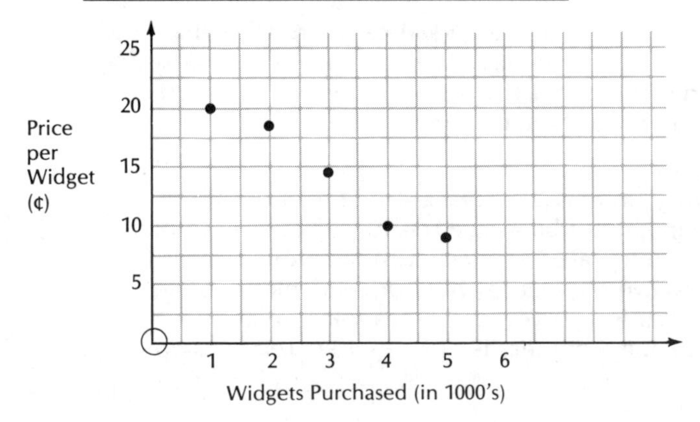

From the scatter diagram, there appears to be a *negative correlation* between the number of widgets purchased and each price.

EXERCISE 9-5

A **1.** For each of the following indicate whether a positive, negative, or zero correlation would be expected.

- **a.** height and mass
- **b.** the amount of rainfall and crop productivity
- **c.** the number of hours you studied last night and the amount of snowfall
- **d.** the number of hours spent training by a runner and the time taken to run a race
- **e.** the number of weeks spent in a speed-reading program and the number of words that can be read in a minute
- **f.** the number of weeks spent on a diet and the number of kilograms lost
- **g.** car speed maintained from Toronto to Ottawa and the time taken to drive the distance
- **h.** the number of hours of sunshine this week and a person's shoe size.

B **2.** Use the data from exercise 1 of lesson 9-4 and refer to the scatter diagrams. What type of correlation (positive, negative, or zero) exists between each of the following pairs of subjects?

- **a.** Math and Science
- **b.** Math and Music
- **c** Math and English

3. Use the data from exercise 2 of lesson 9-4 and refer to the scatter diagram. What type of correlation exists between a baby's age and the number of minutes spent playing with the toy?

4. Use the data from exercise 3 of lesson 9-4 and refer to the scatter diagram. What type of correlation exists between advertising dollars spent and the number of pens sold.

5. **a.** Using the scatter diagrams from exercise 1 of lesson 9-4, draw a straight line on the scatter diagram that you feel is the best line to represent the data for Math and Science and Math and Music.

b. Use the lines from part **a** to estimate a student's grade for each situation.

- **i.** in Science, if the student obtained a grade of 70 in Math
- **ii.** in Music, if the student obtained a grade of 70 in Math

9-6 The Line of Best Fit

During the Lion's last hockey game, the coach recorded the number of times each player was on the ice when a goal was scored against the team and the number of times each player was on the ice when a goal was scored for the team. The results for four players are shown in the table below.

Player's Name	Number of times on ice when goal is scored	
	against	for
Vince	1	1
Peggy	2	3
Jeff	3	2
Greg	4	5

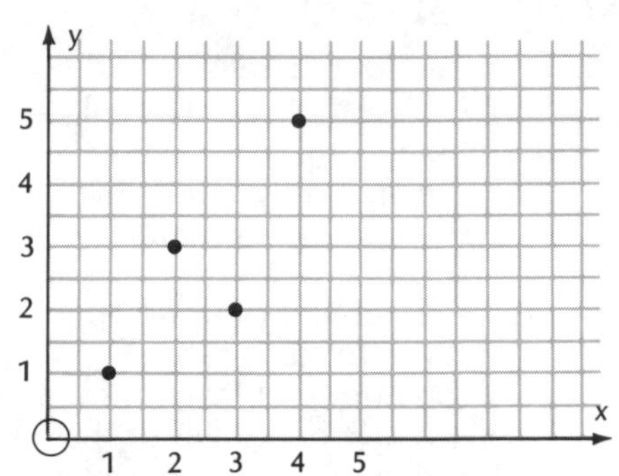

The scatter diagram at the right suggests a *positive linear correlation*. From this, you can try to draw a line that best fits the data. There are *many* possibilities.

You could try drawing a line through the points (1, 1) and (4, 5). As you can see, there are two points *not* on this line. The *difference* between the observed value and the corresponding point on the line is called the **deviation.**

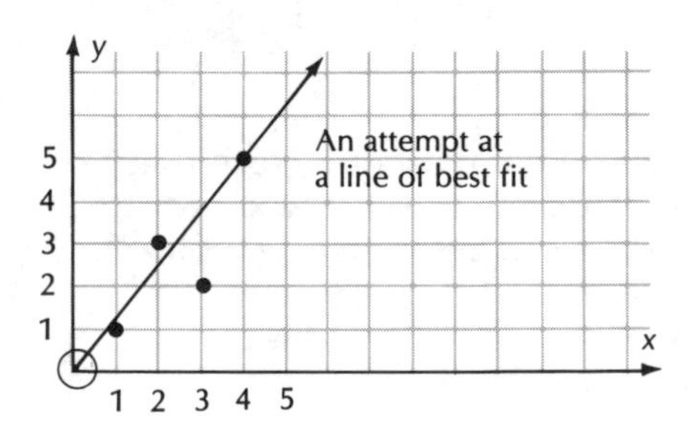

To find the deviation, first find an equation of the line through (1, 1) and (4, 5), using the form $y = mx + b$.

$$m = \frac{5-1}{4-1} = \frac{4}{3}$$

$$y - 5 = \frac{4}{3}(x - 4)$$

$$y = \frac{4}{3}x - \frac{1}{3}$$

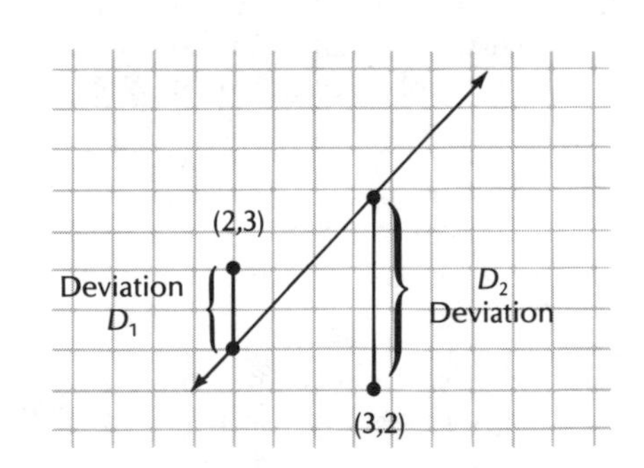

If $x = 2$, then $y = \frac{4}{3}(2) - \frac{1}{3} = \frac{7}{3}$.

This gives a deviation of $\frac{7}{3} - 3 = -\frac{2}{3}$. So, $D_1 = -\frac{2}{3}$.

If $x = 3$, then $y = \frac{4}{3}(3) - \frac{1}{3} = \frac{11}{3}$.

This gives a deviation of $\frac{11}{3} - 2 = \frac{5}{3}$. So, $D_2 = \frac{5}{3}$.

The idea is to keep the sum of the squares of these deviations as small as possible.

Square the deviations to calculate the *magnitude* of the deviations from the point on the line.

In this case, $D_1^2 + D_2^2 = \left(-\frac{2}{3}\right)^2 + \left(\frac{5}{3}\right)^2$

$$= \frac{4}{9} + \frac{25}{9}$$
$$= \frac{29}{9}$$
$$= 3.\overline{2}$$

Try moving the line and see what happens. The next attempt at finding a **line of best fit**, or a line that best represents the data, is the line $y = x$.

Find all four deviations.

D_1: $1 - 1 = 0$
D_2: $2 - 3 = -1$
D_3: $3 - 2 = 1$
D_4: $4 - 5 = -1$

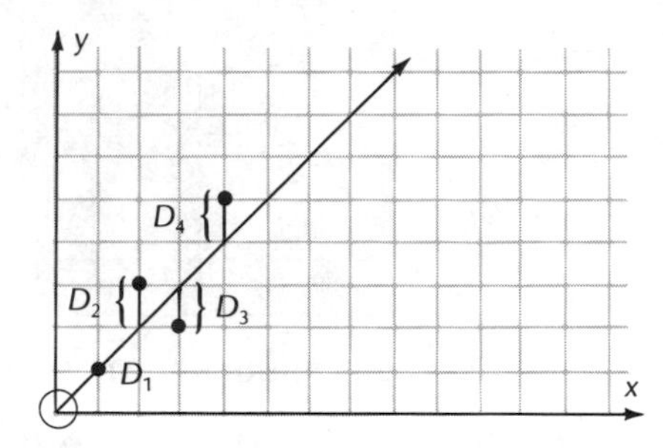

Find the sum of the squares of the deviations.

$$D_1^2 + D_2^2 + D_3^2 + D_4^2 = 0^2 + (-1)^2 + (1)^2 + (-1)^2 = 3$$

As you can see, this result is smaller than the first result. This means that $y = x$ is a *better* line to represent the data than $y = \frac{4}{3}x - \frac{1}{3}$.

The intention is to find *the best line.*

You can find the line of best fit by minimizing the sum of the squares of the deviations. The resulting line is called the **least squares line** and it can be obtained by using the equation

$y = mx + b$, where

$$m = \frac{n(\Sigma xy) - (\Sigma x)(\Sigma y)}{n(\Sigma x^2) - (\Sigma x)^2} \quad \text{and} \quad b = \frac{(\Sigma y)(\Sigma x^2) - (\Sigma x)(\Sigma xy)}{n(\Sigma x^2) - (\Sigma x)^2}.$$

For the Lion's hockey team the equation of the least squares line is obtained as follows.

x	y	x^2	xy
1	1	1	1
2	3	4	6
3	2	9	6
4	5	16	20
10	11	30	33

$$m = \frac{4(33) - (10)(11)}{4(30) - (10)^2} = 1.1$$

$$\text{and } b = \frac{(11)(30) - (10)(33)}{4(30) - (10)^2} = 0$$

Therefore, the equation of the least squares line is $y = 1.1x$.
This is the best line to fit the data.

EXAMPLE 1: In a recent study, a school principal asked ten students how many books they read each month and compared the results with each student's school average. The results are shown in the table at the right. Find an equation of the least squares line.

Number of books read per month (x)	Average grade (y)
3	57
4	80
4	72
2	58
5	89
3	63
4	65
5	84
3	75
2	48

First, organize the data into a table. Find the total for each column.

x	y	x^2	xy
3	57	9	171
4	80	16	320
4	72	16	288
2	58	4	116
5	89	25	445
3	63	9	189
4	65	16	260
5	84	25	420
3	75	9	225
2	48	4	96
35	691	133	2530

Since there are ten pieces of data, then $n = 10$.

Substitute known values into the equation for the least squares line.

$$m = \frac{n(\Sigma xy) - (\Sigma x)(\Sigma y)}{n(\Sigma x^2) - (\Sigma x)^2} \quad \text{and} \quad b = \frac{(\Sigma y)(\Sigma x^2) - (\Sigma x)(\Sigma xy)}{n(\Sigma x^2) - (\Sigma x)^2}.$$

$$= \frac{10(2530) - (35)(691)}{10(133) - (35)^2} \qquad = \frac{(691)(133) - (35)(2530)}{10(133) - (35)^2}$$

$$\doteq 10.6 \qquad \doteq 31.9$$

Therefore, the least squares line is $y = 10.6x + 31.9$.

A line of least squares can be used to make predictions.

EXAMPLE 2: **a.** Using the least squares line obtained in Example 1, predict the average grade of a student who reads six books per month.

$$y = 10.6x + 31.9$$
$$y = 10.6(6) + 31.9$$
$$= 95.5$$

A student might expect to receive a grade of 95.5 if he or she read six books per month.

b. Using the least squares line obtained in Example 1, predict the average grade of a student who reads no books per month.

$$y = 10.6x + 31.9$$
$$y = 10.6(0) + 31.9$$
$$= 31.9$$

A student might expect to receive a grade of 31.9 if he or she does not read any books.

EXERCISE 9-6

B **1.** Ten males were asked their height, in centimetres, and mass, in kilograms. The results are shown at the right.

a. Draw a scatter diagram for this data.
b. Sketch a curve of best fit.
c. Find an equation of the least squares line.
d. Make a prediction about a person's mass if he is 183 cm tall.
e. Make a prediction about a person's height if his mass is 81 kg.

Height (cm) x	Mass (kg) y
157	52
178	70
160	68
183	82
165	73
170	64
173	69
175	80
163	71
168	66

2. Seven women over the age of 20 were asked their heights and the heights of their mothers. The results are shown at the right.

a. Draw a scatter diagram for this data.
b. Sketch a curve of best fit.
c. Find an equation of the least squares line.
d. Predict a mother's height if her daughter is 170 cm tall.

Daughter's Height (in cm) x	Mother's Height (in cm) y
155	152
152	157
178	168
160	163
165	163
168	170
157	163

3. Use the data from exercise 1 of lesson 9-4.

a. Find an equation of the least squares line relating Math and Science.
b. Find an equation of the least squares line relating Math and Music.
c. Predict the Science and Music grades if a student's Math grade is 76.
d. Predict the Science and Music grades if a student's Math grade is 50.

4. Use the data from Example 1 of lesson 9-5.

a. Find an equation of the least squares line.
b. Predict the amount spent on repairs if a car is six years old.
c. Predict the age of the car if $1000 was spent on repairs last year.

5. Use the data from Example 2 of lesson 9-5.

a. Find an equation of the least squares line.
b. Predict the price per widget if 6000 widgets are purchased.
c. Predict the number of widgets that must be purchased if the price per unit is 6¢.

6. A certain automobile has been found to have the following relationship between the speedometer reading and the rear axle gear ratio when the engine turns at 2800 rev/min.

Rear axle gear ratio	Speedometer reading (km/h)
3.68 : 1	50
4.12 : 1	40
3.23 : 1	60

a. Plot the results on a scatter diagram.
b. Sketch a curve of best fit.
c. Find an equation of the least squares line.
d. Predict the speedometer reading for a rear axle gear ratio of 3.5 : 1.

9-7 Correlation Coefficient

The contestants in a recent figure skating competition were ranked according to their standing in the compulsory figures and in free skating. The results are given in the table below.

Contestant	Compulsory Figures Ranking	Free Skating Ranking
A	3	2
B	4	4
C	1	3
D	5	6
E	6	5
F	2	1

The *ranking* for each contestant indicates where each contestant placed in that area of the competition.

To determine if there is a relationship between a contestant's ranking in the compulsory figures and their ranking for the free skating routine, a number called the **rank correlation coefficient** is calculated.

The rank correlation coefficient is calculated using the equation

$$r_{\text{rank}} = 1 - \frac{6\sum d^2}{n(n^2-1)},$$

where r_{rank} is the rank correlation coefficient, n is the number of pairs of data, and d is the difference between the two rankings.

By organizing this data in a table it is easier to calculate the rank correlation coefficient.

Contestant	Compulsory Figures Ranking	Free Skating Ranking	Difference d	d^2
A	3	2	$3-2=1$	1
B	4	4	$4-4=0$	0
C	1	3	$1-3=-2$	4
D	5	6	$5-6=-1$	1
E	6	5	$6-5=1$	1
F	2	1	$2-1=1$	1
Total				8

$$r_{\text{rank}} = 1 - \frac{6\sum d^2}{n(n^2-1)} \qquad n = 6$$

$$= 1 - \frac{6(8)}{6(36-1)}$$

$$= 1 - 0.228\,571\,4$$

$$= 0.77$$

This result shows a high positive correlation between contestants' standings in compulsory figures and their standings in free skating. This means that a skater who ranks high on compulsory figures is expected to perform well in free skating.

Consider the situation where the results of the two events are identical.

Contestant	Compulsory Figures Ranking	Free Skating Ranking	Difference d	d^2
A	3	3	0	0
B	4	4	0	0
C	1	1	0	0
D	5	5	0	0
E	6	6	0	0
F	2	2	0	0
Total				0

Calculate the rank coefficient of correlation.

$$\begin{aligned} r_{\text{rank}} &= 1 - \frac{6(0)}{6(36-1)} \\ &= 1 - 0 \\ &= 1 \end{aligned}$$

Each contestant's rank is identical for both areas of the competition. This is called a **perfect positive correlation** and gives a rank coefficient of correlation equal to 1. .

If the rankings for each contestant are completely reversed, the following results are obtained.

Contestant	Compulsory Figures Ranking	Free Skating Ranking	Difference d	d^2
A	3	4	−1	1
B	4	3	1	1
C	1	6	−5	25
D	5	2	3	9
E	6	1	5	25
F	2	5	−3	9
Total				70

$$\begin{aligned} r_{\text{rank}} &= 1 - \frac{6(70)}{6(36-1)} \\ &= 1 - 2 \\ &= -1 \end{aligned}$$

This is called a **perfect negative correlation**. A perfect negative correlation always has a rank correlation of −1.

Data with no correlation has a correlation coefficient equal to 0.

The closer r_{rank} is to 1, the higher the positive correlation. The closer r_{rank} is to −1, the higher the negative correlation. When r_{rank} is close to zero, there is little or no correlation.

EXERCISE 9-7

A **1.** In a talent competition, contestants were ranked by two judges.

Contestant	Judge A	Judge B
Raquel	1	2
Mark	2	1
Keith	3	4
Greg	4	3
Sherri	5	5

Is there a correlation between the two judges' opinions?

B **2.** A restaurant critic was asked to rank ten restaurants and to calculate the average price of a dinner for two people at each restaurant.

a. Rank each restaurant price from highest to lowest.
b. Calculate the rank coefficient of correlation.
c. What conclusions can be made?

Restaurant	Critics Ranking	Average Price
A	3	$94.68
B	4	$76.13
C	7	$45.29
D	10	$12.62
E	1	$91.62
F	9	$36.37
G	5	$62.13
H	2	$87.50
I	8	$44.29
J	6	$66.89

3. Using the data from exercise 2 of lesson 9-6, the daughters' and mothers' heights are ranked.

The mothers' heights, in order, are 152, 157, 163, 163, 163, 168, 170. The heights in position 3, 4, and 5 are the same. The mean rank $\left(\frac{3+4+5}{3} = 4\right)$ is assigned to this data.

a. Find the rank correlation coefficient for this data.
b. What conclusions can be made?

Rank of Daughters' Heights	Rank of Mothers' Heights
2	1
1	2
7	6
4	4
5	4
6	7
3	4

4. Use the data from exercise 6 of lesson 9-6.
a. Rank the data.
b. Find the correlation coefficient.
c. What conclusions can be made?

5. Use the data from exercise 1 of lesson 9-4.
a. Rank the students' scores for each subject area.
b. Find the coefficient of correlation for each pair of subjects.
i. Math and English
ii. Math and Music
iii. Math and Science
c. What conclusions can be made?

Review

1. Don found that cooking one slice of bacon in his microwave oven took 1 minute, two slices took $1\frac{1}{2}$ minutes, four slices took $2\frac{1}{2}$ minutes, and six slices took $3\frac{1}{2}$ minutes.

   a. Make a scatter diagram using the number of slices of bacon as the *x*-coefficient and the number of minutes as the *y*-coefficient.

   b. What appears to be the type of correlation?

   c. Draw a line that best fits the data.

   d. Calculate the estimated *regression line* using the method of least squares.

   e. Using the equation from part **d**, predict the cooking time for five slices of bacon.

   f. Using the equation from part **d**, predict how many slices of bacon Don could cook in four minutes.

2. Eight grade 12 students were asked the average number of hours they spent watching television each night and the average number of hours they spent doing homework every day. The results are given in the table below.

Student	Number of hours watching television (x)	Number of hours doing homework (y)
Ann	1	3
Warren	1.5	2.5
Beth	3	1.25
Clarence	2	1
Joel	3	0.75
Anthony	5	0.5
Janet	0.5	3.5
Karen	1.5	2

   a. Make a scatter diagram for this data.

   b. What is the type of correlation for this data?

   c. Draw a line that best fits the data.

   d. Calculate the estimated regression line using the method of least squares.

   e. Predict the number of hours spent doing homework by someone who watches four hours of television per evening.

   f. Rank the data.

   g. Calculate the rank coefficient of correlation.

   h. What conclusions can be made regarding the number of hours spent doing homework and the number of hours spent watching television?

Test

1. The Superclean Carpet Company hired 30 students to solicit business using the telephone. The supervisor decided to track the number of phone calls made by each student on Monday. The results are shown at the right.

37	43	52	64	41
58	40	31	33	57
58	62	67	36	35
32	42	61	43	47
47	50	30	51	58
59	56	32	39	58

   a. Organize the data using a stem and leaf plot. Use 3, 4, 5, and 6 as the stems.
   b. Find the lower quartile score, the median score, and the upper quartile score.
   c. Draw a 50% box and whisker plot to represent the data.
   d. What is the percentile rank for a person who made 42 phone calls?
   e. Organize this data into a frequency distribution using groups 30-39, 40-49, 50-59, and 60-69. Also include columns for frequency (*f*), midpoint of the interval (*x*), subtotal (*fx*), deviation (*d*), and deviation squared (d^2).
   f. Draw the frequency polygon for this frequency distribution.
   g. Use the frequency distribution to calculate the mean, median, mode, range, mean deviation, and standard deviation.
   h. Why is the median calculated in part **b** different from the median calculated in part **g**?

2. The Allsports Athletics Company decided to analyse the relationship between the number of phone calls made and the amount of sales generated by each caller. Ten employees were chosen at random and the results shown in the table were obtained.

Employee	Number of calls made on Monday (*x*)	Amount of sales generated by calls (*y*)
Paul	37	$150
Gord	47	$187
Carl	43	$181
Marsha	62	$550
Nicole	67	$529
Danny	58	$460
Steve	32	$63
Tasha	36	$172
Marla	58	$367
Khuong	56	$322

   a. Plot a scatter diagram.
   b. What type of correlation does this resemble?
   c. Draw a line of best fit.
   d. Calculate an equation for a line of best fit using the method of least squares.
   e. Make a prediction about the amount of sales generated when 50 calls are made.
   f. Make a prediction about the number of calls made if $600 in sales are generated.
   g. The supervisor at Allsports Athletics would like each caller to generate $350 in sales per evening. How many calls would each employee have to make to achieve the goal?

   j. If an average phone call takes 2.5 min to complete and a salesperson must generate $350 in sales, how long would it take to reach this goal? If a salesperson is paid 5% commission on sales, how much money does a salesperson make per hour if the goal is reached?

Cumulative Review

1. Sketch the graph of $y = \dfrac{1}{2 - x}$ showing any asymptote and excluded regions.

2. **a.** How much does the value of 2^t increase as the value of t increases by 1?

   b. What happens to the value of 2^{-t} as the value of t increases by 1?

3. A new delivery truck depreciates 30%/a in the first year and 20%/a each subsequent year. What is the depreciated value, after four years, of a truck that was purchased for $50 000?

4. Use a calculator to evaluate each exponential.

   a. $(0.47)^{\frac{2}{9}}$ **b.** $(56.2)^{-\frac{1}{6}}$.

5. Solve for x.

   a. $\log_4 x = 3$ **b.** $\log_x 32 = \frac{5}{3}$

6. Find the value of k such that $x - 3$ is a factor of $6 - 3x^4 - x^2 + 3kx^3 - 8x$.

7. The linear speed of the end of a rotating arm, 15.3 cm from the centre of rotation, is 17π cm/s. What is the angular velocity of the arm, in radians per second?

8. Prove that $\dfrac{\sin(x - y)}{\sin y} + \dfrac{\cos(x - y)}{\cos y} = \dfrac{\sin x}{\sin y \cos y}$.

9. Find an equation of the image of the circle defined by

   $x^2 + y^2 - 2x + 4y = 0$ under the stretch transformation $(x, y) \rightarrow \left(2x, \frac{1}{2}y\right)$.

10. Sketch the graph of each curve and solve for x and y.

    $x^2 + y^2 = 36$
    $x^2 - y^2 = 36$

11. A parabola is defined by $(x + 2)^2 = 24(y - 5)$.

    a. Sketch the parabola.
    b. Find the focus of the parabola and an equation of the directrix.

12. Vigorous exercise increases a person's pulse rate. After exercising, the pulse rate decreases exponentially. After a 5 km run, Sarah's pulse rate is 140 beats/min. Three minutes later, her pulse rate is 120 beats/min. If Sarah's normal pulse rate is 70 beats/min, how long after the run will it take for her pulse rate to reach 90 beats/min?

13. Solve the system of equations.

    $\dfrac{x^2}{4} - \dfrac{y^2}{25} = 1$
    $x^2 + y^2 = 4$

10 Congruence and Parallelism

10-1 The Language of Geometry

Euclid of Alexandria, who lived about 300 B.C., wrote the *Elements*, a set of 13 books that organized geometry in a logical sequence, with each statement following from the previous one. Euclid, who founded a school in Alexandria, compiled his text from the works of earlier mathematicians but the organization of the book was his own. Although very little is known of Euclid's life, he is remembered as a prominent mathematician and teacher whose text dominated the teaching of geometry for over two thousand years. The reasoning methods used in Euclid's *Elements* are of particular interest in this unit.

Many methods of reasoning can be used to make decisions. There are two main types of reasoning that form the basis for deriving conclusions.

Inductive reasoning is often used in science. A scientist gathers a series of individual facts through a set of experiments and then tries to relate them to form a general conclusion. Conclusions derived through inductive reasoning can be proved false if just one trial produces results that differ from the rest.

Deductive reasoning begins with a set of well-defined general ideas, or assumptions. A set of rules and a series of steps are then used to arrive at other ideas or conclusions. Consider the following example of deductive reasoning.

i. If you have exactly 17 cents in your pocket, then you have at least four coins in your pocket.
ii. You have fewer than four coins in your pocket.
iii. *Conclusion:* You do not have exactly 17 cents in your pocket.

This general statement accepted as true.

When using deductive reasoning, justification must be given for each statement that is made. The kinds of justifications that can be used in a proof by deductive reasoning, or a **deduction**, are given information, postulates, previously proven statements, undefined terms, and defined terms.

A **postulate**, or **axiom**, is a statement that is generally accepted and need not be proved.

Three examples of postulates are given below.

There exists one, and only one, line that contains two distinct points.
Two distinct straight lines intersect in, at most, one point.
Any three non-collinear points determine a plane.

Euclid described these as assumptions.

A **theorem** is a statement that has been proved.

An **undefined term** is a basic notion, so fundamental that it cannot be defined using other terms. Examples of undefined terms are *point, line, plane,* and *space*.

A **defined term** is one that can be explained using previously defined terms or commonly accepted undefined terms. A good definition of a term has three characteristics.

1. The definition places the object in a known set.
2. The definition states the property that distinguishes the new term from all other members of the set.
3. The definition is *reversible*. That is, if the subject and predicate are interchanged, the meaning of the statement does not change.

For example, *rhombus* is a defined term. The definition is given below.

A rhombus is a quadrilateral which has four equal sides.

Known set (quadrilateral) — Distinguishing property (four equal sides)

A quadrilateral that has four equal sides is a rhombus.

The definition is reversible.

Deductive reasoning can be used to prove some statements about geometrical figures. Theorems are used as authorities in further proofs and are given specific names in order to make them easier to remember and quote.

.E 1: Write a definition for each term. Draw a diagram to illustrate the term.

a. acute angle

An acute angle is an angle whose measure is greater than 0° and less than 90°.

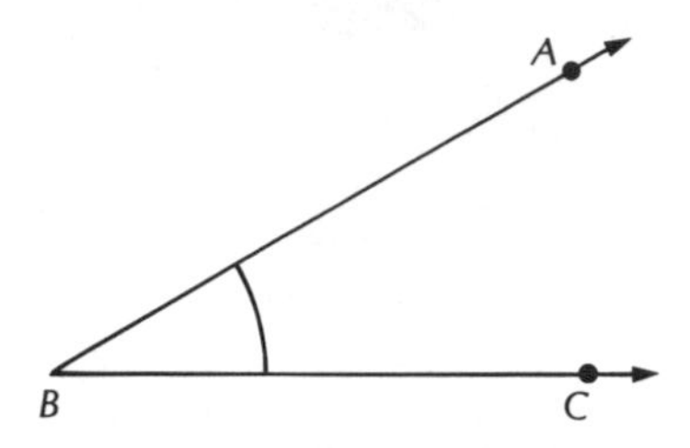

$\angle ABC$ is an acute angle.

b. trapezoid

A trapezoid is a quadrilateral containing an opposite pair of sides that are parallel.

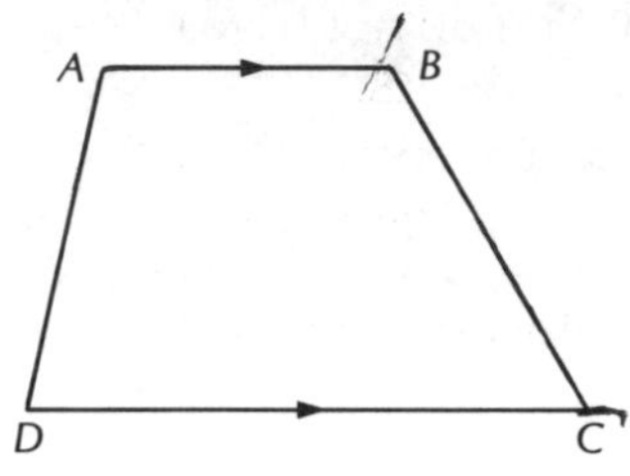

ABCD is a trapezoid.

EXAMPLE 2: Explain why each given definition does not have the characteristics of a good definition. Write a good definition for each term.

a. Parallel lines are lines that do not intersect.

Reasons: Two lines that are in different planes might not meet but they are not necessarily parallel.

New definition: Parallel lines are coplanar lines that do not intersect.

b. A quadrilateral consists of four line segments.

Reasons: The term has not been placed into a known set. Four line segments do not necessarily form a closed figure.

New definition: A quadrilateral is a polygon that has four sides.

Note that a polyg
defined as a close

c. Acute triangle—three acute angles.

Reasons: The definition is not a complete sentence; it does not place the term in a known set. Three acute angles do not necessarily form a triangle.

New definition: An acute triangle is a triangle in which each angle is acute.

EXERCISE 10-1

A **1.** Explain, in your own words, the meaning of the undefined terms: point, line, plane, space.

2. Use the three characteristics of a good definition to define each given term.

a. bicycle **b.** locker **c.** school

3. Explain why each given definition does not have the characteristics of a good definition. Then write a good definition for each term.

a. A circle is the set of all points that are the same distance from a given point.

b. An altitude of a triangle is a line segment from one vertex of the triangle to a point on the opposite side.

c. A rectangle has four congruent angles.

d. A square is a quadrilateral having four congruent sides.

e. The diameter of a circle contains the centre.

4. A list of terms is given: acute angle, obtuse angle, straight angle, reflex angle, bisector of an angle, perpendicular to a line, perpendicular bisector. Select the term that best describes each given diagram.

i.

ii.

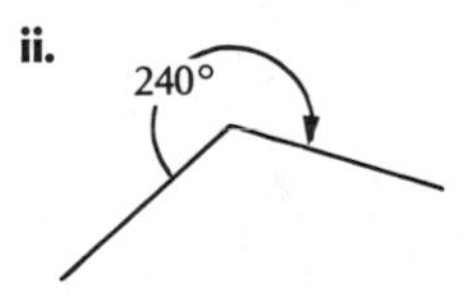

iii.

iv.

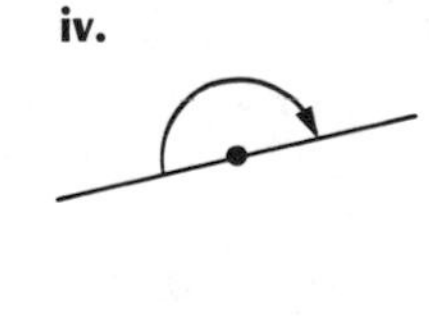

v.

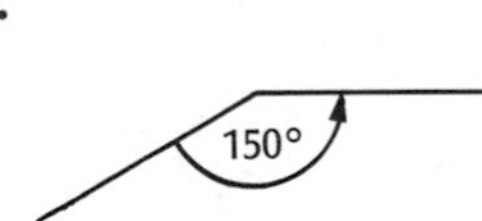

vi.

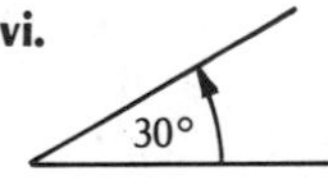

vii.

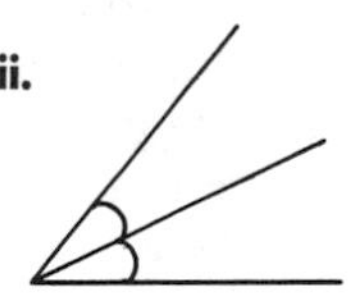

5. Cut out a large triangle from a piece of newspaper.

a. Fold the triangle to find each of the following.

i. the **midpoint** of each side
ii. a **median**
iii. the **bisector of an angle**
iv. an **altitude**
v. the **perpendicular bisector** of one side

b. Define each term given in part **a.**

6. For the diagram given at the right, identify each of the following:
   a. four pairs of adjacent angles
   b. two pairs of vertically opposite angles
   c. four pairs of supplementary angles
   d. one pair of complementary angles
   e. two obtuse angles
   f. two reflex angles
   g. two perpendicular lines
   h. an obtuse angle adjacent to $\angle ACB$
   i. four collinear points

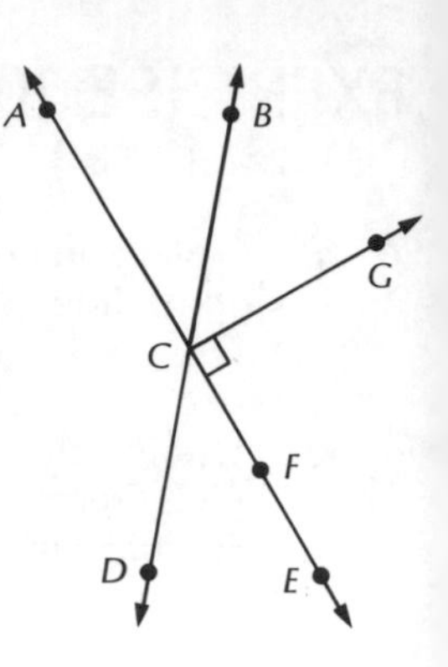

B 7. Name the polygon having the given number of sides.

a. 3	b. 4	c. 5	d. 6
e. 7	f. 8	g. 9	h. 10

8. The supplement of a given angle is three times as large as the angle. Find the measure of the given angle.

9. The complement of a given angle is three times as large as the angle. Find the measure of the given angle.

10. The supplement of a given angle is 30° more than twice the measure of the angle. Find the measure of the given angle.

11. For the diagram given at the right, identify each of the following.
    a. three points coplanar with A, B, and D
    b. a point collinear with C and E
    c. the intersection of the line containing A and C with the line containing J and B
    d. the intersection of the plane containing A, B, and D with the plane containing F, G, and K
    e. the intersection of the plane containing C, D, and F with the plane containing I, J, and D
    f. the plane(s) parallel to the plane containing I, L, and H
    g. the plane(s) perpendicular to the plane containing D, K, and F

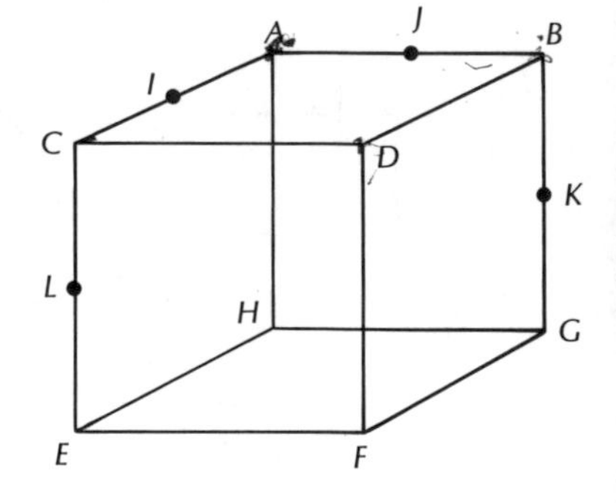

12. What can you conclude from the given information?

    $\overline{AC}$ bisects $\overline{DB}$.
    $\overline{DB}$ bisects $\overline{AC}$.
    $AE = DE$

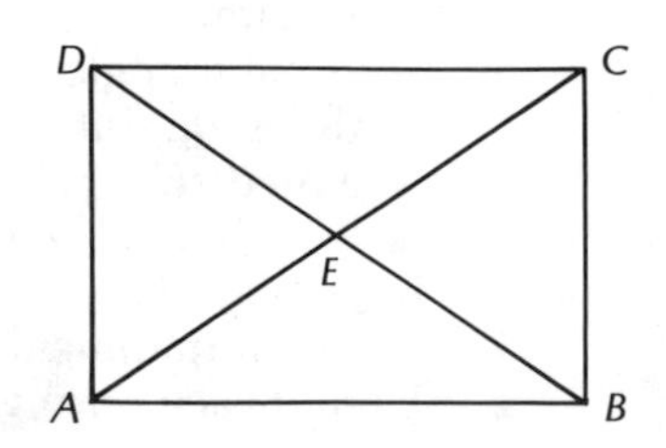

13. A and B are two points on a number line with coordinates 8 and 32, respectively. C is the midpoint of $\overline{AB}$, and D is the midpoint of $\overline{AC}$. Sketch a diagram and find each of the following.

a. AC **b.** AD
c. the coordinate of C **d.** the coordinate of D

14. Prove that when an obtuse angle is bisected, the result is two acute angles.

15. What type of angle is formed when a reflex angle is bisected? Explain.

C 16. Classify each statement as true or false. Justify your answer.

a. Two planes always intersect.
b. Two planes can intersect in only one point.
c. A line intersects a plane in, at most, one point.
d. Two lines must intersect in only one point.
e. Any three points determine a plane.
f. If two distinct planes intersect, they do so on a line.
g. Two intersecting lines determine a plane.
h. Two lines intersect in, at most, one point.

17. Start with a rectangular piece of paper.

- Fold a corner.
- Fold the adjacent corner so that the edges touch, as shown.

Explain why $\angle ABC$ is a fixed size no matter where the first fold is made.

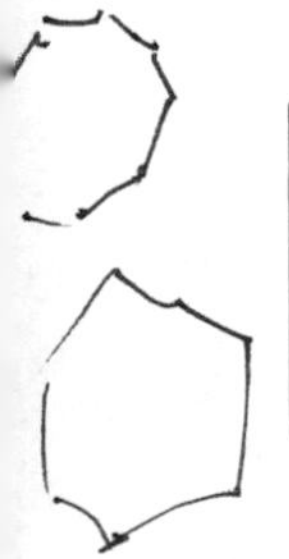

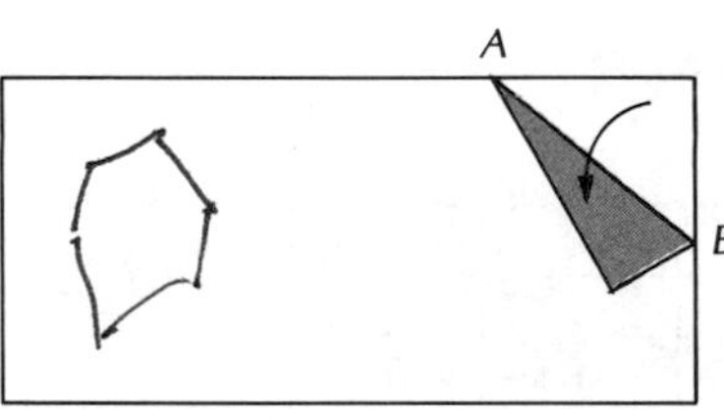

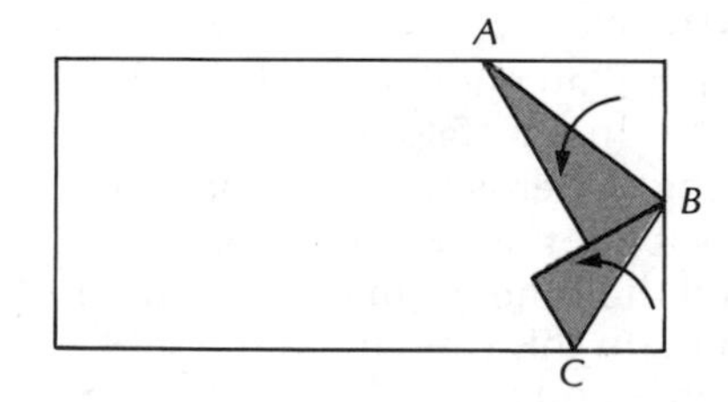

EXTRA

Cutting Cubes

Can a cube be cut by a plane to produce the following figures? For each figure that can be formed, describe the cut that produces the figure.

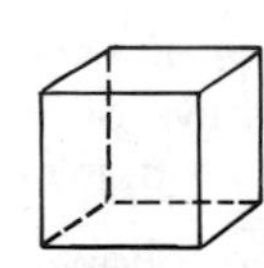

a. an isosceles triangle
b. an equilateral triangle
c. a square
d. a rectangle
e. a pentagon
f. a polygon with more than six sides

10-2 Logical Reasoning

When making a decision, it is often necessary to use logical reasoning. Do I need to take an umbrella? How many books do I need for this morning's classes? Will my parents be pleased to see my report card?

Consider the following situation.

When Toni's computer doesn't work,
she suspects that a fuse has blown.

To verify this, she plugs her desk lamp into the same plug as her computer. Toni's reasoning is as follows:

If the desk lamp works in this plug,
then the fuse is working.

or

The fact that the desk lamp works in
this plug **implies** that the fuse is working.

If-then statements are called **conditional statements** or **implications**. The structure of an implication can be studied using symbols.
If p and q represent sentences, then each implication can be written in the form "If p then q."

Symbolically, "If p then q" is written as $\boldsymbol{p \Rightarrow q}$ and is read "p implies q". Here, p is called the *hypothesis* and q is called the *conclusion*.

Suppose your teacher made the following statement, which you understood to be a promise.

If you pass the June examination, then you will get a pass mark for the course.

This promise is an implication that can be judged as true or false by determining under what conditions the promise was kept or broken. Suppose you passed the June exam and you got a failing mark. In this case, the promise was broken—and this is the only way to break the promise. For all other cases, the promise is judged to be true. All cases can be summarized in a "truth" table, as shown at the right.

p	q	$p \quad q$
T	T	T
F	F	T
F	T	T
T	F	F

Why are the first 3 cases true?

A conditional statement, $p \Rightarrow q$, is false only if p is true and q is false.

The **converse** of a statement is a statement in which the hypothesis and conclusion have been interchanged. If a statement, $p \Rightarrow q$, is true, its converse, $q \Rightarrow p$, is not necessarily true.

Consider the following statement and its converse.

If it snows, then Shirley wears a coat. $\quad p \Rightarrow q$
If Shirley wears a coat, then it snows. $\quad q \Rightarrow p$

The converse is not necessarily true.

A statement and its converse can be combined to form a **biconditional statement**. "If A then B" and "if B then A" can be combined into one biconditional statement:

A if, and only if, B, or $A \Leftrightarrow B$.

EXAMPLE 1: Write a conclusion for each pair of statements, where possible.

a. *Given:* 1. If it rains, the grass will get wet. $A \Rightarrow B$ "then" is understood.
2. It is raining. A
Conclusion: The grass will get wet. B

b. *Given:* 1. A triangle is equilateral if, and only if, it is equiangular. $A \Leftrightarrow B$
2. A triangle is equiangular. B
Conclusion: The triangle is equilateral. A

c. *Given:* 1. All students at LaSalle Secondary School study mathematics.
2. Rick is a student at LaSalle Secondary School.
Conclusion: Rick studies mathematics.

You could write this as: If a student attends LaSalle Secondary School, then the student studies mathematics.

Notice that, since Rick is a particular student at LaSalle Secondary School, then he must study mathematics.

d. *Given:* 1. Some dogs enjoy swimming.
2. Ladee is my dog.
You cannot conclude that "Ladee enjoys swimming," since it is not clear that the second statement is a particular case of the first. Ladee could belong to the set of dogs who dislike swimming.

This in *not* the same as the statement "All dogs enjoy swimming".

A true implication must be true in every case. If one case can be found for which the statement is false, then the implication is false. A case for which an implication is found to be false is called a **counter-example**.

EXAMPLE 2: Show that each given statement is false by finding a counter-example.

a. All even numbers are positive.
Counter-example: -4 is an even number that is not positive.

b. Every furry animal is a dog.
Counter-example: A cat is a furry animal that is not a dog.

EXERCISE 10-2

A **1.** Rewrite each statement as a conditional statement.

a. Opposite sides of a parallelogram are equal in length.
b. A person eighteen years of age or older can vote.
c. Supplementary angles are two angles whose sum is 180°.
d. An equilateral triangle has three equal angles.
e. Water boils at a temperature of 100 °C.

2. Write the converse of each conditional sentence. Is the converse true?

a. If I exercise regularly, then I will be fit.
b. If Al walks in the rain, he gets wet.
c. If you come to my house tonight, you will have pizza for dinner.
d. If Jenny is in Grade 12, she studies English.
e. If a number ends in 0 or 5, it is divisible by 5.
f. If a number ends in 2, then the number is exactly divisible by 2.
g. If two numbers are odd, then their sum is even.
h. If one number is odd and a second number is even, then their product is even.

3. Refer to each statement given in exercise 2. If the converse is true, combine the statement and its converse into an "if, and only if" statement.

4. For each of the following, determine whether the conclusion follows logically from the given information.

a. If the cost of gasoline increases, it will cost Sindy more to run her car.
The cost of running Sindy's car increased this year.
Therefore, the cost of gasoline has increased.

b. Some cats are pets.
A cat has fur.
Therefore, some pets have fur.

c. Every musician plays an instrument.
Steve is a musician.
Therefore, Steve plays the saxophone.

d. Passengers on the Via train to Vancouver must have seat reservations.
Mr. Forest is going to Vancouver.
Therefore, Mr. Forest must have a seat reservation on the Via train.

5. State whether each implication is true or false. Assume that the variables have domain ***R***, the real numbers.

a. $x = 5 \Rightarrow x^2 = 25$
b. $y < 0 \Rightarrow y^2 > 0$
c. $a = -4 \Rightarrow a^2 = -16$
d. $x = 6 \Rightarrow x > -3$
e. $a^2 = 25 \Rightarrow a = 5$
f. $3x - 2 = 4 \Rightarrow x = 2$
g. $x \leq 8 \Rightarrow -8 \leq -x$
h. $y = 10 \Rightarrow 3y - 3 < 7$
i. b is a multiple of 3 $\Rightarrow$ b is a multiple of 9
j. x is a multiple of 9 $\Rightarrow$ x is a multiple of 3

B **6.** Write a conclusion, if possible, given the following facts.

a. If it is snowing, then it is cold outside. It is cold outside.

b. If Greg makes the team, he will be the quarterback. Greg made the team.

c. If the strike is settled by Monday, the workers will return to work on Tuesday. The workers did not return to work on Tuesday.

d. Some of the people in the club were on the social committee. Linda is in the club.

e. A quadrilateral is cyclic if, and only if, its opposite angles are supplementary. The opposite angles of quadrilateral *ABCD* are supplementary.

f. If $x = 5$, then $x^2 = 25$. $x^2 = 25$.

g. All right angles are equal. Angles *P* and *Q* are right angles.

h. A point is on the perpendicular bisector of a line segment if, and only if, it is equidistant from the endpoints of the line segment. *C* is a point not on segment $\overline{AB}$ such that $AC = BC$.

7. Show that each statement is false by finding a counter-example.

a. All integers are either positive or negative.

b. All prime numbers are odd.

c. When a real number is divided by a real number, the result is always a real number.

d. Every quadrilateral with all sides equal is a square.

e. For every whole number n, $n^2 + n + 11$ is a prime number.

8. Michele tutors students who are having difficulty with grade 9 mathematics. These students make many of the same common errors. Michele has found that the best way of convincing them that their methods are wrong is to find a counter-example. Show that each of the given equations is wrong by finding a counter-example.

a. $\frac{1}{p} + \frac{1}{q} = \frac{1}{p+q}$

b. $\frac{1}{p} + \frac{1}{q} = \frac{2}{p+q}$

c. $\frac{a}{b} \times \frac{c}{d} = \frac{ad}{bc}$

d. $\sqrt{a^2 + b^2} = a + b$

e. $\frac{a}{a+b} = \frac{1}{b}$

f. $\sqrt{-a}$ is undefined.

9. Billy's older brother, Michael, made the following promise: "If I get home early, I will take you to the park." For each of the following, decide whether Michael kept his promise.

a. Michael came home early and took Billy to the park.

b. Michael came home early and didn't take Billy to the park.

c. Michael didn't come home early and didn't take Billy to the park.

d. Michael didn't come home early and he still took Billy to the park.

Application

An electrical circuit can be illustrated by diagrams as shown.
The intended flow of electricity is from point A to point B. p is a gate that determines whether electricity flows from A to B.

When p is open, current cannot flow from A to B.
In this case, p is false.

When p is closed, current can flow from A to B.
In this case, p is true.

Circuits can be set up as series circuits or as parallel circuits.

Series Circuit: "and" gates

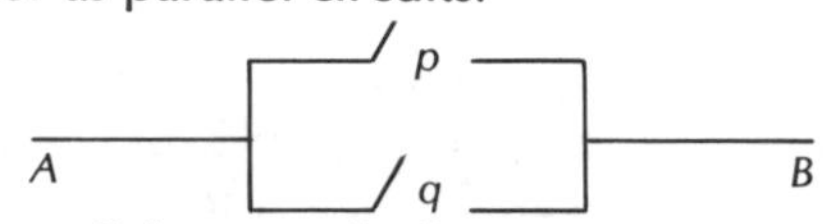

Parallel Circuit: "or" gates

For current to flow from A to B in a series circuit, both p and q must be closed.

Current will flow from A to B in a parallel circuit, if either p or q is closed.

If a gate is closed, label it T. If it is open, label it F. If current can flow through a circuit, label it T. If current cannot flow through the circuit, label it F.

Complete the two tables below, using T to indicate that current can flow or F to indicate that current cannot flow.

The series circuit is the same as
p **and** q.

Series Circuit

p	q	Circuit
T	T	
T	F	
F	T	
F	F	

The parallel circuit is the same as
p **or** q.

Parallel Circuit

p	q	Circuit
T	T	
T	F	
F	T	
F	F	

Now consider a more complicated series of switches where the notation $\sim p$ means "p is false," or "p is not true".

For current to flow from A to B, ($\sim p$ and q) must be true or (p and q) must be true. Notice that if the p gate is open, the $\sim p$ gate must be closed.

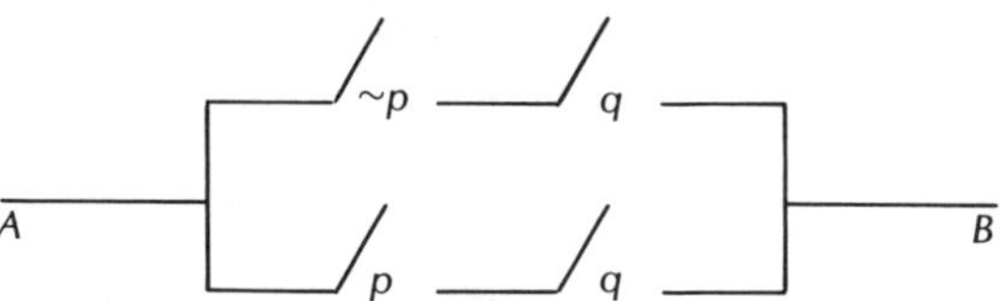

Complete the following table to determine which values of p and q will allow the current flow from A to B.

p	q	$\sim p$	$\sim p$ and q	p and q	($\sim p$ and q) or (p and q)
T	T				
T	F				
F	T				
F	F				

10-3 Indirect Proof

In mathematics, there are various methods of proof. The proofs that you have studied in this unit until now have been *direct proofs.*

Sometimes, it can be easier to reason *indirectly* than to find a direct proof. In order to understand indirect proof, it is necessary to understand what is meant by the **negation** of a statement.
The negation of a statement p, is written "*not p*" or $\sim p$.

	Statement		Negation	
1.	Kelly is in this class.	(T)	Kelly is not in this class.	(F)
2.	Allan does not like sweets.	(T)	Allan does like sweets.	(F)
3.	A triangle has 3 sides.	(T)	A triangle does not have 3 sides.	(F)
4.	$6+5=11$	(T)	$6+5\neq 11$	(F)
5.	$5\times 4=15$	(F)	$5\times 4\neq 15$	(T)
6.	$18\div 3\neq 5$	(T)	$18\div 3=5$	(F)
7.	p	(T)	$\sim p$	(F)
8.	If today is Saturday, then this is a weekend.	(T)	If today is Saturday, then today is not a weekend.	(F)
9.	If p, then q.	(T)	If p, then $\sim q$.	(F)

Notice that if a statement is true, its negation is false.

Negate the conclusion.

An **indirect proof** is a form of reasoning whereby a statement is proved true by proving that its negation is false. The steps for an indirect proof are as follows.

To prove a statement true by an indirect proof:

- Assume that the negation of the statement is true.
- Reason to find a contradiction of known facts (one counter-example is sufficient to prove a statement false).
- Conclude that the assumption is false.
- Conclude that the statement to be proved is true.

Or negate the conclusion.

EXAMPLE 1: Assume that $a > b$ and a contradiction of a known fact is found. What conclusion can you make?

You can conclude that $a > b$ is false.
Therefore, $a \not> b$ is true.
However, you cannot conclude that $a < b$ since it is possible that $a = b$.

Notice in Example 1, $a \not> b$ means $a < b$ or $a = b$, which is usually written as $a \leq b$. When comparing numbers like a and b, there are three cases to consider.

$$a < b, \quad a = b, \quad a > b.$$

To prove any one of the cases to be true by indirect reasoning, you only need to prove the other two cases false

EXAMPLE 2: Prove that if x is an integer and x^2 is odd, then x is odd.

Given: x is an integer and x^2 is odd — List all possibilities.
Prove: x is odd — Assume that the negation of the conclusion is true.
Proof: (indirect)
Since x is an integer, either x is odd or x is even.
Assume that x is even. — Reason logically until you reach a contradiction of a known fact.
Then $x = 2n$, where $n \in \mathbf{Z}$.
$x^2 = (2n)(2n)$ — $4n^2$ is divisible by 2.
$= 4n^2$ — Conclude that what you assumed to be true is false. Therefore, what you want to prove is true.
But $4n^2$ is even.
Thus, x^2 is even.
This contradicts the given information.
So, the assumption that x is even must be false.
Therefore x is odd.

EXAMPLE 3: A group of children consists of twins and triplets. There are 48 children altogether. Prove that the number of sets of triplets must be even.

Let x represent the number of sets of twins and y represent the number of sets of triplets.
The number of children is given by
$2x + 3y$, where $x, y \in \mathbf{Z}$.
$\therefore 2x + 3y = 48$
An integer is either even or odd. Assume that the number of sets of triplets is odd.
Let $2n + 1$ represent the number of sets of triplets, where $n \in \mathbf{Z}$.
That is, $y = 2n + 1$.
$2x + 3(2n + 1) = 48$ — Substitute for y in the equation.
$2x + 6n + 3 = 48$
$2x + 6n = 45$
$2(x + 3n) = 45$
Since $x, 3n \in \mathbf{Z}$, then $x + 3n$ is an integer and $2(x + 3n)$ is even.
Thus, $2(x + 3n) \neq 45$. — This is a contradiction.

Therefore, the assumption that the number of sets of triplets is odd is false. It follows that the number of sets of triplets is even.

EXERCISE 10-3

A **1.** Write the negation of each statement.

a. $\angle A = \angle B$
b. $18 - x > 12$
c. $\angle PQR$ is an acute angle.
d. $6 - 3x \neq 15$
e. Shirley is an artist.
f. Howard enjoys classical music.
g. Claire does not drive.
h. Ari does not play golf.
i. If Molly plays tennis regularly, then she improves her game.
j. If x is an even integer, then x is divisible by 2.
k. If it is winter, then Merle cannot ski.

2. An indirect proof is to be used to prove each given statement. State the assumption that would be used in the proof.
   a. $\angle ABC$ is a right angle.
   b. $\triangle XYZ$ is isosceles.
   c. It is raining outside.
   d. T is the midpoint of $\overline{RS}$.
   e. $a^2 + b^2 = c^2$
   f. Janicė uses a microcomputer.
   g. $|2i| \neq -2$
   h. You cannot see Polaris.
   i. If Mario swims, then he will practise the front crawl.
   j. If $2x + 7 = 15$, then $x \neq 5$.

3. Sandy has shown that $a > b$ is a false statement. Can Sandy now conclude that $a < b$ is a true statement? Explain.

4. While trying to prove that $m \parallel n$, Sean proved that $m \perp n$ is false. Can he conclude that $m \parallel n$? Explain.

5. In order to prove that $a \neq b$ by an indirect proof, what must be disproved?

B 6. Prove each statement using an indirect proof.
   a. If a is an odd integer, then a^2 must be odd.
   b. $\sqrt{10} \neq 3$
   c. If b is odd, then $3b + 1$ is even.
   d. If x is a prime number greater than 2, then x is odd.
   e. If p and q are odd integers, then pq is odd.
   f. If Michael was born in a leap year, then his 17th birthday occurs in an odd-numbered year.

7. Prove that a collection of dimes and quarters with a total value of \$3.40 consists of an even number of quarters.

8. Prove that three angles of a quadrilateral cannot each be equal to 120°.

9. Prove that if $5x + 6y = 142$ and $x, y \in \mathbf{Z}$, then x is an even number.

10. Prove that it is impossible for $5x + 6y$ to be equal to an odd number if x is even and $x, y \in \mathbf{Z}$.

11. The sum of the interior angles of a triangle is 180°. If two angles of a triangle are equal, prove that the measure of the third angle must be even.

12. Allison has an even number of coins consisting of nickels and dimes. Prove that the value of the coins is even.

13. To prove that $\sqrt{2}$ is an irrational number, an indirect proof can be used.
    Either $\sqrt{2}$ is irrational or rational.
    Assume that $\sqrt{2}$ is a rational number.
    $\therefore \sqrt{2} = \frac{a}{b}$, where $a, b \in \mathbf{Z}$, and $\frac{a}{b}$ is expressed in lowest terms.
    Square both sides and multiply by b^2.
    $2b^2 = a$
    Find a contradiction that proves that $\sqrt{2}$ is irrational.

C 14. Prove that $\sqrt{3}$ is irrational.

Review of Theorems and Postulates

1. **Opposite Angle Theorem (OAT)**
When two lines intersect, vertically opposite angles are equal.

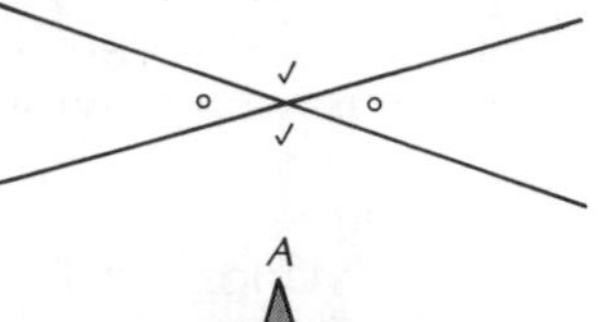

2. **Isosceles Triangle Theorem (ITT)**
If a triangle is isosceles, then the angles opposite the equal sides are equal. That is, if $AB = AC$, then $\angle ABC = \angle ACB$.
Notice that the converse of **ITT** is also true. That is, if $\angle ABC = \angle ACB$, then $AB = AC$.

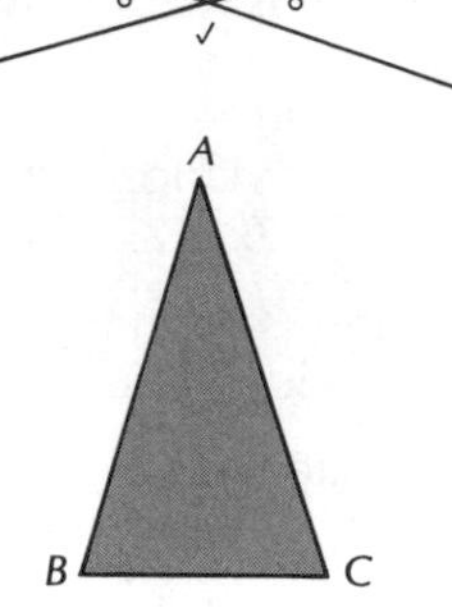

A **corollary** to a theorem is a new theorem which follows easily as an extension of the first theorem.

Corollary to ITT:
A triangle is equilateral if, and only if, it is equiangular.

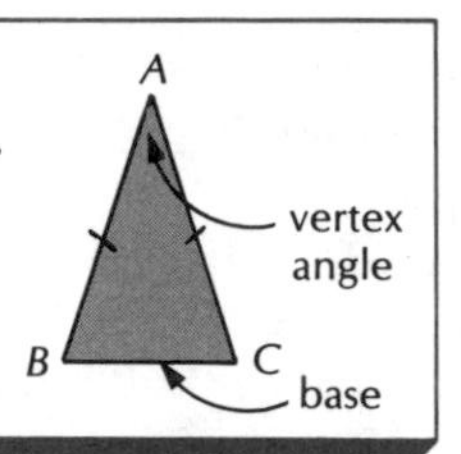

In an isosceles $\triangle ABC$, in which $AB = AC$, the base is defined to be the third side, $\overline{BC}$. The angle formed by the two equal sides is called the **vertex** angle.

3. **Properties of an Isosceles Triangle (PIT)**

a. The bisector of the vertex angle of an isosceles triangle is also the altitude to the base.

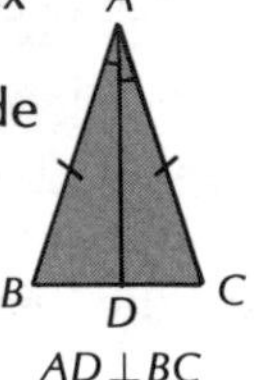

$AD \perp BC$

b. The altitude to the base of an isosceles triangle is also the perpendicular bisector of the base.

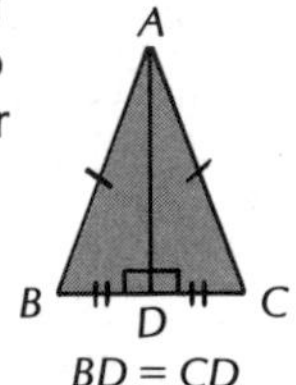

$BD = CD$

c. An isosceles triangle has one line of symmetry, that is, the altitude to its base.

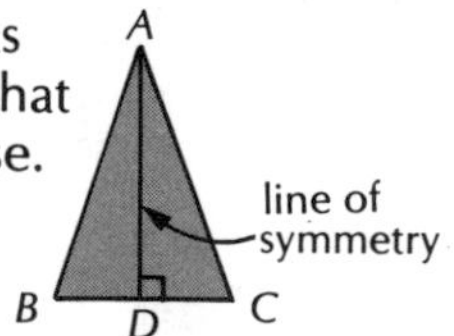

d. The median to the base of an isosceles triangle is perpendicular to the base and the median bisects the vertex angle.

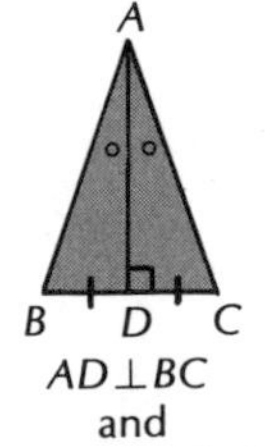

$AD \perp BC$
and
$\angle BAD = \angle CAD$

For any isosceles triangle, the altitude, the perpendicular bisector of the base, the bisector of the vertex angle, the median to the base, and the line of symmetry are the same line.

Two triangles are congruent if, and only if, their corresponding sides and angles are equal.

$$\triangle ABC \cong \triangle DEF$$

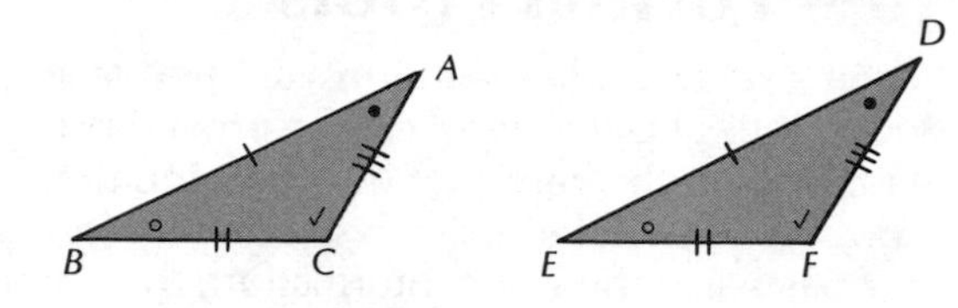

4. SAS Congruence Postulate
If two sides and the contained angle of one triangle are equal to two corresponding sides and the contained angle of another triangle, then the triangles are congruent.

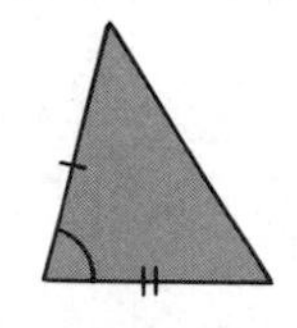
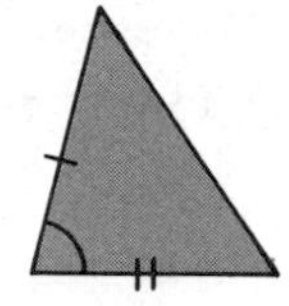

5. SSS Congruence Postulate
If three sides of one triangle are equal to three corresponding sides of another triangle, then the triangles are congruent.

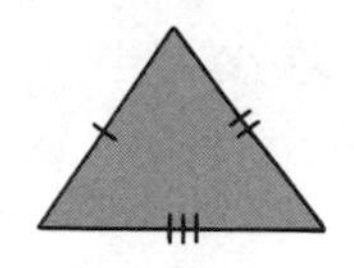
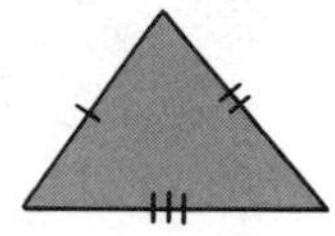

6. ASA or AAS Congruence Postulate
If two angles and a side of one triangle are equal to two angles and the corresponding side of another triangle, then the triangles are congruent.

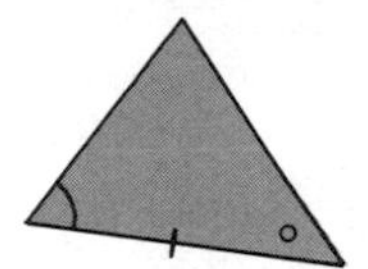
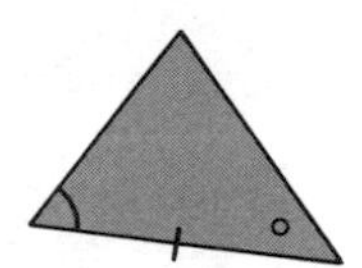

7. Perpendicular Bisector Theorem (PBT)
A point is on the perpendicular bisector of a line segment if, and only if, it is equidistant from the endpoints of the segment.

If $\overline{PD}$ is the perpendicular bisector of $\overline{AB}$, then $PA = PB$. If $PA = PB$, then P is on the perpendicular bisector of $\overline{AB}$.

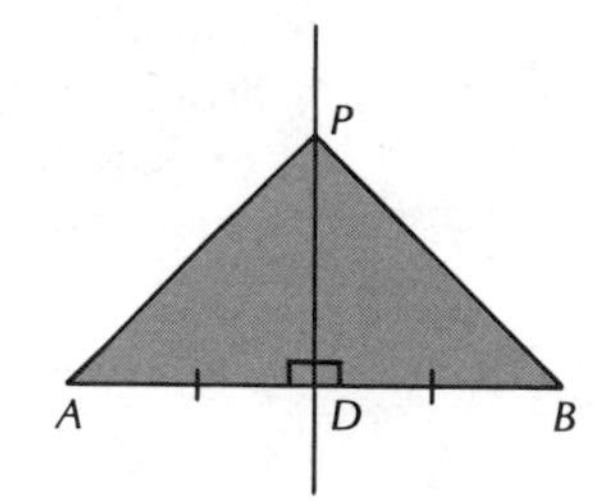

8. Angle Bisector Theorem (ABT)
A point is on the bisector of an angle if, and only if, it is equidistant from the arms of the angle.

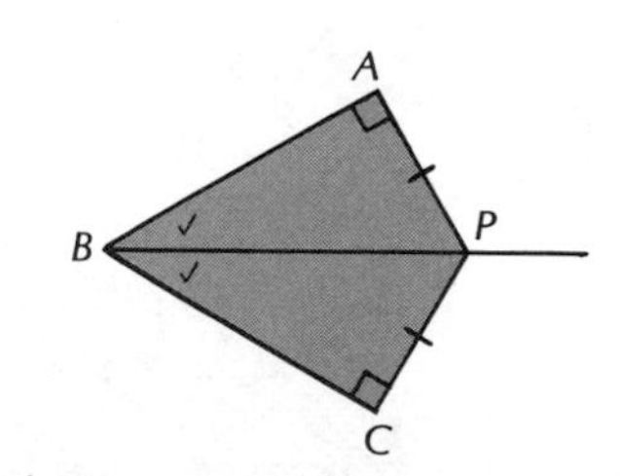

9. Pythagorean Theorem (PT)
The square of the length of the hypotenuse of a right-angled triangle is equal to the sum of the squares of the lengths of the other two sides.

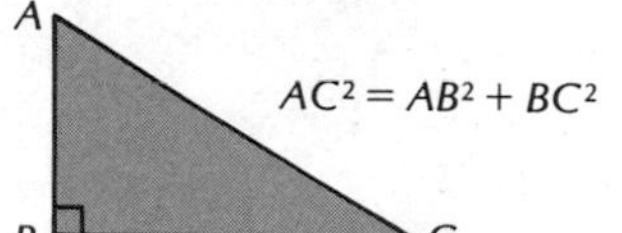

10-4 Formal Proofs

When a set of undefined terms, defined terms, and postulates is given, new deductions and theorems can be proved using the logic of deductive reasoning. In this section, postulates and theorems are used to give formal proofs. A **formal deduction** is a four-part format for writing a proof. The four parts are: the given information, the statement that is to be proved, a diagram, and the formal proof, which contains statements and authorities. Use words like "thus" or "therefore" or a symbol, like $\therefore$, to indicate the conclusion.

EXAMPLE 1: In $\triangle ABC$, $AB = AC$. D is in the interior of $\triangle ABC$ such that $\angle DBC = \angle DCB$. Prove that $\angle ABD = \angle ACD$.

Given: $\triangle ABC$, $AB = AC$,
D is in $\triangle ABC$ such that $\angle DBC = \angle DCB$
Prove: $\angle ABD = \angle ACD$

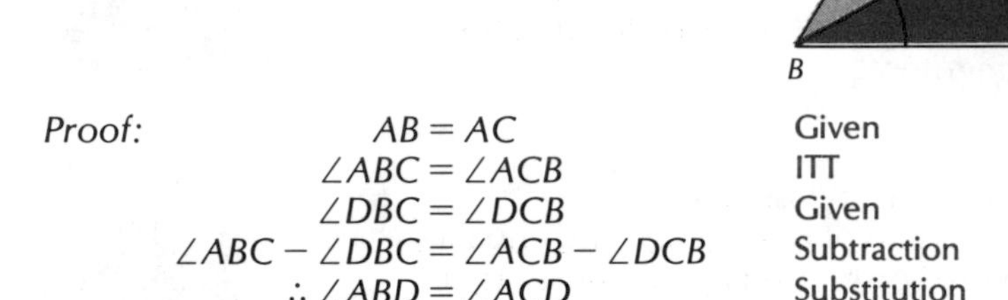

Proof:

Statement	Authority
$AB = AC$	Given
$\angle ABC = \angle ACB$	ITT
$\angle DBC = \angle DCB$	Given
$\angle ABC - \angle DBC = \angle ACB - \angle DCB$	Subtraction
$\therefore \angle ABD = \angle ACD$	Substitution

EXAMPLE 2: In $\triangle ABC$, median $\overline{AD}$ is drawn to side $\overline{BC}$. Prove that the perpendiculars from vertices, B and C to median $\overline{AD}$, extended, are equal.

Given: $\triangle ABC$, median $\overline{AD}$,
$\overline{BE} \perp \overline{AD}$,
$\overline{CF} \perp \overline{AD}$ extended
Prove: $BE = CF$

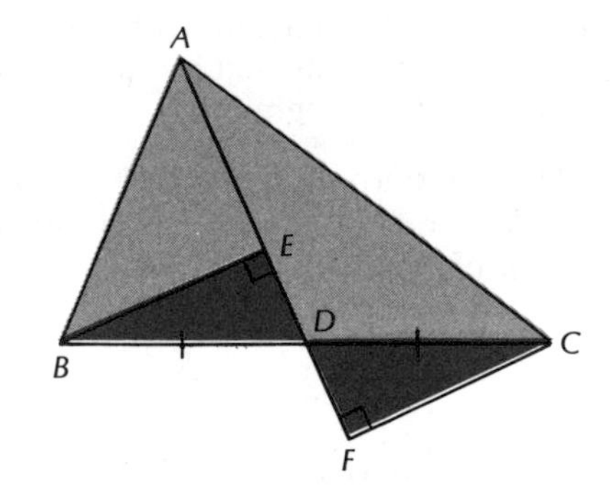

Proof: For $\triangle BED$ and $\triangle CFD$,

Statement	Authority
$\angle BED = \angle CFD$ $= 90°$.	Definition of perpendicular lines
$\angle EDB = \angle FDC$	OAT
$BD = CD$	Given
$\triangle BED \cong \triangle CFD$	AAS
$\therefore BE = CF$	Congruent triangles

Recall that $\cong$ means "is congruent to".

A congruence theorem involving right-angled triangles is proved below.

> **Hypotenuse-Side Theorem (HST)**
> If the lengths of the hypotenuse and one side of a right-angled triangle are equal to the lengths of the hypotenuse and one side of another right-angled triangle, then the triangles are congruent.

Given: $\triangle ABC$ and $\triangle DEF$ such that $\angle B = \angle E = 90°$, $AC = DF$, $AB = DE$

Prove: $\triangle ABC \cong \triangle DEF$

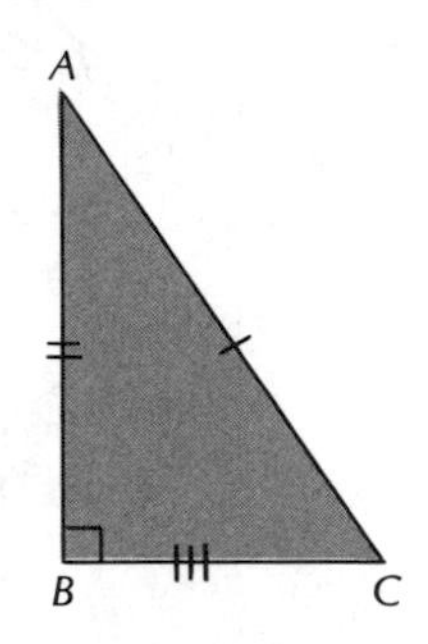

Proof: In $\triangle DEF$, extend $\overline{FE}$ to meet G such that $GE = BC$.
For $\triangle ABC$, $\triangle DEF$, and $\triangle DEG$,

Statement	Reason
$AB = DE$.	Given
$\angle ABC = 90°$	Given
But $\angle DEF + \angle DEG = 180°$	Definition of a straight angle
and $\angle DEF = 90°$	Given
$\therefore \angle DEG = 90°$	Subtraction
$BC = EG$	Construction
$\therefore \triangle ABC \cong \triangle DEG$	SAS
$DG = AC$	Congruent triangles
But $AC = DF$	Given
$\therefore DG = DF$	Substitution
$\angle DGE = \angle DFE$	ITT
$\angle DGE = \angle ACB$	Congruent triangles
$\therefore \angle DFE = \angle ACB$	Substitution

For $\triangle ABC$ and $\triangle DEF$,

Statement	Reason
$AB = DE$.	Given
$\angle ABC = \angle DEF$	Given
$\angle ACB = \angle DFE$	Proved above
$\therefore \triangle ABC \cong \triangle DEF$	AAS

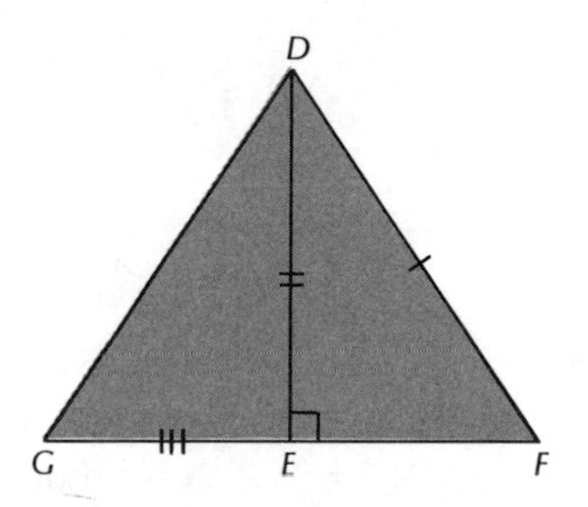

EXERCISE 10-4

A **1.** Rewrite the statement of each given theorem as a biconditional statement.

a. Isosceles Triangle Theorem
b. Perpendicular Bisector Theorem
c. Angle Bisector Theorem

2. Which pairs of triangles are congruent? State reasons.

a.

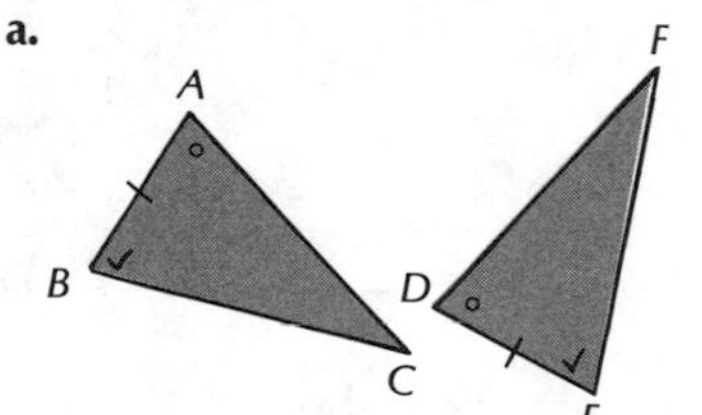

b.

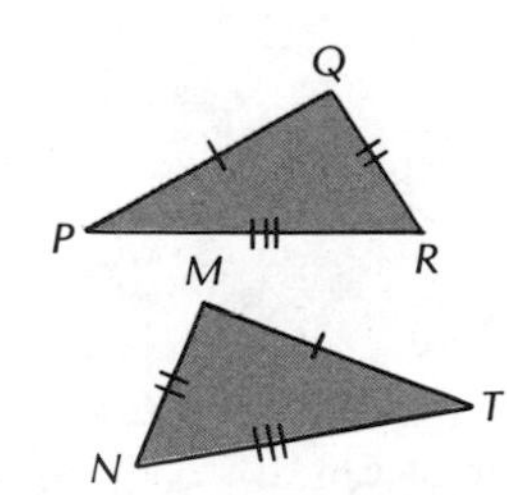

c.

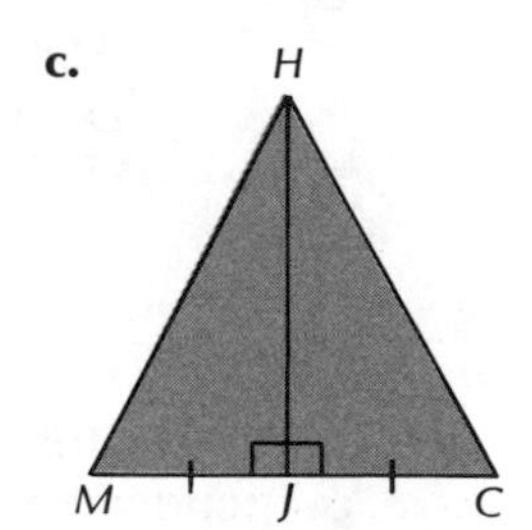

d.

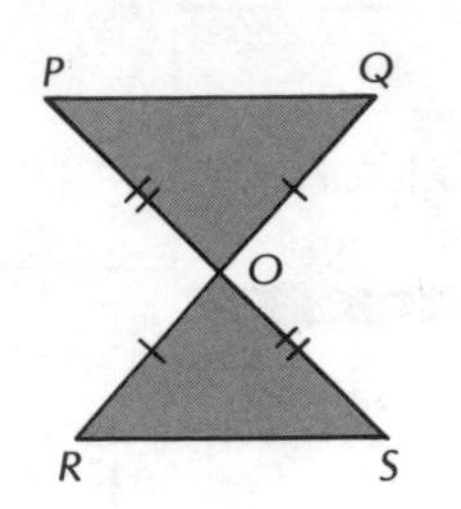

e.

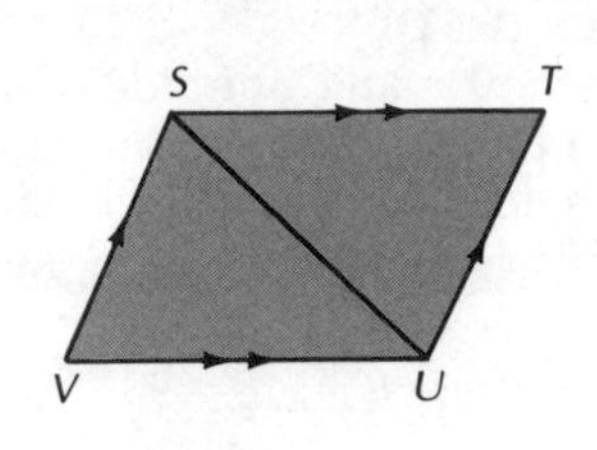

f.

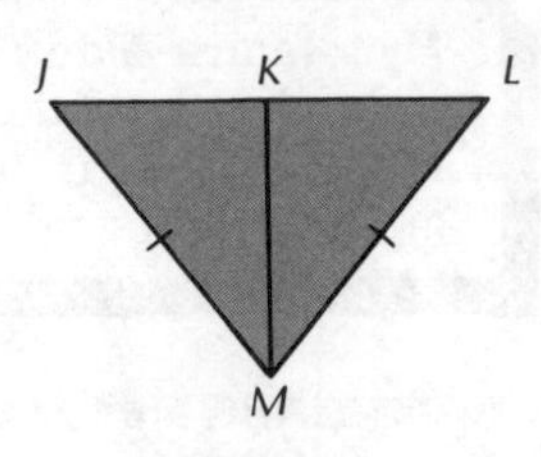

g.

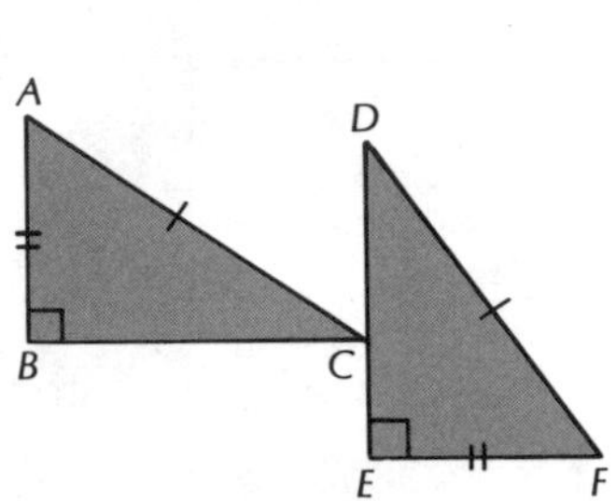

h.

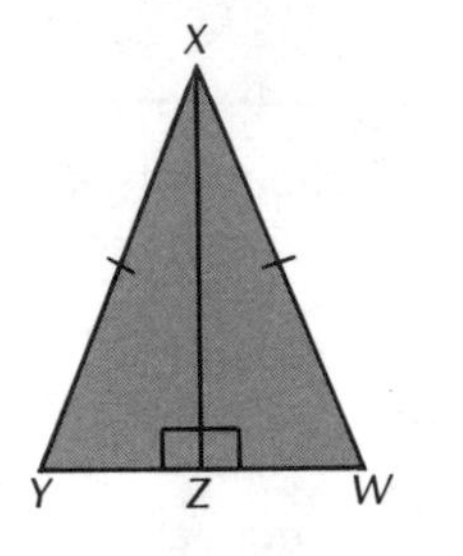

i.

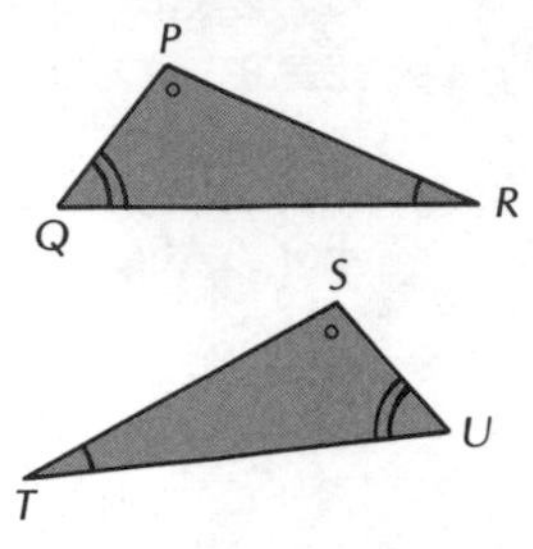

B **3.** Find the values of the variables.

a.

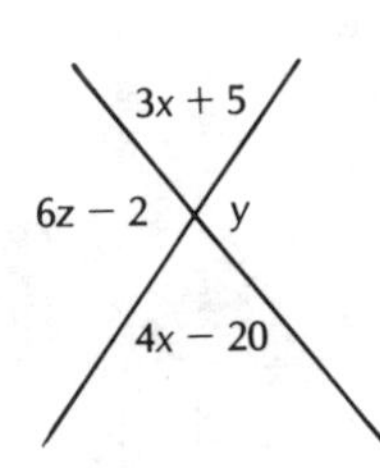

b.

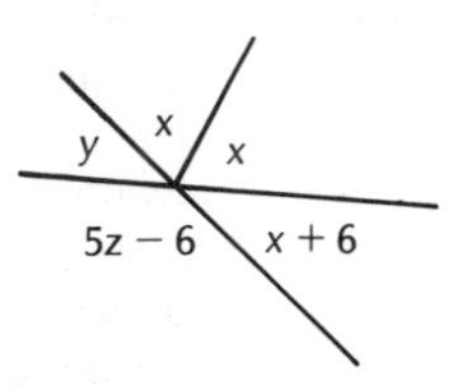

c.

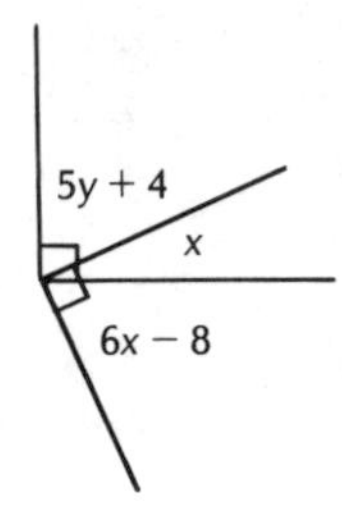

4. For $\triangle XYZ$, $XY = XZ$. W is in the interior of $\triangle XYZ$ such that $WY = WZ$. Prove that $\angle XYW = \angle XZW$.

5. In quadrilateral $PQRS$, $PQ = PS$, $QR = SR$. Prove that $\angle PQR = \angle PSR$.

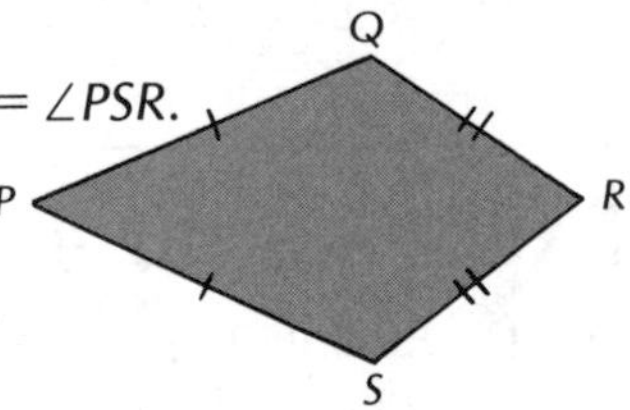

6. In quadrilateral $ABCD$, diagonal $\overline{AC}$ is the perpendicular bisector of diagonal $\overline{BD}$. Prove that $\overline{AC}$ bisects both $\angle BAD$ and $\angle BCD$.

7. Given: $AD = CD$,
$\angle ADE = \angle CDF$,
$\overline{BD} \perp \overline{EF}$

Prove: $\overline{DB} \perp \overline{AC}$

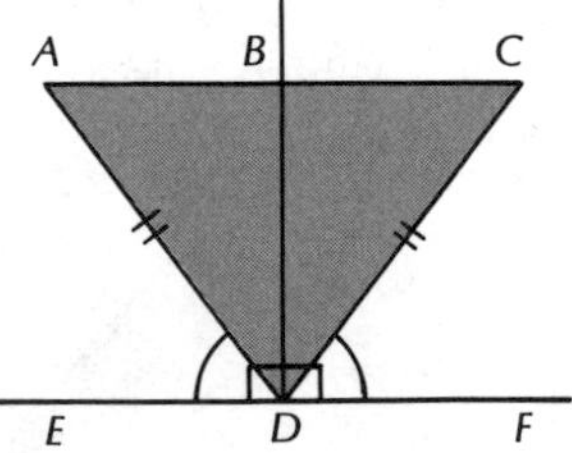

8. In quadrilateral $PQRS$, $PQ = PS$ and $QR = SR$. Prove that $\overline{PR}$ is the perpendicular bisector of $\overline{QS}$.

9. Prove that the bisectors of the angles of a triangle are concurrent (that is, they all contain one point).
(*Hint:* Let D be the intersection of the bisectors of $\angle ABC$ and $\angle ACB$. Prove that $\overline{AD}$ bisects $\angle BAC$.)

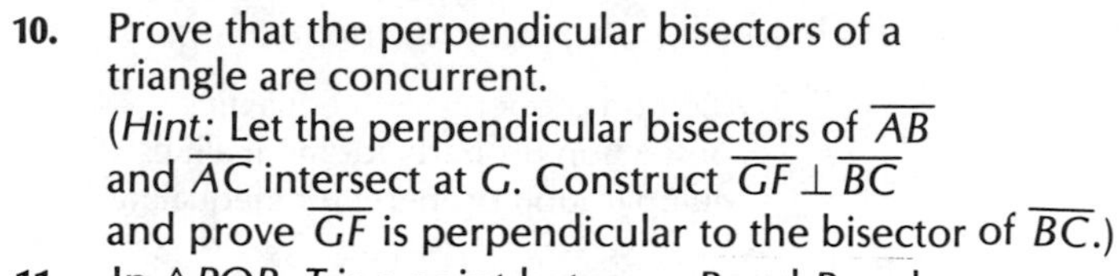

10. Prove that the perpendicular bisectors of a triangle are concurrent.
(*Hint:* Let the perpendicular bisectors of $\overline{AB}$ and $\overline{AC}$ intersect at G. Construct $\overline{GF} \perp \overline{BC}$ and prove $\overline{GF}$ is perpendicular to the bisector of $\overline{BC}$.)

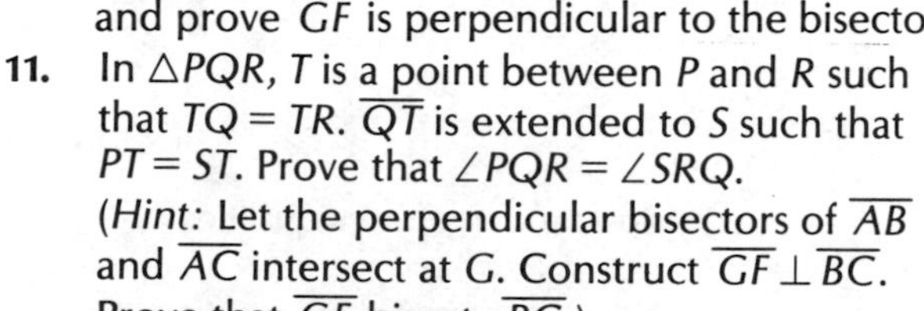

11. In $\triangle PQR$, T is a point between P and R such that $TQ = TR$. $\overline{QT}$ is extended to S such that $PT = ST$. Prove that $\angle PQR = \angle SRQ$.
(*Hint:* Let the perpendicular bisectors of $\overline{AB}$ and $\overline{AC}$ intersect at G. Construct $\overline{GF} \perp \overline{BC}$. Prove that $\overline{GF}$ bisects $\overline{BC}$.)

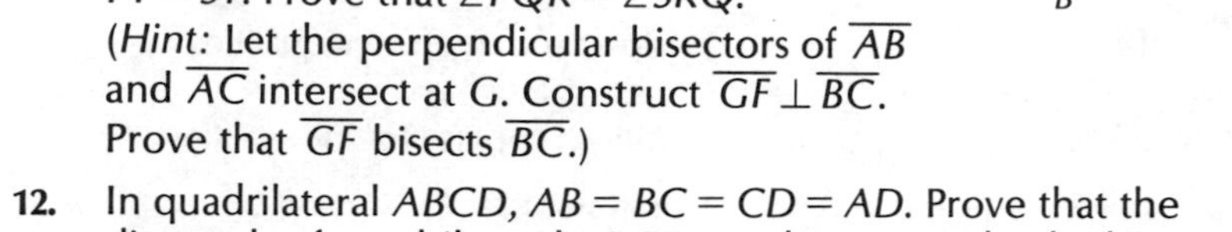

12. In quadrilateral $ABCD$, $AB = BC = CD = AD$. Prove that the diagonals of quadrilateral $ABCD$ are the perpendicular bisectors of each other.

13. $\triangle ABC$ is equilateral. Equilateral triangles ABD, ACF, and BEC are constructed such that D, E, and F are outside $\triangle ABC$.
 a. Prove that D, A, F, and D, B, E, and E, C, F are collinear.
 b. Prove that $AE = BF = CD$.

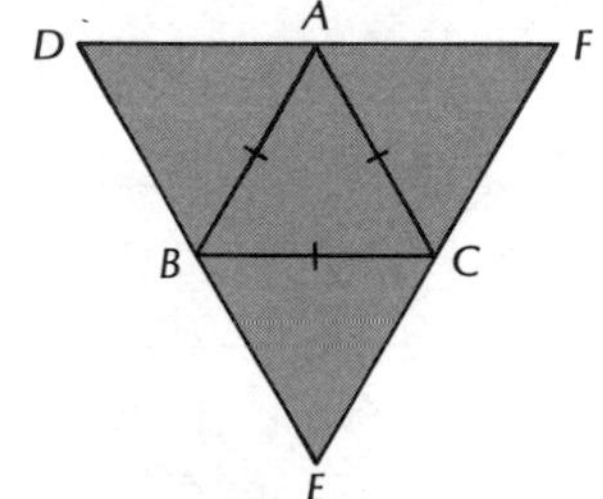

14. $\triangle ABC$ is isosceles such that $AB = AC$. M is the midpoint of side $\overline{BC}$. N and P are points on $\overline{AB}$ and $\overline{AC}$, respectively, such that $\angle NMB = \angle PMC$.
Prove each statement.
 a. $NM = PM$ b. $\triangle ANP$ is isosceles.

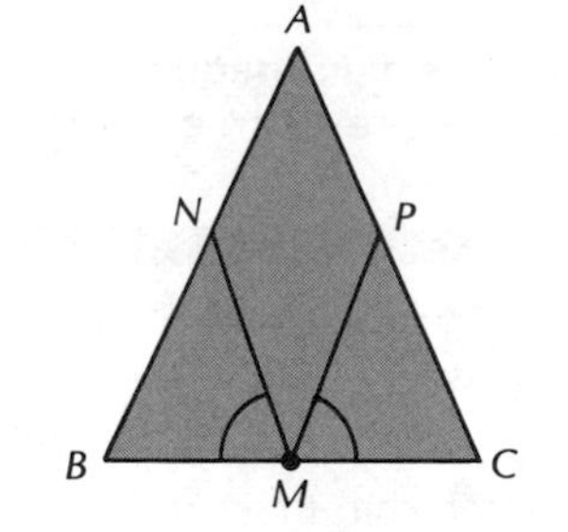

C 15. S is a point on $\overline{XY}$ and T is a point on $\overline{XZ}$ in $\triangle XYZ$. $\overline{SZ}$ and $\overline{TY}$ intersect at W such that $SZ = TY$ and $WY = WZ$. Prove that $\triangle XYZ$ is isosceles and that $\overline{XW}$ extended is a median of $\triangle XYZ$.

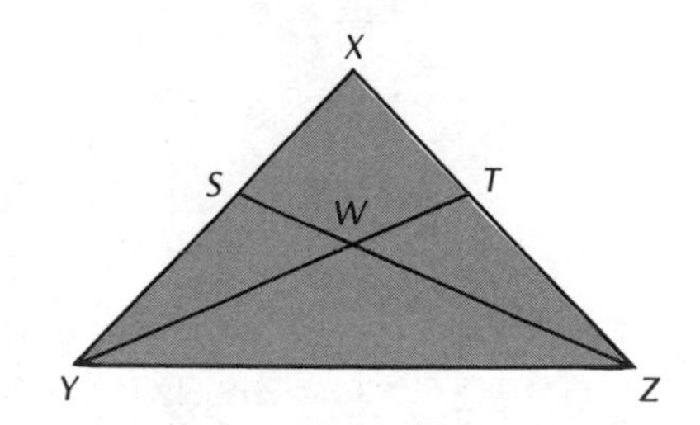

10-5 Proofs Involving Inequalities

In Lesson 10-4, the proofs considered had conclusions that were equalities. The direct method of proof was used. This lesson contains proofs involving inequalities. Some of these conclusions are best proved by the indirect method of proof.

For the exercises in this lesson, you can use the following properties of inequalities.

i. If $a > b$, then $a + c > b + c$. — Addition property for inequalities
$a - c > b - c$ — Subtraction property for inequalities
$ac > bc$, if $c > 0$ — Multiplication property for inequalities
$ac < bc$, if $c < 0$
$\frac{a}{c} > \frac{b}{c}$, if $c > 0$
$\frac{a}{c} < \frac{b}{c}$, if $c < 0$ — Division property for inequalities

ii. If $a > b$ and $b > c$, then $a > c$. — Transitive property for inequalities

iii. $a > b$ if, and only if, $a = b + c$, where $c > 0$. — Definition of $>$

EXAMPLE 1:

a. *B* is between *A* and *C*

$AB + BC = AC$
$\therefore AC > AB$ and $AC > BC$

b. $\angle\theta$ and $\angle\alpha$ are adjacent angles

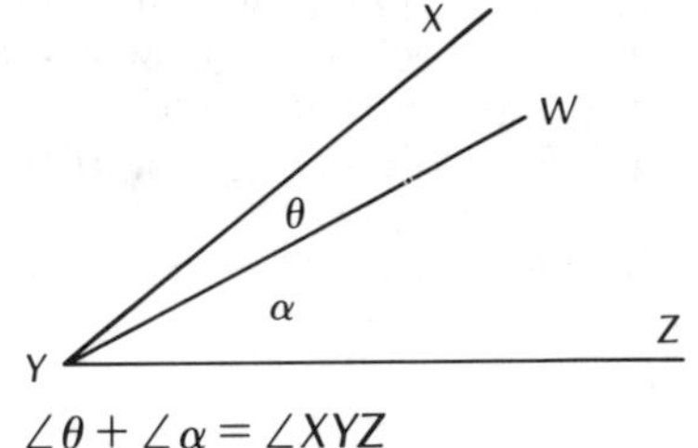

$\angle\theta + \angle\alpha = \angle XYZ$
$\angle XYZ > \angle\theta$ and $\angle XYZ > \angle\alpha$

> **Exterior Angle Inequality Theorem (EAIT)**
> The measure of an exterior angle of a triangle is greater than the measures of either of the non-adjacent interior angles.

Given: $\triangle ABC$, with $\overline{BC}$ extended to *D* to form exterior $\angle ACD$
Prove: $\angle ACD > \angle CAB$

Proof: *E* is the midpoint of $\overline{AC}$. Join *B* and *E*, and extend the segment to *F* such that $BE = FE$. Join *F* and *C*.
For $\triangle ABE$ and $\triangle CFE$,

Statement	Reason
$AE = CE.$	Definition of midpoint
$\angle AEB = \angle CEF$	OAT
$BE = FE$	By construction
$\triangle ABE \cong \triangle CFE$	SAS
$\therefore \angle ECF = \angle EAB = \angle CAB$	Congruent triangles
But $\angle ECF + \angle FCD = \angle ACD$	Addition property
$\angle ACD > \angle ECF$	Inequality assumption
$\therefore \angle ACD > \angle CAB$	Substitution

EXAMPLE 2: Prove that if the length of one side of a triangle is greater than the length of another side, the angle opposite the greater side is greater than the angle opposite the smaller side.

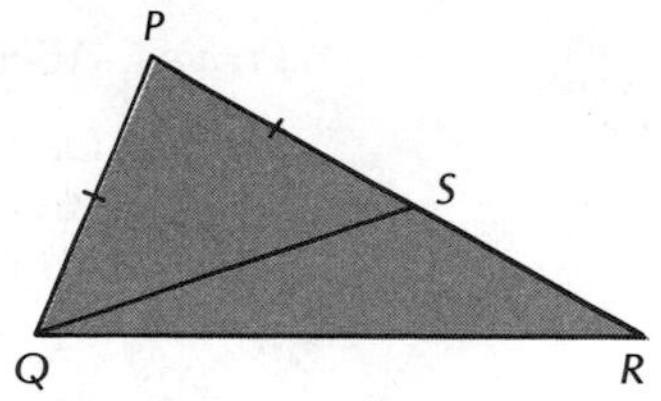

Given: $\triangle PQR$, with $PR > PQ$

Prove: $\angle PQR > \angle PRQ$

Proof: S is a point on $\overline{PR}$ such that $PS = PQ$.
Join Q and S.

$\angle PQS = \angle PSQ$	ITT
But $\angle PQR > \angle PQS$	Inequality assumption
and $\angle PSQ > \angle PRQ$	EAIT
so $\angle PQS > \angle PRQ$	Substitution
$\therefore \angle PQR > \angle PRQ$	Transitive property for inequalities

The method of indirect proof is often used to prove inequalities.

EXAMPLE 3: Prove that if the measure of one angle of a triangle is greater than the measure of another, the side opposite the greater angle is longer than the side opposite the smaller angle.

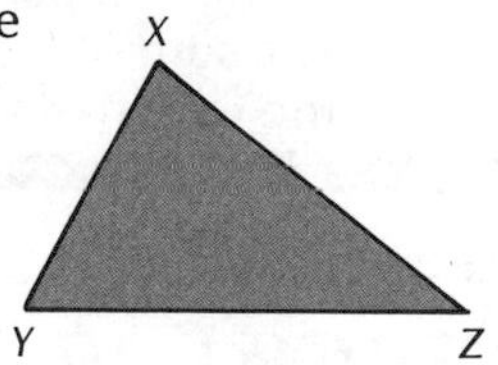

Given: $\triangle XYZ$, with $\angle XYZ > \angle XZY$

Prove: $XZ > XY$

Proof: Either $XZ > XY$, $XZ = XY$, or $XZ < XY$.

Case i. Assume that $XZ = XY$.
$\angle XYZ = \angle XZY$ ITT

But this contradicts the given information that $\angle XYZ > \angle XZY$.

Thus, the assumption that $XZ = XY$ is false.

Case ii. Assume that $XY > XZ$.
$\therefore \angle XZY > \angle XYZ$ By Example 2

But this contradicts the given information that $\angle XYZ > \angle XZY$.

Thus, the assumption that $XY > XZ$ is false.

Because $XZ = XY$ is false and $XY > XZ$ is false, it follows that $XZ > XY$.

EXAMPLE 4: Prove that the sum of the lengths of any two sides of a triangle is greater than the length of the third side.

Given: $\triangle ABC$

Prove: $AB + AC > BC$

Proof: Extend $\overline{BA}$ to P such that $AP = AC$. Join P and C.

Statement	Reason
$\angle ACP = \angle APC$	ITT
$\angle PCB = \angle PCA + \angle ACB$	
$\angle PCB > \angle ACP$	Definition of $>$
$\therefore \angle PCB > \angle APC$	Substitution
$PB > BC$	Proved in Example 3
But $PB = AB + AP$	Construction
$\therefore PB = AB + AC$	Substitution
$\therefore AB + AC > BC$	Substitution

SUMMARY OF TRIANGLE INEQUALITIES

1. The angle opposite the longest side of a triangle is the largest angle; the angle opposite the shortest side of a triangle is the smallest angle.
2. The side opposite the largest angle of a triangle is the longest side; the side opposite the smallest angle of a triangle is the shortest side.
3. The sum of the lengths of any two sides of a triangle is greater than the length of the third side.

EXERCISE 10-5

A 1. Identify the largest angle and the smallest angle for each triangle.

a.

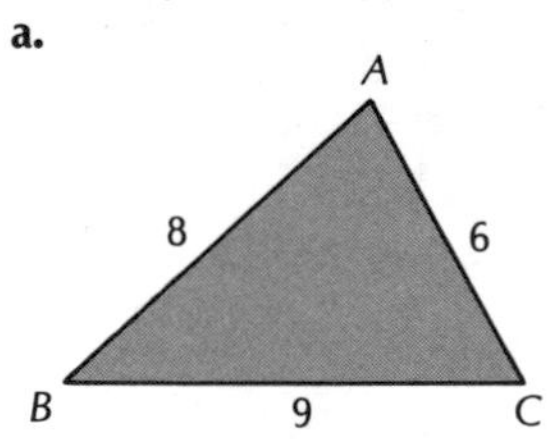

b.

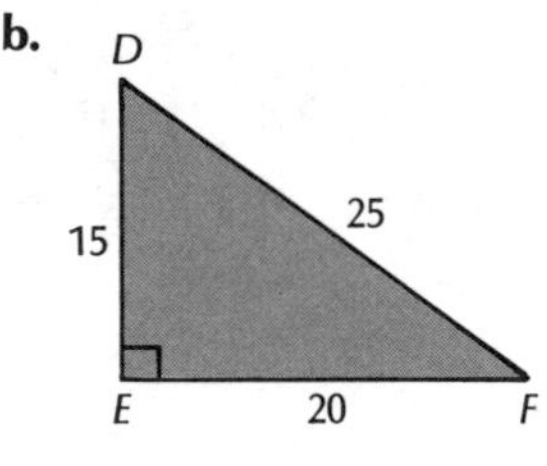

c.

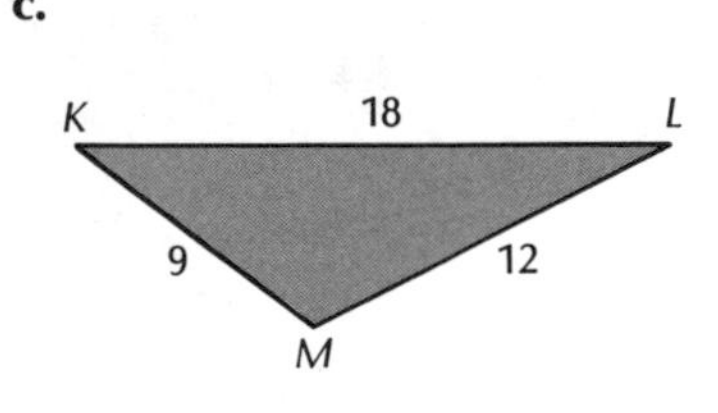

2. List the lengths of the sides of each triangle in decreasing order.

a.

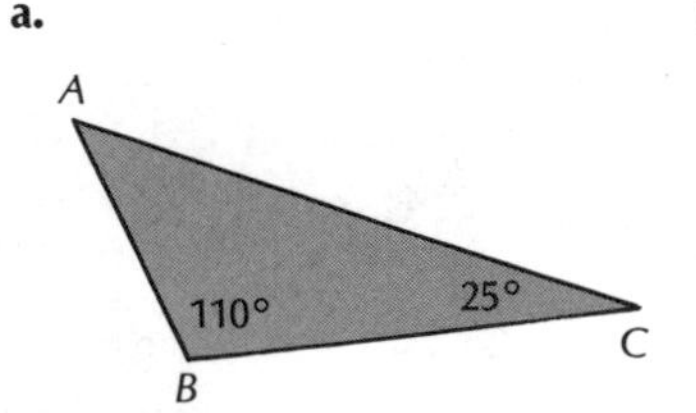

b.

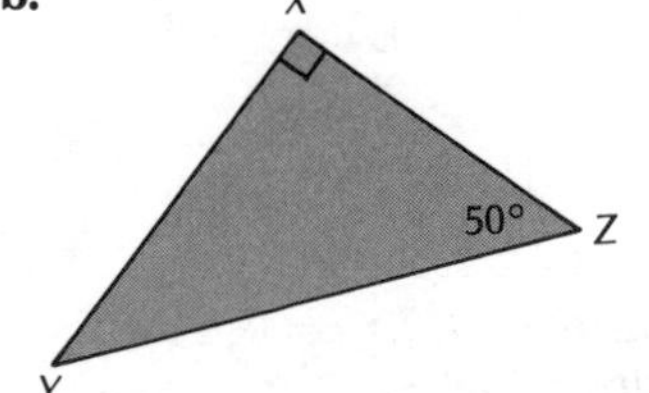

c.

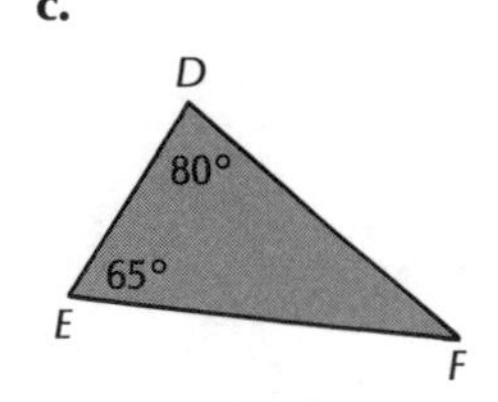

3. Is it possible to have a triangle with sides measuring the given lengths?
   a. 3, 4, 6 **b.** 5, 5, 10 **c.** 4, 4, 4 **d.** 5, 8, 15 **e.** 8, 9, 10

B 4. Find the lengths of the sides of all isosceles triangles having a perimeter of 16 cm if the measures of all the sides are integers.

5. In $\triangle ABC$, $\angle B \neq \angle C$. Prove that $AB \neq AC$.

6. W is the midpoint of side $\overline{YZ}$ in $\triangle XYZ$. $\overline{XW}$ is not perpendicular to $\overline{YZ}$. Prove that $XY \neq XZ$.

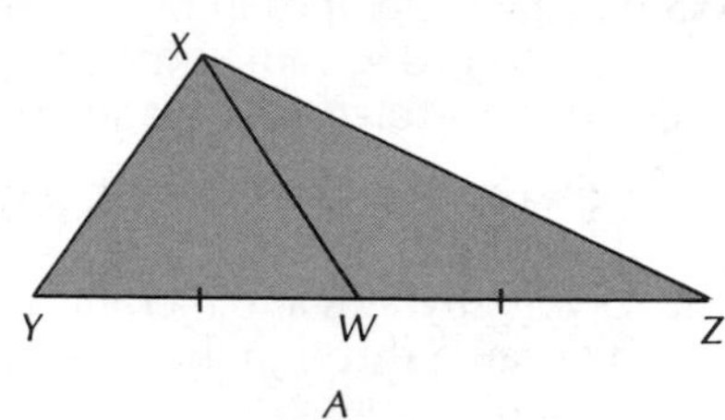

7. In $\triangle ABC$, D is on side $\overline{BC}$ such that $\overline{AD} \perp \overline{BC}$. Prove that if $AB \neq AC$, then $BD \neq DC$.

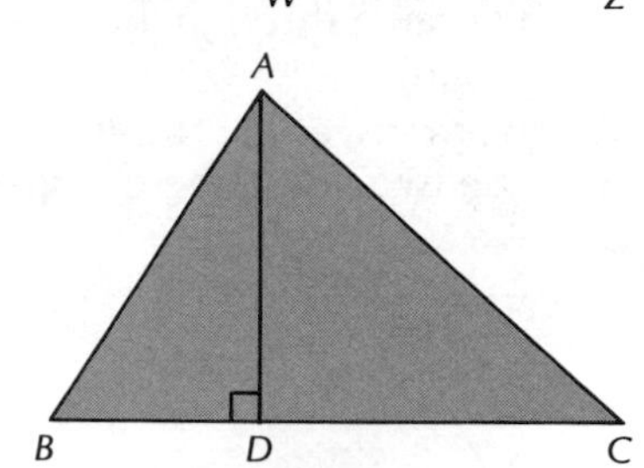

8. Prove that the bisectors of two angles of a triangle are never perpendicular.

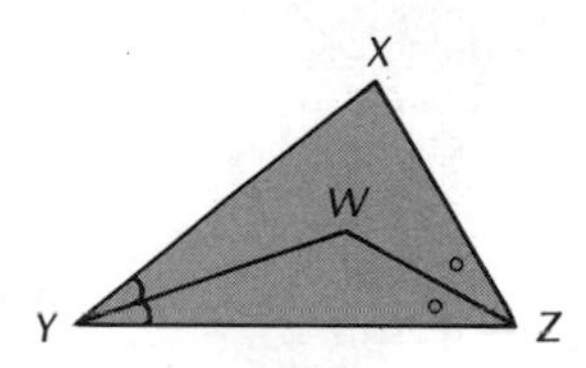

9. Quadrilateral $ABCD$ is a trapezoid such that $\overline{AB} \parallel \overline{DC}$. If $\overline{AD}$ is not parallel to $\overline{BC}$, prove that neither diagonal of $ABCD$ bisects the other.

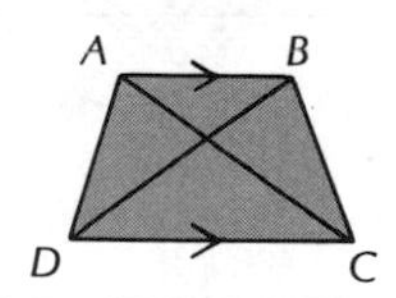

10. In $\triangle ABC$, $\angle BAC = 90°$. $\overline{AD}$ is the altitude from A to $\overline{BC}$. Prove that $AB + AC < BC + 2AD$.

C 11. Prove that the perpendicular from any vertex, P, of a triangle, $\triangle PQR$, to the opposite side, $\overline{QR}$, is the shortest segment from the vertex to that side. Consider both cases, as shown.

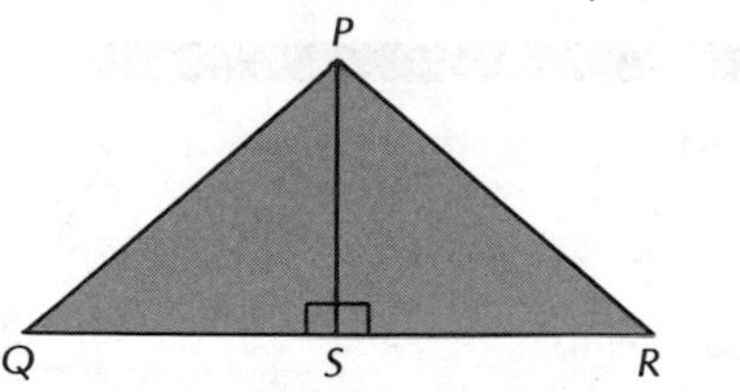

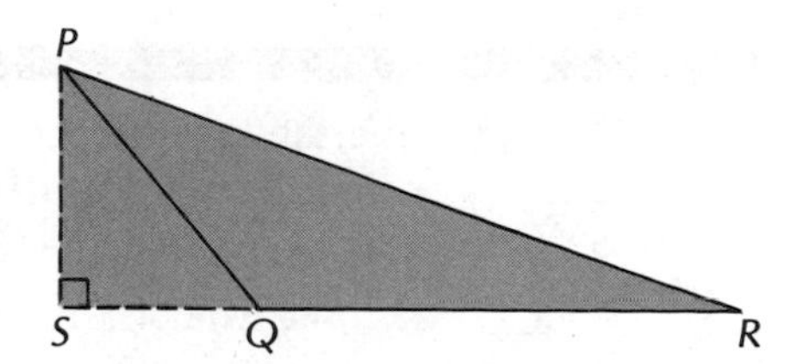

12. In $\triangle ABC$ and $\triangle DEF$, $AB = DE$, $BC = EF$, and $AC > DF$. Prove that $\angle ABC > \angle DEF$.

10-6 Properties of Parallel Lines

Parallel lines have an important role in architectural structures. Doors, windows, and walls generally depict parallel lines and planes.
parallel lines and planes.

Parallel lines are lines in the same plane such that the lines do not intersect. In order to prove some fundamental properties of parallel lines, the following postulates are assumed.

1. Either two distinct lines in the same plane are parallel or they intersect in, at most, one point.
2. Given any line and a point not on the line, one, and only one, line can be drawn through the given point, parallel to the given line. (Playfair's Axiom)

When a transversal crosses two lines, it forms a number of pairs of angles with the two lines. These angles are given special names.

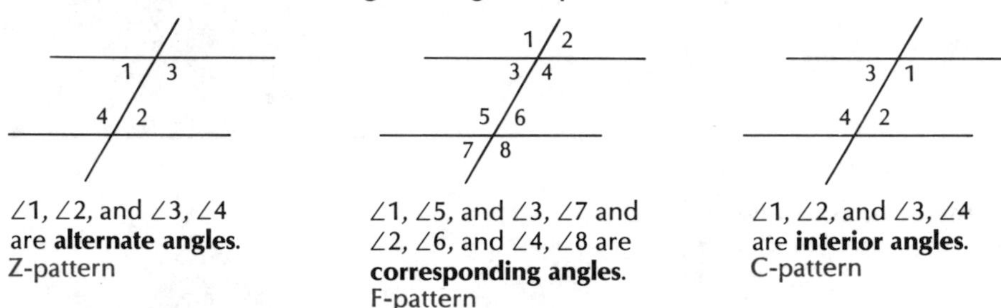

$\angle 1$, $\angle 2$, and $\angle 3$, $\angle 4$ are **alternate angles**.
Z-pattern

$\angle 1$, $\angle 5$, and $\angle 3$, $\angle 7$ and $\angle 2$, $\angle 6$, and $\angle 4$, $\angle 8$ are **corresponding angles**.
F-pattern

$\angle 1$, $\angle 2$, and $\angle 3$, $\angle 4$ are **interior angles**.
C-pattern

The proof of the following biconditional theorem uses the indirect method of proof.

Parallel Lines Theorem (PLT)
Two straight lines are parallel if, and only if, a transversal intersecting both lines forms equal pairs of alternate angles.

PLT involves a statement and its converse, PLT-i and PLT-ii. A proof of these two theorems follows.

PLT-i
If a transversal intersects two lines such that alternate angles are equal, then the two lines are parallel.

Given: $\overline{XW}$ is a transversal that intersects $\overline{AB}$ and $\overline{CD}$ at Y and Z, respectively, such that $\angle AYZ = \angle YZD$.

Prove: $\overline{AB} \parallel \overline{CD}$ The symbol $\parallel$ means "is parallel to".

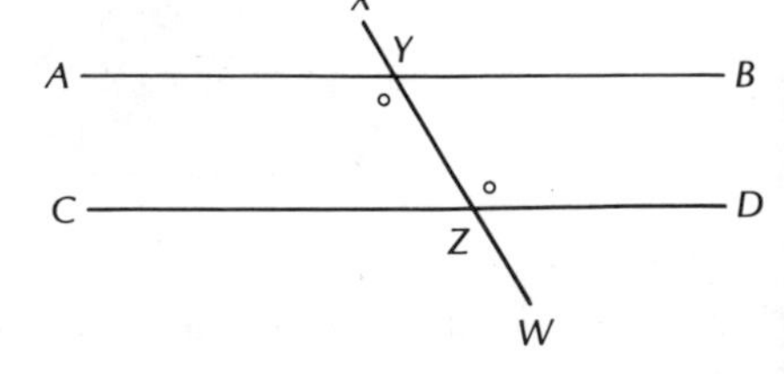

Proof: Either $\overline{AB} \parallel \overline{CD}$ or $\overline{AB}$ is not parallel to $\overline{CD}$.
Assume that $\overline{AB}$ is not parallel to $\overline{CD}$.
Thus, $\overline{AB}$ and $\overline{CD}$, extended, intersect at a point T.
In $\triangle YZT$, $\angle AYZ > \angle YZD$. EAIT
But this contradicts the given information that $\angle AYZ = \angle YZD$.
Thus, the assumption that $\overline{AB}$ is not parallel to $\overline{CD}$ is false.
$\therefore \overline{AB} \parallel \overline{CD}$

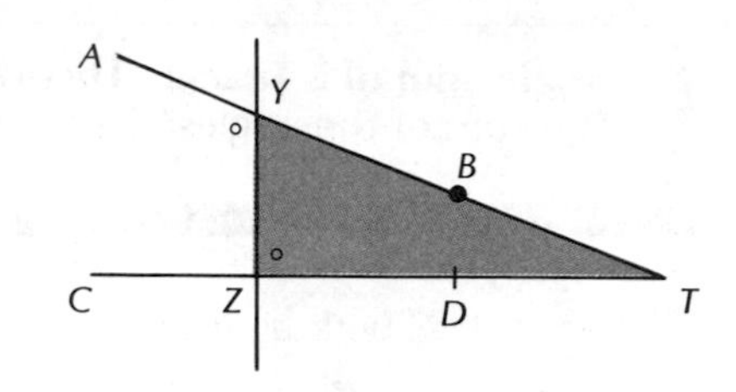

Corollaries to PLT-i:
1. If a transversal intersects two lines such that corresponding angles are equal, then the two lines are parallel.
2. If a transversal intersects two lines such that interior angles are supplementary, then the two lines are parallel.

PLT-ii
If two parallel lines are cut by a transversal, then pairs of alternate angles are equal.

Given: $\overline{AB} \parallel \overline{CD}$, $\overline{XW}$ intersects $\overline{AB}$ at Y and $\overline{CD}$ at Z

Prove: $\angle AYZ = \angle YZD$

Proof: Either $\angle AYZ = \angle YZD$ or $\angle AYZ \neq \angle YZD$.
Assume that $\angle AYZ \neq \angle YZD$.
Construct $\overline{EF}$, containing Y, such that $\angle EYZ = \angle YZD$.
Then $\overline{EF} \parallel \overline{CD}$. PLT-i
But $\overline{AB} \parallel \overline{CD}$. Given
This contradicts Playfair's Axiom.
Therefore, the assumption that $\angle AYZ \neq \angle YZD$ is false.
$\therefore \angle AYZ = \angle YZD$

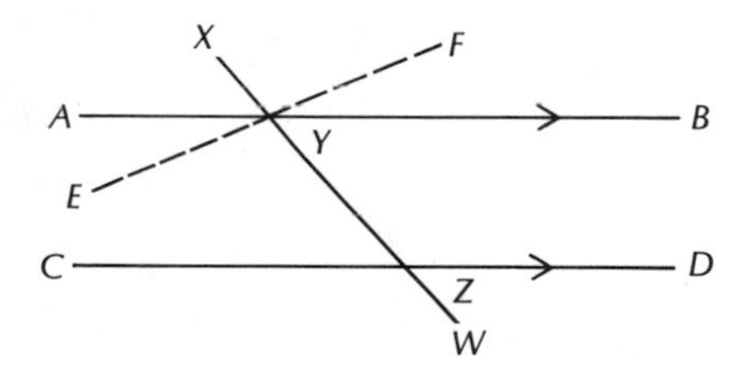

Corollaries to PLT-ii:
1. Two parallel lines that are cut by a transversal form pairs of corresponding angles that are equal.
2. Two parallel lines that are cut by a transversal form pairs of interior angles that are supplementary.

The Parallel Lines Theorem can be used to prove other theorems.

Angle Sum of a Triangle Theorem (AST)
The sum of the angles of a triangle is 180°.

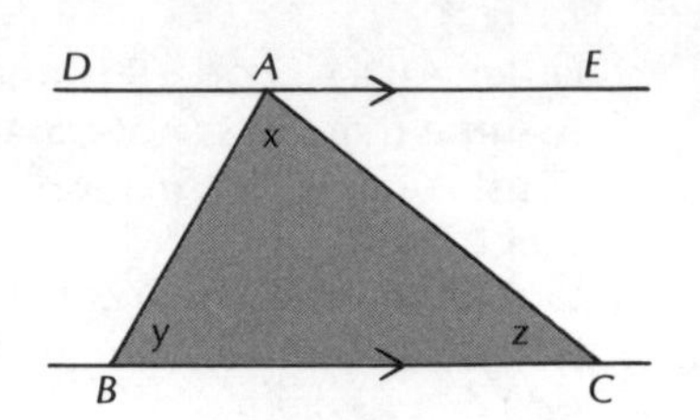

Given: $\triangle ABC$ with angles x, y, and z.

Prove: $\angle x + \angle y + \angle z = 180°$

Proof: Construct $\overline{DAE}$ parallel to $\overline{BC}$. — Playfair's axiom

Statement	Reason
Construct $\overline{DAE}$ parallel to $\overline{BC}$.	Playfair's axiom
$\angle DAB = \angle y$	PLT: alternate angles
$\angle EAC = \angle z$	PLT: alternate angles
$\angle x + \angle DAB + \angle EAC = 180°$	Straight angle
$\therefore \angle x + \angle y + \angle z = 180°$	Substitution

Exterior Angle Theorem
An exterior angle of a triangle is equal to the sum of the two non-adjacent interior angles.

The proof of this theorem follows as a corollary of AST.

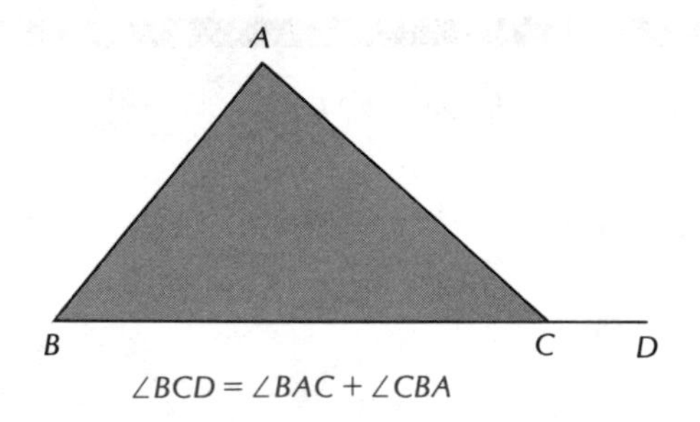

$\angle BCD = \angle BAC + \angle CBA$

EXAMPLE 1: Find the values of x, y, and z.

a.

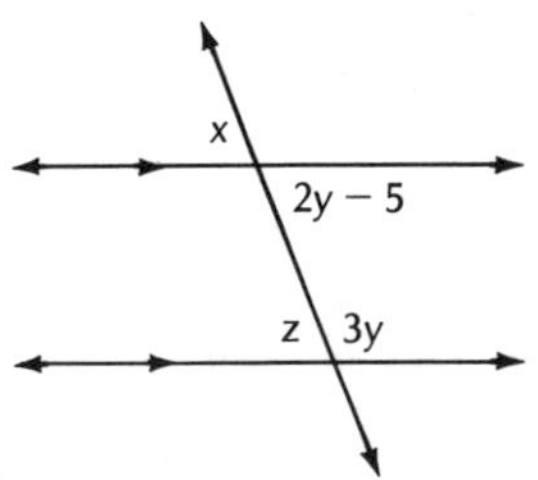

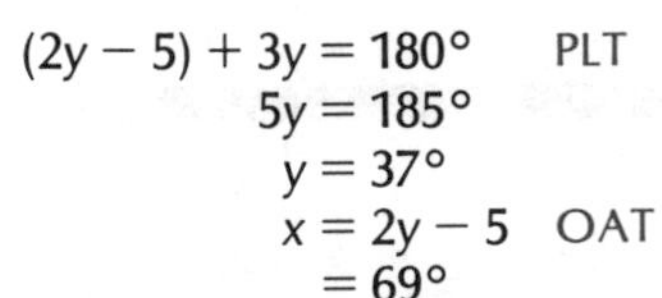

$(2y - 5) + 3y = 180°$ PLT
$5y = 185°$
$y = 37°$
$x = 2y - 5$ OAT
$= 69°$
$z = 69°$ PLT

b.

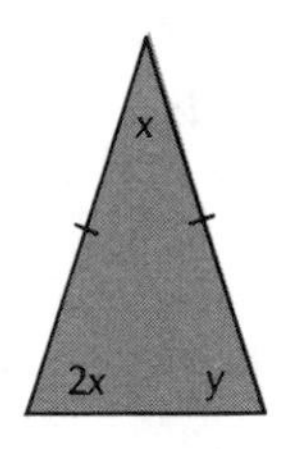

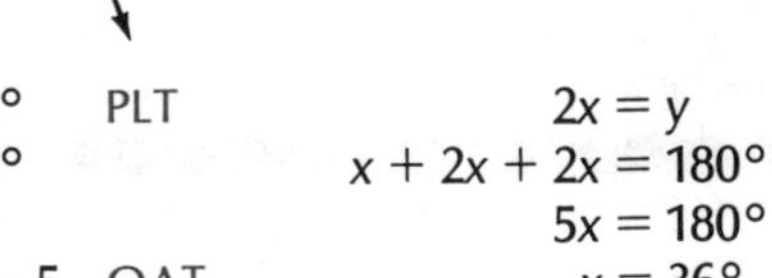

$2x = y$ ITT
$x + 2x + 2x = 180°$ AST
$5x = 180°$
$x = 36°$
$y = 72°$

c.

$x = 55° + 42°$ AST
$x = 97°$

EXAMPLE 2: $\triangle XYZ$ is isosceles, with $XY = XZ$. A line is drawn perpendicular to $\overline{YZ}$, intersecting $\overline{YZ}$ at Q, $\overline{XY}$ at R, and $\overline{ZX}$, extended, at P. Prove that $XP = XR$.

Given: $\triangle XYZ$, $XY = XZ$, $\overline{PQ} \perp \overline{YZ}$ as shown in the diagram.

Prove: $XP = XR$

Proof:

$XY = XZ$	Given
$\angle XYZ = \angle XZY$	ITT
In $\triangle RYQ$, $\angle YRQ + \angle Y + 90° = 180°$ ①	AST
In $\triangle PZQ$, $\angle QPZ + \angle Z + 90° = 180°$ ②	AST
$\angle YRQ = \angle ZPQ$	Subtract ① and ②.
$\angle YRQ = \angle PRX$	OAT
$\angle ZPQ = \angle PRX$	Substitution
$\therefore XP = XR$	ITT

EXERCISE 10-6

A 1. Classify each pair of angles as alternate, corresponding, or interior, if possible.

a. $\angle 2$ and $\angle 10$
b. $\angle 7$ and $\angle 12$
c. $\angle 8$ and $\angle 11$
d. $\angle 14$ and $\angle 16$
e. $\angle 6$ and $\angle 9$
f. $\angle 4$ and $\angle 16$
g. $\angle 1$ and $\angle 8$
h. $\angle 2$ and $\angle 3$

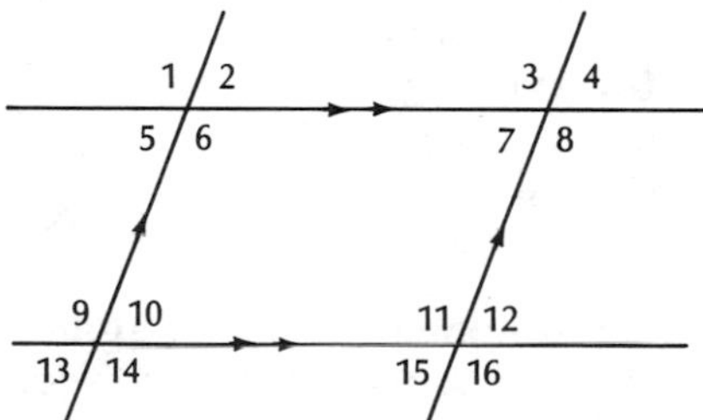

2. In exercise 1, if $\angle 4 = 55°$, find the measure of each remaining angle.

3. Find the measure of each indicated angle.

a.

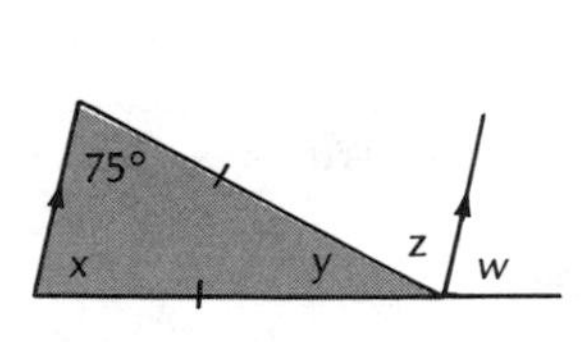

b.

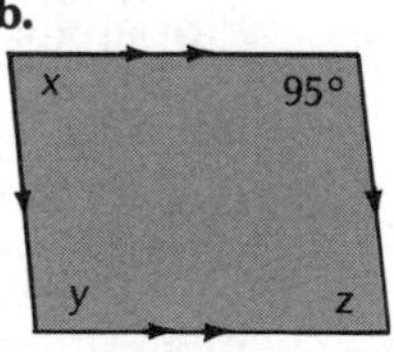

c.

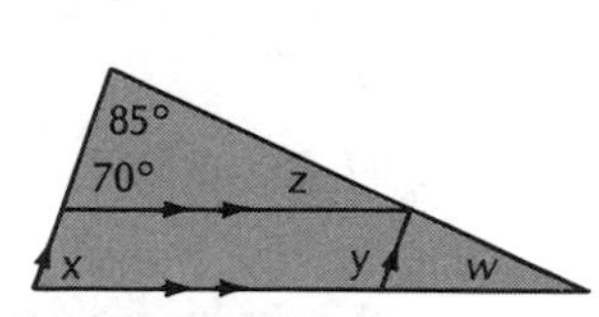

d.

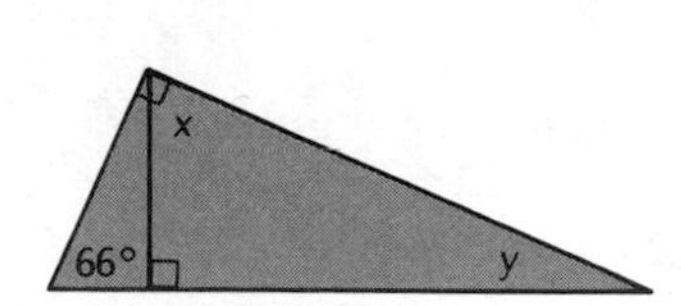

e.

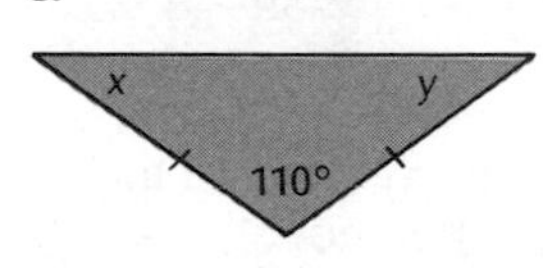

f.

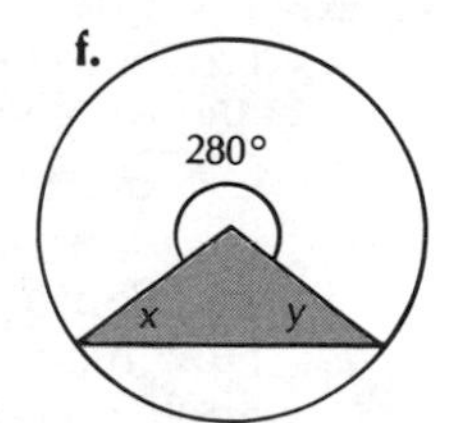

B **4.** *Given:* $\triangle ABC$, as shown at the right
Prove: $\angle 1 + \angle 4 = 180°$

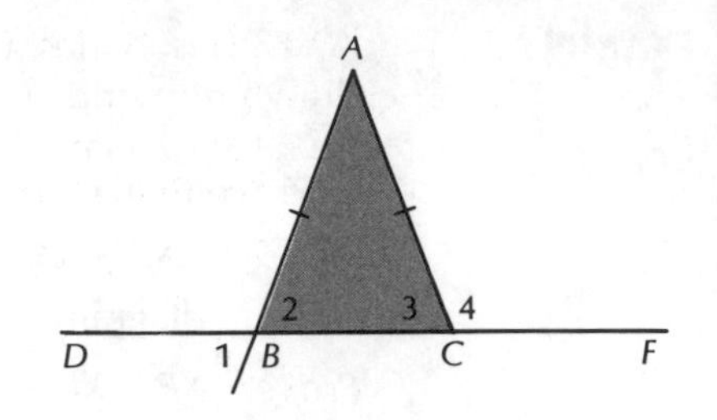

5. $\overline{PZ}$ bisects exterior angle XZW of $\triangle XYZ$.
If $\overline{PZ} \parallel \overline{XY}$, prove that $\triangle XYZ$ is isosceles.

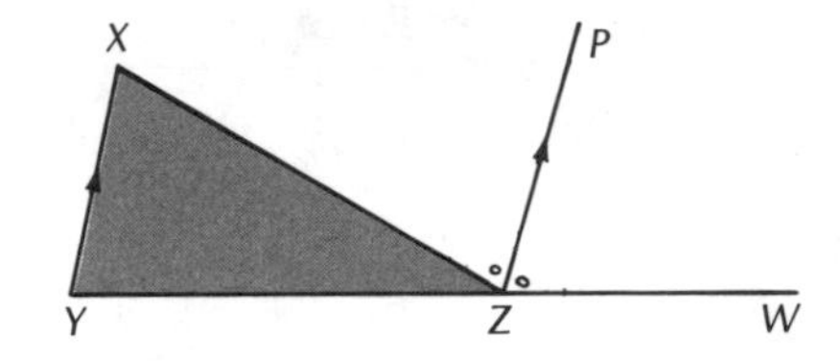

6. $\triangle ABC$ is isosceles, with $AB = AC$.
$\overline{CB}$ is extended to D such that $AB = BD$.
Prove that $\angle DAC = 180° - 3\angle ADB$.

7. For each polygon, select a vertex and draw diagonals from the vertex to each of the other vertices of the polygon. Use AST to determine the interior angle sum of each polygon.

a. a quadrilateral
b. a pentagon
c. a hexagon
d. a decagon
e. an n-gon

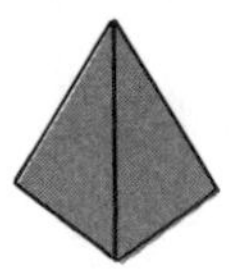

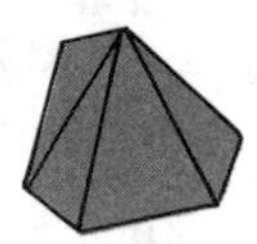

8. An **exterior angle** of a polygon is an angle formed by one side of a polygon and the extension of the adjacent side.

a. Find the sum of the exterior angles of a quadrilateral, a pentagon, a hexagon, and an octagon.

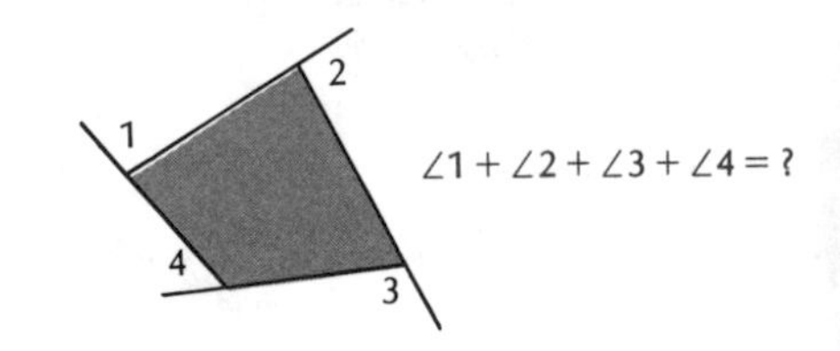

b. Prove that the sum of the exterior angles of an n-gon is 360°.

9. How many sides does a polygon have with the given interior sums?
a. 1080° **b.** 1980° **c.** 3780° **d.** 4500°

10. A **regular polygon** is a polygon with all sides equal and all angles equal.

a. Prove that each angle of a regular polygon measures $\frac{180(n-2)}{n}$ degrees.

b. Find the measure of each angle of a regular pentagon, a regular octagon, and a regular 50-gon.

c. How many sides does a regular polygon have if each interior angle measures 156°?

10-7 Deductions Involving Quadrilaterals

The theorems in previous lessons can be used to analyse quadrilaterals. Recall the definitions of some special quadrilaterals.

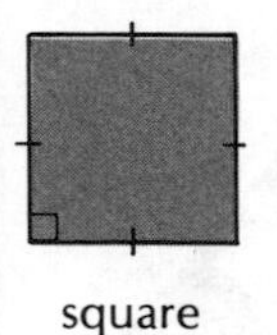
square

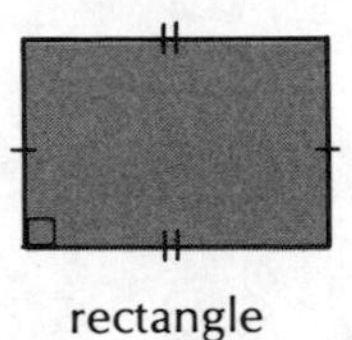
rectangle

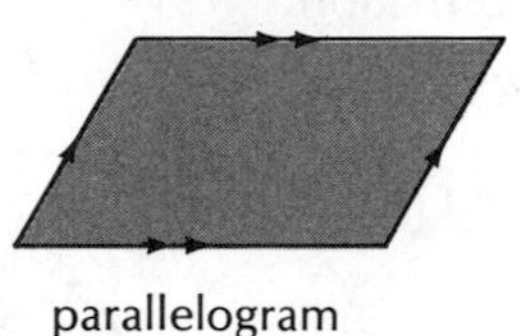
parallelogram

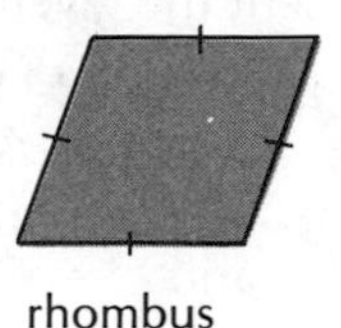
rhombus

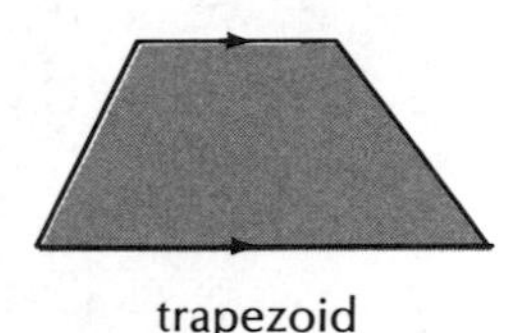
trapezoid

EXAMPLE 1: Prove that a rhombus is a parallelogram.

Given: Rhombus $ABCD$ with $AB = BC = CD = AD$

Prove: $ABCD$ is a parallelogram

Proof: Draw diagonal $\overline{AC}$.
For $\triangle ABC$ and $\triangle ADC$,

Statement	Reason
$AB = DC$.	Given
$BC = AD$	Given
$AC = AC$	Common side
$\triangle ABC \cong \triangle ADC$	SSS
$\angle 1 = \angle 2$	Congruent $\triangle$'s
$\therefore \overline{AD} \parallel \overline{BC}$	PLT: alternate angles
$\angle 3 = \angle 4$	Congruent $\triangle$'s
$\therefore \overline{AB} \parallel \overline{DC}$	PLT: alternate angles

Thus, $ABCD$ is a parallelogram. Definition of parallelograms

EXAMPLE 2: Prove that if a quadrilateral has one pair of sides that are both equal and parallel, the quadrilateral is a parallelogram.

Given: Quadrilateral $ABCD$, with $AD = BC$ and $\overline{AD} \parallel \overline{BC}$

Prove: $ABCD$ is a parallelogram

Proof: Draw diagonal $\overline{AC}$.
For $\triangle ABC$ and $\triangle ADC$,

Statement	Reason
$AD = BC$.	Given
$\overline{AD} \parallel \overline{BC}$	Given
$\angle 1 = \angle 2$	PLT: alternate angles
$AC = AC$	Common side
$\triangle ABC \cong \triangle ADC$	SAS
$\angle 3 = \angle 4$	Congruent $\triangle$'s
$\therefore \overline{AB} \parallel \overline{DC}$	PLT: alternate angles

Thus, $ABCD$ is a parallelogram. Definition of parallelograms

EXAMPLE 3: In trapezoid $PQRS$, $\overline{PQ} \parallel \overline{SR}$, $\overline{PS}$ is not parallel to $\overline{QR}$, and $PS = QR$. Prove that $\angle PSR = \angle QRS$.

First, draw a diagram to represent the given information.

Given: Trapezoid $PQRS$ such that $\overline{PQ} \parallel \overline{SR}$, $\overline{PS}$ is not parallel to $\overline{QR}$ and $PS = QR$

Prove: $\angle PSR = \angle QRS$

Proof: Since $\overline{PS}$ is not parallel to $\overline{QR}$, there must exist a point T on $\overline{SR}$ or on $\overline{SR}$ extended, such that $\overline{QT} \parallel \overline{PS}$. Join P and T.

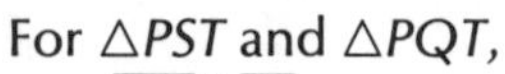

For $\triangle PST$ and $\triangle PQT$,

$\overline{PQ} \parallel \overline{ST}$. $\therefore \angle 1 = \angle 2$	PLT: alternate angles
$\overline{PS} \parallel \overline{QT}$ $\therefore \angle 3 = \angle 4$	PLT: alternate angles
$PT = PT$	Common side
$\triangle PST \cong \triangle PQT$	ASA
$PS = QT$	Congruent $\triangle$'s
But $PS = QR$.	Given
$\therefore QT = QR$	Substitution
$\angle QTR = \angle QRT$	ITT
$\angle PSR = \angle QTR$	PLT: corresponding angles
$\therefore \angle PSR = \angle QRT = \angle QRS$	Substitution

EXERCISE 10-7

A 1. Which of the following statements are true?

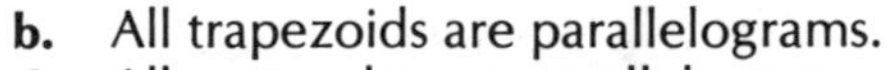

- **a.** All squares are rhombuses.
- **b.** All trapezoids are parallelograms.
- **c.** All parallelograms are trapezoids.
- **d.** All rectangles are parallelograms.
- **e.** All rhombuses are parallelograms.
- **f.** All squares are rectangles.

B 2. Prove each statement.

- **a.** The lengths of opposite sides of a parallelogram are equal.
- **b.** The lengths of opposite angles of a parallelogram are equal.
- **c.** The diagonals of a parallelogram bisect each other.

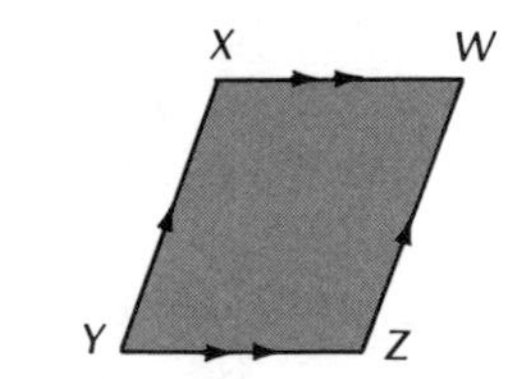

The results of exercise 2 can be named the *Properties of a Parallelogram* and can be used to prove further statements.

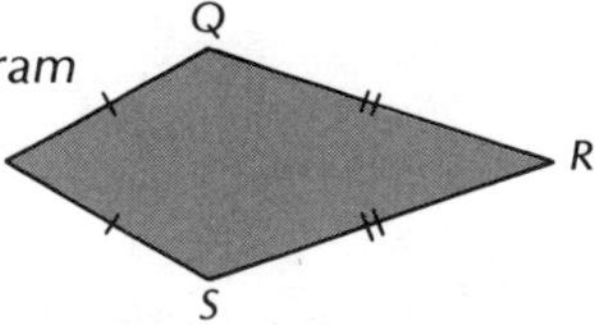

3. For quadrilateral $PQRS$, $PQ = PS$ and $QR = SR$. Prove that $\overline{PR}$ is the perpendicular bisector of $\overline{QS}$.

4. For quadrilateral $PQRS$, $PQ = PS$ and $\overline{PS} \parallel \overline{QR}$.
Prove that $\overline{SQ}$ bisects $\angle PQR$.

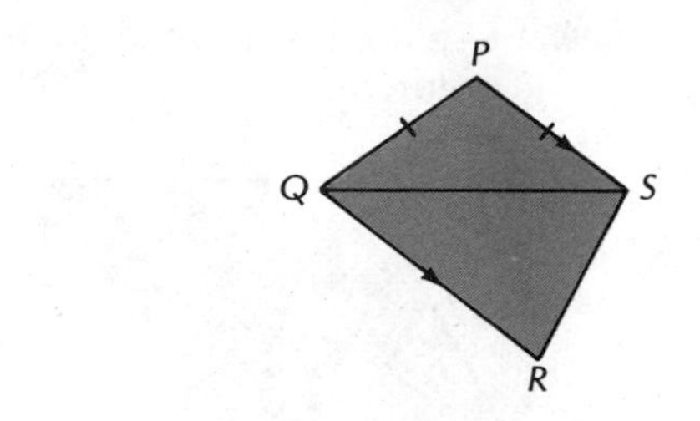

5. For trapezoid $ABCD$, $\overline{AD} \parallel \overline{BC}$. E is in the interior of trapezoid $ABCD$ such that $\overline{ED}$ bisects $\angle ADC$ and $\overline{EC}$ bisects $\angle BCD$. Prove that $\angle DEC = 90°$.

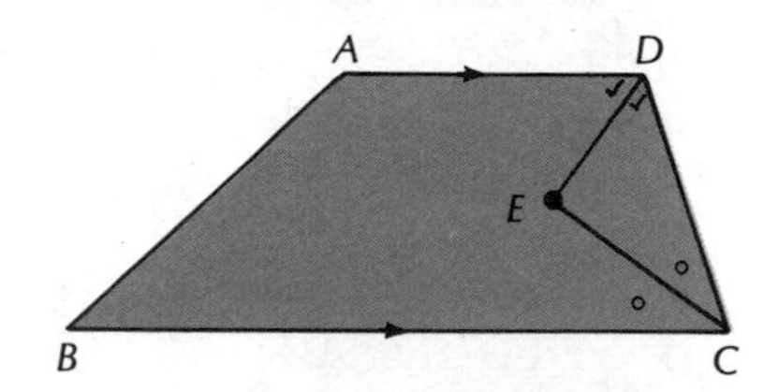

6. A and B are points on diagonal $\overline{XZ}$ of parallelogram $XYZW$, such that $XA = ZB$. Prove that $\overline{AW} \parallel \overline{YB}$.

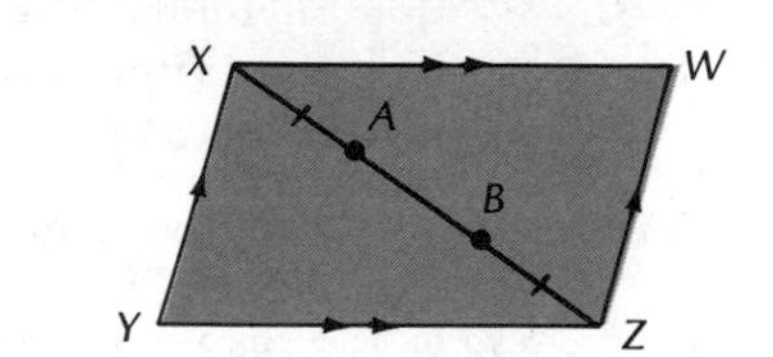

7. Prove each statement for any quadrilateral.

a. If both pairs of opposite sides of a quadrilateral are equal, the quadrilateral is a parallelogram.

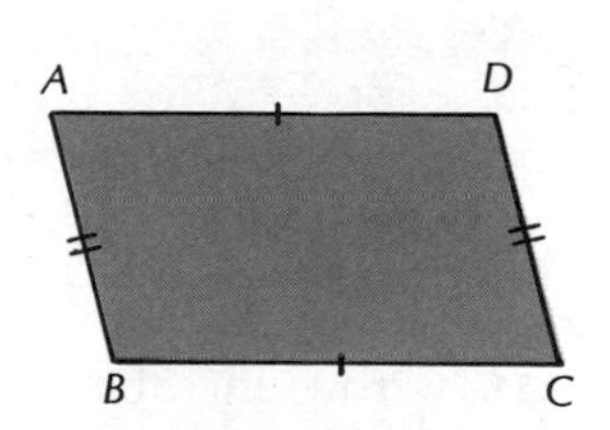

b. If the diagonals of a quadrilateral bisect each other, the quadrilateral is a parallelogram.

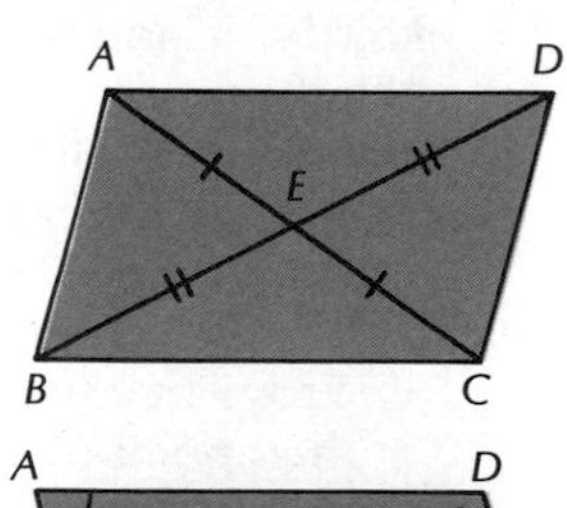

c. If both pairs of opposite angles of a quadrilateral are equal, the quadrilateral is a parallelogram.

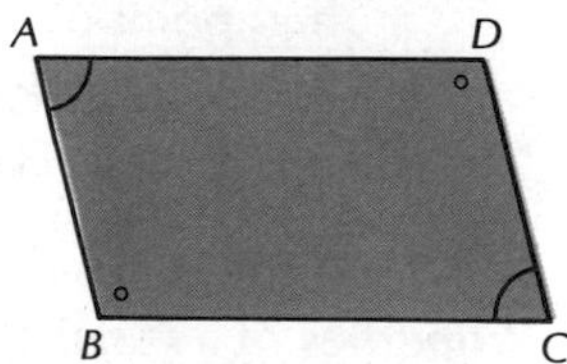

8. Prove that the diagonals of a rhombus are the perpendicular bisectors of each other.

9. Use the results of exercise 8 to find the measure of each indicated segment.

a.

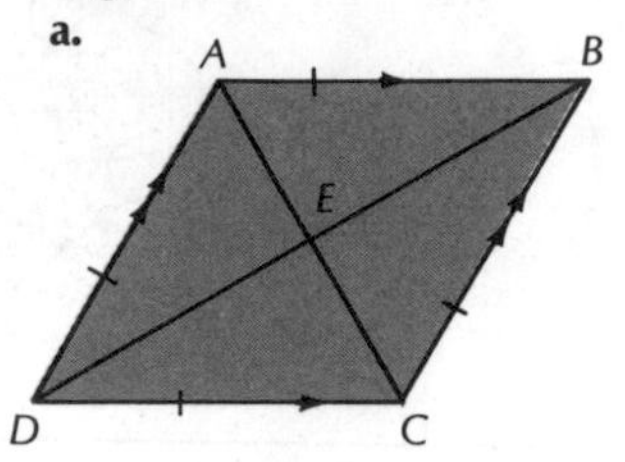

Given: $AB = 13$, $AE = 5$
Find the lengths of $\overline{AC}$ and $\overline{BD}$.

b.

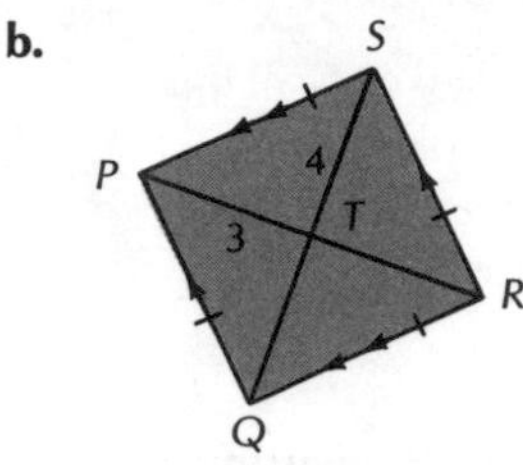

Find the length of $\overline{PQ}$.

c.

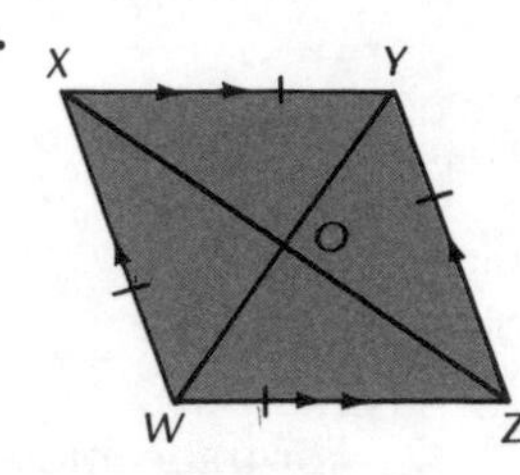

Given: $XY = 25$, $XO = 24$
Find the length of $\overline{YO}$.

10. For trapezoid $ABCD$, $\overline{AB} \parallel \overline{DC}$ and $\angle ADC = \angle BCD$. Prove that $AD = BC$.

11. For quadrilateral $ABCD$, $\overline{DA} \perp \overline{BA}$, $\overline{DC} \perp \overline{BC}$, $\angle ABD = \angle CBD$. $\overline{AE}$ is drawn perpendicular to $\overline{BC}$ such that E is on $\overline{BC}$. Prove that $\overline{AC}$ bisects $\angle EAD$.

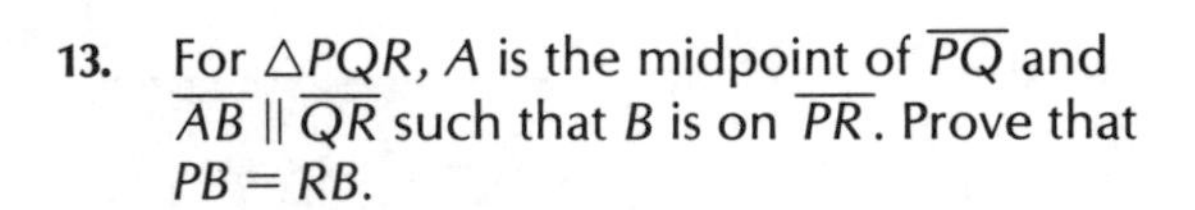

C 12. P, Q, R, and S are the midpoints of the sides of rectangle $ABCD$, as shown. Prove that $XYZW$ is a parallelogram.

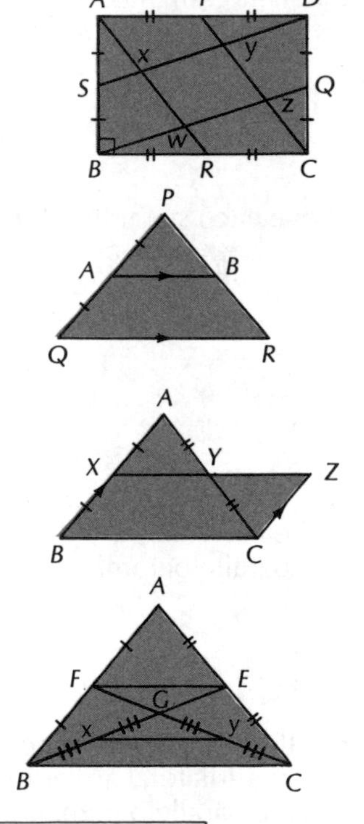

13. For $\triangle PQR$, A is the midpoint of $\overline{PQ}$ and $\overline{AB} \parallel \overline{QR}$ such that B is on $\overline{PR}$. Prove that $PB = RB$.

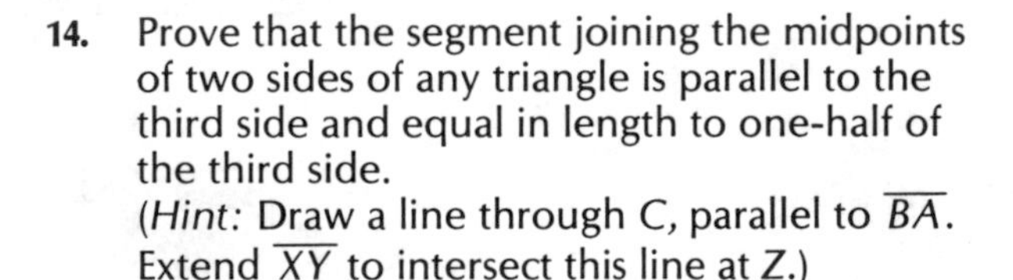

14. Prove that the segment joining the midpoints of two sides of any triangle is parallel to the third side and equal in length to one-half of the third side.
(*Hint:* Draw a line through C, parallel to $\overline{BA}$. Extend $\overline{XY}$ to intersect this line at Z.)

15. For $\triangle ABC$, medians $\overline{BE}$ and $\overline{CF}$ intersect at G. Prove that the medians of a triangle meet at their point of trisection. (Join X and Y, the midpoints of $\overline{GB}$ and $\overline{GC}$. Prove that $FG = \frac{1}{3}FC$ and $EG = \frac{1}{3}EB$.)

Properties of a Parallelogram

1. The lengths of opposite sides of a parallelogram are equal.
2. The measures of opposite angles of a parallelogram are equal.
3. The diagonals of a parallelogram bisect each other.

10-8 Basic Properties of Translations

A **translation** is a transformation that moves all points the same distance in the same direction. The images seen as Marco glides downhill on his skateboard show an example of a translation.

A translation is a transformation defined by the mapping
$(x, y) \rightarrow (x + a, y + b)$ or, more concisely, by $[a, b]$.

Consider the following:

The translation in which points move 3 units to the right and 2 units down can be described as follows.
$(x, y) \rightarrow (x + 3, y - 2)$, or $[3, -2]$.
Notice that the image of $P(2, 6)$ under the translation
$(x, y) \rightarrow (x + 3, y - 2)$ is $(2 + 3, 6 - 2)$, or $(5, 4)$.

Under a translation, all points in the plane move the same distance in the same direction.

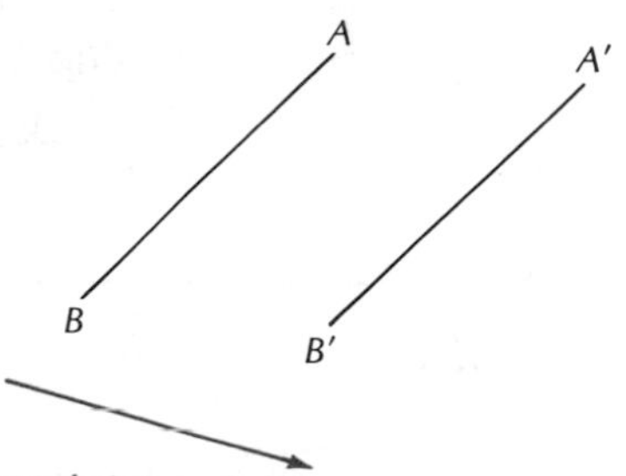

A translation can be described by a translation arrow or by a *vector* showing a point and its image, like $\overrightarrow{AA'}$.

The properties of a translation can be stated briefly, as follows.

i. If $A \rightarrow A'$ and $B \rightarrow B'$ under a translation, then $AA' = BB'$, and $\overrightarrow{AA'} \parallel \overrightarrow{BB'}$.
ii. A figure and its image under a translation are congruent.

A transformation that preserves length is called an **isometry**.
Since a translation preserves length, a translation is an isometry.

EXAMPLE 1: Find the image of $P(5, -3)$ under each translation.

a. $(x, y) \rightarrow (x - 7, y + 2)$ **b.** $(x, y) \rightarrow (x, y - 5)$
c. translation vector $[2, 4]$

a. $P(5, -3) \rightarrow (5 - 7, -3 + 2) = P'(-2, -1)$
b. $P(5, -3) \rightarrow (5, -3 - 5) = P'(5, -8)$
c. $P(5, -3) \rightarrow (5 + 2, -3 + 4) = P'(7, 1)$

EXAMPLE 2: A and B are centres of congruent circles. A line parallel to $\overline{AB}$ intersects the circle with centre A at points C and D and the circle with centre B at points E and F. Prove that $CD = EF$ and $\overline{CA} \parallel \overline{EB}$.

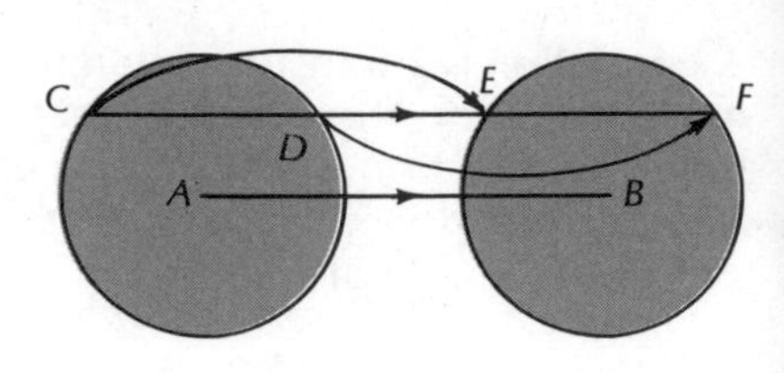

Under a translation, a figure and its image are congruent. A and B are the centres of two congruent circles. Thus, the circle with centre B is the image of the circle with centre A under the translation $\overrightarrow{AB}$.

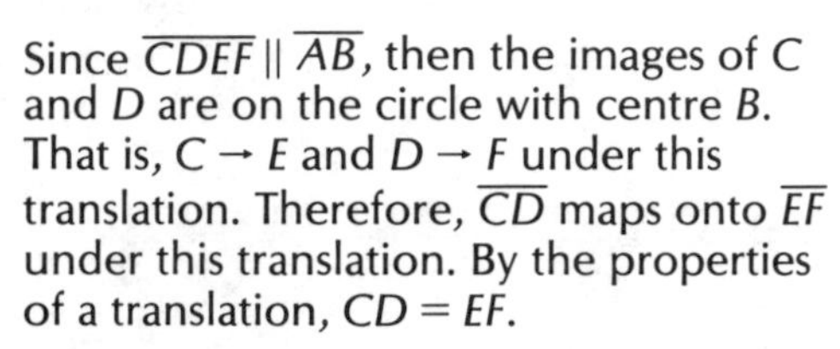

Since $\overline{CDEF} \parallel \overline{AB}$, then the images of C and D are on the circle with centre B. That is, $C \rightarrow E$ and $D \rightarrow F$ under this translation. Therefore, $\overline{CD}$ maps onto $\overline{EF}$ under this translation. By the properties of a translation, $CD = EF$.

Also, since $A \rightarrow B$ and $C \rightarrow E$ under the translation, then $\overline{CA} \rightarrow \overline{EB}$. By definition, $\overline{CA} \parallel \overline{EB}$.

EXERCISE 10-8

A

1. State the image of each point under the translation $(x, y) \rightarrow (x - 4, y + 1)$.

a. $T(4, 0)$ **b.** $R(-2, 8)$ **c.** $U(5, -3)$ **d.** $S(0, -7)$ **e.** $W(-1, -3)$

2. The image of a point under the translation $[-4, 3]$ is the point $(5, -2)$. Find the coordinates of the original point.

3. Copy each figure shown below on graph paper. Graph the image of each figure under the translation indicated by the given translation arrow.

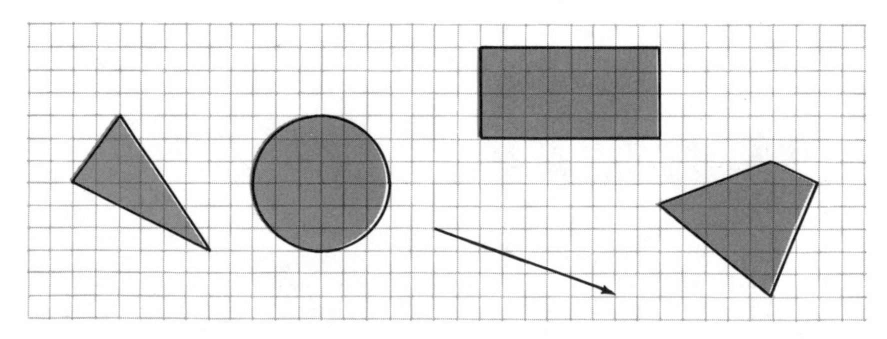

B 4. Under a translation, $\triangle ABC \rightarrow \triangle DEF$. $\overline{AH}$ and $\overline{DG}$ are altitudes of the two triangles, respectively. Prove that $AH = DG$.

5. Prove that a median of a triangle and its image under a translation are equal.

6. Quadrilaterals $PQRS$ and $TSRU$ are two parallelograms having the same base, $\overline{SR}$. Prove that $\triangle PTS \cong \triangle QUR$.

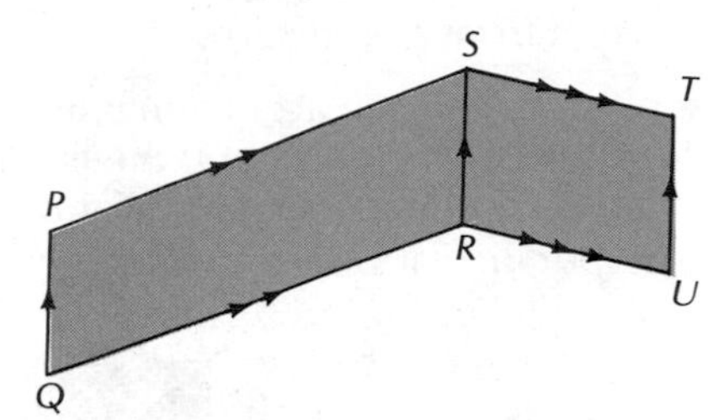

7. P and Q are the centres of two congruent circles. A line parallel to $\overline{PQ}$ intersects the circles at X, Y, Z, and W, as shown. Prove that $XY = ZW$, $XZ = YW$ and $\overline{ZP} \parallel \overline{WQ}$.

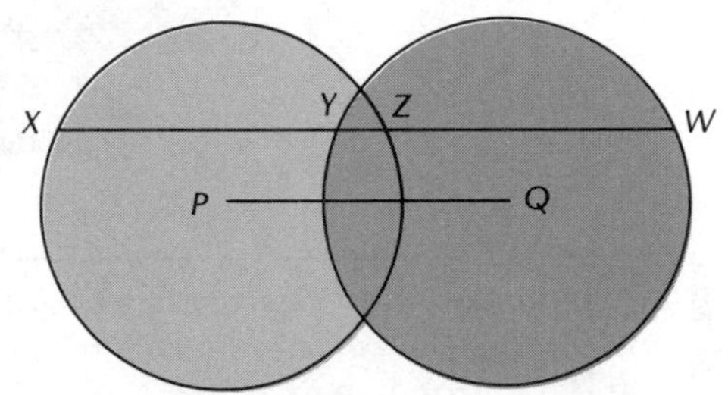

8. Quadrilateral $ABCD$ is a parallelogram.
   a. Show that $\overline{CD}$ is the image of $\overline{BA}$ under a translation.
   b. Prove that $AD = BC$.

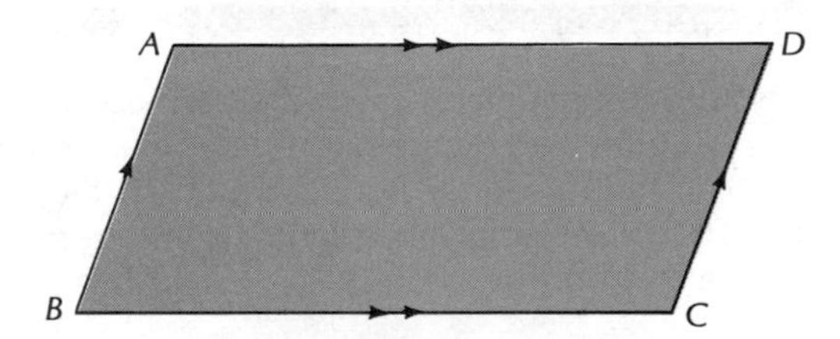

9. In parallelogram $PQRS$, M and N are the midpoints of sides $\overline{PQ}$ and $\overline{SR}$, respectively. Prove that $\overline{MN} \parallel \overline{PS}$.

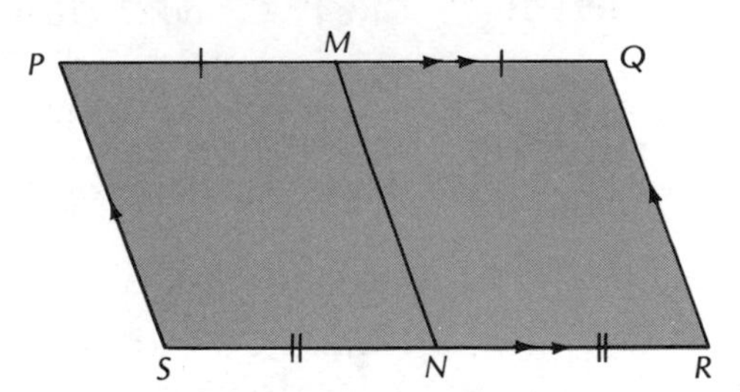

10. In the given diagram, $\triangle AMP \rightarrow \triangle PNC$ under a translation, and $\triangle AMP \rightarrow \triangle MBN$ under a translation. Prove each statement.
   a. $\overline{AB}$, $\overline{BC}$, and $\overline{AC}$ are line segments.
   b. $MBNP$ is a parallelogram.
   c. $\triangle MBN \rightarrow \triangle PNC$ under a translation.
   d. $MP = \frac{1}{2}BC$
   e. Area of $\triangle MNP = \frac{1}{4}$(area of $\triangle ABC$).

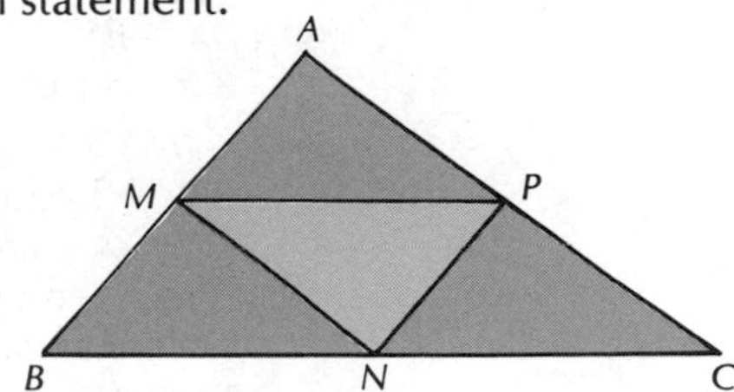

10-9 Basic Properties of Reflections

When you stand in front of a mirror, you see an image of yourself which appears to be as far away behind the mirror as you are in front of the mirror.

In a plane, a line can act in a manner similar to that of the mirror. In the given diagram, the line *m* is a line of reflection. If a point, *P*, is reflected in *m* to produce the image, *P′*, then *m* is the perpendicular bisector of segment $\overline{PP'}$.

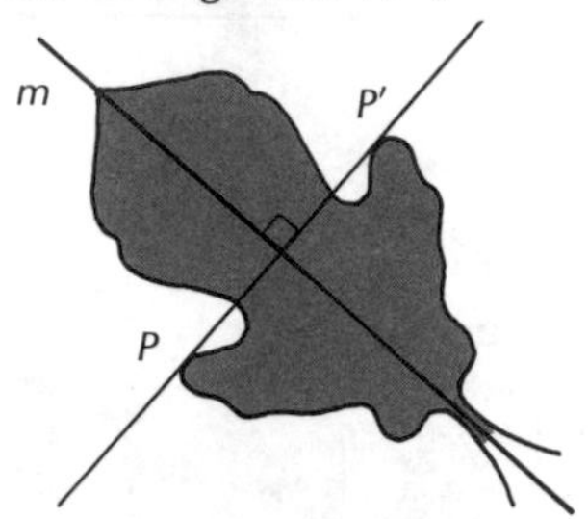

A **reflection** in a line, *m*, is a transformation that maps *P* onto *P′*, such that if *P* is not on line *m*, then *m* is the perpendicular bisector of $\overline{PP'}$, and if *P* is on line *m*, $P = P'$.

Additional properties of a reflection are given below.

i. A figure and its reflection image are congruent.
ii. Each point on the reflection line is its own reflection image.
iii. The point of intersection of a line segment with its image lies on the reflection line.

EXAMPLE 1: *Given:* C_1 and C_2 are two congruent circles with centres *X* and *Y*, respectively.
C_1 and C_2 intersect at *A* and *B*.

Prove: C_2 is the reflection image of C_1 in $\overline{AB}$.

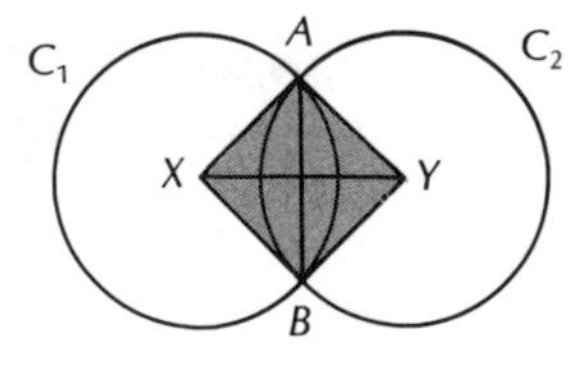

Proof:

Statement	Reason
$C_1 \cong C_2$	Given
$AX = AY$	Definition of congruent circles
A is on the perpendicular bisector of $\overline{XY}$.	PBT
$BX = BY$	Definition of congruent circles
B is on the perpendicular bisector of $\overline{XY}$.	PBT

$\overline{AB}$ is the perpendicular bisector of $\overline{XY}$.
Thus, $X \to Y$, $A \to A$, and $B \to B$ under a reflection in $\overline{AB}$.
Also, C_1 maps onto a congruent circle with centre *Y*, which is congruent to C_2.
Therefore, $C_1 \to C_2$ under a reflection in $\overline{AB}$.

EXAMPLE 2: For $\triangle ABC$, $AB = AC$ and $\overline{AM}$ is a median. Show that $\overline{AM}$ is the line of reflection that maps B onto C.

Given: $\triangle ABC$ in which $AB = AC$.
$\overline{AM}$ is a median.

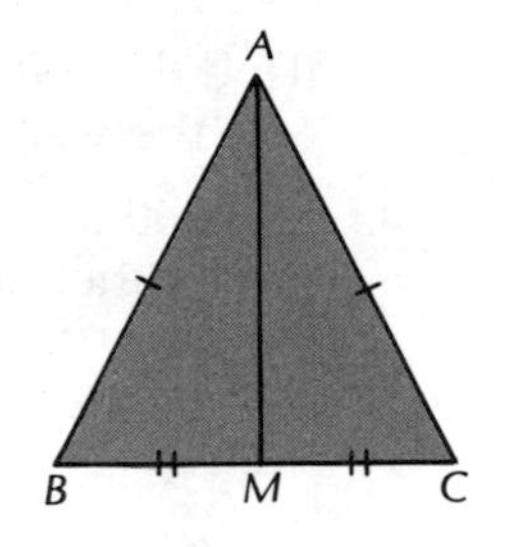

Prove: $\overline{AM}$ is the line of reflection that maps B onto C.

Proof: Prove that $\overline{AM}$ is the perpendicular bisector of $\overline{BC}$.

For $\triangle ABM$ and $\triangle ACM$,

$AB = AC.$	Given
$MB = MC$	Definition of a median
$AM = AM$	Common segment
$\triangle ABM \cong \triangle ACM$	SSS
$\angle AMB = \angle AMC$	Congruent triangles
$\angle AMB + \angle AMC = 180°$	Straight angle
$\angle AMB = \angle AMC = 90°$	Division

Thus, $\overline{AM}$ is the perpendicular bisector of $\overline{BC}$.
Therefore, $\overline{AM}$ is the line of reflection that maps B onto C.

EXERCISE 10-9

A **1.** Copy each figure shown below on grid paper. Graph the image of each figure in the reflection line, *m*.

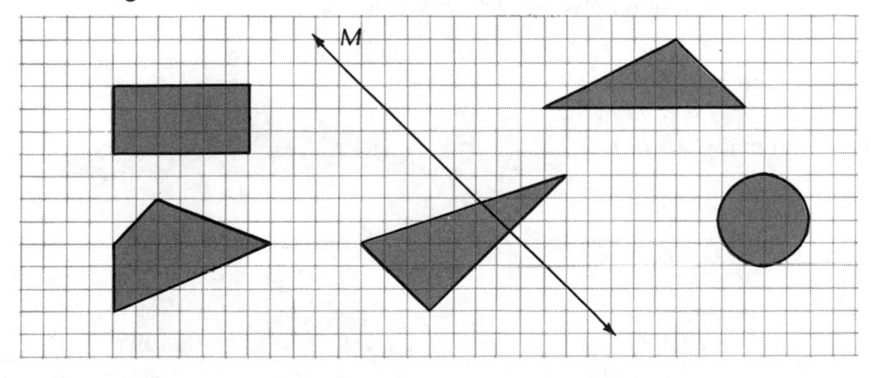

2. Find the image of $P(4, 3)$ under reflection in each given line.
   a. the x-axis b. the y-axis c. the line $y = x$ d. the line $y = -x$

3. Find the reflection image of $P(a, b)$ in each given line.
   a. the x-axis b. the y-axis c. the line $y = x$ d. the line $y = -x$

B 4. Prove that two intersecting lines are images of each other after reflection in the bisector of the angle formed by them.

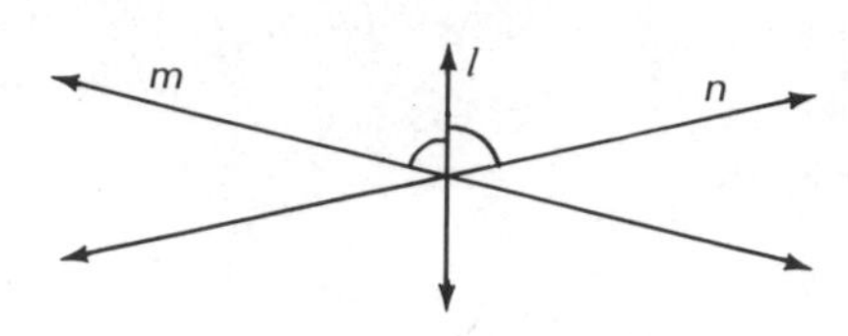

5. Prove that a circle is its own image after reflection in any diameter.

6. Two congruent circles intersect at P and Q. A line through P intersects the circles at A and B, respectively, such that $\overline{APB} \perp \overline{PQ}$. Prove that $AQ = BQ$.

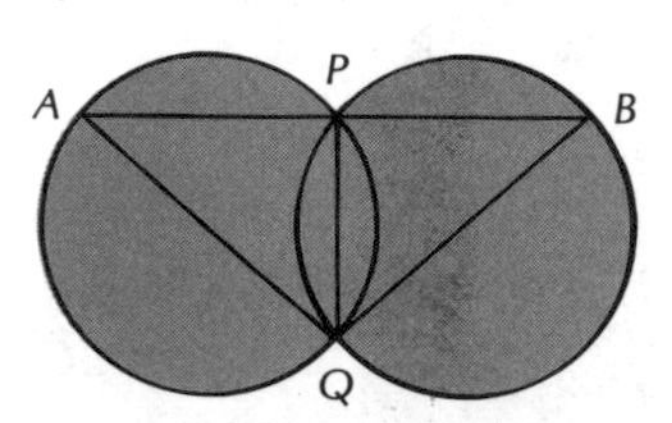

7. Two circles with centres at P and Q intersect at X and Y. Prove that $\overline{PQ}$ is the line of reflection that maps X onto Y.

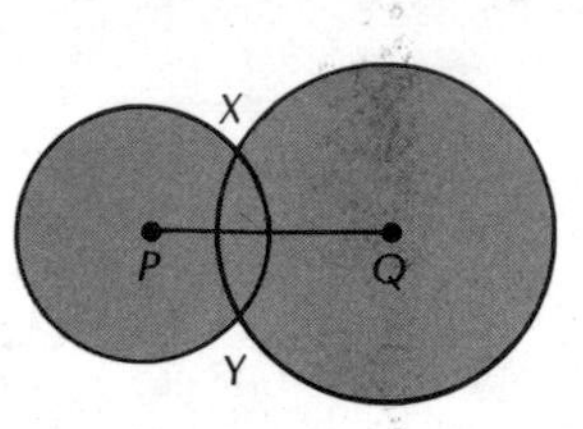

8. For parallelogram $ABCD$, diagonals $\overline{AC}$ and $\overline{BD}$ intersect at E. Under what conditions is vertex A reflected about $\overline{BD}$ onto vertex C?

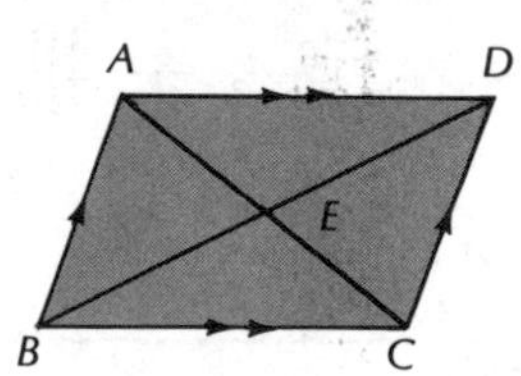

9. The image of $\overline{AB}$, when it is reflected in line l, is $\overline{A'B'}$. If $\overline{AB}$ and its image intersect at a point, P, prove each statement.
   a. P is on line l.
   b. Line l bisects the angle between $\overline{AB}$ and $\overline{A'B'}$.

10. $\angle ABC$ is bisected by $\overline{BD}$. Prove that if $AB = CB$, $\overline{BD}$ is the line of reflection that maps $\overline{AB}$ onto $\overline{CB}$.

11. For trapezoid $ABCD$, $\overline{AD} \parallel \overline{BC}$ and $\angle ABC = \angle DCB$. Use the properties of reflections to prove that $\angle BAD = \angle CDA$.

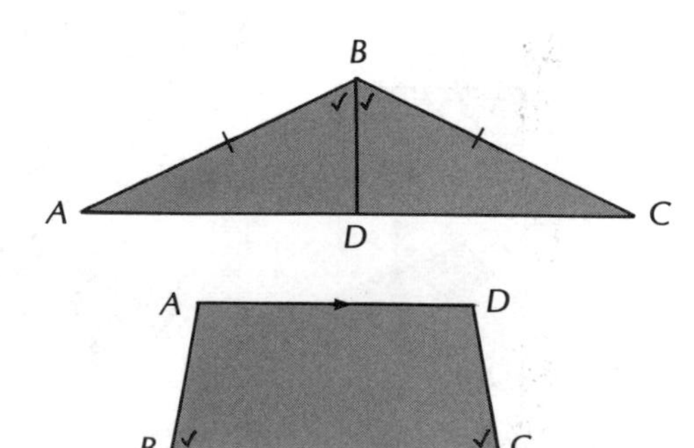

Application

Snookered

In the game of snooker, the cue ball (white ball) is "shot" in a straight line, aimed to strike another ball. Sometimes a third ball lies between the cue ball and the intended target. In such a case, a player is said to be "snookered".

1. The cue ball is at A and the intended target is B, but the player is still snookered. To hit the target at B, a player can bounce the cue ball off the rubber cushion, $\overline{ZW}$, to succeed. (This is called a cushion shot.)
   - **a.** B' is the reflection of B in $\overline{ZW}$. Show that if you aim for B', the ball should hit B.
   - **b.** Show that the player can use any of the four sides of the rectangle for a one-cushion shot.
   - **c.** Show by an indirect method that the path $AP + PB$ is minimized when $\angle 1 = \angle 2$.
   - **d.** Explain how a one-cushion shot is related to reflection in a mirror.

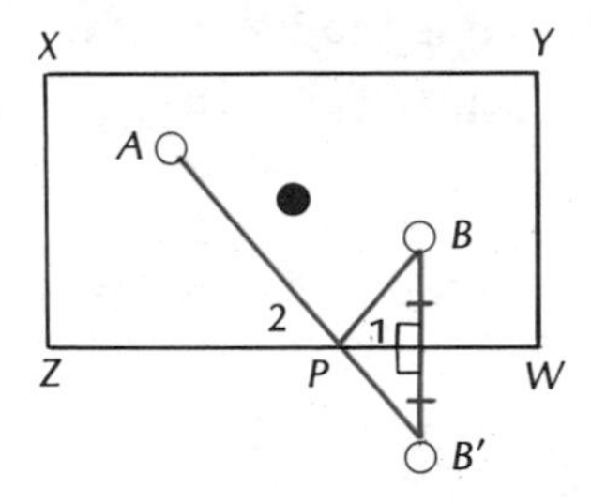

2. If a player is "double" snookered—that is, other balls prevent a one-cushion shot, the player can try a two-cushion shot, as illustrated in the diagram. If B' is the reflection image of B in $\overline{XY}$ and B'' is the reflection image of B' in $\overline{ZX}$, extended, show that the following holds.
   - **a.** Directing the cue ball from A to B'' enables the player to hit the intended target at B.
   - **b.** The total distance travelled by the cue ball, from A to B, is equal to AB''.
   - **c.** The path of the cue ball is the same as a light ray reflected in two mirrors.

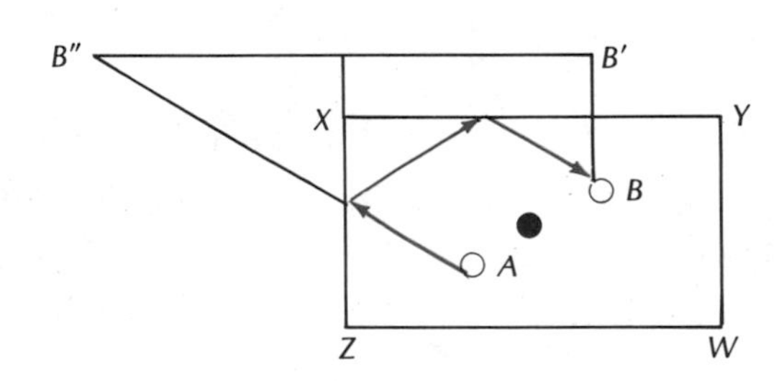

3. Show how a player could make a three-cushion shot using the given diagram. (There are many possible paths.)

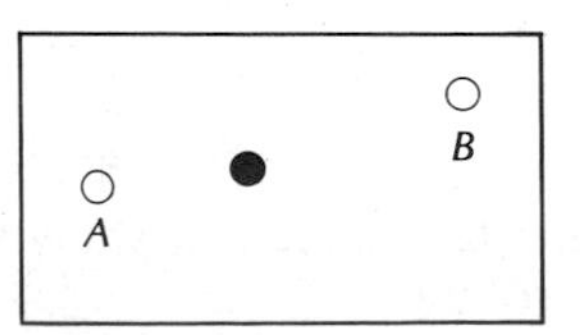

10-10 Basic Properties of Rotations

The movement of the pedals on a bicycle illustrates another type of transformation, that is, a rotation. As you pedal the bicycle, each pedal rotates to a new position, the same distance away from the centre of rotation.

A **rotation** about a point, O, through $\theta°$ is a transformation such that if $P \rightarrow P'$, then $OP = OP'$, and $\angle POP' = \theta°$.

In the diagram below, $\overline{PQ}$ maps onto $\overline{P'Q'}$ under a rotation of $\theta°$ about O, the **centre of rotation.** θ is called the **angle of rotation**.

A counter-clockwise rotation is defined to be positive; a clockwise rotation is defined to be negative.

EXAMPLE 1: Prove that a rotation about a point is an isometry.

To show that a rotation is an isometry, it is necessary to prove that under a rotation, segments map onto new segments of equal length.

Given: $\overline{PQ}$ maps onto $\overline{P'Q'}$ under a rotation of $\theta°$ about O.

Prove: $PQ = P'Q'$

Proof:

$OP = OP'$ and $OQ = OQ'$	Definition of rotation
$\angle POP' = \angle QOQ' = \theta°$	Definition of rotation
$\angle POQ = \angle P'OQ'$	Subtraction of common $\angle P'OQ$
$\triangle POQ \cong \triangle P'OQ'$	SAS
$PQ = P'Q'$	Congruent triangles

Therefore, a rotation is an isometry.

EXAMPLE 2: Prove that a triangle maps onto a congruent triangle under a rotation about a given point.

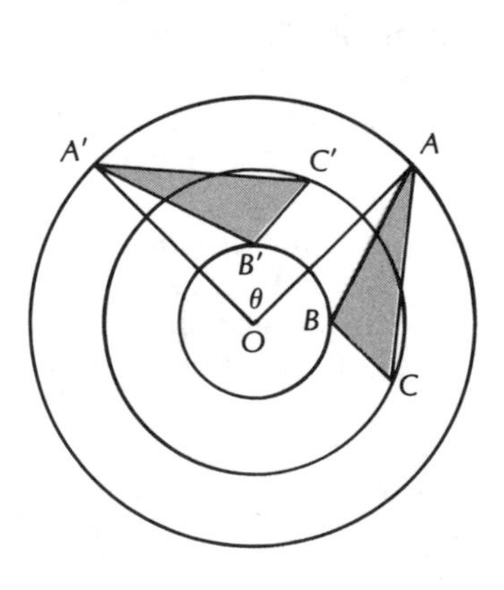

In the diagram, $\triangle ABC$ is rotated about point O in a counter-clockwise direction to give the image $\triangle A'B'C'$.

$AB = A'B'$	From Example 1
$BC = B'C'$	From Example 1
$AC = A'C'$	From Example 1
$\triangle ABC \cong \triangle A'B'C'$	SSS

Therefore, a triangle maps onto a congruent triangle under a rotation.

Similarly, it can be shown that all figures map onto congruent figures under a rotation.

A **half-turn** is a rotation of 180° about a point.
If $A \rightarrow A'$ under a half-turn about centre O, then $OA = OA'$ and $\angle AOA' = 180°$.

The following properties of a half-turn can be established.

i. A segment and its image under a half-turn are parallel.
ii. The centre of rotation is the midpoint of a segment joining a point and its half-turn image.

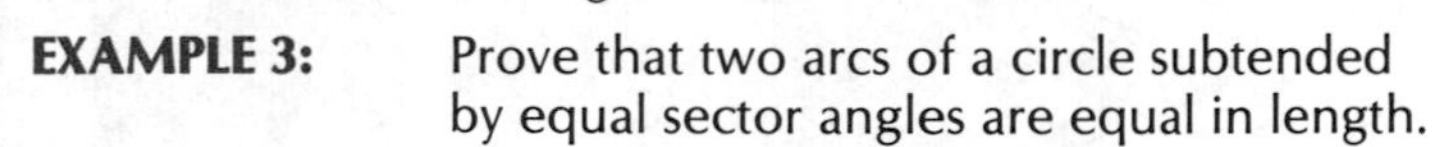

EXAMPLE 3: Prove that two arcs of a circle subtended by equal sector angles are equal in length.

Given: The circle shown at the right, with centre O, sector angles such that $\angle AOB = \angle COD = \theta°$

Prove: Arc BA = arc CD

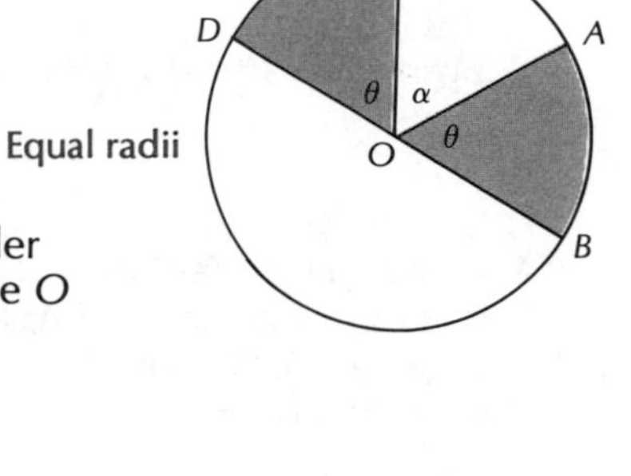

Proof: Consider a rotation of $(\theta + \alpha)°$, where $\alpha = \angle AOC$, $OB = OC$ and $OA = OD$	Equal radii
$\angle BOC = \angle AOD = (\theta + \alpha)°$.	
Therefore, $B \rightarrow C$ and $A \rightarrow D$ under a rotation of $(\theta + \alpha)°$ about centre O and arc $BA \rightarrow$ arc CD under this rotation.	
Therefore, arc BA = arc CD.	

EXAMPLE 4: For parallelogram $ABCD$, E is the midpoint of diagonal $\overline{AC}$. Prove that $BE = DE$ and that B, E, and D are collinear.

Given: Parallelogram $ABCD$, E is the midpoint of diagonal $\overline{AC}$

Prove: $BE = DE$ and that B, E, and D are collinear

Proof: $AE = CE$	Given
$A \rightarrow C$ and $C \rightarrow A$ under a half-turn about centre E.	
So $\overline{AB} \rightarrow \overline{CX}$, for some point X, under the half-turn.	
$\overline{AB} \parallel \overline{CX}$,	Property of a half-turn
and $AB = CX$.	Rotation is an isometry
But $\overline{AB} \parallel \overline{CD}$,	
and $AB = CD$,	Given parallelogram
so $\overline{CD} \parallel \overline{CX}$,	Transitivity
and $CD = CX$.	Transitivity
Thus, $\overline{CD} = \overline{CX}$.	Segments share a common point, C
Also, $X = D$	
and $\overline{AB} \rightarrow \overline{CD}$ under the half-turn about E.	
$B \rightarrow D$ under the half-turn about E.	
Thus $BE = ED$	Isometry
and B, E, and D are collinear.	$\angle BED = 180°$

EXERCISE 10-10

A 1. Copy each given figure on grid paper. Graph the image of each figure using the indicated rotation.

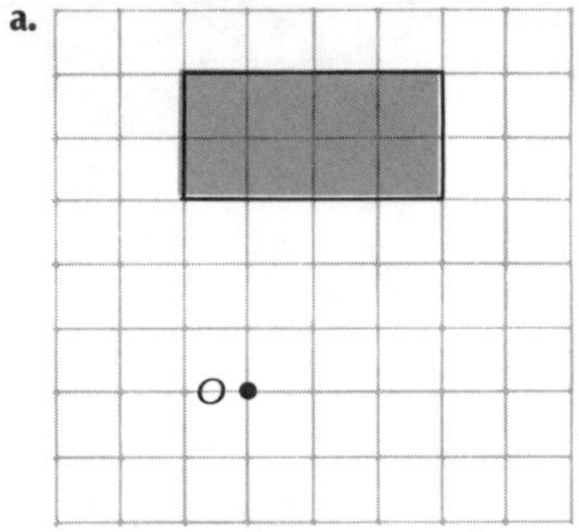

a. a positive quarter-turn about O

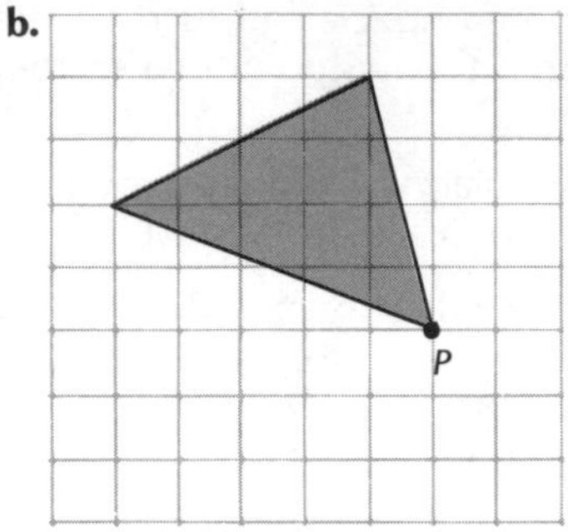

b. a half-turn about P

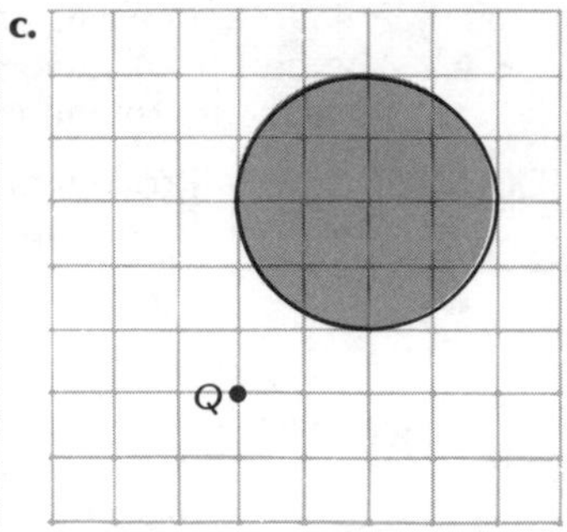

c. $-90°$ about Q

2. A rotation of $+90°$ about O is equivalent to a rotation of $-270°$ about O. State another name for each rotation.

a. a half-turn about O **b.** a quarter-turn about O
c. $-45°$ about O **d.** $150°$ about O

3. Plot $A(2, 3)$, $B(4, -1)$, $C(5, 0)$, and $D(6, -3)$ on a graph. Plot the image of each point under the given rotation.

a. $90°$ about O **b.** a half-turn about O
c. $-90°$ about O **d.** $-270°$ about O

4. Find the image of (a, b) under each rotation.

a. a half-turn about O **b.** a positive quarter-turn about O

B 5. Prove that two chords of a circle subtended by equal sector angles are equal in length.

6. The diagonals of quadrilateral $ABCD$ bisect each other at E. Prove that $ABCD$ is a parallelogram.

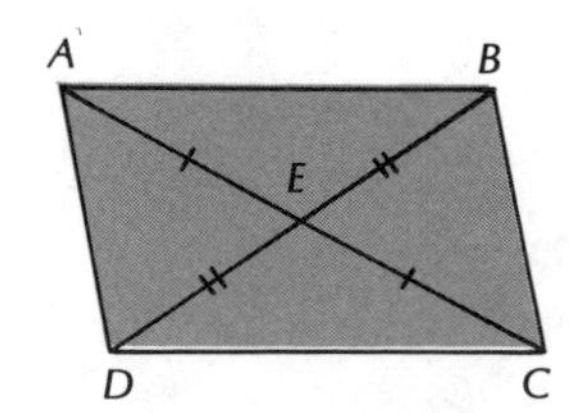

7. A line, m, maps onto a line, n, under a rotation of $\theta°$ about point O. Point O is not on either m or n. Prove that one of the angles between m and n is equal to $\theta°$.
(*Hint:* Construct $\overline{OP} \perp m$ such that P is on m. Find P'. The image of m is perpendicular to $\overline{OP'}$.)

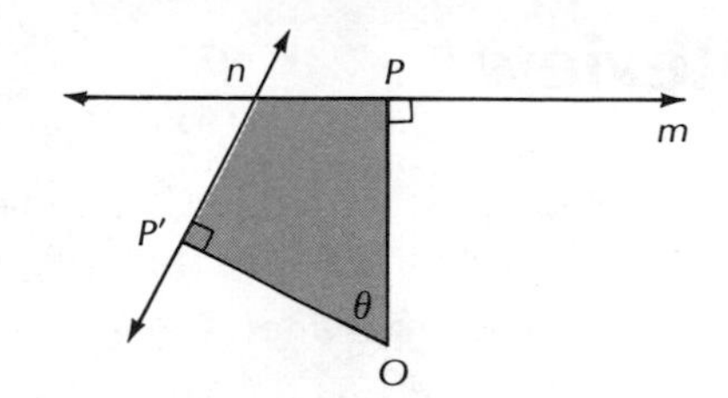

8. Quadrilateral $ABCD$ is given with $AB = AC$, $AD = AE$, $\angle BAC = 30°$, and $\angle DAE = 30°$.
   a. What rotation maps B onto C and D onto E?
   b. Prove that $BD = CE$.
   c. Find the measure of the acute angle between $\overline{BD}$ and $\overline{CE}$.

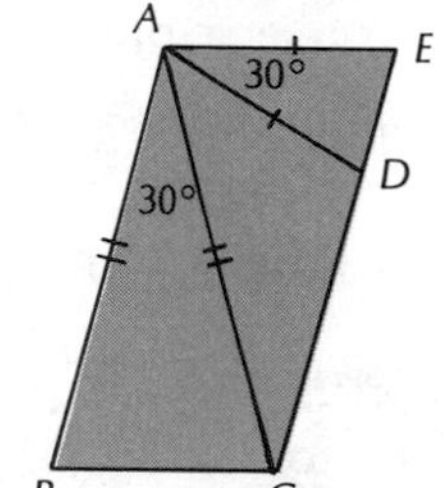
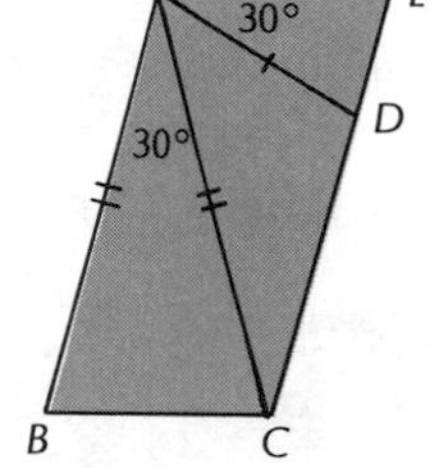

9. $\overline{PQ}$ and $\overline{RS}$ are two segments that bisect each other at T. Join P to R and S to Q. Prove that $\triangle PRT$ is congruent to $\triangle QST$ and that $\overline{PR} \parallel \overline{QS}$.

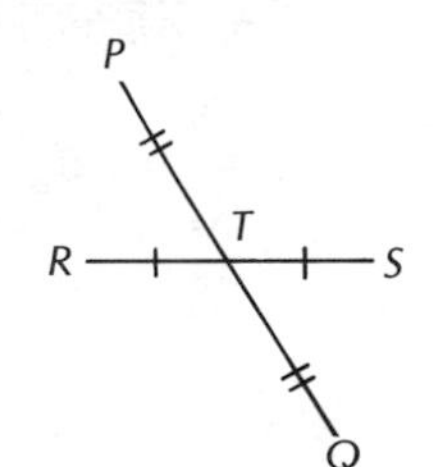

10. $\overline{XY} \parallel \overline{VW}$ and $\overline{XW}$ intersects $\overline{VY}$ at Z such that $XZ = WZ$. Prove that $XY = WV$, $\overline{XV} \parallel \overline{YW}$, and $XV = WY$.

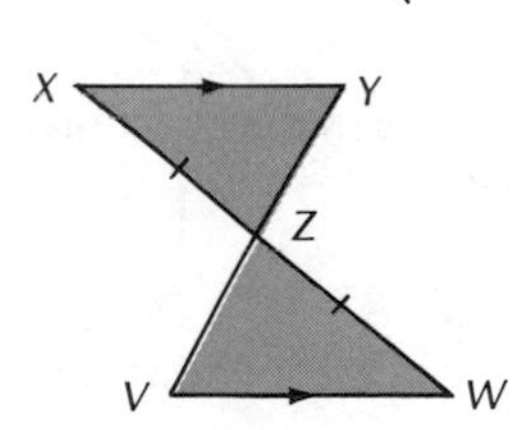

11. Two squares, $ABCD$ and $CEFG$, are given, such that C is at the origin, and E is on the x-axis.
   a. Find the image of $\triangle BCE$ under a clockwise rotation of 90° about centre C.

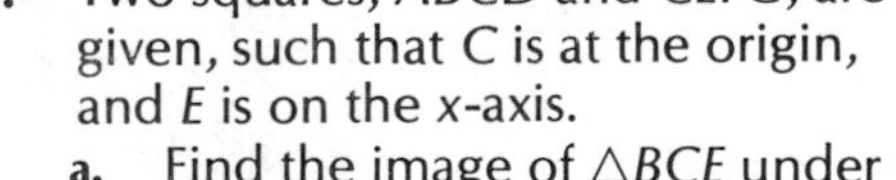

   b. Prove that $BE = DG$.
   c. Prove that $\overline{BE} \perp \overline{DG}$.

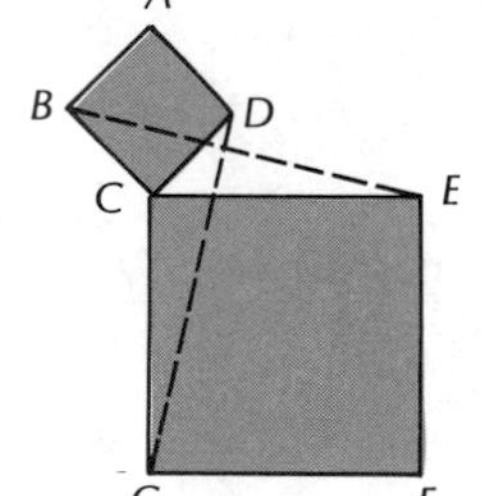

12. $\triangle ABC$, with vertices $A(0, 6)$, $B(0, 0)$, and $C(3, 0)$, and $\triangle CDE$, with vertices $C(3, 0)$, $D(9, 0)$, and $E(9, 3)$, are given.
   a. Graph $\triangle ABC$ and $\triangle CDE$ on the same set of axes.
   b. Find the centre of rotation for which $\triangle ABC \rightarrow \triangle CDE$.
   c. Find the angle of rotation for which $\triangle ABC \rightarrow \triangle CDE$.

Review

1. Define each term using a complete sentence.
   Use a diagram, where possible, to illustrate the term.

   a. concurrent lines
   b. median of a triangle
   c. trapezoid
   d. supplementary angles

2. Write the converse of the given statement. Is the converse true?

   a. If a triangle is isosceles, then the angles opposite the equal sides are equal.

   b. If $x = 6$, then $x^2 = 36$.

3. Are the conclusions valid?

   a. $\overline{AB} \parallel \overline{CD}$ or $AB \neq CD$
   $AB = CD$
   Conclusion: $\overline{AB} \parallel \overline{CD}$

   b. Some of the students in 12A take math.
   Stephen is in 12A.
   Conclusion: Stephen takes math.

4. For $\triangle ABC$, $AB = AC$. $\overline{BC}$ is extended by its own length to E. $\overline{AB}$ is extended by its own length to D. Prove that $\angle CAE = \angle BDC$.

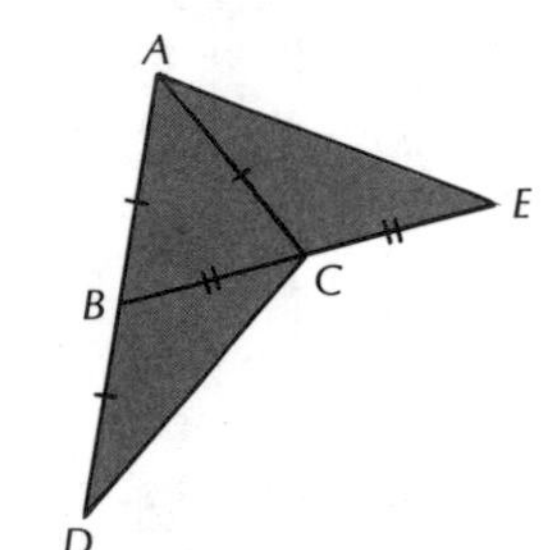

5. Use transformations to prove both parts of the Isosceles Triangle Theorem.

6. For $\triangle XYZ$, $XZ = YZ$. $\overline{YZ}$ is extended to W.
   If $\overline{PZ} \parallel \overline{XY}$, prove that $\overline{PZ}$ bisects $\angle XZW$.

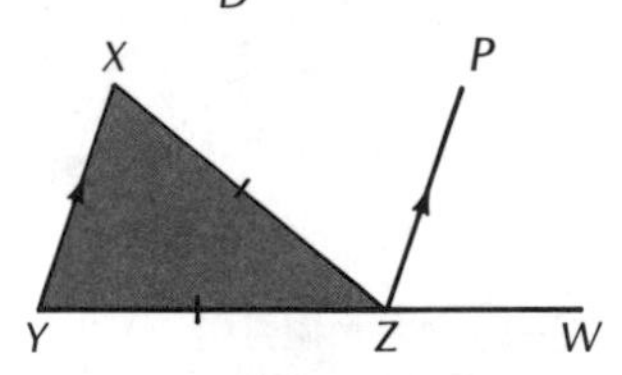

7. For trapezoid $ABCD$, $\overline{AD} \parallel \overline{BC}$ and $AB = DC$.
   Prove that $\angle ABC = \angle DCB$.

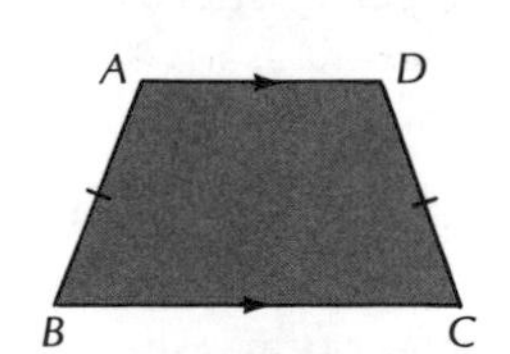

8. Use an indirect proof to prove each statement.

   a. If x is an integer and x^3 is odd, then x is odd.

   b. A tiled wall in a bathroom is made up of tiles in the shape of triangles and squares, as shown. There are 1875 tiles altogether. Thus, there must be an odd number of squares.

9. For quadrilateral $XYZW$, the diagonals bisect each other. Use transformations to prove that $XYZW$ is a parallelogram.

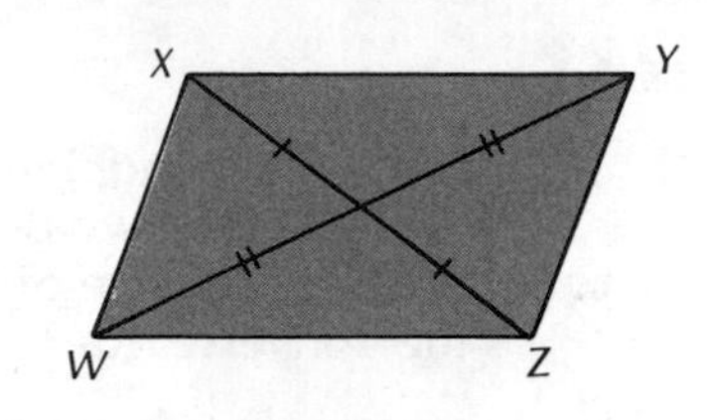

10. For $\triangle XYZ$, $\overline{XW}$ bisects $\angle YXZ$ in $\triangle XYZ$. Prove the following statements.
   a. $XZ > WZ$
   b. $XY > YW$
   c. $XZ + XY > YZ$

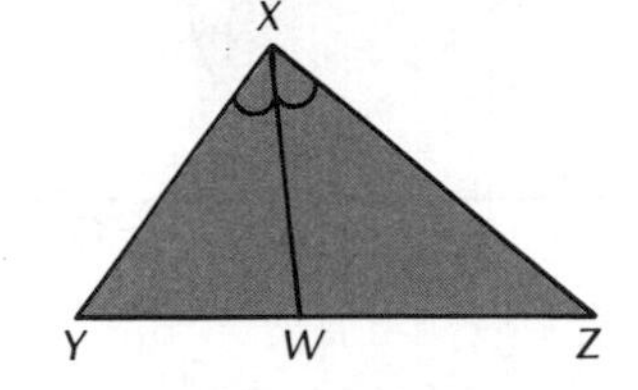

11. As shown, $\overline{AB}$ and $\overline{CD}$ are chords of two concentric circles, with centre O. Prove that $\overline{AB} \parallel \overline{CD}$.

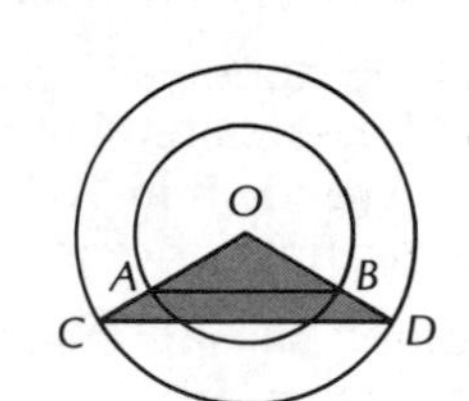

12. The diagonals of quadrilateral $ABCD$ intersect at E. Prove that $AB + BC + CD + AD > AC + BD$.

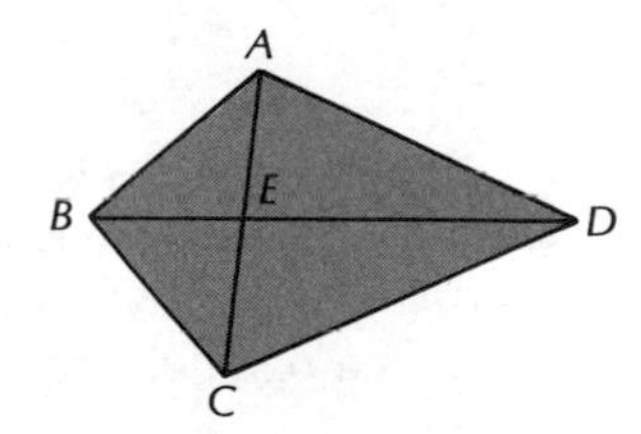

13. As shown in the diagram, $XY > XZ$, and $PZ = WY$. Prove that $YP > WZ$.

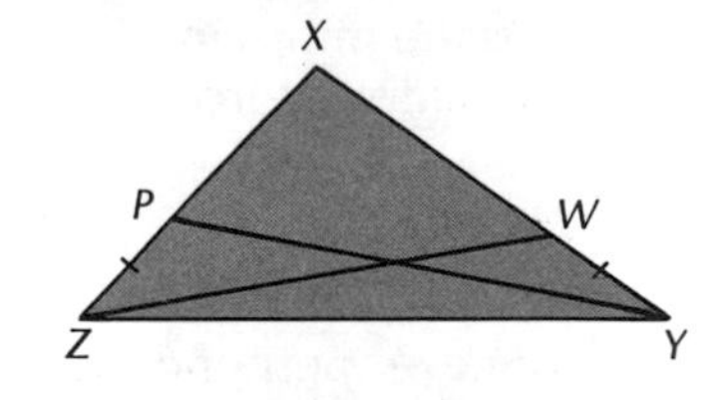

14. In the given diagram, $\overline{AE} \parallel \overline{BD}$, $\overline{BC} \parallel \overline{AD}$, $AE = BC$, and $AD = BD$. Prove each statement.
   a. $AC = BE$

   b. $\overline{EC} \parallel \overline{AB}$

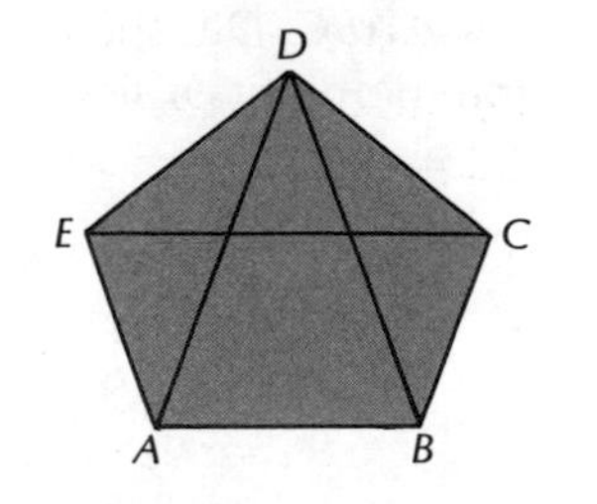

Test Unit 10

1. **a.** Rewrite as a conditional sentence:
   The product of two odd numbers is an odd number.
   b. Write the converse of the conditional sentence given in part **a.** Is the converse true?

2. Find the size of each indicated angle.

a.

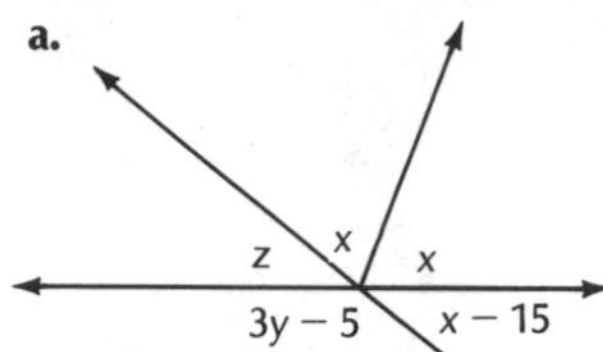

b.

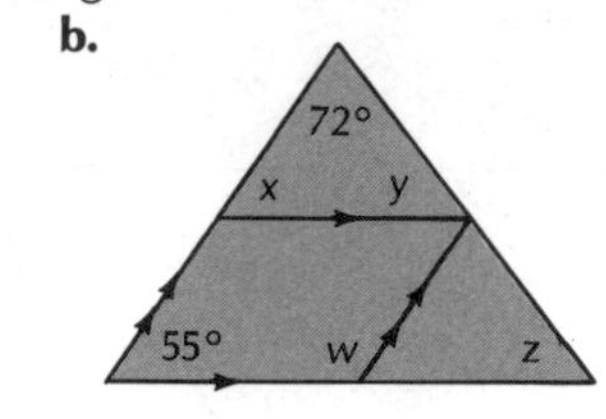

c.

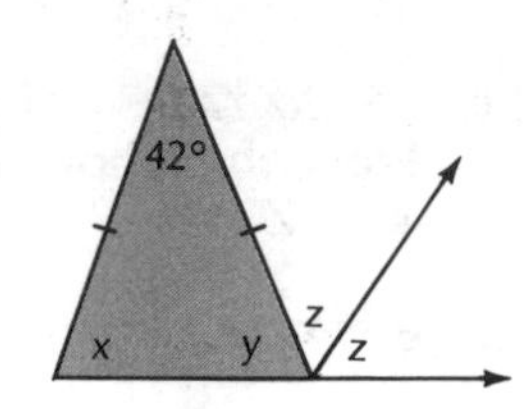

3. $\triangle ABC$ is scalene. Prove that $\angle A \neq \angle B$.

4. All the students in class 12C are at least 16 years old. Pair this statement with each statement below. Then, write a conclusion, if possible.
   a. Wendy is in 12C. **b.** Patrick is 17 years old.
   c. Lianne is not in 12C. **d.** Neil is 15 years old.

5. Point P is inside $\triangle ABC$.
   Prove that $AB + AC > PB + PC$.

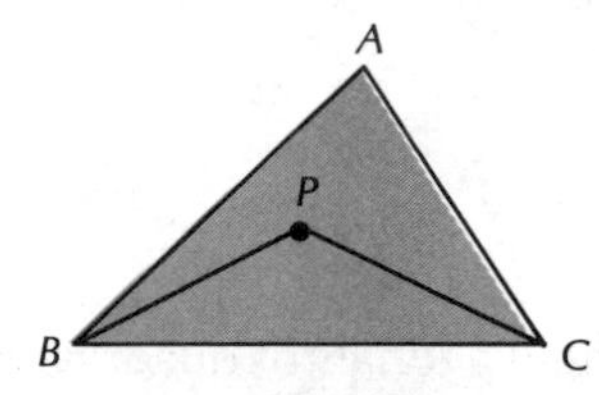

6. Quadrilateral $PQRS$ is a parallelogram. T is a point on $\overline{PS}$ such that $\overline{TQ}$ bisects $\angle PQR$, and U is a point on $\overline{QR}$ such that $\overline{SU}$ bisects $\angle PSR$. Prove that $STQU$ is a parallelogram.

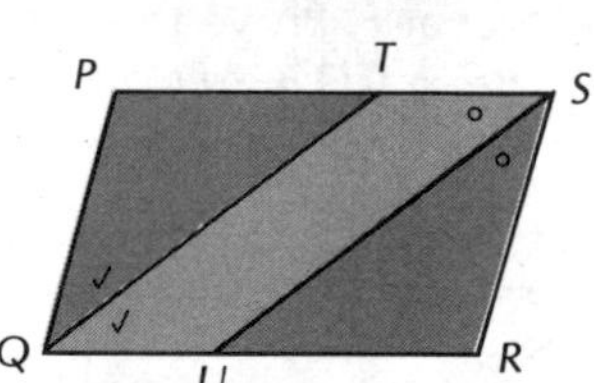

7. $\triangle XYZ$ is a right-angled triangle with $\angle XZY = 90°$. W is the midpoint of the hypotenuse. Prove that W is equidistant from the vertices of $\triangle XYZ$.

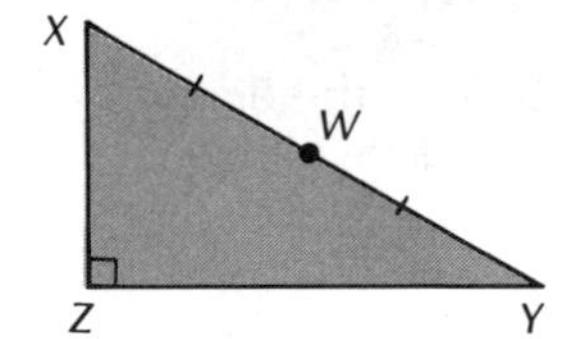

8. Prove that the bisectors of two angles of a triangle are never perpendicular.

9. For $\triangle ABC$, D is the midpoint of side $\overline{AB}$ and E is the midpoint of side $\overline{AC}$. Prove that $\overline{DE} \parallel \overline{BC}$ and $DE = \frac{1}{2}BC$.

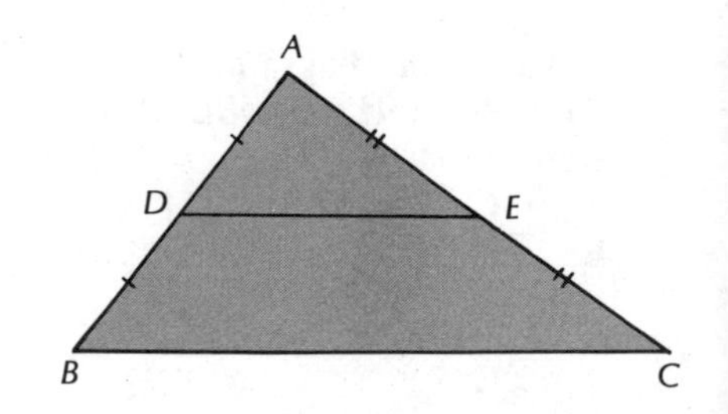

Cumulative Review

1. Write an equation of the circle with centre $C(2, -3)$ and radius $\sqrt{5}$.

2. A radioactive substance has a half-life of 16 d.
How many grams of a 500 mg supply remains after 56 d?

3. Evaluate.
   a. $27^{\frac{2}{3}}$ b. $\left(\frac{1}{32}\right)^{\frac{3}{5}}$

4. Susan deposits \$4000 in a bank. What amount will this accumulate to at the end of 3 a, if the bank pays an interest rate of 6%/a, compounded semiannually?

5. Evaluate:
   a. $\log_5 5^{-2}$ b. $\log_2 16^3$

6. Factor $(x + 2)^2 + 3(x + 2) + 2$.

7. Divide $(y^5 + 4y^4 + 2y^2 + 4)$ by $(y + 4)$. Give the answer in the form $P(x) = D(x)Q(x) + R(x)$.

8. The terminal ray of an angle, θ, in standard position, contains $(8, -15)$.
   a. Find $\sin\theta$ and $\cos\theta$. b. Show that $\tan^2\theta + 1 = \sec^2\theta$.

9. A ship's captain sights the top of a lighthouse that is on top of a cliff. The angle of elevation is 46.5°. After sailing 2000 m directly away from the cliff, the angle of elevation is 32.4°. How many metres above the sea is the lighthouse?

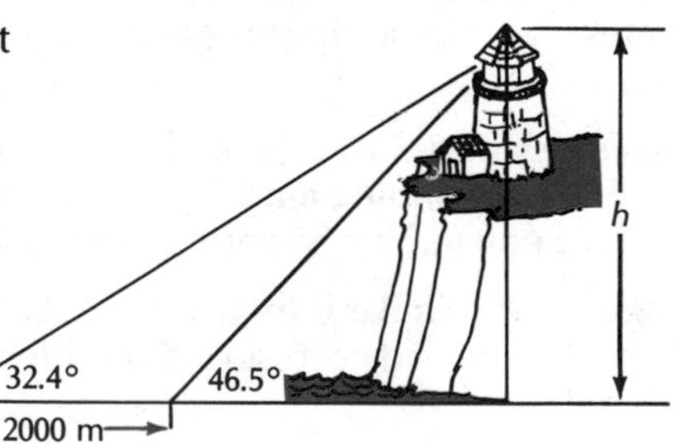

10. Find the length of an arc of a circle, with a radius 15 cm, that subtends an angle of 140° at the centre. Leave your answer in terms of π.

11. A function is defined by $y = -2\cos 3x$.
    a. Find the period and amplitude of the function.
    b. Sketch the graph of the function, for $0 \leq x \leq 2\pi$.

12. Prove that $(\sin\theta + \cos\theta)^2 = 1 + \sin 2\theta$.

11 Similar Figures

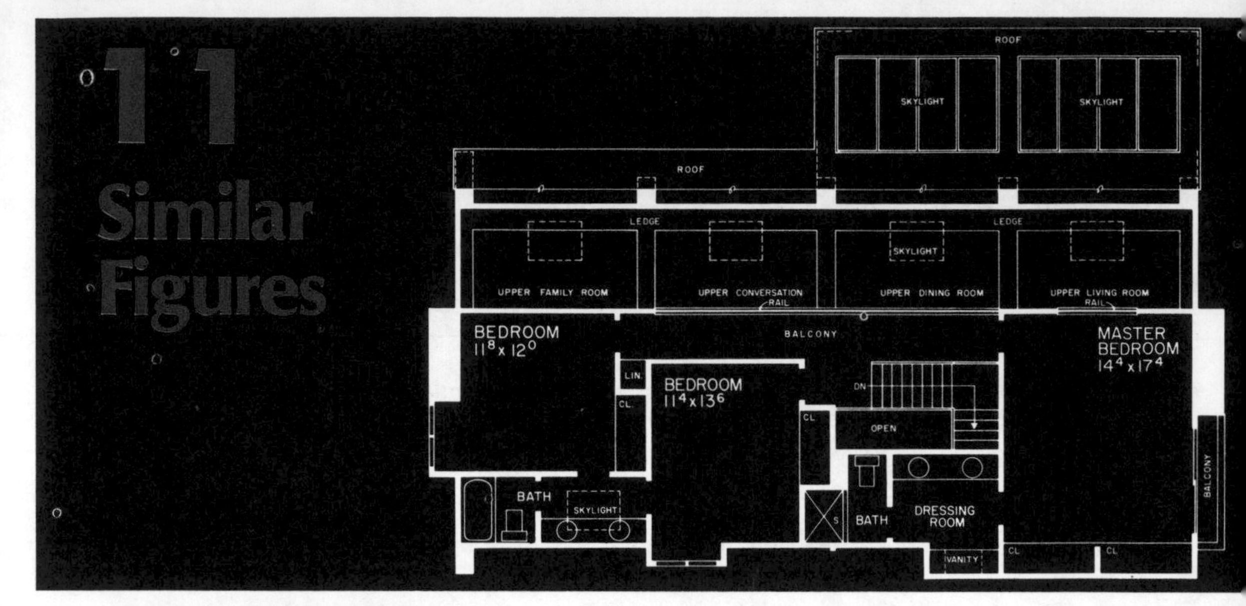

11-1 Similar Figures

The images you see on a television screen are identical in shape to the actual objects and people being shown. A telescope and a microscope both show enlarged images of the objects being viewed. The objects and their images have the same shape, and so they are examples of *similar* figures. To remodel a kitchen, you need a plan. A drawing of the room, in which measurements are drawn to scale, can be of great assistance in deciding where each cupboard and appliance will be located. This scale drawing illustrates how similar figures can be used to help in the design of the kitchen.

The scale drawing shown is similar to a view of the kitchen from above. The ratios of corresponding lengths, shown in the scale drawing, to the actual lengths are equal. That is, corresponding lengths are proportional.

Two figures are **similar** if their vertices can be paired so that corresponding angles are equal and corresponding sides are proportional. Consider the figures below.

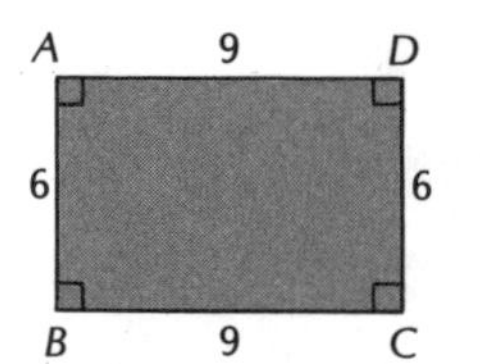

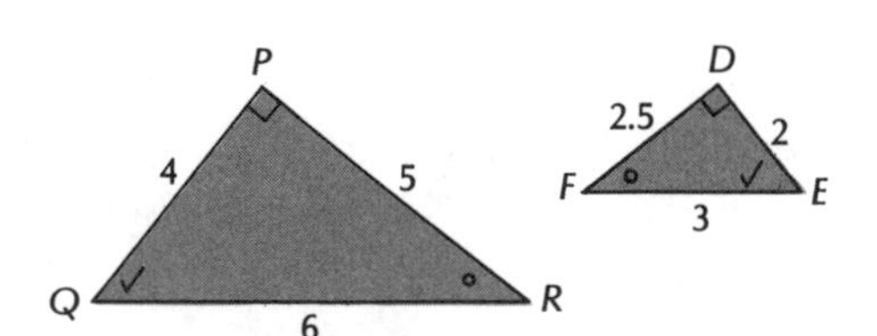

$\angle A = \angle X, \angle B = \angle Y, \angle C = \angle Z, \angle D = \angle W$

$\frac{AB}{XY} = \frac{BC}{YZ} = \frac{CD}{ZW} = \frac{AD}{XW} = \frac{3}{2}$

Rectangle $ABCD \sim$ Rectangle $XYZW$

$\angle P = \angle D, \angle Q = \angle E, \angle R = \angle F$

$\frac{PQ}{DE} = \frac{QR}{EF} = \frac{PR}{DF} = \frac{2}{1}$

$\triangle PQR \sim \triangle DEF$

Note that $\sim$ is the symbol for "is similar to."

The ratio of the lengths of two corresponding sides of two similar figures is called the **scale factor**. The scale factor of rectangle *ABCD* to rectangle *XYZW* is $\frac{3}{2}$, or 3:2. The scale factor of $\triangle PQR$ to $\triangle DEF$ is $\frac{2}{1}$ or 2:1.

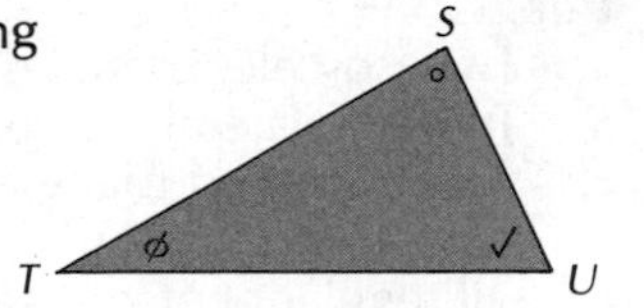

The names of similar figures are written so that corresponding vertices are in the same order. This notation is used throughout this unit. Therefore, $\triangle STU \sim \triangle HMJ$ implies that $\angle S = \angle H$, $\angle T = \angle M$, and $\angle U = \angle J$. Also, $\frac{ST}{HM} = \frac{TU}{MJ} = \frac{SU}{HJ}$.

EXAMPLE 1: Two similar polygons are shown. What is the scale factor of *ABCD* to *XYZW*? of *XYZW* to *ABCD*? Find the measure of each unknown side.

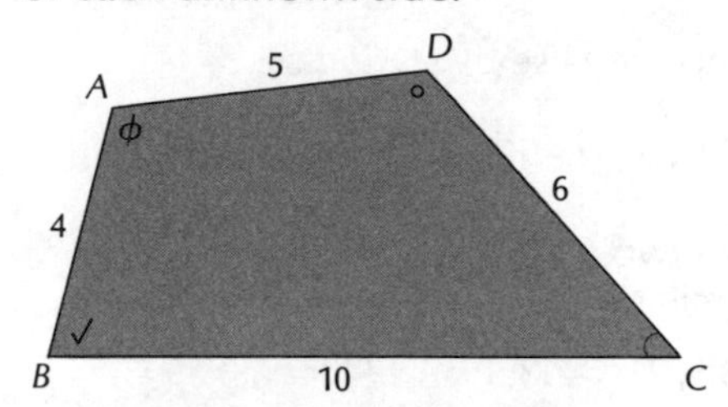

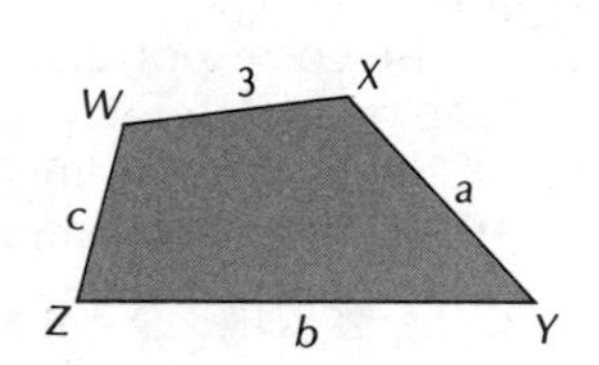

Since the polygons are similar,
$\angle A = \angle X$, $\angle B = \angle Y$, $\angle C = \angle Z$, and $\angle D = \angle W$.
Therefore, $\overline{AD}$ and $\overline{XW}$ are corresponding sides.
The scale factor of *ABCD* to *XYZW* is $\frac{5}{3}$. The scale factor of *XYZW* to *ABCD* is $\frac{3}{5}$.

To find the value of a and c, notice that
$$\frac{5}{3} = \frac{AD}{XW} = \frac{AB}{XY} = \frac{BC}{YZ} = \frac{CD}{ZW}.$$
So,
$$\frac{5}{3} = \frac{4}{a}, \quad \frac{5}{3} = \frac{10}{b}, \quad \text{and } \frac{5}{3} = \frac{6}{c}.$$
$$5a = 12 \qquad 5b = 30 \qquad 5c = 18$$
$$\therefore a = 2.4 \qquad b = 6 \qquad c = 3.6$$
Solve each equation.

EXAMPLE 2: For the given diagram, $ABCDE \sim XYZTW$. Find the lengths of $\overline{CB}$, $\overline{XW}$, $\overline{WT}$, and $\overline{TZ}$.

Since the figures are similar,
$$\frac{AB}{XY} = \frac{BC}{YZ} = \frac{CD}{ZT} = \frac{DE}{TW} = \frac{AE}{XW}.$$
So, $\frac{2}{4} = \frac{g}{6} = \frac{4}{a} = \frac{3}{b} = \frac{5}{h}$.

The scale factor of *ABCDE* to *XYZTW* is $\frac{1}{2}$.

Therefore, $g = 3$, $a = 8$, $b = 6$, and $h = 10$.

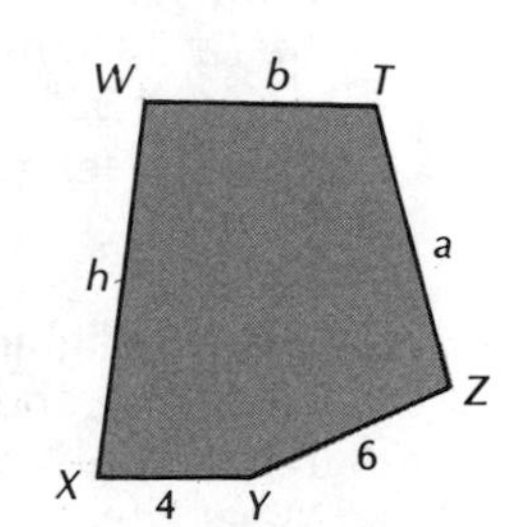

EXERCISE 11-1

A **1.** Determine whether the given statement is true. If the statement is false, make an appropriate change so that the new statement is true.

a. Two isosceles triangles are always similar.
b. Two equilateral triangles are always similar.
c. A right-angled triangle cannot be similar to a scalene triangle.
d. Two right-angled triangles are always similar.
e. All regular pentagons are similar.

2. For each pair of similar figures, identify pairs of equal angles. Then write a pair of ratios that relate the lengths of corresponding sides.

a. $\triangle PQR \sim \triangle IJK$ **b.** $PQRS \sim JKLM$

3. Show that the following statements are false by stating a counter-example.

a. If the corresponding sides of two quadrilaterals are equal, then the quadrilaterals are similar.
b. If the corresponding angles of two quadrilaterals are equal, then the quadrilaterals are similar.

B **4.** $\triangle PQR \sim \triangle STU$, $PQ = 4.8$, $PR = 3.5$, $TU = 13.5$, and $SU = 6.3$. Find the lengths of $\overline{QR}$ and $\overline{ST}$.

5. $\triangle ABC \sim \triangle XZY$, $\angle ABC = 35°$, and $\angle XZY = 80°$. Find the measures of $\angle ACB$, $\angle BAC$, and $\angle YXZ$.

6. Each pair of figures is similar. Find the lengths of the unknown sides.

a.

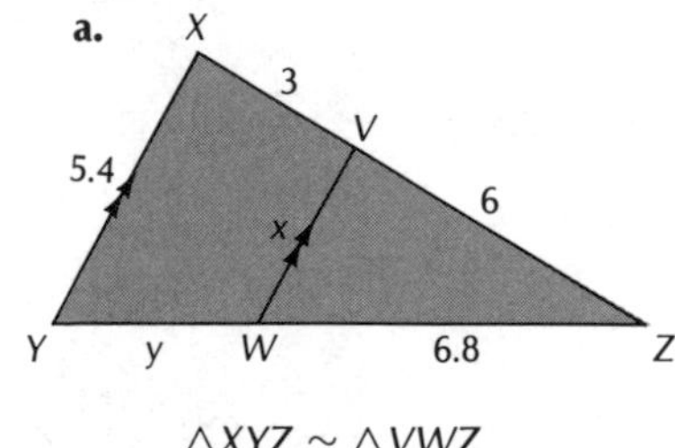

$\triangle XYZ \sim \triangle VWZ$

b.

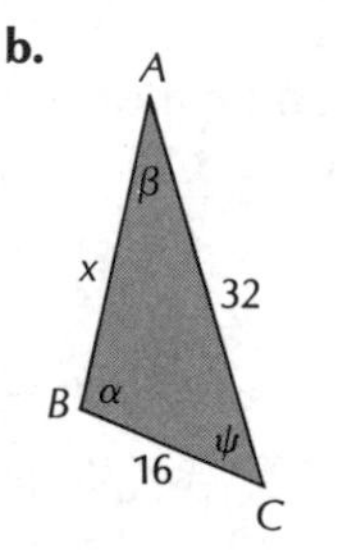

c.

7. In $\triangle ABC$, M is the midpoint of side $\overline{AB}$ and N is the midpoint of side $\overline{AC}$. $MN = 12.5$, $BC = 25$, $AC = 15$ and $\angle BAC = 90°$. $\triangle AMN \sim \triangle ABC$. Find the lengths of $\overline{AB}$ and $\overline{AM}$.

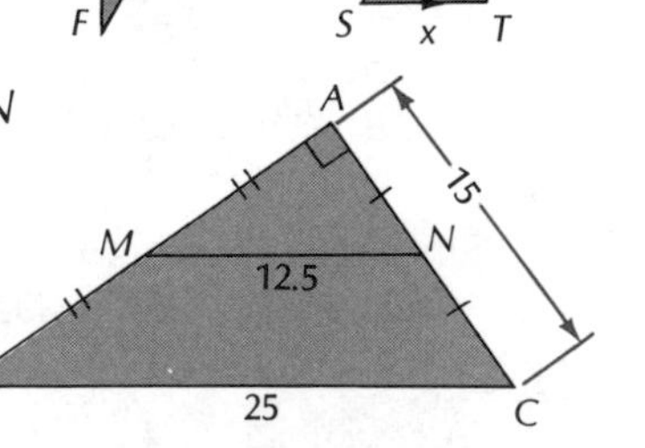

8. Use a straightedge and a protractor to draw two triangles with bases 5 cm long and 10 cm long and base angles of 30° and 70°, respectively. Measure the third angles and the remaining sides. What conclusion can you make regarding the two triangles?

9. A rectangle, 24 cm long, is cut into four congruent pieces, as shown. If each piece is similar to the original rectangle, find the width of the rectangle.

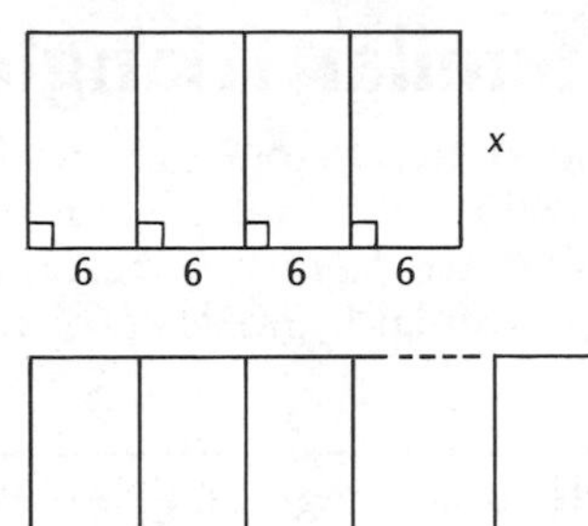

C 10. A rectangle, ky units long and x units wide, is cut into k congruent rectangles. Each rectangle is similar to the original rectangle, as in exercise 9. If x, y, and k are integral lengths, show that k must be a perfect square.

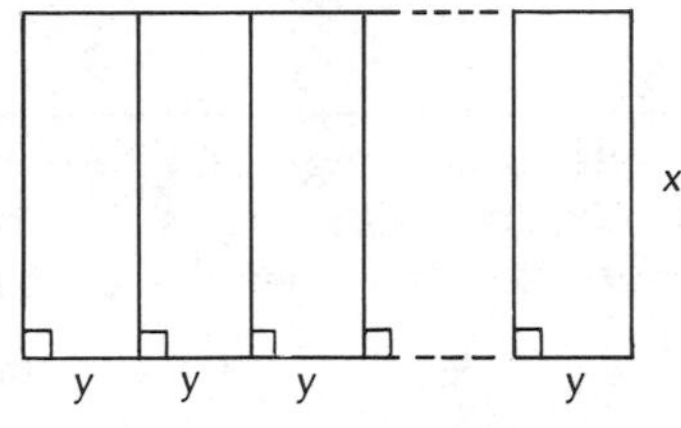

Application

Scale Drawings

Whether you are planning to build a deck, renovate a kitchen, or have a house built, it is essential that the project be well-planned. One method of ensuring success is to use a scale drawing. The project can be mapped out on a grid. On the grid, one unit can represent whatever length is convenient, depending on the detail required for the plan.

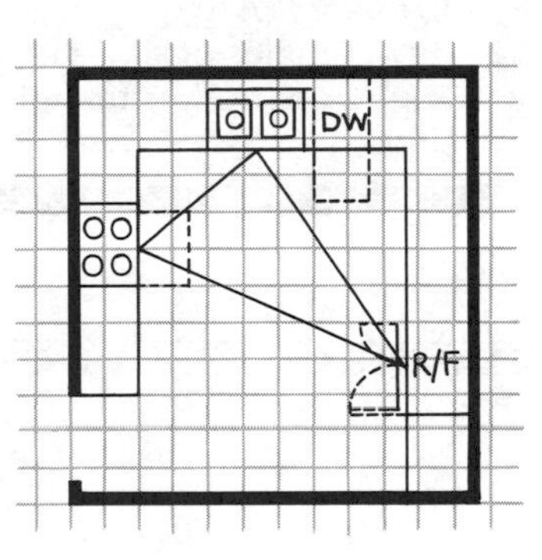

The scale used in planning the kitchen shown at the right is 1 unit represents 0.5 m. Each measurement should be taken as accurately as possible. For example, measure from the window to the door, from the door to the corner, and so on. When all the measurements of a wall are finished, total all the measurements and check your results by taking an overall measurement. It is essential to check the "squareness" of the room's corners. This can be done using the Pythagorean Theorem.

Ensure that the kitchen has an efficient "work triangle" between the sink, the stove, and the refrigerator. If the distance is too large, you may feel that you are taking too many steps; if it is too small, you may feel too cramped. Depending upon the shape of the room, a layout that provides both convenience and safety is ideal.

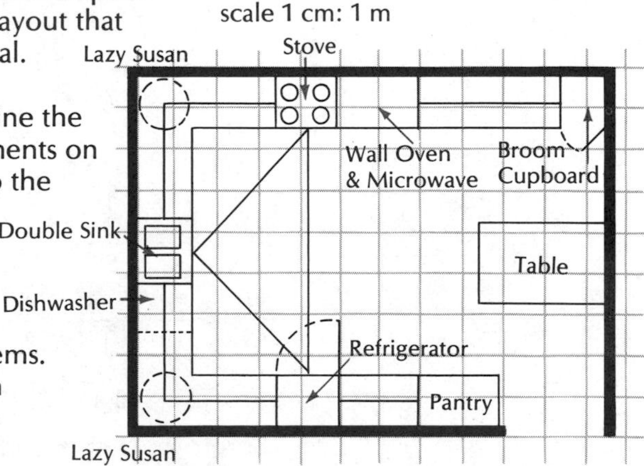

1. For the plan shown at the right, determine the following measurements. (All measurements on the scale drawing should be accurate to the nearest half-centimetre.)
   a. the length and width of the room
   b. the perimeter of the work triangle
   c. the size of the table

2. Determine the scale size of the given items.
   a. a table that measures 0.9 m by 1.2 m
   b. a cupboard that is 0.8 m wide
   c. a sink that is 1.22 m wide

11-2 Similar Triangles: AAA~

By definition, two triangles are similar if pairs of angles are equal and sides are proportional. In exercise 8 of lesson 11-1, it was found that two triangles are similar if two pairs of corresponding angles are equal. This leads to the following postulate, and its corollary, for similar triangles.

Angle Angle Angle Similarity Postulate (AAA~)
If corresponding angles of two triangles are equal, then the triangles are similar.

$\triangle XYZ \sim \triangle PQR$

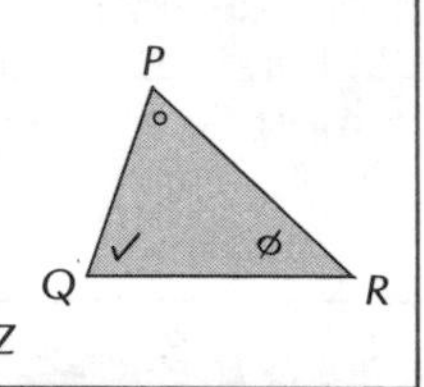

Corollary (AA~)
If two angles of one triangle are equal to two angles of another triangle, then the triangles are similar.

EXAMPLE 1: $\overline{PT}$ and $\overline{QS}$ intersect at R such that $\overline{PQ} \parallel \overline{TS}$. $PQ = 24$, $QR = 18$, $TR = 10$, and $SR = 12$. Find the lengths of $\overline{PR}$ and $\overline{TS}$.

Given: $\overline{PT}$ and $\overline{QS}$ intersect at R. $\overline{PQ} \parallel \overline{TS}$, $PQ = 24$, $QR = 18$, $TR = 10$, and $SR = 12$.

Find: The lengths of $\overline{PR}$ and $\overline{TS}$

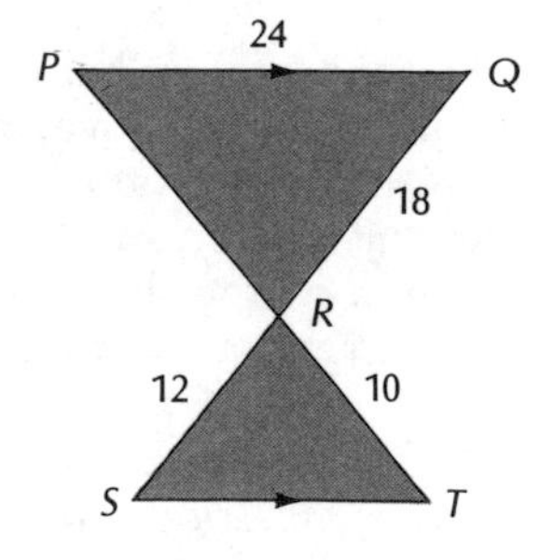

Solution: For $\triangle PQR$ and $\triangle TSR$,

$\angle P = \angle T$,	PLT
and $\angle Q = \angle S$.	PLT
$\therefore \triangle PQR \sim \triangle TSR$	AA~

$\frac{PQ}{TS} = \frac{PR}{TR} = \frac{QR}{SR}$ Corresponding sides of similar triangles

$\frac{24}{TS} = \frac{PR}{10} = \frac{18}{12} = \frac{3}{2}$. That is, $\frac{24}{TS} = \frac{3}{2}$ and $\frac{PR}{10} = \frac{3}{2}$.

So, $3(TS) = 48$ and $2(PR) = 30$.

Therefore, $TS = 16$ and $PR = 15$.

EXAMPLE 2: For $\triangle XYZ$, A is on $\overline{XY}$ and B is on $\overline{XZ}$ such that $\overline{AB} \parallel \overline{YZ}$. Prove that $(XA)(XZ) = (XB)(XY)$.

Given: For $\triangle XYZ$, A is on $\overline{XY}$ and B is on $\overline{XZ}$ such that $\overline{AB} \parallel \overline{YZ}$.

Prove: $(XA)(XZ) = (XB)(XY)$

Proof: Proving that $(XA)(XZ) = (XB)(XY)$ is equivalent to proving that $\dfrac{XA}{XY} = \dfrac{XB}{XZ}$.

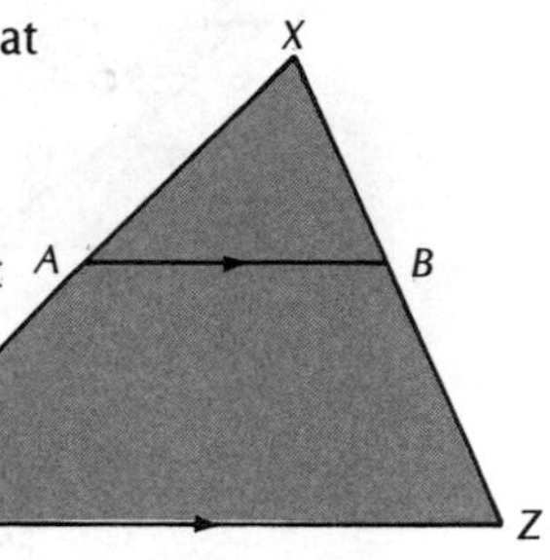

To do this, first prove that $\triangle XAB \sim \triangle XYZ$.

For $\triangle XAB$ and $\triangle XYZ$,	
$\angle XAB = \angle XYZ$	PLT
and $\angle XBA = \angle XZY$.	PLT
$\therefore \triangle XAB \sim \triangle XYZ$	AA~

If two triangles are similar, their sides are proportional.

$$\frac{XA}{XY} = \frac{XB}{XZ} \quad \text{Definition of similar triangles}$$

$$\therefore (XA)(XZ) = (XB)(XY)$$

EXERCISE 11-2

A **1.** Prove that each pair of triangles shown is similar. Then write a statement relating ratios of corresponding sides of each pair of triangles.

a. $\triangle WVZ \sim \triangle XYZ$ **b.** $\triangle ABC \sim \triangle DBE$

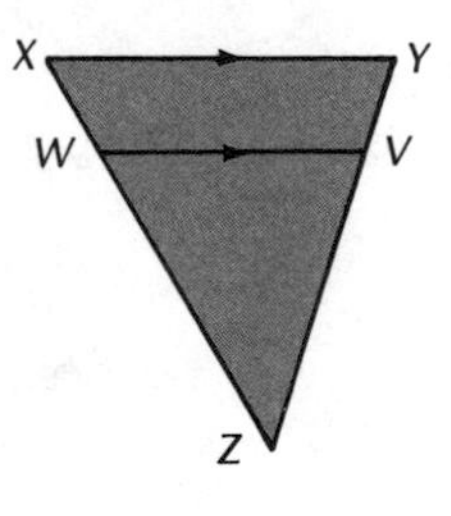

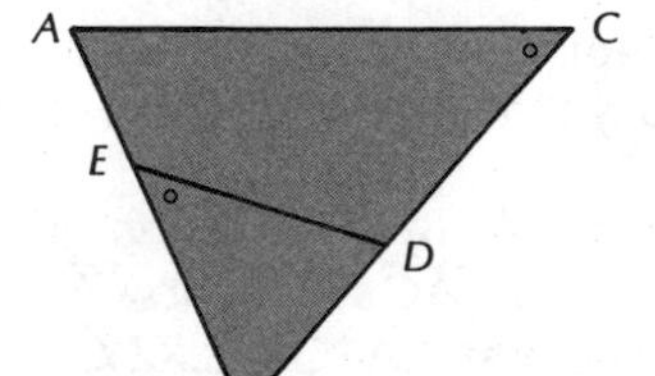

c. $\triangle XYZ \sim \triangle TXZ$ **d.** $\triangle DEF \sim \triangle MNO$

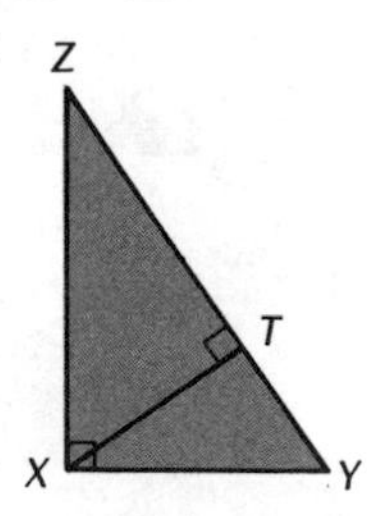

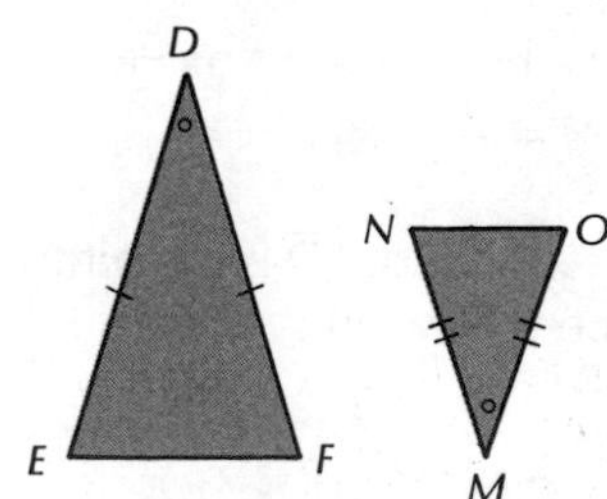

B **2.** Find the length of each unknown side.

a.

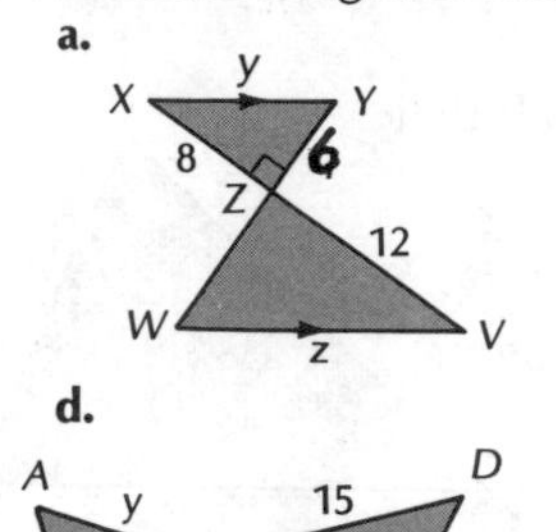

b.

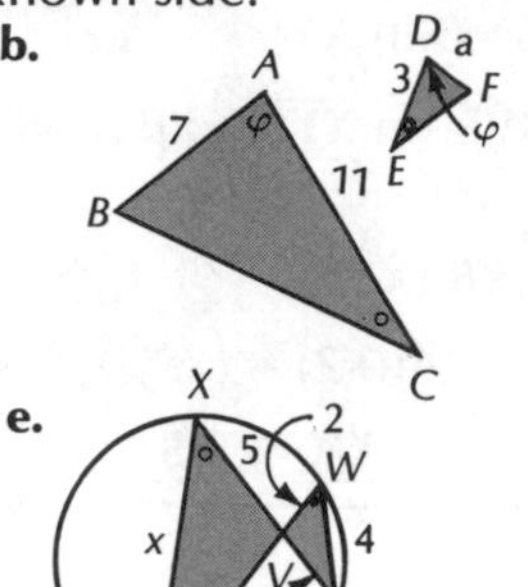

c.

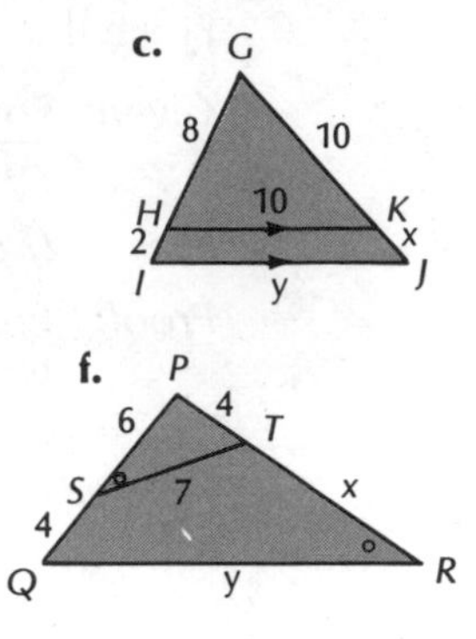

d. **e.** **f.**

3. In trapezoid $ABCD$, $\overline{AB} \parallel \overline{DC}$. Diagonals $\overline{AC}$ and $\overline{BD}$ intersect at E such that $AE : EC = 1:3$. Prove that $DC = 3(AB)$.

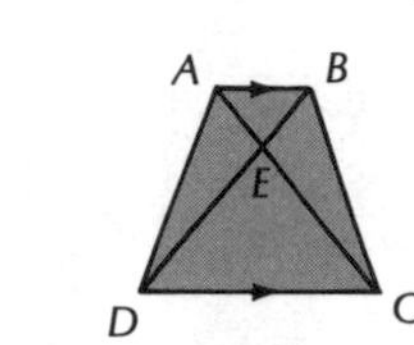

4. In $\triangle ABC$, D is on $\overline{AB}$ and E is on $\overline{AC}$ such that $\angle ADC = \angle AEB$. $\overline{DC}$ and $\overline{EB}$ intersect at F. Prove that $DF : EF = BF : CF$.

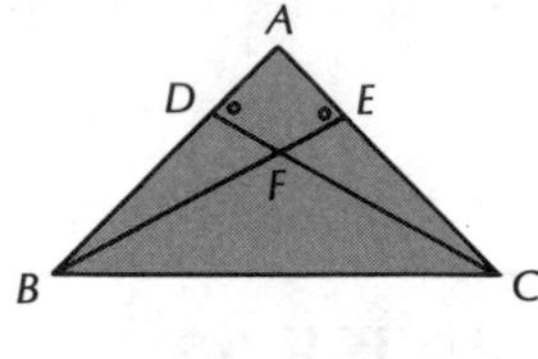

5. $\triangle ABC \sim \triangle XYZ$. $\overline{AM}$ *and* $\overline{XN}$ are the altitudes from A and X, respectively. Prove that

$$\frac{AM}{XN} = \frac{AB}{XY}.$$

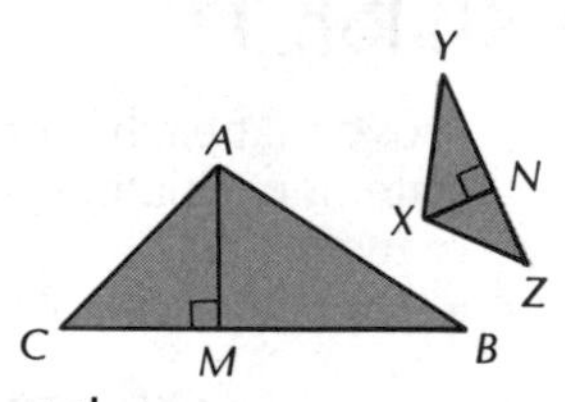

6. Find the height of a flagpole that casts a shadow 16 m long at the same time of day that a person 1.8 m tall casts a shadow 1.2 m long.

7. In $\triangle ABC$, X is on side $\overline{BC}$ and Y is on side $\overline{AB}$ such that $\overline{XY} \parallel \overline{AC}$. Z is on $\overline{AC}$ such that $\overline{XZ} \parallel \overline{AB}$. If $\overline{YZ} \parallel \overline{BC}$, prove that $\triangle ABC \sim \triangle XZY$.

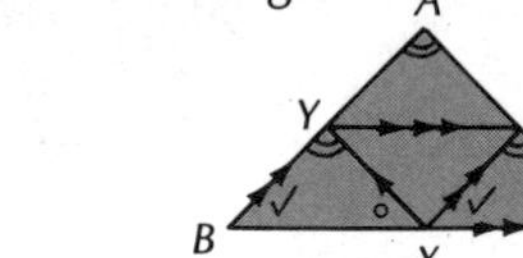

8. In $\triangle PQR$, M is the midpoint of side $\overline{PQ}$ and N is on $\overline{PR}$ such that $\overline{MN} \parallel \overline{QR}$.

a. Prove that N is the midpoint of $\overline{PR}$.

b. Prove that $MN = \frac{1}{2}(QR)$.

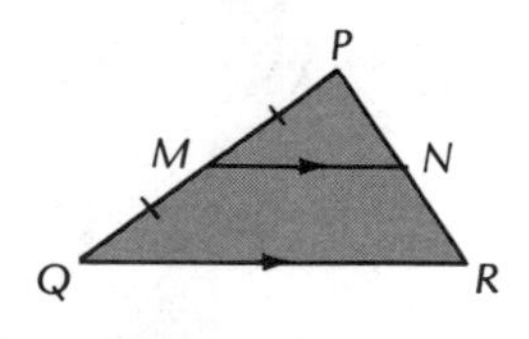

9. In $\triangle ABC$, $\angle BAC = 90°$ and $\overline{AD}$ is the altitude from A to $\overline{BC}$. Prove the following.

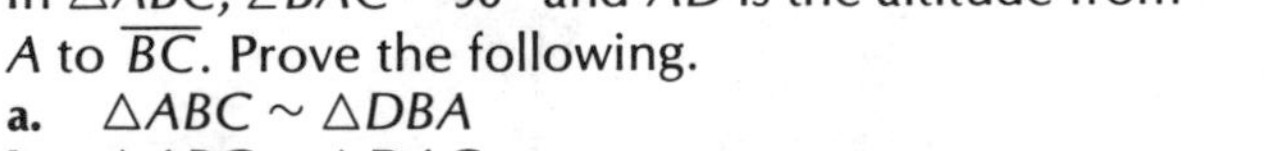

a. $\triangle ABC \sim \triangle DBA$

b. $\triangle ABC \sim \triangle DAC$

c. $\triangle DBA \sim \triangle DAC$

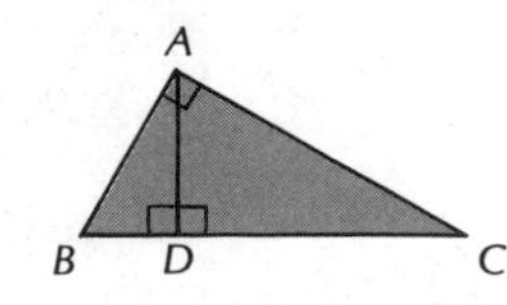

EXTRA The Golden Rectangle

For centuries, the **golden rectangle** has been found to be especially pleasing to the eye. In the Middle Ages, it was thought to have "divine proportions." It is often used in art and in architecture because of its harmonious proportions.

In the golden rectangle, the length and width satisfy the equation:

$$\frac{l}{w} = \frac{l + w}{l}.$$

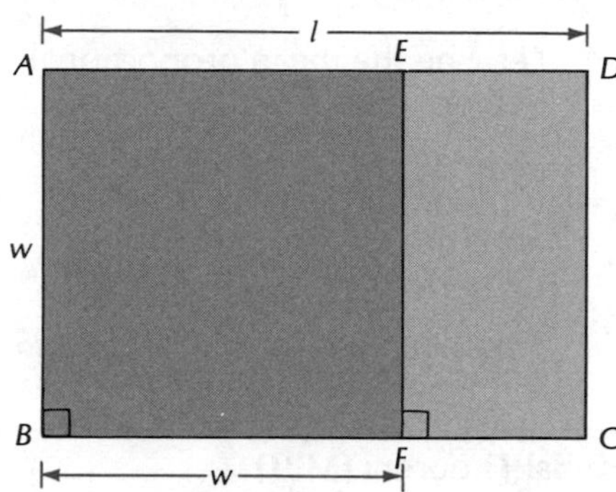

If a square is drawn inside the rectangle on the shorter side, the rectangle that remains is similar to the original rectangle.

1. If *ABCD* is a golden rectangle, show that rectangle *CDEF* is also a golden rectangle.
2. If *ABCD* is a golden rectangle, and $\overline{BC}$ is 8 cm long, what is the length of $\overline{AB}$?
3. Find the **golden ratio**, or the ratio of the length of the longer side of *ABCD* to the length of the shorter side.
4. In order to find a numerical value for $l : w$, consider the following exercise.

   Let a segment that is $x + 1$ units long be divided into two parts to form the length and width of a golden rectangle.
   Let the two parts be x and 1.

   $$\therefore \frac{x + 1}{x} = \frac{x}{1}$$

   A ——— x ——— C — 1 — B

   Thus, the ratio $l : w$ is $x + 1 : x$ or, more simply, $x : 1$.

   Solve the quadratic equation $x^2 - x - 1 = 0$ for x. This will result in the ratio $l : w$, or the golden ratio.
   (Notice that one of the roots is inadmissible, since a length cannot be negative.)
5. The golden ratio has some interesting properties. Use a calculator to evaluate the following. Compare the results.

   a. x **b.** x^2 **c.** $\frac{1}{x}$ **d.** $1 - x$

11-3 Theorems Proved by Similar Triangles

The concept of similar triangles can be used to prove further theorems.

By definition, x is the **mean proportional** between a and b if $a:x = x:b$, that is, if $x^2 = ab$. The mean proportional is also referred to as the **geometric mean**.

EXAMPLE 1:

a. Find the mean proportional between 5 and 125.

Let x be the mean proportional between 5 and 125.

$$\frac{5}{x} = \frac{x}{125}$$

$$x^2 = 625$$

$$x = \pm 25$$

The mean proportionals are ± 25.

b. Six is the mean proportional between 8 and another number. Find the other number.

Let x be the other number.

$$\frac{8}{6} = \frac{6}{x}$$

$$8x = 36$$

$$x = 4.5$$

The other number is 4.5.

Mean Proportional Theorem (MPT)

The altitude to the hypotenuse of a right-angled triangle is the mean proportional to the resulting segments of the hypotenuse, and each side about the right angle is the mean proportional to the hypotenuse and the adjacent segment of the hypotenuse.

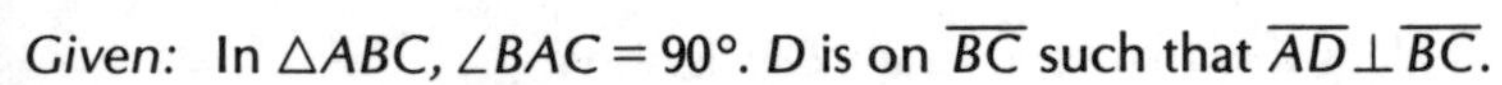

Given: In $\triangle ABC$, $\angle BAC = 90°$. D is on $\overline{BC}$ such that $\overline{AD} \perp \overline{BC}$.

Prove: **a.** $AD^2 = (BD)(DC)$ **b.** $AB^2 = (BC)(BD)$ **c.** $AC^2 = (BC)(DC)$

Proof: **a.** Proving $AD^2 = (BD)(DC)$ is equivalent to proving $\frac{BD}{AD} = \frac{AD}{DC}$.

To do this, prove that $\triangle ABD \sim \triangle CAD$. Because you know only that $\angle BDA = \angle ADC = 90°$, you must first prove that another pair of angles is equal.

Statement	Reason
For $\triangle CBA$ and $\triangle ABD$,	
$\angle BDA = \angle BAC = 90°$,	Given
$\angle B = \angle B$, and so	Common angle
$\angle BAD = \angle C$.	Angle sum of a triangle
For $\triangle ABD$ and $\triangle CAD$,	
$\angle BDA = \angle ADC = 90°$, and so	Given
$\angle BAD = \angle C$.	Proved above
So, $\triangle ABD \sim \triangle CAD$.	AA~
$\frac{BD}{AD} = \frac{AD}{DC}$	Corresponding sides of similar triangles
$\therefore AD^2 = (BD)(DC)$	

The proofs of parts **b** and **c** of MPT are left to the exercises.

EXAMPLE 2: Find the lengths of the unknown sides of the given triangle.

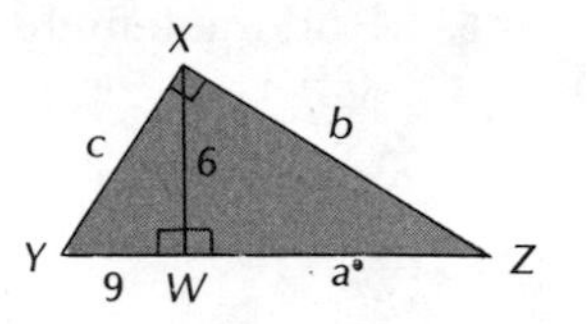

$6^2 = 9a$	$b^2 = (9 + a)a$	$c^2 = (9 + a)9$	MPT
$36 = 9a$	$b^2 = (13)(4)$	$c^2 = (13)(9)$	Substitution
$a = 4$	$b = 2\sqrt{13}$	$c = 3\sqrt{13}$	

The Mean Proportional Theorem can be used to prove a very famous theorem, the Pythagorean Theorem. There have been several proofs for this theorem, but the one shown below is both simple and elegant.

The Pythagorean Theorem (PT)
The square on the hypotenuse of a right-angled triangle is equal to the sum of the squares on the other two sides.

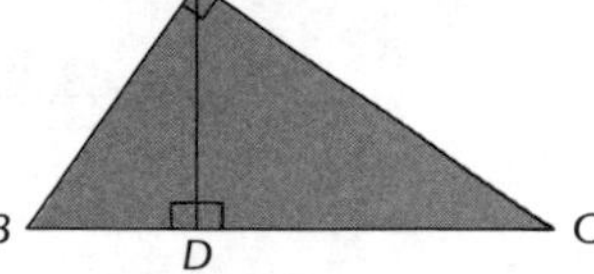

Given: $\triangle ABC$ in which $\angle BAC = 90°$

Prove: $AB^2 + AC^2 = BC^2$

Proof: Draw $\overline{AD}$, the altitude from A to $\overline{BC}$.

$AB^2 = (BC)(BD)$	MPT
$AC^2 = (BC)(DC)$	MPT
$AB^2 + AC^2 = (BC)(BD) + (BC)(DC)$	Addition
$= BC(BD + DC)$	Distributive property
But $BD + DC = BC$	
$AB^2 + AC^2 = (BC)(BC)$	Substitution
$\therefore AB^2 + AC^2 = BC^2$	

EXERCISE 11-3

A **1.** Find the mean proportional between each pair.

a. 9, 4 **b.** 5, 20
c. 8, 9 **d.** $6a$, $16a$
e. 13, 25 **f.** $8x^3$, $32x$
g. $a^3 + a^2b$, $a + b$ **h.** $2\sqrt{3}$, $6\sqrt{3}$

2. The mean proportional between 5 and another number is 15. Find the number.

3. The mean proportional between 6 and x is $2\sqrt{15}$. Solve for x.

4. Three numbers that satisfy the Pythagorean relationship, $a^2 + b^2 = c^2$, are called **Pythagorean triples**. Which of the following are Pythagorean triples?

a. 9, 40, 41 **b.** 16, 30, 35

5. **a.** Show that $a^2 + b^2$, $a^2 - b^2$, and $2ab$ are Pythagorean triples.
b. Find six sets of Pythagorean triples.

B

6. Find the lengths of the unknown sides.

a.

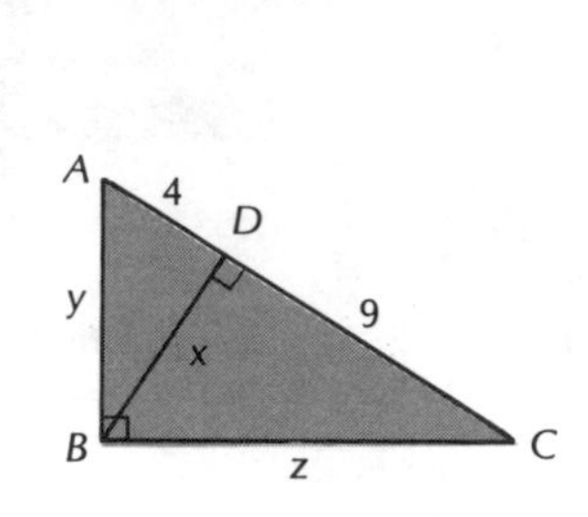

b.

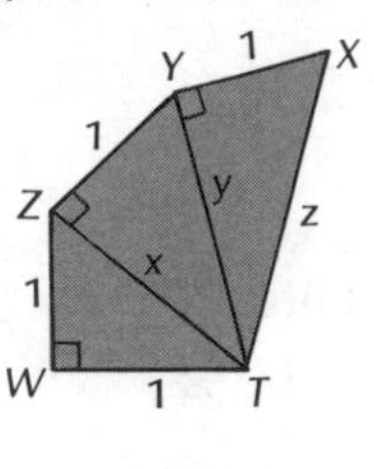

c.

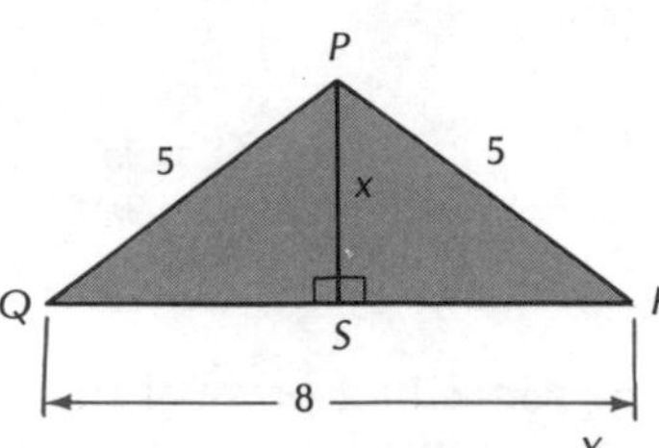

d.

P
y
8
z
Q
x
S
4
R

e.

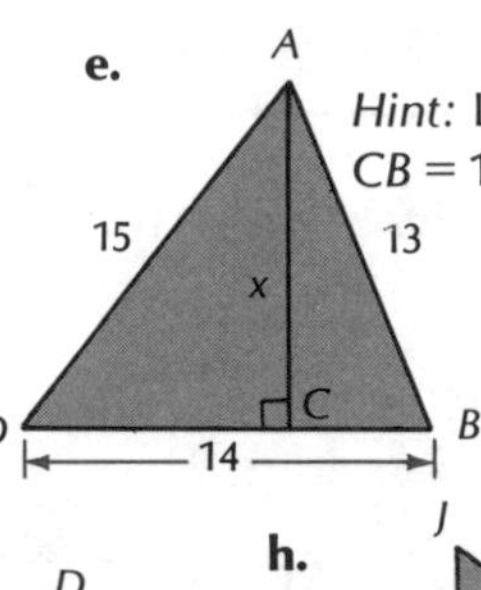

Hint: Let $DC = y$ and $CB = 14 - y$.

f.

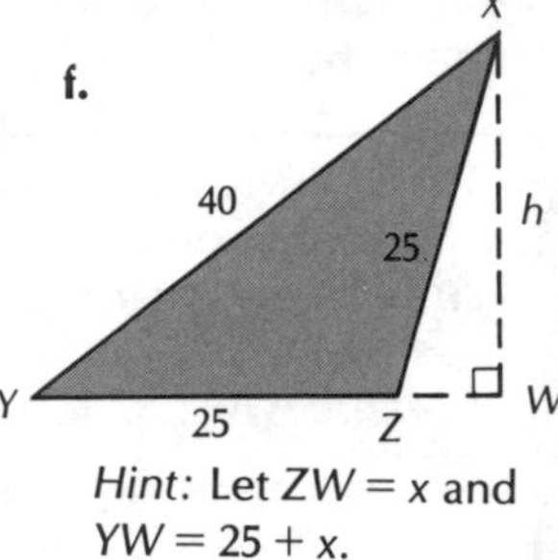

Hint: Let $ZW = x$ and $YW = 25 + x$.

g.

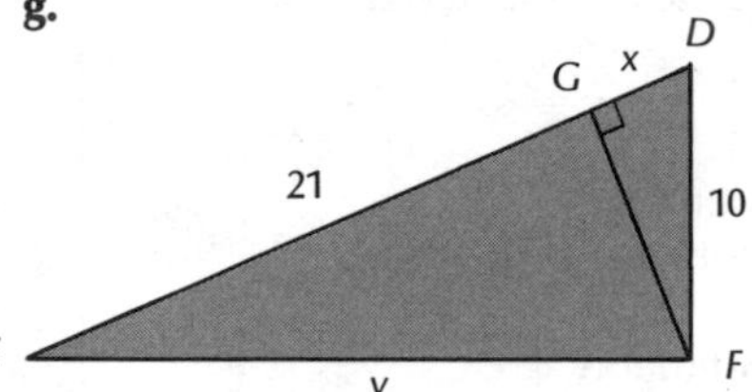

h.

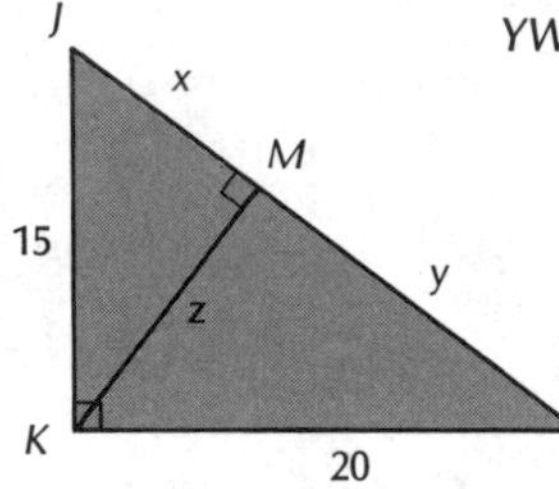

7. In $\triangle ABC$, $\angle BAC = 90°$. D is on $\overline{BC}$ such that $\overline{AD} \perp \overline{BC}$. Prove the following.
   a. $AB^2 = (CB)(DB)$ b. $AC^2 = (BC)(DC)$
   (These prove the last two parts of the Mean Proportional Theorem.)

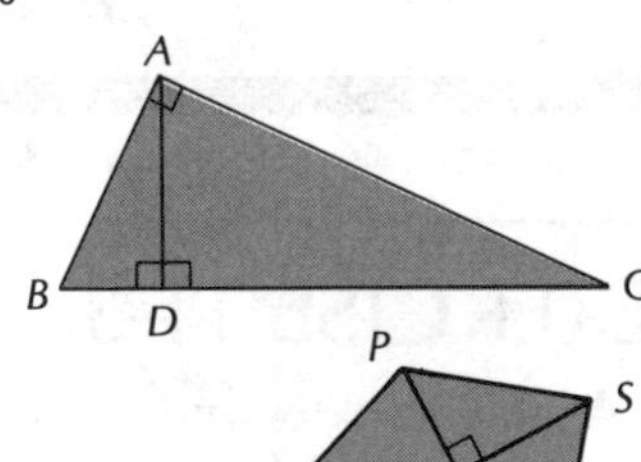

8. The diagonals of quadrilateral $PQRS$ are perpendicular. Prove that $PS^2 + QR^2 = PQ^2 + RS^2$.

P
S
T
Q
R

9. In $\triangle ABC$, $\angle BAC = 90°$ and $\overline{AD}$ is the altitude from A to $\overline{BC}$. $\overline{AD}$ is extended to E such that $\overline{EB} \perp \overline{AB}$. Prove that $(BD)(CB) = (AE)(AD)$.

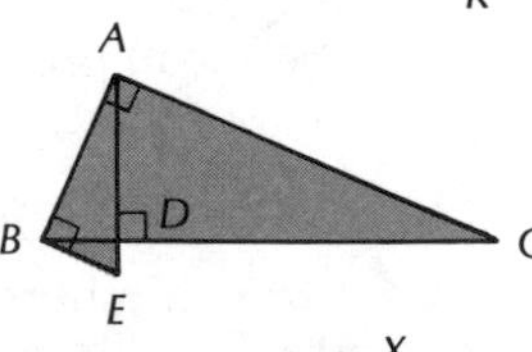

10. In $\triangle XYZ$, $\angle YXZ = 90°$. W is a point on $\overline{YZ}$ such that $\overline{XW} \perp \overline{YZ}$. Prove that $\frac{XY^2}{XW^2} = \frac{YZ}{WZ}$.

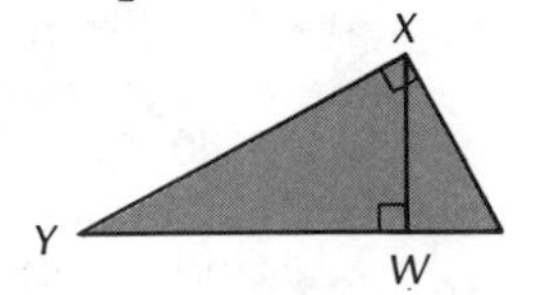

EXTRA Using the Mean Proportional Theorem for Constructions

1. The Mean Proportional Theorem can be used to construct a square equal in area to a given rectangle.

Given: Rectangle $ABCD$

Construct: A square, equal in area to rectangle $ABCD$

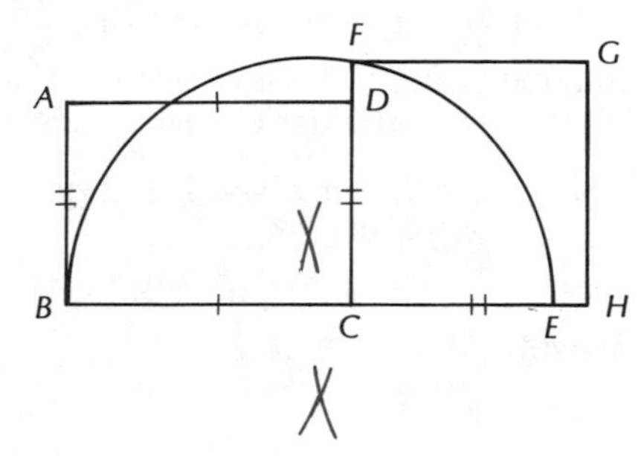

Construction: Extend $\overline{BC}$ to E such that $CE = CD$. Construct a circle with $\overline{BE}$ as diameter. Extend $\overline{CD}$ to intersect the circle at F. On $\overline{CF}$, construct square $CFGH$.

Prove: Square $CFGH$ is equal in area to rectangle $ABCD$.

Hint: An angle inscribed in a semicircle is a right angle.

2. a. Construct a segment that is $\sqrt{10}$ units long.

Recall that in a right-angled triangle, as shown, $p^2 = xy$.

Construct a segment, $BC = 7$ units, with D on $\overline{BC}$ such that $BD = 2$ units.
Construct $\overline{AD} \perp \overline{BC}$.
Construct a circle with $\overline{BC}$ as diameter. Extend $\overline{DA}$ to intersect the circle at E. Prove that $DE = \sqrt{10}$.

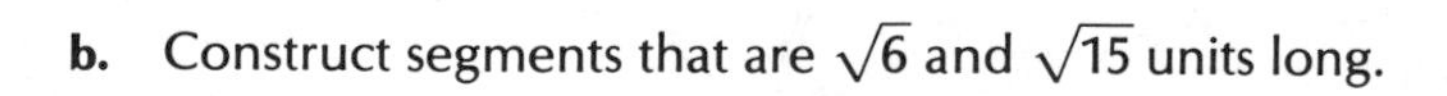
b. Construct segments that are $\sqrt{6}$ and $\sqrt{15}$ units long.

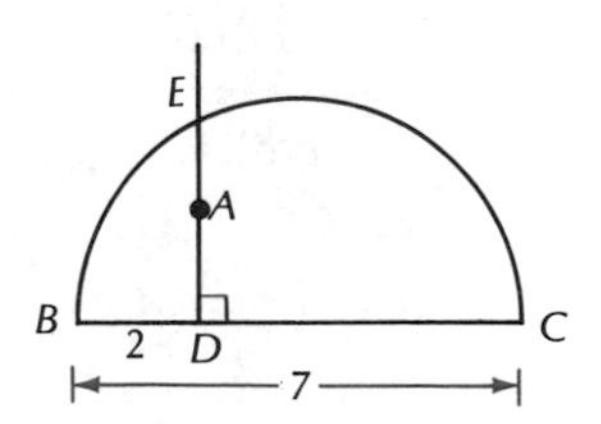

11-4 Parallelism Proportionality Theorem

In this lesson, the proof of a biconditional theorem, which will be very useful for work with similar triangles, is given.

Parallelism Proportionality Theorem (PPT)
A line is parallel to one side of a triangle if, and only if, it divides the other two sides in the same ratio.

This theorem is proved in two parts.

i. If a line that intersects two sides of a triangle is parallel to the third side, then the line divides the two sides in equal ratios.

Given: $\triangle ABC$, in which D is a point on $\overline{AB}$ and E is a point on $\overline{AC}$ such that $\overline{DE} \parallel \overline{BC}$

Prove: $AD:DB = AE:EC$

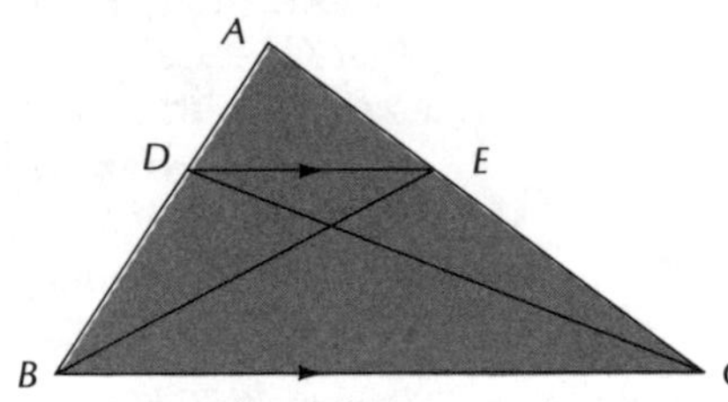

Proof: Construct $\overline{CD}$ and $\overline{BE}$.
$\triangle EDB$ and $\triangle DEC$ are two triangles on the same base, $\overline{DE}$.
$\triangle EDB$ and $\triangle DEC$ lie between the same parallel lines, $\overline{DE}$ and $\overline{BC}$.
Therefore, the altitudes from B and C to base $\overline{DE}$ are equal.
$\therefore$ Area $\triangle EDB$ = Area $\triangle DEC$ — Same base, equal heights

$$\frac{\text{Area } \triangle ADE}{\text{Area } \triangle EDB} = \frac{\text{Area } \triangle ADE}{\text{Area } \triangle DEC}$$ Division

Construct $\overline{EF}$ and $\overline{DG}$, the altitudes of $\triangle ADE$.

Area $\triangle ADE = \frac{1}{2}(AD)(EF)$ — Area of a triangle $= \frac{1}{2}bh$

Area $\triangle EDB = \frac{1}{2}(DB)(EF)$

Area $\triangle ADE = \frac{1}{2}(AE)(DG)$

Area $\triangle DEC = \frac{1}{2}(EC)(DG)$

$$\frac{\frac{1}{2}(AD)(EF)}{\frac{1}{2}(DB)(EF)} = \frac{\frac{1}{2}(AE)(DG)}{\frac{1}{2}(EC)(DG)}$$ Substitution

$$\frac{AD}{DB} = \frac{AE}{EC}$$ Division

ii. If two sides of a triangle are divided in equal ratios, then the segment joining the points of division is parallel to the third side.

Given: $\triangle ABC$, in which D is on $\overline{AB}$ and E is on $\overline{AC}$ such that $AD:DB = AE:EC$

Prove: $\overline{DE} \parallel \overline{BC}$

Proof: (Indirect)

Either $\overline{DE} \parallel \overline{BC}$ or $\overline{DE}$ is not parallel to $\overline{BC}$.

Assume that $\overline{DE}$ is not parallel to $\overline{BC}$.

Therefore, there must be a point F on $\overline{AC}$ such that $\overline{DF} \parallel \overline{BC}$.

$\therefore \dfrac{AD}{DB} = \dfrac{AF}{FC}$ PPT–i

$AD:BD = AE:EC$ Given

This means that both E and F divide $\overline{AC}$ in the same ratio, $AD:DB$.

But this is a contradiction.

So, the assumption that $\overline{DE}$ is not parallel to $\overline{BC}$ is false.

$\therefore \overline{DE} \parallel \overline{BC}$

EXAMPLE 1: For $\triangle PQR$, find the measure of $\overline{PS}$.

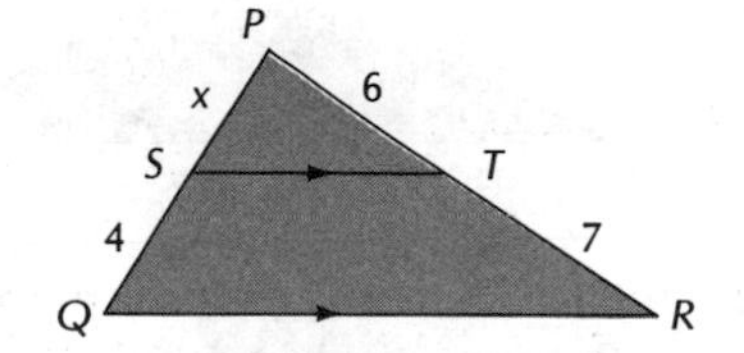

$\dfrac{6}{7} = \dfrac{PS}{4}$ PPT

$7(PS) = 24$

$\therefore PS = \frac{24}{7}$

EXAMPLE 2: $\overline{ZM}$ and $\overline{YN}$ are medians of $\triangle XYZ$, as shown. Prove that $\overline{MN} \parallel \overline{YZ}$.

Given: $\triangle XYZ$, in which M is the midpoint of $\overline{XY}$ and N is the midpoint of $\overline{XZ}$

Prove: $\overline{MN} \parallel \overline{YZ}$

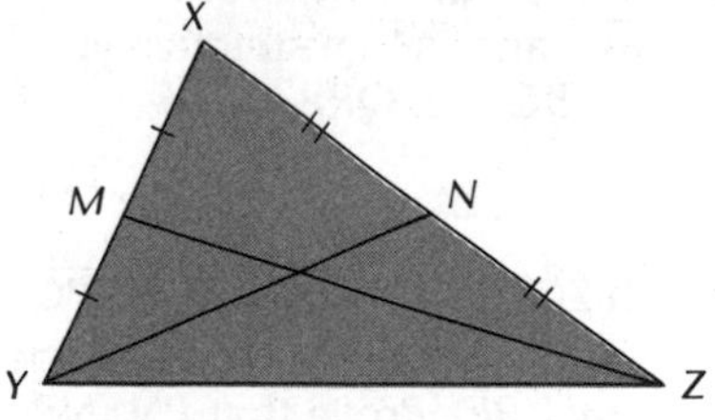

Proof: Join M to N.

$XM = MY$ and $XN = NZ$.	Given
$\dfrac{XM}{MY} = \dfrac{1}{1}$ and $\dfrac{XN}{NZ} = \dfrac{1}{1}$.	Division
$\dfrac{XM}{MY} = \dfrac{XN}{NZ}$	Substitution
$\therefore MN \parallel YZ$	PPT

EXERCISE 11-4

A **1.** Find the measure of each unknown side.

a.

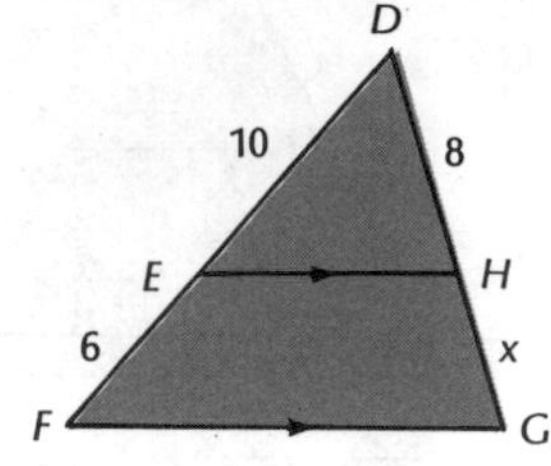

b.

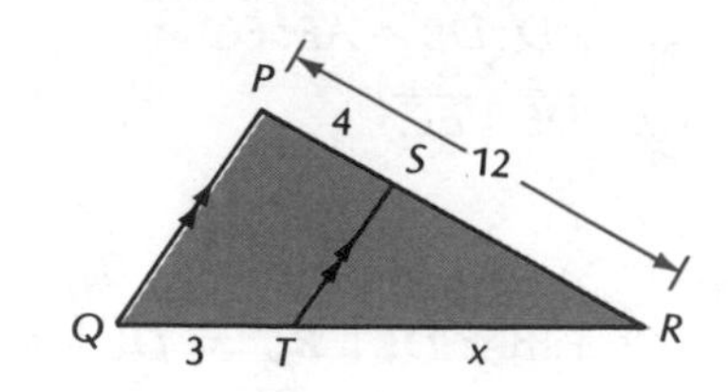

c.

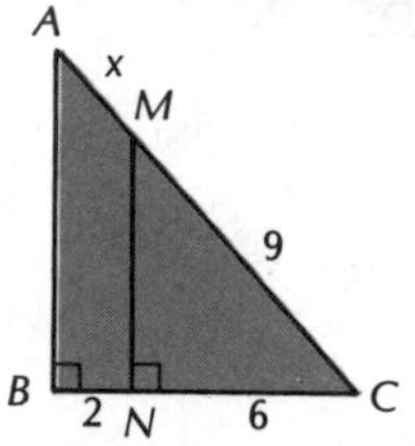

d.

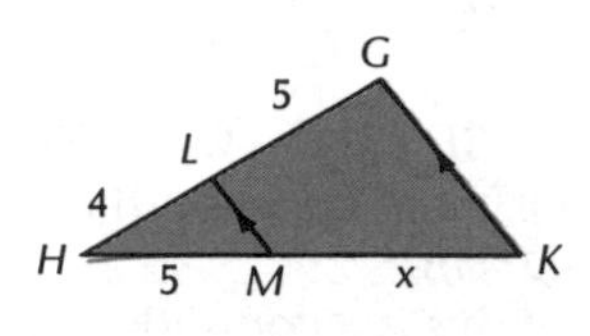

B **2.** Identify pairs of parallel lines. Justify your answers.

a.

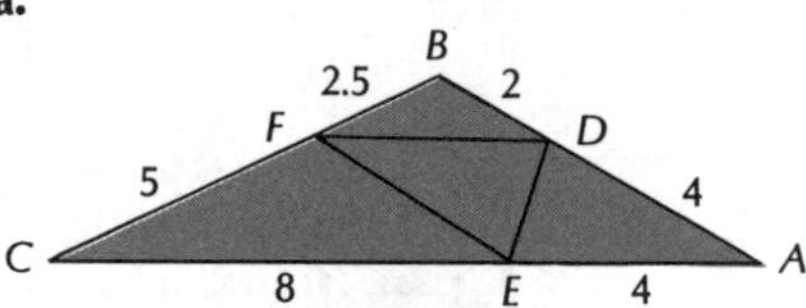

b. Join R and T, and prove that $\overline{RT} \parallel \overline{Q}$

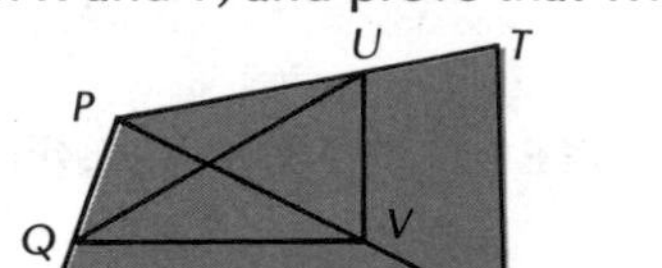

3. In $\triangle PQR$, L, M, and N are points on $\overline{PQ}$, $\overline{PR}$, and $\overline{QR}$, respectively, such that $\overline{LM} \parallel \overline{QR}$.
If $QL:LP = RN:NQ$, prove that $\overline{MN} \parallel \overline{PQ}$.

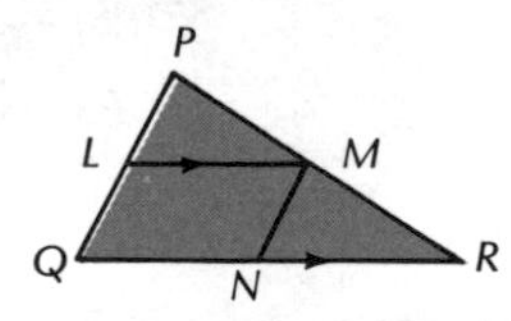

4. In $\triangle ABC$, P, Q, and R are midpoints of sides $\overline{AB}$, $\overline{BC}$, and $\overline{AC}$, respectively. Prove that $\triangle ABC \sim \triangle QRP$.

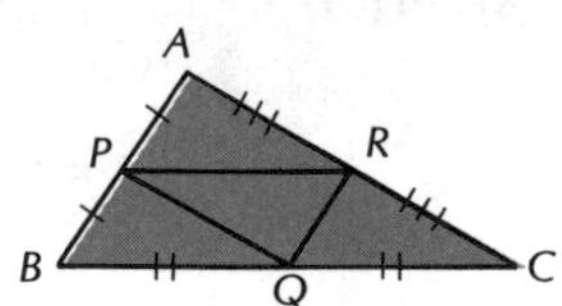

5. In $\triangle PQR$, L is a point on $\overline{PQ}$, N is a point on $\overline{PR}$, and M is a point on $\overline{QR}$ such that $\overline{LN} \parallel \overline{QR}$ and $\overline{LM} \parallel \overline{PR}$. Prove that $PN:NR = RM:MQ$.

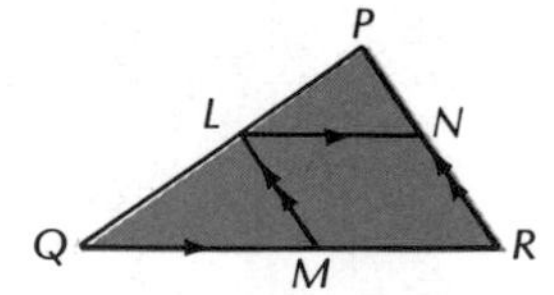

6. In $\triangle ABC$, D is on $\overline{BC}$ such that $\overline{AD}$ bisects $\angle BAC$. $\overline{BA}$ is extended to E such that $\overline{CE} \parallel \overline{AD}$. Prove that $(BD)(AC) = (DC)(AB)$.

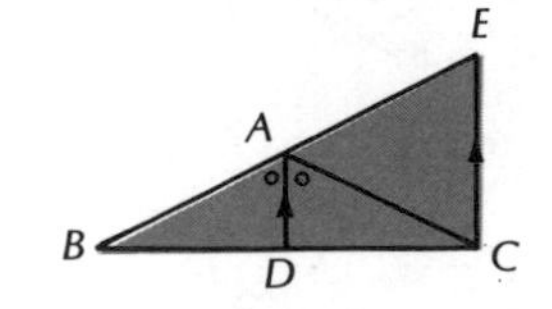

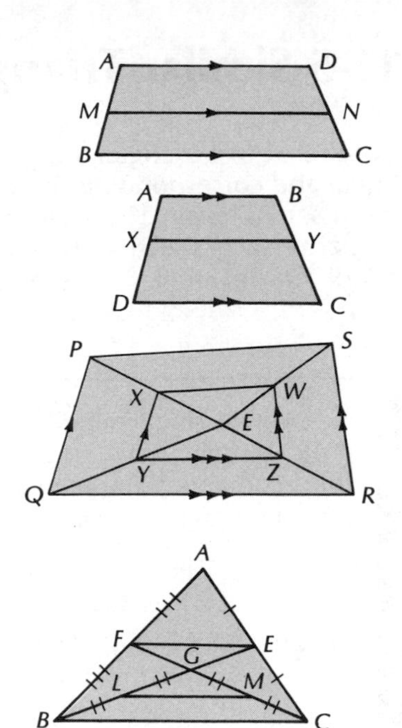

7. In trapezoid $ABCD$, $\overline{AD} \parallel \overline{BC}$. M is a point on $\overline{AB}$ and N is a point on $\overline{CD}$ such that $\overline{MN} \parallel \overline{BC}$. Prove that $AM:MB = DN:NC$.

8. In trapezoid $ABCD$, $\overline{AB} \parallel \overline{DC}$. X is on $\overline{AD}$ and Y is on $\overline{BC}$ such that $AX:XD = BY:YC$. Prove that $\overline{XY} \parallel \overline{DC}$.

9. E is any point inside quadrilateral $PQRS$. X is any point on $\overline{PE}$. Y is a point on $\overline{QE}$ such that $\overline{XY} \parallel \overline{PQ}$. Z is a point on $\overline{ER}$ such that $\overline{YZ} \parallel \overline{QR}$. W is a point on $\overline{ES}$ such that $\overline{ZW} \parallel \overline{RS}$. Prove that $\overline{XW} \parallel \overline{PS}$.

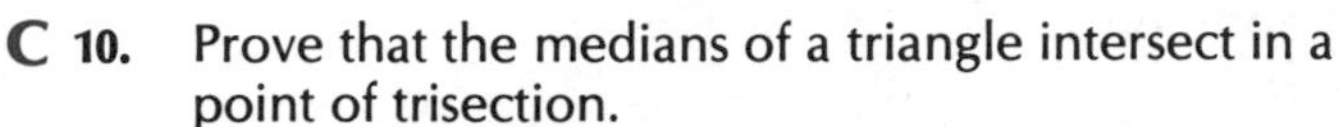

C 10. Prove that the medians of a triangle intersect in a point of trisection.

Given: Medians $\overline{BE}$ and $\overline{CF}$ of $\triangle ABC$ intersect at G. L is the midpoint of $\overline{BG}$. M is the midpoint of $\overline{GC}$.

Prove: $FG = GM = MC$, $EG = GL = LB$, and $\dfrac{FG}{GC} = \dfrac{1}{2}, \dfrac{EG}{GB} = \dfrac{1}{2}$.

11. Prove that the bisector of one angle of a triangle divides the opposite side into segments that are proportional to the adjacent sides.

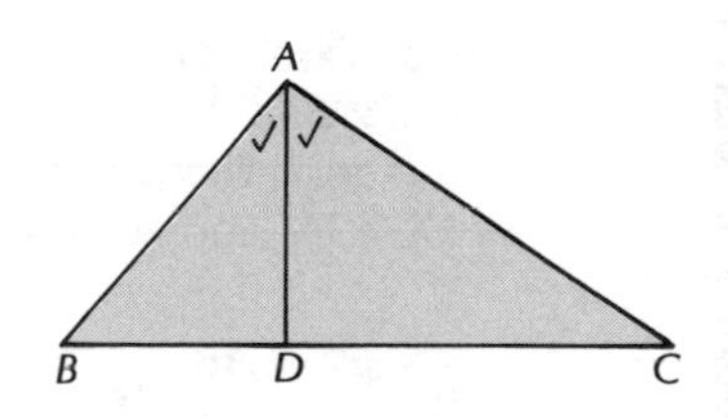

Given: $\triangle ABC$, such that D is on $\overline{BC}$ and $\angle BAD = \angle DAC$

Prove: $BD:DC = BA:AC$

Hint: Extend $\overline{BA}$ to E such that $\overline{AD} \parallel \overline{EC}$.

EXTRA — Dividing a Line Segment into a Given Ratio

Divide $\overline{XY}$ in the ratio $3:4$.

Draw any convenient $\angle ZXY$.
On $\overline{XZ}$, mark 7 equal segments,
$XA = AB = BC = CD = DE = EF = FG$.
Draw $\overline{GY}$.
Construct $\overline{CM}$ parallel to $\overline{GY}$, such that M is on $\overline{XY}$.
$\overline{XM}:\overline{MY} = 3:4$.

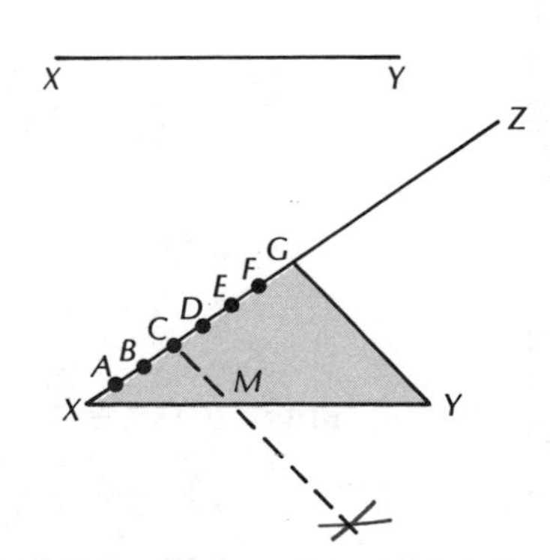

1. Justify the above construction.
2. Describe how to divide a given segment in the ratio $2:3$.
3. Describe how to divide a given segment in the ratio $1:3:4$.

11-5 Similar Triangle Theorems: SAS$\sim$ and SSS$\sim$

Recall that two triangles are similar if pairs of corresponding angles are equal and corresponding sides are proportional. The AAA$\sim$ Postulate, discussed in lesson 11-2, provides one set of conditions sufficient for similarity. In this section, two more theorems dealing with sufficient conditions for similarity are discussed.

Side Angle Side Similarity Theorem (SAS$\sim$)
If two triangles have one pair of equal angles and if the corresponding sides containing these angles are proportional, then the triangles are similar.

Given: $\triangle ABC$ and $\triangle DEF$, in which $\angle BAC = \angle EDF$ and $AB:DE = AC:DF$

Prove: $\triangle ABC \sim \triangle DEF$

Proof: Translate $\triangle DEF$ such that $D \rightarrow A$ and $\angle BAC = \angle EDF$, and such that X is the image of E and Y is the image of F.

Statement	Reason
$AX = DE$ and $AY = DF$	Definition of a translation
$\frac{AB}{DE} = \frac{AC}{DF}$	Given
$\frac{AB}{AX} = \frac{AC}{AY}$	Substitution
But $AB = AX + XB$ and $AC = AY + YC$.	
$\frac{AX + XB}{AX} = \frac{AY + YC}{AY}$	Substitution
$\frac{AX}{AX} + \frac{XB}{AX} = \frac{AY}{AY} + \frac{YC}{AY}$	
$\frac{XB}{AX} = \frac{YC}{AY}$	Subtraction
$\overline{XY} \parallel \overline{BC}$	PPT
	PLT
$\triangle AXY \sim \triangle ABC$	AA$\sim$
But $\triangle AXY \cong \triangle DEF$	Property of a translation
$\therefore \triangle DEF \sim \triangle ABC$	Substitution

Recall that $\cong$ means "is congruent to".

Side Side Side Similarity Theorem (SSS~)
If the sides of two triangles are in proportion, then the triangles are similar.

Given: $\triangle ABC$ and $\triangle DEF$, in which $AB:DE = BC:EF = AC:DF$

Prove: $\triangle ABC \sim \triangle DEF$

Proof: Let X be a point on $\overline{AB}$ (or $\overline{AB}$ extended) such that $AX = DE$.
Let Y be a point on $\overline{AC}$ (or $\overline{AC}$ extended) such that $AY = DF$.
For $\triangle AXY$ and $\triangle ABC$,

$\angle BAC = \angle XAY.$	Common angle
$AB:DE = AC:DF$	Given
$AB:AX = AC:AY$	Substitution
$\triangle AXY \sim \triangle ABC$	SAS~
$\therefore AB:AX = BC:XY$	Corresponding sides of similar triangles
But $AB:DE = BC:EF$	Given
and $AX = DE.$	Construction
$\therefore BC:XY = BC:EF$	Substitution
$XY = EF$	
$\triangle AXY \cong \triangle DEF$	SSS
$\angle EDF = \angle XAY$	Congruent triangles
But $\angle XAY = \angle BAC.$	Common angle
For $\triangle ABC$ and $\triangle DEF$,	
$\angle EDF = \angle BAC.$	Proved above
$AB:DE = AC:DF$	Given
$\therefore \triangle ABC \sim \triangle DEF$	SAS~

EXAMPLE 1: Q is the midpoint of $\overline{XY}$ and R is the midpoint of $\overline{XZ}$ in $\triangle XYZ$. Prove that $QR = \frac{1}{2}YZ$.

Given: $\triangle XYZ$, such that Q is the midpoint of $\overline{XY}$ and R is the midpoint of $\overline{XZ}$

Prove: $QR = \frac{1}{2}YZ$

Proof: For $\triangle XYZ$ and $\triangle XQR$,

Q is the midpoint of XY.	Given
$XQ:XY = 1:2$	Definition of midpoint
R is the midpoint of XZ.	Given
$XR:XZ = 1:2$	Definition of midpoint
$XQ:XY = XR:XZ$	Substitution
$\angle YXZ = \angle XQR$	Common angle
$\triangle XYZ \sim \triangle QXR$	SAS~
$QR:YZ = XQ:XY = 1:2$	Corresponding sides of similar triangles
$\therefore QR = \frac{1}{2}YZ$	Multiplication

EXAMPLE 2: In $\triangle ABC$, D is on $\overline{AB}$ and E is on $\overline{AC}$ such that $AD = 12$, $DB = 6$, $AE = 10$, and $EC = 5$. If $DE = 14$ and $BC = 21$, prove that $\overline{DE} \parallel \overline{BC}$.

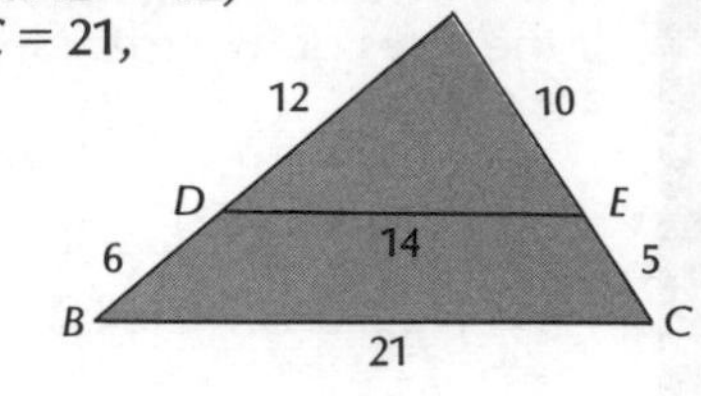

Given: $\triangle ABC$, in which D is on $\overline{AB}$ and E is on $\overline{AC}$ such that $AD = 12$, $DB = 6$, $AE = 10$, $EC = 5$, $DE = 14$, and $BC = 21$.

Prove: $\overline{DE} \parallel \overline{BC}$

Proof: For $\triangle ADE$ and $\triangle ABC$,

$\frac{AD}{AB} = \frac{12}{18} = \frac{2}{3}$, $\frac{AE}{AC} = \frac{10}{15} = \frac{2}{3}$, and $\frac{DE}{BC} = \frac{14}{21} = \frac{2}{3}$. Division

$\triangle ABC \sim \triangle ADE$ SSS~

$\angle ADE = \angle ABC$ Corresponding angles of similar triangles

$\therefore \overline{DE} \parallel \overline{BC}$ PLT

EXERCISE 11-5

A 1. Prove that the given pairs of triangles are similar. State any possible conclusions about equal angles, lengths of sides, or parallel segments.

a.

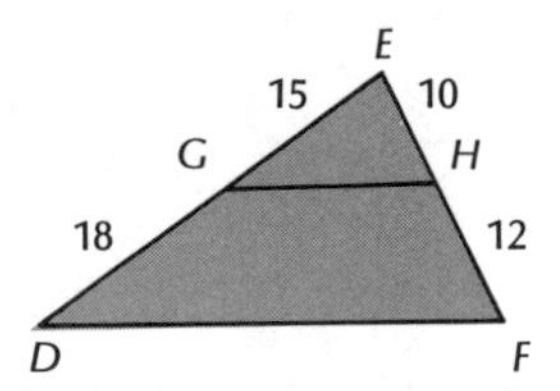

b.

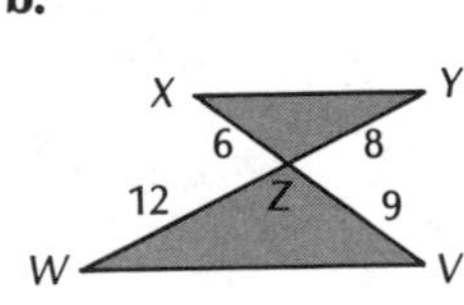

c.

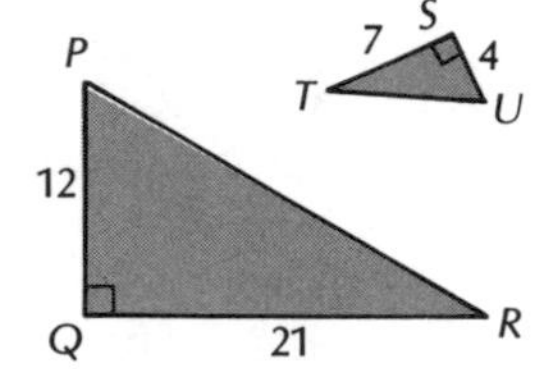

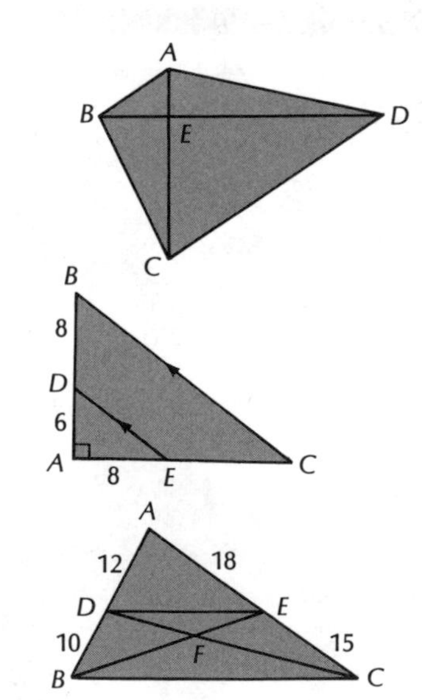

B 2. In quadrilateral $ABCD$, diagonals $\overline{AC}$ and $\overline{BD}$ intersect at E such that $AE : EC = BE : ED$. Prove that $ABCD$ is a trapezoid.

3. In $\triangle XYZ$, $\overline{XY}$ is extended to P and $\overline{XZ}$ is extended to Q such that $(XY)(XP) = (XZ)(XQ)$. Prove that $\angle YPZ = \angle ZQY$.

4. In $\triangle ABC$, $\angle BAC = 90°$. D is a point on $\overline{AB}$ such that $AD = 6$ and $DB = 8$. If E is a point on $\overline{AC}$ such that $AE = 8$ and $\overline{DE} \parallel \overline{BC}$, find the measures of $\overline{EC}$, $\overline{DE}$, and $\overline{BC}$.

5. In $\triangle ABC$, D is on side $\overline{AB}$ and E is on side $\overline{AC}$. $AD = 12$, $DB = 10$, $AE = 18$, and $EC = 15$. $\overline{DC}$ and $\overline{BE}$ intersect at F. Prove that $\triangle DFE \sim \triangle CFB$.

6. In quadrilateral $ABCD$, $\angle ABC = \angle ADC$ and $AB : CD = BC : DA$. Prove that $ABCD$ is a parallelogram.

Review

1. In $\triangle ABC$, D is on $\overline{BC}$ and E is on $\overline{AC}$ such that $\overline{AD}$ and $\overline{BE}$ are altitudes. $\overline{AD}$ and $\overline{BE}$ intersect at F. Prove the following.
   a. $\triangle ADC \sim \triangle AEF$ **b.** $\triangle AEF \sim \triangle BDF$

2. In $\triangle ABC$, $\angle A$ is a right angle. D is any point on $\overline{AB}$ and E is on $\overline{BC}$ such that $\overline{DE} \perp \overline{BC}$. Prove that $(DB)(CA) = (CB)(DE)$.

3. In $\triangle PQR$, W is any point on $\overline{QR}$. X is a point on $\overline{QW}$ and Y is a point on $\overline{PW}$ such that $\overline{XY} \parallel \overline{QP}$. Z is a point on $\overline{WR}$ such that $\overline{YZ} \parallel \overline{PR}$. Prove that $\triangle PQR \sim \triangle YXZ$.

4. In $\triangle ABC$, D is a point on side $\overline{AB}$ such that $(AB)(AD) = AC^2$. Prove that $\angle ACD = \angle B$.

5. Find the measure of each unknown side.

a.

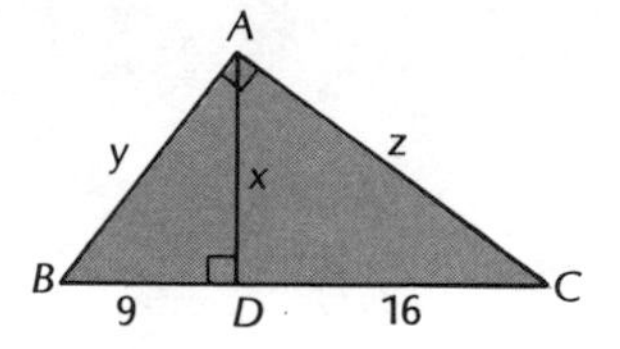

b.

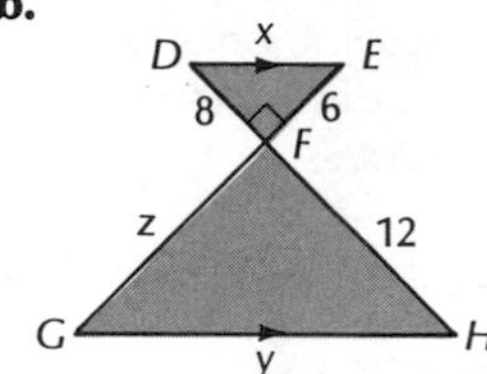

c.

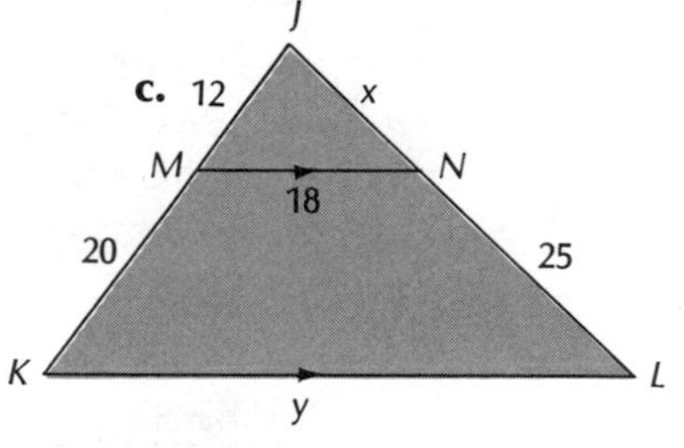

• **d.**

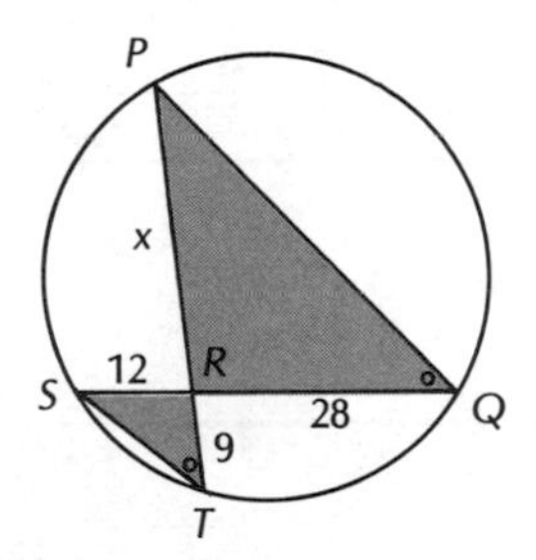

• **e.**

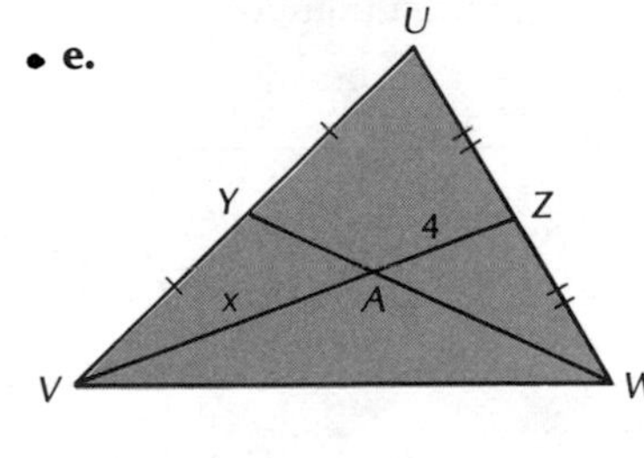

• 6. $ABCD$ is a parallelogram. P and Q are midpoints of $\overline{AD}$ and $\overline{BC}$, respectively. Prove that $\overline{AQ}$ and $\overline{PC}$ intersect diagonal $\overline{BD}$ in a point of trisection.

7. In $\triangle ABC$, D is a point on side $\overline{AB}$ and E is a point on side $\overline{AC}$ such that $\overline{DE} \parallel \overline{BC}$. F is any point on $\overline{BC}$. $\overline{AF}$ intersects $\overline{DE}$ at G. Prove that $DG : GE = BF : FC$.

8. In $\triangle ABC$, $\angle BAC = 90°$ and $\overline{AD}$ is the altitude from A to $\overline{BC}$. Prove that $AB^2 : AC^2 = BD : CD$.

9. In two quadrilaterals, corresponding sides are proportional and two pairs of corresponding angles are equal. Prove that the two quadrilaterals are similar.

11-6 Applying Similar Triangles

Similar triangles can be used to solve problems in construction, mapping, surveying, and to calculate distances that cannot be directly measured. Consider the following problem.

EXAMPLE: Janet wants to measure the distance across a river. She draws a scale diagram to represent the following measurements. She positions a marker, B, on the bank directly across from a tree, A. Then, Janet marks points C, D, and E as indicated in the diagram.

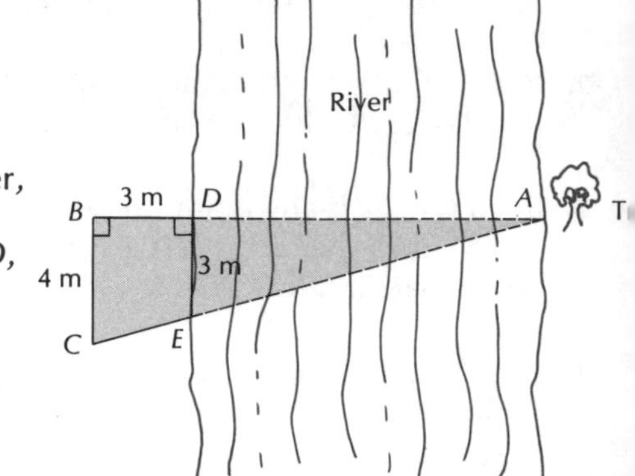

She now has sufficient information to calculate AD, the distance across the river.

For $\triangle ABC$ and $\triangle ADE$,

$\angle BAC = \angle DAE.$	Common angle
$\angle ABC = \angle ADE$	Constructed equal to 90°
$\triangle ABC \sim \triangle ADE$	AA~
$\frac{AB}{AD} = \frac{BC}{DE}$	Corresponding sides of similar triangles
$\frac{AD+3}{AD} = \frac{4}{3}$	Substitution
$3AD + 9 = 4AD$	
$AD = 9$	

Therefore, the river is 9 m wide.

EXERCISE 11-6

In the exercises, prove that a pair of triangles is similar before equating a pair of ratios. Use a calculator where appropriate.

B

1. Jason wanted to know the approximate height of the tree across the street. He noticed that the length of his shadow was 2.5 m and the length of the tree's shadow was 5.5 m. If Jason is 1.8 m tall, how high is the tree?

2. One method for calculating the height of an object is to use a mirror. Kelly places a mirror on level ground so that she can see the top of a tree. Kelly is 168 cm tall and her eyes are about 12 cm from the top of her head. She is standing 1.5 m from the mirror and 6.0 m from the base of the tree. Find the height of the tree. (Hint: From physics, it is known that $\angle\theta = \angle\varphi$.)

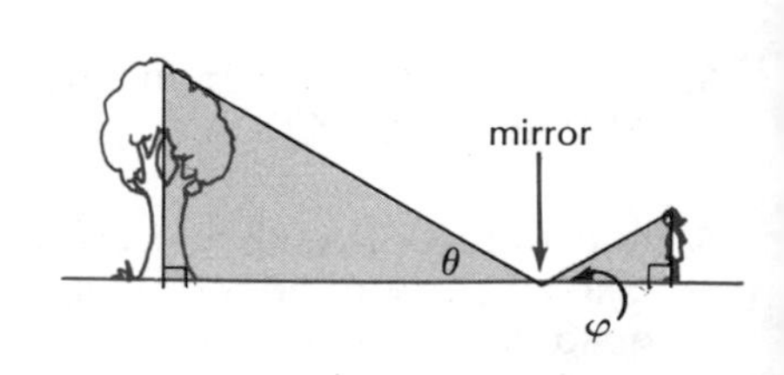

3. Geoff wants to measure the length of his roof from its peak to the eave, but he cannot reach the peak. Instead, he measures two "sample" dimensions at the eave and at the side of the house. Calculate the distance from the eave to the peak.

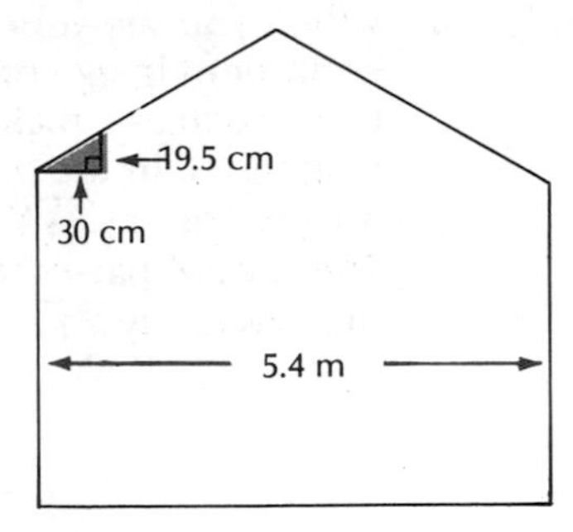

4. A pantograph is a tool used to draw a plane figure similar to a given plane figure. It is especially useful for enlarging or reducing maps or other drawings. A pantograph can be made by pinning four rods together at S, T, U, and B in the form of a parallelogram with extended sides. Points A, B, and C remain collinear. Fix point C to the drawing board. As the pointer traces the figure from B to B', the pen moves from A to A'. This produces an enlargement of the original figure. To reduce the original figure, interchange the pen and the pointer. Show that $BB' : AA'$ is the ratio of the reduction or enlargement.

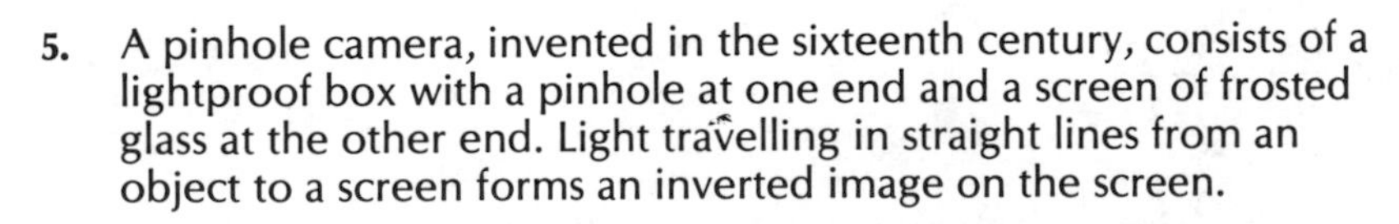

5. A pinhole camera, invented in the sixteenth century, consists of a lightproof box with a pinhole at one end and a screen of frosted glass at the other end. Light travelling in straight lines from an object to a screen forms an inverted image on the screen.

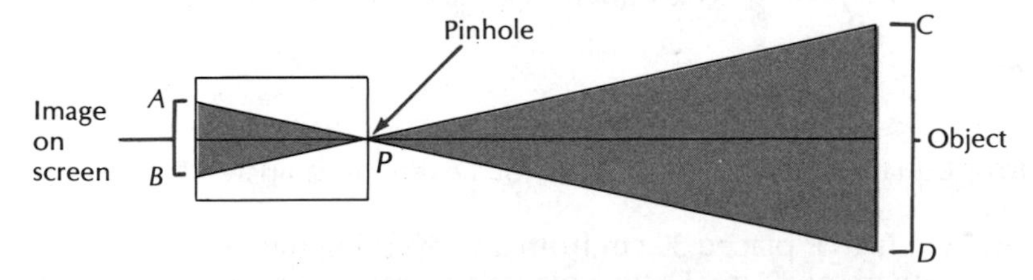

a. Calculate the distance from the pinhole to a building 190 m high, whose image is 8 cm high in a pinhole camera that is 12 cm long.

b. Calculate the height of a man 3 m away from a pinhole camera that is 5 cm long if his image is 3 cm long.

C 6. When you see your reflection in a plane mirror, you see a congruent image of yourself. However, when a curved mirror is used, such as a makeup mirror or a shaving mirror, the image is magnified. In the diagram, two rays of light are used to locate the image. The ray $\overrightarrow{AVY}$ obeys the laws of reflection, that is, $\angle\theta = \angle\varphi$. The ray $\overrightarrow{AZ}$ passes through the focus, F, and is reflected parallel to the axis as ray $\overrightarrow{ZY}$.

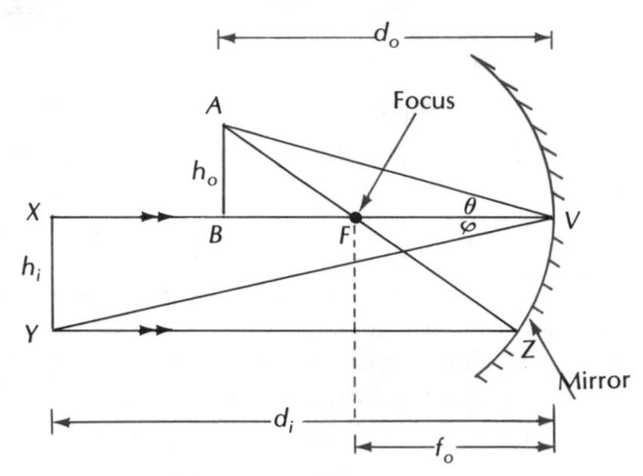

h_o = height of object = AB
h_i = height of image = XY
d_o = distance of object from mirror = BV
d_i = distance of image from mirror = XV
f = distance from the focus to the vertex of the mirror = FV

a. Prove that $\triangle ABF \sim \triangle ZVF$.
(For a small mirror, you can disregard the slight error caused by the curvature of the mirror.)

b. Prove that $\dfrac{h_o}{h_i} = \dfrac{d_o - f}{f}$.

c. Prove that $\dfrac{1}{d_o} + \dfrac{1}{d_i} = \dfrac{1}{f}$. This equation is called the **mirror equation.**

7. Use the mirror equation derived in the previous exercise to answer the following.

a. A candle 5 cm high is placed 30 cm from a converging mirror with a focal length of 20 cm. Draw a diagram to represent the situation. Determine the height of the image and its distance from the mirror.

b. A converging mirror has a focal length of 15 cm. Where should an object be placed so that its image will be twice as tall as the object?

11-7 Areas of Similar Figures

When Toni sets the prices for the various sizes of pizza at her restaurant, she uses the fact that the price of a pizza varies directly as the area of the top of the pizza.

TONI'S PIZZA

	SMALL (25 cm)	MED. (35 cm)	LARGE (40 cm)
Plain	\$5.25	10.30	13.45
Special	\$6.50	12.75	16.65

The area of a circle is given by πr^2.

For example, Toni's small Special pizza costs \$6.50.

$$\text{price} = k\pi r^2, \text{ where } k \text{ is a constant}$$
$$6.50 = k\pi(25)^2$$
$$k\pi = 6.50 \div 625 = 0.0104$$

The price formula can be written as

$$\text{price} = 0.0104r^2.$$

Toni can use this formula to calculate the prices of the other special pizzas. (Notice that the prices are rounded off to the nearest 5¢.)

Ratio of the areas of two circles is $\dfrac{\pi(r_1)^2}{\pi(r_2)^2} = \dfrac{(r_1)^2}{(r_2)^2}$

So, the area of a circle is proportional to the square of its radius.

Now consider the areas of two similar triangles, $\triangle ABC$ and $\triangle DEF$.

Given: $\triangle ABC \sim \triangle DEF$

Find: $\dfrac{\text{Area } \triangle ABC}{\text{Area } \triangle DEF}$

Solution: Draw altitudes, $\overline{AX}$ and $\overline{DY}$, from two corresponding vertices, A and D.

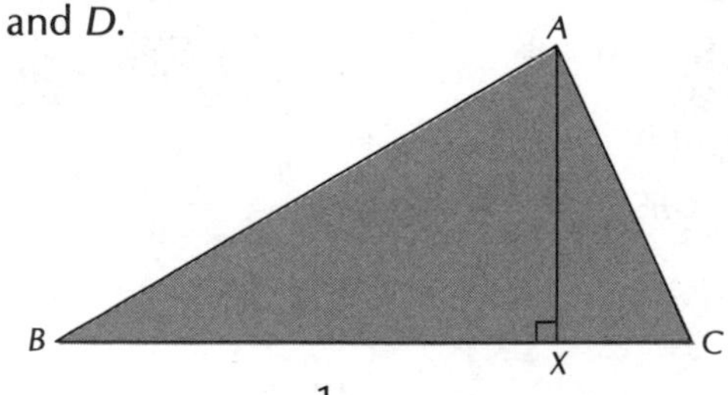

$\dfrac{\text{Area } \triangle ABC}{\text{Area } \triangle DEF} = \dfrac{\frac{1}{2}(BC)(AX)}{\frac{1}{2}(EF)(DY)}$ — Area of a triangle = $\frac{1}{2}$(base)(height)

$\dfrac{\text{Area } \triangle ABC}{\text{Area } \triangle DEF} = \left(\dfrac{BC}{EF}\right)\left(\dfrac{AX}{DY}\right)$ — Division

For $\triangle ABX$ and $\triangle DEY$,

$\angle ABX = \angle DEY$ — Corresponding angles in similar triangles

$\angle AXB = \angle DYE = 90°$ — Definition of an altitude

$\triangle ABX \sim \triangle DEY$ — AA~

$\dfrac{AB}{DE} = \dfrac{AX}{DY}$ — Corresponding sides of similar triangles

But $\triangle ABC \sim \triangle DEF$. Given

$\dfrac{AB}{DE} = \dfrac{BC}{EF}$ Corresponding sides of similar triangles

$\therefore \dfrac{BC}{EF} = \dfrac{AX}{DY}$ Substitution

$\therefore \dfrac{\text{Area } \triangle ABC}{\text{Area } \triangle DEF} = \left(\dfrac{BC}{EF}\right)\left(\dfrac{BC}{EF}\right)$ Substitution

and $\dfrac{\text{Area } \triangle ABC}{\text{Area } \triangle DEF} = \dfrac{BC^2}{EF^2}$.

But $\dfrac{AB}{DE} = \dfrac{BC}{EF} = \dfrac{AC}{DF}$. Corresponding sides of similar triangles

$\therefore \dfrac{\text{Area } \triangle ABC}{\text{Area } \triangle DEF} = \dfrac{BC^2}{EF^2} = \dfrac{AB^2}{DE^2} = \dfrac{AC^2}{DF^2}$ Subsitution

> The ratio of the areas of two similar triangles is equal to the ratio of the squares of corresponding sides.
>
> *or*
>
> The areas of similar triangles are proportional to the squares of corresponding sides.

EXAMPLE 1: In $\triangle ABC$, D is a point on side $\overline{AB}$ and E is a point on side $\overline{AC}$ such that $AD = 4$, $BD = 8$, $AE = 6$, and $EC = 2$.

i. Find $\dfrac{\text{area } \triangle ADE}{\text{area } \triangle ABC}$. **ii.** Find $\dfrac{\text{area } \triangle ADE}{\text{area } DBCE}$.

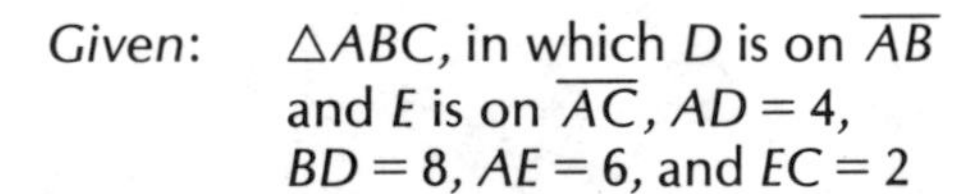

Given: $\triangle ABC$, in which D is on $\overline{AB}$ and E is on $\overline{AC}$, $AD = 4$, $BD = 8$, $AE = 6$, and $EC = 2$

Solution: For $\triangle ADE$ and $\triangle ACB$,

$\dfrac{AD}{AC} = \dfrac{4}{8} = \dfrac{1}{2}$. Division

$\dfrac{AE}{AB} = \dfrac{6}{12} = \dfrac{1}{2}$ Division

$\dfrac{AD}{AC} = \dfrac{AE}{AB}$ Substitution

$\angle A = \angle A$ Common angle

$\triangle ADE \sim \triangle ACB$ SAS~

$\dfrac{\text{area } \triangle ADE}{\text{area } \triangle ABC} = \dfrac{AD^2}{AC^2} = \dfrac{4^2}{8^2} = \dfrac{1}{4}$ Ratio of areas of similar triangles

Let area $\triangle ADE = k$ and area $\triangle ABC = 4k$.
Then area $DBCE = 3k$.

$\therefore \dfrac{\text{area } \triangle ADE}{\text{area } DBCE} = \dfrac{k}{3k} = \dfrac{1}{3}$ Division

The property of areas of similar triangles can be extended to other similar figures. For example, consider two similar quadrilaterals, $ABCD$ and $XYZW$.

EXAMPLE 2: *Given:* $ABCD \sim XYZW$, with measures of sides as shown in the diagram

Prove: $\dfrac{\text{area } ABCD}{\text{area } XYZW} = \dfrac{AB^2}{XY^2} = \dfrac{BC^2}{YZ^2} = \dfrac{CD^2}{ZW^2} = \dfrac{AD^2}{XW^2}$

Proof: Draw diagonals $\overline{AC}$ and $\overline{XZ}$.

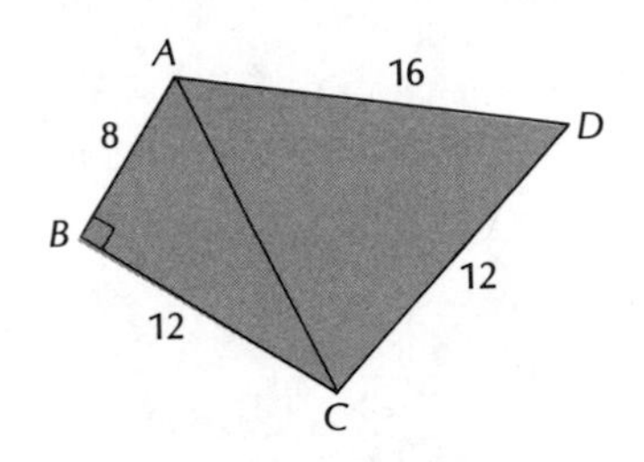

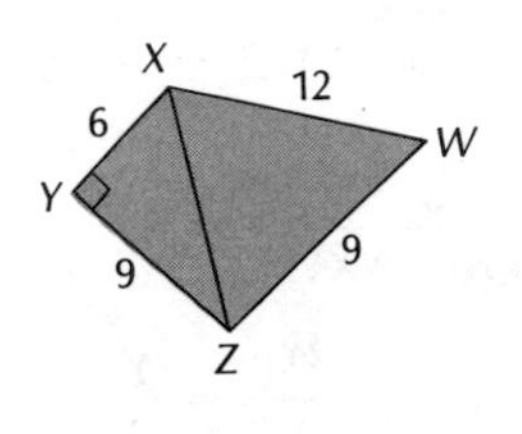

$\dfrac{\text{area } \triangle ABC}{\text{area } \triangle XYZ} = \dfrac{AC^2}{XZ^2}$ — Ratio of areas of similar triangles

But $AC^2 = 8^2 + 12^2$. — Pythagorean Theorem

$AC = \sqrt{208}$ or $4\sqrt{13}$

Similarly, $XZ = 3\sqrt{13}$.

$\dfrac{\text{area } \triangle ABC}{\text{area } \triangle XYZ} = \dfrac{AC^2}{XZ^2} = \dfrac{16}{9}$ — Division

Similarly, $\dfrac{\text{area } \triangle ACD}{\text{area } \triangle XZW} = \dfrac{AC^2}{XZ^2} = \dfrac{16}{9}$. — Ratio of areas of similar triangles

$\therefore$ 9 (area $\triangle ACD$) = 16 (area $\triangle XZW$) — Multiplication

and area $\triangle ABC = \frac{16}{9}$(area $\triangle XYZ$)

Similarly, area $\triangle ACD = \frac{16}{9}$(area $\triangle XZW$)

$$\frac{\text{area } ABCD}{\text{area } XYZW} = \frac{\text{area } \triangle ABC + \text{area } \triangle ACD}{\text{area } \triangle XYZ + \text{area } \triangle XZW} = \frac{\frac{16}{9}(\text{area } \triangle XYZ + \text{area } \triangle XZW)}{\text{area } \triangle XYZ + \text{area } \triangle XZW} = \frac{16}{9}$$

But $\dfrac{AB^2}{XY^2} = \dfrac{BC^2}{YZ^2} = \dfrac{CD^2}{ZW^2} = \dfrac{AD^2}{XW^2} = \dfrac{16}{9}$.

$\therefore \dfrac{\text{area } ABCD}{\text{area } XYZW} = \dfrac{AB^2}{XY^2} = \dfrac{BC^2}{YZ^2} = \dfrac{CD^2}{ZW^2} = \dfrac{AD^2}{XW^2}$

The theorem that follows is useful for work with areas of triangles.

Ratios of Areas of Triangles Theorem (RAT)
If two triangles have equal altitudes, the ratio of their areas is equal to the ratio of their bases.

Given: In $\triangle XYZ$, W is a point on side $\overline{YZ}$.

Prove: $\dfrac{\text{area } \triangle XYW}{\text{area } \triangle XWZ} = \dfrac{YW}{WZ}$

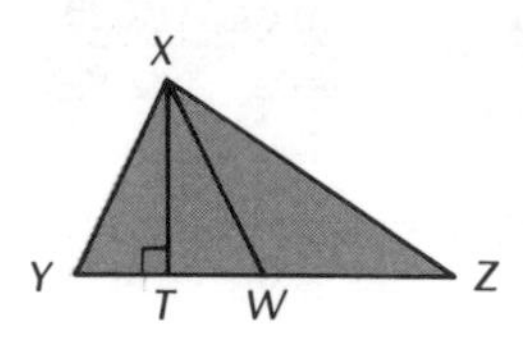

Proof: Construct altitude $\overline{XT}$.

$\text{area } \triangle XYW = \frac{1}{2}(YW)(XT)$

$\text{area } \triangle XWZ = \frac{1}{2}(WZ)(XT)$ — Area of a triangle $= \frac{1}{2}bh$

$\dfrac{\text{area } \triangle XYW}{\text{area } \triangle XWZ} = \dfrac{\frac{1}{2}(YW)(XT)}{\frac{1}{2}(WZ)(XT)}$ — Division

$\therefore \dfrac{\text{area } \triangle XYW}{\text{area } \triangle XWZ} = \dfrac{YW}{WZ}$

EXAMPLE 3: Find each ratio.

a. $\dfrac{\text{area } \triangle ABD}{\text{area } \triangle ADC}$ **b.** $\dfrac{\text{area } \triangle ABE}{\text{area } \triangle ABD}$ **c.** $\dfrac{\text{area } \triangle ABE}{\text{area } \triangle ABC}$

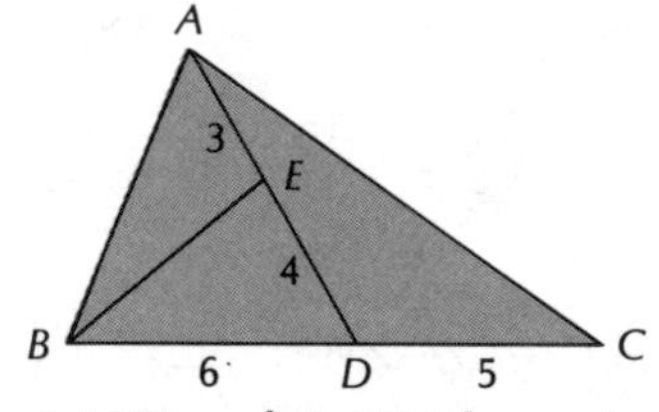

a. $\triangle ABD$ and $\triangle ADC$ have the same altitude from A.

$\therefore \dfrac{\text{area } \triangle ABD}{\text{area } \triangle ADC} = \dfrac{BD}{DC} = \dfrac{6}{5}$ — RAT

b. $\triangle ABE$ and $\triangle ABD$ have the same altitude from B.

$\therefore \dfrac{\text{area } \triangle ABE}{\text{area } \triangle ABD} = \dfrac{AE}{AD} = \dfrac{3}{7}$ — RAT

c. $\triangle ABD$ and $\triangle ABC$ have the same altitude from A.

$\dfrac{\text{area } \triangle ABD}{\text{area } \triangle ABC} = \dfrac{BD}{BC} = \dfrac{6}{11}$ — RAT

$\therefore \text{area } \triangle ABD = \frac{6}{11}(\text{area } \triangle ABC)$ — Multiplication

and $\text{area } \triangle ABE = \frac{3}{7}(\text{area } \triangle ABD)$

$\therefore \text{area } \triangle ABE = \frac{3}{7}\left[\frac{6}{11}(\text{area } \triangle ABC\right]$ — Multiplication

$\dfrac{\text{area } \triangle ABE}{\text{area } \triangle ABC} = \dfrac{18}{77}$ — Division

EXERCISE 11-7

A **1.** Prove that each pair of figures is similar. Find the ratios of the indicated areas.

a. $\dfrac{\text{area } \triangle PST}{\text{area } \triangle PQR}, \dfrac{\text{area } \triangle PST}{\text{area } QRTS}$

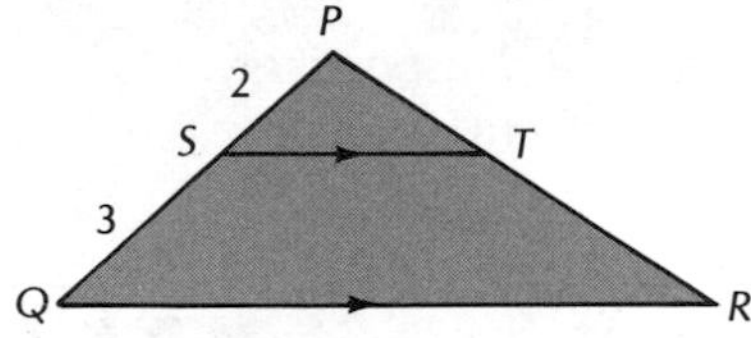

b. $\dfrac{\text{area } \triangle ABC}{\text{area } \triangle ACD}, \dfrac{\text{area } \triangle ACD}{\text{area } \triangle DBC}$

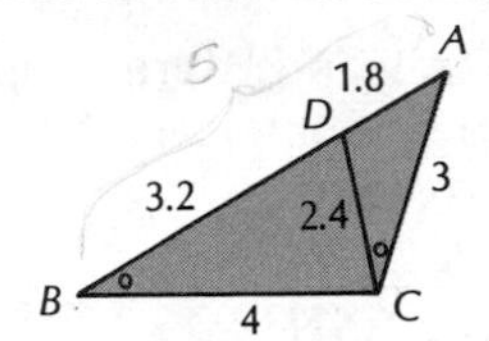

c. $\dfrac{\text{area } \triangle DEF}{\text{area } \triangle HGF}$

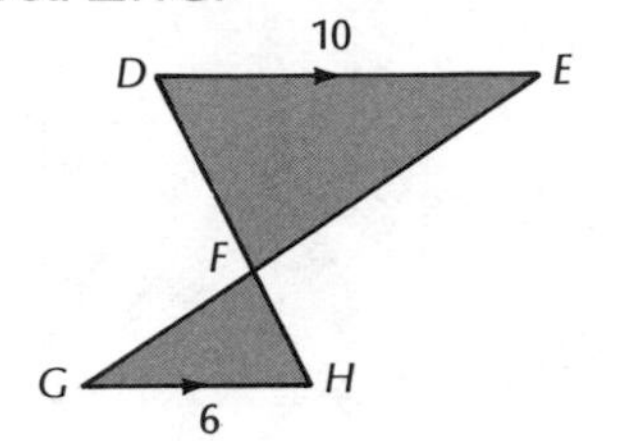

d. $\dfrac{\text{area } ABCD}{\text{area } ABFE}, \dfrac{\text{area } EFCD}{\text{area } ABFE}$

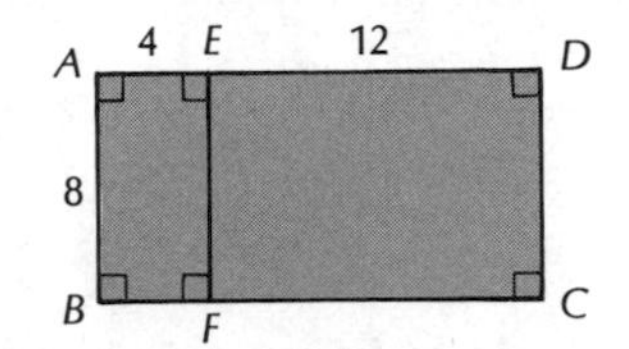

2. In $\triangle ABC$, D is on side $\overline{AB}$ and E is on side $\overline{AC}$ such that $\overline{DE} \parallel \overline{BC}$.

a. If $AD = 6$ and $DB = 5$, find the ratio area $\triangle ADE$: area $\triangle ABC$.

b. If area $\triangle ADE$: area $DBCE = 9:7$, find the ratio $AD:DB$.

c. If $AE:EC = 4:9$, find the ratio area $DBCE$: area $\triangle ABC$.

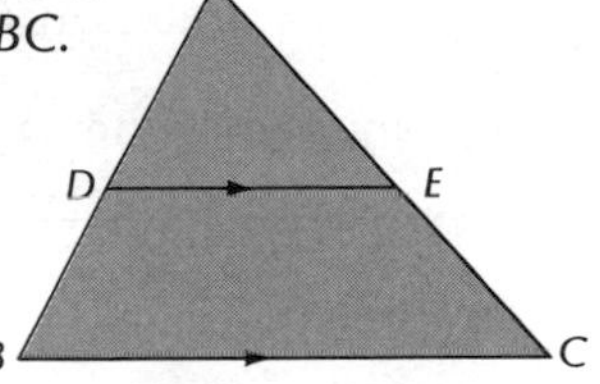

B **3.** Parallelogram $ABCG \sim$ parallelogram $HBDE$.
Area $ABCG = 50 \text{ cm}^2$ and area $HEDB = 72 \text{ cm}^2$.
If $AH = AG = 5$ cm, find the lengths of the sides of $HBDE$.

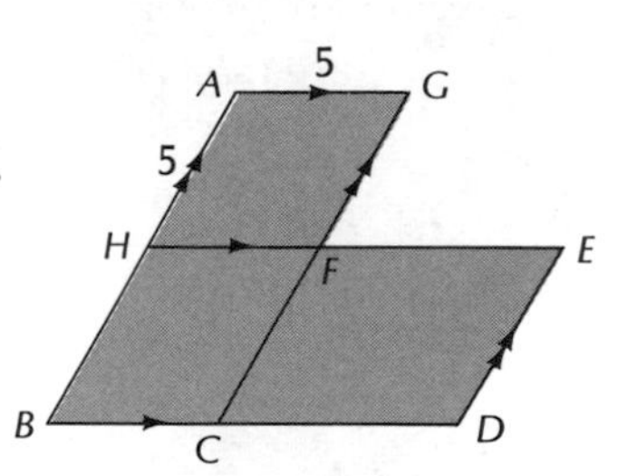

4. The Gibsons have just built a patio with the plan shown at the right. Their neighbours decide to build a similar patio with 125% more area.

a. What is the ratio of corresponding sides of the two patios?

b. Determine the dimensions of the larger patio.

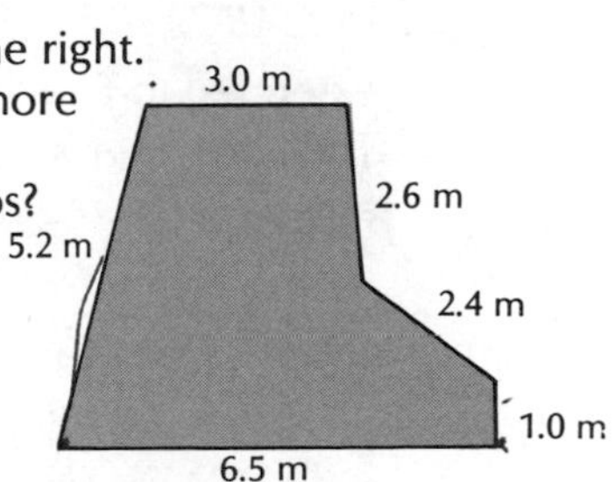

5. In trapezoid $ABCD$, $\overline{BC} \parallel \overline{AD}$. The diagonals intersect at E. Prove the following.

a. $\dfrac{\text{area } \triangle AED}{\text{area } \triangle CEB} = \dfrac{AD^2}{CB^2}$

b. $\dfrac{\text{area } \triangle ABE}{\text{area } \triangle DEC} = \dfrac{1}{1}$

6. In $\triangle STU$, V and W are midpoints of sides $\overline{ST}$ and $\overline{SU}$, respectively. $\overline{VU}$ and $\overline{WT}$ intersect at X. $ST = 12$ cm, and $SU = 16$ cm. Find the following ratios.

a. $\dfrac{\text{area } \triangle SVW}{\text{area } \triangle STU}$

b. $\dfrac{VW}{TU}$

c. $\dfrac{\text{area } \triangle XVW}{\text{area } \triangle XUT}$

d. $\dfrac{\text{area } \triangle VZX}{\text{area } \triangle WUX}$

7. For the given triangles, determine the indicated ratios.

a.

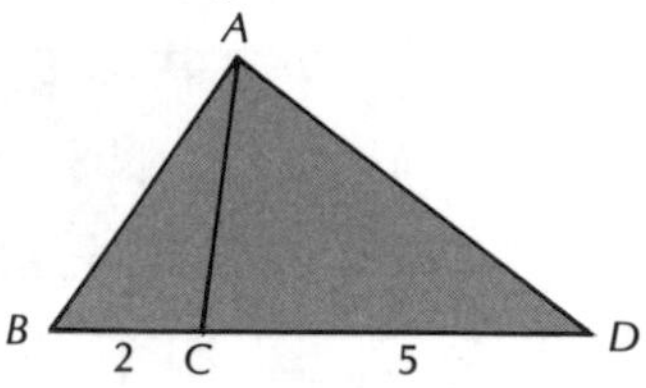

$\dfrac{\text{area } \triangle ABC}{\text{area } \triangle ACD}, \dfrac{\text{area } \triangle ACD}{\text{area } \triangle ABD}$

b.

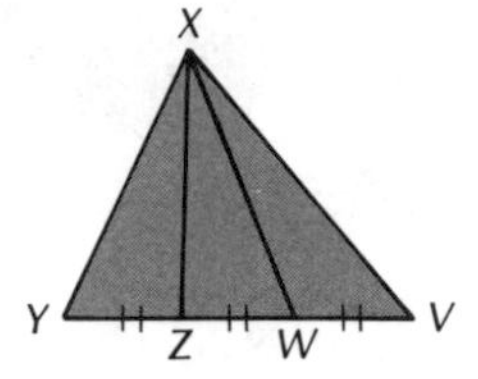

$\dfrac{\text{area } \triangle XYZ}{\text{area } \triangle XZW}, \dfrac{\text{area } \triangle XWY}{\text{area } \triangle XVW}, \dfrac{\text{area } \triangle VZX}{\text{area } \triangle XYV}$

8. In the diagram, $XA : AY = 2 : 1$ and $YW : WZ = 3 : 5$. Find each ratio.

a. $\dfrac{\text{area } \triangle XWZ}{\text{area } \triangle XYZ}$

b. $\dfrac{\text{area } \triangle XBC}{\text{area } \triangle XWZ}$

c. $\dfrac{\text{area } \triangle XBC}{\text{area } \triangle XYZ}$

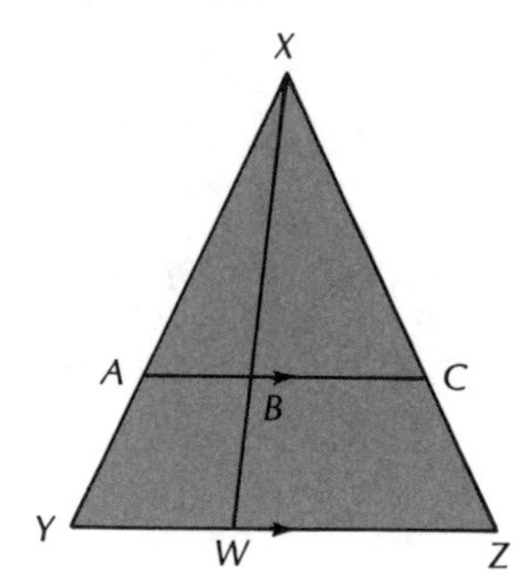

9. In $\triangle ABC$, $AB = AC$. $\overline{CB}$ is extended to D such that $BD = 2AB$. $\overline{BC}$ is extended to E such that $CE = \frac{1}{2}AC$. $\overline{AB}$ is extended to F such that $\overline{DF} \perp \overline{AB}$, and $\overline{AC}$ is extended to G such that $\overline{EG} \perp \overline{AC}$. Find area $\triangle ADF$: area $\triangle AEG$.

C 10. In $\triangle XYZ$, medians $\overline{XP}$ and $\overline{YQ}$ intersect at R. Prove the following.

a. $\dfrac{\text{area } \triangle PQR}{\text{area } \triangle XYR} = \dfrac{1}{4}$

b. $\dfrac{\text{area } \triangle PQR}{\text{area } \triangle XYZ} = \dfrac{1}{12}$

11-8 Volumes of Similar Solids

Special Offer!
Shampoo
50% more at
no extra cost

A manufacturer sells a 300 mL bottle of shampoo in a container that is 14 cm high. For a special promotion, a similar container is designed that contains a bonus of 50% more shampoo at no extra cost.

The concept of similar figures can be extended to three dimensions. Two solids are similar if corresponding dimensions are proportional and corresponding angles are equal.

In the situation above, the original container is a cylinder. To determine the size of the larger container, you must know the relationship between volumes of similar solids and corresponding lengths. For two cylinders to be similar:

i. their bases, which are two circles, are similar, and
ii. the ratio of their heights is equal to the ratio of the radii of the bases.

Let the ratio of corresponding lengths be $1:k$.
Therefore, the radius of a cylinder similar to a cylinder having radius r and height h has radius kr and height kh.

$$\frac{\text{volume of cylinder 1}}{\text{volume of cylinder 2}} = \frac{\pi r^2 h}{\pi (kr)^2 kh} = \frac{\pi r^2 h}{\pi k^3 r^2 h} = \frac{1}{k^3}$$

> In general, if two solids are similar, the ratio of their volumes is equal to the ratio of the cubes of corresponding sides.

EXAMPLE 1: What is the height of the shampoo bottle to be used in the promotion described above?

Let V_1 represent the volume of the original bottle and h_1 be the height, where $h_1 = 14$.
Let V_2 represent the volume of the new bottle and h_2 be the height.
Since V_2 is 50% more than V_1, then $V_2 = 1.5V_1$.

$$\frac{V_1}{V_2} = \frac{(h_1)^3}{(h_2)^3}$$

$$\frac{V_1}{1.5V_1} = \frac{14^3}{(h_2)^3}$$

$$\frac{1}{1.5} = \frac{2744}{(h_2)^3}$$

$$(h_2)^3 = 4116$$

$$h_2 \doteq 16.026$$

Volumes of similar solids

r_1 r_2 V_1 V_2 $h_1 = 14$ cm h_2

Therefore, the height of the shampoo bottle used in the promotion is approximately 16 cm.

EXAMPLE 2: Two similar pyramids have volumes 9 and 576 cubic units. Find the ratios of each of the following.

a. the heights **b.** the areas of the bases **c.** the lateral surface areas

The ratio of their volumes is 9 : 576, or 1 : 64, or $1:4^3$.

a. The ratio of corresponding heights is 1 : 4.

b. The ratio of the areas of similar figures is equal to the ratio of the squares of corresponding sides. Although the shape of the base is not known, the ratio of the base areas is $1:4^2$, or 1 : 16.

c. A pyramid consists of an n-sided base and n triangles.
The lateral surface area of the smaller pyramid
= base area + area of n triangles.
The lateral surface area of the larger pyramid
= 16(base area) + 16(area of n triangles)
= 16(surface area of the smaller pyramid)
The ratio of their lateral surface areas is 1 : 16.

EXERCISE 11-8

A **1.** Are the given pairs of solids similar? Explain.

a.

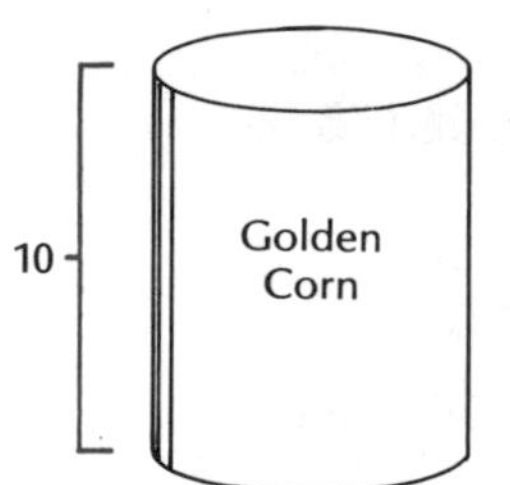

b.

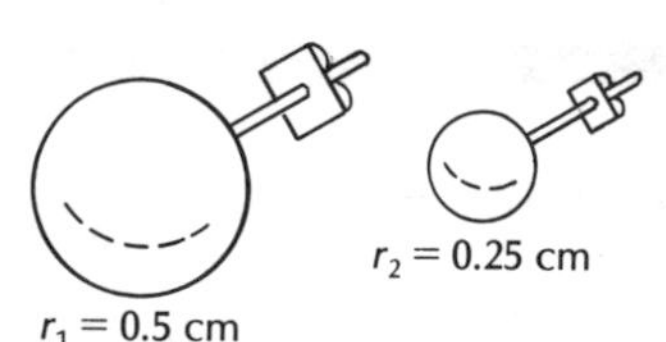

c.

d.

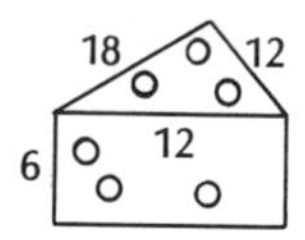

2. The corresponding edges of two solids have the given ratio. Find the ratio of their volumes.

a. 5 : 7 **b.** 3.2 : 1.5 **c.** $\sqrt{7}:\sqrt{10}$

3. Two similar solids have volumes in the given ratio. Find the ratio of corresponding sides.

a. 216 : 1331 **b.** 320 : 625 **c.** 108 : 1372

B **4.** For each of the given pairs of similar solids, determine each unknown value.

a.

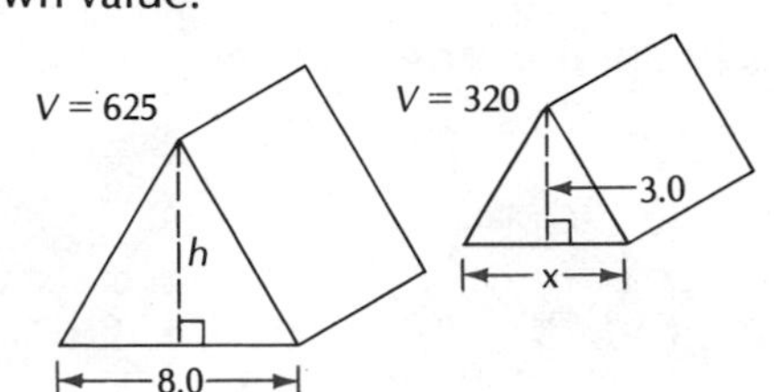

b.

V

V = 648

6

9

c.

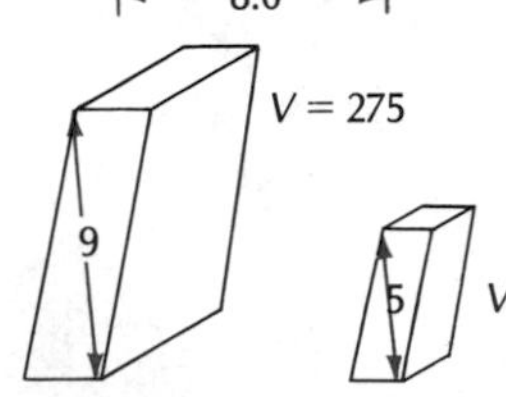

d.

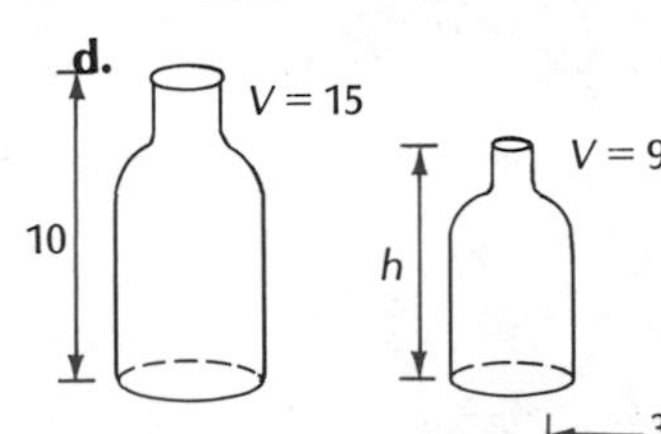

5. In the diagram, Drum 1 holds 100 L. What volume can be contained in Drum 2?

3

1.8

5

3

Drum 2

Drum 1

6. A triangular pyramid has an altitude of 7.5 m and a volume of 135 m³. What is the altitude of a similar pyramid having a volume of 40 m³?

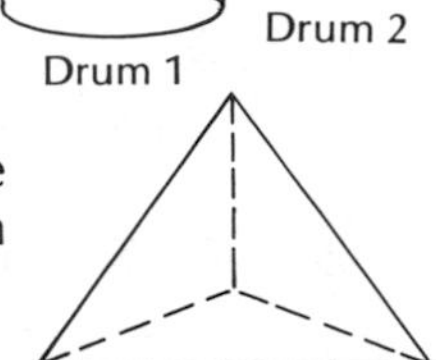

7. Hay is bundled into bales with a mass of 25 kg and having dimensions 40 cm × 40 cm × 70 cm. If bales with a mass of 30 kg are to be made, what will be the new dimensions? (Note that a modern baling machine only allows the length of the bale to be altered. Assume that mass varies directly as volume.)

8. A 4 L can of camp fuel is 25 cm high. A 2 L can has a similar shape. What is the height of the 2 L can?

9. A 3 L box of plaster of paris is 21 cm high. What volume of plaster of paris is in a similar box, 15 cm high?

10. The size of a television screen is measured diagonally. How many times as large (surface area) is a 66 cm screen compared with a 48 cm screen?

11. Two spheres have diameters 25 cm and 35 cm.

a. What is the ratio of their surface areas? **b.** What is the ratio of their volumes?

12. Two similar cylinders have lateral surface areas 49π and 121π square units.

a. Find the ratio of their heights. **b.** Find the ratio of their volumes.

C **13.** The boxes shown are similar. The volume of the larger box is 36 cm³ and its lateral surface area is 72 cm². If the lateral surface area of the smaller box is 18 cm², find its volume.

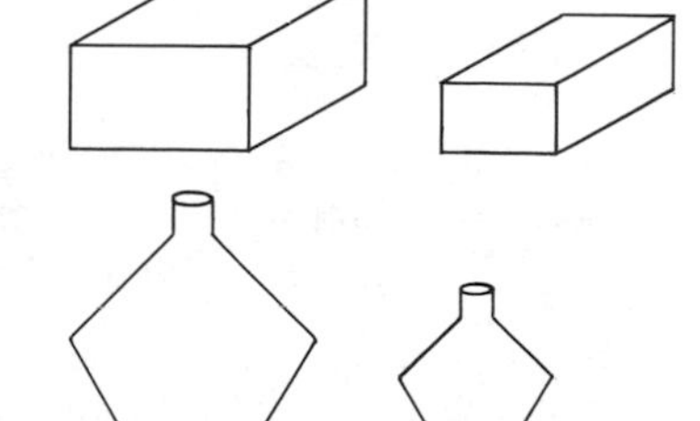

14. The bottles shown are similar. The surface area of the larger bottle is 700 cm² and its volume is 400 mL. If the smaller bottle holds 50 mL, what is its surface area?

Review

1. Find the measure of each unknown side. Justify your answers.

a. A, D, E, 8, B, x, C

b.

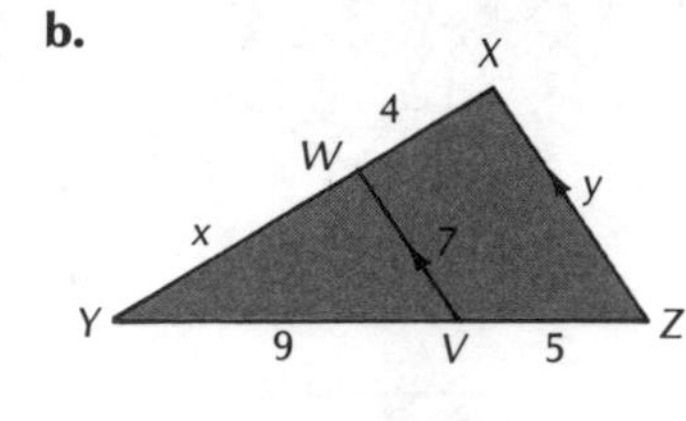

c.

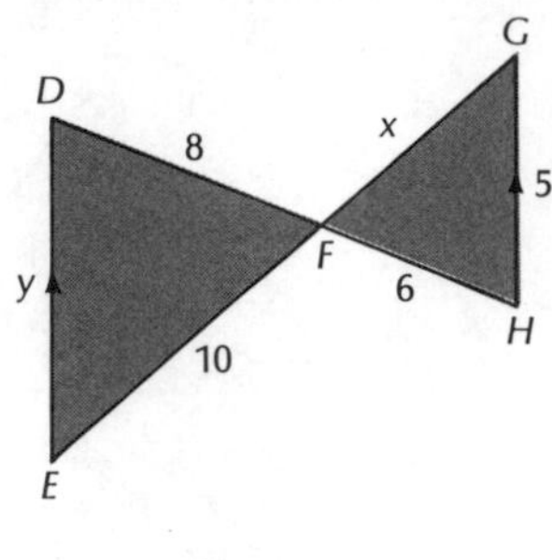

d. J, y, 3, M, K, x, N, 4, 7, z, L

e.

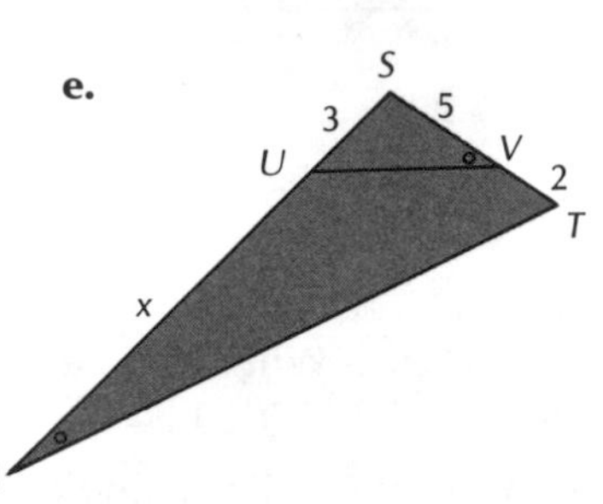

f.

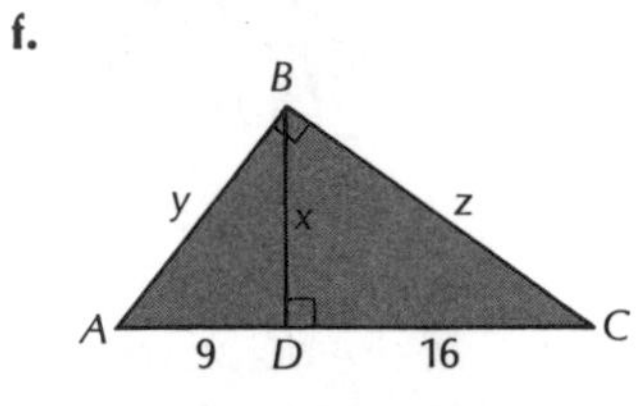

2. For $\triangle PQR$, A, B, and C are the midpoints of sides $\overline{PQ}$, $\overline{PR}$, and $\overline{QR}$, respectively. Prove that the triangle formed by joining A, B, and C is similar to $\triangle PQR$.

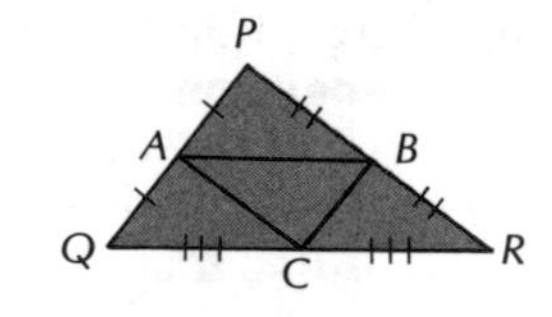

3. Prove that the quadrilateral formed by joining the midpoints of the sides of quadrilateral $ABCD$ is a parallelogram.

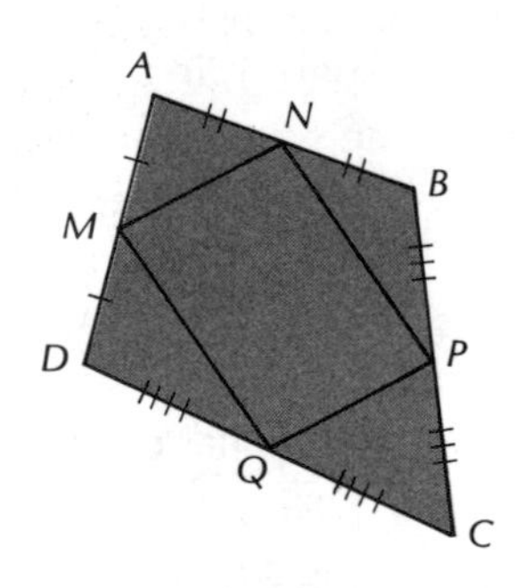

4. For quadrilateral $PQRS$, X is a point on $\overline{PQ}$ and Y is a point on diagonal $\overline{PR}$ such that $\overline{XY} \parallel \overline{QR}$. Z is a point on $\overline{PS}$ such that $\overline{YZ} \parallel \overline{RS}$. Prove that $\overline{XZ} \parallel \overline{QS}$.

5. Prove that the ratio of the altitudes of two similar triangles is equal to the ratios of corresponding sides.

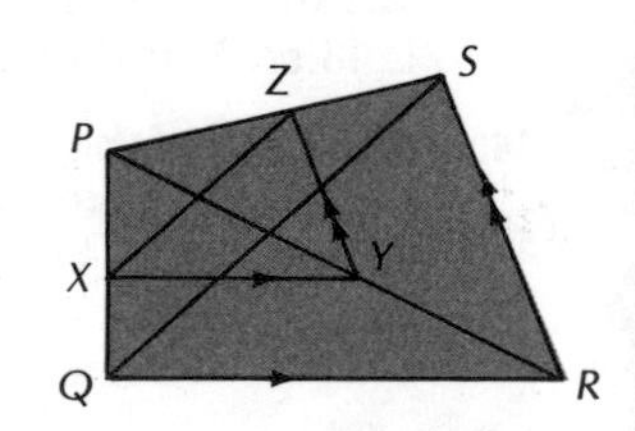

6. For $\triangle PQR$, S is any point on side $\overline{QR}$. A is on side $\overline{PQ}$ and C is on side $\overline{PR}$ such that $\overline{AC} \parallel \overline{QR}$. $\overline{AC}$ intersects $\overline{PS}$ at B. If $PA = 6$, $PB = 5$, $QS = 4$, $SR = 10$, and $AQ = 10$, find each ratio.

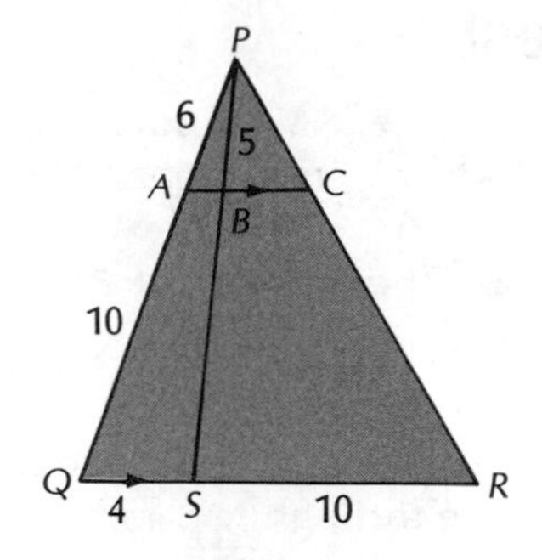

a. $\dfrac{\text{area } \triangle PAB}{\text{area } \triangle PQS}$ b. $\dfrac{\text{area } \triangle PQS}{\text{area } \triangle PSR}$

c. $\dfrac{\text{area } \triangle PQS}{\text{area } \triangle PQR}$ d. $\dfrac{\text{area } \triangle PAB}{\text{area } \triangle PQR}$

7. For $\triangle ABC$, P is on side $\overline{AB}$ and Q is on side $\overline{AC}$ such that $\overline{PQ} \parallel \overline{BC}$. $\overline{PC}$ and $\overline{QB}$ intersect at T. R is the midpoint of $\overline{BT}$, and S is the midpoint of $\overline{CT}$. If $AP = 3$ and $PB = 5$, find each ratio.

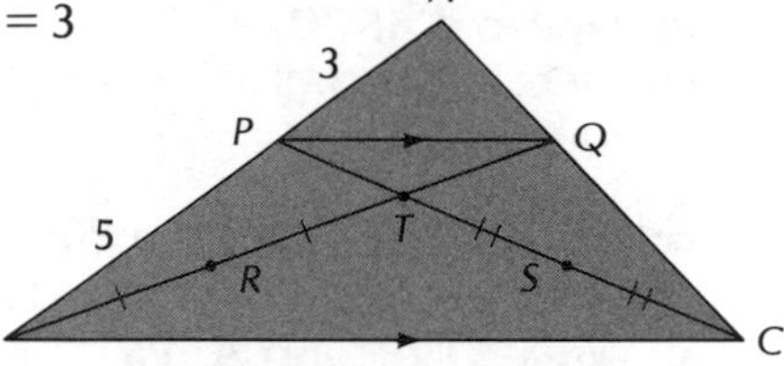

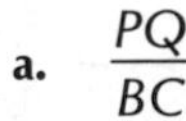

a. $\dfrac{PQ}{BC}$ b. $\dfrac{PQ}{RS}$ c. $\dfrac{\text{area } \triangle APQ}{\text{area } \triangle ABC}$

d. $\dfrac{\text{area } PQCB}{\text{area } \triangle APQ}$ e. $\dfrac{\text{area } \triangle PQT}{\text{area } \triangle SRT}$

8. A fence post 1.3 m high casts a shadow 0.9 m long. At the same time of day, a hydro pole casts a shadow 4 m in length. Find the height of the hydro pole.

9. Two similar cylinders have volumes of 81 cm³ and 375 cm³. Find the ratio of:

a. the heights. b. the bases.

10. Two spheres have radii 8 cm and 10 cm. Find the ratio of:

a. the surface areas. b. the volumes.

11. Two soft-drink bottles, similar in shape, have volumes of 750 mL and 1.5 L. The height of the smaller bottle is 30 cm. What is the height of the larger bottle?

12. For trapezoid $ABCD$, $\overline{AB} \parallel \overline{DC}$. P is a point on $\overline{AD}$ and Q is a point on $\overline{BC}$ such that $AP : PD = BQ : QC$. Prove that $\overline{PQ} \parallel \overline{AB}$.

13. For acute $\triangle ABC$, altitudes $\overline{AD}$, $\overline{BE}$, and $\overline{CF}$ intersect at O. Prove that $(AB)(AF) = (AD)(AO) = (AC)(AE)$.

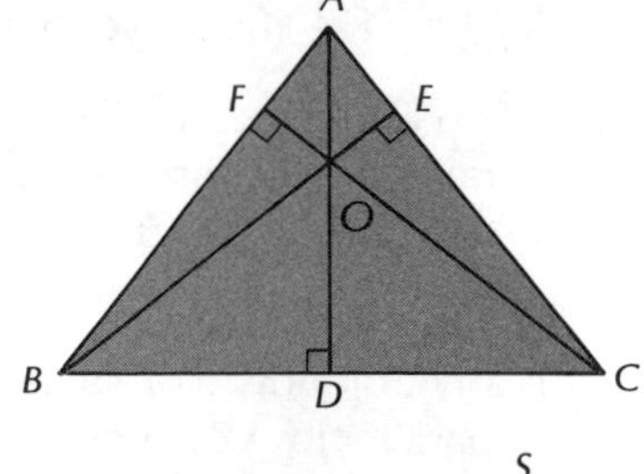

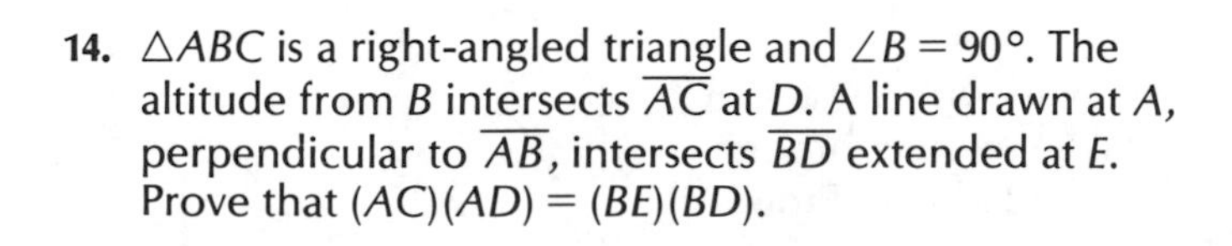

14. $\triangle ABC$ is a right-angled triangle and $\angle B = 90°$. The altitude from B intersects $\overline{AC}$ at D. A line drawn at A, perpendicular to $\overline{AB}$, intersects $\overline{BD}$ extended at E. Prove that $(AC)(AD) = (BE)(BD)$.

15. For $\triangle PQR$, $\angle SPR$ is an exterior angle. The bisector of $\angle SPR$ intersects $\overline{QR}$ extended at T. Prove that $QT : RT = QP : PR$.
Hint: Draw $\overline{RV} \parallel \overline{TP}$, where V is a point on $\overline{PQ}$.

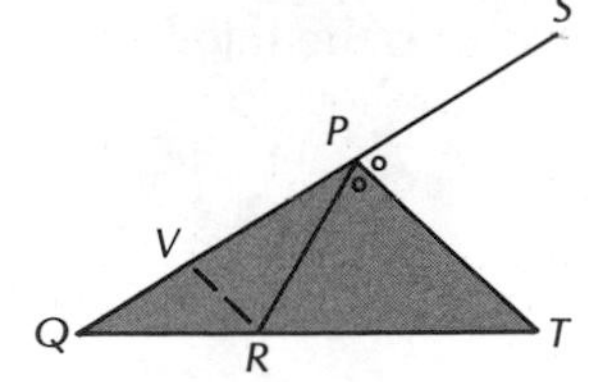

Test Unit 11

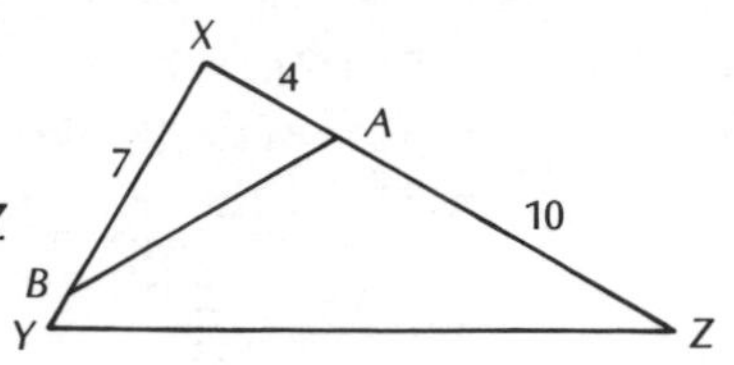

1. In $\triangle XYZ$, A is a point on side $\overline{XZ}$ and B is a point on side $\overline{XY}$ such that $XA:XB = XY:XZ$. If $XB = 7$, $XA = 4$, and $AZ = 10$, find each of the following.
   a. the measure of $\overline{BY}$ **b.** area $\triangle XBA$: area $ABYZ$

2. In $\triangle PQR$, M and N are midpoints of sides $\overline{PQ}$ and $\overline{PR}$, respectively. A line through N parallel to $\overline{PQ}$, intersects $\overline{QR}$ at X. Prove that X is the midpoint of $\overline{QR}$.

3. In trapezoid $ABCD$, $\overline{AB} \parallel \overline{DC}$. Diagonals $\overline{AC}$ and $\overline{BD}$ intersect at E such that $AE = 4$, $BE = 5$, and $DE = 7$. Find:
   a. the measure of $\overline{EC}$. **b.** area $\triangle AEB$: area $\triangle CED$.

4. Side $\overline{QR}$ of parallelogram $PQRS$ is extended to T such that $RT = 8$ cm. $\overline{PT}$ intersects $\overline{SR}$ at V. If $PS = 12$ cm, find each ratio.
   a. area $\triangle TVR$: area $\triangle PVS$ **b.** area $\triangle TVR$: area $\triangle TPQ$

5. In $\triangle DEF$, $\angle EDF = 90°$. $\overline{DG}$, the altitude from D to $\overline{EF}$, intersects $\overline{EF}$ at G such that $EG = 9$ cm and $GF = 25$ cm. Find each indicated length.
   a. DE **b.** DF **c.** DG.

6. Two similar triangular pyramids have heights of 6 m and 8 m. Find the ratio of:
   a. the volumes. **b.** the surface areas.

7. Two similar cylinders have volumes of 4725π and 1400π cubic units.
   a. What is the ratio of their heights?
   b. If the larger cylinder has a height of 21 units, what is the height of the smaller cylinder?
   c. What is the ratio of the areas of their bases?

8. For rectangle $ABCD$, $BC > AB$. A perpendicular from A intersects diagonal $\overline{BD}$ at E, and a perpendicular from C intersects $\overline{BD}$ at F. If $BE = EF = FD$, prove that $AB^2 = \frac{1}{2}BC^2$.

9. $\overline{AD}$ is an altitude of $\triangle ABC$. A line through X on $\overline{AB}$, parallel to $\overline{BC}$, intersects $\overline{AD}$ at Y and $\overline{AC}$ at Z. Prove that $XZ:BC = AY:AD$.

10. $\overline{XM}$ is a median of $\triangle XYZ$. B is any point on $\overline{YM}$ and A is any point on $\overline{XM}$ such that $\overline{AB} \parallel \overline{XY}$. A line through B, parallel to $\overline{XZ}$, intersects $\overline{XM}$ extended at C. Prove that M is the midpoint of $\overline{AC}$.

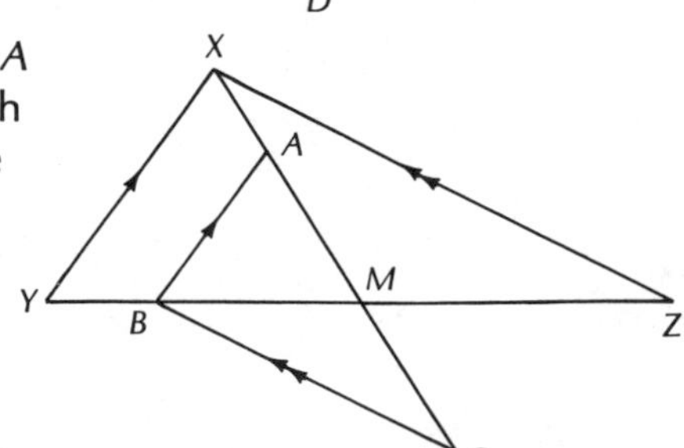

Cumulative Review

1. Consider the function $f: x \rightarrow x^2 - 2$.
   a. Find the domain and range of f.
   b. Sketch the graph of f.
   c. Find a defining equation for f^{-1}.
   d. Sketch the graph of f^{-1}.

2. Find an equation of the image of $y = x^2 - 4x$ under a horizontal stretch by a factor of 2 and the translation $(x, y) \rightarrow (x + 1, y - 2)$.

3. An object cools in a room according to the formula
   $$T = a + Ae^{-bt},$$
   where a is the room temperature in degrees Celsius,
   A is the difference in temperature of the object and the room at the start ($t = 0$), and
   T is the Celsius temperature t min after temperature measurements start.

   When an apple pie was removed from the oven, its temperature was 200°C. Ten minutes later the pie had cooled to 160°C. Pies should not be eaten until their temperature is 30°C or less. If room temperature was 25°C, what was the least time one had to wait before eating the freshly baked pie?

4. Solve the equation $3^x = \frac{1}{15}$.

5. Prove that $x - 2$ is a factor of $x^5 - x^4 - x^3 - x^2 + x - 6$.

6. Beatrice lives directly south of factory A. Factory B is N45°W of factory A. Beatrice hears the noon whistle from factory A at 4 s past noon and the one from factory B at 7 s past noon. If the velocity of sound is 320 m/s, find the distance between the two factories.

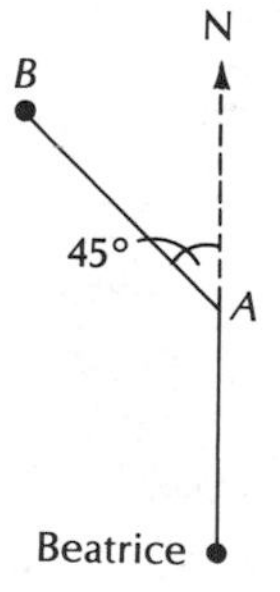

7. Solve the given system of equations.
   $$2x^2 + y^2 = 11$$
   $$y = x^2 - 4$$

8. Given parallelogram $ABCD$, E and F are midpoints of $\overline{AD}$ and $\overline{BC}$, respectively.
   Prove the following.
   a. $\overline{AF} \parallel \overline{EC}$
   b. $DK = KM$
   c. $\overline{AF}$ and $\overline{EC}$ divide the diagonal $\overline{BD}$ into three equal segments.

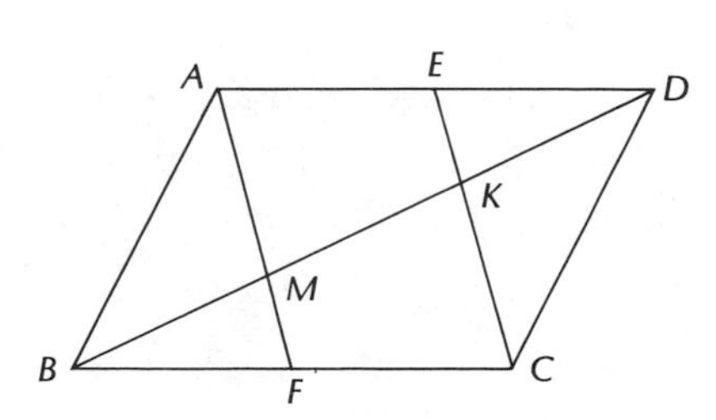

9. Prove $\dfrac{\cos\theta}{1 + \sin\theta} + \dfrac{\cos\theta}{1 - \sin\theta} = 2\sec\theta$.

12 The Circle

12-1 The Circle: A Review

The circle and the sphere can be seen all around you: in nature, in architecture, and in the construction of modern machinery. It is apparent that the symmetric properties of the circle make it the essential base of such important items as wheels and gears, as shown in the ten-speed bicycle above.

In this lesson, the vocabulary related to the circle is reviewed, along with solving numerical problems involving the circle.

A **circle** is the set of all points in a plane equidistant from a given point, the **centre**. The fixed distance is called the **radius**.

The diagram below illustrates many of the terms associated with the circle.

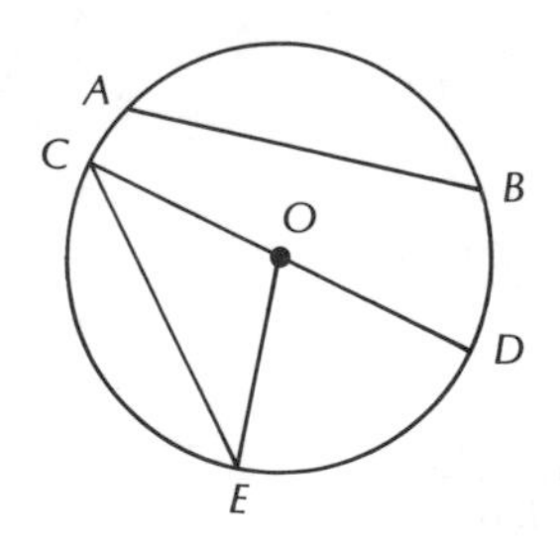

O is the **centre**. The line segment $\overline{OE}$ is a **radius** since its endpoints are O and a point, E, on the perimeter.

The segment $\overline{AB}$ is a **chord**.

Diameter $\overline{CD}$ is a chord that contains the centre.

The set of points on the perimeter of the circle between A and B and containing A and B is **arc** AB.

The region bounded by arc AB and chord $\overline{AB}$ is a **segment** of the circle.

The region bounded by radii $\overline{OE}$, $\overline{OD}$, and arc $\overline{ED}$ is a **sector**, EOD.

The angle formed by radii $\overline{OE}$ and $\overline{OD}$ is a **sector angle**, $\angle EOD$.

Chord $\overline{AB}$ forms two arcs. The **minor arc** AB bounds a sector whose angle measures $\theta°$, such that $0° < \theta < 180°$. The **major arc** AEB bounds a sector whose angle is a reflex angle, $\angle AOB$, measuring $(360 - \theta°)$.

Congruent circles are circles that have the same radius.

Concentric circles are circles that lie in the same plane and have the same centre.

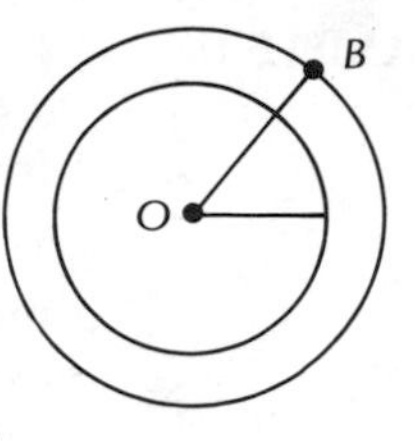

$\overline{OB}$ and $\overline{OA}$ are radii.

The measure of the perimeter of a circle is called the **circumference**. Many centuries ago, mathematicians discovered that the ratio of the circumference of a circle to its diameter is a constant value known as π (pi).

An approximate value of π, determined by Archimedes (287–212 B.C.), is $3\frac{10}{71} < \pi < 3\frac{1}{7}$.

In 1794, Adrien Marie Legendre showed that π is irrational. Although there is no finite decimal that is exactly equal to π, the value of π can be calculated correctly to any desired number of decimal places using an infinite series and a computer. Commonly used approximations for π are 3.14 and $\frac{22}{7}$.

> The length of the circumference of a circle is $C = \pi d$ or $C = 2\pi r$, where d is the diameter and r is the radius of the circle.

The area of a circle can be approximated by dividing it into n congruent sectors and finding the areas of the corresponding triangles. As n becomes very large some observations can be made.

- The sum of the areas of the triangles approximates the area of the circle.
- The sum of the lengths of the bases of the triangles approximates the circumference of the circle.

area of a triangle $= \frac{1}{2}bh$

area of a circle $\doteq n\left(\frac{1}{2}bh\right)$

$$A \doteq \frac{1}{2}nbh \quad ①$$

Notice that when n is large, the measure of the circumference is approximately equal to the sum of the bases of the triangles, nb. Also, the height of each triangle is approximately equal to the radius. To find the exact area of the circle, substitute $C = 2\pi r$ for nb and r for h in equation ①.

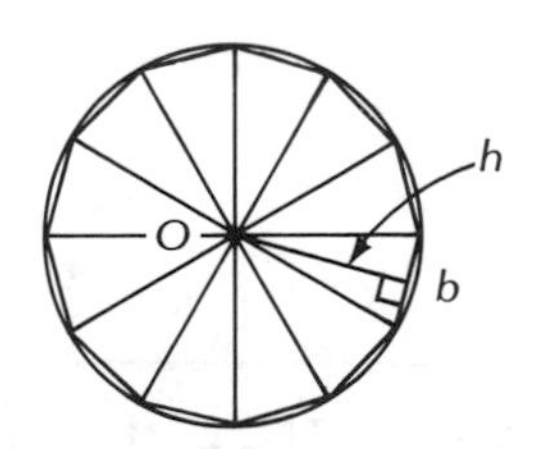

$$A = \frac{1}{2}(2\pi r)r$$

$$\therefore A = \pi r^2$$

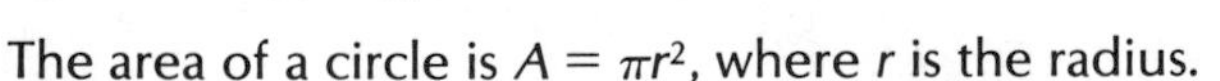

The area of a circle is $A = \pi r^2$, where r is the radius.

A **sphere** is the set of all points in three-dimensional space that are equidistant from a given point.

Many of the properties of a circle are shared by the sphere.

EXAMPLE 1: Find the area of a sector of a circle with radius 9 cm and a sector angle of 60°. (Use 3.14 as an approximation for π.)

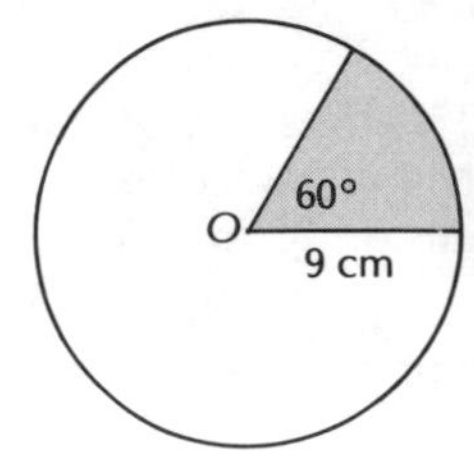

The area of the sector is proportional to the measure of the sector angle. Consider the circle as a sector having a sector angle of 360°. Then the area of a sector having a sector angle of 60° is $\frac{60}{360}$ of the area of the circle.
In general,

$$\text{area of a sector} = \frac{\text{sector angle}}{360} \times (\text{area of the circle})$$

For the sector defined above,

$$\text{area of the sector} = \frac{60(81\pi)}{360} \qquad \pi r^2 = 9^2\pi = 254.34$$

$$\doteq 42.39$$

The area of the sector is 42.4 cm², correct to one decimal place.

EXAMPLE 2: Find the length of the arc bounding the sector given in Example 1.

The length of the arc is proportional to the measure of the sector angle. Consider the circle as a sector having a sector angle of 360°. Then the length of an arc having a sector angle of 60° is $\frac{60}{360}$ of the length of the circumference of the circle.
In general,

$$\text{length of an arc} = \frac{\text{sector angle}}{360} \times (\text{circumference})$$

For the sector defined above,

$$\text{length of the arc} = \frac{60(2\pi r)}{360} \qquad 2\pi r = 18\pi$$

$$\doteq 9.42$$

The length of the arc is 9.4 cm, correct to one decimal place.

EXERCISE 12-1

A 1. Point P is a point inside a circle with centre O.
   a. How many chords can you draw that contain P?
   b. How many radii can you draw that contain P?

2. For a circle with radius 16 cm and a sector angle with the given measure, find the area of each sector.
   a. 90° **b.** 50° **c.** 175° **d.** 100°

3. Find the length of the arc that bounds each sector defined in exercise 2.

4. Find the radius of a circle with circumference 40π units long.

5. Find the diameter of a circle with area 225π square units.

B 6. Find the measure of each indicated sector angle.

a.

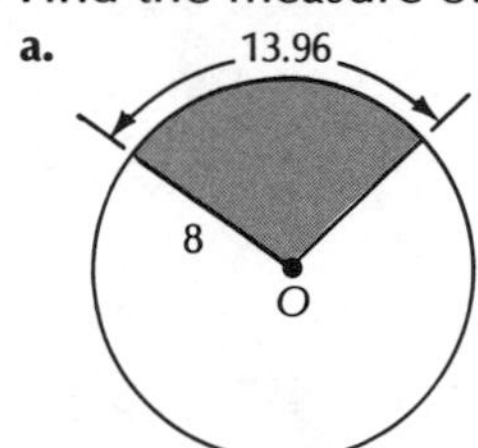

b.

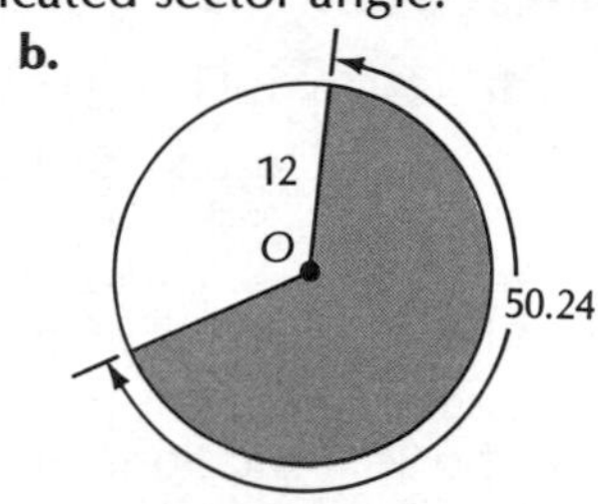

c.

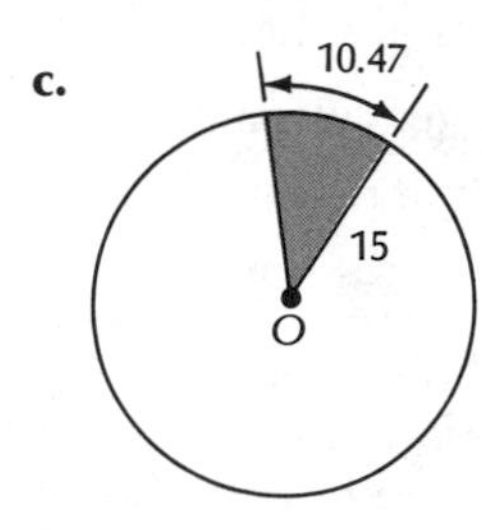

7. Find the measure of each indicated sector angle.

a.

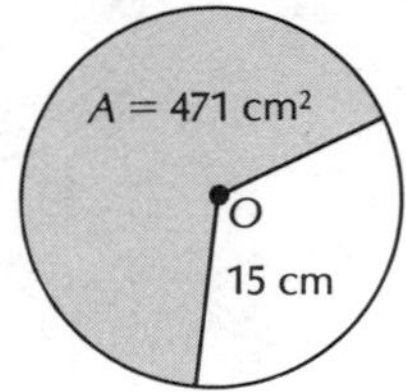

b.

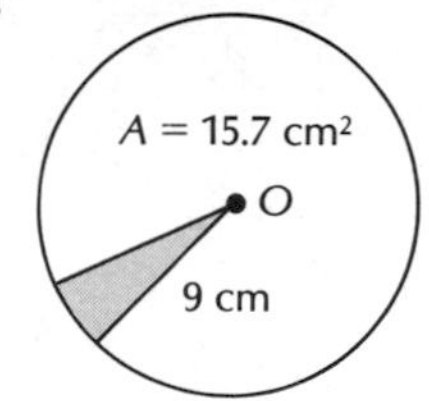

c.

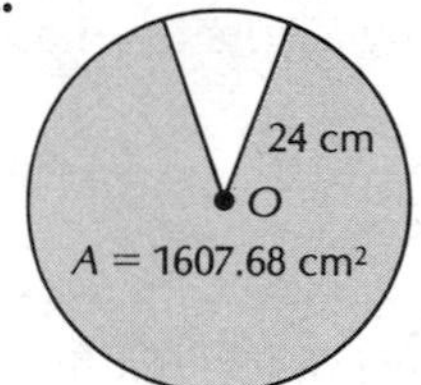

8. The neck band of Kevin's shirt is 38 cm long. What is the approximate diameter of Kevin's neck?

9. The outdoor track at Colonel By High School is constructed around a playing field with straight sides 100 m long and semicircular ends with a diameter of 80 m. The track has a constant width of 10 m. Find the perimeter of the outside of the track. What is the area of the track?

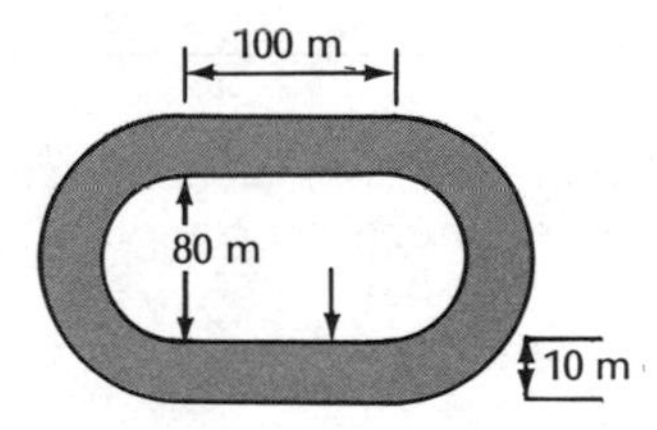

10. Semicircles are constructed such that their diameters lie on the sides of a right-angled triangle, as shown. Show that the area of the semicircle constructed on the hypotenuse of the triangle is equal to the sum of the areas of the semicircles constructed on the other two sides.

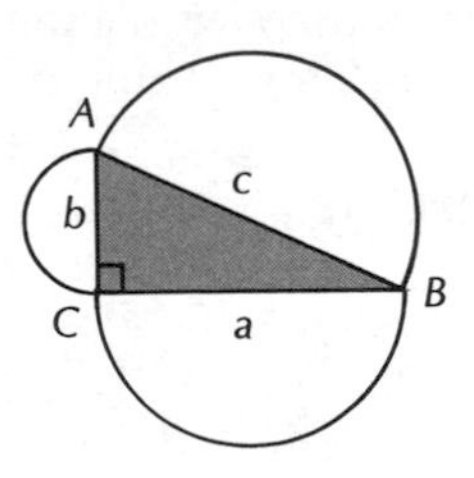

11. If s represents the length of an arc of a circle with radius r and A represents the area of the corresponding sector, prove that $A = \frac{1}{2}sr$.

12. a. Find the area of a sector having an arc length of 22.3 cm and radius 16 cm.

12-2 Chord Properties of a Circle

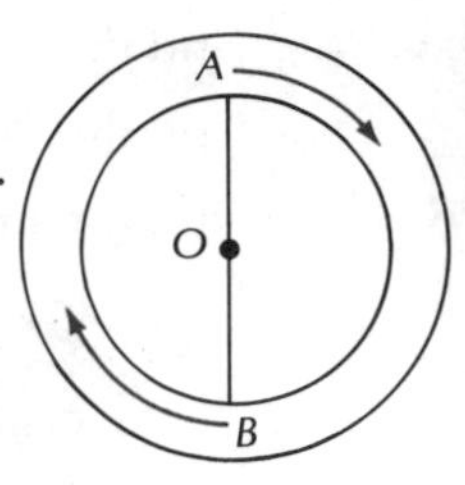

Suppose Adrienne and Blair are sprinting over a 1000 m course around a circular school track with circumference 1500 m. Each girl runs clockwise along the inside lane, starting at the endpoints of one diameter of the track. Where are their respective finishing points?

Each girl runs along an arc of length 1000 m. Each arc covers $\frac{1000}{1500}$ of the circumference of the track, and so each arc forms a sector angle measuring

$$\frac{1000}{1500} \times 360°, \text{ or } 240°.$$

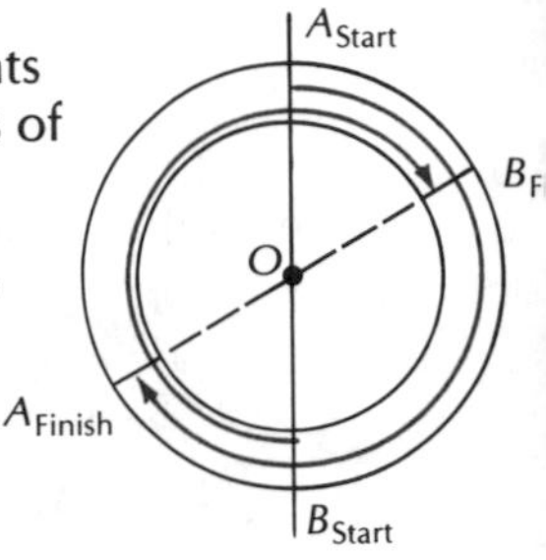

The finish points are found by rotating the starting points through 240°. Rotations are isometries, so the diameter $\overline{AB}$ formed by the starting points is mapped to another diameter by the 240° rotation. Thus, the endpoints of the image diameter, $\overline{A'B'}$, are the girls' finishing points.

Therefore, the girls' finishing points are 240° clockwise around the track, directly across from each other.

The examples that follow are simplified by using two circle properties. Every circle has **infinite rotational symmetry**. That is, every rotation of the circle about centre O produces an image that coincides with the circle.

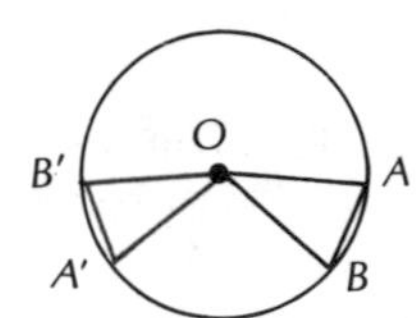

Every circle has **bilateral symmetry** for any diameter of the circle. That is, the circle reflects onto itself when a diameter is used as a line of reflection.

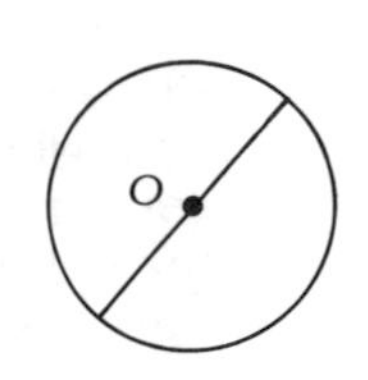

Thus, arcs map onto congruent arcs under a rotation about the centre of the circle. Every diameter of a circle is a line of symmetry of the circle.

EXAMPLE 1: *Given:* Circle with centre O, chord $\overline{AB}$, chord $\overline{CD}$, arc AB = arc CD

Prove: $AB = CD$

Proof: Rotate arc AB about centre O.
Arc AB = arc CD
Thus, arc $AB \to$ arc CD under a rotation about O.
Since $A \to C$, $B \to D$, and lengths are preserved under a rotation, $AB = CD$.

Thus, equal arcs subtend equal chords.

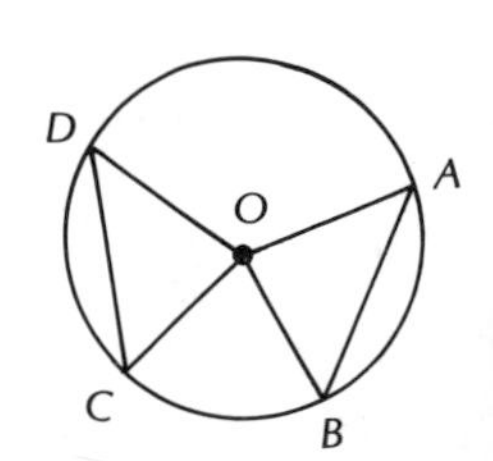

Use the diagram given in Example 1 to prove Example 2.

EXAMPLE 2: *Given*: The diagram for Example 1, $AB = CD$

Prove: $\angle AOB = \angle COD$

Proof: Rotate $\triangle AOB$ about centre O such that $\overline{AB} \rightarrow \overline{CD}$, and $\angle AOB \rightarrow \angle COD$.
Since the measures of angles are preserved under a rotation, $\angle AOB = \angle COD$.

Thus, equal arcs subtend equal sector angles.

EXAMPLE 3: *Given*: Circle with centre O, sector $\angle AOB$.
$AB = A'B'$

Prove: arc AB = arc $A'B'$.

Proof: Rotate $\angle AOB$ about O such that $A \rightarrow A'$ and $B \rightarrow B'$.

$\angle AOB = \angle A'OB'$	Definition of rotation
$OA = OA'$ and $OB = OB'$	Equal radii
$\triangle AOB \cong \triangle A'OB'$	SAS
$\therefore AB = A'B'$	Congruent $\triangle$'s
$\therefore$ arc AB = arc $A'B'$	Definition of rotation

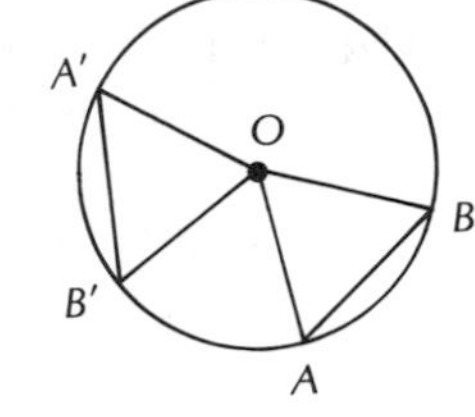

Therefore, equal chords subtend equal arcs.

EXAMPLE 4: *Given*: Circle with centre O and sector $\angle AOB$.
Rotate $\angle AOB$ about O such that $A \rightarrow A'$ and $B \rightarrow B'$. By definition of a rotation, $\angle AOB = \angle A'OB'$.

Prove: arc AB = arc $A'B'$

Proof:

$A \rightarrow A'$ and $B \rightarrow B'$	Given
arc $AB \rightarrow$ arc $A'B'$	Rotation
$\therefore$ arc AB = arc $A'B'$	Definition of a rotation

Thus, equal sector angles subtend equal arcs.

EXAMPLE 5: *Given*: Circle with centre O, chord $\overline{AB}$

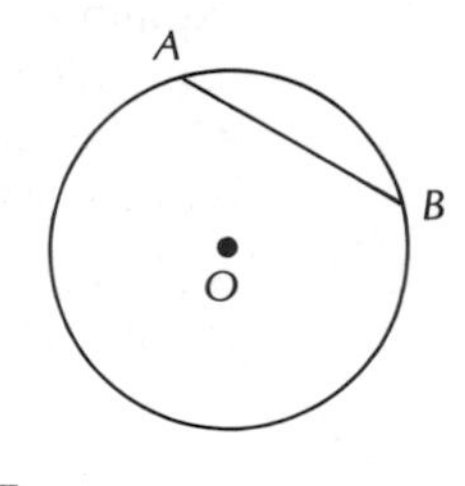

Prove: O lies on the perpendicular bisector of $\overline{AB}$.

Proof: Construct radii $\overline{OA}$ and $\overline{OB}$.
$OA = OB = r$
O is equidistant from endpoints A and B.
$\therefore O$ lies on the perpendicular bisector of $\overline{AB}$. PBT

Thus, the centre of a circle lies on the perpendicular bisector of a chord of the circle.

EXAMPLE 6: *Given*: Circle with centre O, chord $\overline{AB}$

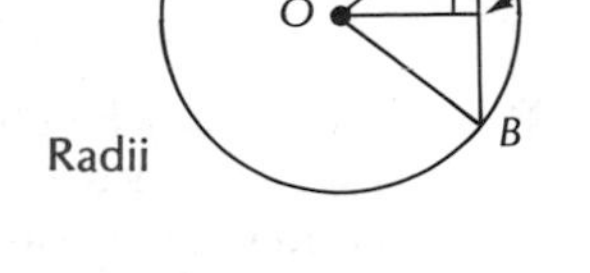

Prove: The perpendicular from O to $\overline{AB}$ bisects $\overline{AB}$.

Proof: Join O to endpoints A and B.
$OA = OB = r$ Radii
$\triangle AOB$ is isosceles.
Construct altitude $\overline{OC}$ to base $\overline{AB}$.
$\overline{OC}$ is the perpendicular bisector of $\overline{AB}$. PIT

Thus, the perpendicular from the centre of a circle to a chord bisects the chord.

The results of the preceding examples are known as the Chord Properties.

Chord Properties

1. Equal arcs subtend equal chords.
2. Equal arcs subtend equal sector angles.
3. Equal chords subtend equal arcs.
4. Equal sector angles subtend equal arcs.
5. The centre of a circle lies on the perpendicular bisector of a chord of the circle.
6. The perpendicular from the centre of a circle to a chord bisects the chord.

EXAMPLE 7: Find the length of a chord, $\overline{AB}$, of a circle with radius 13 cm, given that the chord is 5 cm from centre O.

Construct $\overline{OD} \perp \overline{AB}$.

$OD = 5$ cm	Given
$OA = 13$ cm	Given
$OA^2 = AD^2 + OD^2$	PT
$169 = AD^2 + 25$	
$AD^2 = 144$	
$\therefore AD = 12$	
But the perpendicular bisector from O to $\overline{AB}$ bisects $\overline{AB}$.	Chord Property
$\therefore AB = 2AD = 24$	

Therefore, the length of $\overline{AB}$ is 24 cm.

EXERCISE 12-2

A 1. Explain each given circle property and illustrate the explanation using a circular piece of paper.
   a. A circle has infinite rotational symmetry.
   b. Every diameter of a circle is a line of symmetry for the circle.

2. A chord is 24 cm from the centre of a circle with radius 25 cm. What is the length of the chord?

3. Find the length of each indicated segment.

a.

b.

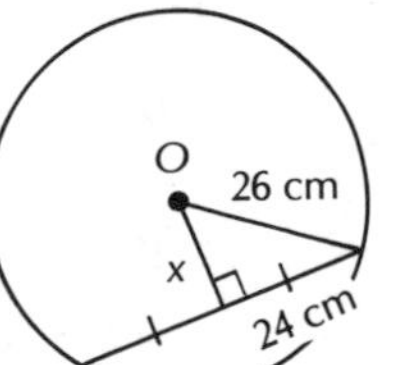

c.

d.

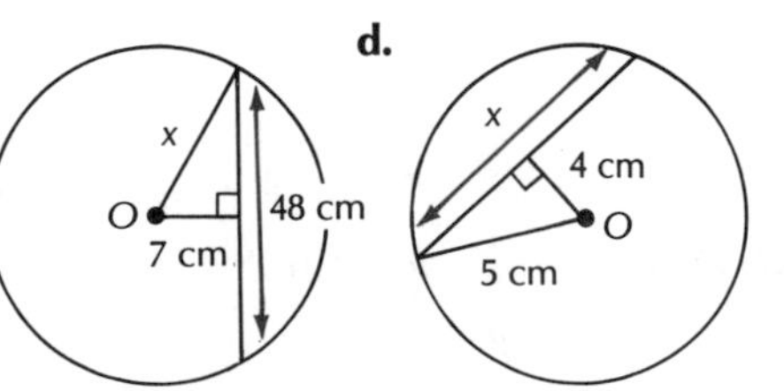

B 4. Two parallel chords, $\overline{AB}$ and $\overline{CD}$, on opposite sides of the centre of a circle, are 24 cm and 10 cm long, respectively. If the diameter of the circle is 26 cm, what is the distance between the two chords?

5. If the two chords given in exercise 4 lie on the same side of the centre, what is the distance between the two chords?

6. $\overline{XY}$ and $\overline{PQ}$ are parallel chords of a circle with centre O. Diameter $\overline{AD}$ intersects $\overline{XY}$ at B and intersects $\overline{PQ}$ at C. Prove that if $XY = PQ$, then $AB = DC$.

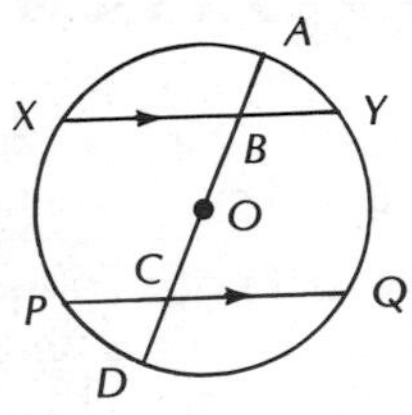

7. Prove that equal chords are the same distance from the centre of a circle.

8. Two concentric circles sharing centre O, are shown. $\overline{AB}$, a chord of the larger circle, is 48 cm long and is tangent to the smaller circle such that $\overline{OC} \perp \overline{AB}$. Find the radius of the larger circle if the radius of the smaller circle is 7 cm.

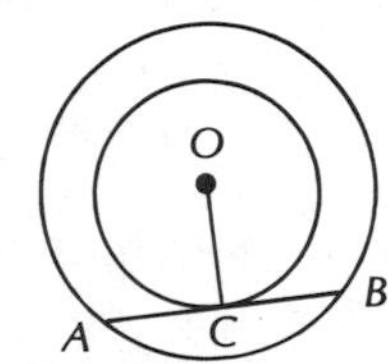

9. A, B, and C are three non-collinear points. Describe a method for constructing a circle that contains A, B, and C. Justify your construction.

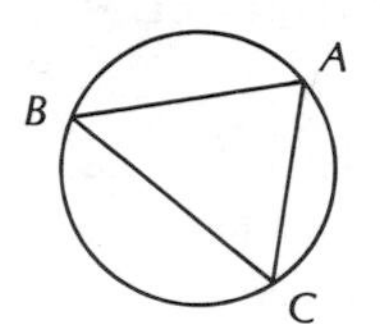

10. $\overline{PQ}$ and $\overline{XY}$ are chords in two concentric circles with centre O. If P, X, Y, and Q are collinear, prove that $PX = QY$.

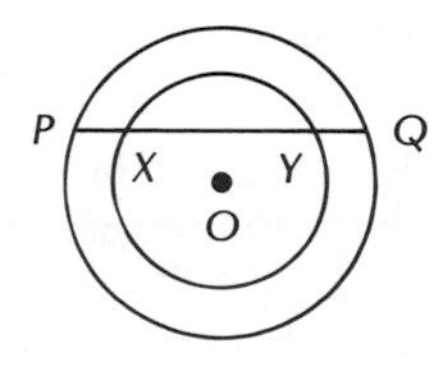

11. $\overline{XY}$ and $\overline{YZ}$ are two equal chords in a circle. W is a point on the circle such that $\overline{YW}$ bisects $\angle XYZ$. Prove that the centre of the circle lies on $\overline{YW}$.

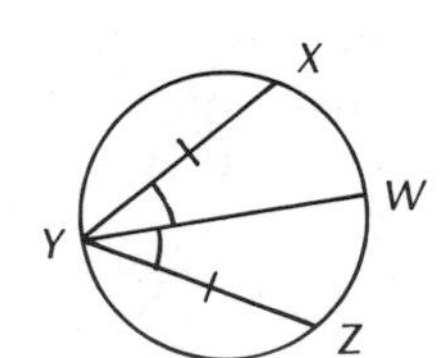

12. Three chords, $\overline{PQ}$, $\overline{QR}$ and $\overline{PR}$, are equidistant from the centre of a circle. What type of triangle is $\triangle PQR$? Prove your conclusion.

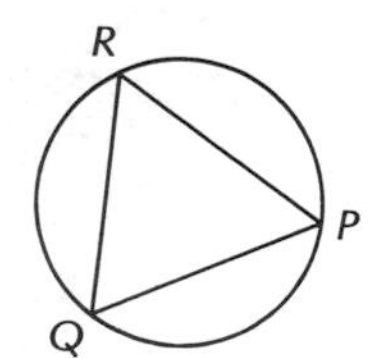

13. In the diagram at the right, $\overline{CO}$ bisects $\angle ACE$. Prove that $AC = EC$.

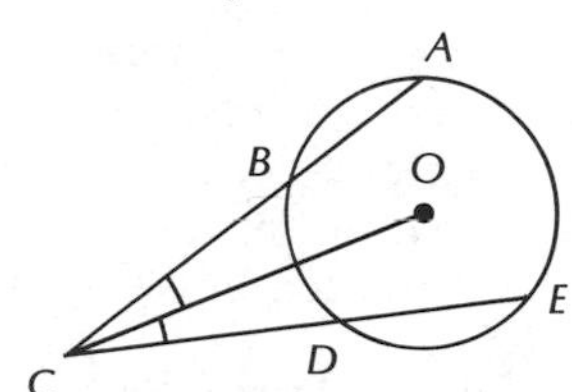

Application

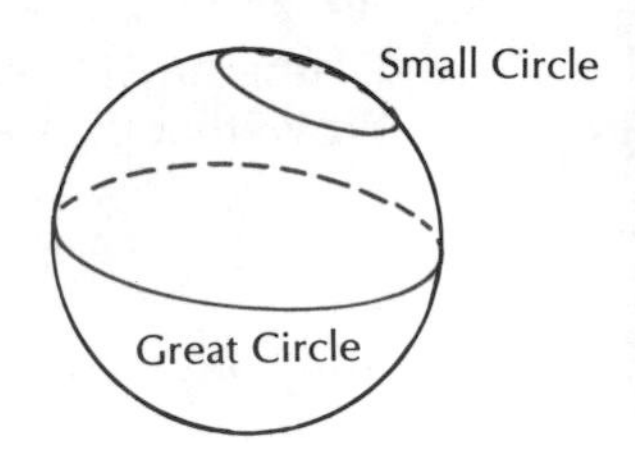

A **sphere** is a surface consisting of the set of all points in three dimensional space that are equidistant from a fixed point.

A **great circle** of a sphere is the largest circle that can be drawn on the surface of a sphere. A great circle is formed by cutting a sphere in half such that its centre is the centre of the sphere. A **small circle** is any circle drawn on a sphere's surface that is not a great circle. Thus, it does not pass through the sphere's centre.

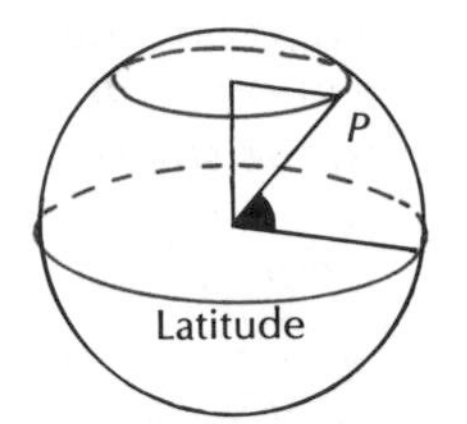

Although Earth is not a perfect sphere, it is sufficient to treat Earth as a sphere for most calculations. Earth rotates around one diameter with endpoints called the North Pole and the South Pole. The **equator** is a great circle located midway between the North and South Poles. Small circles parallel to the equator are called **parallels of latitude.**

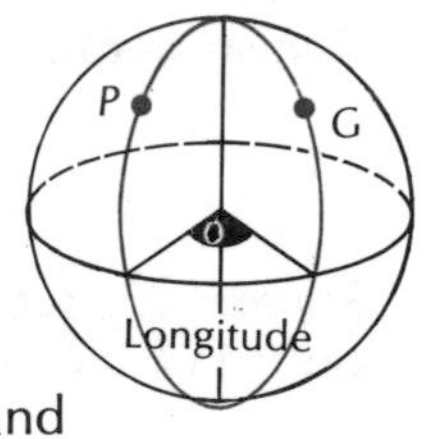

Great circles that pass through the North and South Poles are called **meridians.** A **meridian of longitude** is a semicircle, or one-half of a meridian, with endpoints at the North and the South Poles. The zero meridian, or 0° longitude, is called the **prime meridian,** and passes through the Royal Observatory at Greenwich, England.

Any point on Earth can be named by using two coordinates, latitude and longitude. The latitude of a point *P*, is the measure of the angle between the radius through *P* and the equatorial plane. The longitude of *P* is the measure of the angle between intersecting planes formed by the great circle of the prime meridian through Greenwich and the great circle of the meridian that passes through *P*.

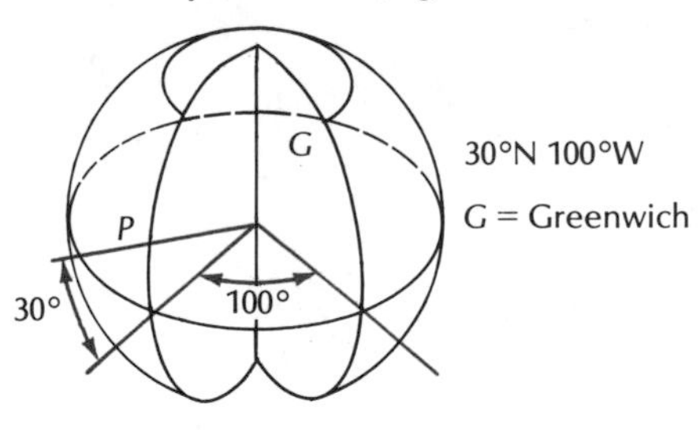

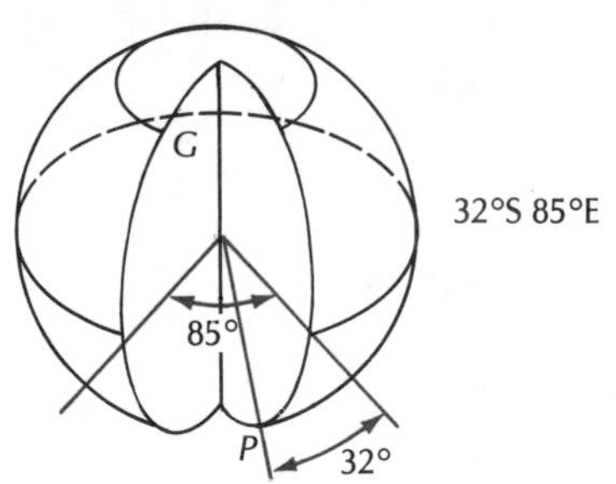

The distance between two points on Earth is measured along the shorter geodesic line, or the shorter arc between two points on the great circle joining the two points. This distance can be determined by the angle subtended at the centre of the sphere by the shorter arc of the great circle joining the two points. Distances are measured in nautical miles. A **nautical mile** is the distance between any two points, *P* and *Q*, on Earth's surface, where $\angle POQ = \left(\frac{1}{60}\right)^{\circ}$, or 1′(one minute). One nautical mile is equal to 1852 m.

EXAMPLE: P and Q are points on the equator with longitudes 74°E and 28°W, respectively.

a. Find the measure of the angle subtended at the centre of Earth by P and Q.

b. Calculate the great circle distance between P and Q on Earth's surface, to the nearest nautical mile.

a. The two points have the same latitude since they are on the equator. Therefore, it is necessary to consider only the longitude. Because P and Q are on opposite sides of Greenwich, the angle subtended at the centre of Earth is the sum of the two longitudes, or 102°.

b. An angle of $\left(\frac{1}{60}\right)^\circ$ at the centre of Earth subtends an arc of 1 nautical mile. Find the distance subtended by an angle of 102° at the centre of Earth.

$1^\circ \rightarrow 60$ nautical miles

$\therefore 102^\circ \rightarrow 102 \times 60$ nautical miles

So, P and Q are 6120 nautical miles apart.

EXERCISE

1. The geographical coordinates of Winnipeg are approximately (50°N, 96°W). Use a globe to find the latitude and longitude of Ottawa, Vancouver, Halifax, Paris, and Tokyo.

2. Calculate the great circle distances between two points on the surface of Earth if the points subtend angles with the given measurements at Earth's centre.

   a. 30° b. 45° c. 95° d. 120° e. 135°

3. Determine the geographical coordinates of each point shown below.

a.

b.

c.

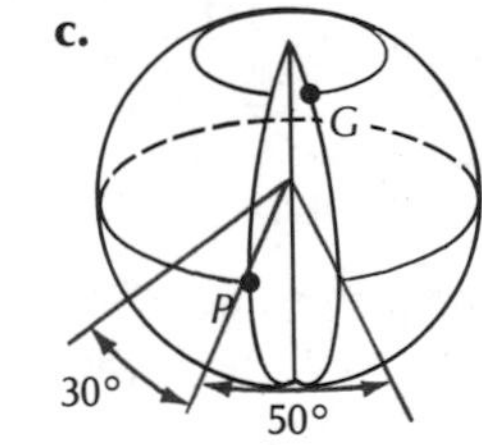

d.

e.

f.

4. Find the distance between the following places, expressed to the nearest nautical mile.

   a. A(54°N, 0°E), B(11°N, 0°E)

   b. C(45°N, 12°E), D(22°S, 12°E)

12-3 Angle Properties of a Circle

An angle whose vertex is on the circumference of a circle and whose rays pass through the circle is an **inscribed angle**. An angle whose vertex is the centre of a circle and whose rays are radii of the circle is a **sector angle** or **central angle**. An **inscribed** or **cyclic polygon** is a polygon that has all of its vertices on the circumference of a circle.

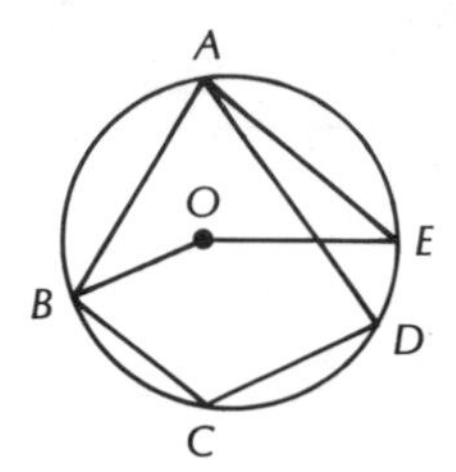

O is the centre.

$\angle ABC$, $\angle BCD$, $\angle CDA$, $\angle DAB$, $\angle EAB$ are inscribed angles.

$\angle BOE$ is a sector angle.

$\angle BAE$ and $\angle BOE$ are both subtended by arc *BE*.

ABCD is an inscribed quadrilateral.

In this section, the relationship between inscribed angles and sector angles subtended by the same arc is explored.

> **Inscribed Angle Theorem (IAT)**
> The measure of an angle inscribed in a circle is one-half the measure of the sector angle subtended by the same arc.

Case a

$\overline{BC}$ is a diameter.

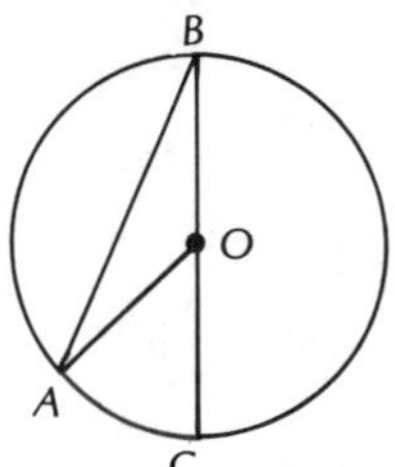

Case b

A, *C* lie on opposite sides of diameter *BD*.

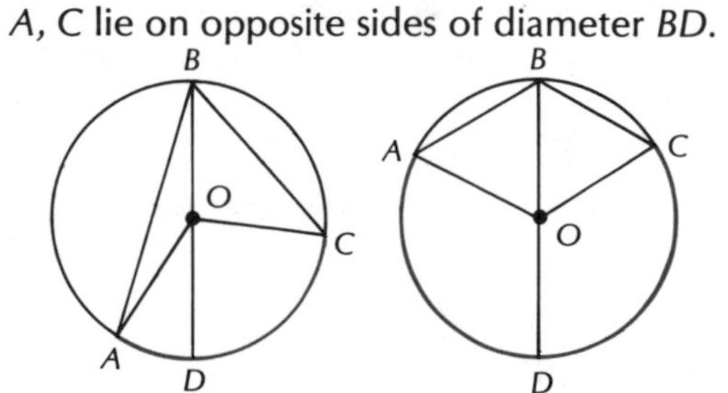

Case c

Arc *AC* lies on one side of $\overline{BD}$.

The diagrams above show the four possible cases in which a sector angle and an inscribed angle are subtended by the same arc. The proof of IAT is given below.

Given: Circle with centre *O*, inscribed $\angle ABC$ and central $\angle AOC$ both subtend arc *AC*.

Prove: $\angle ABC = \frac{1}{2}\angle AOC$, or $\angle AOC = 2\angle ABC$

Proof: For case **a**,

$AO = BO$	Equal radii
$\angle OBA = \angle OAB$	ITT
$\angle AOC = \angle OBA + \angle OAB$	EAT
$\angle AOC = \angle OBA + \angle OBA = 2\angle OBA$	Substitution
But $\angle OBA$ is the same as $\angle ABC$.	
$\therefore \angle AOC = 2\angle ABC$	Substitution

For case **b**, draw diameter $\overline{BD}$.

$\angle AOD = 2\angle ABD$	Proved in case **a**
$\angle DOC = 2\angle DBC$	Proved in case **a**
$\angle AOD + \angle DOC = 2\angle ABD + 2\angle DBC$	Addition
$\therefore \angle AOC = 2\angle ABC$	Substitution

For case **c**, draw diameter $\overline{BD}$.

$\angle AOD = 2\angle ABD$	Proved in case **a**
$\angle COD = 2\angle CBD$	Proved in case **a**
$\angle AOD - \angle COD = 2\angle ABD - 2\angle CBD$	Subtraction
$\therefore \angle AOC = 2\angle ABC$	Substitution

Corollaries to IAT

1. Inscribed angles subtended by the same arc are equal.
2. Angles inscribed in a semicircle are right angles.
3. Opposite angles of a cyclic quadrilateral are supplementary.
4. An exterior angle of a cyclic quadrilateral is equal to the interior angle at the opposite vertex.

EXAMPLE 1: Find the value of each indicated unknown angle.

a.

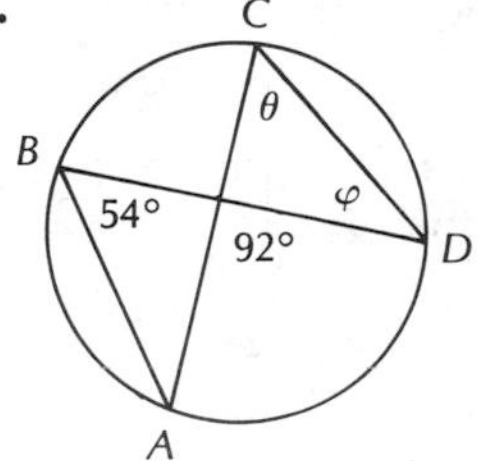

b.

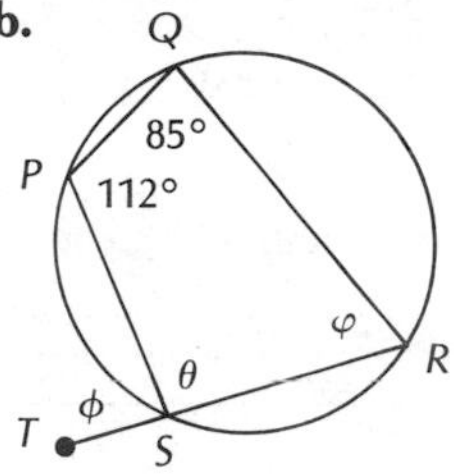

c.

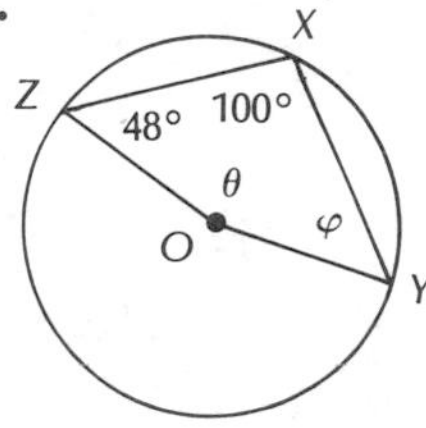

a. $\theta = 54°$ — IAT–inscribed angles subtended by arc AD

$\theta + \varphi = 92°$ — EAT

$\varphi = 38°$ — Subtraction

b. $\theta = 180 - 85 = 95°$ — IAT–opposite angles of an inscribed quadrilateral are supplementary.

$\varphi = 180 - 112 = 68°$ — IAT–opposite angles of a cyclic quadrilateral are supplementary

$\phi = 85°$ — IAT–exterior angle of an inscribed quadrilateral

c. $\angle ZXY = 100°$ — Given

reflex $\angle ZOY = 200°$ — IAT–sector angle is double the inscribed angle subtended by major arc ZY.

$\theta = 360 - 200 = 160°$ — Complete revolution is 360°

$\varphi = 360 - (48 + 100 + 160) = 52°$ — Angle sum of a quadrilateral

EXAMPLE 2: Two circles with unequal radii intersect at points P and Q. Two points, R on one circle and S on the other circle, are selected such that R, P, and S are collinear. Prove that $\angle RQS$ remains constant, independent of the choice of point R.

Given: Two distinct circles with unequal radii, intersecting at P and Q. Also, R, P, and S are collinear, as shown.

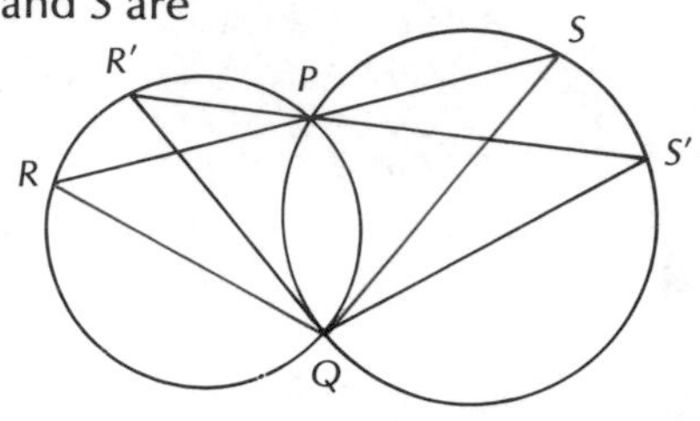

Prove: $\angle RQS$ remains constant.

Proof: Let R' and S' be points on the two circles such that R', P, and S' are collinear points.

$\angle PRQ = \angle PR'Q$	IAT–inscribed angles subtended by arc PQ
$\angle PSQ = \angle PS'Q$	IAT–inscribed angles subtended by arc PQ
But $\angle PRQ + \angle RQS + \angle PSQ = 180°$	AST
and $\angle PR'Q + \angle R'QS' + \angle PS'Q = 180°$	AST
$\therefore \angle RQS = \angle R'QS'$	Subtraction

Therefore, $\angle RQS$ remains constant, independent of the location of point R on the circumference of one circle.

Summary

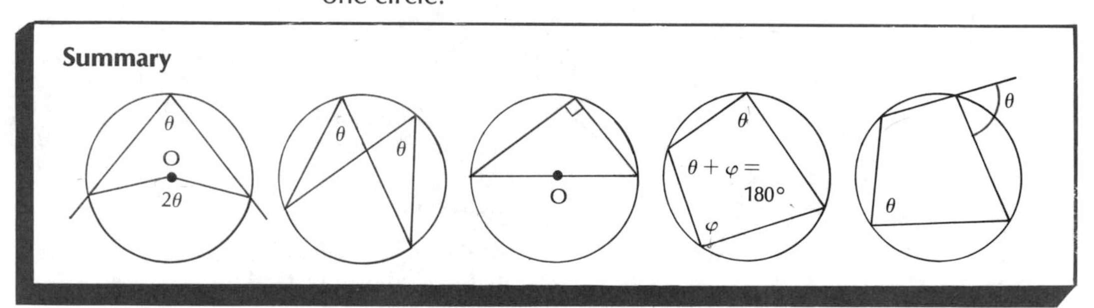

EXERCISE 12-3

A 1. Find the measure of each unknown angle. O is the centre of the circle.

a.

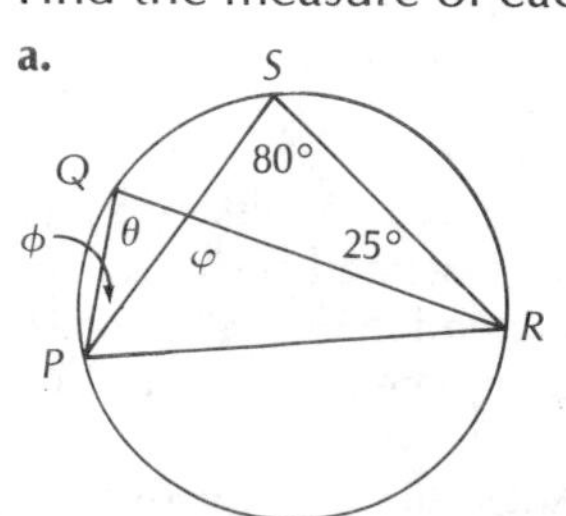

b.

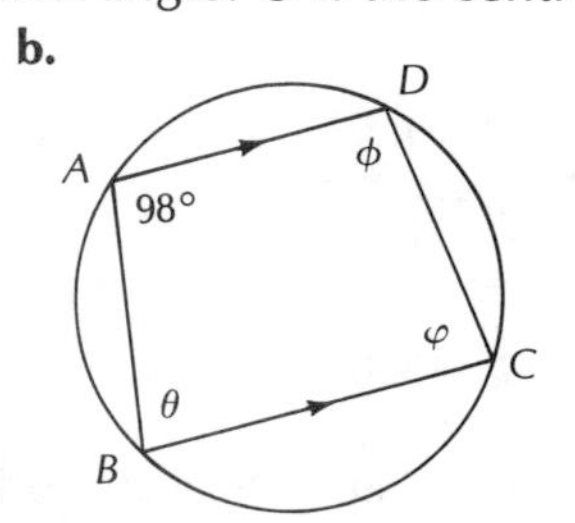

c.

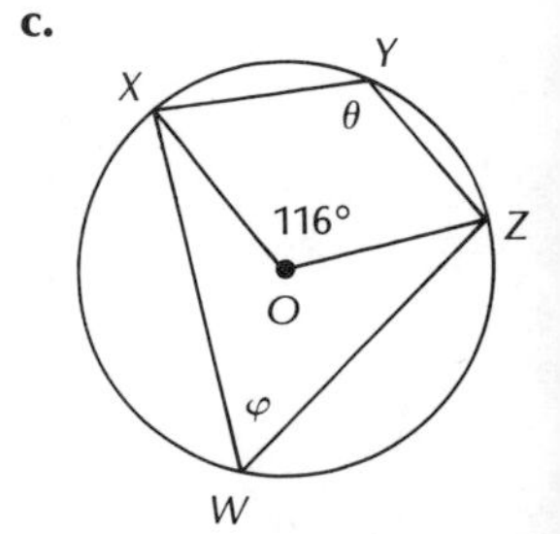

d.

F G E H φ θ 120° O

e.

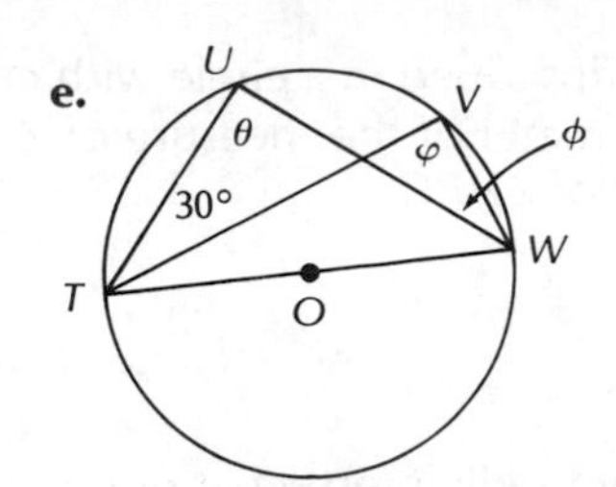

f.

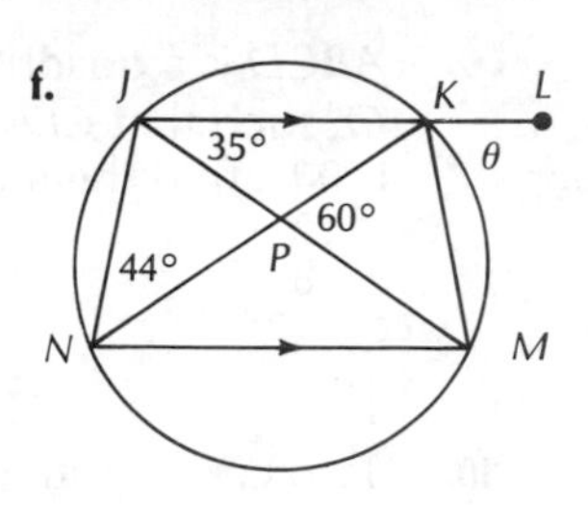

2. Prove that equal chords of a circle subtend equal inscribed angles.

3. Prove that equal inscribed angles of a circle subtend equal chords.

B 4. $\triangle ABC$ is inscribed in a circle with centre O. E is a point in $\triangle ABC$ such that $\overline{EA}$ bisects $\angle CAB$ and $\overline{EB}$ bisects $\angle CBA$. If $\overline{AB}$ is a diameter, find the measure of $\angle AEB$.

5. A, B, C, and D are four points on a circle occuring in the given order. If $\angle CAD = 32°$, $\angle ABD = 36°$, and $\angle ADB = 54°$, find the measure of each angle of quadrilateral $ABCD$.

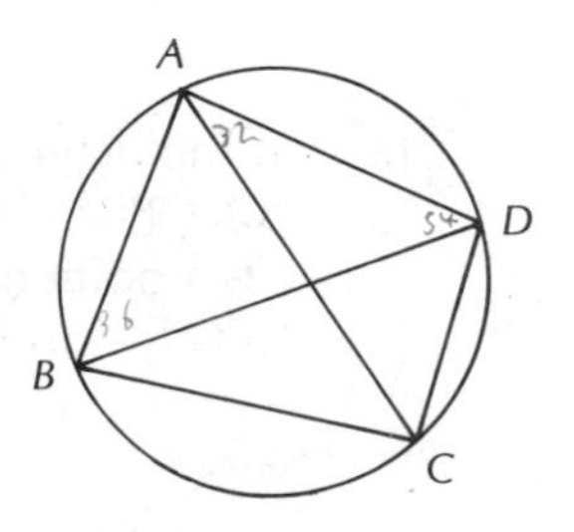

6. $PQRS$ is a trapezoid inscribed in a circle with $\overline{PQ} \parallel \overline{RS}$. Diagonals $\overline{PR}$ and $\overline{QS}$ intersect at T. Prove that $\triangle PQT$ and $\triangle RTS$ are isosceles.

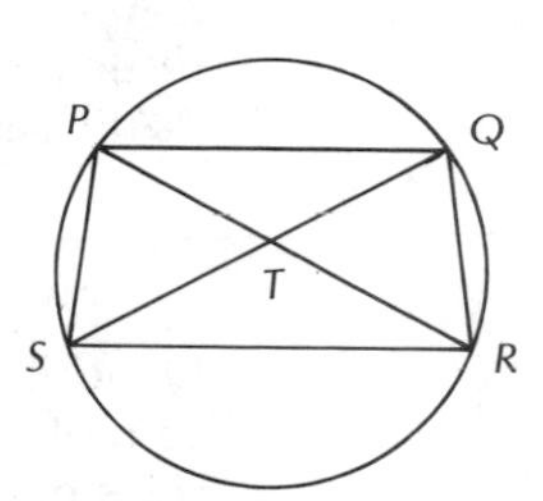

7. $ABCD$ is a cyclic quadrilateral in which $AB = CD$. Prove that $AC = BD$.

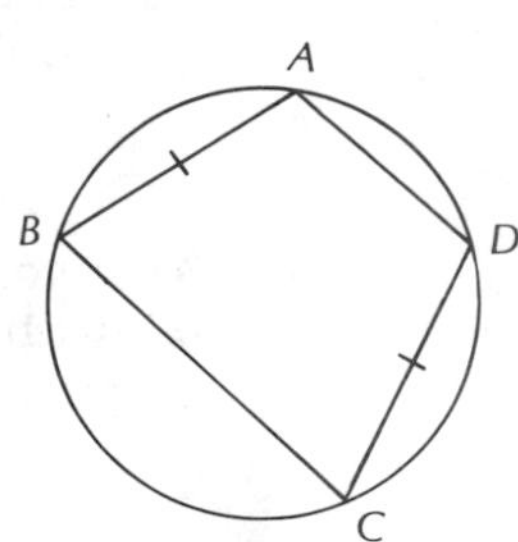

8. $\triangle PQR$ is an equilateral triangle inscribed in a circle. S and T lie on minor arc PQ and minor arc PR, respectively, such that $QS = RT$. Prove that $\triangle SQP \cong \triangle TRP$.

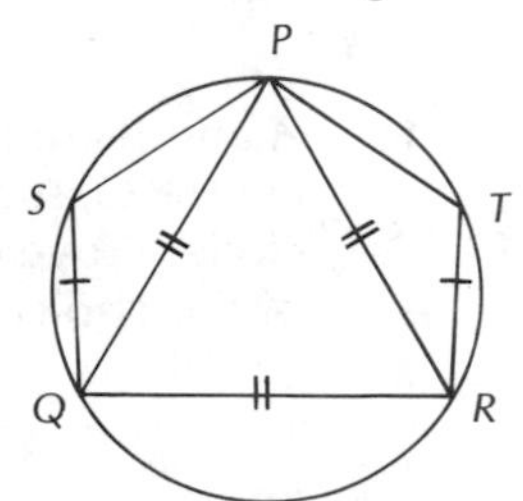

9. *ABCD* is a quadrilateral inscribed in a circle with centre *O*, such that $\overline{CD}$ is a diameter. If the measure of $\angle AOD$ is 80°, find the measure of $\angle ABC$.

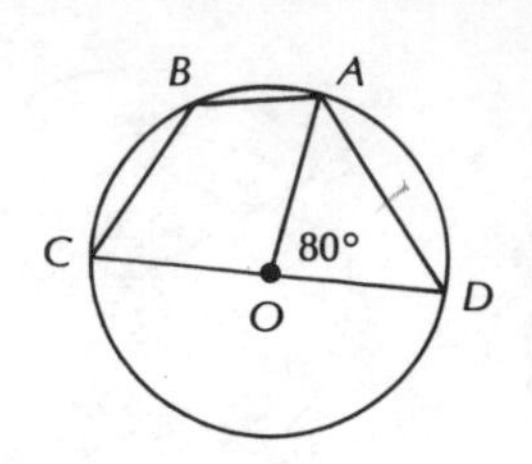

10. Two circles with different radii intersect at points *X* and *Y*. Points *A* and *B* are on one circle, and points *C* and *D* are on the other circle such that $\overline{AXD} \parallel \overline{BYC}$. Prove that $\overline{AB} \parallel \overline{DC}$.

11. *PQRS* is an inscribed quadrilateral. $\overline{QP}$ and $\overline{RS}$ are extended to intersect at a point *T* outside the circle. Prove that the angles of $\triangle TQS$ are equal to the corresponding angles of $\triangle TRP$.

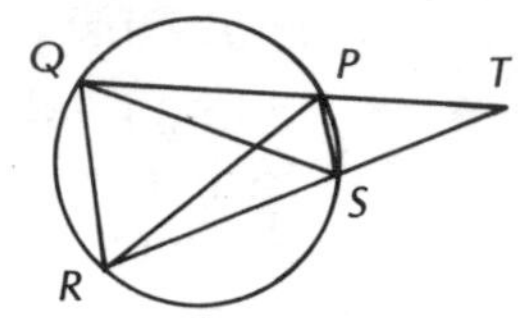

12. In the diagram at the right, $\triangle PQR$ is isosceles with $PQ = PR$. *S* is a point on the circle between *P* and *R*. *T* is a point on $\overline{QS}$ such that $QT = SR$. Prove that $\triangle PQT \cong \triangle PRS$.

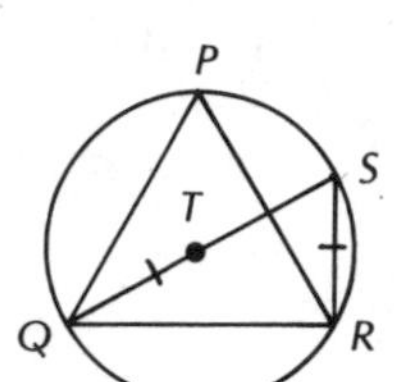

C **13.** **a.** $\triangle ABC$ is inscribed in a circle. Find the sum of the three inscribed angles subtended by the sides of $\triangle ABC$, as shown.

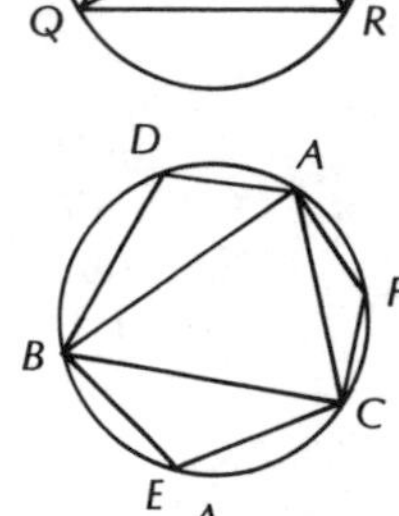

b. Quadrilateral *ABCD* is inscribed in a circle. Find the sum of the four inscribed angles subtended by the sides of quadrilateral *ABCD*, as shown.

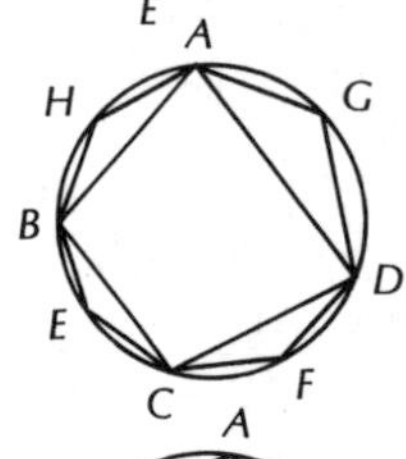

c. An *n*-gon is inscribed in a circle. Find the sum of the *n* inscribed angles, as shown, subtended by the sides of the *n*-gon.

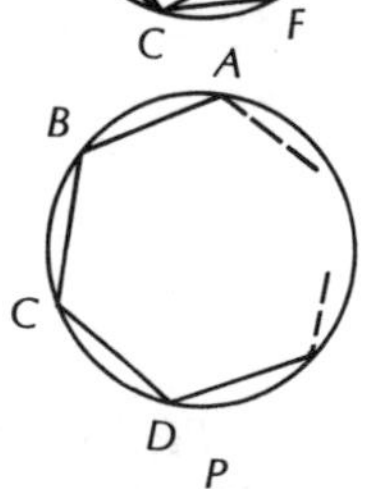

14. *A* and *B* are to points on a diameter of a circle with centre *O*, such that $OA = OB$. *P* is any point on the circle. Prove that $PA^2 + PB^2$ is a constant independent of the choice of *P*. (*Hint:* Construct $\overline{PX} \perp \overline{AB}$.)

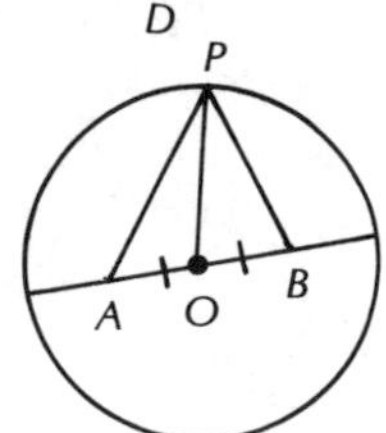

Review

1. Given the circle at right with centre O, identify each of the following.
   a. the radii
   b. the diameters
   c. the sector angles
   d. the inscribed angles
   e. the cyclic quadrilaterals
   f. the sectors subtended by minor arcs
   g. the boundaries of a semicircle
   h. the sectors subtended by major arcs

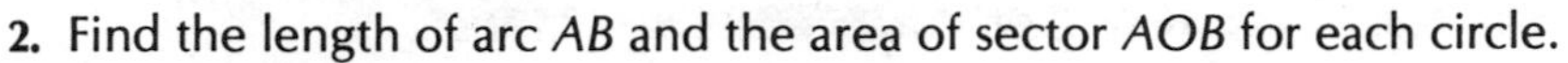

2. Find the length of arc AB and the area of sector AOB for each circle.

a. 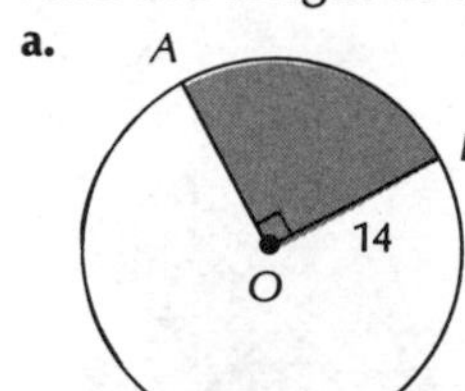

b. 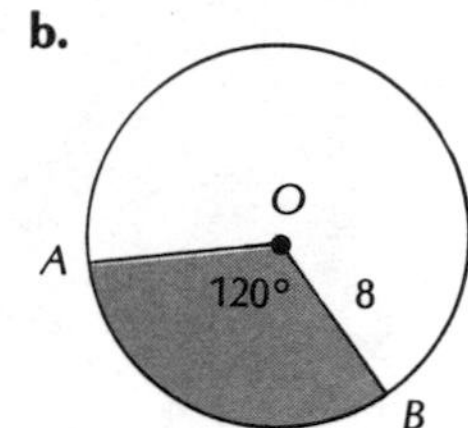

c. 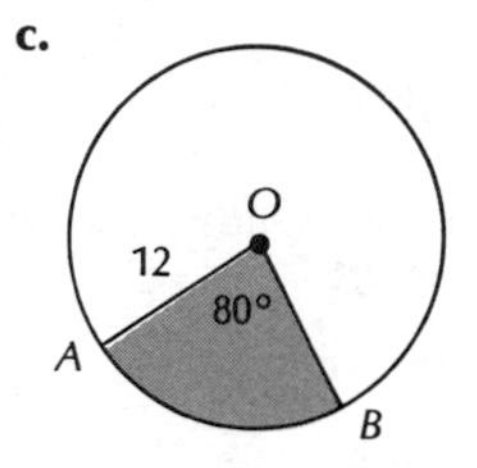

d. 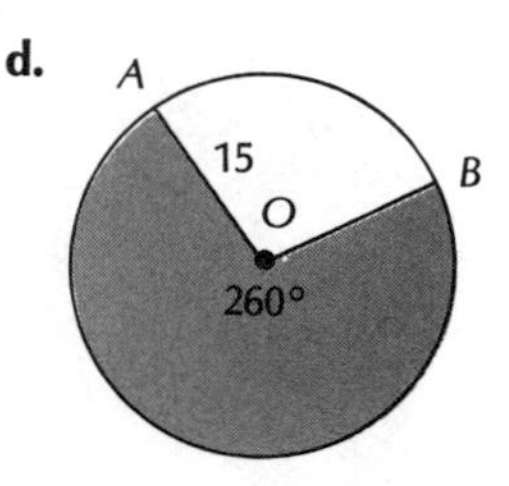

3. For each circle, find the indicated length.

a. 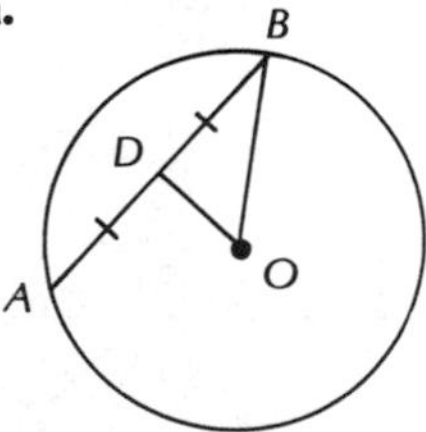

$AB = 16$, $DO = 6$
Find OB.

b. 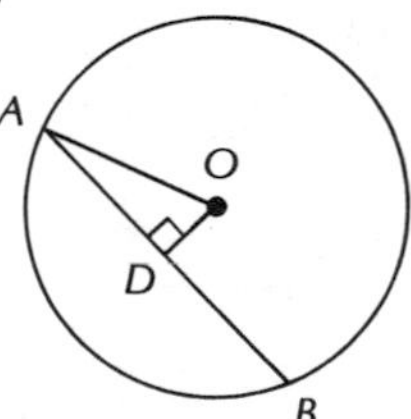

$AO = 13$, $DO = 5$
Find AB.

c. 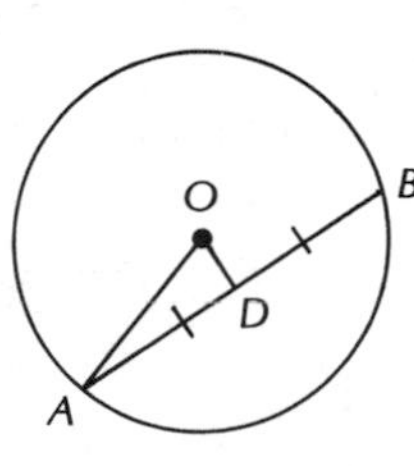

$OA = 25$, $AB = 48$
Find DO.

d. 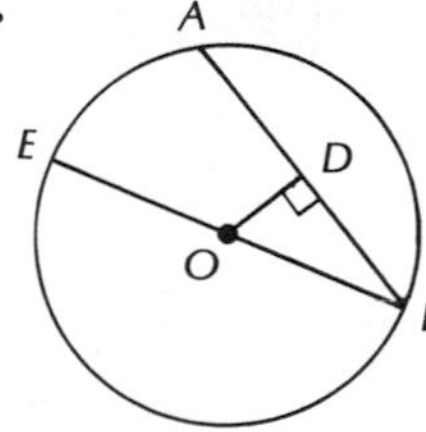

$EB = 10$, $DO = 4$
Find AB.

4. Two parallel chords on opposite sides of the centre of a circle are 32 cm and 24 cm long, respectively. If the radius of the circle is 20 cm, how far apart are the chords?

5. If the chords given in exercise 4 lie on the same side of the centre of the circle, how far apart are they?

6. Find the measure of each unknown angle.

a. 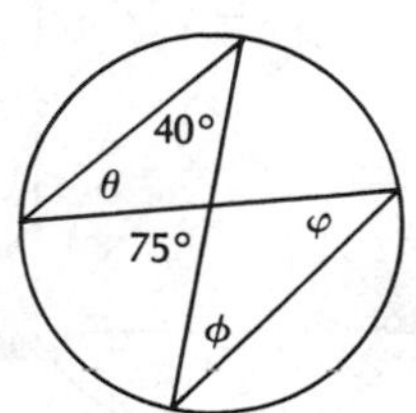

b. 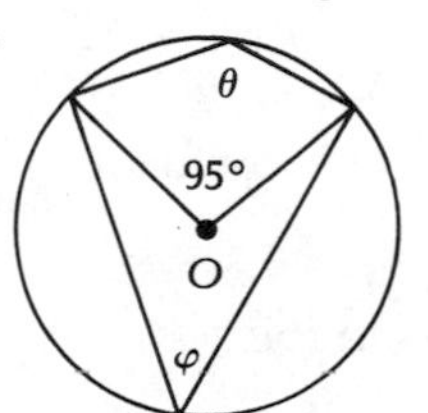

c. 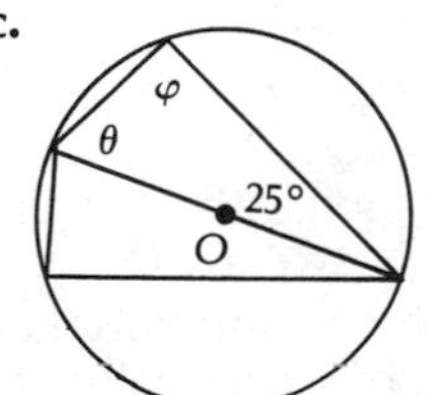

d. 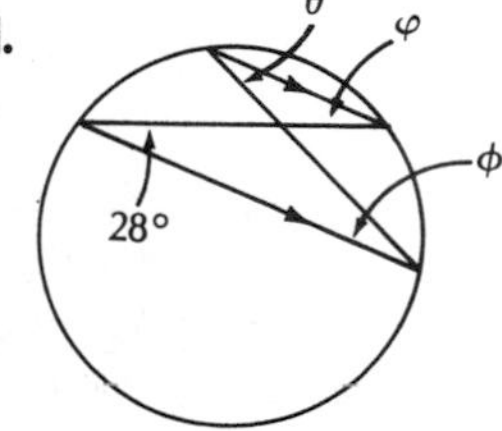

7. $XYZW$ is a cyclic quadrilateral. Diagonals $\overline{XZ}$ and $\overline{WY}$ intersect at point T. Prove that $\triangle XTW \sim \triangle YTZ$ and that $(XT)(TZ) = (WT)(TY)$.

12-4 Concyclic Points Theorem (CPT)

The converse of the Inscribed Angle Theorem is established in this lesson. Notice that a set of points is **concyclic** if all the points lie on one circle.

> **Concyclic Points Theorem (CPT)**
> If a line segment subtends two equal angles at points on the same side of the segment, then the segment is a chord of a circle such that the vertices of the angles and the endpoints of the chord are concyclic points.

The proof of this theorem is given below.

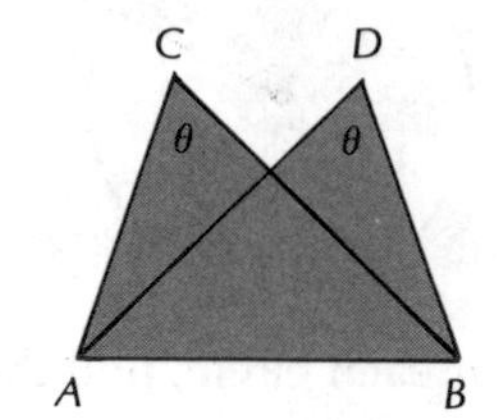

Given: C and D are points on the same side of $\overline{AB}$ such that $\angle ACB = \angle ADB$.

Prove: A, B, C, and D are concyclic points.

Proof: (Indirect) Construct a circle through A, B, and C and suppose it does not pass through D. Then either D is in the interior or the exterior of the circle.

Case 1: D is in the interior of the circle.
Extend $\overline{AD}$ to intersect the circle at E.

$\angle ADB > \angle AEB$	EAT
$\angle ADB = \angle ACB$	Given
$\therefore \angle ACB > \angle AEB$	Substitution

But this contradicts the fact that
$\angle ACB = \angle AEB$ by IAT.
Therefore, the assumption that D is in the interior of the circle is false.

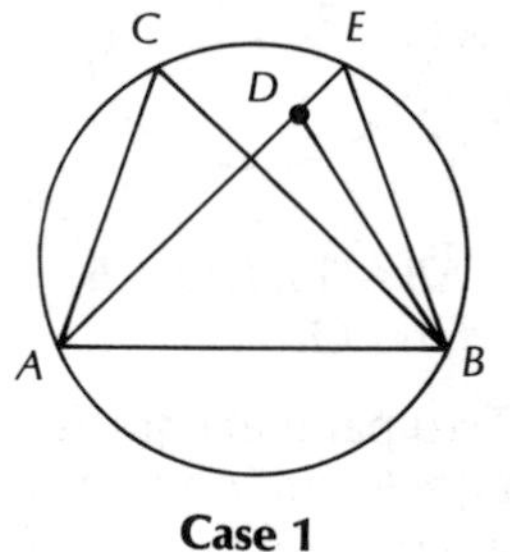

Case 1

Case 2: D is in the exterior of the circle. If D is in the exterior of the circle, then $\overline{AD}$ must intersect the circle at a point, say E.

$\angle AEB > \angle ADB$	EAT
$\angle ACB = \angle ADB$	Given
$\therefore \angle AEB > \angle ACB$	Substitution

But this contradicts the fact that
$\angle AEB = \angle ACB$ by IAT.
Therefore, the assumption that D is in the exterior of the circle is false.

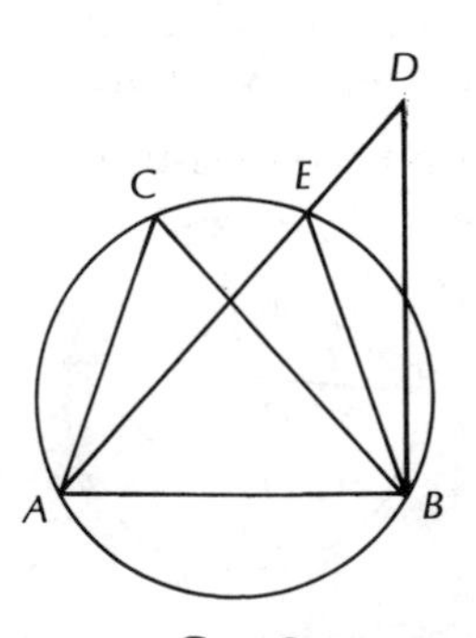

Case 2

Therefore, D is on the circumference of the circle containing points A, B, and C.

Corollaries to CPT

1. If the hypotenuse of a right-angled triangle is the diameter of a circle, then the vertex of the right-angled triangle is on the circle.
2. If a quadrilateral has one pair of opposite angles that are supplementary, then the quadrilateral is a cyclic quadrilateral.
3. If an exterior angle of a quadrilateral is equal to the interior angle at the opposite vertex, then the quadrilateral is a cyclic quadrilateral.

EXAMPLE 1: Prove Corollary 2 of the Concyclic Points Theorem.

Given: Quadrilateral $ABCD$, such that A, B, and D are concyclic points on a circle with centre O and $\angle BAD + \angle BCD = 180°$

Prove: C is on the circle.

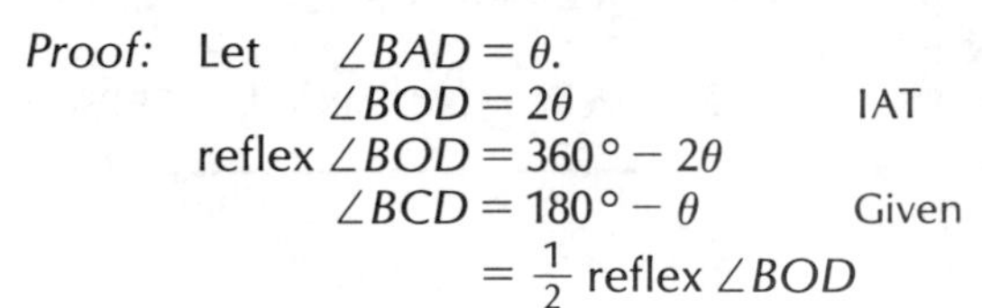

Proof: Let $\angle BAD = \theta$.
$\angle BOD = 2\theta$ IAT
reflex $\angle BOD = 360° - 2\theta$
$\angle BCD = 180° - \theta$ Given
$= \frac{1}{2}$ reflex $\angle BOD$

By IAT, C is on the circumference of the circle.

The proofs of the other corollaries are left to the exercises.

EXAMPLE 2: Prove that if altitudes $\overline{XA}$ and $\overline{ZB}$ of $\triangle XYZ$ are constructed such that they intersect at point W, then B, Y, A, and W are concyclic points.

Given: $\triangle XYZ$ with altitudes $\overline{XA}$ and $\overline{ZB}$ that intersect at W

Prove: B, Y, A, and W are concyclic points.

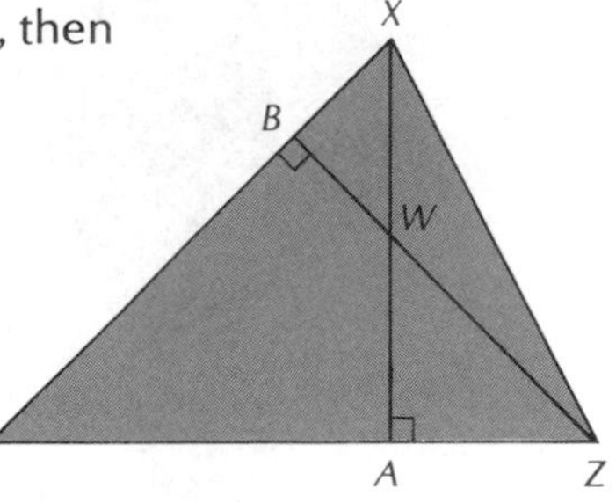

Proof: In quadrilateral $BYAW$,
$\angle WBY = \angle WAY = 90°$. Definition of altitudes
Thus, one pair of opposite angles is supplementary.
$BYAW$ is a cyclic quadrilateral. CPT–Corollary 2
Therefore, B, Y, A, and W are concyclic points.

Notice that B, X, Z, and A are concyclic points since $\overline{XZ}$ subtends $\angle ZBX$ and $\angle ZAX$ such that $\angle ZBX = \angle ZAX$.

EXAMPLE 3: Prove that an isosceles trapezoid having only one pair of parallel sides is a cyclic quadrilateral.

Given: Trapezoid $ABCD$ with $\overline{AD} \parallel \overline{BC}$, $\overline{AB}$ is not parallel to $\overline{DC}$, and $AB = DC$.

Prove: $ABCD$ is an inscribed quadrilateral.

Proof: Construct $\overline{DE} \parallel \overline{AB}$ such that E is on $\overline{BC}$.

$ABED$ is a parallelogram.	Definition
$AB = DE$	Property of a parallelogram
$AB = DC$	Given
$DE = DC$	Substitution
$\angle DEC = \angle DCE$	ITT
$\angle DEB = \angle BAD$	Property of a parallelogram
$\angle DEB + \angle DEC = 180°$	$\angle BEC$ is a straight angle.
$\angle BAD + \angle DCE = 180°$	Substitution

Thus, opposite angles of quadrilateral $ABCD$ are supplementary.
Therefore, $ABCD$ is a cyclic quadrilateral. CPT

EXERCISE 12-4

A **1.** From the diagram shown at the right, identify three sets of four concyclic points.

2. **a.**

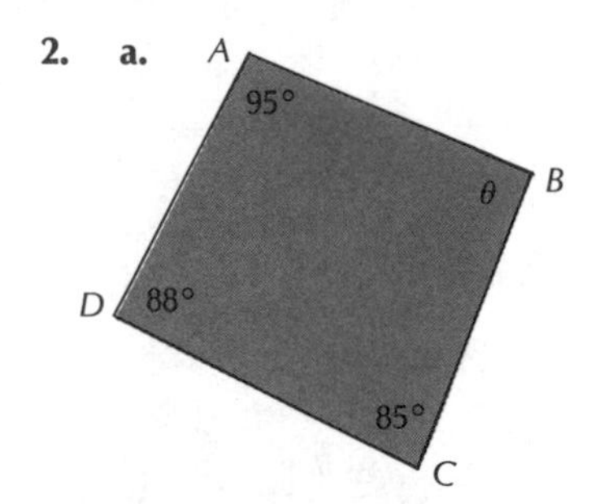

Prove that $ABCD$ is a cyclic quadrilateral, and find the value of x.

b. Prove that $PSTR$ and $SVTQ$ are cyclic quadrilaterals.

c.

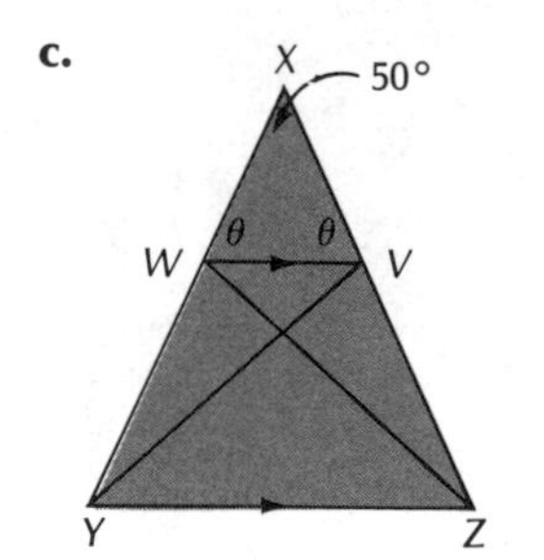

Prove that W, V, Z, and Y are concyclic points and find the value of x.

3. Prove that the vertices of a rectangle are concyclic.

4. Prove the following corollaries of the Concyclic Points Theorem.

a. If the hypotenuse of a right-angled triangle is the diameter of a circle, then the vertex of the right-angled triangle is on the circle.

b. If an exterior angle of a quadrilateral is equal to the interior angle at the opposite vertex, then the quadrilateral is a cyclic quadrilateral.

5. Prove that the midpoint of the hypotenuse of a right-angled triangle is equidistant from its vertices.

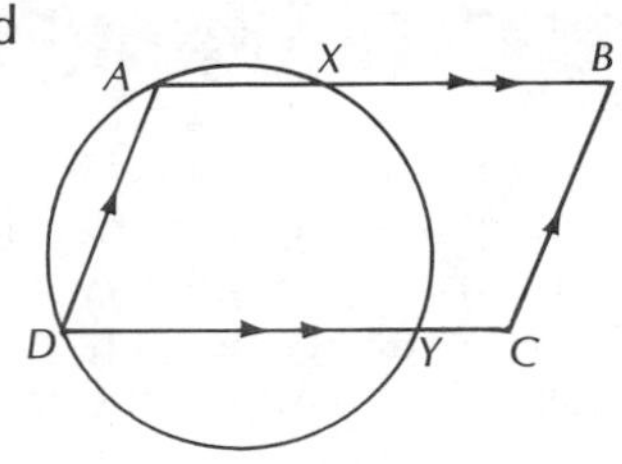

B 6. In parallelogram $ABCD$, $AB > AD$. X and Y are points on $\overline{AB}$ and $\overline{DC}$, respectively, such that A, X, Y, and D are concyclic points. Prove that X, Y, C, and B are concyclic points.

7. The diagonals of quadrilateral $PQRS$ intersect at T such that $\angle QPT = 45°$, $\angle QTR = 85°$, $\angle RPS = 62°$, and $\angle PRS = 40°$. Prove that $PQRS$ is a cyclic quadrilateral and find the measure of $\angle QRP$.

8. A is a point on side $\overline{XW}$ of parallelogram $XYZW$ such that $XY = YA$. Prove that $AYZW$ is a cyclic quadrilateral.

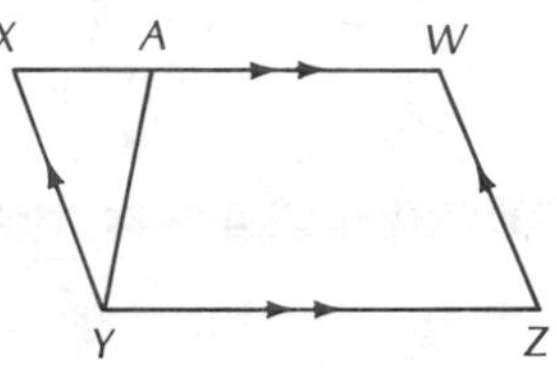

9. Altitudes $\overline{RS}$ and $\overline{QT}$ of acute $\triangle PQR$ intersect at W. Prove that $\angle SPW = \angle STW$ and $\angle SQW = \angle TRW$.

10. $\triangle XYZ$ is isosceles such that $XY = XZ$. A circle with diameter $\overline{XY}$ intersects $\overline{YZ}$ at W. Prove that $\overline{XW}$ bisects $\angle YXZ$.

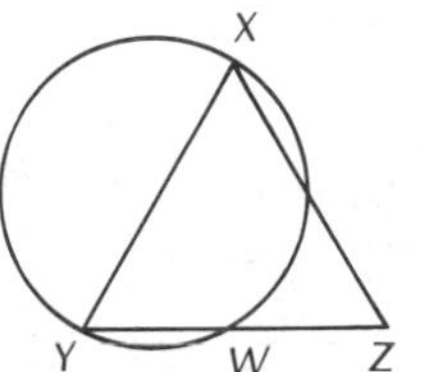

11. $ABCD$ is a parallelogram. E is a point on $\overline{AD}$ and F is a point on $\overline{BC}$ such that A, E, F, and B are concyclic points. Prove that $\angle FEC = \angle FDC$.

12. In $\triangle XYZ$, $\angle XYZ = 90°$. A is a point on $\overline{XY}$. A circle with diameter $\overline{AX}$ intersects $\overline{XZ}$ at B. Prove that A, B, Z, and Y are concyclic points.

13. Prove that a cyclic trapezoid is isosceles. That is, it has two equal sides.

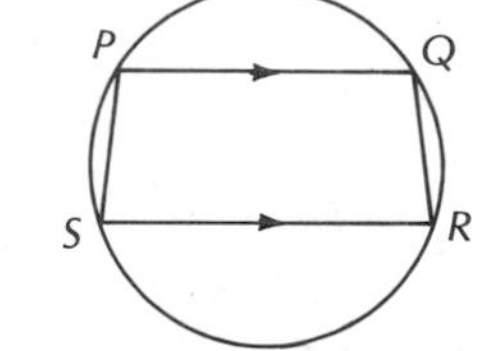

14. $\overline{AXB}$ is parallel to base $\overline{YZ}$ of $\triangle XYZ$. $\overline{AZ}$ intersects $\overline{XY}$ at C and $\overline{BY}$ intersects $\overline{XZ}$ at D such that $\overline{CD} \parallel \overline{YZ}$. Prove that if $CDZY$ is a cyclic quadrilateral, then $ACDB$ is also a cyclic quadrilateral.

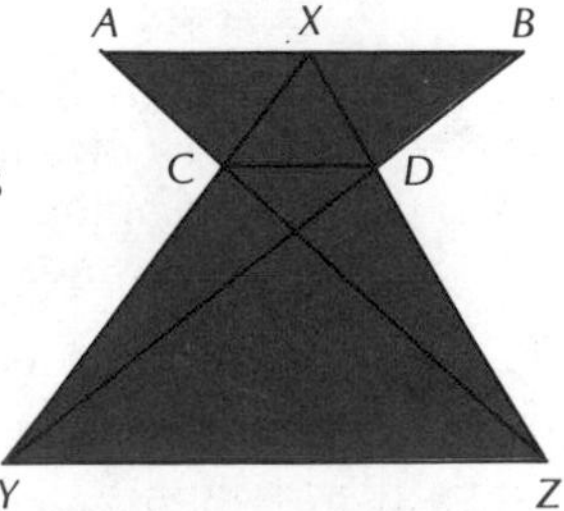

12-5 Tangent Properties of a Circle

Tangents to circles have many practical applications. Pulleys are one way that tangents to circles are used. A combination of pulleys and ropes can be used to increase lifting capacity, as seen in venetian blinds, belt drives, hoisting apparatus, and many other applications.

A line that intersects a circle in only one point is a **tangent** to the circle. The intersection point is called the **point of contact**, or the **tangent point**.

Tangent Theorem for Circles
A line is tangent to a circle if, and only if, the line is perpendicular to a radius at the point of contact.

The statement of this theorem contains the expression, "if, and only if" and is, therefore, a biconditional statement. It is necessary to prove two cases: the statement and its converse.

Case 1: If a line is tangent to a circle, then it is perpendicular to the radius at the point of contact.

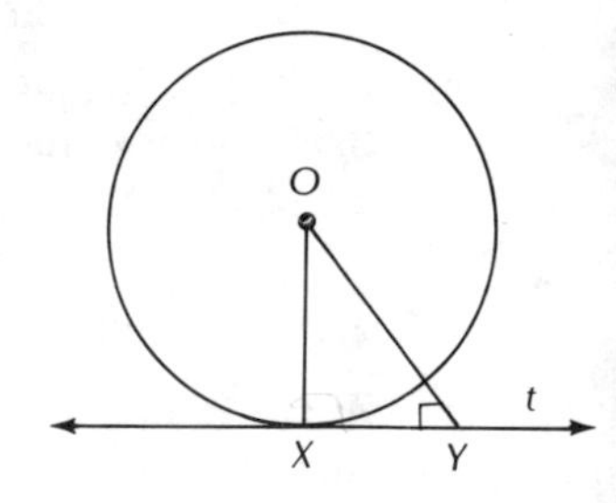

Given: A tangent t to a circle with centre O, X is the point of contact of the tangent.

Prove: $\overline{OX} \perp t$

Proof: (Indirect) Assume that $\overline{OX}$ is not perpendicular to t.
Then there is a point Y outside the circle such that $\overline{OY} \perp t$.
Thus, $\triangle OYX$ is a right-angled triangle with hypotenuse $\overline{OX}$.
$\therefore OX^2 = OY^2 + XY^2$ — Pythagorean Theorem
$OX > OY$
$r > OY$ — r is the radius of the circle.
Thus, Y is contained inside the circle.
But this contradicts the given condition, so the assumption must be false.
$\therefore OX \perp t$

Case 2: If a line is perpendicular to the radius of a circle at a given point on the circle, then the line is tangent to the circle at that point.

Given: P is a point outside a circle with centre O. X is a point on the circle such that $\overline{PX} \perp \overline{OX}$.

Prove: $\overline{PX}$ is tangent to the circle.

Proof: (Indirect) Assume that $\overline{PX}$ is not tangent to the circle.

Thus, $\overline{PX}$ intersects the circle in another point, say Y.

$\angle PXO = 90°$	Definition
$\angle YXO = 90°$	Definition of a straight angle
But $OX = OY$	Equal radii
$\therefore \angle OYX = 90°$	ITT
$\therefore \overline{OX} \parallel \overline{OY}$	PLT

Recall that parallel line segments do not intersect.

Thus, the assumption that $\overline{PX}$ is not tangent to the circle is false.
Therefore, $\overline{PX}$ is tangent to the circle.

Since the statement and its converse are both true, the theorem is proved.

EXAMPLE: Find the length of a tangent segment, $\overline{AB}$, from a point A, 10 cm from the centre, O, of a circle with radius 6 cm.

$\overline{OB} \perp \overline{AB}$	Tangent Theorem for Circles (TTC)
$OB^2 + AB^2 = OA^2$	Pythagorean Theorem
$36 + AB^2 = 100$	
$AB^2 = 64$	
$AB = 8$	

Therefore, the tangent segment, $\overline{AB}$, is 8 cm long.

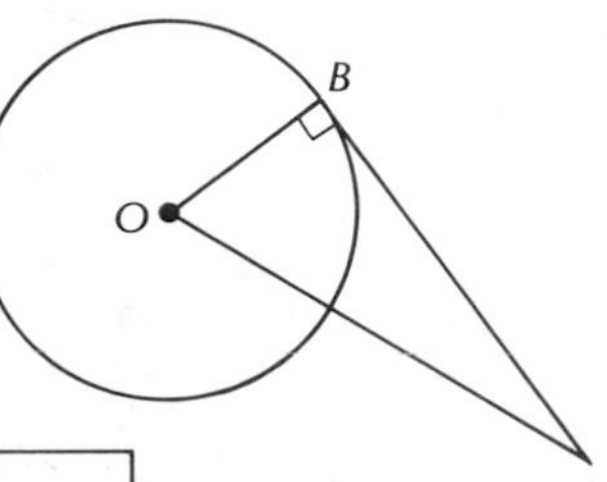

Tangent Segment Theorem
Tangent segments from a point outside a circle are equal in length.

The proof of the Tangent Segment Theorem follows.

Given: $\overline{PA}$ and $\overline{PB}$ are tangent segments to a circle with centre O.

Prove: $PA = PB$

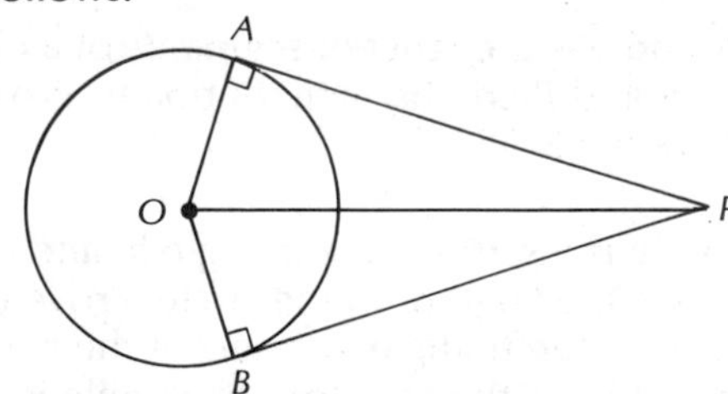

Proof: Construct $\overline{OA}$ and $\overline{OB}$.

$OA = OB$	Equal radii
$OP = OP$	Common Side
$\angle OAP = \angle OBP = 90°$	Tangent Theorem for Circles
$OP^2 = PA^2 + OA^2$ and $OP^2 = PB^2 + OB^2$	Pythagorean Theorem
$PA^2 + OA^2 = PB^2 + OB^2$	Substitution
$PA^2 = PB^2$	Subtraction
$\therefore PA = PB$	Square root

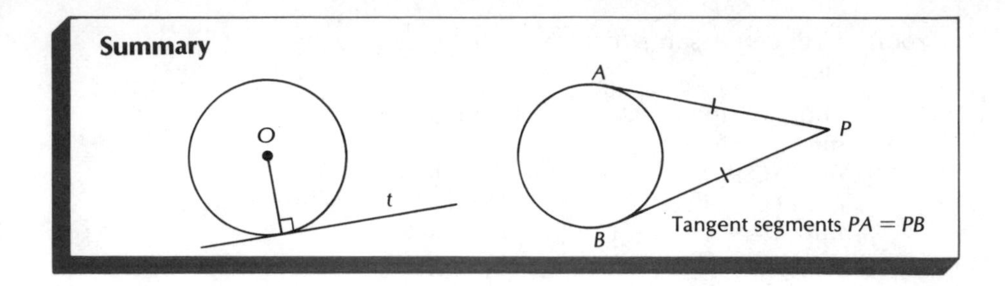

EXERCISE 12-5

A 1. Find the lengths of each indicated segment.
O is the centre of each circle and $\overline{AB}$ is a tangent.

a. $OA = 8$
$OB = 10$
Find AB.

b. $BD = 18$
$CD = 10$
Find AB.

c. 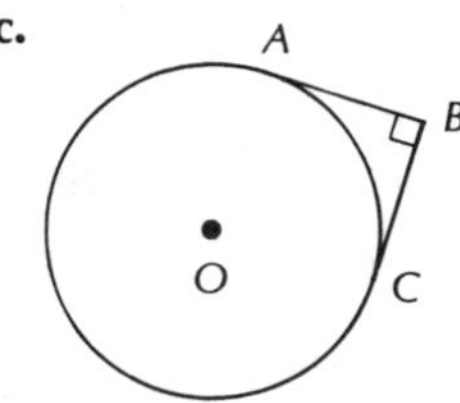

$AO = 6$
Find AB and AC.

d. 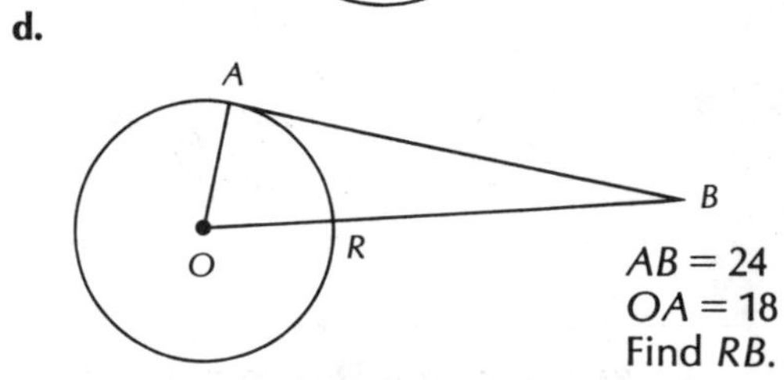

$AB = 24$
$OA = 18$
Find RB.

B 2. A is a point outside a circle with centre O. Points B and C lie on the circle such that $\overline{AB}$ and $\overline{AC}$ are tangent segments. Prove that $\overline{AO}$ is the perpendicular bisector of $\overline{BC}$.

3. $\overline{PA}$ and $\overline{PB}$ are tangent segments of a circle with centre O such that A and B are the tangent points. Prove that $\angle APO = \angle BPO$ and $\angle AOP = \angle BOP$.

4. A circle is inscribed in a triangle if, and only if, all three sides of the triangle are tangent to the circle. Prove that the bisectors of the angles of the triangle intersect at the centre of the inscribed circle. A point is on the bisector of an angle if, and only if, it is equidistant from the rays of the angle.

5. An **escribed** circle of a triangle is tangent to one side of the triangle and the other two sides extended. Construct the bisectors of the two exterior angles formed by the three tangents. Prove that the bisectors of these angles intersect at the centre of the escribed circle.

6. Two concentric circles with centre O are shown at the right. $\overline{XY}$ and $\overline{PQ}$ are chords of the larger circle such that each is tangent to the smaller circle. Prove that $XY = PQ$.

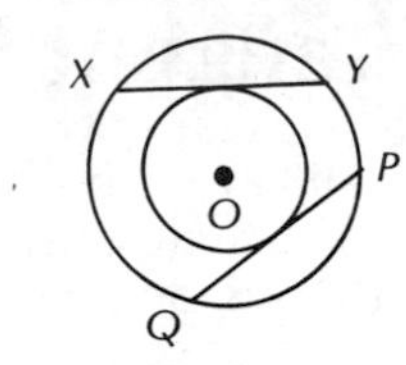

7. $\overline{PA}$ and $\overline{PB}$ are tangent segments to a circle with centre O, as shown. $\overline{AC}$ is a diameter of the circle. Prove that the measure of $\angle CAB$ is one-half the measure of $\angle APB$.

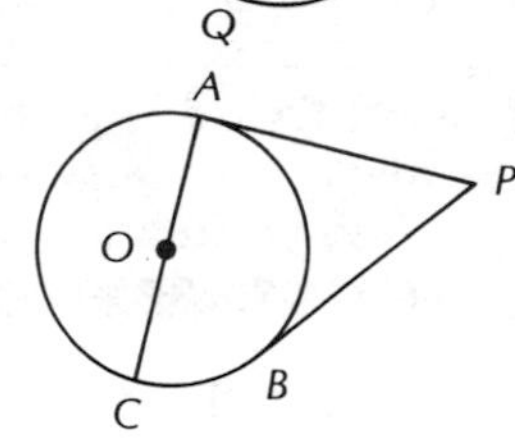

8. In the diagram at the right, $\overline{XY}$, $\overline{XP}$, and $\overline{PW}$ are tangent to the circle with centre O, and tangent points Y, Z, and W, respectively. If $\overline{XY} \parallel \overline{PW}$, prove that $\angle XOP$ is a right angle.

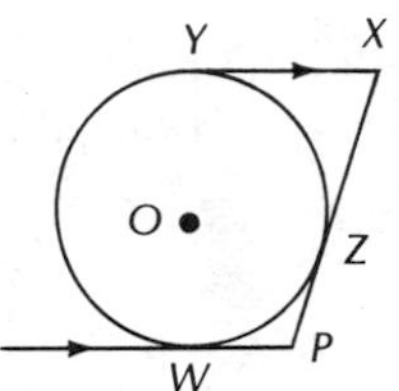

9. $\overline{XY}$ is a chord of a circle with centre O. Z is a point on the circle such that $\angle ZXY = \angle YXO$. The tangent at Y intersects $\overline{XZ}$ extended at W. Prove that $\angle ZWY = 90°$.

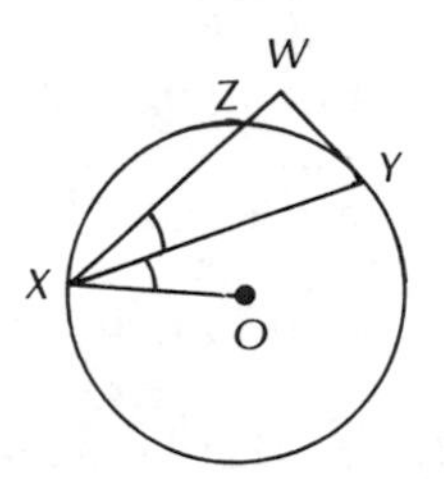

10. Two concentric circles have radii 7 cm and 25 cm. Find the length of a chord of the larger circle that is tangent to the smaller circle.

11. Tow circles with centres P and Q, and radii r_1 and r_2, respectively, are tangent at point R.
    a. Draw two diagrams that represent the two possible situations.
    b. Prove that P, Q, and R are collinear for each case.
    c. Prove that either $PQ = r_1 + r_2$ or $PQ = r_1 - r_2$, where $r_1 > r_2$.

C 12. Two circles with centres P and Q, and radii 6 cm and 20 cm, respectively, are externally tangent at R. S is on the smaller circle and T is on the larger circle such that $\overline{ST}$ is tangent to both circles. Find the measure of $\overline{ST}$.

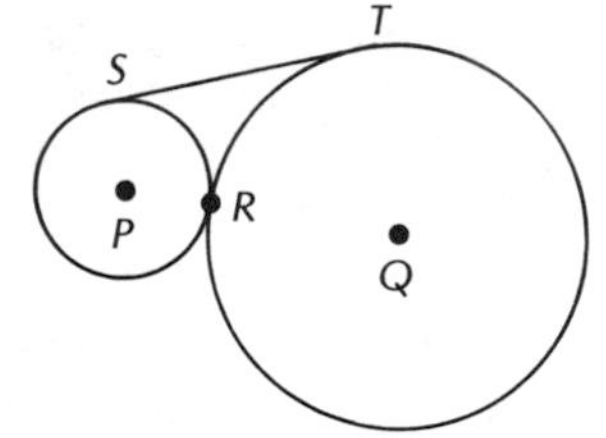

13. A belt and pulley system is set up so that the distance between the centres of the two pulleys is 20 cm. Find the length of the belt for each case shown below if the diameters of the pulleys are 6 cm and 8 cm.

a.

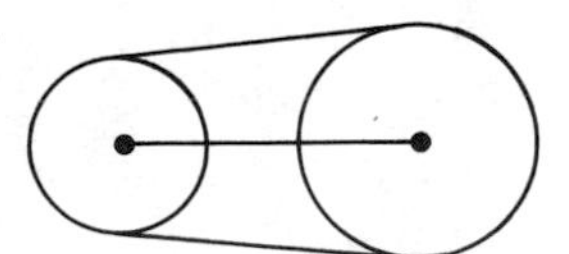

b.

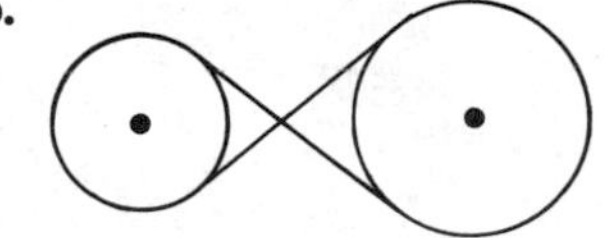

12-6 Tangent Chord Theorem

An interesting relationship between the chords, the angles, and the tangents of a circle exists. It is proved using the chord properties, angle properties, and tangent properties studied in previous lessons of this unit.

> **Tangent Chord Theorem (TCT)**
> The angle between a tangent and a chord of a circle is equal to the inscribed angle on the opposite side of the chord.

The proof is given below.

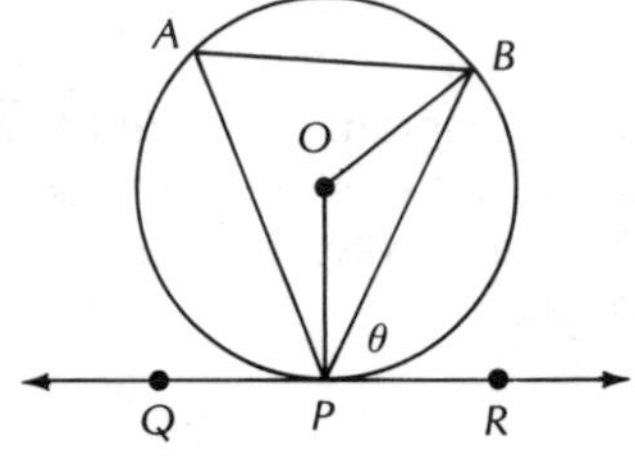

Given: $\overline{QPR}$ is tangent to a circle with centre O.
$\overline{PB}$ is any chord, and $\angle PAB$ is an inscribed angle.

Prove: $\angle PAB = \angle BPR$

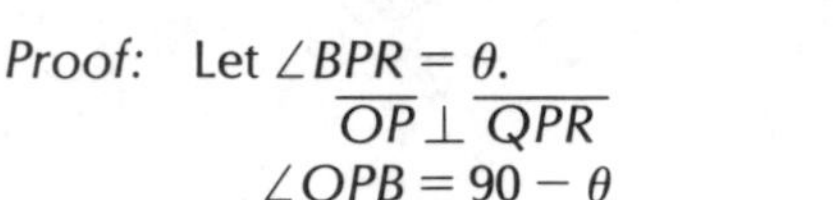

Proof: Let $\angle BPR = \theta$.

$\overline{OP} \perp \overline{QPR}$	Tangent Theorem for Circles
$\angle OPB = 90 - \theta$	
But $OP = OB$.	Equal radii
$\angle OBP = 90 - \theta$	Isosceles Triangle Theorem
$\angle POB = 180 - 2(90 - \theta) = 2\theta$	Angle sum of triangle
$\angle PAB = \theta$	Inscribed Angle Theorem
$\therefore \angle PAB = \angle BPR$	

EXAMPLE 1: Find the measure of each indicated angle.

a.

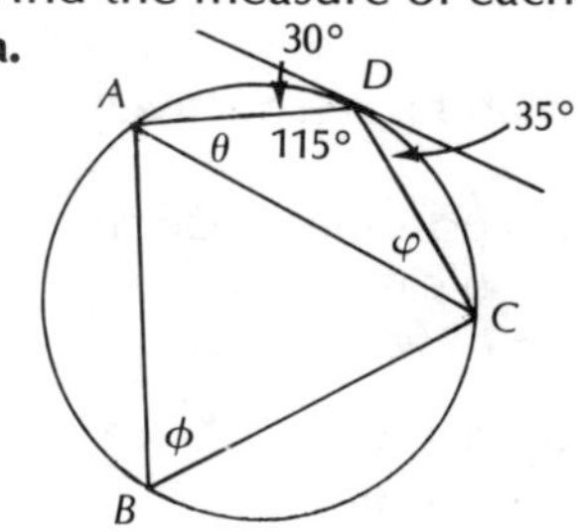

b.

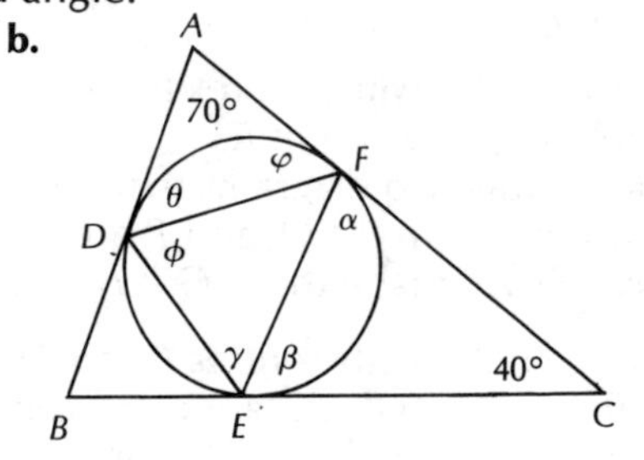

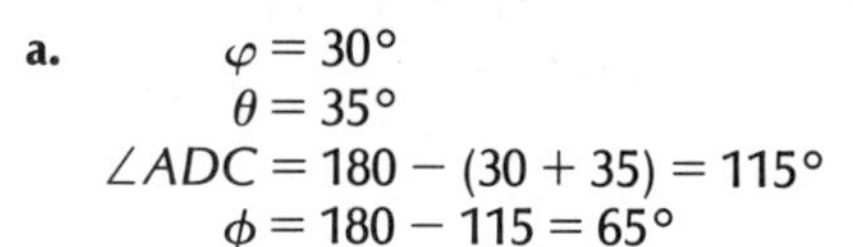

a.

$\varphi = 30°$	TCT
$\theta = 35°$	TCT
$\angle ADC = 180 - (30 + 35) = 115°$	Straight angle
$\phi = 180 - 115 = 65°$	IAT–opposite angles of an inscribed quadrilateral are supplementary.

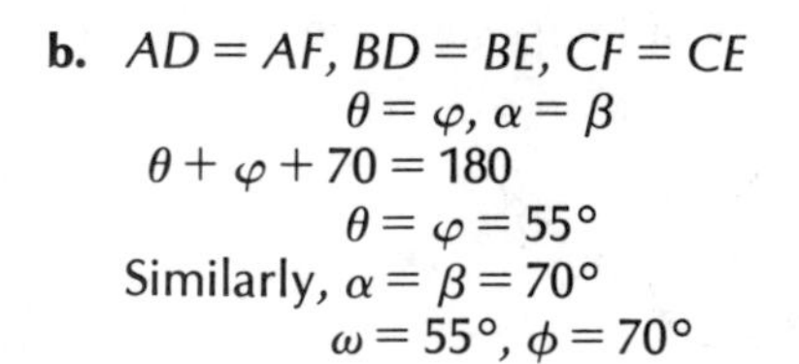

b.

$AD = AF$, $BD = BE$, $CF = CE$	Tangent Segment Theorem
$\theta = \varphi$, $\alpha = \beta$	ITT
$\theta + \varphi + 70 = 180$	AST
$\theta = \varphi = 55°$	
Similarly, $\alpha = \beta = 70°$	
$\omega = 55°$, $\phi = 70°$	TCT

EXAMPLE 2: Two circles intersect at points X and Y. A is a point on one circle while B and C are points on the other circle such that A, X, and B are collinear and A, Y, and C are collinear. Prove that the tangent at A is parallel to $\overline{BC}$.

Given: Two circles intersect at X and Y. A, X, B and A, Y, C are collinear sets of points, as shown. $\overline{DE}$ is tangent to the smaller circle at A.

Prove: $\overline{BC} \parallel \overline{DAE}$

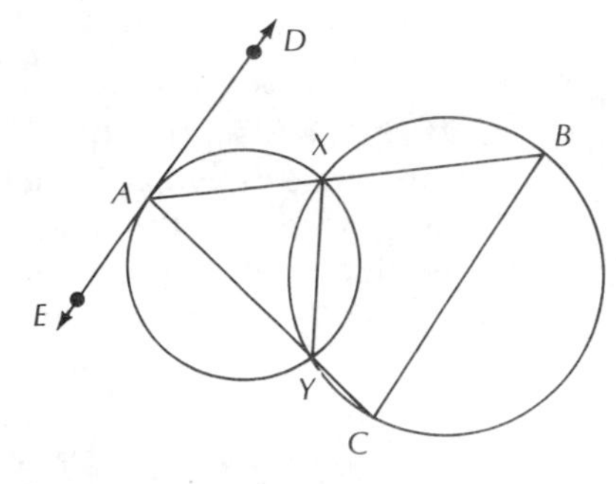

Proof:	
$\angle DAX = \angle XYA$	TCT
$\angle XYA = \angle XBC$	IAT–exterior angle of an inscribed quadrilateral is equal to the interior angle at the opposite vertex.
$\angle DAX = \angle XBC$	Substitution
$\therefore \overline{BC} \parallel \overline{DAE}$	PLT–alternate angles

EXERCISE 12-6

A **1.** Find the measure of each unknown angle.

a.

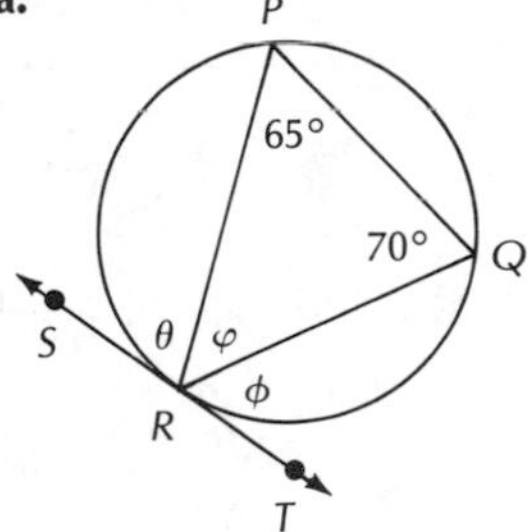

b.

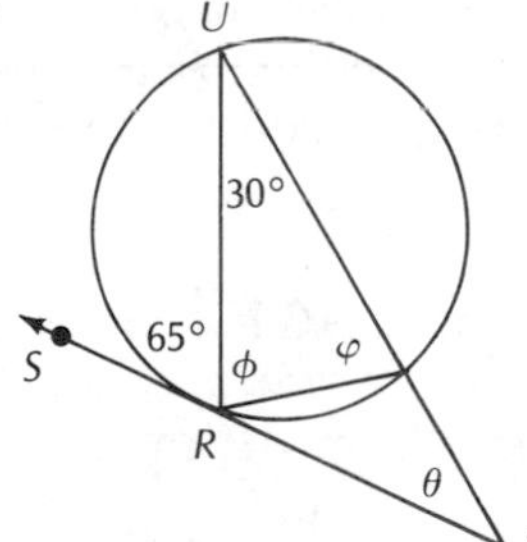

$\overline{ST}$ is tangent to the circle at R.

c.

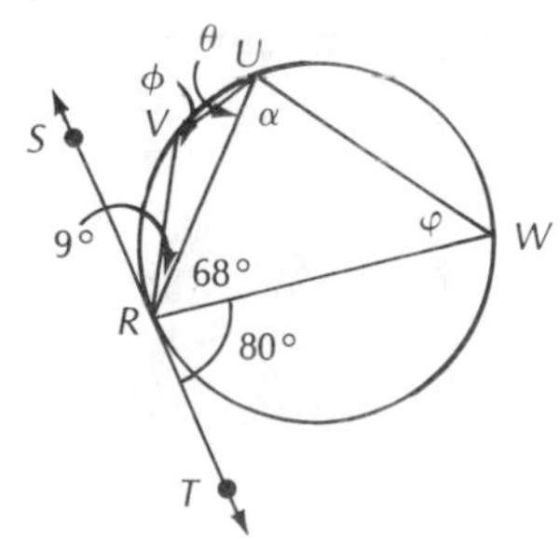

d.

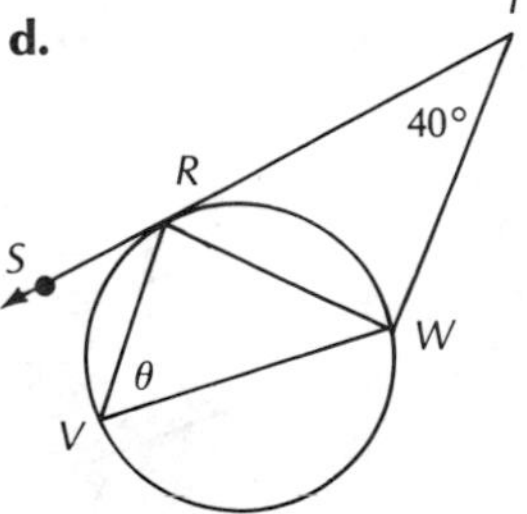

$\overline{ST}$ is tangent at R and $\overline{TW}$ is tangent at W.

e.

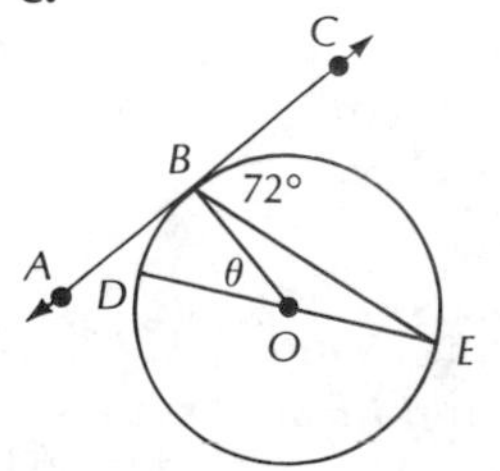

$\overline{AB}$ is tangent at B. O is centre of the circle.

f.

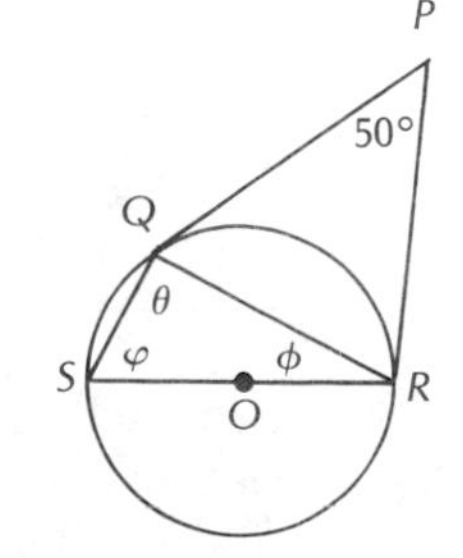

$\overline{PQ}$ and $\overline{PR}$ are tangent segments.

B **2.** $\triangle XYZ$ is inscribed in a circle. $\overline{AB}$ is tangent to the circle at Y, as shown. If $XZ = YZ$, prove that $\overline{ZY}$ bisects $\angle XYB$.

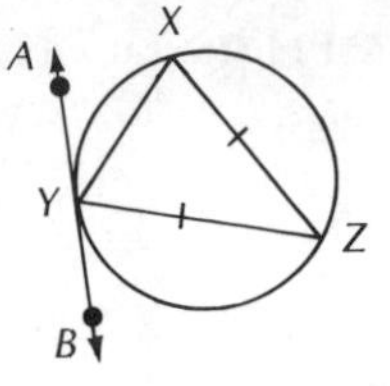

3. $ABCD$ is an inscribed quadrilateral in which $\overline{AB} \parallel \overline{DC}$. A tangent is drawn at D such that the smaller angle between $\overline{CD}$ and the tangent is 62°. If $\angle BAC = 33°$, find the value of each given angle.

a. $\angle ACD$ **b.** $\angle DAC$

c. $\angle ABC$ **d.** $\angle ADC$

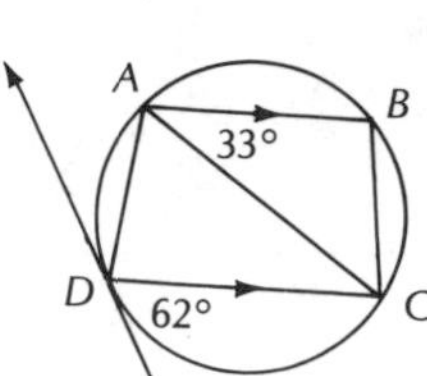
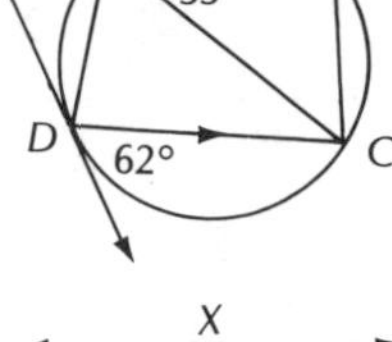

4. $\triangle XYZ$ is inscribed in a circle. A tangent to the circle at X is parallel to $\overline{YZ}$. Prove that $\triangle XYZ$ is isosceles.

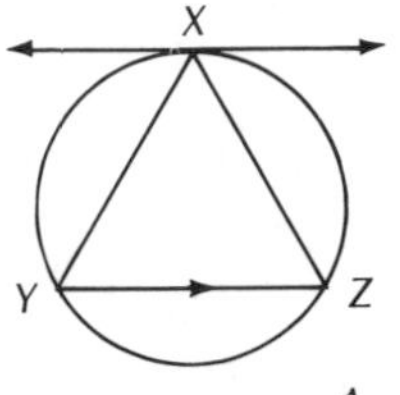

5. A circle is inscribed in $\triangle ABC$, with points of contact D, E, and F on sides $\overline{AB}$, $\overline{AC}$, and $\overline{BC}$, respectively. In $\triangle ABC$, $\angle ABC = 35°$ and $\angle ACB = 65°$. Find the measure of each angle of $\triangle DEF$.

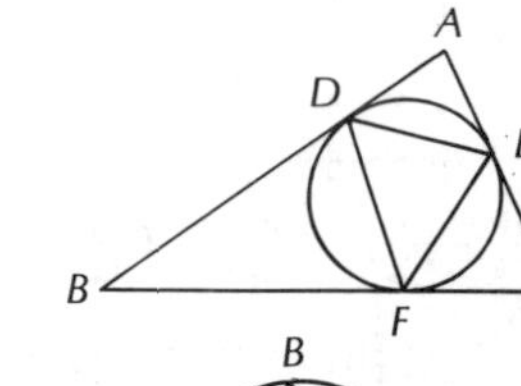

6. $\triangle ABC$ is inscribed in a circle. If $\angle A = 60°$ and $\angle B = 75°$, find the number of degrees in the three angles of the triangle formed by drawing tangents to the circle at A, B, and C.

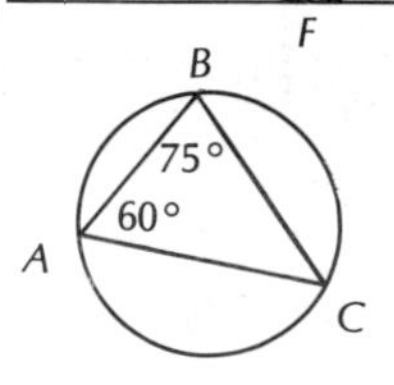

7. $\overline{BA}$ is tangent to a circle at A. $\overline{AC}$ is a chord of the circle. D is a point in the circle, as shown, such that $AD = CD$. Prove that D is equidistant from $\overline{AB}$ and $\overline{AC}$.

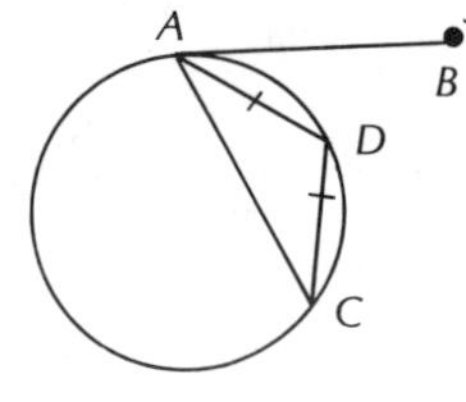

8. Quadrilateral $ABCQ$ is inscribed in a circle such that diagonal $\overline{AC}$ is parallel to $\overleftrightarrow{PQR}$, the tangent to the circle at Q. Prove that $\angle ABC = 2\angle PQA$.

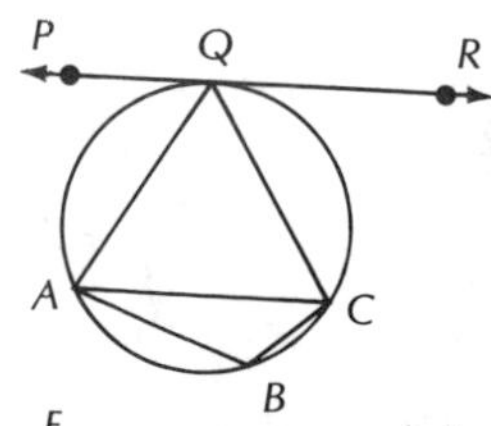

9. Two circles intersect at points D and F. $\overleftrightarrow{ABC}$ is tangent to the smaller circle at B. $\overline{BD}$ and $\overline{BF}$ are extended to intersect the larger circle at E and G, respectively. Prove that $\overleftrightarrow{ABC} \parallel \overline{EG}$.

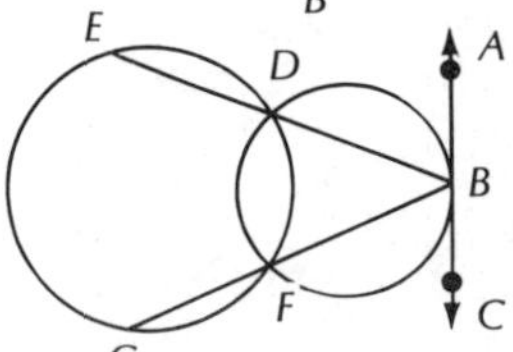

10. Two circles are externally tangent at B. $\overline{AB}$ and $\overline{BC}$ are diameters of the two circles. $\overline{CD}$ is tangent at D to the circle containing A and B. Prove the following.

  a. $\overline{BD}$ bisects $\angle ABE$.

  b. $\angle ABD = \angle DAB + \angle BCE$

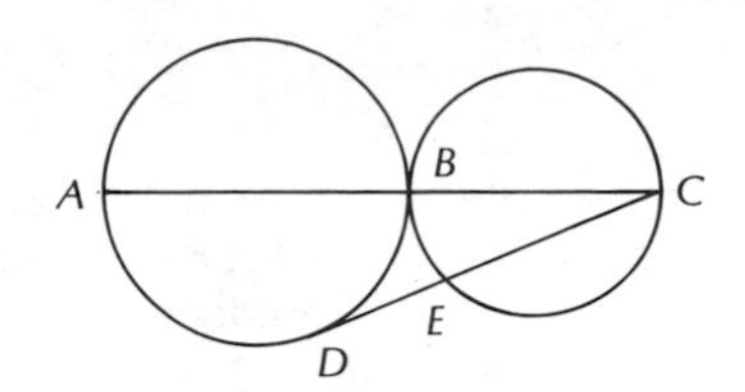

11. In $\triangle ABC$, $\angle BAC = 76°$ and $\angle ACB = 45°$. An escribed circle touches $\overline{BC}$ at P, $\overline{AB}$ extended at Q, and $\overline{AC}$ extended at R. Find the measure of each angle of $\triangle PQR$.

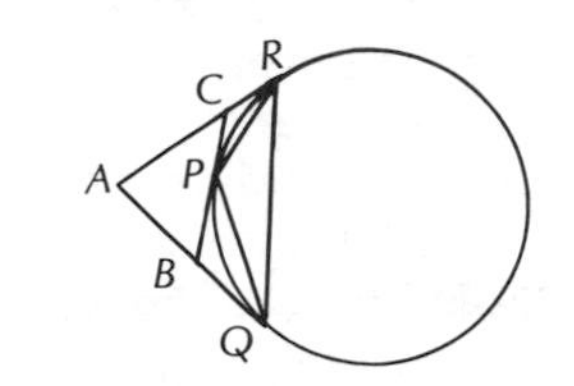

12. Quadrilateral $ABCD$ is inscribed in a circle such that $\overline{AB} \parallel \overline{DC}$. $\overline{EB}$ is tangent to the circle at B such that D, C, and E are collinear. Prove that $\angle BEC = \angle ADB$.

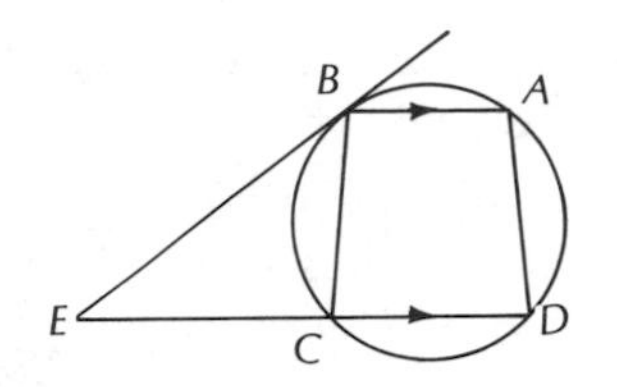

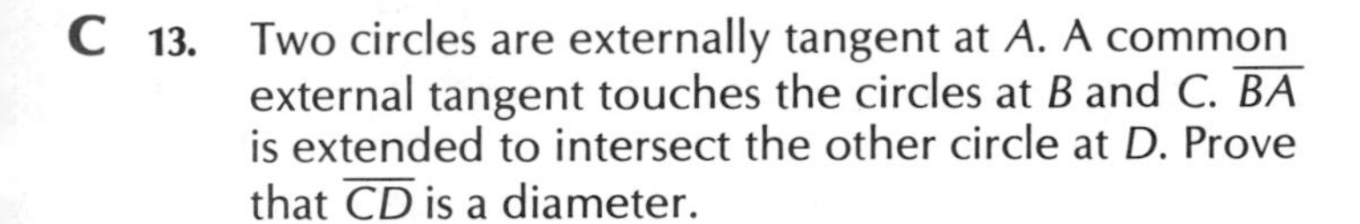

C 13. Two circles are externally tangent at A. A common external tangent touches the circles at B and C. $\overline{BA}$ is extended to intersect the other circle at D. Prove that $\overline{CD}$ is a diameter.

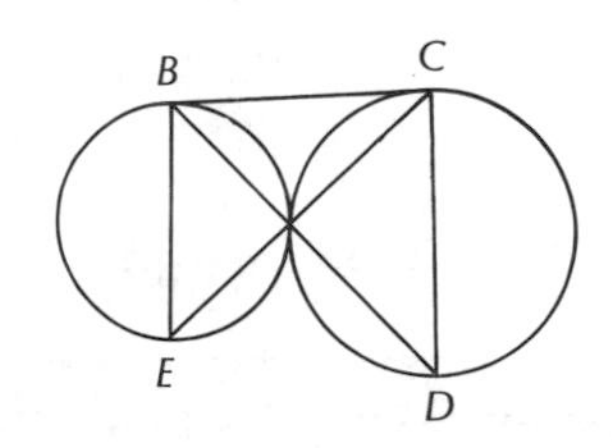

EXTRA

Curvature

The cover of this textbook shows a close-up of Ted Bieler's sculpture *Ziggurat* (1985). The entire sculpture, constructed of laminated birch in interwoven concentric circles, is shown at the right. The patterns of the circles are reminiscent of radio wave patterns, or of ripples that intersect when two stones are thrown into still water.

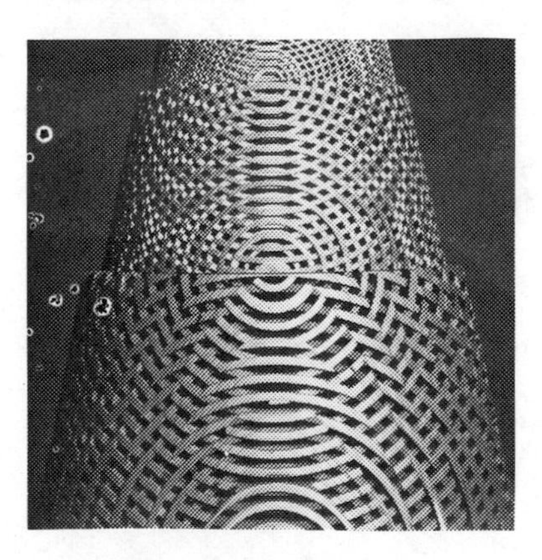

The edges of the smaller circles, near the common centre, are "more curved" than the larger circles. That is, a portion of a large circle approaches closer and closer to a tangent at a given point, as the radius increases.

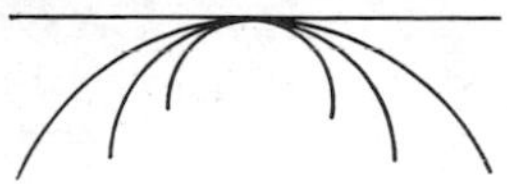

A measure of this property is called the **curvature** of the circle and is given by the reciprocal of the radius $\frac{1}{r}$. What meaning would be given to a curve if its curvature is given as zero?

12-7 Tangent Secant Theorem

Another interesting relationship exists between the lengths of tangents and secants from any point P outside a circle. The product of the distances from P to the point of contact of the tangent through P with the circle, or the intersection points of a secant through P and the circle, is a constant.

> **Tangent Secant Theorem**
> If the secant from an external point P intersects a circle at points A and B and the tangent from P contacts the same circle at T, then $PT^2 = (PA)(PB)$.

A secant is a line which intersects a circle in two points.

The proof of this theorem is given below.

Given: Secant from point P, outside a circle intersects the circle at A and B. $\overline{PT}$ is tangent to the circle at T.

Prove: $PT^2 = (PA)(PB)$

Proof: Join T and A, and T and B.
In $\triangle PTA$ and $\triangle PBT$,

$\angle APT = \angle TPB$	Common angle
$\angle PTA = \angle PBT$	TCT
$\triangle PTA \sim \triangle PBT$	AA~
$\frac{PT}{PB} = \frac{PA}{PT}$	Similar Triangles
$PT^2 = (PA)(PB)$	

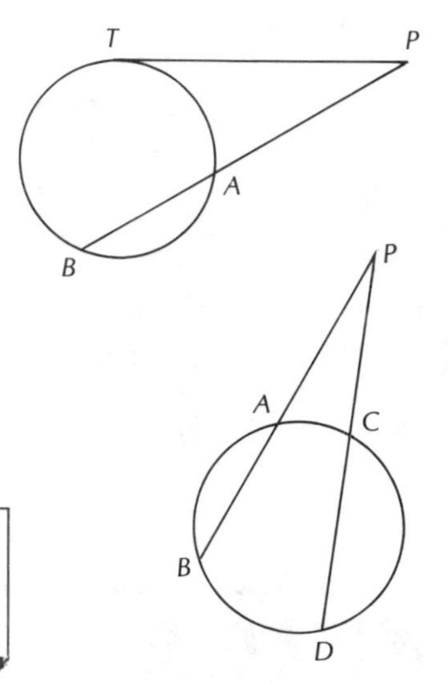

> **Corollary to the Tangent Secant Theorem**
> If two secants from an external point, P, intersect a circle at A, B, and C, D, respectively, then $(PA)(PB) = (PC)(PD)$.

EXAMPLE 1:

a. *Given:* $XZ = 6$, $ZW = 18$
Find: XY

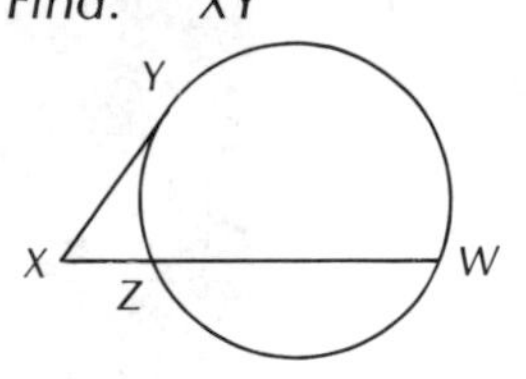

$XY^2 = (XZ)(XW)$ Tangent Secant Theorem

$XY^2 = 6(24)$
$= 144$
$XY = \pm 12$
-12 is an inadmissible solution.
$\therefore XY = 12$

b. *Given:* $AB = 12$, $BC = 6$, $DE = 3$
Find: EC

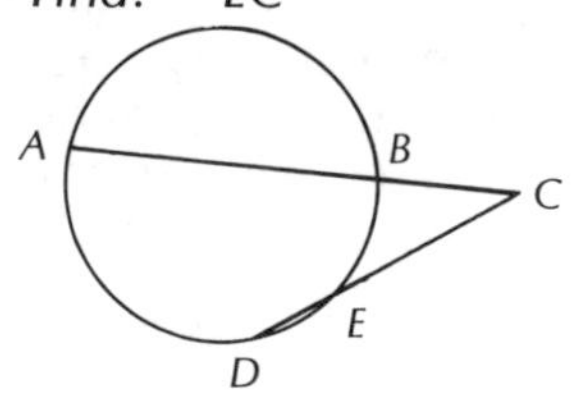

$(CA)(CB) = (CD)(CE)$ Tangent Secant Theorem

$18(6) = (3 + x)x$, where $x = EC$
$108 = 3x + x^2$
$0 = x^2 + 3x - 108$
$0 = (x + 12)(x - 9)$
$x = -12$ or $x = 9$
-12 is an inadmissible solution.
$\therefore EC = 9$

EXAMPLE 2: Two circles intersect at X and Y. Tangent segments $\overline{PA}$ and $\overline{PB}$ are drawn from a point P, on $\overline{XY}$, extended, to the two circles. Prove that the two tangent segments are equal in length.

Given: Two circles intersect at X and Y.
$\overline{PA}$ and $\overline{PB}$ are tangent to the circles at A and B, respectively.

Prove: $PA = PB$

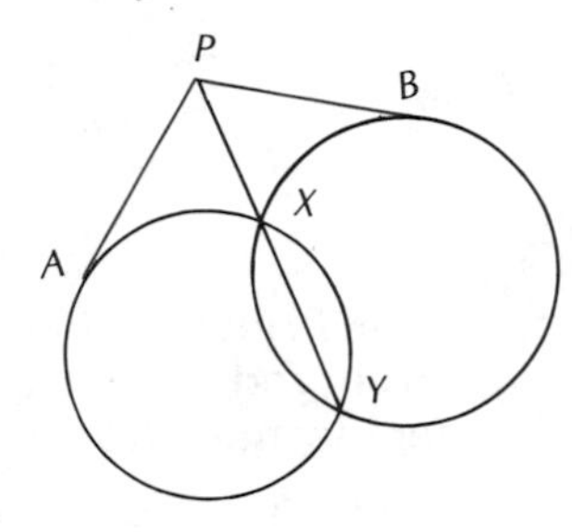

Proof:

$PA^2 = (PX)(PY)$	Tangent Secant Theorem
$PB^2 = (PX)(PY)$	Tangent Secant Theorem
$PA^2 = PB^2$	Substitution
$\therefore PA = PB$	

EXAMPLE 3: $\triangle PQR$ is inscribed in a circle. Point S is on $\overline{PQ}$ and point T is on $\overline{PR}$ such that $\overline{ST}$ is parallel to the tangent that contains P. Prove that $(PQ)(PS) = (PR)(PT)$.

Given: $\triangle PQR$, inscribed in a circle.
$\overleftrightarrow{APB}$ is tangent to the circle at P.
$\overline{ST} \parallel \overleftrightarrow{APB}$

Prove: $(PQ)(PS) = (PR)(PT)$

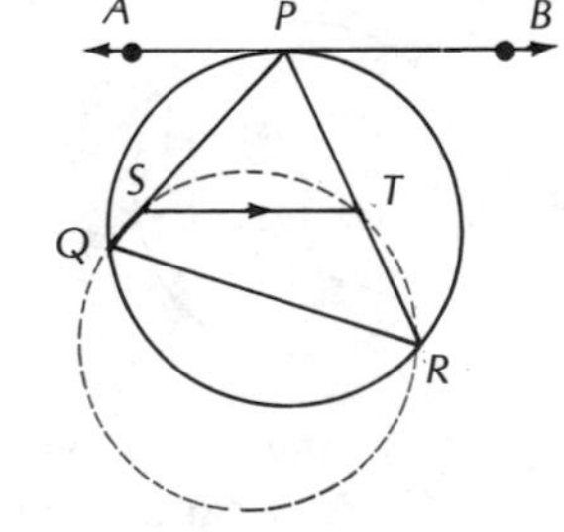

Proof: Show that $STRQ$ is a cyclic quadrilateral such that $\overline{PQ}$ and $\overline{PR}$ are secants of the circle.

$\angle BPT = \angle PQR$	TCT
$\angle BPT = \angle PTS$	PLT–alternate angles
$\angle PQR = \angle PTS$	Substitution

$STRQ$ is an inscribed quadrilateral. CPT

$\overline{PQ}$ and $\overline{PR}$ are secants to the circle passing through S, T, R, and Q. Now apply the corollary of the Tangent Secant Theorem.

$\therefore (PQ)(PS) = (PR)(PT)$ Tangent Secant Theorem

EXERCISE 12-7

A **1.** Find the length of each indicated segment.

a.

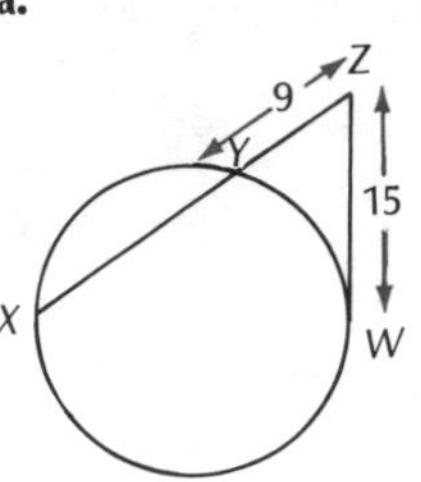

Find XY.

b.

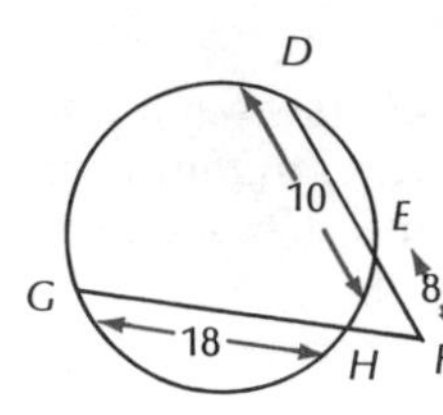

Find HF.

c.

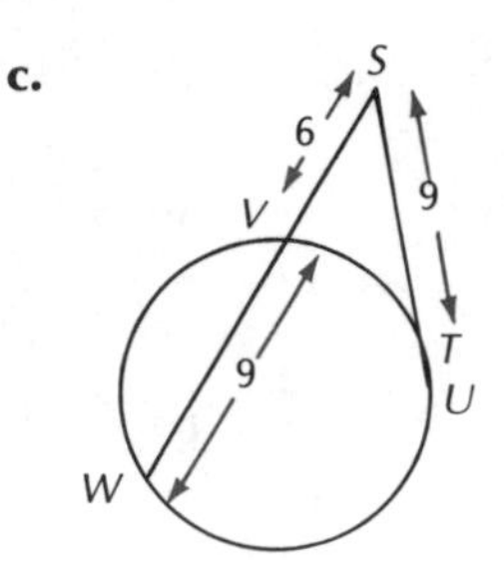

Find SU.

2. A secant from a point, P, intersects a circle at B and C such that $PB = 20$ cm and $BC = 16$ cm. Find the length of the tangent segment from P to the circle.

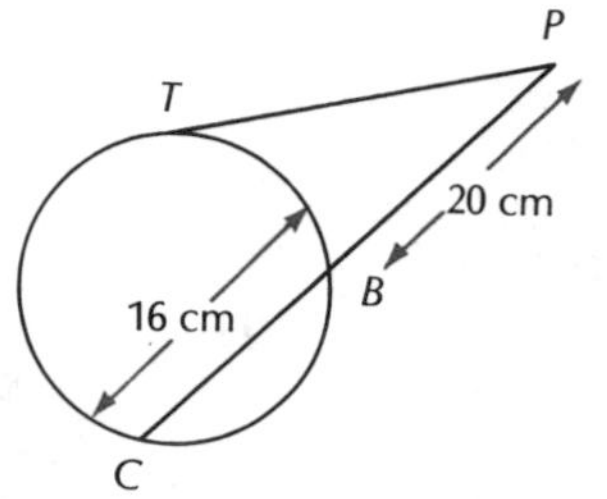

B **3.** Two secants $\overline{RS}$ and $\overline{RT}$, from a point R outside a circle also intersect the circle at points W and V such that W lies between S and R, and V lies between T and R. The tangent segment from R is 18 cm long. If $RS = TV = 27$ cm, find the lengths of $\overline{RW}$, $\overline{RV}$, and $\overline{RT}$.

4. Solve for x.

a.

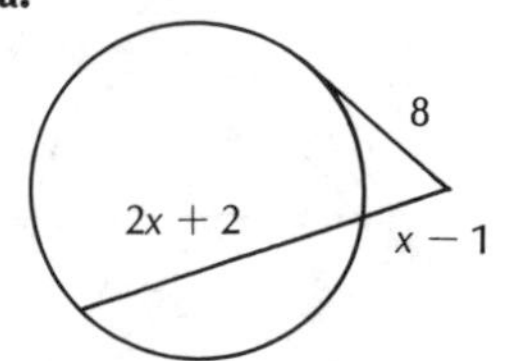

b.

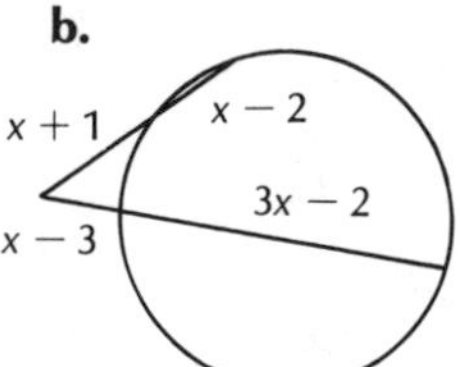

c.

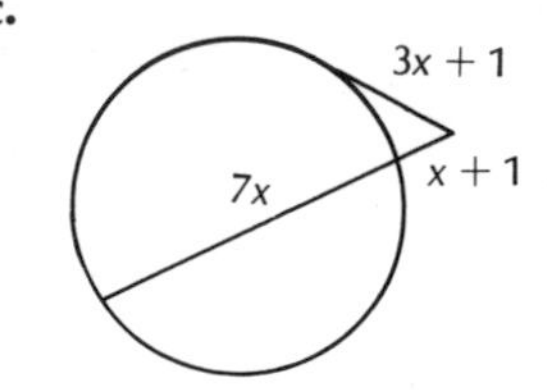

5. $\overline{AE}$ is tangent to two circles, as shown. $\overline{ABC}$ and $\overline{AFG}$ are secants to the two circles. Prove that $(AB)(AC) = (AF)(AG)$.

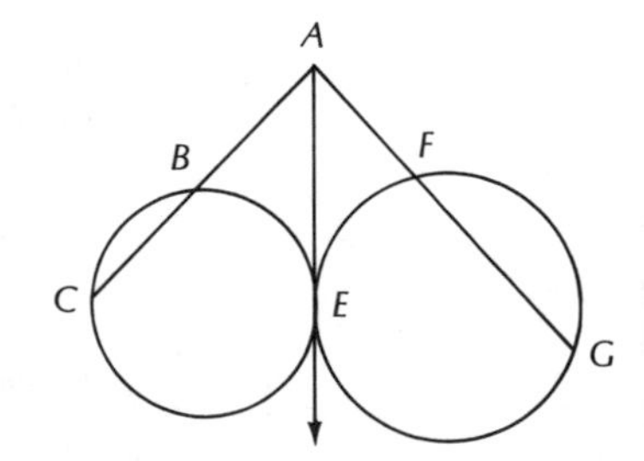

6. Prove the corollary of the Tangent Secant Theorem.

7. Two circles intersect at A and B. A tangent common to both circles touches them at X and Y, respectively. Prove that the line containing chord $\overline{AB}$ bisects $\overline{XY}$.

8. Secant $\overline{ABC}$ intersects a circle with centre O, at B and C. Prove that $(AB)(AC) = OA^2 - OB^2$.

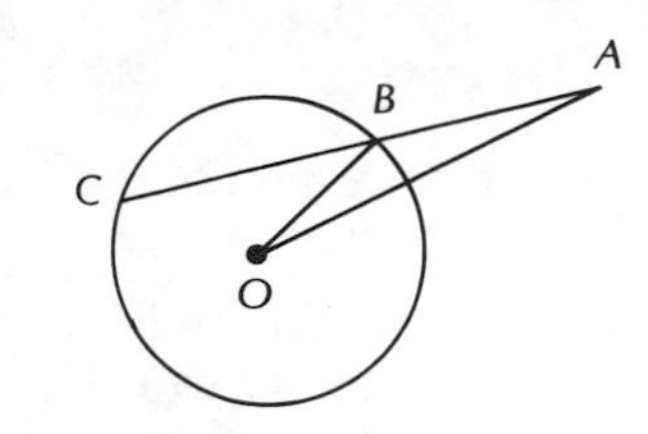

9. $\triangle PQR$ is right-angled at Q. S is on $\overline{PQ}$ and T is on $\overline{PR}$ such that $\overline{ST} \perp \overline{PR}$. Prove that $(PS)(PQ) = (PT)(PR)$.

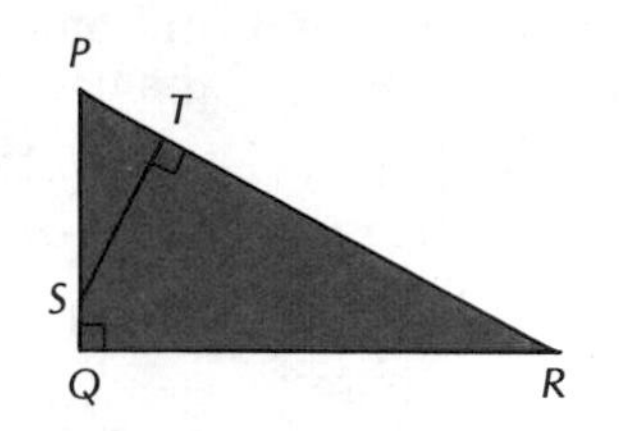

10. $\overline{BY}$ and $\overline{CX}$ are altitudes of acute $\triangle ABC$. Prove that $(AX)(AB) = (AY)(AC)$.

11. $\triangle XYZ$ is isosceles such that $XY = XZ$. The bisectors of $\angle Y$ and $\angle Z$ intersect $\overline{XZ}$ at A and intersect $\overline{XY}$ at B. Prove that $(XB)(XY) = (XA)(XZ)$.

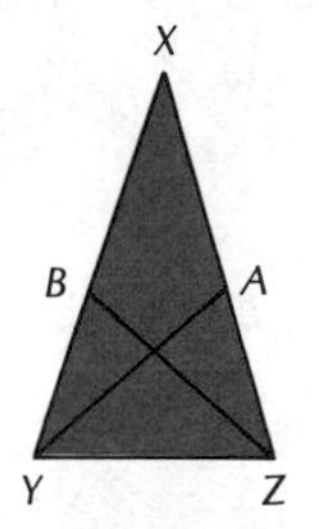

12. In $\triangle ABC$, $\angle BAC = 90°$. D is on $\overline{BC}$ such that $\overline{AD} \perp \overline{BC}$.

a. Prove that $\overline{AB}$ is tangent to the circle through A, C, and D.

b. Prove that $AB^2 = (BD)(BC)$.

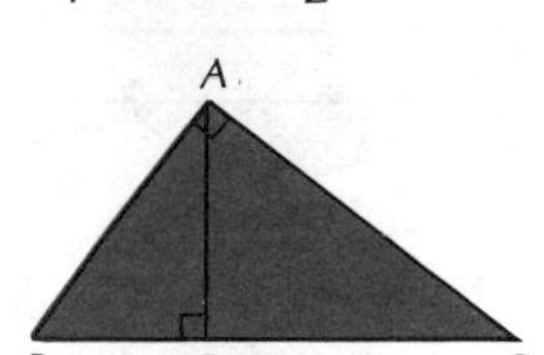

C **13.** $\overline{AD}$ is tangent to a circle at D, and $\overline{DE}$ is a diameter of the circle. For any point, P, on $\overline{AD}$, $\overline{PE}$ intersects the circle at F. Prove that $(PE)(EF)$ is a constant, no matter where P lies on $\overline{AD}$.

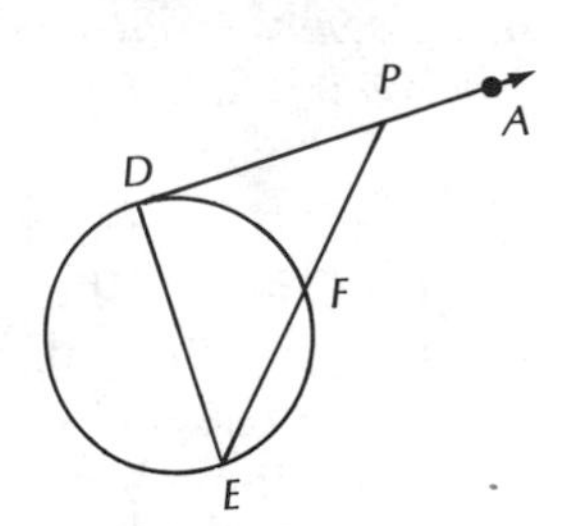

14. Two circles intersect at points X and Y. $\overline{XY}$ is extended to A. Secant $\overline{ADE}$ is drawn to one circle and secant $\overline{ABC}$ is drawn to the other circle. Prove that E, D, B, and C are concyclic points.

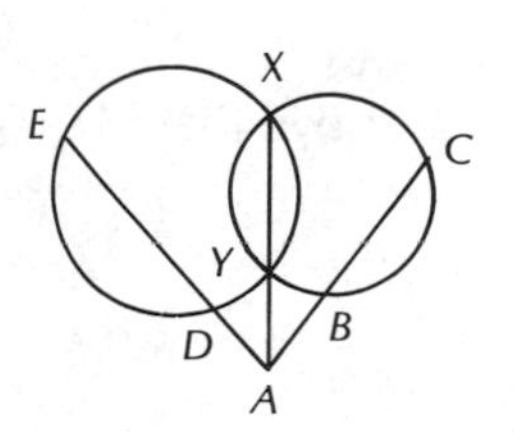

Review

1. Find the area of the sector of a circle with radius 7 cm if the sector angle measures 65°.
2. Find the length of an arc of a circle with radius 15 mm if the sector angle measures 140°.
3. A chord is 8 cm from the centre of a circle with diameter 20 cm. Find the length of the chord.
4. A chord 48 cm long is 10 cm from the centre of a circle. Find the length of the radius of the circle.
5. Find the measure of each unknown angle. O is the centre of the circle.

a. 50°, φ, 95°, θ, ϕ

b. 80°, 115°, φ, θ

c. 112°, θ, O

d.

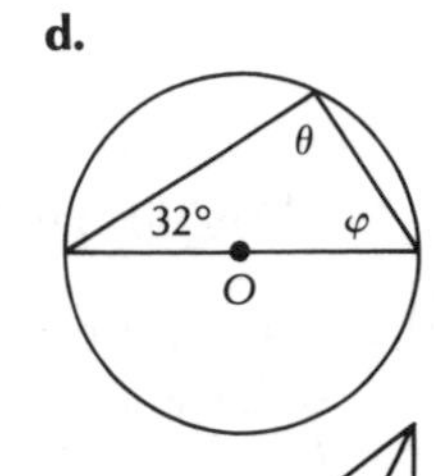

e.

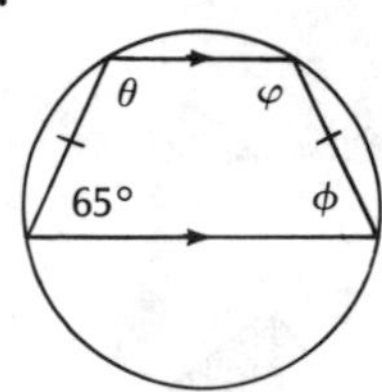

f. t, 70°, ϕ, φ, θ, 85°

g.

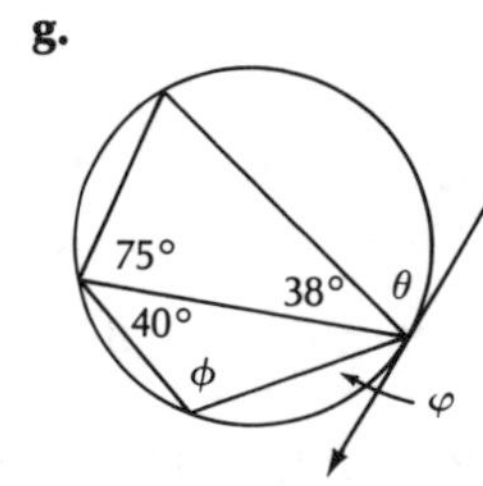

h.

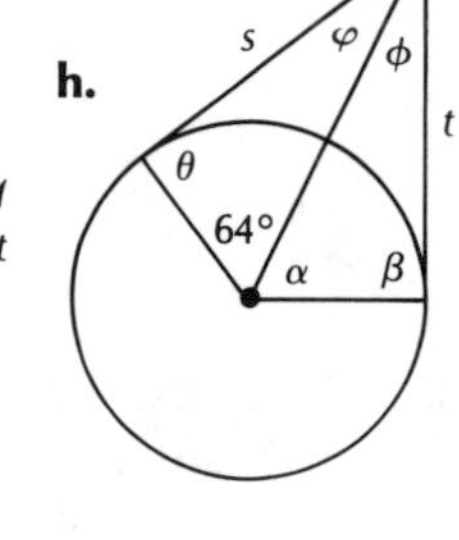

6. $\overline{PR}$ is a tangent to two circles with centres O and S such that the points of contact are P and R, respectively. If $\overline{PR}$ intersects $\overline{OS}$ at Q, prove that $\triangle POQ \sim \triangle RSQ$.

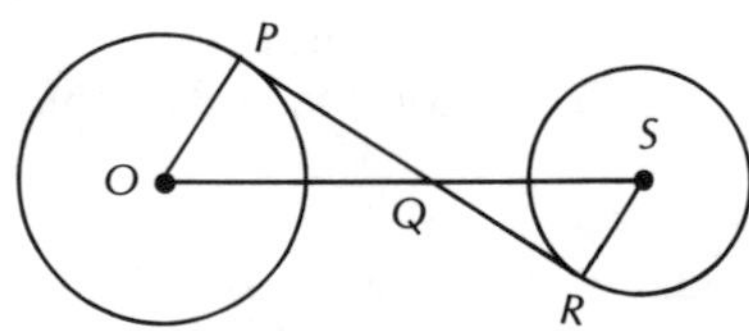

7. $\overline{RU}$ and $\overline{ST}$ are each tangent to two circles with centres O and P. The points of contact are R, S, T, and U, as shown. $\overline{RU}$ and $\overline{ST}$ intersect at W. $WS = 6$ cm, $WU = 4$ cm, and $OR = 8$ cm.
   a. Prove that O, W, and P are collinear points.
   b. Find the lengths of $\overline{RU}$, $\overline{PT}$, and $\overline{OP}$.

8. $\overline{AD}$ and $\overline{BC}$ are chords of a circle. $\overline{AD}$ and $\overline{BC}$ intersect at E. Prove that $(AE)(ED) = (CE)(EB)$.

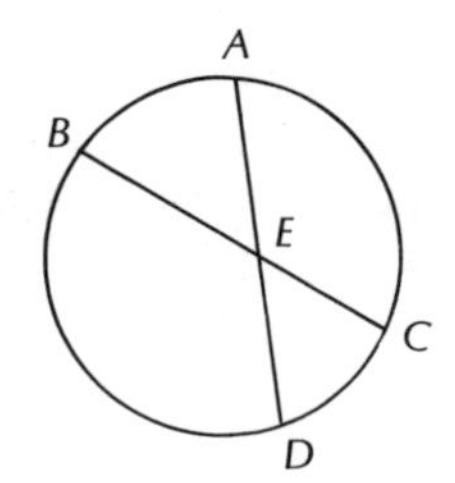

9. Three circles with centres P, Q, and R are externally tangent to each other, as shown. Their radii are 3 cm, 4 cm, and 5 cm, respectively.
   a. Prove that P, A, Q and P, B, R and Q, C, R are collinear sets of points.
   b. Find the perimeter of $\triangle PQR$.

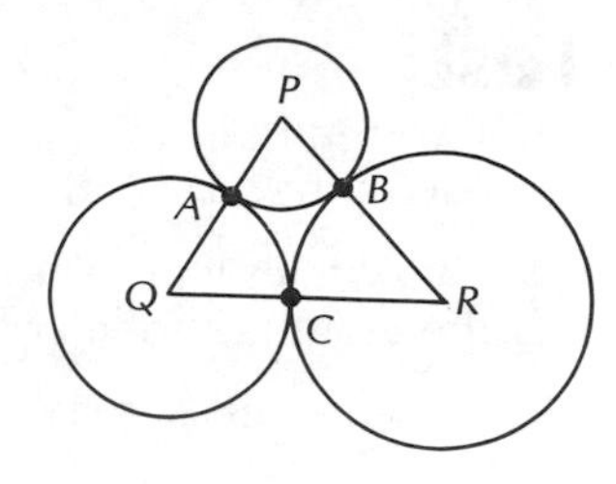

10. Two concentric circles have radii 6 cm and 10 cm. Find the length of the chord of the larger circle that is tangent to the smaller circle.

11. A secant from a point, P, outside a circle intersects the circle at A and B such that $PA = 8$ cm and $PB = 1$ cm. A second secant from P intersects the circle at C and D such that $PC = 6$ cm. Find the measure of each segment.
   a. $\overline{CD}$ b. the tangent segment from P to the circle

12. $\triangle ABC$ is inscribed in a circle. The tangents at A and C intersect at X, the tangents at A and B intersect at Y, and the tangents at B and C intersect at Z. If $\angle XYZ = 44°$ and $\angle YXZ = 76°$, find the measure of each angle of $\triangle ABC$.

13. $\triangle APC$ is inscribed in a circle. B lies on the circle such that $\overline{BP}$ bisects $\angle APC$. The tangent at B intersects $\overline{PA}$ extended at Q and intersects $\overline{PC}$ extended at R. Prove that $\overline{AC} \parallel \overline{QR}$.

14. $\overline{CD}$ is a diameter of a circle with centre O. P lies on $\overline{DC}$ extended, and Q lies on $\overline{CD}$ extended such that O is the midpoint of $\overline{PQ}$. A and B are points on the circle and lie on the same side of $\overline{CD}$ such that $\overline{PA}$ and $\overline{QB}$ are tangent segments. Prove that $ABQP$ is a trapezoid.

15. $XYZW$ is a quadrilateral inscribed in a circle such that $XW = YZ$. Prove that $XYZW$ is a trapezoid.

16. $\overline{AB}$ is a diameter of a circle with centre O. Chord $\overline{AD}$ is extended to intersect the tangent at B at point C. E is the midpoint of $\overline{AD}$. Prove that $(AE)(AC) = 2AO^2$.

17. Chords $\overline{AB}$ and $\overline{CD}$ of a circle intersect at E. L is the midpoint of $\overline{CE}$ and M is the midpoint of $\overline{BE}$. Prove that A, S, M, and L are concyclic points.

18. A and D are points on two concentric circles. The tangent from D intersects the tangent from A at point B, as shown. Prove that $DOBA$ is a cyclic quadrilateral.

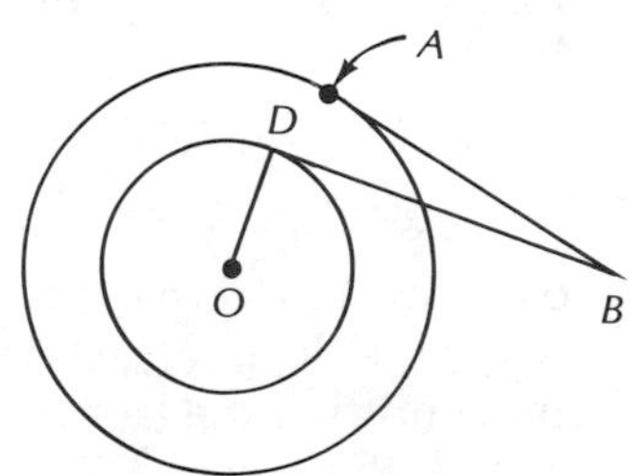

19. C and D are two fixed points on a circle. A is the midpoint of arc CD. A chord, $\overline{AB}$, is drawn to intersect $\overline{CD}$ at M. Prove that the value of $(AM)(AB)$ remains constant, independent of the position of B.

Test

Unit 12

1. Two segments, $\overline{PA}$ and $\overline{PB}$, tangent to a circle form an angle of 60° with each other. Find the length of arc AB if the radius of the circle is 6 cm.

2. Two circles with diameters 12 cm and 27 cm are externally tangent. Find the length of their common external tangents.

3. Find the measure of each unknown angle. (Note: t is a tangent and O is the centre.)

a. 37°, θ, φ, O

b. 84°, 120°, φ, θ

c. s, α, ϕ, t, θ, 64°, φ, O, β

d.

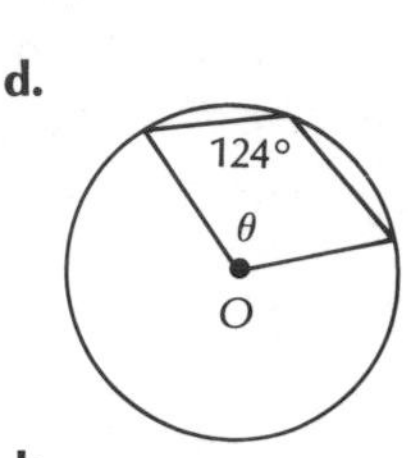

e. θ, φ, 72°, ϕ

f.

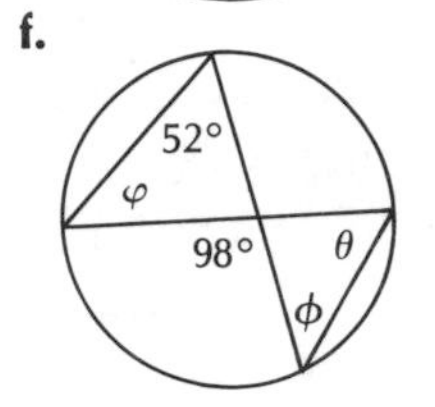

g.

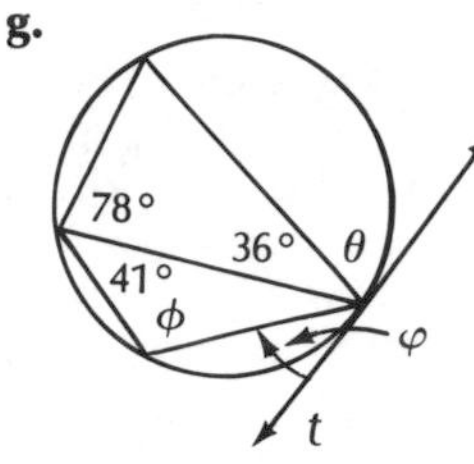

h.

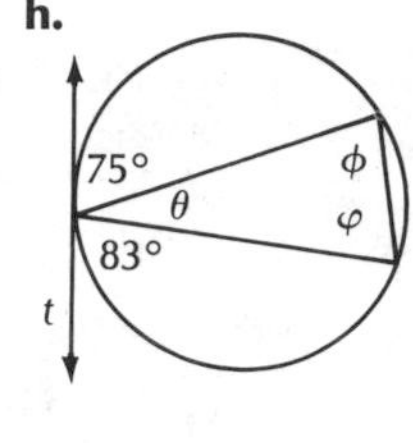

4. Solve for x.

a. x, 7, 48

b.

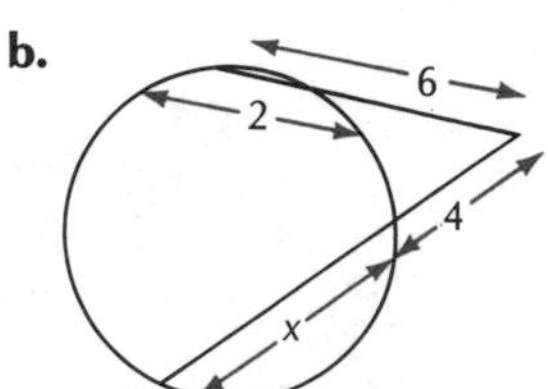

c.

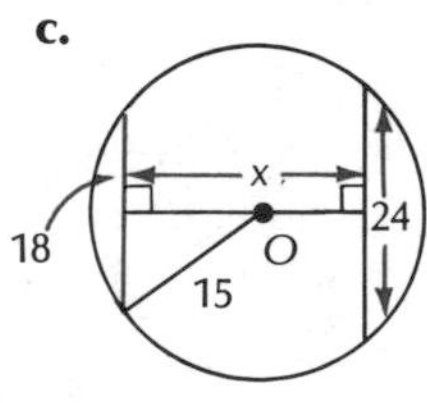

d.

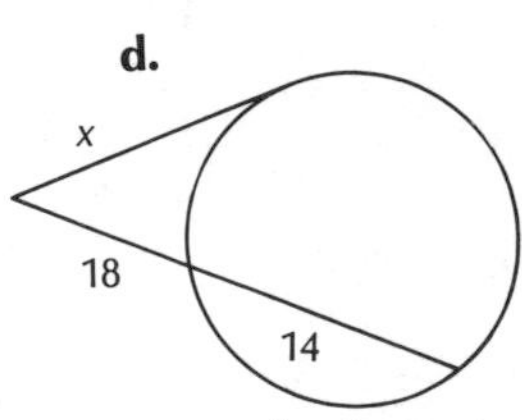

x is a tangent.

5. Quadrilateral $PQRS$ is inscribed in a circle. Find the sum of the four inscribed angles subtended by the sides of $PQRS$.

6. $\overline{XB}$ and $\overline{ZA}$ are altitudes of $\triangle XYZ$ that intersect at C. Prove that $\angle XCA = \angle XYZ$.

7. $\triangle ABC$ is inscribed in a circle. The tangents at A and B intersect at D, the tangents at A and C intersect at E, and the tangents at B and C intersect at F. If $\angle BAC = 38°$ and $\angle ABC = 75°$, find the measure of each angle of $\triangle DEF$.

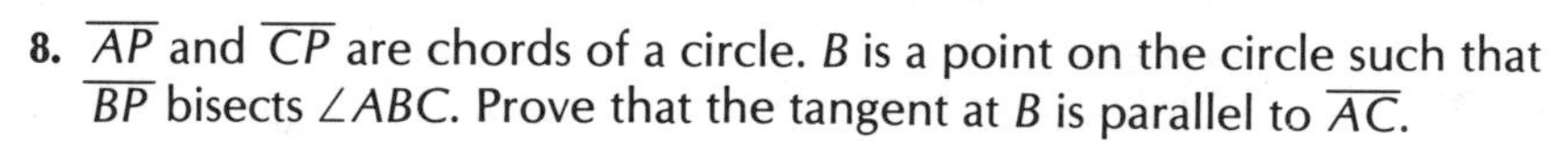

8. $\overline{AP}$ and $\overline{CP}$ are chords of a circle. B is a point on the circle such that $\overline{BP}$ bisects $\angle ABC$. Prove that the tangent at B is parallel to $\overline{AC}$.

9. Two circles are internally tangent at B. $\overline{BC}$, a chord of the larger circle, intersects the smaller circle at D. $\overline{BF}$, a second chord of the larger circle, intersects the smaller circle at E. Prove that $\overline{ED} \parallel \overline{FC}$.

B, E, D, F, C

10. Two circles are externally tangent at T. AB is the segment that is tangent to both circles at A and B. $\overline{AT}$ and $\overline{BT}$ are extended to intersect the circles at P and Q, respectively. Prove that $AT:BT = BQ:AP$.

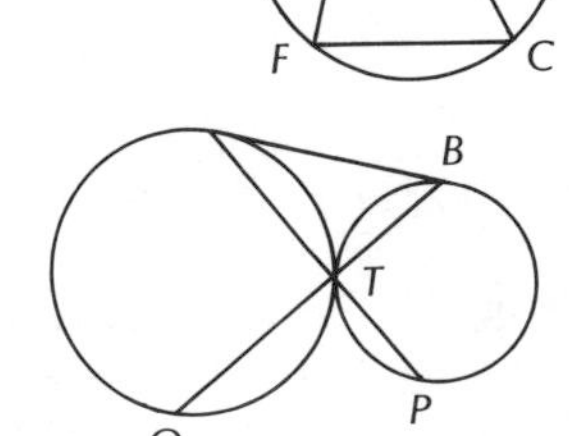

Cumulative Review

1. Find the solution set for each of the following.
   a. $|3x+2|=7$ b. $|2x+1|<7$

2. Given that $f(x)=3x+4$ and $g(x)=x^2-1$, find an equation of the composite functions $f\circ g$ and $g\circ f$.

3. The formula
$$P=101.3\left(\frac{1}{2}\right)^{\frac{h}{5.2}}$$
gives the atmospheric pressure, P, in kiloPascals (kPa), at an altitude h kilometres above sea level.
   a. What is the atmospheric pressure at sea level?
   b. Find the atmospheric pressure at an altitude of 26 km above sea level.
   c. Find the altitude at which the atmospheric pressure is 25 kPa.

4. Use a calculator to evaluate each of the following.
   a. $(1.2)^{3.4}$ b. $(6.2)^{\sqrt{2}}$ c. $(\sqrt{2})^{\sqrt{3}}$

5. If 2 and -3 are zeros of the polynomial $x^4+8x^3+7x^2-36x-36$, find all linear factors.

6. Prove that $\dfrac{\sec x+\tan x}{\sec x-\tan x}=\dfrac{1+2\sin x+\sin^2 x}{\cos^2 x}$.

7. A bridge, whose elliptical section is shown, is 40 m wide at water level and is 10 m above the water at its highest point. Can a barge 20 m wide and 8 m high pass under the bridge?

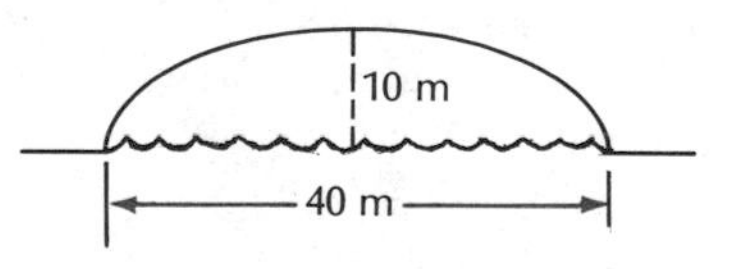

8. A rectangle has an area of 240 m². If its length and width are both decreased by 5 m, the area decreases by 130 m². Find the length and width of the rectangle.

9. The Nature Valley Ice Cream Company sells their ice cream to supermarkets in 5 different container sizes. The sizes are 0.5 L, 1 L, 2 L, 3 L, 4 L, and 6 L. A local grocery store feels that they are stocking too many sizes and decides to keep track of the amount of each size they sell over the next month.
   a. Draw a circle graph to display this data.
   b. Find the mean, median, and mode.
   c. Find the range, mean deviation, and standard deviation.

Size (litres)	Number sold
0.5	10
1	85
2	72
4	57
6	5

10. Given the parabola $(x+2)^2=24(y-5)$,
   a. sketch the parabola.
   b. find its focus and an equation of its directrix.

Glossary

a-b-c triangle The standard presentation of a triangle where vertices A, B, and C are opposite sides a, b, and c, respectively.

Absolute value The positive distance of a number from zero. The absolute value of n is written $|n|$.

Acute angle An angle measuring less than 90°.

Additive inverse The number which, when added to a given number, gives a sum of zero.

Adjacent side (ADJ) For a given angle in a right-angled triangle, the side which is adjacent to the angle and is not the hypotenuse.

Adjacent angles Two non-overlapping angles that share a common side and vertex.

Algebraic expression A mathematical expression containing sums, products, differences, or quotients involving variables.

Alternate angles Angles on opposite sides of a transversal that cuts two lines.

Altitude (of a triangle) A perpendicular line segment drawn from a vertex to the opposite side.

Ambiguous case (SSA) If two sides and a non-contained angle of a triangle are given, four possible triangles can be drawn.

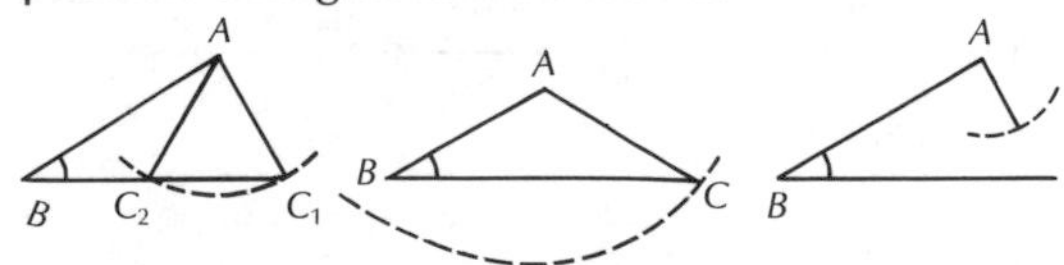

Amplitude In periodic motion, the amplitude is one-half the distance between the maximum and minimum values of the function.

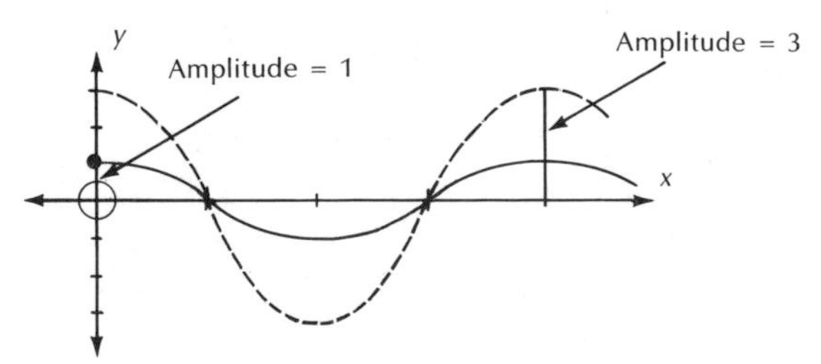

Amplitude modulation (AM) The encoding of a carrier wave by varying its amplitude in accordance with an input signal.

Angle of depression The angle between the horizontal and the line of sight to a point below the horizontal.

Angle of elevation The angle between the horizontal and the line of sight to a point above the horizontal.

Angle of rotation The measure of the difference in direction between the initial and the terminal rays of an angle.

Angular velocity The rate of change in the angle of rotation with respect to time.

Antipodal point The opposite ends of any diameter of a sphere.

Arc A part of a circle's circumference.

Argand plane The plane in which complex numbers are represented by rectangular coordinates. The horizontal axis is called the *real axis* and the vertical axis is called the *imaginary axis*.

Arithmetic mean The average value of an arithmetic sequence found by dividing the sum of all the terms in the sequence by the number of terms in the sequence.

Arrow diagram A diagram used to represent a relation. The domain and range are separated and arrows pair each member of the domain with the member it corresponds to in the range.

Associative property The property stating that, when three or more numbers are added or multiplied, the operations can be performed in any order.

$(a + b) + c = a + (b + c)$

$(a \times b) \times c = a \times (b \times c)$

Assumption A statement that is generally accepted as true, without proof. (also **axiom** or **postulate**)

Asymptote A line that a curve approaches indefinitely, yet never intersects.

Axiom A statement that is generally accepted as true, without proof. (also **assumption** or **postulate**)

Axis of Symmetry The line about which a figure is symmetrical.

Bar graph A graph displaying data in which the length of each bar is proportional to the number it represents.

Base (in a power) The factor repeated in a power.

Base (of a polygon) Any face of a polygon.

Biconditional statement A conditional statement and its converse combined.

Bilateral symmetry An object has bilateral symmetry if it maps onto itself under a reflection line.

Binomial A polynomial consisting of two terms.

Bisect To divide into two congruent parts.

Bisector of an angle The ray that divides a given angle into two equal adjacent angles.

Box and whisker plot An arrangement of data which facilitates a quick summary by highlighting the median, the extremes, and the hinge points.

Cartesian coordinate plane A rectangular coordinate plane.

Cast rule A method for remembering which trigonometric functions are positive in each quadrant. Cosines are positive in quadrant IV, all functions in quadrant I, sines in quadrant II, and tangents in quadrant III.

Central angle An angle with its vertex at the centre of a circle and bounded by two radii. (also **sector angle**)

Centre of a circle The point that is the same distance from all points in a circle.

Centre of an ellipse The middle point and the intersection point of the major and minor axes of an ellipse.

Centre of rotation The point about which a figure is rotated.

Centroid The point where the medians of a triangle intersect.

Chord (of a circle) A line segment with endpoints on the circumference of a circle.

Circle The set of all points in a plane that are equidistant from a fixed point, the centre. It can be represented by an equation of the form $(x + h)^2 + (y + k)^2 = r^2$, for $C(h, k)$ and radius r.

Circle graph The percentage of all data that a certain type of data represents is illustrated by a sector of the circle, such that the ratio of the sector angle to 360° is equal to the percentage of the whole population this data represents.

Circumference The perimeter of a circle.

Coefficient The numerical factor of an algebraic term.

Collinear points Points that lie on the same straight line.

Commutative property The property stating that two numbers can be added or multiplied in any order.

$a + b = b + a$

$a \times b = b \times a$

Complementary angles Two angles with measures that sum to 90°.

Complementary trigonometric functions Any pair of trigonometric functions such that the value of a given angle under one function is equal to the value of the angle's complement under the other function.

Complete the square The process of adding a term to a given expression so that the result is a perfect square trinomial.

Complex number A number of the form $a + bi$, where a and b are real numbers and $i^2 = -1$. $\boldsymbol{C}$ represents the set of complex or imaginary numbers.

Complex plane A rectangular coordinate system used to represent the complex number system. The real components are represented along the horizontal axis and the imaginary components are shown along the vertical axis.

Composite function For two given functions, f and g, the composite function $f \circ g$ is the function that maps each element in the domain of g onto an element in the range of f.
$f \circ g = f(g(x))$

Composition of transformations The process of performing successive transformations one after another.

Concentric circles Circles that lie in the same plane and have the same centre.

Concurrent lines Two or more lines that intersect in one point.

Concyclic points Points that lie on the circumference of the same circle.

Conditional statement A statement in the form "If p, then q". (also **implication**)

Cone A solid bounded by a circle and all line segments from a point outside the plane of the circle to all the points of the circle.

Congruent figures Figures with the same size and shape.

Conic section The figure which results from the intersection of a plane and a cone.

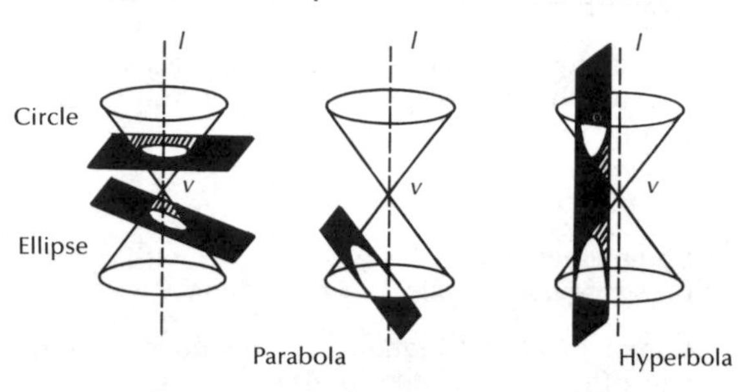

Conjugate axis The line segment that is the perpendicular bisector of the segment joining the foci of a hyperbola.

Conjugates The numbers $a\sqrt{b} + c\sqrt{d}$ and $a\sqrt{b} - c\sqrt{d}$, where a, b, c, d are rational, are called conjugates. Their product has the form $a^2b - c^2d$, which is a rational number. The expressions $a + bi$ and $a - bi$ are *complex conjugates*, with real number product $a^2 + b^2$.

Constant A quantity with a fixed value in a specified mathematical context.

Constant difference of a hyperbola The constant result of subtracting the square of the length of the conjugate axis from the square of the length of the transverse axis of a hyperbola.

Constant function A function of the form $f(x) = k$, where k is any number. It is represented graphically by a straight line parallel to the x-axis.

Constant of proportionality The constant k in a direct, inverse, or partial variation.

Constant of variation In an equation of the form $y = kx$ $(k = 0)$, which specifies a linear direct variation, k is the constant of variation. It is also called the *constant of proportionality*.

Constant sum of ellipse The sum of the squares of the lengths of the major and minor axes of an ellipse.

Contained angle The angle between two given sides of a polygon.

Continuous function If a function $f(x)$ tends toward a function $f(a)$ when x approaches a from a value $x = a \pm \epsilon$, no matter how small ϵ is, then $f(x)$ is continuous.

Continuous graph A graph that is defined for all elements of the real numbers, no matter how close together, is a continuous graph.

Converse A statement in the form "If q, then p", given the original implication "If p, then q".

Coordinate plane A number grid on a plane with an x-axis and a y-axis.

Coordinates The two numbers in an ordered pair that locate a point on a grid.

Coplanar lines Lines that lie in the same plane.

Corollary A theorem that follows directly as an extension of another theorem and is deducible from the first theorem.

Correlation A term used to indicate an obvious relation between two variables of statistical data, as displayed by some scatter diagrams.

Corresponding angles For a transversal that intersects two lines, the angles on the same side of the transversal and on the same side of each line.

Cosine For a given angle in a right-angled triangle, the ratio of the length of the adjacent side to the length of the hypotenuse.

Coterminal Angles Two angles defined by the expression $(\theta \pm 360n)$, $n \in \mathbf{Z}$ are coterminal angles. They share the same initial ray and terminal ray when they are in standard position.

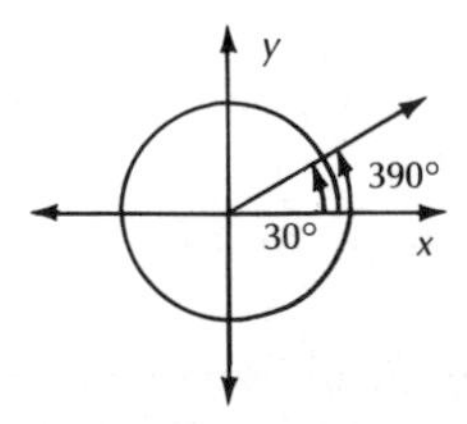

Counter-example A counter-example of an assumption is any application of the assumption for which the result is not the expected result. It is used to prove an *if-then* statement false.

Cube root The number which, when cubed, results in a given number.

Cumulative frequency The cumulative frequency of a set of events is the sum of all the frequencies of the events.

Curvature The curvature of a circle at any point on the circumference is the constant value $\frac{1}{r}$. The curvature of the arc of a figure is measured by the angle between the tangents drawn at the endpoints of the arc.

Curvilinear correlation Two factors of a frequency distribution have a curvilinear correlation if the appearance of the scatter diagram of their values can be approximated by a curved line.

Cyclic polygon A polygon with all its vertices on the circumference of the same circle. (also **inscribed polygon**)

Deductive reasoning The method of proof that involves reasoning from general, accepted statements to particular statements.

Defined term A term that can be explained using only other terms.

Degree A rotation of $\frac{1}{360}$ part of a complete revolution.

Degree of a polynomial The greatest degree of any term within the polynomial.

Degree of a term The maximum value of the exponents of the variables in the term.

Dependent events Two or more events such that the result of one event affects the results of the events that follow.

Descartes rule of signs In a polynomial expression, if there are two positive terms or two negative terms in succession, then there is a negative root. If two consecutive terms have alternate signs, there is a positive root.

Deviation Variation from a standard of reference, or the mean in a sequence.

Diagonal A line segment joining any two non-adjacent vertices of a polygon.

Diameter A chord of a circle that passes through its centre.

Difference For any two real numbers a and b, the difference, $a - b$, is the number whose sum with b is equal to a.

Difference of squares A binomial consisting of a squared term minus a different squared term.

Dilatation A transformation for which the shape of the image is the same as the shape of the object but the image may be enlarged or reduced in size.

Direct congruence Two or more figures having the same size, shape, and orientation.

Direct proof A proof of a statement that contains only true statements and conclusions that are equalities.

Direct variation A function of two variables, say x and y, defined by an equation of the form $y = kx$, where $k \neq 0$.

Directrix A fixed line about which a conic section is drawn.

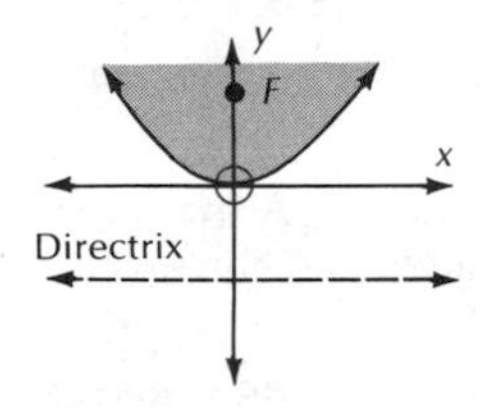

Discriminant The expression $b^2 - 4ac$ is called the discriminant of the quadratic equation $ax^2 + bx + c = 0$. It determines the nature of the roots of the equation.

Displacement The distance travelled in a given direction.

Distinct real root A root of a polynomial expression that is a member of the real numbers and has multiplicity equal to 1.

Distributive property The property that a product of a sum or difference can be written as a sum of or difference between two products.

$a \times (b + c) = (a \times b) + (a \times c)$
$a \times (b - c) = (a \times b) - (a \times c)$

Dodecagon A polygon with twelve sides.

Domain The set of the first elements of the ordered pairs of a relation.

Double root (of an equation) Two equal solutions to a quadratic equation $ax^2 + bx + c = 0$.

Double-angle formulas Formulas used to determine the trigonometric values of an angle of twice the measure of a given angle for which the trigonometric values are known.

e Euler's constant base of a natural logarithm, approximately equal to 2.7.

Edge The intersection of two faces of a three-dimensional figure.

Elimination A process of solving a system of equations whereby two or more simultaneous equations are combined so that one variable is removed and the number of equations reduced by one.

Ellipse The set of all points, P, in the plane such that the sum of the distances from P to the endpoints of a given line segment is a given constant k.

Entire radical A radical that contains no coefficients outside the radical sign.

Equation A mathematical statement showing two or more numbers or quantities equal.

Equilateral triangle A triangle with three congruent sides and three congruent angles.

Equivalent equations Equations that are obtained by performing the same operation on each side of a given equation.

Equivalent fractions Fractions that reduce to the same lowest terms.

Equivalent ratios Ratios that can be expressed as equivalent fractions.

Equivalent vectors Vectors that have the same magnitude and direction.

Escribed circle A circle drawn externally to a polygon to touch three consecutive sides with the first and third sides extended.

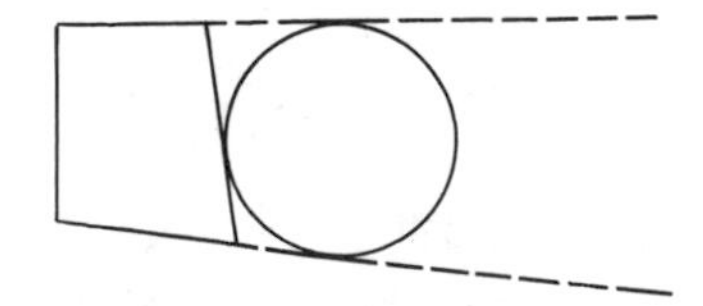

Event Any set of possible outcomes.

Experimental probability of an event The frequency of the occurrence of an event in a sample, divided by the total sample size.

Exponent (in a power) The number of times the base occurs as a factor.

Exponential equation An equation of the form $y = ab^x$, where the variable x appears in the exponent.

Expression A combination of mathematical symbols, variables, and numerals.

Exterior angle inequality The measure of an exterior angle of a triangle is greater than the measure of each of the non-adjacent angles.

Exterior angles Angles on the outside of two lines cut by a transversal.

Extraneous root A solution to a radical expression which, when substituted into the expression, does not give the expected result. It usually arises when the two sides of a radical expression are squared to obtain the solution.

Extreme value The highest or lowest value of the frequency or the dependent variable in a statistical distribution.

Factor Any one of the numbers or expressions or variables used in multiplication to form a product.

Fibonacci sequence The arithmetic sequence 1, 1, 2, 3, 5, 8, 13, . . . defined by the equation $f(n) = f(n-1) + f(n-2)$.

Focal radius The line segment joining a point on the circumference of an ellipse to a focus.

Focus A fixed point about which a conic section, a hyperbola, an ellipse, or a parabola, is oriented.

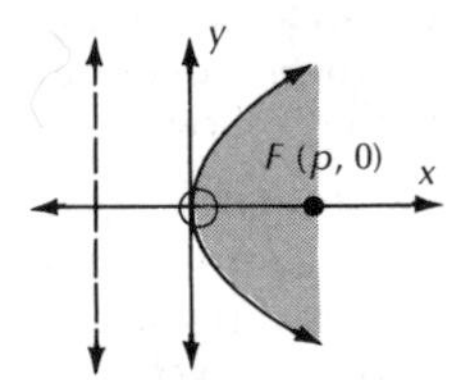

Formal deduction A format for presenting a proof of a statement using the given information, the statement to be proved, a diagram (if appropriate), and the proof itself.

Formula An equation that states a rule about quantities represented by variables.

Frequency The number of times a particular value in a set of data occurs.

Frequency distribution table A table that shows the frequencies of values in a set of data, often including columns for cumulative frequency, midpoint of interval, and subtotal.

Frequency modulation (FM) The encoding of a carrier wave by varying its frequency in accordance with an input signal.

Frequency polygon The graph of a frequency distribution consisting of a set of points obtained by finding the midpoint of each interval and plotting the frequency associated with each midpoint.

Function A relation in which each element of the domain corresponds to exactly one element of the range.

Fundamental period The initial period of a periodic function. It is found by letting $t=0$ in the equation $y=a\sin(n\theta + \epsilon)$.

General equation of a figure The equation defining a figure centred about any point on the Cartesian plane.

Geometric mean The term between two given terms of a geometric sequence. If r, s, and t are positive numbers such that $\frac{r}{s} = \frac{s}{t}$, then s is the geometric mean between r and t.

Glide reflection A transformation that is the combination of a reflection in a line and a translation parallel to the line.

Golden rectangle A rectangle such that the length, l, and the width, w, satisfy the equation $\frac{l}{w} = \frac{l+w}{l}$.

Great circle The circle formed when a plane intersects the centre of a sphere.

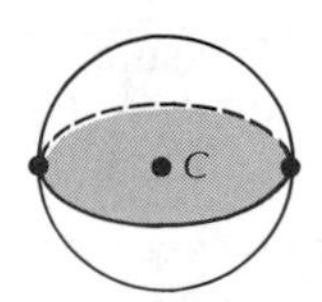

Greatest common factor (GCF) The largest number that is a factor of each of a set of numbers or the expression that has the greatest degree and numerical coefficient common to each of a set of expressions. (also **greatest monomial factor for polynomials**)

Greatest monomial factor for polynomials The largest number that is a factor of each of a set of numbers or the expression that has the greatest degree and numerical coefficient common to each of a set of expressions. (also **greatest common factor**)

Half-angle formulas Formulas used to determine the trigonometric values of an angle that is half the measure of a given angle for which the trigonometric values are known.

Half-life The time it takes until half of the original amount of a radioactive substance remains.

Half-turn symmetry A property exhibited in a figure for which there is a mapping that maps the figure onto itself under a rotation of 180°.

Height (of a polygon) The length of a perpendicular line segment from any vertex to the opposite side (or an extension of the opposite side).

Histogram A graph used to display frequency distribution of data using touching bars such that the height of the bars represents frequencies and the width of the bars represents interval width.

Horizontal line test If a horizontal line intersects the graph of a function f in two or more places, then f^{-1} is not a function.

Hyperbola The name of the shape of a graph of inverse variation which can be represented by an equation of the form $xy = k$, where $k \neq 0$.

Hyperbolic trajectory The hyperbola-shaped path of a moving particle or body.

Hypotenuse (HYP) The side opposite the right angle in a right-angled triangle.

Hypothesis The "p" statement in a conditional statement.

Identity elements 0 is the identity for addition and 1 is the multiplicative identity. $a + 0 = a$ and $a \times 1 = a$

Identity function The function I which maps every member of its domain onto itself.

Image The figure resulting from a transformation.

Imaginary number A number of the form $a + bi$, where $i = \sqrt{-1}$ and $b \neq 0$.

Imaginary component In the complex number $a + bi$, b is the imaginary component.

Imaginary zero The zero of a polynomial equation for which the root is an imaginary number.

Implication A statement in the form "If p, then q". (also **conditional statement**)

In phase Two points with the same relative position on a periodic curve are in phase.

Inadmissible root A solution of an equation which has no meaning in the context of the application.

Inconsistent equations A system of equations that has no solution. The equations of parallel lines are inconsistent because they do not intersect.

Independent events Events that have no effect on one another.

Indirect proof A method of proof that involves assuming that the conclusion of the statement to be proved is false and then working towards a contradiction.

Inductive reasoning A method used in proving that a particular proposition, $P(n)$, is true for *all* values of n. First prove that $P(1)$ is true. Then show that if $P(k)$ is true, $P(k + 1)$ is true.

Inequality A mathematical statement that one quantity is greater than ($>$) or less than ($<$) another.

Infinite rotational symmetry A figure has infinite rotational symmetry if, when rotating the figure about its centre by any angle, however small, it maps onto itself.

Initial ray Usually the positive x-axis, it is the original position of a ray before it is rotated to form an angle.

Inscribed angle An angle formed by two chords of a circle with a common vertex in the circle.

Inscribed polygon A polygon with each of its vertices on the circumference of a circle. (also **cyclic polygon**)

Integers The set of numbers consisting of $\{\ldots, -2, -1, 0, 1, 2, \ldots\}$. The integers are denoted by $\boldsymbol{Z}$.

Integral exponent An exponent that is an integer.

Interior angles Two angles on the inside of two lines cut by a transversal, and on the same side of the transversal.

Interquartile range The range between any two of the three values that divide a frequency distribution into four equal parts.

Intersecting lines Lines that have one point in common.

Interval (of statistical data) A set consisting of all the numbers between a pair of given numbers.

Inverse of a function The inverse of a function f is the function f^{-1} such that the composite $f(f^{-1}(x)) = 1$ for all x in the domain of f^{-1} and $f^{-1}(f(x)) = 1$ for all x in the domain of f.

Inverse variation A function of two variables, say x and y, defined by an equation of the form $xy = k$, where $k \neq 0$.

Irrational number A number that cannot be expressed as the quotient of two integers and whose decimal expansion neither terminates nor repeats.

Isolating a variable In a formula, solving for one variable in terms of the others.

Isometry A transformation that preserves distance between points.

Isosceles triangle A triangle with two congruent sides and two congruent angles.

Joint variation A function of more than two variables. A joint variation of x, y, and z is defined by an equation of the form $z = kxy$, where k is a constant.

Lateral surface area The sum of the areas of all lateral faces (all the faces of a three-dimensional figure excluding the bases).

Latus rectum The line segment drawn through the focus of a conic section that is perpendicular to the diameter and that intersects the curve of the conic section.

Law of Sines A trigonometric equivalence, used to determine the missing angle and side measures when at least one side and its opposite angle are known.

Least common multiple (LCM) The smallest non-zero number that is a multiple of each of two or more given numbers.

Least squares line A line determined by the *method of least squares*, that is, by minimizing the sum of the squares of the deviations of the given data.

Like radicals Radicals that have the same radicand when expressed in simplest form.

Line graph A graph made up of line segments used to show data representing changes over a period of time.

Line of best fit A trend line that is sketched to best approximate the distribution in a scatter diagram.

Line of sight A direct (imaginary) line from an observer to a sighted object.

Line of symmetry A line that divides a figure into two congruent parts that are reflection images of each other.

Linear correlation Two factors of a statistical distribution are said to have a linear correlation when the appearance of the scatter diagram of their values can be approximated by any straight line except a horizontal line.

Linear direct variation An equation of the form $y = kx, k \neq 0$.

Linear equation An equation of degree one that can be put into the form $Ax + By = C$ (where A and B not both equal to 0).

Linear function A function that is represented by a straight-line graph.

Linear programming The process of using inequalities to optimize business opportunities.

Linear relation A relation that is represented by a straight-line graph.

Linear term For a polynomial, a linear term has degree one.

Linear velocity Rate of change of displacement.

Linear-quadratic system A system of equations that consists of at least one equation of degree one and at least one equation of degree two but contains no equations of any greater degree.

Locus of points The figure formed by the set of all points and only those points that satisfy one or more specified conditions.

Logarithm The exponent which changes a given number, called the *base*, into any required number.

Lower quartile The set of percentiles between 0% and 25%.

Magnitude The absolute value of a number or a vector; size.

Magnitude of a complex number The real number value of the complex variable that is determined by

$$|a + bi| = \sqrt{a^2 + b^2}.$$

Magnitude of deviation The largest amount of the variation of a set of data about a given value or the mean of the data.

Major and minor arcs of a circle A chord $\overline{YZ}$, that is not a diameter, determines a major arc YXZ and a minor arc YZ. The measure of the minor arc is the measure of its central angle $\angle YOZ$. The measure of a major arc is found by subtracting the measure of the minor arc from 360°.

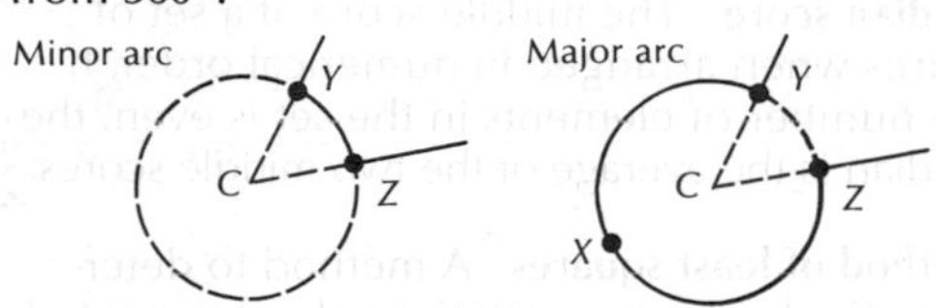

Major axis The chord of an ellipse that contains the ellipse's foci and centre.

Major sector of a circle A sector of a circle greater than a semicircle. Its central angle measure is in the range $180° < \theta < 360°$.

Many-to-one correspondence A relation in which more than one element in the domain corresponds to the same element in the range.

Mapping A correspondence of points or elements under some transformation or rule.

Maximum value The value of a function that occurs at the highest stationary point of the graph of the function. The point whose y-coordinate is the greatest value the function can have.

Mean The sum of a given set of values divided by the number of values.

Mean deviation The average variation from a standard of reference in a statistical distribution.

Measure of central tendency A single value representative of a set of data, such as mean, median, or mode.

Measure of variation The measure of the amount that output data in a statistical distribution deviates or varies within a given range or about an average value.

Median (of a triangle) A segment joining a vertex to the midpoint of the opposite side.

Median (statistics) The middle value of a set of data when the data are listed in numerical order.

Median fit line In a scatter diagram displaying either positive or negative correlation, a fitted line found by dividing the graph into three regions and using the medians of *x* and *y* values in the outer regions.

Median score The middle score of a set of scores when arranged in numerical order. If the number of elements in the set is even, the median is the average of the two middle scores.

Method of least squares A method to determine the best representative value for a set of data. It is based on the reasoning that this occurs when the sum of the squares of the deviations is a minimum.

Midpoint The point in a line segment that bisects the line.

Minimum value of a quadratic or trigonometric function The value of a function that occurs at the lowest stationary point of the graph of the function. The value whose *y*-coordinate is the least value the function can have.

Minor axis The chord of an ellipse that contains the ellipse's centre and that is perpendicular to the axis that contains the ellipse's foci.

Minor sector of a circle A sector of a circle less than a semicircle. Its central angle measure is in the range $0° < \theta < 180°$.

Mirror equation The sum of the reciprocals of the distance of the object from a mirror and the distance of the image from the mirror is equal to the reciprocal of the distance of the focus from the vertex of the mirror.

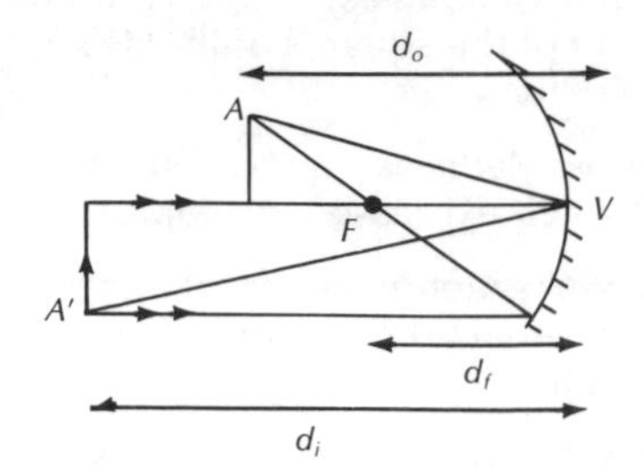

Mode The most frequently occurring value in a set of data.

Monomial A single-term expression that is either a numeral, one or more variables, or a product of a numeral and one or more variables.

Moving average A form of statistical average obtained by choosing a chronological range of values within a distribution and calculating the mean of each, such that the whole moving average has several successive values.

Multiple roots Repeated roots in the factored form of a polynomial equation.

Multiplicative inverse The number that a given number is multiplied by to yield a product of one.

Multiplicity of a root The multiplicity of a root in a polynomial equals the frequency of occurrences of the root in the factored form of the polynomial.

Mutually exclusive events Events that do not have common outcomes.

Natural logarithm Logarithm to the base e, where $e \doteq 2.71828$.

Natural numbers The set of all positive integers $\{1, 2, 3, \ldots\}$.

Negation of a statement A denial or contradiction of a given statement formed by placing the phrase "It is not true that . . ." before the statement.

Negative correlation A relationship between two statistical variables such that one variable tends to increase as the other decreases.

Negative reciprocals Two numbers whose product is -1.

Nested form of a polynomial A polynomial written in the form $x[\ldots(x[x(x-a)-b]-c)\ldots]-n$.

No correlation Two factors of a statistical distribution are said to have no correlation when the appearance of the scatter diagram of their values can only be approximated by a horizontal line.

Obtuse angle An angle that measures between 90° and 180°.

One-to-one correspondence A relation in which each element of the domain corresponds to exactly one element of the range and each element of the range corresponds to exactly one element of the domain.

Opposite side (OPP) For a given angle in a right-angled triangle, the side that is opposite the angle.

Opposite angles Angles formed by two intersecting lines that have a common vertex and are opposite to each other.

Order of rotational symmetry The number of times that the tracing of a figure fits onto the figure in one full turn.

Ordered pair A pair of numbers in which the order is important. $(3, -2)$ and $(-2, 3)$ are different ordered pairs.

Orientation The determination of direction in terms of standard directions such as clockwise and counterclockwise, or north, east, south, and west.

Origin The point where the x-axis and the y-axis intersect.

Outcome The result obtained from an action or an experiment.

Pantograph A tool used to copy a plane figure to a desired scale.

Parabola The name of the shape of a graph of quadratic direct variation that can be represented by an equation in the form $y = kx^2$, where $k \neq 0$.

Parabolic trajectory The parabola-shaped path of a moving particle or body.

Paraboloid A three dimensional parabola.

Parallel lines Lines in a plane that do not intersect.

Parallel planes Planes in space that do not intersect.

Parallelogram A quadrilateral with opposite sides parallel.

Partial variation A function of two variables, say x and y, defined by an equation of the form $y = kx + b$.

Percentile A statistical term used to describe a value that divides a range of a set so that a given percentage is lower than it.

Percentile ranking To assign a relative position in a number scale of 100 equal divisions of a range of a set of statistical data. It states the value below which a given percentage of the data lies.

Perfect correlation A relationship between two sets of data such that one is wholly dependent on the other and so the coefficient is equal to ± 1.

Perfect square A number whose square root is an integer.

Period The length of a phase of a periodic function.

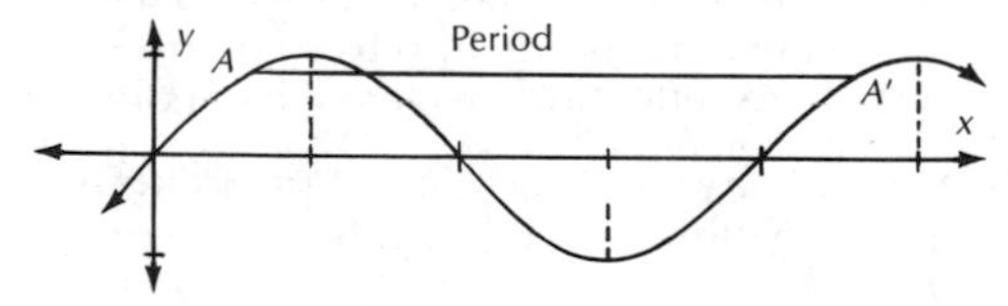

Period (of a repeating decimal) The set of digits that repeat, indicated by a solid line over the period. The period of $\frac{4}{11}$ is 36 since $\frac{4}{11} = 0.363\,636\ldots = 0.\overline{36}$.

Periodic decimal A decimal fraction such that, after a certain decimal place, one digit, or a set of digits in the same order, is repeated indefinitely. (also **repeating decimal**)

Periodic function A function $f(x)$ such that for every element x in the domain of f and for some constant $p \geq 0$, $f(x + p) = f(x)$. The function repeats the same value at equal intervals of the independent variable.

Periodic motion Motion that repeats the action at equal intervals of time.

Perpendicular bisector The line that bisects a segment and is perpendicular to it.

Perpendicular lines Lines that form 90° angles when they intersect.

Phase A stage in periodic or simple harmonic motion. An object completes a period of motion from phase to repeated phase.

Phase shift The horizontal translation of a periodic or trigonometric function.

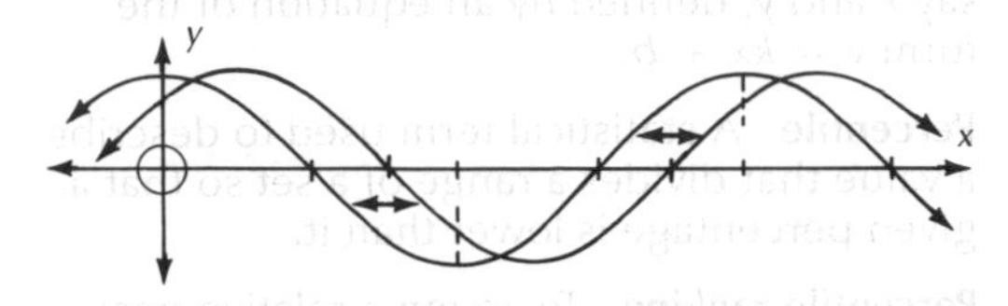

Pi (π) The ratio of the circumference of a circle to its diameter. $\pi \doteq 3.1416$

Piecewise linear Functions are said to be piecewise linear if their graphs consist of a line and line segments.

Plane A flat surface that has no thickness, extends infinitely in all directions, and contains the whole of a straight line drawn through any two points in it.

Plane figure A set of points in a plane.

Plane of symmetry A plane that divides a three-dimensional figure into two congruent parts that are reflection images of each other.

Plane symmetry A three-dimensional figure has plane symmetry if it has at least one plane of symmetry.

Point A point has an exact position. It has neither magnitude nor direction and is shown by a dot.

Point of contact The point where a plane or line is tangent to a given curve. It is also called the *point of tangency*.

Point symmetry A figure has point symmetry if there is a point O such that the figure maps onto itself under a rotation about O.

Point-slope form of a linear equation The equation of a straight line written in the form $y - y_1 = m(x - x_1)$, where (x_1, y_1) is a point on the line and m is the slope.

Polygon A closed figure whose sides are three or more line segments.

Polynomial A monomial or a sum of monomials.

Positive angle An angle determined by rotating the terminal ray in a counterclockwise direction.

Positive correlation A relationship between two statistical variables such that both variables tend to increase or decrease together.

Postal function A function consisting of disjointed constant functions over finite domains. This is also called a **step function**.

Postulate A statement that is generally accepted as true without proof. (also **assumption** or **axiom**)

Primary trigonometric function The functions sin*x*, cos*x*, and tan*x* are the primary trigonometric functions.

Principal square root (of a positive number) The positive square root.

Prism A three-dimensional figure whose bases are congruent polygons in parallel planes and whose faces are parallelograms.

Probability The ratio of the number of times a certain outcome can occur to the total possible outcomes.

Proportion An equality of ratios. The first and last terms are the *extremes*; the middle terms are the *means*.

Pure imaginary number A complex number $a + bi$, where $a = 0$.

Pyramid A three-dimensional figure whose base is a polygon and whose lateral faces are triangles.

Pythagorean identities The trigonometric identities involving the sine, cosine, and tangent functions and based on the Pythagorean Theorem of an *a-b-c* triangle, $a^2 + b^2 = c^2$.

Pythagorean triples Any three natural numbers a, b, and c satisfying the equation $a^2 + b^2 = c^2$.

Quadrant One of the four regions into which the coordinate axes separate the plane.

Quadrantal angle An angle whose initial ray is the positive x-axis and whose terminal ray is collinear with the x-axis or the y-axis. Thus, its measure is $\frac{n\pi}{2}$ rad.

Quadratic direct variation A function of two variables, say x and y, defined by an equation of the form $y = kx^2$, where $k \neq 0$.

Quadratic equation An equation of degree two that can be put into the form $Ax^2 + Bx + C = 0$ $(A \neq 0)$.

Quadratic formula The solutions of the general quadratic equation $ax^2 + bx + c = 0$, $(a \neq 0)$ are given by the quadratic formula $x = \frac{-b \pm \sqrt{b^2 - 4ac}}{2a}$.

Quadratic function A quadratic equation that satisfies the properties of a function.

Quadratic inverse variation A function of two variables, say x and y, defined by an equation of the form $x^2y = k$, where $k \neq 0$.

Quadratic-quadratic system of equations A system of two or more quadratic equations.

Quadratic trinomial A three-term polynomial of degree two.

Quotient identities The trigonometric identities for the tangent and cotangent functions, found by dividing one of the sine function or the cosine function by the other.

Radian A unit of angular measure. The measure of 1 rad is assigned to an angle subtended by an arc of length r equal to the length of the radius, r, of the circle.

Radical expression An expression containing a square root.

Radius A line segment that joins the centre of a circle to any point on its circumference.

Random number table A table of the digits 0 through 9 such that each digit is equally likely to occur in any place on the table.

Random sample A sample such that each member of the population is equally likely to appear.

Range (of a relation) The set of the second elements of the ordered pairs of a relation.

Range (of statistical data) The difference between the smallest and largest values of a set of data.

Range of variation For a frequency distribution, the difference between the highest and lowest values.

Rank correlation coefficient A measure of the interdependence of two random variables that have been assigned a relative position in a graded scale. The measure ranges in value from -1 to $+1$.

Ratio The relation existing between two quantities of the same kind. The ratio of x to y is $\frac{x}{y}$.

Rational expression An expression that contains variables in the denominator.

Rational numbers The set of numbers that can be expressed as the quotient of two integers, such that the divisor is not zero.

Rational roots Roots of a polynomial that can be expressed by rational numbers.

Rationalizing the denominator The process of changing the denominator from an irrational number to a rational number.

Raw data Data that has not yet been organized.

Ray Part of a line extending without end in one direction only.

Real component of a complex number In the complex number $a + bi$, a is the real component.

Real number Any number that is either a rational number or an irrational number.The set of real numbers is denoted by ***R***.

Reciprocal The number that a given number is multiplied by to yield a product of 1.

Reciprocal identities Every non-zero real number, r, has a reciprocal, or multiplicative inverse, such that the product of the number and its reciprocal is 1.

Reciprocal trigonometric functions Two trigonometric functions whose product is 1.

Rectangular hyperbola A hyperbola whose asymptotes are perpendicular. In this case the conjugate and transverse axes are equal.

Rectangular prism A prism with two parallel congruent rectangular bases.

Rectangular pyramid A pyramid with a rectangular base.

Recursive definition A sequence has a recursive definition if its terms are defined in relation to preceding terms.

Reference angle If an angle θ is not a quadrantal angle, then there is a unique acute angle α such that $\theta + \alpha$ or $\theta - \alpha$ is an integral multiple of 180° and α is a reference angle.

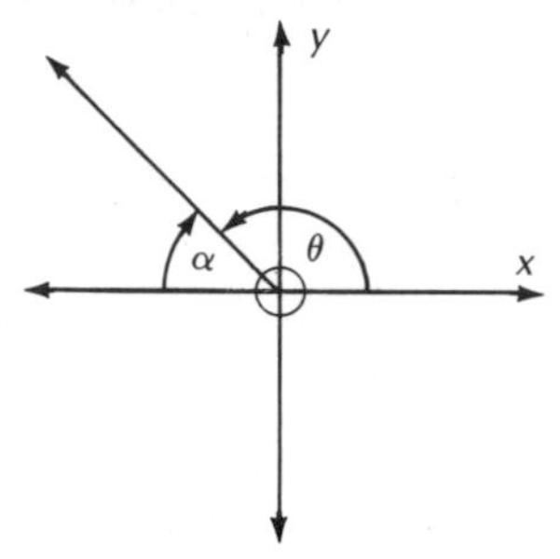

Reflection A transformation that flips the points of a plane over a line.

Reflection line A line in which a figure is reflected (or mapped) onto its image.

Reflex angle An angle that measures between 180° and 360°.

Regression line The line that shows the tendency for the expected value of a random variable to be closer to the mean value of its set than the independent variable used to predict it.

Regular polygon A polygon that is equilateral and equiangular.

Regular polyhedron A polyhedron whose faces are regular congruent polygons.

Relation A set of ordered pairs.

Relative frequency A ratio of the frequency of one element or interval of data to the total frequency.

Repeating decimal A decimal fraction in which, after a certain decimal place, one digit, or a set of digits in the same order, is repeated indefinitely. (also **periodic decimal**)

Replacement set (for a variable) The set of numbers that may be used to replace the variable.

Resultant vector The vector that is obtained by adding or subtracting two or more vectors.

Revolution One complete rotation about an axis or point.

Right angle An angle that measures 90°.

Root (of an equation) A solution of an equation.

Rotation A transformation such that the points of the plane are turned about a fixed point.

Rotational symmetry A figure has rotational symmetry if a tracing of the figure rotates onto itself in less than one full turn.

Scale drawing A drawing of an object with all dimensions in proportion to corresponding actual dimensions.

Scale factor A number representing the amount by which the dimensions of an object are multiplied to get the dimensions of its image.

Scale ratio The ratio of the size of the enlarged or reduced image to the object in a scale drawing.

Scalene triangle A triangle with no congruent sides or angles.

Scatter diagram A statistical graph displaying a two-variable set of data such as a set of points on a coordinate grid.

Scientific notation A method of writing a number as the product of a power of ten and a number between one and ten.

Secant A line that contains a chord, such as $\overleftrightarrow{AB}$.

Sector (of a circle) A region bounded by an arc and two radii.

Sector angle An angle with its vertex at the centre of a circle and bounded by two radii. (also **central angle**)

Segment (of a circle) A region bounded by an arc and a chord.

Semicircle An arc that joins the endpoints of a diameter.

Semi-logarithmic graph paper Graph paper with a uniform x-axis and a logarithmic scale along the y-axis.

Semi-major or semi-minor axis One-half the major or minor axis from the centre of the conic to one vertex or focus.

Similar figures Figures with the same shape but not necessarily the same size.

Sine For a given angle in a right-angled triangle, the ratio of the length of the opposite side to the length of the hypotenuse.

Skew lines Lines that are not parallel and do not intersect. The distance between any pair is defined by the length of the unique line that is perpendicular to both.

Slant asymptote An oblique line that a function, $f(x)$, approaches as x becomes very large.

Slope-intercept form of a linear equation The equation of a straight line in the form $y = mx + b$, where m is the slope of the line and b is the y-intercept.

Slope formula The slope of a line is the ratio $\frac{y_1 - y_2}{x_1 - x_2}$ where (x_1, y_1) and (x_2, y_2) are points on the line.

Slope of a line The steepness of a line; the ratio of the rise of a line to its run.

Small circle The section of the surface of a sphere formed when a plane intersects the sphere anywhere but the centre of the sphere.

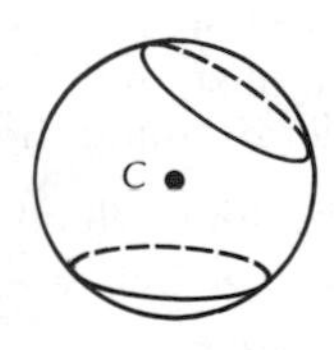

Smoothing (of data) A method for removing extreme highs and lows in statistical data collected over time, by substituting the median of three consecutive values for each original value, excluding the first and last values.

Solid A three-dimensional figure whose inside is completely filled.

Solution set The set of values in the replacement set for a variable that make the sentence true.

Sphere The set of all points in space that are a given distance from a fixed point.

Square root A number that, when multiplied by itself, results in the given number.

Standard deviation The principal square root of the mean value of the squares of the individual deviations in a distribution.

Standard equation of a figure The equation defining a figure in standard position.

Standard form of a linear equation The equation of a straight line written in the form $Ax + By + C = 0$, where $A, B, C \in \mathbf{R}$.

Standard position of a figure The accepted way of showing a figure in the Cartesian coordinate plane by placing the centre of the figure at the origin and placing the foci on the x-axis or the y-axis.

Standard position of an angle The accepted way of presenting an angle in the Cartesian coordinate plane such that its initial ray is collinear with the positive x-axis.

Statistics The study of methods of collecting and analysing data.

Stem and leaf plot An arrangement of data that facilitates the finding of the mean, median, and mode.

Step function See **postal function.**

Straight angle An angle measuring 180°.

Subtend To be opposite to and to delimit, as chord $\overline{AB}$ or arc AB subtends $\angle APB$.

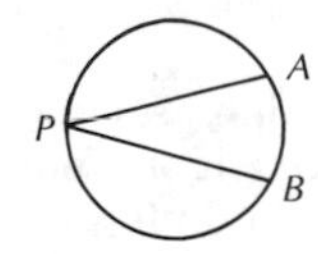

Sum and difference formulas The formulas used to find the trigonometric values of the sum or difference of two or more angles using the trigonometric values of each angle.

Supplementary angles Two angles with measures that sum to 180°.

Surface area The total area of the polygonal regions (faces) of a polyhedron.

Synthetic division A method of using the detached coefficients of a given polynomial to display the process of dividing a polynomial in x by $x - r$.

System of equations A set of equations in the same variables.

System of inequalities A set of inequalities in the same variables.

Tangent (of a circle) A line in the same plane as the circle that has one, and only one, point in common with the circle. The common point is called the point of contact.

Tangent (trigonometry) For a given angle in a right-angled triangle, the ratio of the length of the opposite side to the length of the adjacent side.

Term A mathematical expression using numerals or variables or both to indicate a sum, difference, product, or quotient.

Terminal ray The final position of a ray after it has been rotated to form an angle.

Theorem A statement that has been proved.

Theoretical probability The number of favourable outcomes divided by the number of possible outcomes.

30°-60°-90° triangle A triangle whose three angles measure 30°, 60°, and 90°.

Transformation A one-to-one mapping from a whole plane to a whole plane.

Transversal A line that intersects two or more lines.

Transverse axis The line segment that passes through the foci of a hyperbola. It is the perpendicular bisector of the conjugate axis of the hyperbola.

Trigonometric function A circular function defined in terms of trigonometric ratios. If $P(x, y)$ lies on the circumference of the unit circle, then the trigonometric functions are $\sin\theta = y$, $\cos\theta = x$, and $\tan\theta = \frac{y}{x}$.

Trigonometry An area of mathematical study involving the measurement of triangles.

Trinomial A polynomial consisting of three terms.

Trinomial square A three-term polynomial that is the product of squaring a binomial.

Unbiased sample A sample that gives a good representation the group being studied.

Unit circle A circle whose radius measures 1 unit.

Upper quartile The set of percentiles between 76% and 100%.

Variable A letter used to represent an unknown quantity.

Vector A directed line segment or arrow. The length of the segment is the magnitude of the vector and the direction of the arrow indicates the direction of the vector.

Velocity Speed in a given direction.

Vertex (of a conic section) The point where the parabola intersects the major axis of symmetry of a conic section. Also the maximum or minimum point of the graph of a parabola.

Vertex (of a parabola) The point where a parabola intersects the axis of symmetry.

Vertical line test A test to determine whether a relation is a function. If a vertical line intersects a graph of a relation in two or more distinct points then it is not a function.

Weighted mean The mean value of a set of numbers that have undergone the weighting process.

Weighting The process by which the elements of a set of numbers are assigned coefficients that establish their importance within the set for determining the average.

Whole numbers The set of all natural numbers and zero. $\{0, 1, 2, 3, \ldots\}$

x-axis The horizontal number line in a coordinate plane.

x-intercept The x-coordinate of a point where a graph crosses the x-axis.

y-axis The vertical number line in a coordinate plane.

y-intercept The y-coordinate of a point where a graph crosses the y-axis.

Zeros of a polynomial A number, r, is the zero of a polynomial, $p(x)$, if $p(r) = 0$. A zero of a polynomial, p, is a solution of the equation $p(r) = 0$.

Answers to Exercises

UNIT 1

Exercise 1-1, pages 4-7

1. a. $D = \{-1, 0, 1, 2, 3\}$; $R = \{1, 8, 9, 10, 14\}$
b. $D = \{-3, -1, 1, 3\}$; $R = \{2, 6\}$
c. $D = \{-2, -1, 0, 1, 2\}$; $R = \{0, 1, 3\}$
d. $D = \{-2, -1, 0, 1, 2, 3\}$; $R = \{-2, -1, 0, 1, 2, 3\}$
2. a. function → only one y-coordinate for each x.
b. not a function → two y-coordinates for $x = 4$.
c. function (as in a) **d.** not a function — two y-coordinates for $x = -1, -2$ **e.** not a function → two y-coordinates for $x = 1, 2, 3$ **3. a.** function
b. function **c.** function **d.** function **e.** not a function **f.** function **4. a.** 51 **b.** ± 3
c. ± 2 **d.** -6 **e.** 19 **f.** -1.5 **g.** 0 **h.** $\pm\sqrt{5}$
5. a. $y = 10$ **b.** $y = -2$ **c.** $x = 2$
d. $x = -2$ **e.** $y = 13$ **f.** $x = -3$ **g.** $x = 0$
h. $x = -\frac{1}{3}$
6. a. $D = \{x \mid x \in \boldsymbol{R}, -3 \leq x \leq 4\}$;
$R = \{y \mid y \in \boldsymbol{R}, -1 \leq y \leq 2\}$
b. $D = \{x \mid x \in \boldsymbol{R}, -4 \leq x \leq 5\}$;
$R = \{y \mid y \in \boldsymbol{R}, 0 \leq y \leq 3\}$
c. $D = \{x \mid x \in \boldsymbol{R}, -3 \leq x \leq 4\}$;
$R = \{y \mid y \in \boldsymbol{R}, 2 \leq y \leq 6\}$
d. $D = \{x \mid x \in \boldsymbol{R}, 1 \leq x \leq 6\}$;
$R = \{y \mid y \in \boldsymbol{R}, -4 \leq y \leq 4\}$
7. a. $R(f) = \{2, 5, 8, 11\}$ **b.** $R(g) = \{-2, -1, 2\}$
c. $R(h) = \{\frac{3}{2}, 2, 3, 6\}$
d. $R(p) = \{y \mid y \in \boldsymbol{R}, 0 \leq y \leq 2\sqrt{2}\}$
8. a. $D = \{x \mid x \in \boldsymbol{R}\}$; $R = \{y \mid y \in \boldsymbol{R}, y \geq -5\}$
b. $D = \{x \mid x \in \boldsymbol{R}\}$; $R = \{y \mid y \in \boldsymbol{R}\}$
c. $D = \{x \mid x \in \boldsymbol{R}, x \neq 0\}$; $R = \{y \mid y \in \boldsymbol{R}, y \neq 0\}$
d. $D = \{x \mid x \in \boldsymbol{R}, x \geq 3\}$; $R = \{y \mid y \in \boldsymbol{R}, y \geq 0\}$
e. $D = \{x \mid x \in \boldsymbol{R}, x \neq 1\}$; $R = \{y \mid y \in \boldsymbol{R}, y \neq 0\}$
f. $D = \{x \mid x \in \boldsymbol{R}\}$; $R = \{y \mid y \in \boldsymbol{R}\}$
g. $D = \{x \mid x \in \boldsymbol{R}, x \geq 0\}$; $R = \{y \mid y \in \boldsymbol{R}, y \geq 0\}$
h. $D = \{x \mid x \in \boldsymbol{R}, x \geq -3\}$; $R = \{y \mid y \in \boldsymbol{R}, y \geq 0\}$
i. $D = \{x \mid x \in \boldsymbol{R}, x \neq 2\}$; $R = \{y \mid y \in \boldsymbol{R}\}$
j. $D = \{x \mid x \in \boldsymbol{R}\}$; $R = \{y \mid y \in \boldsymbol{R}, y \geq 0\}$
k. $D = \{x \mid x \in \boldsymbol{R}, x \leq 2\}$; $R = \{y \mid y \in \boldsymbol{R}, y \leq 0\}$
l. $D = \{x \mid x \in \boldsymbol{R}, -2 \leq x \leq 2\}$;
$R = \{y \mid y \in \boldsymbol{R}, 0 \leq y \leq 2\}$
9. a. $4x^2 - 1$ **b.** $x^4 - 1$ **c.** $\frac{x^2}{4} - 1$ **d.** $x^2 + 2x$
e. $k^2 - 1$ **f.** $m^2 - 4m + 3$ **10. a.** $k = -6$
b. $n = 1$ **c.** $a = 5$ **11. a.** function
b. function **c.** not a function **d.** function
e. not a function **f.** function **12. a.** $E = 5.72h$
b. $C = 27.50n + 37.50$
13. a. $D = \{x \mid x \in \boldsymbol{R}, -1 \leq x \leq 4\}$;
$R = \{y \mid y \in \boldsymbol{R}, 1 \leq y \leq 17\}$; function
b. $D = \{x \mid x \in \boldsymbol{R}, 3 \leq x \leq 5\}$;
$R = \{y \mid y \in \boldsymbol{R}, |y| \leq 4\}$; not a function
14. a.

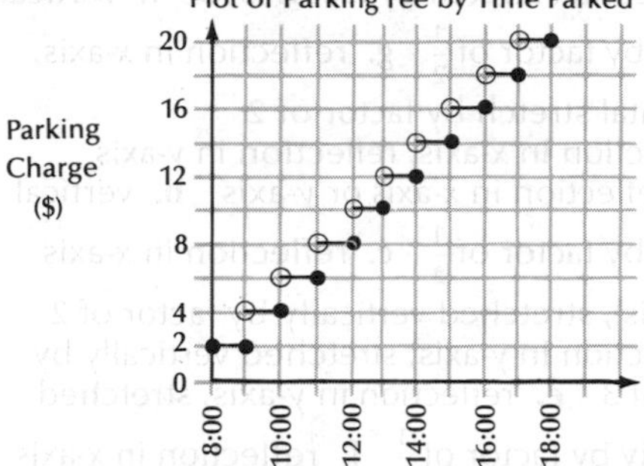

b. The graph's appearance is like a set of steps.

15. a.

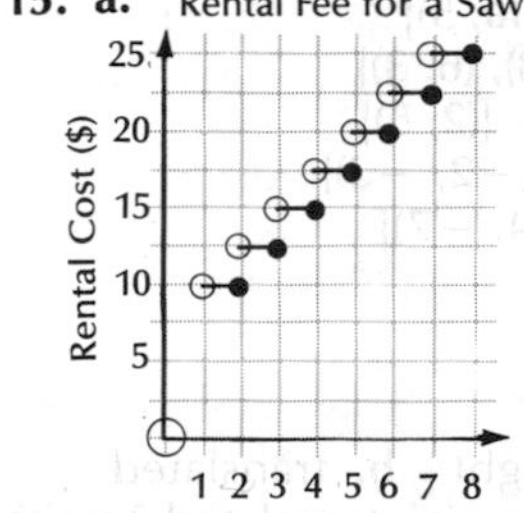

b.

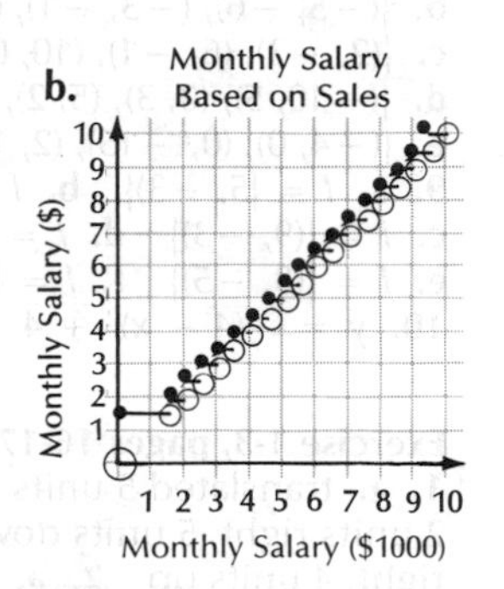

16. a. $y = 2x + 1$ **b.** $y = x^2 - 2$
c. $xy = 8$ **d.** $y = \frac{6}{x - 1}$
17. a. $D = \{x \mid x \neq 1, x \in \boldsymbol{R}\}$; $R = \{y \mid y \neq 1, y \in \boldsymbol{R}\}$
b. $D = \{x \mid x \neq 0, x \in \boldsymbol{R}\}$; $R = \{y \mid y \neq 1, y \in \boldsymbol{R}\}$
c. $D = \{x \mid x \neq 0, x \in \boldsymbol{R}\}$; $R = \{y \mid y \leq 0.25, y \in \boldsymbol{R}\}$

Exercise 1-2, pages 11-13

1. a. reflection in x-axis **b.** translated +4 units to the right **c.** stretched horizontally by a factor of 2 **d.** vertical stretch by a factor of $\frac{1}{2}$
2. c. ellipse: $x^2 + y^2 = 16$; centre (0,0)
3. a. $y = -x^2$ **b.** $y = 3x$ **c.** $y = -\frac{1}{x}$
d. $y = \left(\frac{5}{3}\right)x - 1$ **e.** $y = 2 - \left(\frac{5}{2}\right)x$
4. a. $y = -x^2$ **b.** $y = \frac{x^3}{27}$ **c.** $y = \frac{1}{2}|x|$
d. $y = 2^{-x}$ **6. a.** reflection in y-axis

b. horizontal stretch by factor of $\frac{1}{2}$ **c.** vertical stretch by factor of 3 **d.** reflection in x-axis
e. horizontal stretch by factor of 3 **f.** vertical stretch by factor of $\frac{1}{2}$ **g.** reflection in x-axis, horizontal stretch by factor of 2
h. reflection in x-axis, reflection in y-axis
7. a. reflection in x-axis or y-axis **b.** vertical stretch by factor of $\frac{1}{2}$ **c.** reflection in x-axis (or y-axis), stretched vertically by factor of 2
d. reflection in y-axis, stretched vertically by factor of 3 **e.** reflection in y-axis, stretched vertically by factor of $\frac{1}{2}$ **f.** reflection in x-axis and y-axis, stretched vertically by factor of 2
8. a. $\{(0, -5), (-3, -3), (6, -7), (9, -5)\}$
b. $\{(-5, -6), (-3, -1), (0, 5), (1, -3)\}$
c. $\{(2, -3), (6, -1), (10, 0), (14, 1.5)\}$
d. $\{(-10, 5), (0, 3), (5, 2), (10, 5)\}$
e. $\{(-4, 0), (0, -15), (2, 18), (6, 3)\}$
9. a. $I = \{5, -3)\}$ **b.** $I = \{(2, 5)\}$
c. $I = \{(9, -3)\}$ **d.** $I = \{(-2, -3)\}$
e. $I = \{(8, -5)\}$ **f.** $I = \{(4, -7)\}$
10. $y = -(4 - x)^2 + 4$

Exercise 1-3, pages 16-17

1. a. translated 5 units right **b.** translated 2 units right, 5 units down **c.** translated 3 units right, 4 units up **2. a.** $y = (x - 3)^2$
b. $y = -3x - 1$ **c.** $y = (x - 3)^3 - 2$
4. a. $y = (x - 4)^2$ **b.** $y = -x^2 - 2$
c. $y = \sqrt{-x} + 3$ for $x \leq 0$ **5. a.** reflection in the y-axis **b.** translation 3 units to the right
c. translation 3 units down **d.** vertical stretch by factor of 2, reflection in x-axis **e.** vertical stretch by factor of 3 **f.** translated 3 units up, 1 unit to the left **g.** reflection in x-axis, horizontal stretch by factor of 2 **h.** reflection in the origin
6. a. horizontal stretch by factor of $\frac{1}{3}$; translation 2 units down **b.** translation 1 unit right; translation 3 units down **c.** translation 1 unit right; vertical stretch by factor of 4
d. horizontal stretch by factor of 2; translation 1 unit up **e.** reflection in y-axis; translation 1 unit up **f.** vertical stretch by factor of 2; translation 3 units down **g.** translation 1 unit right; vertical stretch by factor of 5; translation 5 units down
h. translation 2 units right; translation 5 units down **7. a.** $y = \frac{1}{4}x^2 + 3$ **b.** $y = \frac{1}{2(x + 1)}$
c. $y = -3x + 5$ **d.** $y = -\frac{1}{2}(x + 5)$
e. $y = \frac{3}{4}x^2 - 9$ **f.** $y = \frac{1}{x - 1} - \frac{2}{3}$
g. $y = \frac{-(x + 1)^3 - 1}{2}$ **8.** (0, 0)
9. a. translated 2 units down **b.** translated 2 units up; stretched vertically by factor of $\frac{1}{5}$
c. translated 4 units up; reflected in the y-axis; stretched vertically by factor of 5; stretched horizontally by factor of 2 **d.** translated 3 units down; stretched horizontally by factor of 1.5; reflected in the y-axis **e.** translated 3 units up; stretched horizontally by factor of 4
f. translated 2 units up; stretched horizontally by factor of $\frac{1}{3}$; stretched vertically by factor of 0.5
10. reflected in y-axis **11.** $R(x) = 0$

Exercise 1-4, page 20

1. a. 19 **b.** -5 **c.** 4.5 **d.** 0 **e.** 23 **f.** -5
g. -6 **h.** $\frac{56}{3}$ **i.** 14.5
2. a.

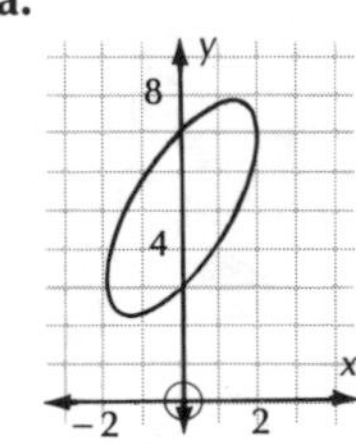

b.

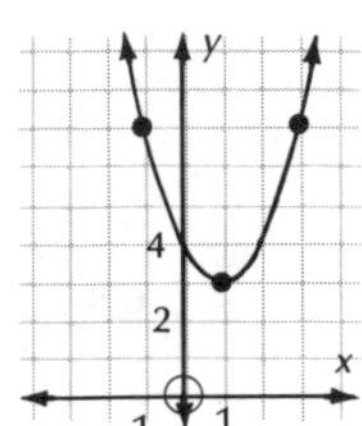

c.

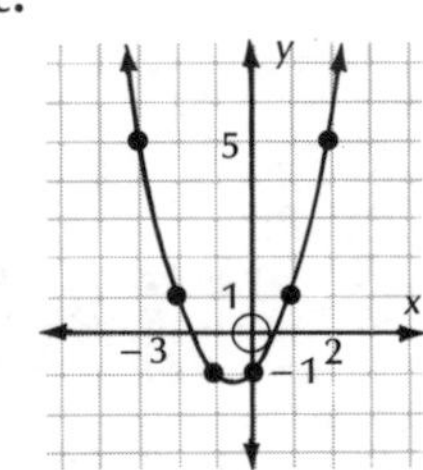

3. a. $(f + g)(x) = x^2 + x - 2$
b. $(f - g)(x) = -x^2 + x$ **c.** $(f + h)(x) = 3x^2 - x$
d. $(g + h)(x) = 4x^2 - 2x$
e. $(h - g)(x) = 2(x^2 - x + 1)$
f. $(f - g + h)(x) = 2x^2 - x + 1$ **4. a.** 10
b. -6 **c.** 24 **d.** 30 **e.** 14 **f.** 16
5. a.

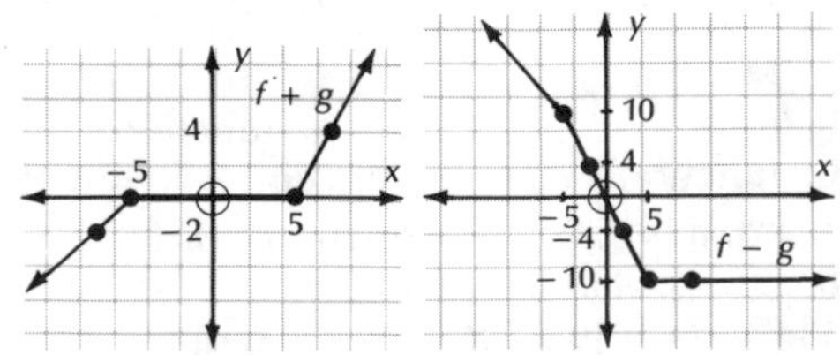

b.

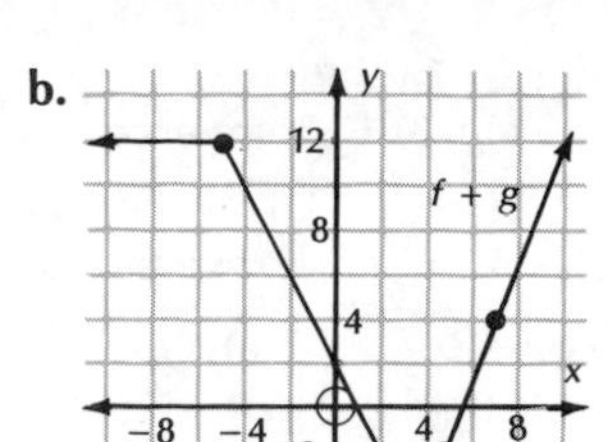

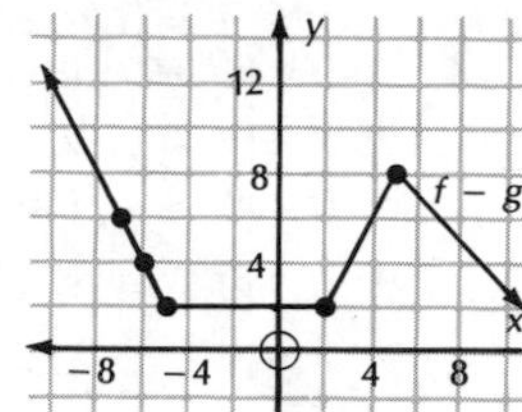

c.

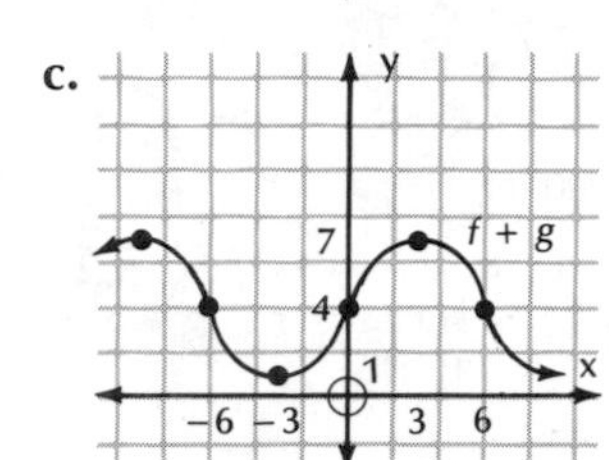

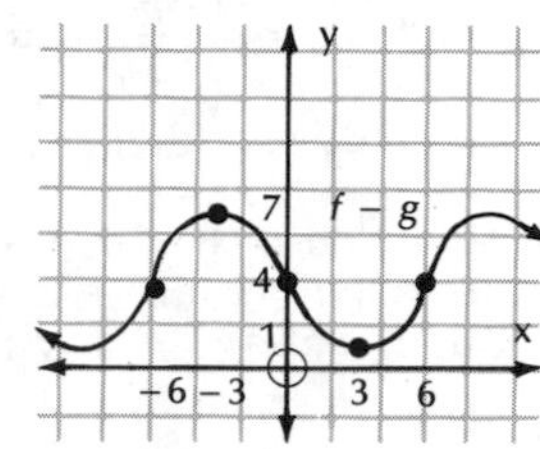

d.

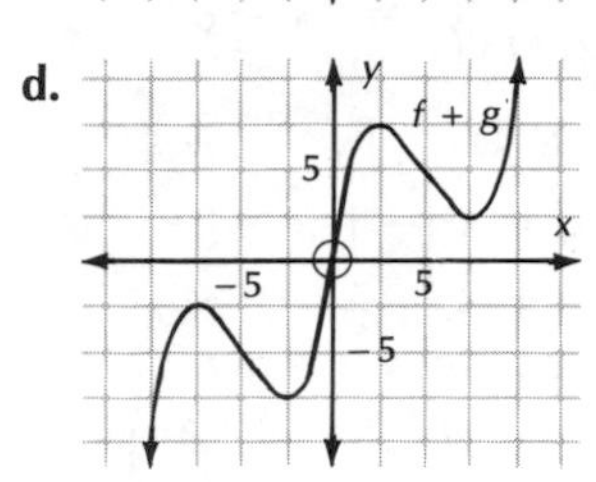

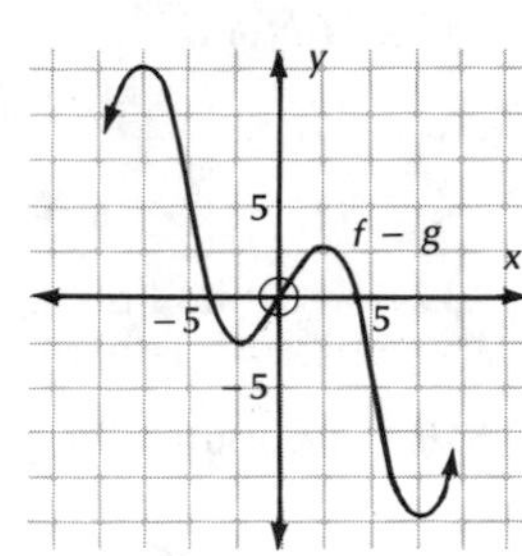

e.

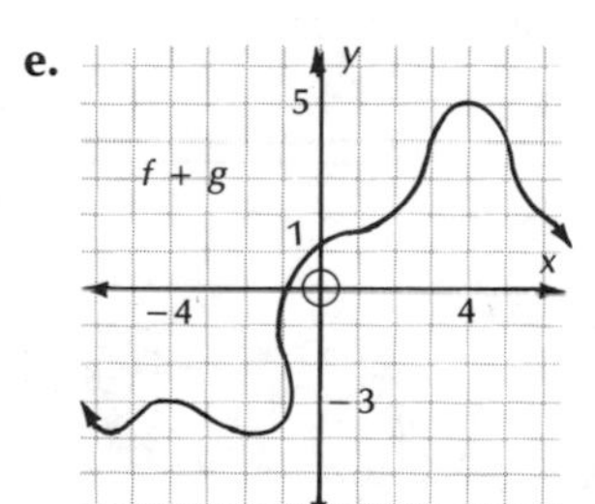

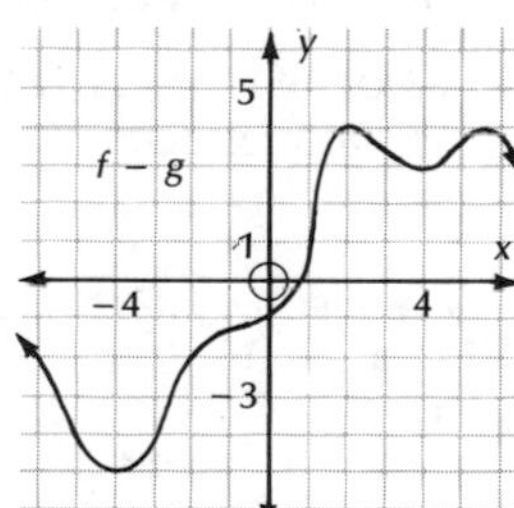

f.

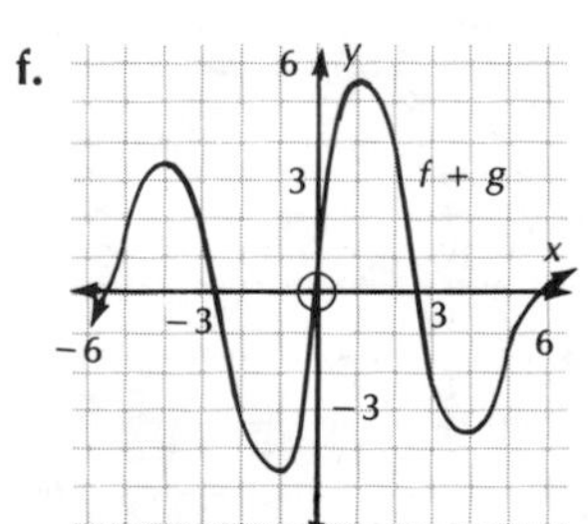

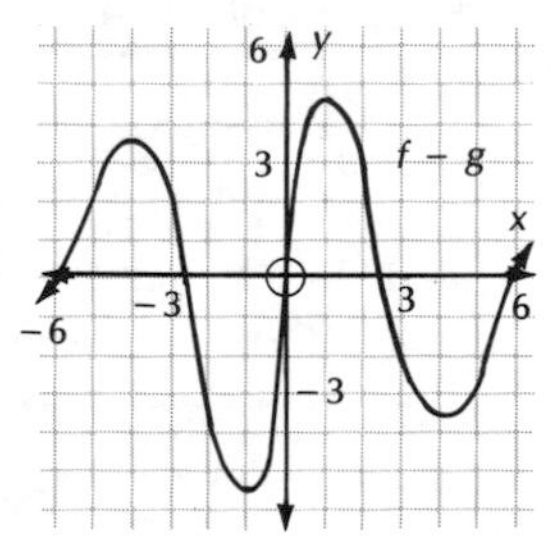

Review, page 21

1. a. $D = \{-2, -1, 0, 2, 3\}$; $R = \{-1, 1, 5, 7\}$; function
   b. $D = \{-1, 0, 1, 2, 3\}$; $R = \{-2, -1, 2, 7\}$; function
   c. $D = \{-5, -1, 2, 3\}$; $R = \{-5, -2, 4, 6, 7\}$; not a function
   d. $D = \{x \mid x \in \boldsymbol{R}, -3 \le x \le 6\}$; $R = \{-2, 1, 3\}$; function
   e. $D = \{x \mid x \in \boldsymbol{R}, 1 \le |x| \le 6\}$; $R = \{y \mid y \in \boldsymbol{R}, 1 \le y \le 6\}$; function
   f. $d = \{x \mid x \in \boldsymbol{R}, x > 0\}$; $R = \{y \mid y \in \boldsymbol{R}, y \ne 0\}$; not a function
2. a. $R(f) = \{-7, -5, -3, -1, 1, 3\}$
   b. $R(f) = \{y \mid y \in \boldsymbol{R}, -2 \le y < 2\}$
3. a. $y = \sqrt{4(x - 4)}$ b. $y = \frac{1}{4}(x - 3)^2$
4. a. translated 1 unit down
   b. vertical stretch by factor of 2
   c. reflection in y-axis
   d. translated 1 unit right, 2 units up
   e. i) reflected in y-axis
   ii) horizontal stretch by factor of 2
   f. i) horizontal stretch by a factor of 2
   ii) translated 3 units up
5. a. 8 b. 14 c. −28 d. 0 e. $x^2 + 5x - 6$
   f. $x^2 - 5x - \dfrac{12}{x} + 8$

Exercise 1-5, pages 24-25

1. a. $f \circ g = \{(0, 3), (1, 5), (3, 1)\}$
   b. $g \circ f = \{-3, 27), (-2, 1), (-1, 3), (1, 3), (2, 1), (3, 27)\}$
   c. $g \circ f(-1) = \{3\}$
   d. $f \circ g(1) = \{5\}$ e. $R(f) = \{5, 3, 1, -1\}$
   f. $D(f) = \{-3, -2, -1, 0, 1, 2, 3\}$
   g. $D(g) = \{0, 1, 2, 3, 4, 5\}$
   h. $R(g) = \{1, 2, 3, 6, 18, 27\}$
   i. $D(g \circ f) = \{-3, -2, -1, 1, 2, 3\}$
   j. $R(f \circ g) = \{1, 3, 5\}$ k. $D(f \circ g) = \{0, 1, 3\}$
   l. $R(g \circ f) = \{1, 3, 27\}$
2. a. 3 b. 10 c. 8 d. 3 e. 10 f. 37 g. 8 h. 48 i. 26 3. a. 3 b. 4 c. −2
4. a. $(f \circ g)(x) = 2x^2 + 3$
   b. $(g \circ f)(x) = 4x^2 - 4x + 3$
   c. $(h \circ f)(x) = \dfrac{1}{2x - 4}$
   d. $(h \circ g)(x) = \dfrac{1}{x^2 - 1}$
   e. $(f \circ h)(x) = \dfrac{2}{x - 3} - 1$
   f. $(g \circ h)(x) = \dfrac{1}{(x - 3)^2} + 2$
5. $R(d) = 38\,500 - 1650(d - 4)^2 - \dfrac{200}{70 - 3(d - 4)^2}$
6. a. $(f \circ g)(x) = \sqrt{x} - 1$; $(g \circ f)(x) = \sqrt{x - 1}$
   $D(f) = \{x \mid x \in \boldsymbol{R}\}$; $R(f) = \{y \mid y \in \boldsymbol{R}\}$
   $D(g) = \{x \mid x \in \boldsymbol{R}, x \ge 0\}$;
   $R(g) = \{y \mid y \in \boldsymbol{R}, y \ge 0\}$

$D(f \circ g) = \{x | x \in \boldsymbol{R}, x \geq 0\}$;
$R(f \circ g) = \{y | y \in \boldsymbol{R}, y \geq -1\}$
$D(g \circ f) = \{x | x \in \boldsymbol{R}, x \geq 1\}$;
$R(g \circ f) = \{y | y \in \boldsymbol{R}, y \geq 0\}$

b. $(f \circ g)(x) = (x + 1)^2$; $(g \circ f)(x) = x^2 + 1$;
$D(f) = \{x | x \in \boldsymbol{R}\}$; $R(f) = \{y | y \in \boldsymbol{R}\}$
$D(g) = \{x | x \in \boldsymbol{R}\}$; $R(g) = \{y | y \in \boldsymbol{R}\}$
$D(f \circ g) = \{x | x \in \boldsymbol{R}\}$; $R(f \circ g) = \{y | y \in \boldsymbol{R}\ y \geq 0\}$
$D(g \circ f) = \{x | x \in \boldsymbol{R}\}$; $R(g \circ f) = \{y | y \in \boldsymbol{R}\ y \geq 1\}$

c. $(f \circ g)(x) = \dfrac{1}{(x + 1)^2} - 1$; $(g \circ f)(x) = \dfrac{1}{x^2}$;
$D(f) = \{x | x \in \boldsymbol{R}\}$;
$R(f) = \{y | y \in \boldsymbol{R}, y \geq -1\}$
$D(g) = \{x | x \in \boldsymbol{R}, x \neq -1\}$;
$R(g) = \{y | y \in \boldsymbol{R}, y \neq 0\}$
$D(f \circ g) = \{x | x \in \boldsymbol{R}, x \neq 1\}$;
$R(f \circ g) = \{y | y \in \boldsymbol{R}, y > -1\}$
$D(g \circ f) = \{x | x \in \boldsymbol{R}, x \neq 1\}$;
$R(g \circ f) = \{y | y \in \boldsymbol{R}, y > 0\}$

7. $d(t) = 3.43\sqrt{3t}$
8. a. $T(d) = 0.003\ 54\ d + 0.0354$ **b.** 9.94 cm
9. a. $L(x) = \sqrt{10x^2}$
b. $M(x) = 125\sqrt{10x^2} + 2700 \doteq 395x + 2700$
10. a. $(f \circ g \circ h)(x) = \dfrac{2x + 1}{x^2}$
b. $(g \circ f \circ h)(x) = \dfrac{1}{x^2}$
c. $(h \circ f \circ g)(x) = \dfrac{1}{x^2 + 2x}$
11. a. $(f \circ g)(x)$, where $g(x) = x^2 - 4$
$f(x) = \sqrt{x}$
b. $(f \circ g)(x)$, where $g(x) = \sqrt{x}$
$f(x) = \dfrac{1}{x}$
c. $(f \circ g)(x)$, where $f(x) = x + 2$
$g(x) = 3x$

Exercise 1-6, pages 28-29

1. a. $\{(-8, -2), (1, 1), (2, 0), (7, 3), (4, -2)\}$; function
b. $\{(-1, -1), (-8, -2), (0, 0), (2, 3), (8, 2)\}$; function
c. $\{(1, -1), (1, 1), (4, -2), (9, 3), (16, 4)\}$; not a function
d. $\{(3, 9), (0, 0), (1, 1), (2, 4), (4, 16)\}$; function
e. $\{(2, -2), (2, 2), (1, -1), (3, 3), (5, 5)\}$; not a function
f. $\{(-1, 3), (2, 3), (7, 8), (8, 7)\}$; function
2. a. not a function **b.** function **c.** function
d. not a function
3. a. $R(f^{-1}) = \{0, 1, 2, 3, 4, 5\}$
b. $D(f^{-1}) = \{x | 0 \leq x \leq 6, x \in \boldsymbol{R}\}$
c. $R(f^{-1}) = \{3, 5, 7, 9\}$
d. $R(f) = \{y | 1 \leq y \leq 5, y \in \boldsymbol{R}\}$;
$D(f^{-1}) = \{x | 1 \leq x \leq 5, x \in \boldsymbol{R}\}$;
$R(f^{-1}) = \{y | -2 \leq y \leq 2\ y \in \boldsymbol{R}\}$

4. a. $(f \circ g)(-2) = -2$; $(f \circ g)(3) = 3$; inverses
b. $(f \circ g) = -1$; $(f \circ g)(0) = 0$; inverses
c. $(f \circ g) = \dfrac{1}{16}$; $(f \circ g)(-3) = \dfrac{1}{9}$; not inverses
d. $(f \circ g)(1) = 1$; $(f \circ g)(-2) = -2$; inverses
5. a. $f^{-1}(x) = \dfrac{x + 2}{3}$ **b.** $f^{-1}(x) = \dfrac{3 - x}{4}$
c. $f^{-1}(x) = \dfrac{2x - 2}{3}$ **d.** $f^{-1}(x) = \dfrac{1}{x}$
e. $f^{-1}(x) = \dfrac{2}{x} + 1$ **f.** $f^{-1}(x) = \dfrac{2}{x} - 3$
g. $f^{-1}(x) = x^2 + 1, x \geq 0$ **h.** $f^{-1}(x) = |\sqrt{x + 2}|$
i. $f^{-1}(x) = -(3x + 2)$ **6. a.** $D = x | x \in \boldsymbol{R}, x \geq 0\}$
b. $D = \{x | x \in \boldsymbol{R}, x \leq 0, x > 3\}$
c. $D = \{x | x \in \boldsymbol{R}, x > 0\}$
7. a. $f^{-1}(x) = \dfrac{x + 1}{2}$ **b.** $f^{-1}(x) = \dfrac{4x - 8}{3}$
c. $f^{-1}(x) = |\sqrt{2x^2}|$ **d.** $f^{-1}(x) = |\sqrt{x + 3}|$
e. $f^{-1}(x) = \dfrac{1}{\sqrt{x}}$ **f.** $f^{-1}(x) = x^2 - 1, x \geq 0$
8. horizontal line test **9. a.** yes **b.** No, because (a, c), $(a, b) \in f$ implies f is not a function.
10. Midpoint of segment is $\left(\dfrac{x + y}{2}, \dfrac{x + y}{2}\right)$; lies on $y = x$. Slope of segment is $\dfrac{x - y}{y - x} = -1$, slope of $y = x$ is 1. So segments are perpendicular.

Exercise 1-7, pages 32-33

1. a. 8 **b.** 2 **c.** −2 **d.** 1 **e.** 3 **f.** −1 **g.** 3
h. −5 **i.** −11 **2. a.** $\{-5, 5\}$ **b.** $\{-3, 3\}$
c. $\{-13, 7\}$ **d.** $\{1, 3\}$ **e.** $\{4, 6\}$ **f.** ϕ **g.** $\{-3, 2\}$
h. $\{-2, 1\}$ **i.** $\{-4, 10\}$ **3. a.** 2 **b.** 5 **c.** 4
d. 1 **e.** 20 **f.** 1
4.

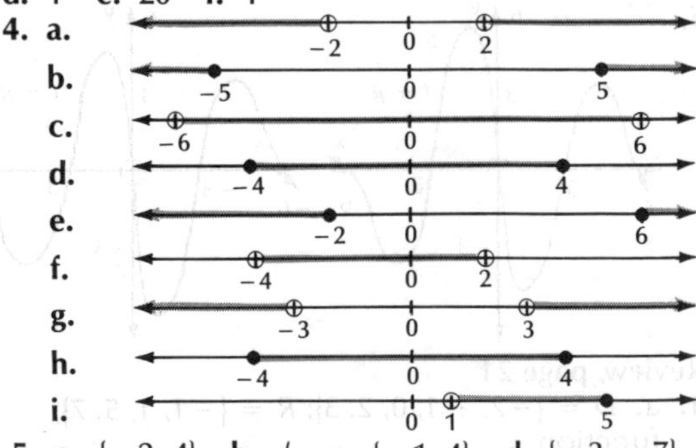

5. a. $\{-2, 4\}$ **b.** ϕ **c.** $\{-1, 4\}$ **d.** $\{-3, -7\}$
e. $\{0, 4\}$ **f.** $\{-3, 1\}$
6. a. −3 0 2
b. −1 0 2

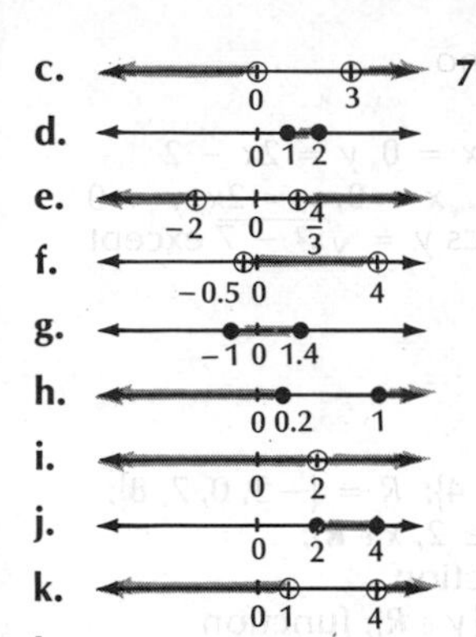

7. c.

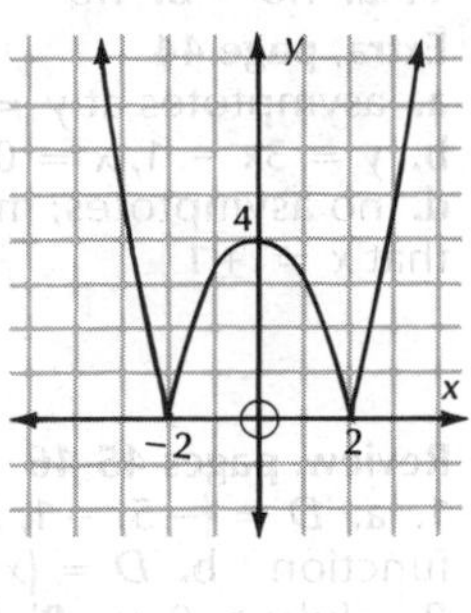

8. c.

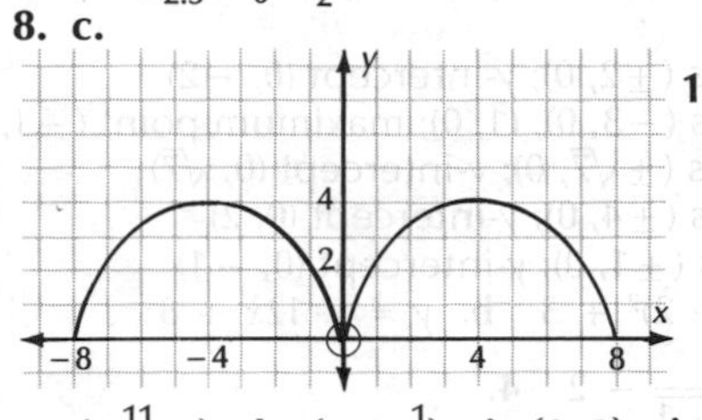

10. a. $\{-5, 5\}$ **b.** $\{-3, +3\}$ **c.** $\{-2, 2\}$ **d.** $\{-7, 7\}$ **e.** $\{-1, 5\}$ **f.** $\{-9, 7\}$ **g.** $\{-\frac{11}{3}, 1\}$ **h.** $\{-2, \frac{1}{2}\}$ **i.** $\{0, 2\}$ **j.** $\{2, \frac{10}{3}\}$

11. a. −1 0 3

b. −1 0 2

c. −2 0 6

d. −8 0 2

12. a. $\{-\frac{4}{3}, 4\}$ **b.** $\{2, -4\}$ **c.** $\{-\frac{7}{3}, -3\}$

d. $\{-\frac{1}{2}, 3\}$

Extra, page 33

$a > 0, b < 0$ or $a < 0, b > 0$;
$a > 0, b > 0$ or $a < 0, b < 0$

Exercise 1-8, pages 38-39

1.	Excluded value	Domain	Range
a.	$x = 3, y = 0$	$\{x \mid x \neq 3\}$	$\{y \mid y \neq 0\}$
b.	$x = -2, y = 0$	$\{x \mid x \neq -2\}$	$\{y \mid y \neq 0\}$
c.	$x = \pm 3, y = 0$	$\{x \mid x \neq \pm 3\}$	$\{y \mid y > 0, y \leq -\frac{1}{9}\}$
d.	$x = \pm 4, y = 0$	$\{x \mid x \neq \pm 4\}$	$\{y \mid y > 0, y \leq -\frac{1}{16}\}$
e.	$x < -2, y \geq 0$	$\{x \mid x \geq -2\}$	$\{y \mid y > 0\}$
f.	$\lvert x \rvert < 5, y \geq 0$	$\{x \mid \lvert x \rvert \geq 5\}$	$\{y \mid y > 0\}$
g.	$\lvert x \rvert \leq 3, y > 0$	$\{x \mid x > 3\}$	$\{y \mid y > 0\}$
h.	$\lvert x \rvert \leq 4, y > 0$	$\{x \mid x > 4\}$	$\{y \mid y > 0\}$
i.	$x > 5, y \geq 0$	$\{x \mid x \leq 5\}$	$\{y \mid y \geq 0\}$
j.	$x \geq -1, y < 1$	$\{x \mid \lvert x \rvert < 1\}$	$\{y \mid y \geq 1\}$
k.	$x \geq 1, y < 1$	$\{x \mid x < 1\}$	$\{y \mid y > 0\}$
l.	$\lvert x \rvert \geq 3, y > 0$	$\{x \mid \lvert x \rvert < 3\}$	$\{y \mid y > \frac{1}{3}\}$

2.

a.		b.	c.	
∞^+		∞^-	0^+	∞^+
∞^-		∞^+	0^-	∞^-
0^+		0^-	0^-	∞^-
0^-		0^+	0^+	∞^+
			∞^+	0^+
			∞^+	0^+

3. a. $x = -2$ **b.** $x = \pm 1$ **c.** $x = 1$
d. $x = -1$ **e.** $x = -4, 0, 8$ **f.** $x = \pm 3$

4. a. $D = \{x \mid x \in \mathbf{R}, x \neq 1\}$; $R = \{y \mid y \in \mathbf{R}, y \neq 0\}$
b. $D = \{x \mid x \in \mathbf{R}, x \neq \pm 4\}$;

$R = \{y \mid y \in \mathbf{R}, y \leq -\frac{1}{16}, y > 0\}$

c. $D = \{x \mid x \in \mathbf{R}, x > 3\}$; $R = \{y \mid y \in \mathbf{R}, y > 0\}$
d. $D = \{x \mid x \in \mathbf{R}, x \neq 3\}$; $R = \{y \mid y \in \mathbf{R}, y \neq 0\}$
e. $D = \{x \mid x \in \mathbf{R}, x \neq \pm 2\}$;
$R = y \mid y \in \mathbf{R}, y \leq -0.25, y > 0\}$
f. $D = \{x \mid x \in \mathbf{R}, x \neq 0\}$; $R = \{y \mid y \in \mathbf{R}, y \neq 3\}$

5.	Excluded Region	Horizontal Asymptote	Vertical Asymptote
a.	$x = 5; y = 0$	$y = 0$	$x = 5$
b.	$x = \pm 1; -3 \geq y \geq 0$	$y = 0$	$x = \pm 1$
c.	$x \leq 5; y = 0$	$y = 0$	$x = 5$
d.	$x = \pm 5; -0.04 \leq y \leq 0$	$y = 0$	$x = \pm 5$
e.	$x = 0; y = 0$	$y = -6$	$x = 0$
f.	$\lvert x \rvert \leq 2; y = 5$	$y = 5$	$x = \pm 2$

	Domain	Range
a.	$\{x \mid x \neq 5\}$	$\{y \mid y \mid > 0\}$
b.	$\{x \mid x \neq \pm 1\}$	$\{y \mid y < -3, y > 0\}$
c.	$\{x \mid x > 5\}$	$\{y \mid y \mid > 0\}$
d.	$\{x \mid x \neq \pm 5\}$	$\{y \mid y < -0.04, y > 0\}$
e.	$\{x \mid x \neq 0\}$	$\{y \mid y \neq -6\}$
f.	$\{x \mid \lvert x \rvert > 2\}$	$\{y \mid y > 5\}$

6. a. $x \neq -5, \quad y \neq 0$

b. $x \neq \pm 2, \quad y > 0, y \leq -\frac{1}{4}$

c. $x \neq -1, 5, \quad y \leq -\frac{1}{2}, \quad y > 0$

d. $x \neq -4, -2, \quad y \geq 1, \quad y < 0$

e. $x \neq \pm 3, \pm 9, \pm 15, \ldots, \quad \lvert y \rvert \geq \frac{1}{4}$

7. a. V.A.: $x = -3$; H.A.: $y = 0$
b. V.A.: $x = \pm 1$; H.A.: $y = 0$;
Excluded $-1 < y \leq 0$
c. V.A.: $x = \pm 5$; H.A.: $y = 0$;
Excluded $\lvert x \rvert \leq 5; y \leq 0$
d. V.A.: $x = -5, 3$; H.A.: $y = 0$;
Excluded $-\frac{1}{16} < y \leq 0$
e. V.A.: $x = -5$; H.A.: $y = 0$;
Excluded $x \leq -5, y \leq 0$
f. V.A.: $x = 2$; H.A.: $y = 0$

8. a. **b.**

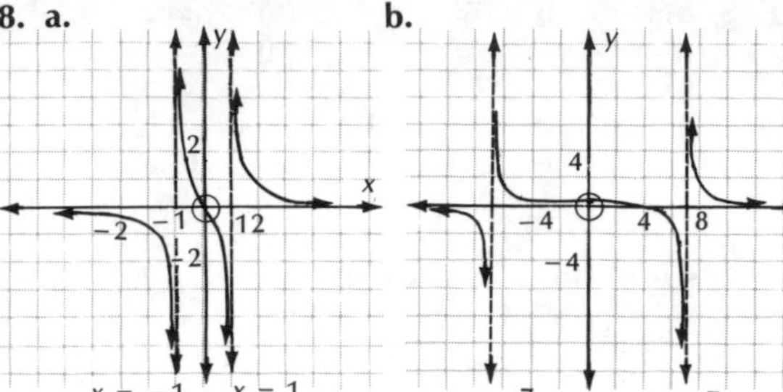

c.

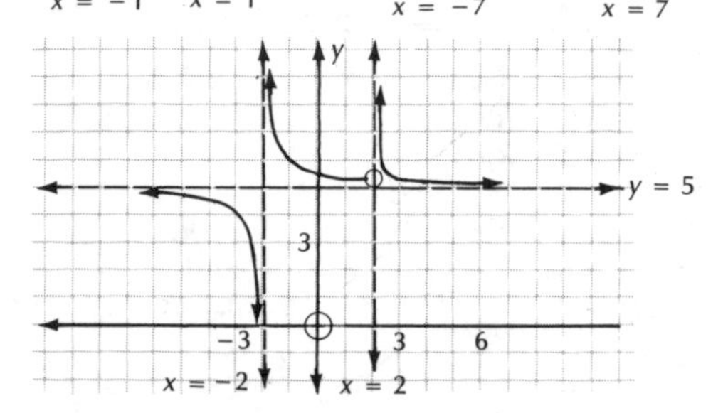

Exercise 1-9, pages 41-43

1. a. periodic, period = 4, amplitude = 1.5
b. non-periodic **c.** non-periodic
d. periodic, period = 5, amplitude = 7.5
e. periodic, period = 8, amplitude = 3
f. periodic, period = 6, amplitude = 4

2. a. non-periodic **b.**

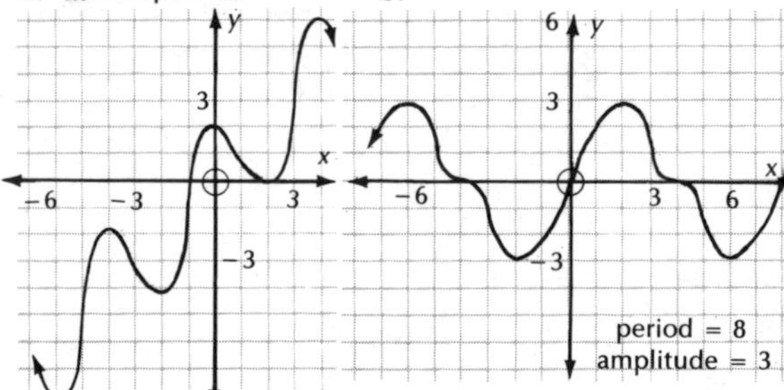

3. a. period = 29d **b.** May 23, June 21, July 20

4.

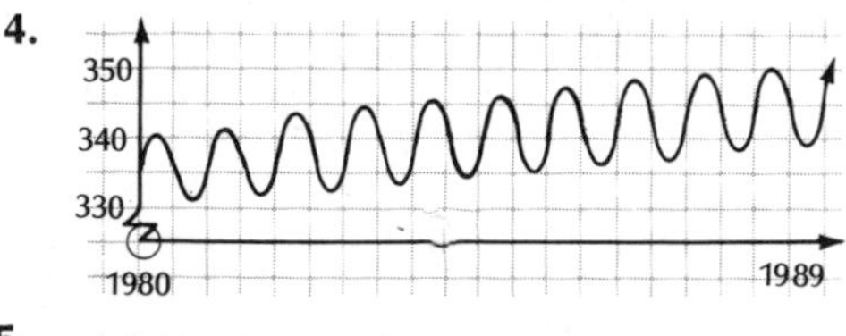

5.

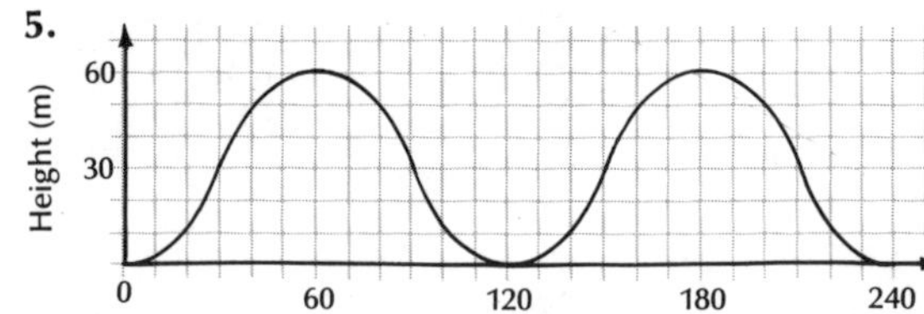

7. a. no **b.** no **c.** no

Extra, page 44

a. asymptotes at $y = 0$, $x = 0$, $y = 2x - 2$
b. $y = 3x - 1$, $x = 0$ **c.** $x = 0$, $y = 2x$, $y = 0$
d. no asymptotes; mimics $y = \sqrt{x^2 - 7}$ except that $x \neq \pm 1$

Review, pages 45-46

1. a. $D = \{-5, -1, 2, 3, 4\}$; $R = \{-3, 0, 7, 8\}$; function **b.** $D = \{x \mid x \geq 2, x \in \boldsymbol{R}\}$; $R = \{y \mid y \geq 0, y \in \boldsymbol{R}\}$; function
c. $D = \{x \mid x \in \boldsymbol{R}\}$; $R = \{y \mid y \in \boldsymbol{R}\}$; function
d. $D = \{x \mid x \geq -3, x \in \boldsymbol{R}\}$; $R = \{y \mid y \in \boldsymbol{R}\}$; not a function
b. x-intercepts $(\pm 2, 0)$; y-intercept $(0, -2)$
c. x-intercepts $(-3, 0)$, $(1, 0)$; maximum point $(-1, 2)$
d. x-intercepts $(\pm\sqrt{7}, 0)$; y-intercept $(0, \sqrt{7})$
e. x-intercepts $(\pm 4, 0)$; y-intercept $(0, 2)$
f. x-intercepts $(\pm 1, 0)$; y-intercept $(0, -1)$
3. a. $y = (x + 2)^2 + 3$ **b.** $y = -12x + 8$
c. $y = \dfrac{1}{\sqrt{-x - 1}} - 2$ **4.**

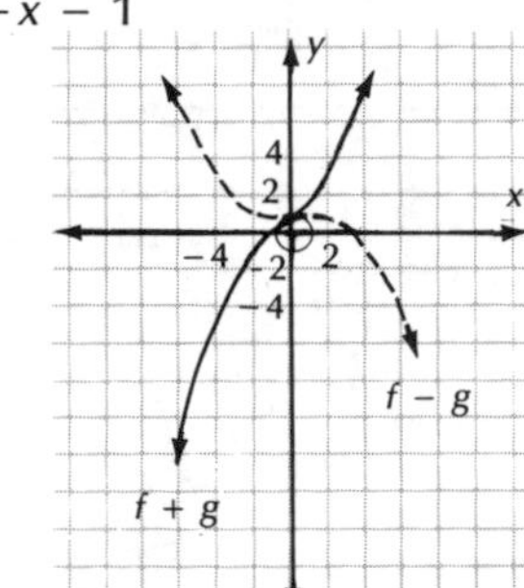

5. a. 9 **b.** 3 **c.** 1 **d.** 6 **e.** 3 **f.** $2x^2 - 7$
g. $4x^2 - 2x - 2$ **h.** $R(f \circ h) = \{-5, -1, 5, 9\}$
i. $R(f \circ g) = \{y \mid y \geq -7, y \in \boldsymbol{R}\}$
j. $D(g \circ h) = \{-2, -1, 0, 1, 2\}$
k. $R(g \circ h) = \{-3, 1, 6, 22\}$
l. $R(g \circ f) = \{y \mid y \geq -2, y \in \boldsymbol{R}\}$
6. a. $T \circ A = 0.003d^2$ **b.** Exposure time to the distance from projector.
7. a. $f^{-1} = \{(1, -2), (1, 2), (5, 0), (6, -4), (7, 3)\}$
b. $y = \dfrac{x - 3}{2}$ **c.** $f: x \rightarrow |\sqrt{x + 2}|$
d. $f\{(x, y) \mid y = \dfrac{2}{x} + 1;\ x, y \in \boldsymbol{R}\}$
8. a. $\{x \mid x \leq -3, x \geq 4, x \in \boldsymbol{R}\}$
b. $\{x \mid 0 \leq x \leq 3, x \in \boldsymbol{R}\}$
c. $\{x \mid |x| > 3, x \in \boldsymbol{R}\}$
d. $\{x \mid -1 \leq x \leq 3, x \in \boldsymbol{R}\}$
e. $\{x \mid x < 2, x > 8, x \in \boldsymbol{R}\}$
f. $\{x \mid -1 < x < 2, x \in \boldsymbol{R}\}$

9. a.

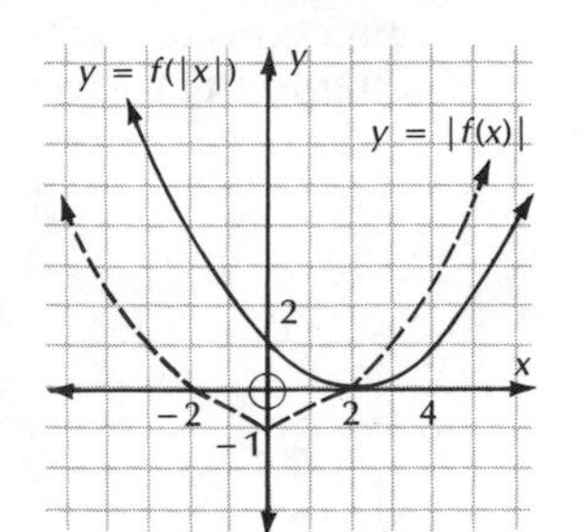

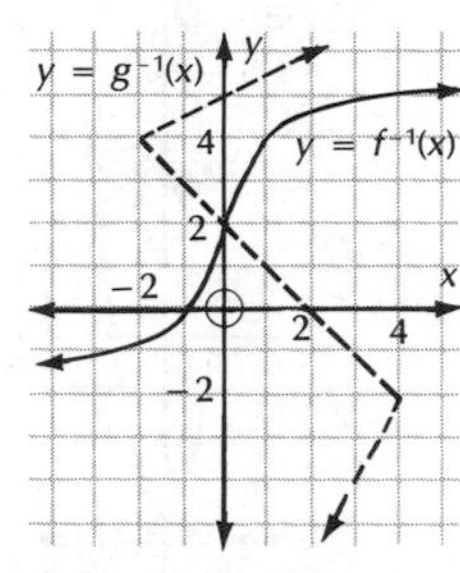

b. $y = |f(x)|$: function; $y = f(|x|)$: function; $y = f^{-1}(x)$: function; $y = g^{-1}(x)$: not a function
10. a. V.A.: $x = -4$; H.A.: $y = 0$
b. V.A.: $x \neq \pm 1$; H.A.: $y = 0$;
Excluded: $-1 < y \leq 0$
c. V.A.: $x = \pm 2$; H.A.: $y = 0$;
Excluded: $|x| < 2, y \leq 0$
11. a. periodic: period = 6, amplitude = 3
b. non-periodic **c.** non-periodic

Test, page 47

1. a. $D(f) = \{-3, -2, -1, 0, 1, 2, 3\}$
b. $R(k) = \{y | y \geq 0, y \in \mathbf{R}\}$ **c.** $R(g^{-1}) = \{0, 1, 2, 3, 4\}$
d. 5 **e.** 8 **f.** no solution **g.** -1 **h.** $\sqrt{14}$
i. $g^{-1} = \{(-4, 0), \{-3, 1), (-1, 2), (2, 3), (5, 4)\}$
j. $f \circ h = \{(0, 1), (0.5, 0), (1, 3), (1.5, 5), (2, 6), (2.5, 8), (3, 10)\}$ **k.** $D(g \circ f) = \{-3, -2, -1\}$
l. $R(h \circ k) = \{y | y \geq -3, y \in \mathbf{R}\}$
2. b. $f^{-1}(x) = \dfrac{4 - x}{2}$; function, $g^{-1}(x) = \sqrt{x + 4}$; not a function **c.** $\dfrac{1}{f(x)}$: $x \neq z$, $y \neq 0$; $\dfrac{1}{g(x)}$: $x \neq 2$; $y < -\frac{1}{4}$, $y > 0$; $(f + g)(x)$; x-intercepts: (0, 0), (2, 0); minimum point (1, −1)

3. a. $f(x + 2) + 2$ **b.** $f\left(\dfrac{x}{2}\right) + 2$ **c.** $-2f(x - 3)$
4. a. $\{x | x \geq 4, x \leq -1, x \in \mathbf{R}\}$
b. $\{x | 4 < x < 6, x \in \mathbf{R}\}$ **c.** $\{x | x \geq 1, x \leq -\frac{7}{3}, x \in \mathbf{R}\}$
5. a. V.A.: $x = 3$; H.A.: $y = 0$ **b.** V.A.: $x = 2$; H.A.: $y = 0$ **c.** V.A.: $x = +2$; H.A.: $y = \frac{1}{2}$;
Excluded: $|x| \geq 2, y < \frac{1}{2}$
6. a. -26 **b.** $p(10) = 5$ **c.** yes **d.** yes

UNIT 2

Exercise 2-1, pages 52-53

1. a. $\frac{1}{8}$ **b.** 3 **c.** 729 **d.** 1 **e.** $-\frac{1}{27}$ **f.** $\frac{1}{49}$
g. 2 **h.** 4 **i.** $\frac{4}{3}$ **j.** 5 **k.** 4 **l.** 10 **m.** 8 **n.** 5
o. 6 **p.** 30 **2.** $-(3^2) = -1 \times 3 \times 3 = -9$, $(-3)^2 = (-3) \times (-3) = 9$ **3.** $\{x | x = 2k + 1, k \in \mathbf{Z}\}$
4. a, c, d, g **5. a.** $5^{\frac{2}{3}}$ **b.** $15^{\frac{1}{2}}$ **c.** $(-25)^{\frac{2}{3}}$
d. $(-8)^{\frac{2}{3}}$ **e.** $\left(\frac{8}{27}\right)^{\frac{1}{3}}$ **f.** $(-32)^{-\frac{4}{5}}$ **g.** $(-27)^{-\frac{2}{3}}$
h. $\left(\frac{36}{49}\right)^{-\frac{3}{2}}$ **6. a.** 2^3 **b.** 2^1 **c.** $\dfrac{3}{(1 - \frac{1}{3^2})}$ **d.** $3^1 + 2^1$
e. $1 - \dfrac{1}{3^1}$ **f.** $1 - \dfrac{1}{2^3}$ **g.** $\dfrac{1}{2^1} - 3$ **h.** 2^2 **7. a.** 1
b. $a^{-\frac{1}{4}}$ **c.** x **d.** $b^{-\frac{1}{6}}$ **e.** $t^{\frac{7}{4}}$ **f.** $x^{-\frac{3}{7}}$ **g.** $y^{-\frac{8}{15}}$
h. $8xy^6$ **i.** $9ab^{\frac{1}{2}}$ **j.** $5x^2y^{-4}$ **k.** $4ab^{-3}$ **l.** $2ab^{-2}$
m. $4x^4y^{-6}$ **n.** $-3x^2y^{-3}$ **o.** $-8^{-1}a^{-3}b^6$ **p.** $9x^4y^{-6}$
8. a. 72 **b.** $a^{-\frac{17}{60}}$ **c.** $\dfrac{x^{\frac{17}{3}}}{y^{\frac{2}{3}}}$ **d.** 18 **9. a.** 1.32
b. 3.49 **c.** 0.00 **d.** 26.79 **e.** 1.79 **f.** 2.33
10. [0.86] [y^x] [5.2] [+/−] [=]
11. a. 0.01 **b.** 0.35 **c.** 0.97 **d.** 45.29
e. 791.96 **f.** 0.00 **g.** 0.43 **h.** 0.99 **12. a.** 3.00
b. 1.65 **c.** 1.61 **d.** 0.13 **13. a.** 9 **b.** 0.34
c. 0.85 **d.** 0.07 **14. a.** 501.19 **b.** 1000
c. 31 622.78 **d.** 199 526.23
15. a.

Magnitude	6	5	4	3	2	1
Brightness	1	2.512	6.310	15.851	39.818	100.023

b. $B_1 = (2.512)^5 B_6 = 100.023\, B_6$ **c.** 20.896 times

Exercise 2-2, page 55

1. a. 49 **b.** 1 **c.** $4^{\sqrt{2}}$ **d.** $3^{\sqrt{10}}$ **e.** $2^{3\sqrt{6}}$ **f.** 7
2. a. 0.71 **b.** 1.02 **c.** 6.70 **d.** 0.54 **e.** 13.12
f. 5.09 **g.** 1 **h.** 7.10 **3. a.** $5^{\sqrt{2}}$ **b.** $3^{\sqrt{2}}$ **c.** π^3
d. $5^{\sqrt{3}}$

5. a.

x	1.08^x
0	1
1	1.08
2	1.17
3	1.26
4	1.36
5	1.47
6	1.59
7	1.71
8	1.85
9	2.00
10	2.16

c. 1.125 (answer will vary) **d.** 1.122 **e.** 4.46 (answers will vary)
6. a. 2 weeks **b.** 5 weeks **c.** 8 weeks **d.** 9 weeks **7. a.** 9.0 s **b.** 14.3 s **c.** 18.0 s

Exercise 2-3, pages 57-58

1. a. 1 **b.** 3 **c.** 4 **d.** -2 **e.** -2 **f.** -4 **g.** -3 **h.** $\frac{3}{2}$ **i.** $\frac{3}{2}$ **j.** 9 **k.** -2 **l.** 2
2. a. $x = 3, -7$ **b.** $y = 5$ **c.** $x = 4$ **d.** $y = -1, -3$ **3. a.** $x^2 = 8^3$ **b.** $y^{-3} = 8^2$ **c.** $z^3 = 27^4$ **d.** $x^{-3} = 8^4$ **e.** $y^5 = 32^3$ **f.** $z^{-3} = 216^2$ **4. a.** $\frac{3}{2}$ **b.** $-\frac{1}{2}$ **c.** $\frac{17}{2}$ **d.** $-\frac{11}{2}$ **e.** $-\frac{1}{2}$ **f.** $\frac{2}{3}$ **g.** $-\frac{6}{5}$ **h.** 6 **i.** -2 **j.** $\frac{7}{4}$ **k.** $\frac{11}{4}$ **l.** 4 **5. a.** 6, $\frac{4}{5}$ **b.** 2 **c.** $-2, -\frac{2}{9}$ **d.** $-\frac{1}{2}$ **e.** 5 **f.** 9, $-\frac{9}{5}$ **6. a.** 30 g **b.** 22.6 g **c.** 35.4 g **d.** 454.1 g; 45.1 g **7.** 4 d **8. a.** 4 **b.** $\frac{5}{2}$ **c.** 6 **d.** 5 **9. a.** 3, -2 **b.** 3, -1 **c.** -2
10. a. 1 **b.** 3 **c.** 0, 2 **d.** 0, 1 **e.** 6 **f.** 0

Application, page 59

1. 12.5% **2.** 0.4% **3.** t ≐ 866 a, at the time of William the Conqueror **4.** about 18 900 years ago

Exercise 2-4, pages 63-64

1. a, b, c, f, satisfy the form $y = a(b^x)$, $a, b \in \boldsymbol{R}$, $b > 0, b \neq 1$. **2. a.** $x = 1$ **b.** y increases **c.** y decreases **d.** $-\infty$ **e.** None **f.** All **3. a.** $f(x) = \frac{16}{3}\left(\frac{3}{4}\right)^x$ **b.** $f(x) = \frac{1}{3}(6)^x$ **c.** $f(x) = \frac{27}{15}\left(\frac{15}{3}\right)^x$ **d.** $f(x) = 8(16)^x$ **e.** $f(x) = 10^x$ **f.** $f(x) = \frac{1}{2}(5)^x$ **4.** $f(x)f(y) = a^xa^y = a^{x+y} = f(x + y)$

5. a. 3 **b.** 81

6. a.

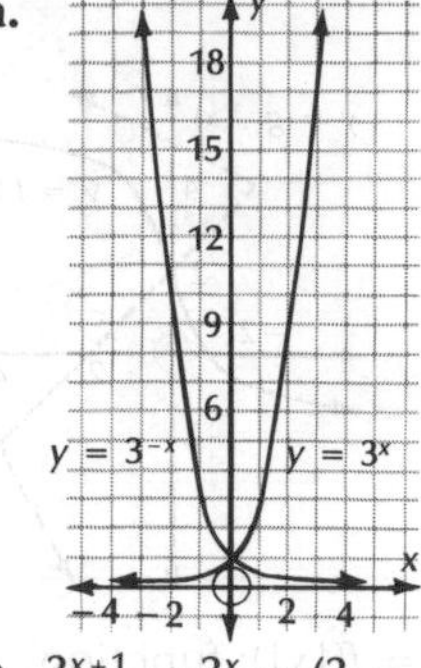

b. The graphs are reflections of each other in the y-axis.

7. a. $3^{x+1} - 3^x = (3 - 1)3^x = 2(3^x)$ **b.** $a(b^x)(b^a - 1)$ **8. a.** 5.196 **b.** 0.192 **9. b. i.** about 1.21 **ii.** about 1.47 **iii.** about 1.77 **iv.** about 2.15 **d. i.** 0.22 **ii.** -0.70 **iii.** -1.92 **iv.** -2.15

10.

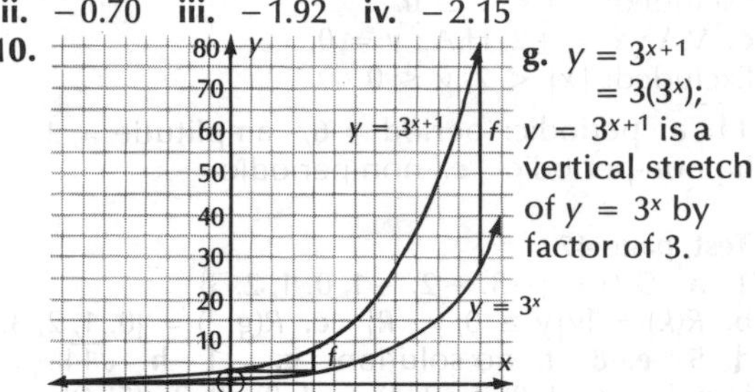

g. $y = 3^{x+1} = 3(3^x)$; $y = 3^{x+1}$ is a vertical stretch of $y = 3^x$ by factor of 3.

11.

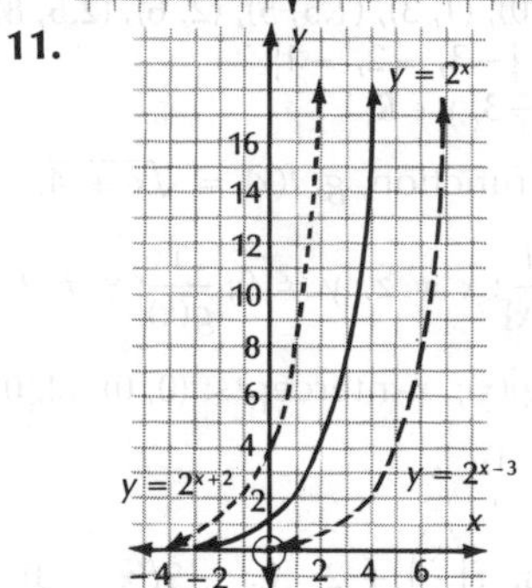

b. i. horizontal translation of -2 units or vertical stretch by factor of 4. **ii.** horizontal translation of $+3$ units or vertical stretch by factor of $\frac{1}{8}$

12. $f(x) = (2^{1.5})^x$ **13.** $\frac{4}{9}$ **14.** -3
15. $f(x + 1) - 5f(x) = 4(5^2)(5^{2x})$, which is divisible by 100.

Application, page 65

1.

A3	A#	B	C	C#	D	D#
220	233	247	262	277	294	311

E	F	F#	G	G#	A4
330	349	370	392	425	440

3. Yes. There exists only one $f(x)$ for every x.
4. Yes. **5.** $f(x) = 220(\sqrt[12]{2})^x$

Exercise 2-5, pages 69-70
1. 1.9% **2. a.** 20 a; 6%/a
b. There are 20 periods at 6%/period.
c. 5 a at 24%/a compounded quarterly; 40 a at 3%/a compounded every two years
3. a. $450(1.07)^8$ **b.** $900(1.08)^{12}$ **c.** $1200(1.10)^6$
d. $800(1.06)^{21}$ **e.** $2100(1.045)^{14}$ **f.** $1000(1.025)^{24}$
g. $1500(1.04)^{6.5}$ **4. a.** 2^t is doubled **b.** 2^t is halved **c.** 2^{-t} is halved. **5. a.** $N = \frac{1}{2}N_0$
b. i. $\frac{1}{4}$ **ii.** $\frac{1}{8}$ **iii.** $\frac{1}{32}$ **6.** 29 749 000; 55 363 000 (to the nearest thousand) **7.** 22 531 000 (to the nearest thousand) **8.** \$1.58 **9.** \$3105.94
10. \$8498.91 **11.** 10%/a, compounded annually
12. $\$3.017 \times 10^{13}$ **13.** No. The pile reaches 9×10^7 km **14.** 20 g **15.** Yes. If the factor was overestimated by 0.03, then the population would be multiplying by a factor of 0.99. It would actually be decreasing. **16.** 67 kPa

Application, page 71
3 min 32.3 s

Exercise 2-6, page 74
1. a. 3.669 296 7 **b.** 1.284 025 4 **c.** 9.974 182 5
d. 0.223 130 2 **e.** 1.395 612 4 **f.** 0.716 531 3

2. a.

x	e^x
−3.0	0.0498
−2.5	0.0821
−2.0	0.1353
−1.5	0.2231
−1.0	0.3679
−0.5	0.6065
0	1
0.5	1.6487
1.0	2.7183
1.5	4.4817
2.0	7.3891
2.5	12.1825
3.0	20.0855

2. c. 0.30; 14.88; 4.48 (Answers will vary)
3. a., c.
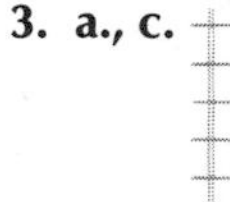
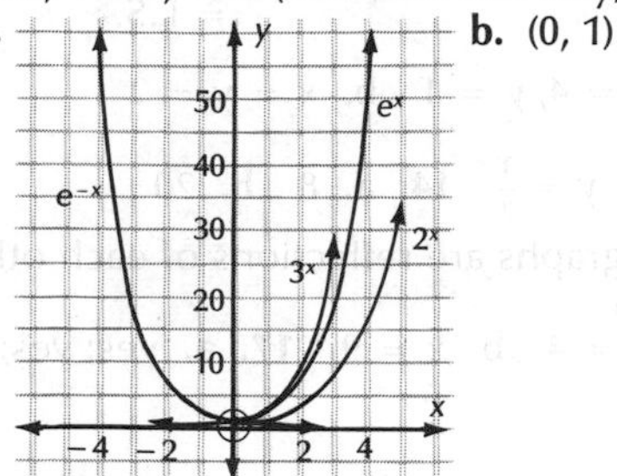

b. (0, 1)

5. a. 0.367 695 4; 0.367 879 6
b. $\frac{e^{-1}}{(0.999)^{1000}} = 1.0005$;
$\frac{e^{-1}}{(0.999\ 999)^{1\ 000\ 000}} = 0.999\ 999\ 5$
6. a. $2^{1.106x}$ **b.** $2^{-2.52t}$ **c.** $e^{0.373x}$
7. a. 69.12°, 60.22°, 52.93°, 46.96° **b.** 17 min 20 s
8. $y = 2\left(e^{\frac{x}{4}} + e^{-\frac{x}{4}}\right)$ **9.**

Application, page 75
1. $a^b = b^a \rightarrow b^a = a^b$; Reflexive property
2. L.S. = R.S. = $\left(\frac{3}{2}\right)^{\frac{27}{4}}$; L.S. = R.S. = $3^{\frac{3\sqrt{3}}{2}}$;
3. L.S. = R.S. = $\left(\frac{n+1}{n}\right)^{\frac{(n+1)^{n+1}}{n^n}}$ **4.** (4, 2), $\left(\frac{27}{8}, \frac{9}{4}\right)$, $\left(\frac{256}{81}, \frac{64}{27}\right)$, $\left(\frac{3125}{1024}, \frac{625}{256}\right)$, $\left(\frac{46\ 656}{15\ 625}, \frac{7776}{3125}\right)$
5. Yes **6.** $n = -\frac{1}{4}$ ∴ $n^n = (-4)^{\frac{1}{4}}$; irrational
7. LS = RS = $n^{\left(\frac{n}{n-1}\right)^{\left(\frac{n}{n-1}\right)}}$ **8.** (2, 4), $\left(3^{\frac{1}{2}}, 3^{\frac{3}{2}}\right)$, $\left(4^{\frac{1}{3}}, 4^{\frac{4}{3}}\right)$, (4, 2), $\left(\frac{3}{2}, 3^{\frac{1}{2}}\right)$ **9.** $x = y$; $x^y = y^x$

Review, pages 76-77
1. a. 216 **b.** $\frac{1}{0.729}$ **c.** 2 **d.** 64 **e.** 4
2. a. $-\frac{4}{3}$ **b.** $\frac{1}{2}$ **c.** $\frac{5}{6}$ **d.** 2 **e.** $\frac{5}{3}$ **f.** $\frac{11}{4}$
3. a. 0.444 **b.** 1.476 **c.** 62.053 **d.** 0.015
e. 1.865 **4. a.** 6.611 **b.** 0.316 **c.** 1.260
d. 6.644 **e.** 0.429 **5. a.** −4 **b.** 3 **c.** 3
d. −1 **e.** 4 **6. a.** 8 **b.** 32 **8. a.** $f(x) = 9\left(\frac{2}{3}\right)^x$
b. $f(x) = 3(4^x)$ **9. a.** about 1.35 **b.** about 43.1
10. $f(x + 1) - f(x) = 99(10^{2x})$ **11.** 44.2 g
12. 904.8 g **13. a.** 0 **b.** 68.8 **c.** 94.5 **d.** 99.7
14. \$88 573.50 **15.** 57 698 000 (to the nearest thousand) **16.** \$2066.87 **17.** \$10 955.62

18. a. 1345.4 g; 1131.4 g; 282.8 g **b.** 0.018 mg **c.** 53.12 mg **19.** 6.03×10^9a

Test, page 78

1. a. 243 **b.** 4 **c.** 0.4 **d.** 3 **2. a.** $\frac{3}{2}$ **b.** $\frac{9}{2}$ **c.** $\frac{5}{9}$ **3. a.** 1.256 **b.** 2.281 **c.** 11.55 **d.** 0.917 **4. a.** 1.937 **b.** 2.255 **c.** 0.958 **d.** 1.17 **5. a.** −4 **b.** $\frac{5}{2}$ **c.** $\frac{3}{2}$ **d.** 1 **6.** points of intersection: (1.32, 3), (−1.32, 3)

7. a. $f(x) = 20\left(\frac{1}{2}\right)^x$ **b.** $f(x) = 6(9)^x$ **8.** 265.2 g **9.** 90 g **10.** 190.2 m **11.** $7183.43

Cumulative Review, page 79

1. a, b, c

2. a.

x	−3	−2	−1	0	1	2	3
y	−27	−8	−1	0	1	8	27

b.

x	−3	−2	−1	0	1	2	3
y	11	6	3	2	3	6	11

c.

x	−2	−1	0	1	2	3	4
y	9	4	1	0	1	4	9

d.

x	−1	0	1	2	3	4	5
y	12	7	4	3	4	7	12

3. a. $f + g$: $x^2 + (y - 7)^2 = 25$; Circle with C(0, 7), $r = 5$.
b. $f + g$: $x^2 + 2x = y$; Parabola with minimum point (−1, −1), x-intercepts −2, 0.

4. a. $f \circ g: x \rightarrow \frac{1}{x^2 - 9}, x \neq \pm 3$ **c.** $x = 3; x = -3$

5. a. vertical translation −3 units **b.** vertical translation +5 units **c.** vertical stretch by factor of 2 **d.** horizontal stretch by factor of $\frac{1}{2}$ **e.** vertical stretch of factor of 6 **f.** horizontal translation +2 units **g.** reflection in x-axis **h.** reflection in the line $y = x$ **i.** vertical stretch by factor of $\frac{1}{2}$

UNIT 3

Exercise 3-1, pages 83-84

1. a. $\log_2 32 = 5$ **b.** $\log_3 9 = 2$ **c.** $\log_5 3125 = 5$ **d.** $\log_7 49 = 2$ **e.** $\log_{16} 4 = \frac{1}{2}$ **f.** $\log_{125} 5 = \frac{1}{3}$ **g.** $\log_{36} 6 = 0.5$ **h.** $\log_{25} 125 = 1.5$ **i.** $\log_a c = b$ **j.** $\log_2 5 = x$ **k.** $\log_a 1 = 0$ **l.** $\log_{1.5} 0.3 = y$

2. a. $2^4 = 16$ **b.** $5^3 = 125$ **c.** $3^4 = 81$ **d.** $7^0 = 1$ **e.** $6^{\frac{1}{2}} = \sqrt{6}$ **f.** $5^{1.5} = 5\sqrt{5}$ **g.** $6^{2.5} = 36\sqrt{6}$ **h.** $4^{0.25} = \sqrt{2}$ **3. a.** 3 **b.** 0 **c.** 1 **d.** 3 **e.** 2 **f.** −1 **g.** −3 **h.** −3 **i.** −2 **j.** x **k.** $\frac{1}{2}$ **l.** x

4. a. 10 **b.** 0 **c.** 21 **d.** 6 **e.** x **f.** −7 **g.** −27 **h.** 0 **5. a.** 3 **b.** $\sqrt[15]{25}$ **c.** 16 **d.** 0.25 **e.** 10^{-10} **f.** $\sqrt{3}$ **g.** 125 **h.** $\frac{64}{343}$

6. b. $\log_2 x = y$; $\log_3 x = y$; $\log_4 x = y$ **c.** (0, 1) **d.** (1, 0)

7. a.

x	$\frac{1}{4}$	$\frac{1}{2}$	1	2	4	8	16
y	−2	−1	0	1	2	3	4

c. 1.58, 2.32, 3.97 **8. a.** −3 **b.** $\frac{2}{3}$ **c.** 0.4 **d.** $\frac{1}{6}$ **e.** $-\frac{2}{3}$ **f.** −1.5 **g.** −3.5 **h.** −1.5 **9. a.** $x = 3$ **b.** $y = -3$ **c.** $x = \frac{5}{3}$ **d.** $x = \frac{1}{49}$ **e.** $y = -4$ **f.** $b = \frac{1}{16}$ **g.** $x = 4\sqrt{2}$ **h.** $y = \frac{1}{27}$ **i.** $a = 0.5$ **j.** $x = \frac{1}{3}$ **k.** $a = 4$ **l.** $y = 243$ **m.** $a = 0.04$ **n.** $x = 7$ **o.** $\{b \mid b \in \boldsymbol{R}, b > 0, b \neq 1\}$ **p.** $x = 27$ **q.** $x = 28$ **r.** $x = 7$ **s.** $x = 30$ **t.** $x = 12$

10. a. $x = 25$ **b.** $y = 2$ **c.** $x = 243$ **d.** $x = 4096$ **11. a.** $x = -3, 4$ **b.** $x = 14$ **c.** $x = 3, 4$ **12. a. i.** 2, 0.5 **ii.** 3, $\frac{1}{3}$

b. Let $x = \log_b a$
$\rightarrow a = b^x$

$$\begin{aligned} \text{R.S.} &= \frac{1}{\log_a b} \\ &= \frac{1}{\log_{b^x} b} \\ &= \frac{1}{\frac{1}{x}} \\ &= x \\ &= \log_b a \\ &= \text{L.S.} \end{aligned}$$

13. a. $x = 4, y = 1$ **b.** $x = y = 2$ **c.** $x = \frac{7}{2}, y = \frac{1}{2}$ **14. a.** 8 **b.** 20

15. The graphs are reflections of each other in the x-axis

16. a. $x = 4$ **b.** $x = 9$ **17. a.** yes; yes; no **b.** 4.75

Exercise 3-2, pages 88-89

1. a. $\log 145 + \log 192$ **b.** $\log_3 1792 + \log_3 853$ **c.** $\log_4 1.56 + \log_4 0.359$ **d.** $\log_5 70.52 + \log_5 8953$ **e.** $\log_2 17 + \log_2 19 + \log_2 152$ **f.** $\log_3 192 + \log_3 273 + \log_3 584$ **2. a.** $\log (7 \times 5)$ **b.** $\log_5 (92 \times 63)$ **c.** $\log_9 (78 \times 952)$ **d.** $\log_6 (9751 \times 1.567)$ **e.** $\log_2 (5 \times 7 \times 10)$ **f.** $\log_3 (82 \times 91 \times 77)$ **3. a.** $\log_5 10 - \log_5 7$ **b.** $\log_2 56 - \log_2 83$ **c.** $\log_7 873 - \log_7 942$ **d.** $\log 0.72 - \log 1.56$ **e.** $\log 1 - \log 10$ **f.** $\log a - \log b$ **4. a.** $\log \frac{17}{95}$ **b.** $\log_3 \frac{60}{20}$ **c.** $\log_4 \frac{872}{2.37}$ **d.** $\log_2 \frac{673}{985}$ **e.** $\log \frac{0.015}{0.7}$ **f.** $\log_5 \frac{190}{23}$ **5. a.** 3 **b.** 4 **c.** 6 **d.** 4 **e.** ± 3 **f.** 3 **6. a.** L.S. = R.S. = 3.487 **b.** L.S. = R.S. = −0.302 **c.** L.S. = R.S. = 0.110 **d.** L.S. = R.S. = −0.187 **7. a.** $\log_3 14$ **b.** $\log_2 4$ **c.** $\log 24$ **d.** $\log_7 5$ **e.** $\log_7 \frac{64}{7}$ **f.** $\log_5 10.5$ **8. a.** 2 **b.** 2 **c.** 3 **d.** 2 **e.** 1.5 **f.** 2 **g.** 2 **h.** 3 **i.** 4 **j.** 2 **k.** 3 **l.** −3 **9. a.** 147 **b.** 128 **c.** 4 **d.** 5 **e.** 9 **f.** 7 **11.** L.S. = 0.268, R.S. = 9.006 **12. a.** $y = \log 2x = \log x + \log 2 = \log x + 0.30$ **b.** $(x, y) \rightarrow (x, y + 0.30)$ **13.** $\log_3 1 = \log_4 1 = \log_5 1 = 0$; The point is (1, 0). **14. a.** $x = \frac{22}{3}$ **b.** $x = 2.2$ **c.** $x = 3$ **d.** $x = 10$ **e.** $x = 1.2$ **f.** no solution; $x = \frac{-1 \pm i\sqrt{7}}{2} \notin R$ **g.** no solution; $x = \frac{7 \pm \sqrt{5}}{2}$ is inadmissible since $x - 5 < 0$ **h.** 144 **15. a.** $T = 366.6$ d **b. i.** 57.765 million km **ii.** 107.584 million km **iii.** 227.842 million km **iv.** 777.890 million km **v.** 1424.820 million km **c. i.** 30 421.5 d **ii.** 59 690.6 d **iii.** 89 963.4 d **16.** $a = -1.75$, $b = -2.25$

Exercise 3-3, pages 91-92

1. a. $2 \log_3 7$ **b.** $3 \log_3 10$ **c.** $-4 \log_7 2$ **d.** $-4 \log_{13} 12$ **e.** $\frac{1}{2} \log_2 10$ **f.** $\frac{1}{2} \log_4 5$ **g.** $0.5 \log_2 7$ **h.** $-0.1 \log_3 5$ **i.** $-3 \log_7 10$ **j.** $\frac{2}{3} \log 2$ **k.** $0.2 \log 5$ **l.** $2 \log \pi$ **2. a.** $\log 2^5$ **b.** $\log_2 7^2$ **c.** $\log_3 10^{0.5}$ **d.** $\log_5 6^{0.75}$ **e.** $\log 8^{-2}$ **f.** $\log_2 7.5^{-1}$ **g.** $\log_3 5^{-0.5}$ **h.** $\log_4 7^{-\frac{2}{3}}$ **3. a.** $5 \log x$ **b.** $\frac{1}{2} \log x$ **c.** $2 \log x + \log y$ **d.** $\frac{3}{4} \log x$ **e.** $2 \log x + 3 \log y$ **f.** $-\log x$ **g.** $\frac{3}{2} \log x$ **h.** $\frac{1}{3} \log xy$ **i.** $\log x + \frac{1}{2} \log y$ **j.** $\frac{1}{2} \log x + \log y$ **4. a.** $x = 25$ **b.** $x = 125$ **c.** $x = 1$ **d.** $x = 4$ **e.** $x = 8$ **f.** $x = 25$ **5. a.** true **b.** true **c.** true **d.** false **e.** false **f.** true **6. a.** $\log A = \log 4 + \log p + 2 \log r$ **b.** $\log V = \log 4 - \log 3 + \log p + 3 \log r$ **c.** $\log T = \log 2 + \log p + \frac{1}{2} \log l - \frac{1}{2} \log g$ **d.** $\log P + 1.4 \log V = \log C$ **7. a.** 2 **b.** 1 **c.** 0 **d.** 1 **e.** 0 **f.** 0 **g.** 3 **h.** $\frac{1}{3}$ **i.** $\frac{5}{6}$ **j.** −0.5 **k.** 0 **l.** 0.5 **8. a.** 1.613 15 **b.** 1.671 94 **c.** 1.898 24 **d.** 0.2263 **e.** 0.511 39 **f.** −0.898 24 **g.** 1.2263 **h.** 3.183 33 **i.** 4.753 51 **j.** 2.1833 **k.** 0.4526 **l.** −0.386 85 **9. a.** $x = 500$ **b.** $y = 3$ **c.** $x = 432$ **d.** $z = 5$ **e.** $x = \frac{10}{9}$ **f.** $x = 14$ **g.** $x = 4$ **h.** $x = 2.5$ **i.** $x = 4$ **j.** $x = 4$

10. a. $1 = \log 10, \quad 0 = \log 1;$
$1 = \log (12 - 2), \quad 0 = \log (3 - 2)$
b. $y = \log x$, vertical asymptote $x = 0$, x-intercept = 1; $y = \log (x - 2)$, vertical asymptote $x = 2$, x-intercept = 3 **c.** $(x, y) \rightarrow (x + 2, y)$; translation 2 units to the right

11. a. $1 = \log 10, \quad 0 = \log 1;$
$1 = \log \sqrt{100}, \quad 0 = \log \sqrt{1}$
b. Each graph has vertical asymptote $x = 0$ and x-intercept = 1. **c.** $(x, y) \rightarrow \left(x, \frac{y}{2}\right)$; horizontal stretch by factor of $\frac{1}{2}$

12. a. $(x, y) \rightarrow (x, 3y)$; horizontal stretch by factor of 3 **b.** $(x, y) \rightarrow (x + 3, y)$; horizontal translation +3 units **c.** $(x, y) \rightarrow \left(x + 3, \frac{y}{2}\right)$; horizontal translation +3 units and horizontal stretch by factor of $\frac{1}{2}$ **d.** $(x, y) \rightarrow (x + 3, -y)$; horizontal translation +3 units and reflection in x-axis

13. $\log_2 3 = \frac{a}{b}$, $a, b \in \mathbf{Z}$, $b \neq 0$ implies $2^a = 3^b$. But 2^a always even, 3^b always odd. This implies $a = b = 0$. Contradiction.

14. $x \geq -5.322$

Review, page 93

1. a. $\log_3 243 = 5$ **b.** $\log_5 390\,625 = 8$ **c.** $\log_{0.5} 0.0625 = 4$ **d.** $\log_{16} 8 = \frac{3}{4}$

e. $\log_4 0.5 = -\frac{1}{2}$ **f.** $\log_x \frac{1}{x^3} = -3$

g. $\log_x \sqrt[3]{x} = \frac{1}{3}$ **h.** $\log_x y = a$

i. $2 - 2\log_3 10 = x + 2$ **2. a.** $5^x = 13$
b. $6^x = 3$ **c.** $8^{-2} = x$ **d.** $3^x = 25$ **e.** $5^{-3} = x$
f. $x^4 = 12$ **g.** $x^{10} = 20$ **h.** $x^{-2} = 0.5$ **3. a.** 3
b. 4 **c.** -5 **d.** 0 **e.** 0.5 **f.** 1.5 **g.** $\frac{4}{3}$

h. -1.2 **4.** $x = \log_2(-4)$ implies $2^x = -4$. There is no number, x, that satisfies this equation.
5. a. $\log_2 17 + \log_2 15$ **b.** $\log_3 0.3 + \log_3 0.5$
c. $\log_4 15 - \log_4 7$ **d.** $\log_3 26 - \log_3 27$
e. $\log 11 + \log 13 + \log 17$ **f.** $2\log x + \log y$
g. $\frac{1}{2}\log x + \frac{1}{2}\log y$ **h.** $\frac{2}{3}\log x$ **6. a.** $\log_2 27$
b. $\log_7 250$ **c.** $\log_3 5$ **d.** $\log 15$ **e.** $\log_2 6x$

f. $\log_5 144x$ **g.** $\log_3 x^{\frac{5}{6}}$ **h.** $\log_{10}(a-1)$ **7. a.** 5
b. 100 **c.** 100 **d.** 1000 **e.** 64 **f.** 3 **g.** $\sqrt{5}$
h. 11 **i.** 10 000 **j.** 5 **k.** 4 **l.** 4 **8. a.** 1.398
b. 2.253 **c.** 3.333 **d.** -0.292 **e.** -2.638
9. a. 3 **b.** 3 **c.** 2 **d.** 2 **e.** 2 **f.** 2
10. a. 0.060 **b.** 0.931 **c.** 0 or 0.239 **11.** 2.6020

Exercise 3-4, pages 95-96

1. a. $x = \log_4 50$ **b.** $x = \log_8 70$ **c.** $x = \log_3 0.5$
d. $\log_2 5 = \frac{x}{x+2}$; $\log_5 2 = \frac{x+2}{x}$
e. $\log_4 7 = \frac{x}{x+5}$; $\log_7 4 = \frac{x+5}{x}$
f. $\log_2 5 = \frac{x+3}{x-1}$; $\log_5 2 = \frac{x-1}{x+3}$
g. $\log_3 5 = \frac{(x+2)}{2x}$; $\log_5 3 = \frac{2x}{x+2}$
h. $\log_y x = \frac{x}{y}$; $\log_x y = \frac{y}{x}$
2. a. 37.154 **b.** 1.030 **c.** 0.0003
d. 537 031.796 **3. a.** $10^{0.398}$ **b.** $10^{1.286}$
c. $10^{-0.631}$ **d.** $10^{-2.125}$ **e.** $10^{-0.477}$ **4. a.** 3.292
b. 2.096 **c.** 5.129 **d.** -0.004 **e.** 1.710
f. 9.006 **g.** 18.012 **h.** -2.173 **i.** 2.435
j. 4.549 **k.** 4.419 **l.** 3.606
5. a. $5^x = 7, x = 1.209$
b. $3^x = 12, x = 2.262$
c. $6^x = 13.2, x = 1.440$
d. $x^{4.7} = 1.25, x = 1.049$
e. $x^{3.2} = 0.57, x = 0.839$
f. $x^{0.75} = 0.25, x = 0.157$

6. a. 6.248 **b.** 2.892 **c.** 1.568 **d.** 1.111
e. -0.822 **f.** -5.919 **g.** 5.733 **h.** 1.270
7. a. $10^{1.505}$ **b.** $10^{5.724}$ **c.** $10^{4.064}$ **d.** $10^{0.018}$
e. $10^{-0.903}$ **f.** $10^{-0.124}$ **g.** $10^{0.452}$ **h.** $10^{0.392}$
8. a. $A = 10^{0.117}$ **b.** $T = 10^{1.301} + 10^{1.903 - 0.013t}$
c. $N = N_0(10^{-0.301})^{\frac{t}{h}}$ **9. a.** 0.431 or 0 **b.** 0.565
c. 1 **d.** 0.5 or 0.792

10. Let $x = a^{\log b}$
$\log x = (\log b)(\log a)$
$= (\log a)(\log b)$
$x = b^{\log a}$
$\therefore a^{\log b} = b^{\log a}$

11. Let $x = \log_a 3$
$= \log_b 27$
$\therefore a^x = 3$
and $b^x = 27$
$(a^x)^3 = b^x$
$(a^3)^x = b^x$
$\therefore a^3 = b$

12. $x = 2, 16$ **13.** $x = 1.854$

Application, page 97

$y = 2.5(7)^x$

Exercise 3-5, pages 100-101

1. a. 12 **b.** $950 **c.** 7.5%/period **2.** 14 a
3. 28 a **4.** 6.5%/a **5. a.** 80 cm^2 **b.** 61.4 cm^2
c. 30.4 d **6.** 5 d **7.** 29%

8. a.

t	$P_{\frac{t}{12}}$
0	$P_0 = A$
12	$P_1 = 1.5A = 1.5P_0$
24	$P_2 = (1.5)^2A = 1.5P_1$
36	$P_3 = (1.5)^3A = 1.5P_2$
⋮	⋮

b. 1960: 140 198 290 tonnes
1970: 196 555 605 tonnes
1980: 275 567 596 tonnes
1990: 386 341 057 tonnes
9. a. 74% **b.** 48 **10. a.** 18 935 a **b.** no
11. 6213 a **12.** 5 **13. a.** $x = 0.000\ 34, y = 2.9$
b. 283 kg

Exercise 3-6, pages 103-104

1. a. $x = \frac{\ln 20}{\ln 3}$ **b.** $t = \frac{\ln 8.2}{\ln 1.5}$
c. $t = \ln 13$ **d.** $x = \frac{\ln 9}{\ln 0.72}$
2. a. 3.912 **b.** 4.605 **c.** 0.693 **d.** -0.580
3. a. 1.046 **b.** 0.861 **c.** 1.099 **d.** -0.580
4. a. 3 **b.** 1 **c.** 0 **d.** -3 **e.** undefined
f. 2 **g.** 5 **h.** -2 **5. a.** $\ln 15$ **b.** $\ln \frac{1}{6}$ **c.** $\ln \frac{1}{8}$

d. $\ln 5e^3$ **e.** $\ln \frac{4}{e^3}$ **f.** $\ln \frac{e^5}{2}$ **6. a.** $x = \ln 3$
b. $x = \frac{1}{2}\ln 3$ **c.** $x = \ln 5e^2$ **d.** $x = -\ln 3$
e. $x = \ln \frac{e^2}{3}$ **f.** $x = \ln \frac{e^5}{2}$ **g.** $x = \ln e$
h. $x = \ln e^{\frac{3}{2}}$ **7. a.** $A = e^{0.934t}$ **b.** $V = V_0e^{-0.009t}$
c. $T = e^{2.96} + e^{4.382-0.104t}$ **8. a.** $y = e^{3.912+0.693x}$
b. $y = e^{0.049x}$ **c.** $y = e^{6.659-0.693x}$ **9.** 1995
10. 32.9 m **11. a.** 0.129 **b.** 78.3 kPa
12. 46.2 min **13.** 69.3 s; 138.6 s **14. a.** 0.012
b. 383.8 m **15. a.** 0.297 **b.** 13.2 cm
16. a. 1.099 **b.** 1.099 or 0.693 **17. a.** 48.6 a
b. 50.3 a

Application, page 105

1. 11.1 times as strong **2. a.** No increase
b. $10^{\left(\frac{R_2 - R_1}{0.67}\right)}$ **c.** $10^{\left(\frac{R_2 - R_1}{0.67}\right)}$

Review, pages 106-107

1. a. -2 **b.** -3 **c.** 12 **d.** $\frac{1}{2}$ **e.** $\frac{1}{5}$

2. a.

x	$f(x)$
-3	$\frac{1}{27}$
-2	$\frac{1}{9}$
-1	$\frac{1}{3}$
0	1
1	3
2	9
3	27

b.

x	$f^{-1}(x)$
$\frac{1}{27}$	-3
$\frac{1}{9}$	-2
$\frac{1}{3}$	-1
1	0
3	1
9	2
27	3

c. $y = \log_3 x$ **3. a.** $\log_3 81 = 4$ **b.** $\log_{0.5}\frac{1}{8} = 3$
c. $\log_4 8 = 1.5$ **d.** $\log_{16}\frac{1}{256} = -2$ **4. a.** $3^5 = 243$
b. $5^{0.5} = \sqrt{5}$ **c.** $32^{-\frac{3}{5}} = \frac{1}{8}$ **d.** $2^{1.5} = 2\sqrt{2}$
5. a. $x = 3$ **b.** $x = 121$ **c.** $y = 8$ **d.** $x = 9$
e. $x = 3$ **f.** $y = 2$ **g.** $x = 0.25$ **h.** $y = \frac{1}{3}$
i. $x = 8$ **j.** $x = 6$ **k.** $x = 79$ **l.** $x = 15$
6. a. $\log 17 + \log 15$
b. $\log_3 17 + \log_3 15 + \log_3 13$
c. $\log_2 12 - \log_2 5$ **d.** $\log 1 - \log 5$
7. a. $3 \log x$ **b.** $3 \log x + 4 \log y$
c. $\frac{1}{2}\log x + \frac{1}{2}\log y$ **d.** $\frac{1}{3}\log x + \frac{2}{3}\log y$

8. a. 196 **b.** 7 **9. a.** $\log 100 = 2$
b. $\log_6 36 = 2$ **c.** $\log_6 18 = 1.613$
d. $\log 1000 - \log_a a^3 = 0$ **10. a.** 0.920 79
b. 1.277 **c.** 2.722 81 **d.** 0.208 37
e. $-0.827\ 09$ **f.** 1.297 97 **11. a.** 416.869
b. 0.018 **c.** 2.355 **d.** 2.396 **12. a.** $x = 2$
b. $z = \sqrt{10}$ **13. a.** $y = 10^{1.236+0.301x}$
b. $y = 10^{0.025t}$ **c.** $y = 10^{1.778+0.191t}$ **14. a.** 4.087
b. -2.096 **c.** -4.322 **d.** 2.996
e. -1.609 **15. a.** 4.25 a **b.** 10.6 a
16. a. 7%/a **b.** 5.6%/a **17. a.** 24 **b.** 53
c. 5 d **18. a.** $k = 0.110$; $D_0 = 12.535$ cm
b. 10.5 a **19. a.** 10.5 times **b.** 25.9%

Test, page 108

1. a. 1000 **b.** 8 **c.** 25 **d.** -2

2.

x	$\frac{1}{8}$	$\frac{1}{4}$	$\frac{1}{2}$	1	2	4	8
y	-3	-2	-1	0	1	2	3

3. a. 0.5 **b.** 5 **c.** 5 **d.** 0.5 **e.** 1.5
4. a. $\log_{16} 4 = 0.5$ **b.** $\log_2 0.5 = -1$
c. $\log_{10} 0.001 = -3$ **d.** $\log_{81} 27 = 0.75$
5. a. $2^{-2} = 0.25$ **b.** $5^1 = 5$ **c.** $9^{0.25} = \sqrt{3}$
d. $10^2 = 100$ **6. a.** $x = 5$ **b.** $x = 100$
c. $x = \frac{4}{3}$ **d.** $x = 8$ **e.** $a = \frac{1}{7}$ **f.** $x = 29$
g. $x = 250$ **h.** $y = 1.5$ **7.** $y = 10^{0.796t-0.432}$
8. a. 0.018 **b.** 1.002 **c.** 1.452 **d.** 4.995
9. a. 4.192 **b.** 2.597 **c.** 1.270 **d.** -1.824
10. a. 7.5%/a **b.** 8%/a **11.** 25 runs
12. a. 100
b. 12.0°C **13. a.** $\{x \mid x > 2, x \in \boldsymbol{R}\}$; $x = 6$
b. $\{x \mid x > 1, x \in \boldsymbol{R}\}$; $x = \sqrt{11}$

Cumulative Review, page 109

1. a. $x = 5$ **b.** $x = -3$ **c.** $x = 6$ **d.** $x = 3$
2. a. $f(x) = 5\left(\frac{3}{4}\right)^x$ **b.** $f(x) = 2(3)^x$ or $f(x) = 2(-3)^x$

3. a. $f{:}x$ is a hyperbola, centre $C(0, 0)$, and horizontal axis the x-axis, vertical axis the y-axis. $g{:}x$ is the graph of $y = x$ translated 3 units to the right.
to the right.
b. $\frac{f}{g} : x$ has $D = \{x \mid x \in \boldsymbol{R}, x \neq 0, 3\}$ and
$R = \{y \mid y \in \boldsymbol{R}, y > 0, y \leq -\frac{4}{9}\}$.
c. $\frac{f}{g}: x \rightarrow \frac{1}{x^2 - 3x}$ **d.** $x = 0, x = 3$

4. 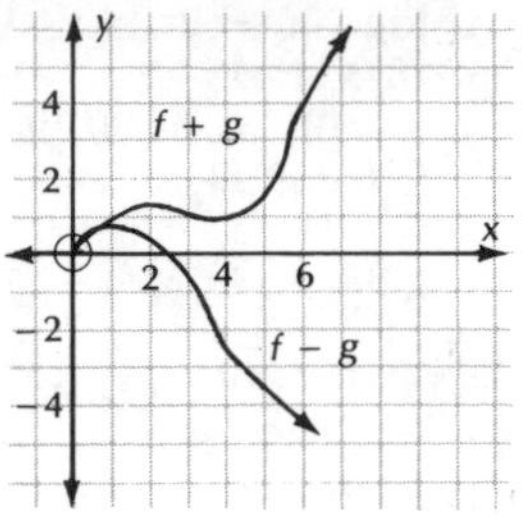

5. a. $|x| > 3$
b. $|x| < 1$
c. $|x| \geq 2$
d. $x < 1, x > 5$
e. $-7 < x < 3$
f. $x \neq -2$
6. a. $x = -3, 7$
b. $x = 0, 4$
c. $x = -5, 3$

7. b. $g^{-1}: x \rightarrow \pm\sqrt{x}$ is a parabola with vertex $V(0, 0)$, opening to the right.
c. When $D_g = \{x | x > 0\}$, then $g^{-1}: x = +\sqrt{x}$, and g^{-1} passes the vertical line test.
d. When $D_g = \{x | x < 0\}$, then $g^{-1}: x = -\sqrt{x}$, and g^{-1} passes the vertical line test.
8. $h^{-1}: x$ fails the vertical line test. For every value of x, there are two values of y.
9. \$2012.20

UNIT 4

Exercise 4-1, pages 112-113

1. a. $a = 3; b = 7$ b. $a = 2; b = 7$ c. $a = 3; b = 4$ d. $a = -6; b = 2$ e. $a = -7; b = -9$ f. $a = 5; b = -4$ 2. a. $(3 + a)(x + y)$ b. $(x - y)(a + b)$ c. $(m + n)(r - s)$ d. $(x + 2y)(p + 3q)$ e. $(3a - b + 2c)(x + y)$ f. $(3x + y - 2)(m - 3)$ 3. a. $(x + 1)(x + 4)$ b. $(x - 6)(x - 4)$ c. $(x + 3)(x - 4)$ d. $(x + 5)(x - 4)$ e. $(y - 5z)(y + 5z)$ f. $\left(m + \frac{1}{2}\right)^2$ g. $(2x - 3y)(2x + 3y)$ h. $(3a - 1)(3a + 1)$ i. $(x + 1)(2x + 15)$ j. $(2x + 3)(x + 1)$ k. $(5x - 1)(x + 7)$ l. $(3x + 4)(x + 6)$ 4. a. $a(x + 1)(x + 2)$ b. $2(x + 3)(x + 4)$ c. $5(x + y)(x + 3y)$ d. $3ab(a - 5b)(a - 2b)$ 5. a. $(a + b)(x + 2)(x + 1)$ b. $(y + 2)(y + 3)(m + n)$ c. $(a - 5)(a + 2)(x - 2y)$ d. $(x + 1)(x - 4)(y - 2)$ 6. a. $(3x - 5)(2x + 5)$ b. $(2x - 3)^2$ c. $(3x + 2)^2$ d. $(4x - 3)(2x - 3)$ e. $(4x + 3)(3x + 2)$ f. $(x - 6)(4x + 3)$ g. $(2x - 9)(2x + 7)$ h. $(4x + 5)(5x + 3)$ i. $(3x - 2)(5x + 2)$ 7. a. $3(4x + 3)(x + 3)$ b. $3r^2(3r^2 - 2q)(3r^2 + 2q)$ c. $p(4q - 3)(q + 5)$ d. $5(5x + 2)(2x - 3)$ e. $2m^2(2n + 5)(2n + 3)$ f. $ab(b - 4a)(b + 4a)$ g. $10p^2r(3q + 2)(2q + 3)$ h. $a(2x - 3)(5x - 3)$ i. $10s^2(2r - 5)(5r + 2)$ j. $2y^2(5x - 2y)^2$ k. $a(a - 1)^2$ l. $2x(x + 3)^2$ m. $2x(x + 4)(x - 4)$ n. $5x(x + 3)(x - 3)$ 8. a. $(x^2 + 1)(x + 1)(x - 1)$ b. $(s^4 + 1)(s^2 + 1)(s + 1)(s - 1)$ c. $(b + 1)^2(b - 1)^2$ d. $(z^2 + 1)(z + 2)(z - 2)$ e. $(2x^2 + 3)(2x + 3)(2x - 3)$ f. $(5r - 2)^2(5r + 2)^2$ 9. a. $k = \pm 5, \pm 7$ b. $k = \pm 2, \pm 7$ c. $k = \pm 5, \pm 7$ d. $k = \pm 7, \pm 8, \pm 13$ e. $k = \pm 4, \pm 7, \pm 11, \pm 17, \pm 28, \pm 59$ f. $\{k \in \mathbf{R}, k \leq \frac{25}{12}\}$ 10. a. $(x + 3 - y)(x + 3 + y)$ b. $(a - b - 2)(a + b + 2)$ c. $(2m - n - 1)(2m + n - 1)$ d. $(3x + 2 - y)(3x + 2 + y)$ e. $(x - y + 1)(x + y + 3)$ f. $(a - b - 2)(a + b + 8)$ g. $(3m + 2n - 5p)(3m + 2n + 5p)$ h. $(2r + 3s + 2q)(2r + 3s - 2q)$ i. $(a + b - c - 1)(a + b + c + 1)$ j. $(y + 3z + x - 2)(y + 3z - x + 2)$

Exercise 4-2, pages 116-117

1. a. $-1, 4$ b. $-2, 7$ c. ± 3 d. $2, 3$ e. $0, 2$ f. $2, -3$ g. $-3, 5$ h. $-3.5, 4$ i. $1.75, -4$ 2. a. $\frac{-3 \pm \sqrt{37}}{2}$ b. no real roots c. $\frac{1}{2}, 1$ d. $-\frac{1}{3}, 2$ e. no real roots f. $\frac{-1 \pm \sqrt{22}}{3}$ g. $\frac{7 \pm \sqrt{29}}{2}$ h. no real roots i. $\frac{1}{3}, 1$ 3. a. $-2 \pm \sqrt{6}$ b. $-1, 7$ c. $\frac{5 \pm \sqrt{37}}{2}$ d. $\frac{-1 \pm \sqrt{21}}{2}$ e. $5 \pm 2\sqrt{7}$ f. $1 \pm \sqrt{6}$ g. $\frac{5 \pm \sqrt{17}}{4}$ h. 1 i. $\frac{1 \pm \sqrt{85}}{6}$ 4. a. -15; no real roots b. 21; 2 distinct real roots c. 29; 2 distinct real roots d. 29; 2 distinct real roots e. 1.45; 2 distinct real roots f. -0.8; no real roots g. 52; 2 distinct real roots h. -27; no real roots i. 14.25; 2 distinct real roots j. -8.32; no real roots 5. width = 25 m; length = 30 m 6. a. $x^2 - 12x + 20 = 0$ b. 5, 12, 13 7. $-1, 0, 1$ or $4, 5, 6$ 8. 2.09 m 9. 43.59 mm 10. 12 km/h 11. 20 cm × 30 cm 12. a. $-1 \pm \sqrt{2}$ b. 0 c. $1 \pm \sqrt{10}$ d. $\frac{4}{3}$ e. $2, -\frac{3}{5}$ f. $-\frac{3}{4}$ 13. a. 5, 2 b. 5, 9 c. $\frac{9}{4}, 7$ d. $-\frac{1}{2}, 4$ e. $-\frac{1}{5}, -8$ f. $-13, \frac{5}{7}$

Exercise 4-3, pages 121-122

1. a. $-2.75, 0.75$ b. $-3.1, -1.2, 1.3$ c. $-0.7, 1.75, 5.0$ d. $0.6, 1.75$
2. a. $T(2) = 0$
$T(-1) = -3$
$T\left(\frac{1}{2}\right) = 1.875$
b. $T(-5) = -45$
$T(-3) = -23$
$T(0) = -5$

c. $R(0) = 1$
$R(-6) = 103$
$R(1.5) = -2$

d. $S(-2) = -16$
$S(5) = 29.5$
$S(-0.2) = 1.316$

e. $Q(-1) = 6.5$
$Q(-2) = 9$
$Q(-2.5) = 10.625$

f. $V(-1) = -2$
$V(-1.1) = -2.641$
$V(-1.2) = -3.368$

3. b, c, d
4.

	a.	b.	c.	d.	e.	f.
−3	13	−58	−51	−1	−4	−4
−2	5	−23	−17	−4	3	0
−1	−1	−6	−1	3	0	−2
0	−5	−1	3	2	5	−4
1	−7	−2	1	−1	6	0
2	−7	−3	−1	24	−9	16
3	−5	2	3	131	−22	50

5. a. −2.7, 0.7 **b.** −3.1, −1.2, 1.3
c. −0.7, 1.8, 5.0 **d.** 0.6, 1.7 **7.** $F(x)$: zeros at −0.79, 3.79 $R(x)$: zero at −1.67 $T(x)$: zero at 0.36
8. a. parabola; zeros at 5, −1; min. at (2, −9)
b. parabola; zeros at 3, −2; min. at (0.5, 6.25)
c. parabola; zeros at 2, 1; min. at (1.5, −0.25)
d. parabola; zeros at −3, −4; min. at (3.5, 48.75)
e. parabola; double zero at 4; min. at (4, 0)
f. parabola; zeros at 0, 2; min. at (1, −3)
g. zeros at ±3, 7; min. at (2.10, −5.05); max. at (−1.43, 16.90)
h. zeros at −4, 1, 5; min. at (3.27, 28.55) max. at (−1.94, 42.03)
i. zeros at ±2, 1, 5; max. at (1.5, 3.06); min. at (−1, −36), (4, −36)
j. zeros at 0, 6, 2, −3.
9. a. $x < -1, x > 2$ **b.** $x < 0, 1 < x < 3$
c. $x < -3, x > 2$ **d.** $x < -1, 0 < x < 5$
e. $|x| > 5$ **f.** $-3 < x < 0, x > 2$
g. $-4 < x < 2, x > 7$ **h.** $x > 0$
11. a. $a = \pm 2$ **b.** $-2 < a < 2$ **c.** $|a| > 2$

Using the Calculator, page 123

1. a. $x[x(x + 3) - 5] - 6$
b. $x(x[x(7x + 3) - 1] + 4) + 1$
c. $x[x(x) - 1]$ **d.** $x[x(5x - 6) + 8] - 9$
e. $x[x(x[x(x) + 3]) - 2] + 5$ **f.** $x[x(2x) - 1] + 6$

Exercise 4-4, page 126

1. a. $6i$ **b.** $10i$ **c.** $3i\sqrt{5}$ **d.** $2i\sqrt{15}$ **e.** $-2i$
f. $3i$ **g.** $2i\sqrt{5}$ **h.** 3 **2. a.** $10 + 3i$ **b.** $8 - 2i$
c. $4 + 4i$ **d.** $7 - i$ **e.** $-1 + 4i$ **f.** $-1 + i$
3. a. $5 + i$ **b.** 5 **c.** $9 + 6i$ **d.** $3 + 22i$
e. $7 - 9i$ **f.** $31 + 17i$ **4. a.** $3 - 2i$ **b.** $2 + i$
c. $-2i$ **d.** 8 **5. a.** $5i\sqrt{5}$ **b.** $7i\sqrt{2}$ **c.** $6i\sqrt{5}$
d. $\sqrt{7} - i\sqrt{6}$ **e.** $7\sqrt{3} - 2i\sqrt{5}$ **f.** $3\sqrt{6} + 9i\sqrt{2}$
6. a. $3i\sqrt{10}$ **b.** $-2i\sqrt{5}$ **c.** $-\sqrt{6}$ **d.** $\frac{3i}{4}$ **e.** $-\frac{1}{3}$
f. $2i$ **g.** $-5i$ **h.** -3 **i.** -1 **7. a.** $5 + 5i$
b. $6 - 2i$ **c.** $27 + 11i$ **d.** $21 + 20i$
e. $25 - 24i$ **f.** $-2 + 6i$ **g.** $5\sqrt{2} + 4i$
h. $-2 - 2i\sqrt{3}$ **i.** $6i$ **8. a.** $x = \pm 3i$
b. $\pm 3i\sqrt{2}$ **c.** $\pm\frac{\sqrt{21}}{3}$ **d.** $\frac{-3 \pm i\sqrt{23}}{2}$ **e.** $1 \pm 3i$
f. $2 \pm 5i$ **g.** $1, \frac{2}{3}$ **h.** $\frac{1 \pm 2i\sqrt{2}}{3}$ **i.** $\frac{5 \pm i\sqrt{11}}{6}$
9. a. 25 **b.** 5 **c.** 2 **d.** 29 **e.** 40 **f.** 9 **g.** 1
h. 25 **10. a.** −1 **b.** $-i$ **c.** 1 **d.** i **e.** −1
f. $-i$ **g.** 1 **h.** i **i.** −1 **j.** 1 **k.** i **l.** $-i$
11. n is odd; $n - 1$ is not divisible by 4.

Application, page 127

3. A complex conjugate is the reflection of a complex number in the real axis.
5. a. $\sqrt{13}$ **b.** $\sqrt{10}$ **c.** 5 **d.** 1 **e.** 1
8. (length of $factor_1$)(length of $factor_2$)
= (length of product
(angle of $factor_1$) + (angle of $factor_2$)
= (angle of product)

Exercise 4-5, page 129

1. a. $3x^2 + 0x - 5$ **b.** $2x^3 + x^2 - 3x + 1$
c. $x^3 - 3x^2 + 2x + 5$ **d.** $2x^4 + 0x^3 + 0x^2 + 3x + 0$
e. $x^3 + 0x^2 + 3x - 4$
f. $x^6 + 0x^5 + 0x^4 - 3x^3 + 0x^2 + 0x + 4$
2. a. $(x - 2)(x - 1) + 3$ **b.** $(x + 3)(-2x + 11) - 30$
b. $(x + 3)(-2x + 11) - 30$
c. $(m + 2)(3m^2 - 7m + 12) - 19$
d. $(2x + 3)(x^2 + 2x - 1) - 5$
e. $(x - 3)(2x^3 + 3x - 1)$ **f.** $(5x - 1)(2x^3 - x + 2) - 1$
3. a. $4x^2 - x - 6 = (x + 4)(4x - 17) + 62$
b. $4x^3 + 3x - 2 = (x + 2)(4x^2 - 8x + 19) - 40$
c. $3x^3 - 7x^2 - 10x + 5 = (3x - 1)(x^2 - 2x - 4) + 1$
d. $2x + 3x^4 + 7 = (x + 3)(3x^3 - 9x + 27x - 79) + 244$
e. $x^3 - x^5 + x - 1 = (x - 1)(-x^4 - x^3 + 1)$
f. $x^4 - 1 + x = (x - 1)(x^3 + x^2 + x + 2) + 1$
4. a. $Q(r) = 3r^2 - 2r; R(r) = 3$
b. $Q(x) = 3x^2 - 2x - 4; R(x) = 0$
c. $Q(x) = 3x^2 + 5x - \frac{3}{2}; R(x) = \frac{9}{2}x + \frac{5}{2}$
d. $Q(t) = 5t^4 + t^2 + 2t + 3; R(t) = 5t - 2$
5. a. 11 **b.** 3

Exercise 4-6, page 130

1. a. $3x^2 - x + 2 = (x - 3)(3x + 8) + 26$
b. $5x^2 + x - 6 = (x - 2)(5x + 11) + 16$
c. $m^3 + 3m^2 - 5m - 2 = (m - 2)(m^2 + 5m + 5) + 8$
d. $3x^3 - 2x^2 + 5x - 1 = (x + 4)(3x^2 - 14x + 61) - 245$
e. $2t^3 - t + 1 = (t + 5)(2t^2 - 10t + 49) - 244$
f. $n^3 - 3n^2 + n + 5 = (n - 2)(n^2 - n - 1) + 3$

g. $p^4 - p^2 + 3 = (p - 4)(p^3 + 4p^2 + 15p + 60) + 243$
h. $x - x^3 + 7 = (x - 8)(-x^2 - 8x - 63) - 497$
i. $3n^2 + n^4 - 2 = (n + 3)(n^3 - 3n^2 + 12n - 36) + 106$
j. $s^4 - s^2 + s + 6 = (s + 2)(s^3 - 2s^2 + 3s - 5) + 16$
k. $2x^2 - 7x + 3 = (2x - 6)\left(x - \frac{1}{2}\right)$
l. $4x^3 - 4x^2 - 9x + 3 = \left(x - \frac{3}{2}\right)(4x^2 + 2x - 6) - 6$
m. $4x^3 - x^2 + 5x - 3 = \left(x - \frac{3}{4}\right)\left(4x^2 + 2x + \frac{13}{2}\right) + \frac{15}{8}$
n. $4x^4 - 3x^2 + x - 1 = \left(x - \frac{3}{2}\right)(4x^3 + 6x^2 + 6x + 10) + 14$

Review, page 131

1. a. $(3x + 2)(x - 2)$ **b.** $(2x - 7)(x + 9)$ **c.** $(x - 9)(4x - 9)$ **d.** $2(3x - 2)(2x + 3)$ **e.** $m^2(4x + 7)(x - 8)$ **f.** $y(2x - 1)(5x + 3)$ **g.** $r(2p - 3q)(4p + q)$ **h.** $a(a + 5)$ **i.** $(7x - 2)(x - 3)$ **2. a.** $P(-1.65) = -0.01$; $P(3.65) = -0.01$ **b.** $P(-0.64) = 0.02$; $P(3.14) = 0.02$ **3. a.** $R = \{y \mid -3 \le y \le 46\}$; Min. at $(2, -3)$; zeros at 0.27, 3.73 **b.** $R = \{y \mid -2.07 \le y \le 47\}$; Max. at $(-0.15, 2.08)$, Min. at $(2.15, -4.08)$; zeros at -0.86, 0.75, 3.11 **4. a.** $-2, 9$ **b.** $\frac{7}{2}, -\frac{5}{6}$ **c.** $\pm\frac{1}{3}, \pm 2$ **d.** $\pm 1, \pm 2$ **e.** ± 3 **f.** $-3, \frac{2}{3}$ **5. a.** $-2 \pm \sqrt{14}$ **b.** $\frac{3 \pm \sqrt{15}}{2}$ **c.** $\frac{3 \pm \sqrt{29}}{2}$ **6. a.** $\frac{5 \pm \sqrt{21}}{2}$ **b.** $\frac{1 \pm \sqrt{85}}{6}$ **c.** $\frac{-1 \pm i\sqrt{39}}{4}$ **d.** $1, -\frac{2}{5}$ **e.** $1, \frac{1}{3}$ **f.** $\frac{-5 \pm \sqrt{1561}}{32}$ **7.** 9 m × 13 m **8. a.** $7 + 3i$ **b.** $-1 - 3i$ **c.** $6i\sqrt{5}$ **d.** $\sqrt{7} - i\sqrt{6}$ **e.** $-15\sqrt{2}$ **f.** 2 **g.** $11 - 3i$ **h.** 13 **i.** $2 - 2i$ **9. a.** $x^3 + 3x^2 - 4x - 12 = (x + 2)(x^2 + x - 6)$ **b.** $3x^3 - 4x^2 - 16x + 5 = (x - 3)(3x^2 + 5x - 1) + 2$ **c.** $x - 2x^3 + 3 = (x - 1)(-2x^2 - 2x - 1) + 2$ **d.** $x^4 - 2x^3 + x - 2 = (x^2 + x - 1)(x^2 - 3x + 4) - 6x + 2$

Exercise 4-7, pages 134-135

1. a. 3 **b.** 19 **c.** -141 **d.** 226 **e.** 113 **f.** -6 **2. a.** no **b.** yes **c.** no **d.** yes **e.** no **f.** no **3. a.** 1 **b.** -2 **c.** ± 1 **d.** $\frac{1}{2}, 1$ **e.** $\pm\frac{1}{2}$ **f.** $1 \pm \sqrt{2}$ **4. a.** $(y + 2)(y^2 - 2y + 4)$ **b.** $(c - 10)(c^2 + 10c + 100)$ **c.** $(2a^2 - b)(4a^4 + 2a^2b + b^2)$ **d.** $\left(r^2 + \frac{1}{5}\right)\left(r^4 - \frac{1}{5}r^2 + \frac{1}{25}\right)$ **5. a.** $-2, -1, 3$ **b.** $\pm\sqrt{7}, 1$ **c.** $-2, \pm\frac{\sqrt{6}}{2}$ **d.** 3 **6. a.** yes **b.** no **c.** no **d.** yes **e.** yes **f.** yes

7. a. $(x - 2)(3x - 5)(2x + 3)$ **b.** $(x + 3)(2x + 3)(x - 4)$ **c.** $(x + 3)(x - 1)(x^2 + x + 1)$ **d.** $(3x + 2)(2x + 1)(2x - 1)$ **e.** $(2x + 3)(x + 2)(x^2 - 2x + 4)$ **f.** $x(2x + 3)^2(2x - 3)$ **g.** $(x + 3)(x - 3)(x + 1)(x^2 - x + 1)$ **h.** $(x - 2)(x^2 + 3)^2$ **8. a.** $(x + 1)(x - 1)(x^2 - x + 1)(x^2 + x + 1)$ **b.** $(4t^2 + s^2)(16t^4 - 4s^2t^2 + s^4)$ **c.** $(y - 1)^2(y^2 + y + 1)^2$ **d.** $(2x + 1)^2(4x^2 - 2x + 1)^2$ **e.** $(m - 1)(m + 3)(m^2 + m + 1)(m^2 - 3m + 9)$ **f.** $(2x + 3)(x - 1)(4x^2 - 6x + 9)(x^2 + x + 1)$ **9. a.** $-6, -\frac{1}{2}, 2$ **b.** $-2, 1, 3$ **c.** $-3, \pm\sqrt{6}$ **d.** $-2, \frac{1}{2}, 1$ **e.** $-3, -\frac{1}{3}, \frac{1}{2}$ **f.** $-1, \frac{1}{2}, 1$

Exercise 4-8, pages 138-139

1. a. $\pm\frac{1}{2}, \pm 1, \pm 2$ **b.** $\pm 1, \pm 2, \pm 3, \pm 6$ **c.** $\pm\frac{1}{3}, \pm\frac{2}{3}, \pm 1, \pm\frac{4}{3}, \pm 2, \pm\frac{8}{3}, \pm 4, \pm 8$ **d.** $\pm\frac{1}{5}, \pm\frac{2}{5}, \pm 1, \pm 2$ **e.** $\pm\frac{1}{4}, \pm\frac{1}{2}, \pm\frac{3}{4}, \pm 1, \pm\frac{3}{2}, \pm 2, \pm 3, \pm 6$ **f.** $\pm\frac{1}{6}, \pm\frac{1}{3}, \pm\frac{1}{2}, \pm\frac{2}{3}, \pm\frac{5}{6}, \pm 1, \pm\frac{5}{3}, \pm 2, \pm\frac{5}{2}, \pm\frac{10}{3}, \pm 5, \pm 10$ **g.** $\pm 1, \pm 2, \pm 4, \pm 8$ **h.** $\pm\frac{1}{7}, \pm\frac{3}{7}, \pm 1, \pm 3$ **2. a.** $-3, 1, 4$ **b.** $-4, -2, 1$ **c.** $-5, -2, 3$ **d.** $-7, -1, 4$ **e.** $-1, \frac{1}{3}, 1, 2$ **f.** $\frac{1}{2}, \pm 3, 4$ **g.** $-\frac{2}{3}, 1, \pm 3$ **h.** $-1, \frac{3}{2}, \pm 2$ **3. a.** $-\frac{4}{3}, 4$ **b.** $\frac{1}{2}, 1$ **c.** $\frac{5}{3}, \frac{3}{2}$ **d.** $-3, -2, \frac{2}{3}$ **e.** $\pm\frac{1}{2}, 5$ **f.** $-3, \frac{1}{2}, \frac{2}{3}$ **g.** $-3, \frac{1}{4}, 1, 2$ **h.** $\pm\frac{1}{3}, \pm 1$ **4. a.** $-3, 1 \pm \sqrt{5}$ **b.** $-2, 1 \pm \sqrt{2}$ **c.** $\frac{1}{2}, 1 \pm \sqrt{10}$ **d.** $\frac{1}{3}, \frac{1 \pm \sqrt{2}}{2}$ **e.** $\frac{1}{2}, \frac{2 \pm 2\sqrt{2}}{3}$ **f.** $-1, 3, 3 \pm 2\sqrt{2}$ **g.** $-3, \frac{1}{3}, \frac{3 \pm \sqrt{5}}{2}$ **h.** $\frac{3}{2}, 2, 3 \pm \sqrt{6}$ **5. a.** $(x + 2)(x - 2)(x - 3)$ **b.** $(x + 2)(2x - 1)(3x - 1)$ **c.** $(x - 2)(x + 3)(4x - 1$ **d.** $(x + 1)(x + 2)(4x - 1)(3x - 1)$ **e.** $(x + 1)(x + 3)(5x - 1)(2x - 1)$ **f.** $(x - 1)(x - 2)(x - 3)(2x - 1)(2x + 1)$ **g.** $(x - 1)(3x + 5)(x^2 + x + 1)$ **h.** $(x - 1)(x + 1)(x - 2)(x^2 + 2x + 4)$ **6. a.** $P(x) < 0$ if $x < 0$; $P(x) < 0$ if $0 < x < \frac{2}{3}$;

$P(x) = 0$ if $x = \frac{2}{3}$; $P(x) > 0$ if $x > \frac{2}{3}$ **b.** no
c. Answers will vary. **7. a.** yes **b.** no **c.** no
d. yes **e.** no **f.** yes
8. By RRT, the denominator of any possible rational root is ± 1.
Thus, all rational roots are integers, but all roots are not necessarily integers.

Exercise 4-9, pages 142-143

1. a. $2, -3, i, -i$ **b.** $\frac{2}{3}, 1, -\frac{5}{2}$ **c.** 3 (double), $-2, \pm\sqrt{5}$ **d.** 0, -3 (double), 2 (triple)
e. 0, 2 (double), -2 (double), 0 (triple)
f. $3 + 4i, 3 - 4i, \frac{2}{5}$ (double) **2. a.** $x^2 + 2x + 5$
b. $x^2 - 6x + 10$ **c.** $x^2 - 4x + 13$
d. $x^2 + 10x + 26$ **e.** $x^3 - 3x^2 + x - 3$
f. $2x^3 - x^2 + 18x - 9$ **g.** $4x^2 - 4x + 10$
h. $12x^3 - 44x^2 + 99x - 50$
3. a. $-2, 1$ **b.** ± 2 **c.** $-1, -\sqrt{5}$
d. $\frac{1 \pm \sqrt{3}}{2}$ **e.** $\frac{1 \pm i}{2}$ **f.** $2, 1 - i$ **g.** $2, 2 + i$
h. $1 - 3i, \frac{2}{3}$ **4. a.** -4 **b.** $-2\sqrt{2}, \pm i\sqrt{2}$
c. $1 - 2i, \frac{1}{2}$ **d.** $-\sqrt{5}, \frac{-3 \pm \sqrt{21}}{2}$ **e.** $2 \pm 3i$
f. $1 - 2i$ (double) **g.** $1 \pm 2i, 3 + i$ **h.** ± 2
5. a. $\pm 1, 3$ **b.** -1, 2 (double) **c.** $-1, \frac{1}{2}$; 2 imaginary roots **6. a.** $2x^2 - 5x - 3$
b. $x^3 - 5x^2 + 7x - 3$ **c.** $x^3 + 2x^2 - 7x - 14$
d. $x^2 - 2x + 5$ **e.** $x^3 - 5x^2 + 8x - 6$
f. $x^4 - 4x^3 + 12x^2 + 4x - 13$ **g.** $x^2 - 2x - 1$
h. $2x^3 - 7x^2 - 2x + 1$
i. $4x^5 - 24x^4 + 49x^3 - 45x^2 + 19x - 3$
j. $x^5 - 17x^4 + 112x^3 - 352x^2 + 516x - 260$

Exercise 4-10, pages 145-147

2. a. III **b.** II **c.** I **d.** IV **e.** V **f.** VI
3. a. III **b.** V **c.** I, II, III **d.** IV, V, VI
e. I, II, III **f.** IV, V, VI
5. a. 4; 2 distinct real roots, 2 imaginary roots.
b. 4 distinct real roots. **c.** 4; 2 distinct real roots, 2 imaginary roots. **d.** 3; 1 double root, 1 real root. **e.** 5; 2 double roots, 1 real root. **f.** 6; 2 distinct real roots, 1 double root, 2 imaginary roots.
imaginary roots.
6. a. $(x - 1)^2(x - 3)$ **b.** $-(x + 2)(x - 2)(x + 3)$
c. $(x + 1)(2x - 1)(x - 3)$ **d.** $(x - 1)(4x - 1)(3x + 4$
e. $(x - 1)(x + 2)(x - 2)^2$ **f.** $-(x - 1)^3(x + 5)$
g. $(x + 2)(x - 2)(2x + 1)(2x - 1)$
h. $(x + 1)^3(3x - 2)$ **i.** $(x + 3)^3(x - 1)^2$
j. $(x + 1)^2(x - 1)(x - 2)(x + 3)$

Extra, page 147

	Number of positive roots	Number of negative roots	Number of imaginary roots	Total
1.	1 1	2 0	0 2	3 3
2.	3 1	0 0	0 2	3 3
3.	3 1	1 1	0 2	4 4
4.	2 0	1 1	0 2	3 3
5.	4 2 0	1 1 1	0 2 4	5 5 5
6.	3 3 1 1	2 0 2 0	0 2 2 4	5 5 5 5

Exercise 4-11, page 149

1. a. 8 **b.** 4 **c.** 12 **d.** 12 **e.** 16 **f.** ± 2
2. a. 8 **b.** 1, 2 **c.** $-1, 3$ **d.** 4 **e.** 2 **f.** 0, 5
3. a. 4 **b.** 3 **c.** 10 **d.** 9 **e.** 3 **f.** 4 **4. a.** 3
b. 5 **c.** 5 **d.** 6 **e.** 3 **f.** 2, 5 **5. a.** 3 **b.** 6
c. 10 **d.** 5 **6. a.** 2 **b.** 6 **c.** 12 **d.** $n^2 - n$
7. $\frac{1 \pm \sqrt{5}}{2}$

Exercise 4-12, page 151

1. a. $-4 \le x \le -2, x \ge 1$ **b.** $1 < |x| < 3$
c. $x \le -2, x \ge 1$ **d.** $x > -3, x \ne -1$
e. $x < 0, \quad x \ne -2$ **f.** $x \le -2, x = 3$
2. a.
b.
c.
d.

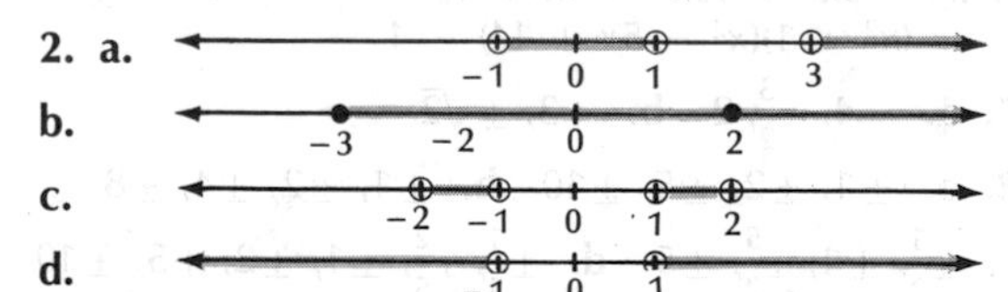

3. a. $1 \le x \le 2$ **b.** $x < -\frac{3}{2}, x > \frac{5}{2}$
c. $-\frac{2}{3} < x < 3$ **d.** $-1 \le x \le 2, x \ge 3$
e. $x \le -\frac{1}{2} \le x \le 3$ **f.** $x > \frac{1}{2}, x \ne 3$
g. $-4 \le x \le \frac{1}{2}, x \ge 1$ **h.** $x < -4, \frac{1}{3} < x < 1$
i. $x < -2, x > 1$ **j.** $-4 \le x \le -\frac{1}{2}, x = 1$

4. a.

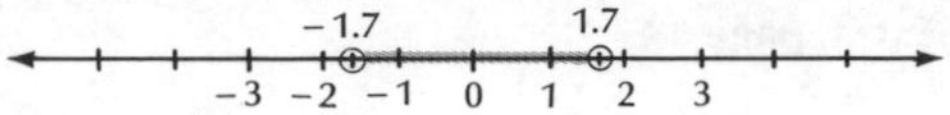

b.

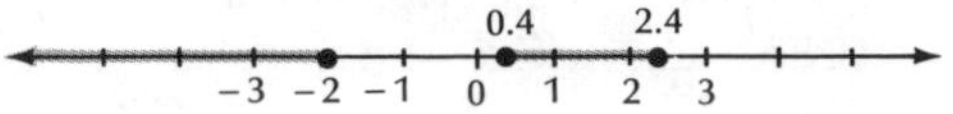

c.

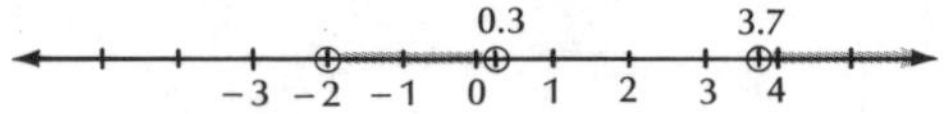

d.

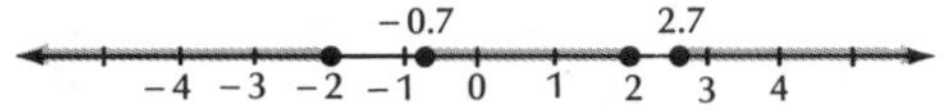

e.

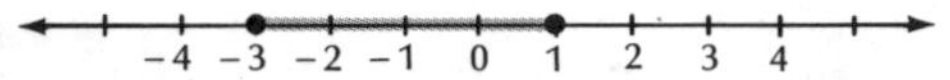

f.

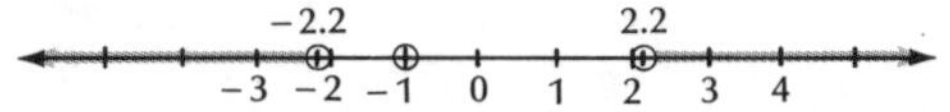

Review, pages 152-153

1. a. $(2x - 1)(3x + 4)$ **b.** $7xy^2(3x + 4)(x - 5)$
c. $(9x^2 - 8)(9x^2 + 8)$ **d.** $(2x - 9y)(9x + y)$
e. $(2x - 5y^2)(4x^2 + 10xy^2 + 25y^4)$
f. $(x + 1)(4x - 15)(x - 1)$ **2. a.** ± 2.24
b. 0.56, 2.86 **4.** 46 **5. a.** $7i$ **b.** 4 **c.** $-5\sqrt{2}$
d. $-2\sqrt{2}$ **e.** $-i\sqrt{6}$ **f.** $-i\sqrt{7}$ **g.** $5i\sqrt{3} - i\sqrt{5}$
h. 34 **i.** $13 - 9i$
6. a. $x^3 + x^2 - 2x - 1 = (x + 1)(x^2 - 2) + 1$
b. $x^3 - 8x^2 + 21x - 20 = (x - 4)(x^2 - 4x + 5)$
c. $5x^3 - 2x^2 + 1 = (x - 3)(5x^2 + 13x + 39) + 118$
d. $x^3 - 4x^2 + x - 4 = (x + 2)(x^2 - 6x + 13) - 30$
e. $x^3 - 3x^2 - x + 1 = (x^2 - x + 1)(x - 2) - 4x + 3$
f. $x^4 - 5x^3 + 15x^2 - 5x + 10$
$= (x^2 + 1)(x^2 - 5x + 14) - 4$
7. a. $-4, -\frac{3}{2}, 2$ **b.** $-3, \pm\sqrt{2}$
8. a. $\pm 1, \pm 2, \pm 5, \pm 10$ **b.** $\pm 1, \pm 2, \pm 4, \pm 8$
c. $\pm\frac{1}{2}, \pm 1, \pm\frac{5}{2}, \pm 5$ **d.** $\pm\frac{1}{5}, \pm\frac{2}{5}, \pm 1, \pm 2, \pm 5, \pm 10$
e. $\pm 1, \pm 2, \pm 3, \pm 4, \pm 6, \pm 12$
f. $\pm\frac{1}{2}, \pm 1, \pm\frac{3}{2}, \pm 2, \pm 3, \pm 6$
g. $\pm\frac{1}{4}, \pm\frac{1}{2}, \pm\frac{3}{4}, \pm 1, \pm\frac{3}{2}, \pm 2, \pm 3, \pm 6$
h. $\pm\frac{1}{6}, \pm\frac{1}{3}, \pm\frac{1}{2}, \pm 1$
9. a. $(x - 3)(x^2 - 2); \pm\sqrt{2}$ **b.** $(x - 1)^2(x + 5); -5$
c. $\left(x - \frac{1}{2}\right)(6x - 4)(x + 1); \frac{2}{3}, -1$
d. $(x - (2 + i))(x - (2 - i))(4x - 3); 2 - i, \frac{3}{4}$
e. $(x - 2)^2(x - 1 + 2i)(x - 1 - 2i); 1 \pm 2i$
10. a. $-1, 4$ **b.** $\frac{5 \pm \sqrt{13}}{6}$ **c.** $-2 \pm i$
d. $-3, \frac{3 \pm i\sqrt{3}}{2}$ **e.** $-3, -1, \frac{1}{2}$ **f.** $1, 1 \pm \sqrt{3}$
g. $1 \pm i, 1$ **h.** $\frac{1}{3}, \pm i$ **i.** $\frac{3}{4}, 1 \pm i$ **j.** $\pm 1, 1 \pm 2i$
11. a. $x^2 - x - 6 = 0$ **b.** $2x^3 + 3x^2 - 1 = 0$
c. $x^2 - 2x + 2 = 0$ **d.** $x^3 - x^2 - 7x + 15 = 0$
e. $x^4 + 2x^2 - 8 = 0$
f. $15x^4 - 103x^3 + 275x^2 - 181x + 26 = 0$
12. a. 4 **b.** 4 **c.** 5 **d.** 3 **e.** 6 **f.** 7
g. 4 **h.** 5 **14. a.** $x < 1, x > 3$ **b.** ϕ
c. $x \leq -2, x \geq \frac{3}{2}$ **d.** $-3 \leq x \leq 4$
e. $x < -1, 2 < x < 3$ **f.** $x < -2, x > 1$

Test, page 154

1. a. $5(x - 1)(x - 2)$ **b.** $2(6x + y)(x - 6y)$
c. $(x^2 + 1)(x^2 - 5)$ **d.** $3y^2(3x - 4)(x + 1)$
e. $(x + 1)(x - 1)(x^2 - x + 1)(x^2 + x + 1)$
f. $(x + 2)(x - 4)(5x - 14)$
2. $\pm\frac{1}{3}, \pm\frac{2}{3}, \pm 1, \pm 2, \pm 3, \pm 6$
3. a. -1 (double), 2 **b.** $\frac{1}{3}, \frac{1}{2}, 2$ **c.** $-\frac{1}{3}, \frac{1}{2}, \frac{3}{2}$
d. $-4, \frac{3 \pm \sqrt{17}}{2}$ **e.** $-2, -1, \pm i$ **f.** $\frac{5}{3}, \frac{1 \pm i\sqrt{3}}{2}$
4. zero at -3.09 **5. a.** $4i\sqrt{3}$ **b.** -10
c. $3i\sqrt{7} - 3i\sqrt{2}$ **d.** $5 + 8i$ **e.** $18 - i$ **f.** i
6. a. $x^3 - 3x^2 - 13x + 10 = (x - 5)(x^2 + 2x - 3) -$
b. $2x^3 - x^2 - 13x - 7 = (2x + 1)(x^2 - x - 6) - 1$
c. $2x^4 - 7x^3 + 12x^2 - 8x + 5$
$= (x^2 - 3x + 4)(2x^2 - x + 1) - x + 1$
7.

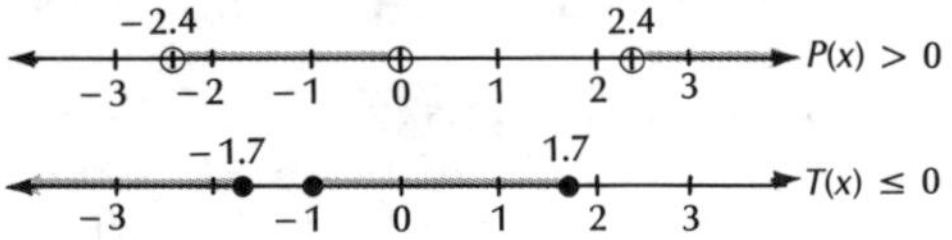

8. a. $x^2 + x - 6$ **b.** $3x^3 - 8x^2 + 7x - 2$
c. $x^3 - 7x^2 + 15x - 25$
d. $x^5 - x^4 + 9x^3 - 7x^2 + 18$ **9. a.** $\frac{2}{3}$ **b.** 5
10. a. 5 **b.** 2 **c.** 7 **d.** 5

Cumulative Review, page 155

1. a. yes; Domain $= \{x \mid x \in \boldsymbol{R}, |x| \leq 5\}$;
Range $= \{y \mid y \in \boldsymbol{R}, -2 \leq y \leq 4\}$
b. no; Domain $= \{x \mid x \in \boldsymbol{R}, -2 \leq x \leq 3\}$;
Range $= \{y \mid y \in \boldsymbol{R}, |y| \leq 2\}$
c. yes; Domain $= \{x \mid x \in \boldsymbol{R}\}$; Range $= \{y \mid y \in \boldsymbol{R}\}$
2. a. 27 **b.** $\frac{256}{81}$ **c.** 8 **d.** $\frac{3}{2}$ **e.** $-\frac{3}{2}$ **f.** $\frac{3}{2}$

3. a. 4 **b.** 0 **c.** 3 **d.** 3 **4. a.** 11 **b.** 7 **c.** 64 **d.** 83 **5.** 5a **6. a.** 1.436 **b.** 1.253 **c.** 0.549 **d.** 3.391 **7. c.** (2, 4), (4, 16), (−0.767, 0.588) **8. a.** 80 W **b.** 26.5 W **c.** 314 d **9.** 4.1 g

UNIT 5

Exercise 5-1, page 159

1.

Function	θ	α
sin	$\frac{9}{41}$	$\frac{40}{41}$
cos	$\frac{40}{41}$	$\frac{9}{41}$
tan	$\frac{9}{40}$	$\frac{40}{9}$
csc	$\frac{41}{9}$	$\frac{41}{40}$
sec	$\frac{41}{40}$	$\frac{41}{9}$
cot	$\frac{40}{9}$	$\frac{9}{40}$

2. a. $x = 37$

Function	θ	α
sin	$\frac{35}{37}$	$\frac{12}{37}$
cos	$\frac{12}{37}$	$\frac{35}{37}$
tan	$\frac{35}{12}$	$\frac{12}{35}$
csc	$\frac{37}{35}$	$\frac{37}{12}$
sec	$\frac{37}{12}$	$\frac{37}{35}$
cot	$\frac{12}{35}$	$\frac{35}{12}$

b. $x = 16$

Function	θ	α
sin	$\frac{16}{65}$	$\frac{63}{65}$
cos	$\frac{63}{65}$	$\frac{16}{65}$
tan	$\frac{16}{63}$	$\frac{63}{16}$
csc	$\frac{65}{16}$	$\frac{65}{63}$
sec	$\frac{65}{63}$	$\frac{65}{16}$
cot	$\frac{63}{16}$	$\frac{16}{63}$

c. $x = 65$

Function	θ	α
sin	$\frac{65}{97}$	$\frac{72}{97}$
cos	$\frac{72}{97}$	$\frac{65}{97}$
tan	$\frac{65}{72}$	$\frac{72}{65}$
csc	$\frac{97}{65}$	$\frac{97}{72}$
sec	$\frac{97}{72}$	$\frac{97}{65}$
cot	$\frac{72}{65}$	$\frac{65}{72}$

3. sine & cosecant; cosine & secant; tangent & cotangent
4. a. 0.7314 **b.** 0.4540 **c.** 8.1443 **d.** 1.1326 **e.** 1.4474 **f.** 1.8572 **g.** 0.1423 **h.** 0.9964
5. a. 55.85° **b.** 65.06° **c.** 36.37° **d.** 73.62° **e.** 65.55° **f.** 44.76° **g.** 25.38° **h.** 48.19° **i.** 51.34° **j.** 38.94° **k.** 46.66° **l.** 68.20°
6. $\sin\theta = \frac{60}{61}$; $\tan\theta = \frac{60}{11}$

7. a. $\sin\theta = \frac{33}{65}$, $\cos\theta = \frac{56}{65}$, $\csc\theta = \frac{65}{33}$, $\sec\theta = \frac{65}{56}$, $\cot\theta = \frac{56}{33}$
b. $\cos\theta = \frac{84}{85}$, $\tan\theta = \frac{13}{84}$, $\csc\theta = \frac{85}{13}$, $\sec\theta = \frac{85}{84}$, $\cot\theta = \frac{84}{13}$
c. $\sin\theta = \frac{2\sqrt{6}}{7}$, $\tan\theta = \frac{2\sqrt{6}}{5}$, $\csc\theta = \frac{7\sqrt{6}}{12}$, $\sec\theta = \frac{7}{5}$, $\cot\theta = \frac{5\sqrt{6}}{12}$
8. $\sin\theta = 0.9479$; $\tan\theta = 2.9741$
9. a. $\cos\theta = 0.5831$, $\tan\theta = 1.3932$, $\csc\theta = 1.2309$, $\sec\theta = 1.7150$, $\cot\theta = 0.7178$
b. $\sin\phi = 0.7773$, $\tan\phi = 1.2356$, $\csc\phi = 1.2865$, $\sec\phi = 1.5896$, $\cot\phi = 0.8093$
c. $\sin\mu = 0.7100$, $\cos\mu = 0.7042$, $\csc\mu = 1.4084$, $\sec\mu = 1.4201$, $\cot\mu = 0.9918$
10. a. 60° **b.** 60° **c.** 30° **d.** 45° **e.** 30° **f.** 53.13° **g.** 48.59° **h.** 66.42°

Exercise 5-2, page 161

1. a. $\frac{7}{25}, \frac{25}{7}$; 1 **b.** $\frac{24}{25}, \frac{25}{24}$; 1 **c.** $\frac{7}{24}, \frac{24}{7}$; 1
2. a. i. $\frac{a}{c}, \frac{c}{a}$; 1 **ii.** $\frac{b}{c}, \frac{c}{b}$; 1 **iii.** $\frac{a}{b}, \frac{b}{a}$; 1
b. i. $\sin\theta\csc\theta = 1$ **ii.** $\cos\theta\sec\theta = 1$ **iii.** $\tan\theta\cot\theta = 1$
3. a. $\frac{27}{36}$ **b.** $\frac{27}{36}$ **c.** $\frac{36}{27}$ **d.** $\frac{36}{27}$ **4. a.** $\frac{b}{a}$ **b.** $\frac{b}{a}$ **c.** $\frac{a}{b}$ **d.** $\frac{a}{b}$ **5.** $\tan\theta = \frac{\sin\theta}{\cos\theta}$; $\cot\theta = \frac{\cos\theta}{\sin\theta}$
7. a.

θ	$90° - \theta$	$\sin\theta$	$\cos(90° - \theta)$
10°	80°	0.1736	0.1736
55°	35°	0.8192	0.8192
63°	27°	0.8910	0.8910
8.4°	81.6°	0.1461	0.1461
20°	70°	0.9397	0.9397
35°	55°	0.8192	0.8192
69°	21°	0.3584	0.3584
12.8°	77.2°	0.9751	0.9751

b. $\sin\theta = \cos(90° - \theta)$; $\cos\theta = \sin(90° - \theta)$
8. a, b, d, e, f, h, i, j

Exercise 5-3, pages 164-167
1. a. 5.63 **b.** 8.59 **c.** 9.19 **d.** 13.40 **e.** 17.44 **f.** 20.31 **g.** 8.63 **h.** 16.35 **2. a.** 44.42° **b.** 57.53° **c.** 32.58° **d.** 35.24° **e.** 61.43° **f.** 71.57° **3.** 27.41 **4.** 53.24 **5.** 7.65 **6.** 55.35° **7. a.** $x = 7.99$, $y = 6.72$, $\theta = 57.25°$ **b.** $x = 6.88$, $y = 4.49$ **c.** $x = 12.93$, $\theta = 51.65°$ **d.** $x = 65$, $y = 97$, $\theta = 47.92°$ **e.** $x = 31.11$, $\theta = 54.73°$ **f.** $x = 55.96$, $y = 58.91$, $\theta = 71.79°$ **g.** $x = 14.38$, $\theta = 31.06°$ **h.** $x = 11.33$, $y = 13.19$, $\theta = 30.78$ **i.** $x = 15.48$, $\theta = 35.54°$
8. $BD = 10.62$ cm; $\angle DBC = 41.25°$
9. $AB = 16.25$ cm; $BC = 15.36$ cm; $AC = 5.29$ cm **10.** 17.08 m **11.** 415.98 m
12. 33.68 m; 50.53 m **13.** 6.70 m **14.** 3254.14 m
15. No, $\theta = 71.03°$ **16.** 189.28 m **17.** 55.71°
18. a. 19.08 m **b.** 16.94° **19. a.** 117 cm **b.** 67.38° **20. a.** 88.39 m **b.** 28.72 m **c.** 55.08 m **d.** 59.05°

Extra, page 167
a. $K = 15.91$; $P = 19.30$ **b.** $K = 77.06$; $P = 43.21$
c. $K = 29.12$; $P = 28.14$ **d.** $K = 8.51$; $P = 16.11$

Exercise 5-4, pages 170-171
1. a. 13.26 cm^2 **b.** 33.11 cm^2 **c.** 14.78 cm^2
2. a. 25.46 cm^2 **b.** 64.95 cm^2 **3.** 147 cm^2
4. a. 63.58 cm^2 **b.** 7492.98 cm^2 **5. a.** 27.89 cm^2 **b.** 61.88 cm^2 **6.** 7.14 cm **7.** 81.48 cm^2
8. a. 53.95 cm^2 **b.** 4.76 cm **9.** 219.33 mm^2
10. 12 mm **11.** 47 313.13 m^2 **12. a.** 6.32 cm **b.** 7.43 cm **13.** 32 cm^2

Exercise 5-5, pages 173-174
1. a. $\frac{\sqrt{3}}{2}$ **b.** $\frac{\sqrt{3}}{3}$ **c.** $\sqrt{2}$ **d.** $\frac{\sqrt{3}}{2}$ **e.** $\frac{2\sqrt{3}}{3}$ **f.** $\sqrt{3}$ **g.** $\frac{\sqrt{2}}{2}$ **h.** 1 **2. a.** 30° **b.** 45° **c.** 30° **d.** 30° **e.** 60° **f.** 45° **3. a.** $\frac{9\sqrt{3}}{2}$ **b.** $\frac{13\sqrt{2}}{2}$ **c.** $\frac{7\sqrt{3}}{3}$ **d.** $15\sqrt{2}$ **e.** $\frac{10\sqrt{3}}{3}$ **f.** $11\sqrt{3}$ **4. a.** $\frac{\sqrt{6}}{2}$ **b.** $\frac{3\sqrt{3}}{2}$ **c.** $\frac{3}{4}$ **d.** $\frac{3 - \sqrt{3}}{3}$ **e.** $2\sqrt{2}$ **f.** 1 **g.** 1 **h.** $\frac{1 + \sqrt{3} + \sqrt{2}}{2}$ **i.** $\frac{\sqrt{6}}{3}$ **j.** $\frac{1 + \sqrt{3} + \sqrt{2}}{2}$
5. a. $\frac{3\sqrt{6}}{2}$ **b.** $2\sqrt{6}$ **c.** $2\sqrt{3}$ **d.** $4\sqrt{6}$ **e.** $2\sqrt{2}$ **f.** $10\sqrt{2}$ **g.** $\frac{10\sqrt{6}}{3}$ **h.** $\frac{5\sqrt{2}}{2}$ **i.** $\frac{5\sqrt{3}}{2}$ **6.** $54\sqrt{3}$ cm^2

7. $98\sqrt{2}$ cm^2 **8.** $10 - 6\sqrt{2}$ cm

Review, page 175
1. a. $\frac{55}{73}$ **b.** $\frac{48}{55}$ **c.** $\frac{55}{73}$ **d.** $\frac{73}{48}$ **e.** $\frac{55}{48}$ **f.** $\frac{73}{55}$
2. a. 28.78° **b.** 45.58° **3.** $\sin\theta = \frac{3\sqrt{13}}{13}$; $\cos\theta = \frac{2\sqrt{13}}{13}$ **4.** $\cos\theta = 0.9825$; $\tan\theta = 0.1897$
5. a. 9.46 **b.** 54.46° **c.** 19.88 **d.** $\theta = 54.47$; $x = 7.14$ **6.** 7.01 cm **7.** $QS = 13.08$ cm; $\angle SQR = 17.76°$ **8.** 7.46 m **9. a.** 61.20 cm^2 **b.** 156.00 cm^2 **10.** 6.83 cm **11. a.** $\frac{3}{2}$ **b.** $\frac{\sqrt{3}}{3}$ **c.** $\frac{\sqrt{3} - \sqrt{2}}{2}$

Exercise 5-6, pages 178-179
1.

	Quadrant			
	I	II	III	IV
x	+	−	−	+
y	+	+	−	−
r	+	+	+	+
$\sin\theta = \frac{y}{r}$	+	+	−	−
$\cos\theta = \frac{x}{r}$	+	−	−	+
$\tan\theta = \frac{y}{x}$	+	−	+	−

2. a. I – sin, cos, tan; II – sin; III – tan; IV – cos
b.

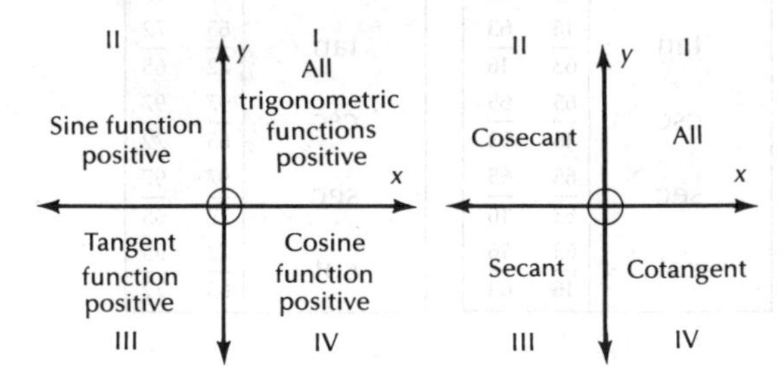

c. I – csc, sec, cot; II – csc; III – cot; IV – sec
3. a. II, III **b.** I, III **c.** III, IV **d.** I, IV
4. a. sin, csc **b.** sin, cos, csc, sec **c.** cos, sec **d.** cos, sec **e.** sin, csc **f.** cos, sec
5. a. II **b.** IV **c.** III **d.** IV
6. a. $\sin\theta = \frac{3}{5}$; $\cos\theta = -\frac{4}{5}$; $\tan\theta = -\frac{3}{4}$
b. $\sin\theta = -\frac{5}{13}$; $\cos\theta = -\frac{12}{13}$; $\tan\theta = \frac{5}{12}$

c. $\sin\theta = -\frac{4}{5}$; $\cos\theta = \frac{3}{5}$; $\tan\theta = -\frac{4}{3}$

d. $\sin\theta = \frac{15}{17}$; $\cos\theta = \frac{8}{17}$; $\tan\theta = \frac{15}{8}$

e. $\sin\theta = \frac{2\sqrt{13}}{13}$; $\cos\theta = -\frac{3\sqrt{13}}{13}$; $\tan\theta = -\frac{2}{3}$

f. $\sin\theta = -\frac{3\sqrt{58}}{58}$; $\cos\theta = \frac{7\sqrt{58}}{58}$; $\tan\theta = -\frac{3}{7}$

7.

	a	b	c	d
$\sin\theta$	$\frac{4}{5}$	$\frac{5\sqrt{34}}{34}$	$\frac{-5\sqrt{41}}{41}$	$-\frac{5\sqrt{26}}{26}$
$\cos\theta$	$\frac{3}{5}$	$\frac{-3\sqrt{34}}{34}$	$\frac{-4\sqrt{41}}{41}$	$\frac{\sqrt{26}}{26}$
$\tan\theta$	$\frac{4}{3}$	$-\frac{5}{3}$	$\frac{5}{4}$	-5
$\csc\theta$	$\frac{5}{4}$	$\frac{\sqrt{34}}{5}$	$-\frac{\sqrt{41}}{5}$	$-\frac{\sqrt{26}}{5}$
$\sec\theta$	$\frac{5}{3}$	$-\frac{\sqrt{34}}{3}$	$-\frac{\sqrt{41}}{4}$	$\sqrt{26}$
$\cot\theta$	$\frac{3}{4}$	$-\frac{3}{5}$	$\frac{4}{5}$	$-\frac{1}{5}$

8.

Terminal Ray	$\sin\theta$	$\cos\theta$	$\tan\theta$
quadrant IV	$-\frac{3}{5}$	$\frac{4}{5}$	$-\frac{3}{4}$
quadrant III	$-\frac{4\sqrt{41}}{41}$	$-\frac{5\sqrt{41}}{41}$	$\frac{4}{5}$
quadrant II	$\frac{5}{13}$	$-\frac{12}{13}$	$-\frac{5}{12}$
quadrant III	$-\frac{3}{4}$	$-\frac{\sqrt{7}}{4}$	$\frac{3\sqrt{7}}{7}$
quadrant IV	$-\frac{\sqrt{21}}{5}$	$\frac{2}{5}$	$-\frac{\sqrt{21}}{2}$
quadrant II	$\frac{3\sqrt{34}}{34}$	$-\frac{5\sqrt{34}}{34}$	$-\frac{3}{5}$

9. a. $\cos\theta = \frac{4}{5}$; $\tan\theta = -\frac{3}{4}$ **b.** $\sin\theta = \frac{3}{5}$; $\tan\theta = \frac{3}{4}$ **c.** $\cos\theta = -\frac{12}{13}$; $\csc\theta = -\frac{13}{5}$

d. $\tan\theta = -\frac{\sqrt{5}}{2}$; $\csc\theta = \frac{3\sqrt{5}}{5}$

e. $\sin\theta = \frac{4}{5}$; $\sec\theta = -\frac{5}{3}$

f. $\cos\theta = \frac{2\sqrt{6}}{5}$; $\cot\theta = -2\sqrt{6}$

Extra, page 179

$n = 10$: $\pi = 2.938\,926$;
$n = 100$: $\pi = 3.139\,526$;
$n = 1000$: $\pi = 3.141\,572$;

Exercise 5-7, pages 182-183

1. a. 30° **b.** 30° **c.** 45° **d.** 60° **e.** 60° **f.** 60° **g.** 45° **h.** 45° **i.** 30° **j.** 40° **2. a.** IV **b.** II **c.** III **d.** II **e.** IV **f.** III **g.** II **h.** IV **i.** III **j.** III **3. a.** $\frac{1}{2}$ **b.** $\frac{\sqrt{2}}{2}$ **c.** $-\sqrt{3}$ **d.** $-\frac{\sqrt{2}}{2}$ **e.** $-\sqrt{3}$ **f.** $-\frac{\sqrt{3}}{2}$ **g.** $-\frac{\sqrt{2}}{2}$ **h.** $\frac{\sqrt{3}}{3}$ **i.** $-\frac{\sqrt{3}}{2}$ **j.** $-\frac{\sqrt{3}}{3}$ **k.** $-\frac{\sqrt{3}}{2}$ **l.** $\frac{1}{2}$ **m.** $-\frac{2\sqrt{3}}{3}$ **n.** $-\sqrt{2}$ **o.** $-\sqrt{3}$ **p.** $\frac{\sqrt{3}}{3}$ **4. a.** $-\frac{1}{2}$ **b.** $-\frac{1}{2}$ **c.** 1 **d.** $-\frac{1}{2}$ **e.** $-\frac{\sqrt{3}}{2}$ **f.** $-\frac{\sqrt{3}}{3}$ **g.** $\frac{\sqrt{2}}{2}$ **h.** $\frac{\sqrt{3}}{2}$ **i.** $-\sqrt{3}$ **j.** 2 **k.** $-\frac{2\sqrt{3}}{3}$ **l.** -2

5.

	0°	90°	180°	270°	360°
$\sin\theta$	0	1	0	−1	0
$\cos\theta$	1	0	−1	0	1
$\tan\theta$	0	*	0	*	0
$\csc\theta$	*	1	*	−1	*
$\sec\theta$	1	*	−1	*	1
$\cot\theta$	*	0	*	0	*

6. a. 0 **b.** undefined **c.** 1 **d.** 0 **e.** 0 **f.** 0 **g.** undefined **h.** 0
7. a. 60°; III or IV; 240° or 300°
b. 60°; I or IV; 60° or 300°
c. 60°; I or III; 60° or 240°
d. 30°; I or IV; 30° or 330°
e. 45°; II or IV; 135° or 315°
f. 45°; II or III; 135° or 225°
g. 30°; I or II; 30° or 150°
h. 45°; III or IV; 225° or 315°
i. 45°; I or IV; 45° or 315°
8. a. 90°, 270° **b.** 90° **c.** 90°, 270°
d. 0°, 180°, 360° **e.** 0°, 180°, 360°
f. 0°, 180°, 360° **10. a.** 180°, 360°, 120°, 240°
b. 45°, 135°, 225°, 315° **c.** 270°, 360°
d. 30°, 150°, 90° **e.** 90°, 270°, 135°, 315°
f. 60°, 300°, 180°

Exercise 5-8, page 185

1. a. 0.5446 **b.** −0.9563 **c.** −1.4281 **d.** −0.9563 **e.** −0.5150 **f.** 3.2709 **g.** −1.5890 **h.** −4.3315 **2. a.** 39° **b.** 18° **c.** 54° **d.** 28° **e.** 15° **f.** 26° **g.** 23° **h.** 82° **3. a.** $-\sin 27°$

b. $-\cos 37°$ **c.** $-\tan 57°$ **d.** $\sec 25°$
e. $-\cos 18°$ **f.** $\tan 83°$ **g.** $\sin 64°$ **h.** $-\cos 4°$
4. a. 38.24°, 141.76° **b.** 147.36°, 212.64°
c. 58.44°, 238.44° **d.** 81.93°, 278.07°
e. 358.38°, 181.62° **f.** 353.13°, 173.13°
g. 56.70°, 303.30° **h.** 293.59°, 246.41°
i. 113.13°, 293.13° **j.** 32.87°, 147.13°
k. 108.55°, 251.45° **l.** 17.14°, 197.14°
5. a. 44.43°, 135.57°, 197.46°, 342.54°
b. 41.81°, 138.19°, 104.48°, 255.52°
c. 48.19°, 131.81°, 228.19°, 311.81°
d. 60°, 180°, 120°, 240°, 300° **e.** 120°, 240°
f. 23.58°, 199.47°, 156.42°, 340.53°
6. a. −0.8177 **b.** 0.7842 **c.** −0.8000
7. a. 210°, 330°, 270°
b. 75.52°, 284.48°, 109.47°, 250.53°
c. 70.53°, 289.47°, 323.13°, 216.87°

Exercise 5-9, pages 188-189

1. a. 8.41 **b.** 8.66 **c.** 11.54 **d.** 18.05 **e.** 2.39
f. 29.16 **g.** 8.69 **h.** 5.26 **i.** 5.59
2. a. 11.53 cm **b.** 10.86 cm **c.** 142.94 m
3. 59.69 m **4.** 744.47 m **5. a.** 4.04 cm
b. 6.06 cm **c.** $\frac{2}{3}$ **6.** 150.53 m **7.** 11.31 m
8. 32.05 cm **9.** AC = 6.78 cm; BC = 5.30 cm
10. 5.23 cm **11.** AC = 7.17 cm; BC = 5.86 cm
12. a. 7.42 cm **b.** 6.31 cm

Exercise 5-10, pages 192-193

1. a. $x < 3.76$ **b.** $x = 3.76$ or $x \geq 8$
c. $3.76 < x < 8$ **2.** $PR = 3.40$ or $PR \geq 11$
3. $2.74 < x < 7$ **4. a.** 0 **b.** 1
5. a. 43.37° or 136.63° **b.** 33.23° or 146.77°
c. no solution **d.** 19.79° **e.** 90°
f. 65.23° or 114.77°
6. a. $\angle ACB$ = 62.03° or 117.97°;
$\angle ABC$ = 85.97° or 30.03°;
AC = 16.94 or 8.50
b. $\angle PQR$ = 38.17° or 141.83°;
$\angle QPR$ = 123.83° or 20.17°;
QR = 16.13 or 6.69
7. a. 43.50° **b.** 23.61° **8.** 82.40° **9.** 58.84°
10. 163.23 m or 116.55 m **11. a.** $\theta = 53.13°$
b. $0 < \theta < 53.13°$ **c.** $\theta > 53.13°$
12. a. $x = 27.71$ or $x \leq 24$ **b.** $24 < x < 27.71$
c. $x > 27.71$

Exercise 5-11, pages 196-197

1. a. 44.42° **b.** 7.86 **c.** 111 **d.** 120° **e.** 7.48
f. 90° **g.** 60° **h.** 7.35 **2. a.** 60° **b.** 31
c. 24.12 **d.** 6.32 **e.** 5.47 **f.** $x = 30.55$;
$\theta = 21.14°$ **3.** 14.35 cm **4.** 117.28° **5.** 87.39°
6. 8.29 m **7.** 25.52° **8.** 3.60 m **9.** 11.40 m
10. 1265.50 km **11.** 8.09 cm **12.** 254.91 m or 281.10 m **13.** 4.16 cm

Extra, page 197

a. 16.89 units^2 **b.** 7.60 units^2 **c.** 11.58 units^2
d. 31.66 units^2

Problem Solving, page 198

1. a. 19.89° **b.** 35.26° **c.** 47.92° **2. a.** 54.74°
b. 70.11° **c.** 42.08° **3.** 45.59 cm **4.** 43.18 m
5. 63.59 m **6.** 88.26° **7.** 11.3 km
8. a. 3219.76 m **b.** 65.67°

Application, page 199

a. 3.090 169 944 **b.** 3.141 075 908
c. 3.141 587 486 **d.** 3.141 592 602
e. 3.141 592 653

Review, pages 200-201

1.

Terminal Ray	$\sin\theta$	$\cos\theta$	$\tan\theta$
Quadrant II	$\frac{7}{25}$	$-\frac{24}{25}$	$-\frac{7}{24}$
Quadrant IV	$-\frac{35}{37}$	$\frac{12}{37}$	$-\frac{35}{12}$
Quadrant III	$-\frac{56}{65}$	$-\frac{33}{65}$	$\frac{56}{33}$
Quadrant II	$\frac{20}{29}$	$-\frac{21}{29}$	$-\frac{20}{21}$

2. a. $\frac{1}{2}$ **b.** $\frac{\sqrt{2}}{2}$ **c.** 0 **d.** $-\frac{\sqrt{3}}{2}$ **e.** undefined
f. 0 **g.** $-\frac{\sqrt{3}}{2}$ **h.** 1 **i.** $-\sqrt{3}$ **j.** $\frac{\sqrt{2}}{2}$
3. a. 78.54°, 281.46° **b.** 302.58°, 237.42°
c. 59.26°, 239.26°
d. 323.13°, 216.87°, 54.46°, 234.46°
e. 56.31°, 123.69°, 236.31°, 303.69°
f. 336.42°, 203.58°, 19.47°, 160.53°
4. $\frac{4\sqrt{33}}{33}$ **5.** 1.0656 **6. a.** 8.84 **b.** no solution
c. 22.62° **d.** 120° **e.** 39.72° or 140.28°
f. 35.81° **g.** 30.10° **h.** 10.25 **i.** 9.25
7. 6. c. is a right-angled triangle.
Thus, use $\sin\theta = \frac{5}{13}$.
8. a. $\theta = 50°$; $x = 10.44$; $y = 6.99$
b. $x = 6.68$; $\theta = 80.18°$; $\phi = 52.82°$
9. 7.00 cm **10.** 7.22 cm **11.** 8.66 cm
12. 33.09° **13.** 130.04 m **14.** 12.58 m
15. 3.68 km **16.** 18.29° **17.** 14.73 km
18. a. $\theta = 60°$, $n \neq -2, -0.5$
b. $\theta = 120°$, $n \neq -0.5, \pm 1$

Test, page 202

1. $\frac{11}{61}$ **2.** -0.9719 **3. a.** $x = 5.25$
b. $\theta = 59.04°$ **c.** $\theta = 35.10°$
d. $x = 8.94; \theta = 70.39°$ **4.** 22.14 cm **5.** 69.44°
6. a. 16.22 cm² **b.** 29.82 cm² **c.** 8 cm²
7. a. $-\frac{\sqrt{3}}{2}$ **b.** $-\frac{\sqrt{2}}{2}$ **c.** $-\frac{\sqrt{3}}{3}$ **d.** $-\sqrt{2}$ **e.** $\sqrt{3}$
8. a. 190.61°, 349.39° **b.** 67.97°, 247.97°
c. 216.87°, 323.13°, 78.46°, 281.54°
9. a. 25.46° **b.** 7.35 **c.** 40.12° **10.** 73.68 m

Cumulative Review, page 203

1. a. $(2y + 5)(y + 1)$ **b.** $(7a - 11)(a + 1)$
c. $(2x + 3)(x + 2)$ **d.** $x(5x + 1)(x + 2)$
e. $5x(2x + 1)(x - 2)$ **f.** $(x - 3)(x + 3)$
g. $(a + b + c)(a + b - c)$
h. $(1 - x - y)(1 + x + y)$
i. $(x - 2)(x + 2)(x^2 + 4)$
2. a. $(x + 2)(x^2 - 2x - 1) + 7$
b. $(x - 2)(3x^2 + 4x + 9) + 13$ **3.** -3
4. a. $f^{-1} = \{(x, y) | y = \frac{x + 4}{3}\}$
b. $g^{-1} = \{(x, y) | y = \sqrt[3]{x}\}$
c. $h^{-1} = \{(x, y) | y = 1 - x^2\}$
5.

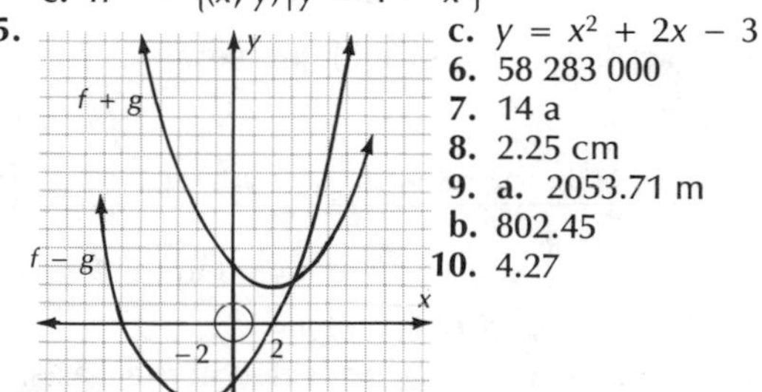

c. $y = x^2 + 2x - 3$
6. 58 283 000
7. 14 a
8. 2.25 cm
9. a. 2053.71 m
b. 802.45
10. 4.27

UNIT 6

Exercise 6-1, pages 207-209

1. a. $\frac{\pi}{6}$ **b.** $\frac{\pi}{3}$ **c.** $\frac{\pi}{2}$ **d.** $\frac{3\pi}{4}$ **e.** $\frac{7\pi}{6}$ **f.** $\frac{5\pi}{3}$ **g.** $\frac{5\pi}{2}$
h. $\frac{\pi}{5}$ **i.** $\frac{11\pi}{9}$ **j.** $\frac{8\pi}{5}$ **k.** $\frac{7\pi}{10}$ **l.** $\frac{11\pi}{15}$ **m.** $\frac{7\pi}{3}$
n. $\frac{14\pi}{5}$ **o.** $\frac{9\pi}{5}$ **2. a.** 60° **b.** 360° **c.** 270°
d. 45° **e.** 150° **f.** 90° **g.** 30° **h.** 140° **i.** 72°
j. 54° **k.** 252° **l.** 260° **m.** 510° **n.** 585°
o. 420° **3. a.** 0.6755 **b.** −0.2272 **c.** 0.0585
d. −0.9999 **e.** 0.3780 **f.** 0.8660 **g.** −0.8660
h. −1.0000 **i.** 0.8090 **j.** −0.1736 **4. a.** 0.96 rad
b. 1.42 rad **c.** 0.90 rad **5. a.** 57.30° **b.** 114.59°
c. 171.89° **6. a.** $\theta = 1.29$ rad **b.** $r = 4.00$
c. $s = 21.00$ **d.** $\theta = 3.75$ rad **e.** $r = 2.56$
f. $s = 40.60$ **g.** $\theta = 3.90$ rad **h.** $s = 25.92$
7. a. 17.71 cm² **b.** 9.45 cm² **c.** 40 cm²
d. 22.64 cm² **e.** 383.72 cm² **8. a.** 0.25 rad
b. 14.32° **9.** 397.9 **10.** 8.38 cm **11.** 11 cm
12. 111.2 km **13. a.** 47.37 m² **b.** 28.81 cm²
14. 71.46 km

Extra, page 209

a. $\tan \theta = FD$ **b.** $\sec \theta = CF$
c. $\csc \theta = CG$ **d.** $\cot \theta = EG$

Exercise 6-2, pages 212-213

1. a. 160 rad **b.** 288 rad **c.** 2.4 rad/s
d. 8.33 rad/s **e.** 0.45 s **f.** 0.95 s **2. a.** 3063 cm
b. 7.8 rad/s **c.** 1.5 m **d.** 11.3 s **e.** 11 309.73 cm
f. 4.44 rad/s **g.** 0.31 m **h.** 6.80 s
3. a. 15.1 m/min **b.** 14.14 m/min **c.** 13.3 rad/s
d. 46.67 rad/min **e.** 6.7 cm **f.** 61.25 cm
4. 0.24 s **5.** 5π **6.** 102.5 m **7.** 23.1 s
8. 23.4 rad/s **9.** 6.2 cm **10. a.** 17.6 rad/s
b. 5.6 m/s **11.** 414 km/min **12.** 1196 km/h
13. a. F is quadrupled. **b.** $F = m\omega^2 r$

Extra, page 213

1. 107 588.79 km/h **2. a.** 0.26 rad/h
b. 1675.52 km/h **c.** 0 **d.** 1099.24 km/h
3. For a satellite launched west to east, initial velocity = 1676 km/h. For a satellite launched east to west, initial velocity = −1676 km/h.

Exercise 6-3, page 217

1. a. II, III **b.** I, II, III, IV **c.** I, IV **d.** II, IV

2.

Function	Domain
sine	$\{\theta \mid \theta \in \mathbf{R}\}$
cosine	$\{\theta \mid \theta \in \mathbf{R}\}$
tangent	$\{\theta \mid \theta \in \mathbf{R}, \theta \neq k\pi + \frac{\pi}{2}, k \in \mathbf{Z}\}$
cosecant	$\{\theta \mid \theta \in \mathbf{R}, \theta \neq k\pi, k \in \mathbf{Z}\}$

Range	Period
$\{\sin\theta \mid -1 \leq \sin\theta \leq 1\}$	2π
$\{\cos\theta \mid -1 \leq \cos\theta \leq 1\}$	2π
$\{\tan\theta \mid \tan\theta \in \mathbf{R}\}$	π
$\{\csc\theta \mid \lvert\csc\theta\rvert \geq 1\}$	2π

3. a. i. $\cot \theta$ is the graph of $\tan \theta$, reflected in the y-axis, translated $\frac{\pi}{2}$ rad to the left. **ii.** $\sec \theta$ is the graph of $\csc \theta$ translated $\frac{\pi}{2}$ rad to the left.

b. i. $D = \{\theta | \theta \in \mathbf{R}, \theta \neq k\pi, k \in \mathbf{Z}\}$, $R = \{\cot \theta | \cot \theta \in \mathbf{R}\}$, period $= \pi$
ii. $D = \{\theta | \theta \in \mathbf{R}, \theta \neq k\pi + \frac{\pi}{2}, k \in \mathbf{Z}\}$, $R = \{\sec \theta | \geq 1\}$, period $= 2\pi$
4. a. $\theta = \frac{\pi}{6}, \frac{5\pi}{6}$ **b.** $\theta = \frac{3\pi}{4}, \frac{7\pi}{4}$ **c.** $\theta = \frac{2\pi}{3}, \frac{4\pi}{3}$
5. a. See page 215. **b.** See page 216. **c.** See **3a**
6. a. $\theta = \frac{\pi}{2}$ **b.** $\theta = \frac{3\pi}{4}, \frac{7\pi}{4}$ **c.** $\theta = \frac{2\pi}{3}, \frac{4\pi}{3}$
7. b. $\theta = \frac{\pi}{4}, \frac{5\pi}{4}$ **8. a.** $p = 6$
b. $g(3) = 0, \ g(3 + p) = 0, p = 6, \therefore g(9) = 0$
9. a. $p = 10$ **b.** $k(3) = k(33) = k(93) = 5$
c. $k(104) = 5; k(210) = -5; k(25) = 5$
10. b. When $\theta = \frac{\pi}{2}$, $\sin \theta = 1$;
When $\theta = \left(\frac{\pi}{2} + 2\pi\right) = \frac{5\pi}{2}$, $\sin \theta = 1$
$\therefore \sin \frac{\pi}{2} = \sin \left(\frac{\pi}{2} + 2\pi\right)$
c. $\alpha = \frac{3\pi}{4}$, $\sin \alpha = \frac{1}{\sqrt{2}}$; $\alpha + 2\pi = \frac{11\pi}{4}$,
$\sin (\alpha + 2\pi) = \frac{1}{\sqrt{2}}$; $\beta = \frac{3\pi}{2}$, $\sin \beta = -1$;
$\beta + 2\pi = \frac{7\pi}{2}$, $\sin (\beta + 2\pi) = -1$
d. $\sin \theta = \sin (\theta + 2\pi)$
11. b. $\theta = \pi, \tan \theta = 0; \theta = \pi + \pi = 2\pi$, $\tan \theta = 0$ **c.** $\tan \theta = \tan (\theta + \pi)$

Exercise 6-4, pages 220-221

1. (period; amplitude) **a.** 2π; 2 **b.** $\frac{\pi}{2}$; 1 **c.** π; 3 **d.** $\frac{\pi}{2}$; $\frac{1}{3}$ **e.** 8π; 5 **f.** 6π; $\frac{2}{3}$ **2. a.** $y = -\sin \theta$
b. $y = \cos 3\theta$ **c.** $y = \frac{3}{4} \sin \theta$ **d.** $y = \tan \frac{\theta}{4}$
3. a. $f(x) = 3 \sin x$ is the graph of $y = \sin x$ with amplitude 3.
b. $h(x) = -\cos x$ is the graph of $y = \cos x$ reflected in the x-axis.
c. $m(x) = \cos 2x$ is the graph of $y = \cos x$ with period $= \pi$.
d. $n(x) = \frac{1}{2} \cos x$ is the graph of $y = \cos x$ with amplitude $\frac{1}{2}$.
e. $p(x) = \sin \frac{x}{2}$ is the graph of $y = \sin x$ with period $= 4\pi$.
f. $f(x) = -\sin x$ is the graph of $\sin x$ reflected in the x-axis.
4. a. $y = 2 \sin \frac{\theta}{2}$ **b.** $y = -\frac{1}{2} \sin \frac{3\theta}{2}$
c. $y = 2 \cos 2\theta$ **d.** $y = -3 \cos 2\theta$
5. a. $y = -\sin \theta$: see 3f
b. $y = \cos 3\theta$: the graph of $y = \cos \theta$ horizontally stretched by a factor of $\frac{2}{3}$
c. $y = \frac{3}{4} \sin \theta$: the graph of $y = \sin \theta$ vertically stretched by a factor of $\frac{3}{4}$
d. $y = \tan \frac{\theta}{4}$, the graph of $y = \tan \theta$ horizontally stretched by a factor of 4
e. $y = 3 \cos 4\theta$: the graph of $y = \cos \theta$, vertically stretched by a factor of 3 and horizontally stretched by a factor of $\frac{1}{4}$
f. $y = -2 \sin 6\theta$: the graph of $y = \sin \theta$ reflected in the θ-axis, vertically stretched by a factor of 2 and horizontally stretched by a factor of $\frac{1}{6}$
6. a. $y = -3 \sin \theta$: $y = \sin \theta$, reflected in θ-axis, amplitude $= 3$
b. $y = 2 \cos 3\theta$: $y = \cos \theta$, amplitude $= 2$, (period) $p = 120°$
c. $y = -\tan 2\theta$; $y = \tan \theta$, vertically stretched by a factor of 2 and reflected in θ-axis
d. $y = 3 \cos \frac{\theta}{2}$: $y = \cos \theta$ with amplitude $= 3$ and $p = 180°$
e. $y = \tan \frac{\theta}{3}$: $y = \tan \theta$ with $p = 540°$
f. $y = -\frac{1}{4} \cos \frac{\theta}{2}$; $y = \cos \theta$ reflected in the θ-axis, with amplitude $= 0.25$, $p = 720°$
g. $y = -\sin 3\theta$: $y = \sin \theta$, reflected in the θ-axis, and $p = 120°$
h. $y = -2 \sin 2\theta$: $y = \sin \theta$, reflected in the θ-axis, amplitude $= 2$, $p = 180°$
i. $y = 3 \cos \frac{\theta}{4}$: $y = \cos \theta$, with amplitude $= 3$, $p = 1440°$
7. a. $y = 2 \sin \frac{3\theta}{2}$: $y = \sin \theta$, amplitude $= 2$, $p = 240°$ **b.** $y = -\cos \frac{2\theta}{3}$: $y = \cos \theta$, reflected in θ-axis, $p = 540°$ **c.** $y = \tan \frac{3\theta}{4}$: $y = \tan \theta$, $p = 240°$ **d.** $y = |\sin \theta|$: $y = \sin \theta$ such that for θ, where $[180 + (360n)]° < \theta < (n + 1)\ 360°$, $\sin \theta$ is reflected in the θ-axis. That is, for all values of θ, $y \geq 0$. **e.** $y = 2|\cos \theta|$: $y = \cos \theta$, amplitude $= 2$ such that for θ, where $[90 + 360n]° < \theta < [270 + 360n]°$, $\cos \theta$ is reflected in the θ-axis. That is, for all values of θ,

$y \geq 0$. **f.** $y = -2|\cos\theta|$: $y = 2|\cos\theta|$ reflected in the θ-axis. That is for all values of θ, $y \leq 0$.

Exercise 6-5, pages 224-225

1. a. phase shift $\frac{\pi}{6}$ rad to the left **b.** vertical translation 3 units down **c.** phase shift 45° right, vertical translation 1 unit up **d.** phase shift π rad right, vertical translation 3 units down **e.** phase shift $\frac{\pi}{3}$ rad left, vertical translation 4 units up **f.** phase shift 30° left, translated $\frac{1}{2}$ unit up.

2. a. $y = \sin\left(x - \frac{\pi}{4}\right)$ **b.** $y = \cos x + 2$ **c.** $y = \tan(x - 90°) - 3$ **d.** $y = 3\sin\left(x - \frac{\pi}{6}\right)$ **e.** $y = -\cos x + 4$ **f.** $y = -3\sin(x + \pi) + 2$

3. a. $y = \sin\theta + 3$ is the graph of $y = \sin\theta$ translated up 3 units.
b. $y = \cos(\theta + 45°)$ is the graph of $y = \cos\theta$ under a phase shift of 45° to the left.
c. $y = \tan(\theta - 90°)$ is the graph of $y = \tan\theta$ under a phase shift of 90° to the right.
d. $y = \sin(\theta + 30°)$ is the graph of $y = \sin\theta$ under a phase shift of 30° to the left.
e. $y = \cos(\theta - 60°) + 2$ is the graph of $y = \cos\theta$ under a phase shift of 60° to the right, translated up 2 units.
f. $y = \sin(\theta + 90°) - 3$ is the graph of $y = \sin\theta$ under a phase shift of 90° to the left, translated 3 units down.

4. a. $y = \sin\left(\theta + \frac{\pi}{4}\right)$ is the graph of $y = \sin\theta$ under a phase shift of $\frac{\pi}{4}$ rad to the left.
b. $y = \cos\theta + 2$ is the graph of $y = \cos\theta$ translated 2 units up.
c. $y = \tan(\theta - 90°) - 3$ is the graph of $y = \tan\theta$ under a phase shift of 90° to the right, translated 3 units down.
d. $y = 3\sin\left(\theta - \frac{\pi}{6}\right)$ is the graph of $y = \sin\theta$ under a phase shift of $\frac{\pi}{6}$ rad to the left, with amplitude increased to 3.
e. $y = -\cos\theta + 4$ is the graph of $y = \cos\theta$ reflected in the θ-axis, translated 4 units up.
f. $y = -3\sin(\theta + \pi) + 2$ is the graph of $y = \sin\theta$ reflected in the θ-axis, under a phase shift of π rad to the left, with amplitude increased to 3, translated 2 units up.

5. a. $y = -\sin(\theta + \pi)$ is the graph of $y = \sin\theta$ reflected in the θ-axis and under a phase shift of π rad to the left.
b. $y = 2\sin\theta - 2$ is the graph of $y = \sin\theta$ with amplitude 2, translated 2 units down.
c. $y = -2\cos\left(\theta + \frac{\pi}{6}\right)$ is the graph of $y = \cos\theta$ reflected in the θ-axis, under a phase shift of $\frac{\pi}{6}$ rad to the left, with amplitude 2.
d. $y = -2\sin\theta + 3$ is the graph of $y = \sin\theta$ reflected in the θ-axis, amplitude 2, translated 3 units up.
e. $y = 3\cos\left(\theta + \frac{\pi}{6}\right)$ is the graph of $y = \cos\theta$ under a phase shift of $\frac{\pi}{6}$ rad to the left, with amplitude 3.
f. $y = -\sin\left(\theta - \frac{\pi}{4}\right) + 1$ is the graph of $y = \sin\theta$ reflected the θ-axis, under a phase shift of $\frac{\pi}{4}$ rad to the right, translated up 1 unit.
g. $y = -\cos\left(\theta + \frac{\pi}{3}\right) + 2$ is the graph of $y = \cos\theta$ reflected in the θ-axis, under a phase shift of $\frac{\pi}{3}$ rad to the left, translated 2 units up.
h. $y = -3\cos\frac{\theta}{2}$ is the graph of $y = \cos\theta$ reflected in the θ-axis, amplitude 3, $p = 4\pi$.
i. $y = 4\sin 2\theta - 1$ is the graph of $y = \cos\theta$ with amplitude 4, $p = \pi$, translated 1 unit down
j. $y = -\tan\left(\theta + \frac{\pi}{2}\right) + 1$ is the graph of $y = \tan\theta$ reflected in the θ-axis, under a phase shift of $\frac{\pi}{2}$ rad to the left, translated 1 unit up.

6. a. The graph $y = \sin(\theta + \pi)$ is the same as the graph $y = \cos\left(\theta + \frac{\pi}{2}\right)$.
b. $\sin(\theta + \pi) = \cos\left(\theta + \frac{\pi}{2}\right)$ for $\theta \in \boldsymbol{R}, 0 \leq \theta \leq 2\pi$

7. a. i. $y = \sin\theta$; $y = \sin(\theta + 2\pi)$; $y = -\sin(\theta + \pi)$ **ii.** $y = \sin\left(\theta + \frac{3\pi}{2}\right)$; $y = -\sin\left(\theta + \frac{\pi}{2}\right)$; $y = \sin\left(\theta - \frac{\pi}{2}\right)$

b. i. $y = \cos\left(\theta - \frac{\pi}{2}\right)$; $y = -\cos\left(\theta + \frac{\pi}{2}\right)$; $y = \cos\left(\theta + \frac{3\pi}{2}\right)$; **ii.** $y = -\cos\theta$; $y = \cos(\theta + \pi)$; $y = \cos(\theta - \pi)$

8. a. $y = \sin\left(2\theta + \frac{\pi}{2}\right)$: the graph $y = \sin\theta$ with $p = \pi$, phase shift $\frac{\pi}{4}$ rad to the left

b. $y = 3\cos\left(2\theta - \frac{\pi}{3}\right)$: $y = \cos\theta$ with $p = \pi$, amplitude 3, phase shift $\frac{\pi}{6}$ rad to the right

c. $y = -\sin(3\theta + \pi) + 1$: $y = \sin\theta$ with $p = \frac{2\pi}{3}$, phase shift $\frac{\pi}{3}$ rad to the left, reflected in the θ-axis, translated 1 unit up.

d. $y = -2\cos\left(2\theta - \frac{\pi}{2}\right) - 2$: $y = \cos\theta$ with $p = \pi$, phase shift $\frac{\pi}{4}$ rad to the right, reflected in the θ-axis, amplitude 2, translated 2 units down

Exercise 6-6, pages 227-228

1. a.

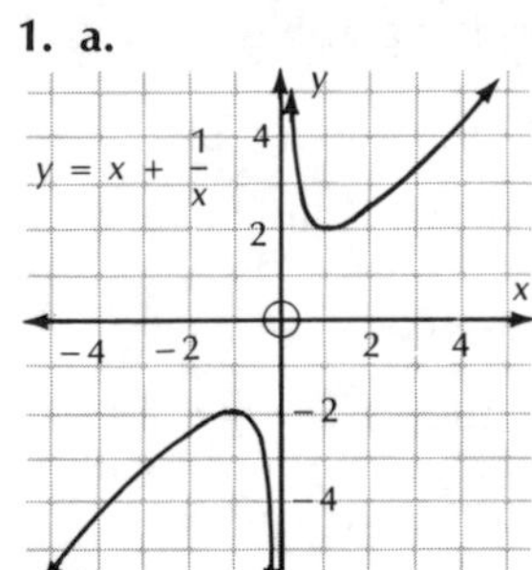

b.

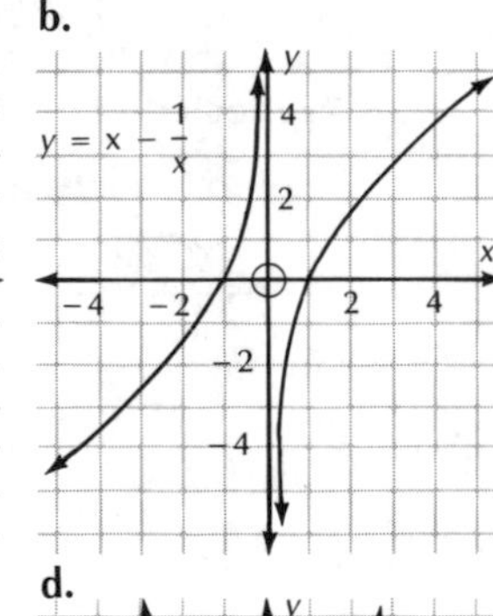

c.

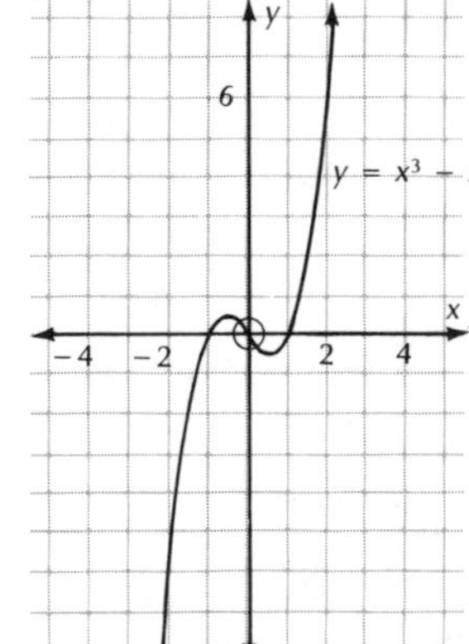

d.

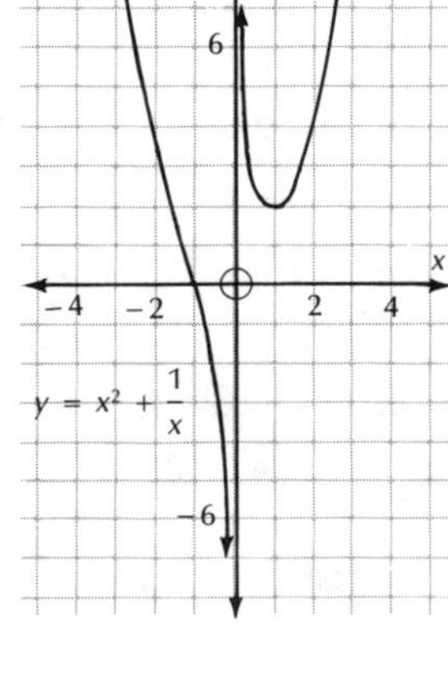

2. a.

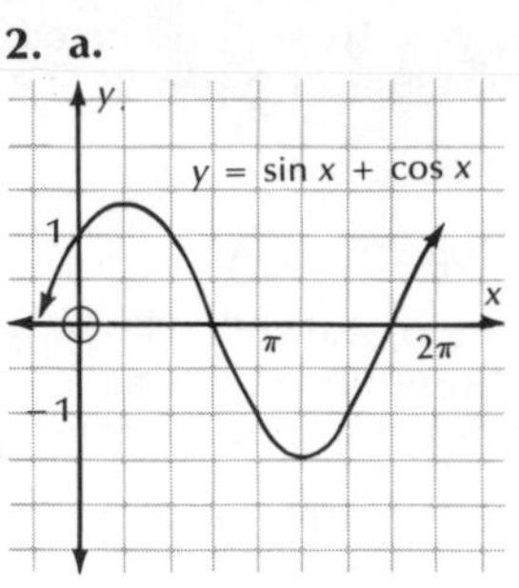

b.

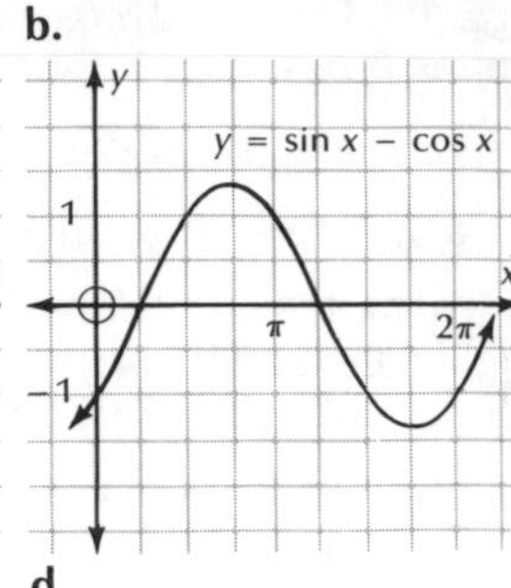

c.

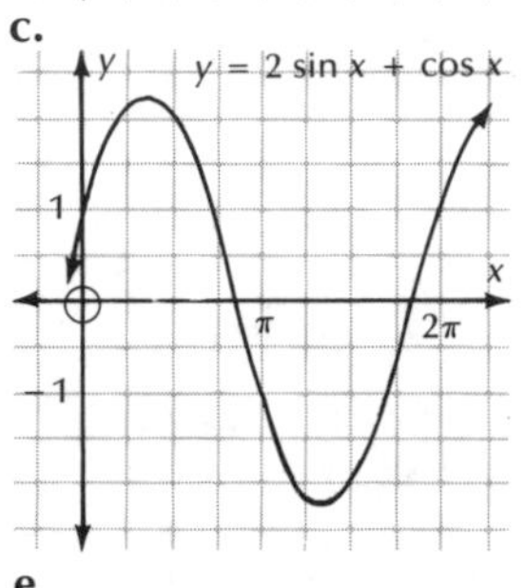

d.

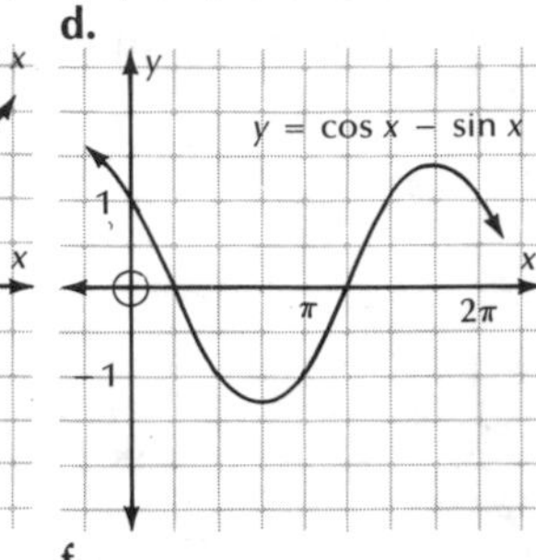

e.

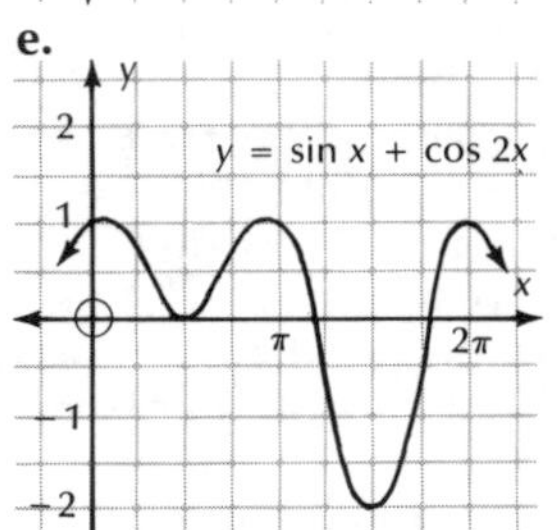

f.

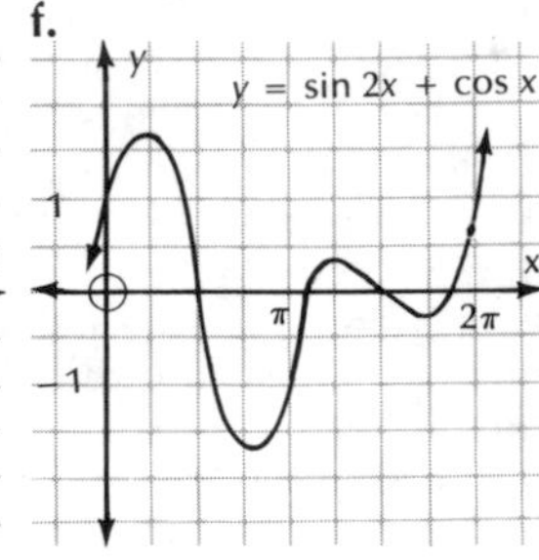

3. a.

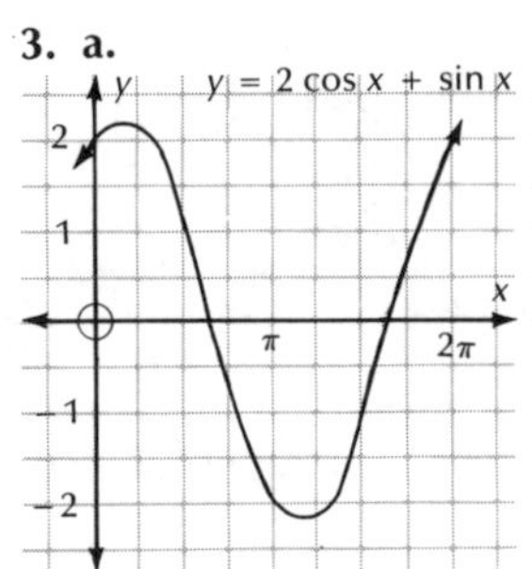

b.

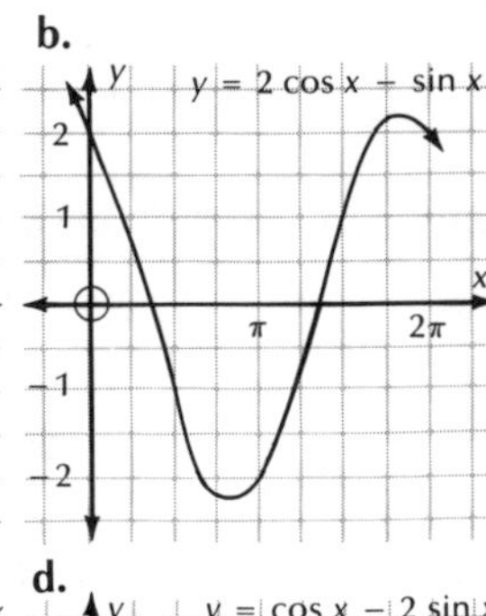

c. **d.**

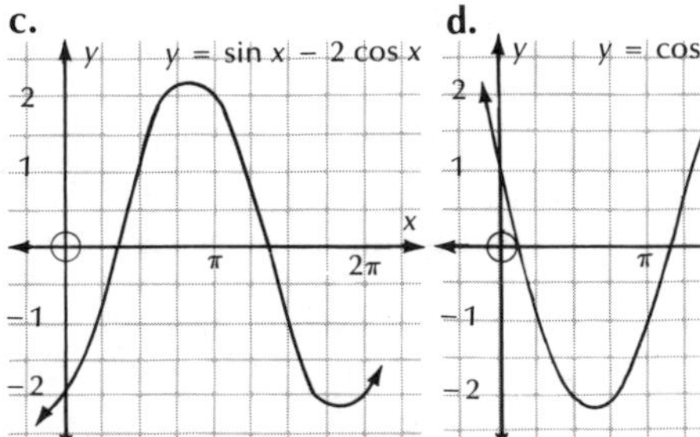

e.

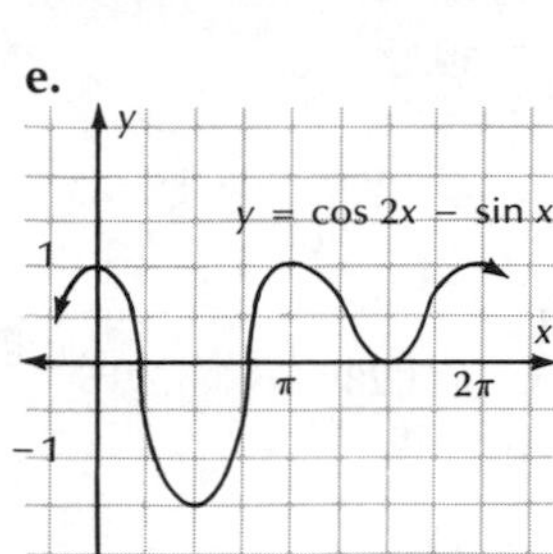

f.

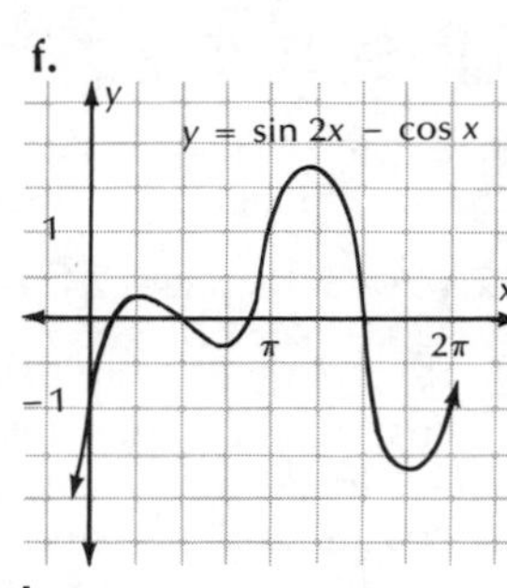

g.

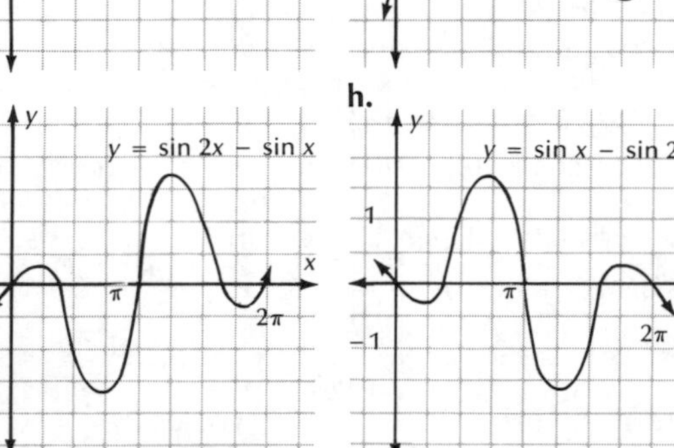

h.

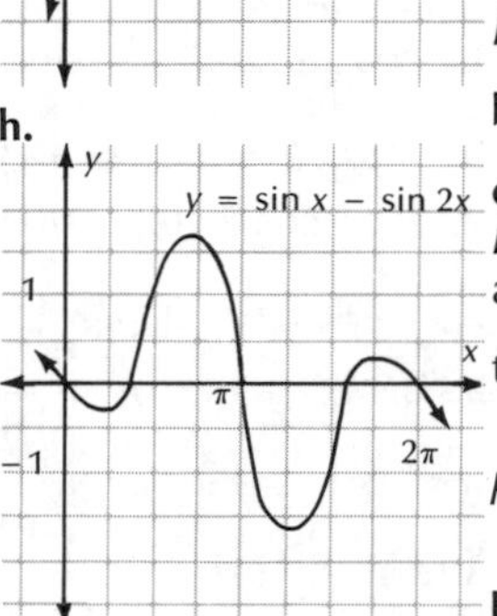

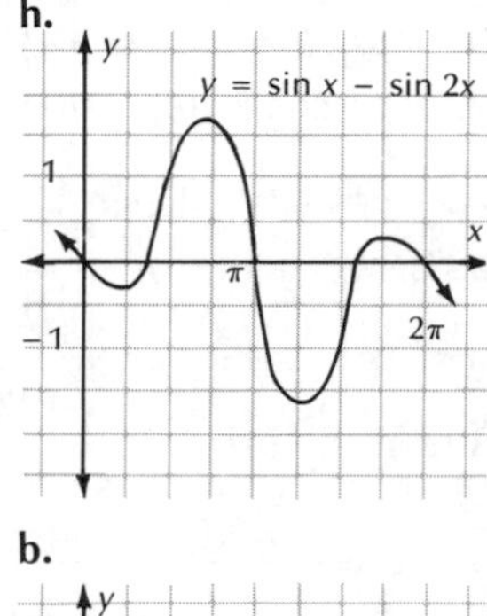

4. a.

b.

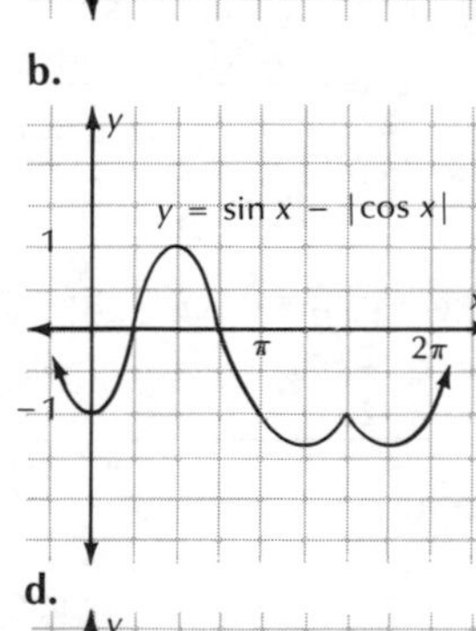

c.

d.

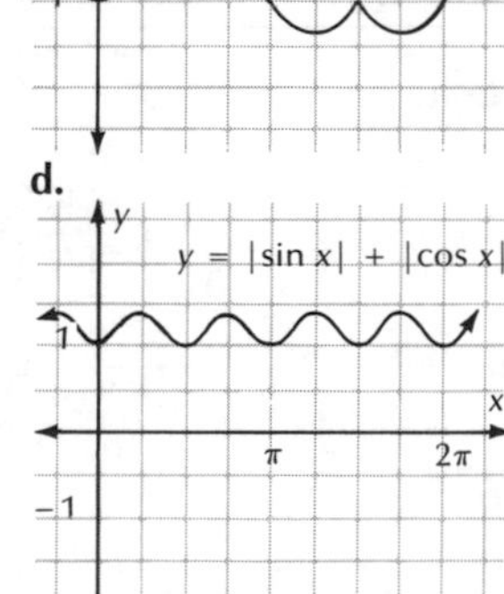

5. a.

b.

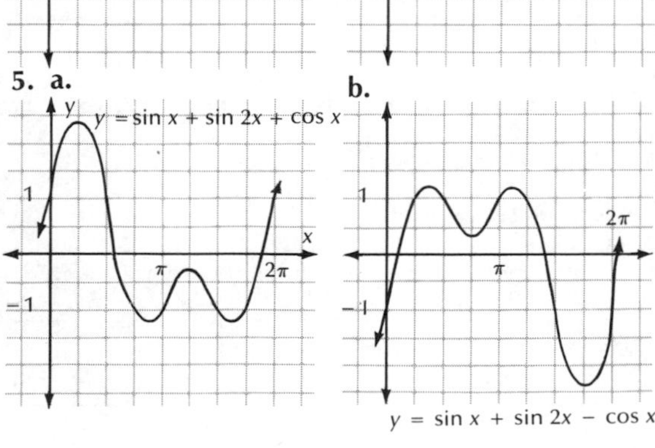

Review, page 229

1. a. $\frac{10\pi}{9}$ **b.** $\frac{2\pi}{5}$ **c.** $\frac{7\pi}{10}$ **d.** $\frac{7\pi}{4}$ **2. a.** 54° **b.** 220° **c.** 108° **d.** 210° **3. a.** $\frac{3}{4}$ rad **b.** $3\frac{1}{3}$ **c.** 10.9 **4. a.** 31.85 cm² **b.** 44.37 cm² **5. a.** 176.8π rad **b.** 442 **6. a.** 0.53 s **b.** 1.33 m **c.** 53.33 rad/s **7.** 28.9 rad **8.** 2.92 cm **9. a.** $D = \{\theta | \theta \in \boldsymbol{R}\}$, $R = \{\cos\theta | -1 \le \cos\theta \le 1, \cos\theta \in \boldsymbol{R}\}$ **b.** $D = \{\theta|\theta \in \boldsymbol{R}, \theta \neq k\pi + \frac{\pi}{2}, k \in \boldsymbol{Z}\}$; $R = \{\tan\theta | \tan\theta \in \boldsymbol{R}\}$ **c.** $D = \{\theta|\theta \in \boldsymbol{R}, \theta \neq k\pi, k \in \boldsymbol{Z}\}$; $R = \{\csc\theta | |\csc\theta| \ge 1, \csc\theta \in \boldsymbol{R}\}$ **10.** $\tan\theta$, amplitude 3, reflected in the θ-axis, vertical translation 1 unit up, phase shift $\frac{\pi}{3}$ rad to the left, $p = \pi$. **11. a.** $y = 2\sin\left(\theta + \frac{\pi}{3}\right) + 3$ **b.** $y = -\cot\left(\theta - \frac{2\pi}{3}\right) - 2$

12. a. See Lesson 6-3, exercise 3**a**.
b. See Lesson 6-3, exercise 3**a**.
c. $y = 2\sin\theta - 1$: graph of $y = \sin\theta$ with amplitude 2, translated 1 unit down.
d. $y = -\sin\left(\theta + \frac{\pi}{6}\right)$: graph of $y = \sin\theta$, reflected in θ-axis, phase shift of $\frac{\pi}{6}$ rad to the left
e. $y = -\cos 2\theta$: graph of $y = \cos\theta$ with $p = \pi$, reflected in the θ-axis
f. $y = \tan\left(\theta - \frac{\pi}{2}\right)$: graph of $y = \tan\theta$, phase shift $\frac{\pi}{2}$ rad to the right
g. $y = -\cos\theta + 2$: graph of $y = \cos\theta$ reflected in θ-axis, translated 2 units up

Exercise 6-7, page 233

1. a. $\cos\theta + \sin\theta$ **b.** $\frac{1}{\cos\theta}$ **c.** $\cos^2\theta$ **d.** $\sin\theta$ **e.** $\frac{1}{\sin\theta\cos\theta}$ **f.** $\csc^2\theta$ **g.** $\sin^2\theta$ **h.** $\frac{\sin\theta - 1}{\sin\theta}$ **i.** $\sin\theta - \cos\theta$ **2. a.** $\sec\theta$ **b.** $\sec^2\theta$ **c.** $\csc\theta$ **d.** $\csc^2\theta$ **e.** $1 + \tan\theta$ **f.** $\cos^2\theta$ **g.** $\cos^2\theta$ **h.** $\frac{\sin\theta + \cos\theta}{\sin\theta - \cos\theta}$ **i.** $\sin\theta\tan\theta$ **3. a.** $-\cos^2\theta$ **b.** $\frac{\sin^2\theta - \cos^2\theta}{\sin^2\theta\cos^2\theta}$ **c.** $-\frac{2\cos\theta}{\sin^2\theta}$ **d.** $\frac{\sin^2\theta}{\cos\theta}$ **e.** 1 **f.** $\sin^2\theta$ **g.** 0 **h.** $1 + \cos\theta$ **i.** $\frac{\cos^2\theta}{\sin^2\theta}$ **4. a.** $\frac{2}{\sin^2\theta}$

b. $-\cot^2\theta$ **c.** $\sec^2\theta$ **d.** $\tan^2\theta$ **e.** $\sin\theta$ **f.** $-\csc^2\theta$ **g.** $-1 - \cos\theta$ **h.** $\sin^2\theta$ **i.** 2 **j.** $\tan^2\theta$ **5. a.** $\sin\theta + 1$ **b.** $-\csc^2\theta$
6. $\sin\theta = \sin\theta$; $\cos\theta = \sqrt{1 - \sin^2\theta}$;
$\tan\theta = \dfrac{\sin\theta}{\sqrt{1 - \sin^2\theta}}$; $\csc\theta = \dfrac{1}{\sin\theta}$;
$\sec\theta = \dfrac{1}{\sqrt{1 - \sin^2\theta}}$; $\cot\theta = \dfrac{\sqrt{1 - \sin^2\theta}}{\sin\theta}$

Exercise 6-9, pages 238-239

1. a. $\theta = \frac{2\pi}{3}, \frac{4\pi}{3}$ **b.** $\theta = \frac{\pi}{4}, \frac{5\pi}{4}$ **c.** $\theta = \frac{3\pi}{2}$ **d.** $\theta = \frac{\pi}{6}, \frac{5\pi}{6}, \frac{7\pi}{6}, \frac{11\pi}{6}$ **2. a.** $\frac{4\pi}{3}, \frac{5\pi}{3}$ **b.** $\frac{\pi}{2}, \frac{3\pi}{2}$ **c.** $\frac{\pi}{3}, \frac{4\pi}{3}$ **d.** $\frac{\pi}{4}, \frac{7\pi}{4}$ **e.** $\frac{\pi}{2}, \frac{3\pi}{2}$ **f.** $\frac{\pi}{6}, \frac{5\pi}{6}$ **g.** $\pi, 2\pi$ **h.** $\frac{\pi}{4}, \frac{7\pi}{4}$ **i.** $\frac{\pi}{3}, \frac{2\pi}{3}$ **3. a.** 29.00°, 151.00° **b.** 136.96°, 223.04° **c.** 58.67°, 238.67° **d.** 228.59°, 311.41° **e.** 48.19°, 311.81° **f.** 194.48°, 345.52° **4. a.** $\frac{\pi}{4}, \frac{5\pi}{4}$ **b.** $\frac{3\pi}{4}, \frac{7\pi}{4}$ **c.** $\frac{\pi}{3}, \pi, \frac{5\pi}{3}, 2\pi$ **d.** $\frac{\pi}{4}, \frac{3\pi}{4}, \frac{5\pi}{4}, \frac{7\pi}{4}$ **e.** $\frac{\pi}{2}, \pi, 2\pi$ **f.** $\pi, \frac{7\pi}{6}, \frac{11\pi}{6}, 2\pi$ **g.** $\frac{\pi}{4}, \frac{3\pi}{4}, \frac{5\pi}{4}, \frac{7\pi}{4}$ **h.** $\frac{\pi}{2}, \frac{7\pi}{6}, \frac{11\pi}{6}$ **i.** $\frac{\pi}{6}, \frac{\pi}{2}, \frac{5\pi}{6}, \frac{3\pi}{2}$ **j.** $\frac{\pi}{3}, \frac{5\pi}{3}$ **k.** $\frac{\pi}{3}, \frac{\pi}{2}, \frac{2\pi}{3}, \frac{3\pi}{2}$ **l.** $\frac{\pi}{2}, \pi, 2\pi$ **5. a.** 41.81°, 138.19° **b.** 109.47°, 180°, 250.53°, 360° **c.** 180°, 221.81°, 318.19°, 360° **d.** 109.47°, 250.53°, 75.52°, 284.48° **e.** 63.43°, 116.57°, 243.32°, 296.57° **f.** 63.43°, 243.43° **g.** 161.57°, 341.57° **h.** 221.81°, 318.19°, 360° **i.** 165.96°, 345.96° **j.** 75.96°, 255.96°
6. a. $\frac{5\pi}{12}, \frac{11\pi}{12}, \frac{17\pi}{12}, \frac{23\pi}{12}$ **b.** $\frac{\pi}{12}, \frac{11\pi}{12}, \frac{13\pi}{12}, \frac{23\pi}{12}$ **c.** $\frac{5\pi}{12}, \frac{7\pi}{12}, \frac{13\pi}{12}, \frac{15\pi}{12}, \frac{21\pi}{12}, \frac{23\pi}{12}$ **d.** $\frac{\pi}{2}$ **7. a.** $\pi, 2\pi$ **b.** $\frac{\pi}{12}, \frac{5\pi}{12}, \frac{7\pi}{12}, \frac{11\pi}{12}, \frac{13\pi}{12}, \frac{19\pi}{12}, \frac{23\pi}{12}, \frac{\pi}{12}$ **c.** $\frac{7\pi}{18}, \frac{11\pi}{18}, \frac{19\pi}{18}, \frac{23\pi}{18}, \frac{31\pi}{18}, \frac{35\pi}{18}$ **d.** $\frac{\pi}{6}, \frac{\pi}{2}, \frac{5\pi}{6}, \frac{7\pi}{6}, \frac{3\pi}{2}, \frac{11\pi}{6}, \frac{\pi}{3}, \frac{4\pi}{3}$
8. a. $\frac{\pi}{6}, \frac{\pi}{3}, \frac{5\pi}{3}, \frac{11\pi}{6}$ **b.** $\frac{\pi}{4}, \frac{5\pi}{4}, \frac{7\pi}{6}, \frac{11\pi}{6}$ **c.** $\frac{\pi}{2}, \pi$ **d.** $\frac{3\pi}{4}, \frac{5\pi}{4}, \frac{\pi}{3}, \frac{4\pi}{3}$ **e.** $\frac{\pi}{2}, \frac{7\pi}{6}, \frac{11\pi}{6}$ **f.** $\frac{\pi}{3}, \pi, \frac{5\pi}{3}$ **g.** $\frac{\pi}{3}, \frac{2\pi}{3}, \frac{4\pi}{3}, \frac{5\pi}{3}$ **h.** $\frac{\pi}{2}, 2\pi$ **i.** $\frac{3\pi}{4}, \frac{7\pi}{4}$
9. a. 90°, 191.54°, 348.46° **b.** 75.96°, 108.43°, 255.96°, 288.43° **c.** 116.57°, 135°, 296.57°, 315°

Exercise 6-10, pages 242–243

1. a. cos 43° **b.** sec 59° **c.** cot 28° **d.** sin 9° **e.** sin 72° **f.** csc 47° **2. a.** −sin 48° **b.** cos 142° **c.** −tan 206°
3. a. $\sin 3\theta \cos\beta - \cos 3\theta \sin\beta$
b. $\cos 2\alpha \cos 3\beta - \sin 2\alpha \sin 3\beta$
c. $\sin\beta \cos\alpha - \cos\beta \sin\alpha$ **4. a.** $\sec\theta$ **b.** $-\csc\theta$ **c.** $-\cot\theta$
7. a. $-\cos\theta$ **b.** $-\sin\theta$ **c.** $-\sin\theta$ **d.** $\cos\theta$ **e.** $\cos\theta$ **f.** $-\cos\theta$ **8. a.** −sin 50° **b.** cos 55° **c.** −cos 40° **d.** sin 15° **e.** sin 15° **f.** −cos 75°
9. a. $\frac{\sqrt{6} - \sqrt{2}}{4}$ **b.** $\frac{\sqrt{6} - \sqrt{2}}{4}$ **c.** $\frac{-\sqrt{6} - \sqrt{2}}{4}$ **d.** $\frac{-\sqrt{6} - \sqrt{2}}{4}$ **e.** $\frac{\sqrt{2} - \sqrt{6}}{4}$ **f.** $\frac{\sqrt{2} - \sqrt{6}}{4}$
10. a. $\sin(2\theta - \beta)$ **b.** $\cos 2\theta$ **c.** $\cos 3\theta$ **d.** $\sin 5\theta$ **e.** $-\cos 8\theta$ **f.** $-\cos 9\theta$
11. a. $\frac{\sqrt{6} - \sqrt{2}}{4}$ **b.** $\frac{\sqrt{6} - \sqrt{2}}{4}$ **c.** $\frac{\sqrt{2} - \sqrt{6}}{4}$
13. e. $PQ = \sqrt{2 - 2\cos(A - B)}$
f. $RT = \sqrt{[\cos(A - B) - 1]^2 + \sin^2(A - B)}$

Exercise 6-11, page 245

1. a. $\frac{24}{25}$ **b.** $\frac{7}{25}$ **c.** $\frac{\sqrt{10}}{10}$ **d.** $\frac{3\sqrt{10}}{10}$
2. a. $\sqrt{\frac{2 - \sqrt{3}}{4}}$ **b.** $\sqrt{\frac{2 + \sqrt{3}}{4}}$ **c.** $\sqrt{\frac{2 - \sqrt{2}}{4}}$ **d.** $\sqrt{\frac{2 + \sqrt{2}}{4}}$ **3. a.** $\frac{840}{841}$ **b.** $-\frac{41}{841}$ **c.** $\frac{3\sqrt{58}}{58}$ **d.** $\frac{7\sqrt{58}}{58}$ **4. a.** $-\frac{720}{1681}$ **b.** $\frac{1519}{1681}$ **c.** $\frac{9\sqrt{82}}{82}$ **d.** $\frac{\sqrt{82}}{82}$
5. a. $\sqrt{\frac{2 - \sqrt{2}}{4}}$ **b.** $\sqrt{\frac{2 + \sqrt{2}}{4}}$ **c.** $-\frac{\sqrt{2}}{2}$ **d.** $\sqrt{\frac{2 - \sqrt{3}}{4}}$ **e.** $\sqrt{\frac{2 + \sqrt{2}}{4}}$ **f.** $-\sqrt{\frac{2 - \sqrt{3}}{4}}$
7. a. $3\sin\theta - 4\sin^3\theta$ **b.** $4\cos^3\theta - 3\cos\theta$
10. a. $\frac{\pi}{3}, \pi, \frac{5\pi}{6}$ **b.** $0, \frac{\pi}{3}, \frac{2\pi}{3}, \pi, 2\pi$

Review, pages 246-247

1. a.

Deg.	60°	150°	225°	140°	126°	108°	70°
Rad.	$\frac{\pi}{3}$	$\frac{5\pi}{6}$	$\frac{5\pi}{4}$	$\frac{7\pi}{9}$	$\frac{7\pi}{10}$	$\frac{3\pi}{5}$	$\frac{7\pi}{18}$

b.

Deg.	80°	50°	77°	162°	199°	219°	466°
Rad.	1.40	0.87	1.35	2.83	3.47	3.82	8.13

2. a. 37.8 units^2 **b.** 33.0 units^2 **c.** 83.1 units^2 **d.** 4.8 units^2 **3. a.** 1.1 s **b.** 2.3 m **c.** 8.6 m
4. $\frac{125\pi}{2}$ rad **5.** 30.6 rad/s
6. a. $D = \{\theta \mid \theta \in \boldsymbol{R}\}$
$R = \{\sin\theta \mid -1 \leq \sin\theta \leq 1, \sin\theta \in \boldsymbol{R}\}$
b. $D = \{x \mid x \in \boldsymbol{R}, x \neq k\pi, k \in \boldsymbol{Z}\}$
$R = \{\cot\theta \mid \cot\theta \in \boldsymbol{R}\}$
c. $D = \{x \mid x \in \boldsymbol{R}, x \neq k\pi + \frac{\pi}{2}, k \in \boldsymbol{Z}\}$
$R = \{\sec\theta \mid |\sec\theta| \geq 1, \sec\theta \in \boldsymbol{R}\}$
7. a. See page 219.
b. $y = -\cos\theta + 1$: graph of $y = \cos\theta$ reflected in the θ-axis, translated 1 unit up.
c. $y = \tan\left(\theta + \frac{\pi}{2}\right)$: graph of $y = \tan\theta$ under a phase shift of $\frac{\pi}{2}$ rad to the left.
d. $y = 2\sin\frac{\theta}{2}$: graph of $y = \sin\theta$, amplitude 2, (period) $p = 2\pi$.
e. $y = 3\cos\theta - 2$: graph of $y = \cos\theta$, reflected in the θ-axis, amplitude 3, translated 2 units down.
f. $y = -\frac{1}{2}\sin\left(\theta - \frac{\pi}{6}\right) - 1$: graph of $y = \sin\theta$, reflected in the θ-axis, amplitude $\frac{1}{2}$, under a phase shift of $\frac{\pi}{6}$ rad to the right, translated 7 units down.
9. a. $\frac{2}{\cos^2\theta}$ **b.** $\frac{1 + \sin\theta}{\cos\theta}$ **c.** $1 - \sin\theta$ **d.** $\frac{\cos\theta}{\sin\theta}$
10. a. $\sec\theta$ **b.** $\cos\theta$ **c.** $\frac{\sin\theta - \cos\theta}{\sin\theta\cos\theta}$
d. $\frac{\cos\theta}{1 - \sin\theta}$ **12. a.** $\pi, 2\pi$ **b.** $\frac{\pi}{2}, \frac{3\pi}{2}$
c. $\frac{5\pi}{12}, \frac{7\pi}{12}, \frac{17\pi}{12}, \frac{19\pi}{12}$ **d.** $\frac{\pi}{3}, \pi, \frac{5\pi}{3}$
13. a. 180°, 360°, 98.2°, 261.8°
b. 41.8°, 138.2°, 194.5°, 345.5°
c. 131.8°, 228.2°, 191.5°, 348.5°
d. 101.5°, 180°, 258.5° **14. a.** $-\frac{\sqrt{2}}{2}$ **b.** $\frac{\sqrt{2} - \sqrt{6}}{4}$
c. $\frac{-\sqrt{2} - \sqrt{6}}{4}$ **d.** $\frac{\sqrt{2} - \sqrt{6}}{4}$ **15. a.** cos 31°
b. $\cos\theta$ **c.** $\cos\theta$ **d.** $\sin\theta$ **e.** $-\cos\theta$ **f.** $\sin\theta$
g. $\sin 5\theta$ **h.** sin 55° **i.** $-\cos 8\theta$ **j.** cos 100°
16. a. $\sqrt{\frac{2 + \sqrt{2}}{4}}$ **b.** $\sqrt{\frac{2 - \sqrt{2}}{4}}$ **c.** $\sqrt{\frac{2 + \sqrt{3}}{4}}$
17. a. $-\frac{240}{289}$ **b.** $-\frac{161}{289}$ **c.** $\frac{5\sqrt{34}}{34}$ **d.** $\frac{3\sqrt{34}}{34}$

Test, page 248

1. a. 35.5°, 0.62 rad **b.** 155°, 2.71 rad **c.** 18°, $\frac{\pi}{10}$ rad **2.** 87.5 units^2, 66.4 units^2 **3. a.** 2.86 cm
b. $\frac{23\pi}{12}$ rad **c.** 0.24 rad/s **4.** 2.55 m/s
5. a. See Lesson 6-4 exercise 3**d**.
b. See Lesson 6-4 exercise 6**g**.
c. $y = \tan\left(\theta - \frac{\pi}{4}\right)$: the graph of $y = \tan\theta$ under a phase shift of $\frac{\pi}{4}$ rad to the right.
d. $y = \sin 2\theta + 2\sin\theta$

θ	$\frac{\pi}{4}$	$\frac{\pi}{2}$	$\frac{3\pi}{4}$	π	$\frac{5\pi}{4}$	$\frac{3\pi}{2}$	$\frac{7\pi}{4}$
y	2.414	2	0.414	0	−0.414	−2	−2.414

6. a. $\frac{2\cos\theta}{\sin^2\theta}$ **b.** $\sin\theta + 1$ **c.** $\frac{1}{\sin\theta\cos\theta}$
d. $2\sin\theta\cos\theta$
8. a. 90°, 270°, 36.9°, 143.1° **b.** 23.2°, 203.2°
c. 90°, 191.5°, 348.5° **d.** 26.6°, 63.4°, 206.6°, 243.4° **9. a.** $\cos\frac{2\pi}{3}$ **b.** $\cos 3\theta$ **c.** $\cos 5\theta$ **d.** $\cos 2\theta$
e. $\sin 4\theta$ **10. a.** $-\frac{120}{169}$ **b.** $\frac{119}{169}$ **c.** $\frac{5\sqrt{26}}{26}$ **d.** $\frac{\sqrt{26}}{26}$

Cumulative Review, page 249

1. $y = 2(x + 3)^2 - 5$ **2. b.** $y = \frac{x - 4}{3}$
c.

x	−5	−3	−1	1	3	4	5
f^{-1}	−3	$-\frac{7}{3}$	$-\frac{5}{3}$	−1	$-\frac{1}{3}$	0	$\frac{1}{3}$

3. a. 9 **b.** 2 **c.** $\frac{8\sqrt{5}}{25}$ **d.** 0.2 **4.** $2204
5. c. $f^{-1}(x) = \sqrt[4]{x}$ **6. a.** $(2a + 1)(a + 4)$
b. $(5x + 4)(2x - 1)$ **c.** $(5y - 2)(2y + 3)$
d. $x(5x + 1)(x + 2)$ **e.** $(8 + 9a)(3 - 8a)$
f. $(3 - x)(1 + 4x)$ **7. a.** $(x + 1)(x - 4)(x - 2)$
b. $(y + 5)(y - 10)(y + 6)$ **8.** 60 km
9. $\angle A = 19.7°$, $\angle B = 28.1°$, $\angle C = 132.2°$
10. a. $x = 8.9$ **b.** $\theta = 136.5°$

UNIT 7

Exercise 7-1, pages 252–253

1. a. $C(1, -4); r = 6$ **b.** $C(0, 2); r = 3\sqrt{2}$
c. $C(0, 0); r = 5\sqrt{2}$ **d.** $C\left(\frac{2}{3}, \frac{1}{4}\right); r = \frac{4\sqrt{2}}{3\sqrt{3}}$
2. a. $(x - 2)^2 + (y + 5)^2 = 9$ **b.** $(x + 5)^2 + y^2 = 45$
c. $(3x - 2)^2 + (3y + 2)^2 = 4$ **d.** $x^2 + y^2 = 5$
3. a. $C(4, -5), r = 3$ **b.** $C(-3, 4), r = 2\sqrt{2}$
c. $C\left(\frac{2}{3}, -\frac{5}{3}\right), r = \frac{5}{3}$ **d.** $C\left(0, \frac{1}{4}\right), r = 1$
4. a. $(x + 2)^2 + (y - 5)^2 = 52$
b. $(x + 7)^2 + (y - 7)^2 = 13$
c. $(x - 5)^2 + (y + 1)^2 = 26$
d. $(x - 4)^2 + y^2 = 36$
5. a. $(x + 2)^2 + (y - 1)^2 = 49$
b. $(x + 2)^2 + (y - 1)^2 = 16$
c. $(x + 2)^2 + (y - 1)^2 = \frac{81}{4}$
6. a. $D = \{x | x \in \boldsymbol{R}, |x| \leq 6\}$;
$R = \{y | y \in \boldsymbol{R}, |y| \leq 6\}$
b. $D = \{x | x \in \boldsymbol{R}, |x| \leq 3\}$;
$R = \{y | y \in \boldsymbol{R}, 2 \leq y \leq 8\}$
c. $D = \{x | x \in \boldsymbol{R}, -1 \leq x \leq 7\}$;
$R = \{y | y \in \boldsymbol{R}, -8 \leq y \leq 0\}$
d. $D = \{x | x \in \boldsymbol{R}, -7 \leq x \leq 3\}$;
$R = \{y | y \in \boldsymbol{R}, 2 \leq y \leq 12\}$
7. $(x \pm 4)^2 + (y \pm 4)^2 = 16$
8. Half circle: $C(0, 0), r = 2$ and
a. $y \geq 0$ **b.** $y \leq 0$ **c.** $x \geq 0$ **d.** $x \leq 0$
9. $(x - 5)^2 + \left(y - \frac{1}{2}\right)^2 = \frac{173}{4}$ **10.** $C(0, -2)$ or $C(0, 8)$
11. a. $C(4, 4)$ or $C(-4, -4)$
b. $(x - 4)^2 + (y - 4)^2 = 32$, or
$(x + 4)^2 + (y + 4)^2 = 32$
12. a. Two circles: $C(0, 0)$ with radii $r_1 = 2$, $r_2 = 5$.
b. The x-axis, the y-axis, and a circle: $C(0, 0), r = 1$
13. a. $3x - 4y + 25 = 0$ **b.** $2x - 3y - 13 = 0$
c. $3x + 4y - 16 = 0$ **d.** $x - 4 = 0$ **13. a.** $\sqrt{58}$
b. $2\sqrt{22}$ **15.** $(x + 2)^2 + (y + 1)^2 = 34$

Extra, page 253

1. a. $\frac{19\sqrt{26}}{26}$ **b.** 0 **2.** $P(2, -3)$ is on the line
$4x + 3y + 1 = 0$ **3. a.** $(x - 2)^2 + (y - 5)^2 = 10$
b. $(x - 3)^2 + (y + 4)^2 = 29$

Exercise 7-2, page 256

1. a. $x^2 + y^2 - 6x + 2y - 39 = 0$
b. $x^2 + y^2 + 10y = 0$ **2. a.** $C(0, 0), r = 5$
b. $C(0, 0), r = 6$ **c.** $C(-4, 2), r = 3\sqrt{2}$
d. $C(0, 1), r = \sqrt{5}$ **e.** $C(3, -4), r = 5$
f. $C(2, -3), r = 0$ **g.** $C(-2, 0), r = \sqrt{29}$
h. $C(0, 3), r = 5$
3. Circle with $r = 0$ is the point $P(2, -3)$.
4. a. $x^2 + y^2 - 6x + 10y + \frac{281}{9} = 0$
b. $x^2 + y^2 + 8x + \frac{4}{3}y + \frac{139}{9} = 0$
c. $x^2 + y^2 - \frac{4}{5}y - \frac{9}{5} = 0$
d. $x^2 + y^2 + \frac{3}{2}x - \frac{1}{2}y + \frac{3}{8} = 0$
5. a. $C(-5, 4), r = \sqrt{39}$ **b.** $C(2, 3), r = 4$
c. $C(3, 0), r = \sqrt{11}$ **d.** $C(2, -4), r = 2\sqrt{5}$
e. $C\left(\frac{1}{4}\right), -\frac{1}{4}), r = \frac{\sqrt{42}}{4}$ **f.** $C\left(-\frac{5}{4}, \frac{3}{4}\right), r = \frac{\sqrt{42}}{4}$
6. a. $x^2 + y^2 - 25 = 0$ **b.** $x^2 + y^2 - 6x + 8y = 0$
c. $x^2 + y^2 + 4x - 10y - 77 = 0$
d. $x^2 + y^2 - 6x + 4y - 21 = 0$
7. a. $x^2 + y^2 + 4x + 6y - 36 = 0$
b. $x^2 + y^2 - 10x + 2y + 1 = 0$
8. a. $x^2 + y^2 - 10x + 4y = 0$
b. $x^2 + y^2 - 2x - 14y + 33 = 0$
9. a. $D = \{x | x \in \boldsymbol{R}, -10 \leq x \leq 0\}$;
$R = \{y | y \in \boldsymbol{R}, -5 \leq y \leq 5\}$
b. $D = \{x | x \in \boldsymbol{R}, 0 \leq x \leq 6\}$;
$R = \{y | y \in \boldsymbol{R}, -5 \leq y \leq 1\}$
10. a. $x^2 + y^2 - 10x - 16 = 0$
b. $x^2 + y^2 + 6x - 4y - 13 = 0$
11. a. $4x + 3y - 20 = 0; 2x - y = 0$ **b.** $C(2, 4)$
c. 25 **d.** $x^2 + y^2 - 4x - 8y - 605 = 0$
12. a. $\sqrt{37}$ **b.** $4\sqrt{3}$

Exercise 7-3, page 260

1. a. $F(9, 0), x = -9$ **b.** $F(0, -6), y = 6$
c. $F\left(0, \frac{3}{2}\right), y = -\frac{3}{2}$ **2. a.** $x^2 = -4y$ **b.** $y^2 = 28x$
c. $3y^2 = 8x$ **3. a.** $V(0, 0), F(0, 3.75)$
b. $V(0, 0), F(1.25, 0)$ **c.** $V(0, 0), F\left(0, -\frac{2}{3}\right)$
d. $V(0, 0), F(-0.5, 0)$ **4.** $5y^2 = 4x$ **5.** $y^2 = -20x$
6. $x^2 = 8y$ **7.** $4x^2 = -9y$ **8.** $3x^2 = 2y$;
$y^2 = -18x$ **9.** $y^2 = 20x$ **10. a.** 8 **b.** 24 **c.** 10
11. a. i. $(-4, 2)$ to $(4, 2)$ **ii.** $(-6, 12)$ to $(-6, -12)$
iii. $(2.5, 5)$ to $(2.5, -5)$ **b.** length $= |4p|$

Exercise 7-4, pages 262–263

1. a. $V(1, -3), F(1, 1)$ **b.** $V(5, 2), F(1, 2)$
c. $V(-4, 1), F(-4, -2)$ **d.** $V(1, -6), F(3, -6)$

2.

	Vertex	Focus	Directrix
a.	$(1, -3)$	$(1, 1)$	$y = -7$
b.	$(5, 2)$	$(1, 2)$	$x = 9$
c.	$(-4, 1)$	$(-4, -2)$	$y = 4$
d.	$(1, -6)$	$(3, -6)$	$x = -1$

3. a. $x = 1$ **b.** $y = 2$ **c.** $x = -4$ **d.** $y = -6$
4. a. $(4, -4)$ **b.** $(0, -3)$ **c.** $(-2, 5)$ **d.** $(-8, 0)$
5. a. $(y - 5)^2 = -28(x + 3)$
b. $(x - 4)^2 = 16(y + 2)$ **c.** $(y + 3)^2 = -16(x - 4)$
d. $(x - 3)^2 = 24(y + 2)$ **e.** $(y + 1)^2 = 12(x - 2)$
f. $(x - 1)^2 = -8(y + 3)$ **6.** $(x + 5) = 24y^2$
7. $x^2 = -24(y + 3)$ **8.** $(y - 2)^2 = -8(x + 3)$
9. $(x - 4)^2 = 8(y - 1)$ **10. a.** $(y + 2)^2 = -14\left(x - \frac{13}{2}\right)$
b. $(x - 4)^2 = -14\left(y - \frac{13}{2}\right)$ **c.** $(y + 2)^2 = -18(x + 5)$
d. $(x - 3)^2 = -18(y + 2)$ **11.** $(x - 2)^2 = 20(y + 3)$
12. $(y + 1)^2 = -16(x + 2)$

13.	Focus	Vertex	Directrix
a.	$(2, -0.5)$	$(2, -3)$	$y = -5.5$
b.	$(-2.5, -3)$	$(-1, -3)$	$x = 0.5$
c.	$(-4, -0.25)$	$(-4, 1)$	$y = 2.25$
d.	$(5.75, -5)$	$(5, -5)$	$x = 4.25$

Extra, page 263
a. The line $9x - 5y = 6$.
b. The circle $\left(x - \frac{11}{3}\right)^2 + \left(y - \frac{11}{3}\right)^2 = \frac{104}{9}$, $r = 2\sqrt{26}$.
c. The hyperbola $\frac{(x + 5)^2}{16} - \frac{y^2}{48} = 1$, $C(-5, 0)$, $F_1(3, 0)$, $F_2(-13, 0)$.
d. The ellipse $\frac{(x - 5)^2}{16} + \frac{y^2}{12} = 1$, $C(5, 0)$, $F_1(7, 0)$, $F_2(3, 0)$.

Review, page 264
1. a. $C(3, -2)$, $r = 2\sqrt{7}$ **b.** $C(3, -4)$, $r = 3$
c. $C(4, -5)$, $r = \sqrt{47}$ **d.** $C(0, 3)$, $r = \sqrt{14}$
2. a. $(x - 4)^2 + (y + 2)^2 = 37$
b. $(x - 5)^2 + (y - 1)^2 = 25$
c. $(x - 7)^2 + (y - 4)^2 = 40$ **3. a.** $C(1, -3)$, $r = 2$
b. $C(3, 0)$, $r = 3$ **4. a.** $(x - 2)^2 + (y + 3)^2 = 25$
b. $(x - 2)^2 + (y + 3)^2 = 36$
5. $x^2 + y^2 - 10x + 2y + 9 = 0$
6. a. $V(0, 0)$, $F(0, -2.5)$, $y = 2.5$
b. $V(3, -2)$, $F(3, 0)$, $y = -4$
c. $V(0, -4)$, $F(3, -4)$, $x = -3$
7. a. $x^2 = -24y$ **b.** $y^2 = 12x$
c. $(x - 2)^2 = 16(y + 5)$ **d.** $(x - 3)^2 = 24(y - 5)$
e. $x^2 = 16(y + 1)$ **f.** $(y + 2)^2 = 12(x - 1)$
8. $x^2 = 16y$ **9.** $x^2 = 36(y + 5)$ **10.** $y^2 = -25x$

11.	Vertex	Focus	Directrix
a.	$(-5, 5)$	$(-3.75, 5)$	$x = -6.25$
b.	$(-3, 1)$	$(-3, 5)$	$y = -3$

12. a. $3x + y = 20$ **b.** $x + y = 8$
13. a. $4\sqrt{2}$ **b.** $2\sqrt{21}$

Exercise 7-5, pages 269-271
1. a. y-axis **b.** x-axis **c.** y-axis
2. a. $V_1(6, 0)$, $V_2(-6, 0)$ **b.** $V_1(4, 0)$, $V_2(-4, 0)$
c. $V_1\left(0, \frac{1}{2}\right)$; $V_2\left(0, -\frac{1}{2}\right)$ **3. a.** $(0, \pm 2\sqrt{5})$ **b.** $(\pm\sqrt{6}, 0)$
c. $(0, \pm 2)$ **4. a.** $(\pm 2, 0)$ **b.** $(0, \pm 0.2)$ **c.** $(\pm 3, 0)$
5. a. $V(\pm 7, 0)$, $B(0, \pm 4)$ **b.** $V(0, \pm 3)$, $B(\pm 2, 0)$
c. $V(0, \pm 0.5)$, $B\left(\pm\frac{1}{3}\right), 0$ **d.** $V(0, \pm 8)$, $B(\pm 5, 0)$
e. $V(0, \pm 2.5)$, $B\left(\pm\frac{5}{3}, 0\right)$ **f.** $V(0, \pm 4)$, $B(\pm 3, 0)$
6. a. $\frac{x^2}{40} + \frac{y^2}{49} = 1$ **b.** $\frac{x^2}{36} + \frac{y^2}{20} = 1$ **c.** $\frac{x^2}{16} + \frac{y^2}{64} = 1$
d. $\frac{x^2}{36} + \frac{y^2}{25} = 1$ **e.** $\frac{x^2}{80} + \frac{y^2}{64} = 1$ **f.** $\frac{x^2}{81} + \frac{y^2}{45} = 1$
7. a. $9x^2 + y^2 = 25$; $V(0, \pm 5)$, $B\left(\pm\frac{5}{3}, 0\right)$
b. $x^2 + 16y^2 = 25$; $V(\pm 5, 0)$, $B(0, \pm 1.25)$
c. $4x^2 + \frac{y^2}{9} = 25$; $V(0, \pm 15)$, $B(\pm 2.5, 0)$
d. $\frac{x^2}{16} + \frac{y^2}{9} = 1$; $V(\pm 4, 0)$, $B(0, \pm 3)$
8. a. $\frac{x^2}{100} + \frac{y^2}{64} = 1$ **c.** $\frac{x^2}{100} + \frac{y^2}{64} = 1$
d. They are identical.
9. $\frac{x^2}{36} + \frac{y^2}{16} = 1$ **10.** $\frac{x^2}{9} + \frac{y^2}{64} = 1$ **11.** $\frac{x^2}{32} + \frac{y^2}{72} = 1$
12. $\frac{x^2}{64} + \frac{y^2}{39} = 1$ **13.** $\frac{x^2}{34} + \frac{y^2}{9} = 1$
14. a. $D = \{x \mid |x| \leq 4, x \in \mathbf{R}\}$; $R = \{y \mid |y| \leq 7, y \in \mathbf{R}\}$
b. $D = \{x \mid |x| \leq 0.5, x \in \mathbf{R}\}$; $R = \{y \mid |y| \leq \frac{1}{3}, y \in \mathbf{R}\}$
c. $D = \{x \mid |x| \leq \frac{2}{3}, x \in \mathbf{R}\}$; $R = \{y \mid |y| \leq \frac{4}{3}, y \in \mathbf{R}\}$
15. $x^2 + 16y^2 = 64$
$\rightarrow 16x^2 + 16y^2 = 64 \therefore x^2 + y^2 = 4$
16. $(x, y) \rightarrow (x, 4y)$ **17.** $(x, y) \rightarrow \left(\frac{xr}{a}, \frac{yr}{b}\right)$
18. a. $\frac{x^2}{84} + \frac{y^2}{63} = 1$ **b.** $\frac{2x^2}{17} + \frac{y^2}{17} = 1$ **19. a.** $\frac{4}{3}$
b. 4 **20.** $\frac{x^2}{100} + \frac{y^2}{16} = 1$ **21.** $\frac{x^2}{a^2} + \frac{y^2}{b^2} = 1$
22. e. An ellipse

Exercise 7-6, page 274

1.	C	F	V	B
a.	$(-3, 2)$	$(-3, 6), (-3, -2)$	$(-3, -3), (-3, 7)$	$(0, 2), (-6, 2)$
b.	$(4, -3)$	$(7, -3), (1, -3)$	$(9, -3), (-1, -3)$	$(4, 1), (4, -7)$
c.	$(-4, -2)$	$(-4, 4), (-4, -8)$	$(-4, 8), (-4, -12)$	$(4, -2), (-12, -2)$
d.	$(1, -4)$	$(\pm 2\sqrt{21} + 1, -4)$	$(11, -4), (-9, -4)$	$(1, 0), (1, -8)$

3. a. $(0, -3 \pm \sqrt{11})$ **b.** $(4 \pm \sqrt{21}, -1)$

4. a. $\frac{(x-3)^2}{36} + \frac{(y-3)^2}{11} = 1$

b. $\frac{(x+4)^2}{7} + \frac{(y-2)^2}{16} = 1$ **c.** $\frac{(x-2)^2}{11} + \frac{(y+3)^2}{36} = 1$

d. $\frac{(x+4)^2}{25} + \frac{(y-1)^2}{16} = 1$ **e.** $\frac{(x-3)^2}{36} + \frac{(y-4)^2}{9} = 1$

f. $\frac{(x+2)^2}{4} + \frac{(y-5)^2}{64} = 1$

5. a. $\frac{(x-1)^2}{36} + \frac{(y+5)^2}{11} = 1$

b. $\frac{(x-2)^2}{33} + \frac{(y+6)^2}{49} = 1$ **6.** $\frac{(x-3)^2}{25} + \frac{(y+5)^2}{16} = 1$

7. $\frac{(x-1)^2}{28} + \frac{(y+3)^2}{64} = 1$ **8.** $\frac{(x+1)^2}{49} + \frac{(y-2)^2}{24} = 1$

9. a. $\frac{x^2}{36} + \frac{y^2}{16} = 1$ **b.** $\frac{x^2}{4} + \frac{y^2}{9} = 1$

10. $\frac{x^2}{16} + \frac{y^2}{9} = 1$

Exercise 7-7, pages 275-276

1. $x^2 = -9y$ **2.** $y^2 = 6x$ **3.** About 265 m

4. $\frac{x^2}{40\,000} + \frac{y^2}{17\,500} = 1$ **5.** 3.69 m

6. $x^2 = -1000y$, 0.081 m **7.** 25.30 cm

8. $\frac{x^2}{56\,250\,000} + \frac{y^2}{56\,000\,000} = 1$

9. $\frac{x^2}{2.25 \times 10^{16}} + \frac{y^2}{2.2496 \times 10^{16}} = 1$; 299 973 332 km

10. Going up: 8 m; Going down 56 m

11. a. $x^2 + y^2 = 1369$ **b.** $2\sqrt{286}$ km N or S

c. (7.8 km E, 36.2 km S) **12. a.** $x^2 + y^2 - 12y = 0$

b. $SM = 11.2$ km; $SP = 4.3$ km

Application, page 277

1. $AB = 85.58$ m; Area = 13 082 m^2 **2.** 123.2 m

3. 141.46 m **4.** 76.39 m

Extra, page 277

$P_1\left(c, \frac{b^2}{a}\right)$ **1.** $\frac{x^2}{64} + \frac{y^2}{36} = 1$ **2.** $\frac{x^2}{4} + \frac{y^2}{36} = 1$

3. $\frac{x^2}{20} + \frac{y^2}{36} = 1$

Review, pages 278-279

1. a. $D = \{x \mid x \in \mathbf{R}, 1 \le x \le 7\}$; $R = \{y \mid y \in \mathbf{R}, -4 \le y \le 2\}$

b. $D = \{x \mid x \in \mathbf{R}, -6 \le x \le 2\}$; $R = \{y \mid y \in \mathbf{R}, -5 \le y \le 3\}$

c. $D = \{x \mid x \in \mathbf{R}, x \le 1\}$; $R = \{y \mid y \in \mathbf{R}\}$

d. $D = \{x \mid x \in \mathbf{R}\}$; $R = \{y \mid y \in \mathbf{R}, y \ge -1\}$

e. $D = \{x \mid x \in \mathbf{R}, |x| \le 3\}$; $R = \{y \mid y \in \mathbf{R}, |y| \le 2\}$

f. $D = \{x \mid x \in \mathbf{R}, |x| \le \sqrt{10}\}$; $R = \{y \mid y \in \mathbf{R}, |y| \le 2\sqrt{2}\}$

2. a. $(x+3)^2 + (y-5)^2 = 72$

b. $(x-2)^2 + (y+4)^2 = 49$

c. $(x-1)^2 + (y-7)^2 = 58$ **3.** $\sqrt{79}$

4. a. $F(-2, 0)$, $x = 2$ **b.** $F(-3, 6)$, $y = -4$

c. $F(-1, 0)$, $x = -3$ **5. a.** $x^2 = -24y$

b. $x^2 = 24(y+2)$ **c.** $y^2 = 12(x-1)$

d. $x^2 = \frac{25}{2}y$ or $y^2 = -\frac{4}{5}x$ **6. a.** $x^2 = -\frac{64}{3}y$

b. 7.31 m

7.	V	F
a.	$(\pm 8, 0)$	$(\pm 2\sqrt{7}, 0)$
b.	$(0, \pm 6)$	$(0, \pm 2\sqrt{5})$
c.	$(\pm 3, 0)$	$(\pm\sqrt{5}, 0)$
d.	$(1, -3), (9, -3)$	$(5 \pm 2\sqrt{3}, -3)$
e.	$(\pm 3, 0)$	$(\pm 2\sqrt{2}, 0)$
f.	$(-7, -12), (-7, 0)$	$(-7, -6 \pm \sqrt{11})$

	B	2a	2b	Constant Sum
a.	$(0, \pm 6)$	16	12	16
b.	$(\pm 4, 0)$	12	8	12
c.	$(0, \pm 2)$	6	4	6
d.	$(5, -5), (5, -1)$	8	4	8
e.	$(0, \pm 1)$	6	2	6
f.	$(-12, -6), (-2, -6)$	12	10	12

8. a. $B(\pm 2, 0)$, $V(0, \pm 6)$ **b.** $B\left(0, \pm\frac{1}{3}\right)$, $V(\pm 0.5, 0)$

c. $B\left(0, \pm\frac{5}{3}\right)$, $V(\pm 2.5, 0)$ **d.** $B(4, -1), (4, -3)$; $V(8, -2), (0, -2)$ **9. a.** $\frac{y^2}{16} + \frac{y^2}{4} = 1$ **b.** $\frac{x^2}{25} + y^2 = 1$

10. a. $\frac{x^2}{48} + \frac{y^2}{64} = 1$ **b.** $\frac{x^2}{144} + \frac{y^2}{64} = 1$

c. $\frac{x^2}{18} + \frac{y^2}{9} = 1$ **d.** $\frac{x^2}{16} + \frac{y^2}{81} = 1$ **e.** $\frac{x^2}{4} + \frac{y^2}{48} = 1$

f. $\frac{x^2}{48} + \frac{y^2}{4} = 1$ **11.** $\frac{(x-4)^2}{16} + \frac{(y+3)^2}{7} = 1$
12. $\frac{x^2}{39} + \frac{y^2}{64} = 1$ **13.** $\frac{(x+2)^2}{16} + \frac{(y-1)^2}{25} = 1$
14. $\frac{x^2}{81} + \frac{y^2}{49} = 1$ **15.** $\frac{4}{3}$ m from the bottom of the oven, centred horizontally.
16. a. $\frac{x^2}{25} + \frac{y^2}{100} = 1$ **b.** $\frac{x^2}{100} + \frac{y^2}{400} = 1$
c. $\frac{x^2}{4} + \frac{y^2}{2500} = 1$ **d.** $\frac{x^2}{16} + \frac{y^2}{64} = 1$
17. a. $\frac{x^2}{9} + \frac{y^2}{25} = 1$ **c.** $\frac{x^2}{9} + \frac{y^2}{25} = 1$
d. They are identical.
18. $x^2 = 75y$; The microphone is located 18.75 cm from the back of the reflector.

Test, page 280

1. a. $C(0, 3); r = 2\sqrt{5}$ **b.** $C(7, -3), r = 7$
2. a. $(x-5)^2 + (y+2)^2 = 20$
b. $(x-3)^2 + (y-7)^2 = 64$ **c.** $x^2 + (y+4)^2 = 58$
d. $(x-4)^2 + (y-4)^2 = 16$ **3. a.** $F(0, 6), y = -6$
b. $F(-8, -3), x = 6$ **c.** $F(0, 4), y = 2$
4. a. $y^2 = -16x$ **b.** $x^2 = -28y$
c. $(y-4)^2 = -8(x+3)$ **d.** $y^2 = -1.8x$
5. a. $F(0, \pm 3\sqrt{3}); V(0, \pm 6); B(\pm 3, 0)$
b. $F\left(\pm\frac{\sqrt{5}}{6}, 0\right)); V\left(\pm\frac{1}{2}, 0\right); B\left(0, \pm\frac{1}{3}\right)$
c. $F(1 \pm \sqrt{21} + 1, -2); V(6, -2)\ (-4, -2);$ $B(1, 0), (1, -4)$ **6. a.** $4x^2 + y^2 = 36$
b. $9x^2 + \frac{y^2}{9} = 36$
c. $x^2 + 36y^2 = 36$ **7.** $F(-4 \pm \sqrt{3}, 1);$ $V_1(-2, 1); V_2(-6, 1)$ **8. a.** $\frac{x^2}{36} + \frac{y^2}{11} = 1$
b. $\frac{x^2}{9} + \frac{y^2}{81} = 1$ **c.** $\frac{x^2}{16} + \frac{y^2}{41} = 1$ **d.** $\frac{x^2}{64} + \frac{y^2}{4} = 1$
9. $\frac{(x-3)^2}{100} + \frac{(y+2)^2}{36} = 1$ **10.** $\frac{x^2}{16} + \frac{y^2}{4} = 1$
11. $4\sqrt{3}$ m apart. The cord is 8 m long.

Cumulative Review, page 281

1. a. 19 **b.** 34 **c.** 257 **d.** 2 **2. a.** $x = -3$
b. $x = 2$ **c.** $x = -2$ **d.** $x = 6$ **3. a.** 10^{1000}
b. $\frac{1}{20\,000}$ **c.** 49 999 **4. a.** 196 **b.** 9 **5. a.** 4.72
b. 12 624.77 **c.** 6.38 **6. a.** $P(t) = P(1.05)^t$
b. 3258 **7. a.** $(3x+2)(2x-3)$ **b.** $(t+7)^2$
c. $(2x-5)(2x+5)$
8. $3x^3 - 2x^2 + 7x - 5$
$= (x+3)(3x^2 - 11x + 40) - 125$

9. a. $\frac{5\sqrt{3}}{3}$ **b.** 14 **c.** $2\sqrt{6}$ **d.** $\frac{\sqrt{6}}{2}$
10. a. 123.11 m **b.** 21.93 m **11.** 24°

UNIT 8

Exercise 8-1, page 285

1. a. $-\frac{2}{3}$ **b.** $-\frac{10}{3}$ **c.** $-\frac{7}{3}$ **2. b.** I, III; II, IV; I, III
3. a. -7 **b.** 3.5 **c.** 4.5 **4. b.** $M = -4, N = 3$
5. a. $(x-3)(y+2) = 12; x = 3, y = -2$
b. $(x+5)(y+2) = 4; x = -5, y = -2$
c. $(x+1)y = -8; x = -1, y = 0$
d. $(x+3)(y-5) = 16; x = -3, y = 5$
e. $(x-4)(y+3) = \frac{1}{2}; x = 4, y = -3$
f. $(x-3)(y-2) = -\frac{1}{3}; x = 3, y = 2$
6. a. $xy = 8$ **b.** $xy = -18$ **7. a.** $x(y-3) = 4$
b. $(x+2)(y-5) = -2$
8. a. $(x-3)(y+4) = 16; x = 3, y = -4$
b. $(x+2)(y+3) = -12; x = -2, y = -3$
c. $x(y+5) = 6; x = 0, y = -5$
d. $(x-2)y = -8; x = 2, y = 0$
9. $18 125

Exercise 8-2, page 289

1.

	x-intercepts	y-intercepts	Vertices
a.	± 6	—	$(\pm 6, 0)$
b.	—	± 7	$(0, \pm 7)$
c.	± 5	—	$(\pm 5, 0)$
d.	—	± 2	$(0, \pm 2)$
e.	$\pm 2\sqrt{5}$	—	$(\pm 2\sqrt{5}, 0)$
f.	—	$\pm\frac{5}{4}$	$\left(0, \pm\frac{5}{4}\right)$

2. a. $m = \pm 3$ **b.** $m = \pm\frac{1}{5}$ **c.** $m = \pm\frac{2}{7}$
3. a. $x \pm y = 0$ **b.** $4x \pm y = 0$ **c.** $x \pm 2y = 0$
d. $2x \pm 5y = 0$ **e.** $3y \pm 2x = 0$ **f.** $3x \pm 2y = 0$

5.

	Equation of Hyperbola
a.	$x^2 - y^2 = 15$
b.	$x^2 - y^2 = -40$
c.	$4x^2 - y^2 = 99$
d.	$x^2 - 9y^2 = -221$
e.	$9x^2 - 25y^2 = 125$

6. a. $9x^2 - 16y^2 = 225$ **b.** $4x^2 - 9y^2 = -441$
7. a. $\frac{x^2}{4} - \frac{y^2}{9} = 1$ **b.** $9x^2 - 16y^2 = 1$
8. c. 45° rotation clockwise
9. a. $y_1 - y_2 = \frac{4}{5}(a - \sqrt{a^2 - 25})$

b. $a = 10; y_1 - y_2 = 1.07$
$a = 20; y_1 - y_2 = 0.51$
$a = 100; y_1 - y_2 = 0.10$

Exercise 8-3, pages 294–295

1. a. x-axis **b.** y-axis **c.** y-axis
2. a. $(\pm 2\sqrt{5}, 0)$ **b.** $(\pm 4, 0)$ **c.** $(0, \pm 0.2)$
3. a. $(\pm 2\sqrt{10}, 0)$ **b.** $(0, \pm 2\sqrt{5})$ **c.** $\left(\pm\frac{\sqrt{5}}{2}, 0\right)$
4. a. $(\pm 2, 0)$ **b.** $(0, \pm 3)$ **c.** $\left(0, \pm\frac{1}{6}\right)$
5. a. Domain: $\{x \mid x \in \boldsymbol{R}\}$; Range: $\{y \mid |y| \geq 5, y \in \boldsymbol{R}\}$
b. Domain: $\{x \mid |x| \geq 4, x \in \boldsymbol{R}\}$; Range: $\{y \mid y \in \boldsymbol{R}\}$
c. Domain: $\{x \mid |x| \geq \frac{1}{3}, x \in \boldsymbol{R}\}$; Range: $\{y \mid y \in \boldsymbol{R}\}$
6. a. $\frac{x^2}{25} - \frac{y^2}{24} = 1$ **b.** $\frac{x^2}{48} - \frac{y^2}{16} = -1$
c. $\frac{x^2}{64} - \frac{y^2}{64} = 1$ **d.** $\frac{x^2}{36} - \frac{y^2}{28} = 1$
e. $\frac{x^2}{8} - y^2 = -1$ **f.** $\frac{x^2}{49} - \frac{y^2}{25} = -1$ **7.** $(0, \pm 5)$
8. $2\sqrt{15}$ **9. a.** $\frac{x^2}{16} - \frac{y^2}{36} = -1$ **b.** $\frac{x^2}{25} - \frac{y^2}{24} = 1$
c. $\frac{x^2}{39} - \frac{y^2}{25} = 1$ **d.** $\frac{x^2}{81} - \frac{y^2}{81} = -1$
e. $\frac{x^2}{20} - \frac{y^2}{16} = -1$ **f.** $\frac{x^2}{57} - \frac{y^2}{64} = -1$
10. $\frac{x^2}{25} - \frac{y^2}{16} = 1$ **11. a.** $\frac{x^2}{36} - \frac{y^2}{4} = 1$
b. $\frac{x^2}{18} - \frac{y^2}{6} = -1$ **12. a.** 16.1 **b.** $\frac{49}{3}$

Exercise 8-4, page 298

1. a. 1 unit right, 2 units down
b. 2 units left, 3 units down
c. 1 unit left, 3 units up
d. 2 units right, 1 unit up
2. a. $\frac{(x-1)^2}{9} - \frac{(y+2)^2}{16} = 1$; $C(1, -2)$
b. $\frac{(x+2)^2}{9} - \frac{(y+3)^2}{16} = 1$; $C(-2, -3)$
c. $\frac{(x+1)^2}{9} - \frac{(y-3)^2}{16} = 1$; $C(-1, 3)$
d. $\frac{(x-2)^2}{9} - \frac{(y-1)^2}{16} = 1$; $C(2, 1)$

3.	Centre C	Vertices V	Endpoints of conjugate axis	Foci F
a.	(1, 3)	(−3, 3), (5, 3)	(1, 0), (1, 6)	(6, 3), (−4, 3)
b.	(−2, 3)	(−2, −5), (−2, 11)	(−8, 3), (4, 3)	(−2, 13), (−2, −7)
c.	(2, −1)	(2, −5), (2, 3)	(0, −1), (4, −1)	$(2, -2\sqrt{5} - 1)$, $(2, 2\sqrt{5} - 1)$
d.	(−1, −3)	(−1, −8), (−1, 2)	(−4, −3), (2, −3)	$(-1, -3 - \sqrt{34})$, $(-1, -3 + \sqrt{34})$

4. a. $\frac{(x-5)^2}{9} - \frac{(y-2)^2}{16} = 1$
b. $\frac{(x+3)^2}{28} - \frac{(y+3)^2}{36} = -1$
c. $\frac{(x+2)^2}{9} - \frac{(y-6)^2}{7} = 1$
d. $\frac{x^2}{11} - \frac{(y+4)^2}{25} = -1$
e. $\frac{(x+1)^2}{3} - (y-2)^2 = -1$
f. $\frac{(x-5)^2}{5} - \frac{(y-1)^2}{4} = 1$
g. $\frac{(x-1)^2}{9} - \frac{(y+4)^2}{16} = -1$
5. a. $4x + 3y = 26$,
$4x - 3y = 14$
b. $6x - 2\sqrt{7}y = 6\sqrt{7} - 18$,
$6x + 2\sqrt{7}y = -18 - 6\sqrt{7}$
c. $\sqrt{15}x - y = 2\sqrt{15} - 6$,
$\sqrt{15}x + y = 6 + 2\sqrt{15}$
d. $5x + \sqrt{11}y = -4\sqrt{11}$,
$5x - \sqrt{11}y = 4\sqrt{11}$
e. $x - \sqrt{3}y = -2\sqrt{3} - 1$, $x + \sqrt{3}y = 2\sqrt{3} - 1$
f. No asymptotes
g. $4x - 3y = 16$,
$4x + 3y = -8$
6. a. $\frac{(x+1)^2}{4} - \frac{(y-4)^2}{21} = 1$
b. $\frac{(x-4)^2}{20} - \frac{(y+6)^2}{16} = -1$
7. a. $\frac{(x-4)^2}{4} - \left(\frac{y+2}{9}\right)^2 = 1$
b. $(x-3)^2 - \frac{(y-3)^2}{9} = -1$

Review, page 299

1.	Vertices	Foci	Conjugate axis
a.	(4, 0), (−4, 0)	(±5, 0)	(0, 3), (0, −3)
b.	(0, 9), (0, −9)	$(0, \pm\sqrt{130})$	(7, 0), (−7, 0)
c.	(0, 2), (0, −2)	$(0, \pm\sqrt{29})$	(5, 0), (−5, 0)

a. $7x \pm 5y = 0$ **b.** $2x \pm 4y = 0$

$10x \pm 7y = 0$ **3. a.** $\frac{x^2}{40} - \frac{y^2}{9} = -1$ **b.** $\frac{x^2}{7} - \frac{y^2}{9} = 1$

$\frac{x^2}{16} - \frac{y^2}{9} = -1$ **d.** $\frac{x^2}{25} - \frac{y^2}{11} = 1$ **4.** $\frac{x^2}{49} - \frac{y^2}{32} = 1$

$\frac{x^2}{72} - \frac{y^2}{72} = -1$ **6.** $\frac{x^2}{9} - \frac{y^2}{16} = -1$

a. $\frac{x^2}{16} - \frac{y^2}{36} = 1$ **b.** $\frac{x^2}{35} - \frac{9y^2}{35} = -1$

$\frac{x^2}{100} - \frac{y^2}{16} = -1$ **8.** $m = \pm 1$

9.

	Centre	Vertices	Foci	Conjugate axis
a.	$(-3, -1)$	$(-3, 3)$, $(-3, -5)$	$(-3, 4)$, $(-3, -6)$	$(0, -1)$, $(-6, -1)$
b.	$(2, -1)$	$(10, -1)$, $(-6, -1)$	$(12, -1)$, $(-8, -1)$	$(2, 5)$, $(2, -7)$

11. a. $\frac{(x+5)^2}{9} - \frac{(y+3)^2}{16} = 1$

b. $\frac{(x+4)^2}{5} - \frac{(y+6)^2}{4} = -1$

12. a. $\frac{(x-1)^2}{16} - \frac{(y+3)^2}{25} = -1$

b. $\frac{(x+2)^2}{4} - \frac{(y-5)^2}{9} = 1$

Exercise 8-5, pages 302-303

1. a. $(8, 4)$ **b.** $(-2, 2)$ **c.** $(5, -2)$ **d.** $(5, -2)$
2. a. 2 **b.** 2 **c.** none **d.** 2 **e.** 3 **f.** 4
g. none **h.** 2 **i.** none **3. a.** $\{(2, 0), (-2, 0)\}$
b. $\{(6, -6), (-6, 6)\}$ **c.** $\{(6, 0), (-6, 0)\}$ **d.** $\{(4, 0)\}$
e. no solution **f.** $\{(3, 4), (-3, -4)\}$
g. $\{(0, 4), (0, -4)\}$
h. $\{(3, -4), (-3, 4), (4, -3), (-4, 3)\}$
i. $(0, 6), (\pm\sqrt{3}, 3)$
4. $\{0, -5\}, \{3, 4\}, \{-3, 4\}$ **5.** $\{-3, -2\}, \{2, 3\}$
6. a. $(3.5, 1.7), (-3.5, -1.7)$ **b.** $(\pm 3.5, \pm 3.5)$
c. $(2.2, 4.5), (-2.2, -4.5)$
7. a. $(x - y - 4)(x - y + 4) = 0$; parallel
b. $(6x - y - 3)(6x + y + 3) = 0$;
intersect at $(0, -3)$
c. $(x - 2y - 6)(x - 2y - 4) = 0$; parallel
d. $(5x - y - 7)(5x + y - 7)$
8. a. $(-2, 2), (2, -2)$ **b.** $(-0.5, 0), (1, 3)$
c. $(0, -3), (2, -1)$ **d.** No solution, parallel lines.

Exercise 8-6, pages 306-307

1. a. $(3, 3\sqrt{3}), (3, -3\sqrt{3})$ **b.** $(\sqrt{6}, -2)$,
$(-\sqrt{6}, -2)$ **c.** $(-2\sqrt{3}, 2\sqrt{3}), (2\sqrt{3}, -2\sqrt{3})$
2. a. $(2, 4), (-2, -4)$ **b.** $(2\sqrt{3}, 2), (-2\sqrt{3}, 2)$
c. $(-3, 3), (-3, -3)$
3. a. $(1, -5), (5, -1)$ **b.** $\left(-\frac{7}{3}, \frac{8}{3}\right), (-1, 4)$
c. $(2, 0), (3, 1)$ **d.** $(8, 5), (-4, -1)$ **e.** $(-1, -3)$
f. No intersection
4. a. $(0, -3), (2, -1)$ **b.** $(-15, -10), (-3, 2)$
c. $\left(-\frac{1}{9}, \frac{34}{9}\right), (-3, -2)$ **d.** $(1, 5)$ **e.** $(4, 2), (-4, -6)$
f. $(-2, 0), \left(\frac{18}{5}, \frac{14}{5}\right)$
5. 8 m × 16 m **6.** $\{3, 5\}, \{-1, 1\}$
7. 9 m × 9 m, and 7 m × 7 m
8. 10 m × 12 m and 8 m × 10 m
9. 5 cm, 12 cm, 13 cm **10.** 5.3 m
11. A_1 = 5 cm × 5 cm; A_2 = 3 cm × 3 cm
12. square: 60 m × 60 m;
rectangle: 100 m × 80 m
13. a. $(-5, -3), (-3, 5)$ **b.** $(0, -2), \left(4, -\frac{14}{3}\right)$
c. $(3, 1), \left(-\frac{27}{5}, -\frac{23}{5}\right)$ **d.** $(-6, -6), (4.5, 8)$
e. $(-6, 0)$ **f.** $(1, 4), (1.5, 5.25)$ **14. a.** $(2, -2)$,
$(-2, 2)$ **b.** $(1, 3), (-0.5, 0)$ **c.** $(0, -3), (2, -1)$
d. no solution

Exercise 8-7, pages 308-309

1. a. $(6, \pm 4), (-6, \pm 4)$ **b.** $(0, \pm 3)$
c. no solution **d.** $(\pm\sqrt{6}, -2)$ **e.** $(\pm 2, 0)$
f. $(2\sqrt{3}, \pm\sqrt{2}), (-2\sqrt{3}, \pm\sqrt{2})$ **2. a.** $(0, -5), (\pm 3, 4)$
b. $(5, 3), (-5, -3), (-3, -5), (3, 5)$
c. $(\sqrt{6}, \sqrt{6}), (-\sqrt{6}, -\sqrt{6}), (2, 3), (-2, -3)$
d. $(\pm 2, 4)$ **e.** $(\pm 1, -3)$ **f.** $(9, \pm 2)$
3. $3\sqrt{2}$ cm, $\sqrt{2}$ cm **4.** 9 m × 9 m and
9 m × 17 m
5. $\{(\pm 2\sqrt{5}, \pm 4)\}$ **6.** 5 m × 10 m **7.** 40¢
8. 650 km/h **9.** Keiji: $800, Takashi: $900
10. 80 cm × 60 cm **11. a.** $(-6, 0)$
b. $(3, -5), (0, 4), (6, 4)$ **c.** $(\pm 4, 5), (0, -3)$
d. $(9, 0), (9, -4)$ **e.** $(6, 5), (0, -5), (8, 3), (-2, -3)$
f. $(\pm 5, -3)$ **g.** $(-2, \pm 4)$ **h.** $(6, 4), (4, 0)$
12. a. $(\pm 3, 0), (0, \pm 3)$ **b.** $(0, 9), (\pm 3, 0)$

Review, pages 310–311

1. a. $(-7, 2)$ **b.** $\left(\frac{1}{2}, \frac{3}{4}\right)$ **c.** $(-6, 4)$ **d.** $(4, -4)$,
$(-4, 4)$ **e.** $(\sqrt{10}, 6), (-\sqrt{10}, 6)$ **f.** $(8, \pm 6), (-10, 0)$
2. a. $(x - 4)(y + 3) = 12$; $x = 4$; $y = -3$
b. $(x + 6)(y + 4) = 3$; asymptotes: $x = -6$;
$y = -4$ **c.** $(x + 1)y = -5$;
asymptotes: $x = -1$; $y = 0$
3. $P = \frac{-17}{3}$ **4. a.** $x \pm y = 0$
b. $y \pm 5x = 0$ **c.** $x \pm 2y = 0$ **5. a.** $\frac{x^2}{9} - \frac{y^2}{16} = 1$
b. $\frac{x^2}{4} - \frac{y^2}{25} = 1$ **c.** $4x^2 - 16y^2 = 1$

Test, page 312

1. a. $P = 3$ **b.** $N = 10$ **2. b.** $N = 2, P = -3$
3. $x^2 - 9y^2 = -27$ **4.** $4x^2 - 25y^2 = -100$
5. Let c be the constant difference or the transverse axis length.
Let b be the conjugate axis length.

	Vertices a	Foci	c	b
a.	$(\pm 1, 0)$	$(\pm\sqrt{17}, 0)$	2	8
b.	$(0, \pm 5)$	$(0, \pm\sqrt{34})$	10	6
c.	$\left(\pm\frac{1}{3}, 0\right)$	$\left(\pm\frac{\sqrt{13}}{6}, 0\right)$	$\frac{2}{3}$	1

6. a. $\frac{x^2}{13} - \frac{y^2}{36} = -1$ **b.** $x^2 - \frac{y^2}{8} = 1$
c. $\frac{x^2}{16} - \frac{y^2}{4} = 1$ **d.** $\frac{x^2}{27} - \frac{y^2}{9} = -1$
7. a. $\frac{(x + 5)^2}{9} - \frac{y^2}{16} = 1$
b. $\frac{(x + 3)^2}{13} - \frac{(y + 1)^2}{36} = -1$

8.

	Centre	Vertices	Foci	Conjugate Axis
a.	$(5, -2)$	$(2, -2)$, $(8, -2)$	$(0, -2)$, $(10, -2)$	$(5, 2)$, $(5, -6)$
b.	$(1, -3)$	$(1, 9)$ $(1, -15)$	$(1, 10)$, $(1, -16)$	$(-4, -3)$, $(6, -3)$

9. a. Asymptotes: $y = -\frac{4}{3}x + \frac{14}{3}, y = \frac{4}{3}x - \frac{26}{3}$
b. Asymptotes: $y = -2.4x - 0.6, y = 2.4x - 5.4$
10. a. $(3, 0)$ **b.** no solution **c.** $(3, 3), (-3, -3)$
11. a. $(-1, 5), (-5, 1)$ **b.** $(-3, -1)$
c. $(-6, -4), (2, 4)$ **d.** $(\pm\sqrt{5}, \pm 2\sqrt{11})$
e. $(4, \pm 2)$ **f.** $(0, -10), (\pm 6, 8)$
12. Fiona invested \$600; Connie invested \$800.

Cumulative Review, page 313

1. $x \leq -3, x \geq \frac{13}{3}$ **2.** $f(x) = 4\left(\frac{3}{4}\right)^x$
3. \$116 000 (to the nearest thousand) **4.** 4
5. $(x - 1), (x + 2)$ **6. a.** $\sin\theta = \frac{4}{5}$; $\cos\theta = -\frac{3}{5}$
b. 126.9° **7.** $x = 23.99$; $y = 20.4$; $\theta = 47°$
8. a. $\frac{\pi}{2}$ rad **b.** $\frac{7\pi}{4}$ rad **c.** $\frac{5\pi}{3}$ rad **d.** $-\frac{2\pi}{5}$ rad
9. a. 60° **b.** 45° **c.** −108° **d.** −105°
10. b. period $= 6\pi$; amplitude $= 3$
11. $\frac{\sin x}{\sin(90° - x)}$ **12.** $C(2, 3)$ $r = 4$

UNIT 9

Exercise 9-1, pages 318-319

1. a. i. 40.9 **ii.** 30 **iii.** 74 **iv.** 64 **b.** There is no mode for runs, and the mode for hits is 1, which is not representative of the central tendency. **c.** 81 **d.** 76

2. a.

Page Numbers	Frequency (f)	Cumulative Frequency	Midpoint of Interval (x)	Subtotal (fx)
1-50	13	13	25.5	331.5
51-100	10	23	75.5	755
101-150	5	28	125.5	627.5
151-200	14	42	175.5	245.7
201-250	13	55	225.5	2931.5
251-300	15	70	275.5	4132.5
301-350	9	79	325.5	2929.5
351-400	10	89	375.5	3755
401-450	11	100	425.5	4680.5
	$n = 100$			$\Sigma fx = 22\ 600$

b. 226; 175.5; 275.5 **3. a.** 79 **b.** 68 **c.** 67
4. a. i. \$1200; \$1050; \$1000 **ii.** \$1090; \$1100; \$1200 **iii.** \$1150; \$1200; \$1000
b. Company *A*: mean, Company *B*: mode, Company *C*: median **5.** yes **6.** 76
7. first moving average = 195;
second moving average = 220;
third moving average = 217.5;
fourth moving average = 237.5;
fifth moving average = 247.5;
sixth moving average = 240;
seventh moving average = 250 **8. a.** 37%
b. 18% **c.** 4050 **d.** 4600

Exercise 9-2, pages 323-324

1. a. \$83.33 **b.** \$54 **c.** \$11.89 **d.** \$17.31
2. a. \$301 375 **b.** \$254 500 **c.** \$104 875
d. \$108 440 **3. a.** Class *A*: 17, Class *B*: 17
b. ranges are equal. **c.** Class *B* **d.** Class *A*: 11.5, Class *B*: 11.5 **e.** Class *A*: 4.9, Class *B*: 7.6
4. a. 5.4 h **b.** 9 h **c.** 2.5 h **d.** 3.0 h
5. the first city
6.

	Becky	Helena	Marge
a.	13.4	13.4	13.4
b.	24	19	7
c.	8.4	8.5	2.4

d. Marge will be selected since she is the most consistent and all three have the same average.

Exercise 9-3, pages 329-330

3.

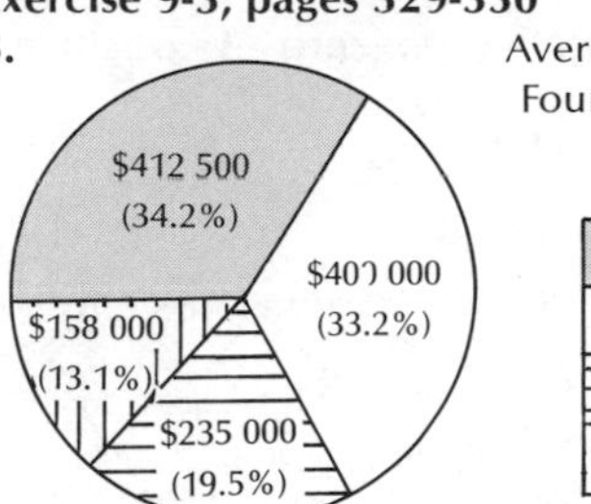

Average Annual Salary for Four Professional Sports (1988)

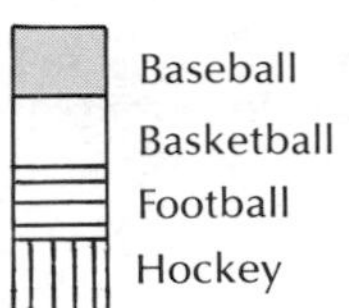

4.

Number of Empty Seats	
Stem	**Leaf**
0	0, 0, 3, 5, 6, 8, 8
1	0, 1, 1, 3, 5, 6, 8
2	2, 5
3	0, 1, 1, 2

6. a. 600 **b.** 600 **c.** 1650

7. a. 19 **b.** 27 **c.** 77.8% **d.** 48.1%

8. a.

Speed at curve (km/h)	
Stem	**Leaf**
3	7, 9
4	0, 6, 9, 9, 9
5	0, 4, 4, 6, 8
6	0, 1, 2, 2, 2, 2, 3, 5, 5, 8
7	1, 2, 2, 3, 3, 4, 4, 5, 5, 5, 6, 6, 6, 6, 7, 8, 8, 9
8	0, 0, 1, 1, 1, 2, 2, 2, 2, 2, 3, 3, 3, 3, 3, 3, 5, 5, 5, 6, 6, 6, 6, 6, 7, 7, 7, 7, 7, 8, 9, 9, 9
9	0, 0, 0, 0, 1, 1, 1, 2, 2, 3, 3, 4, 6, 6, 7, 7, 7, 8, 8, 9
10	0, 1, 3, 5, 6, 9
11	1

d. $Q_L = 73$ $Q_U = 90$ median = 82.5

e.

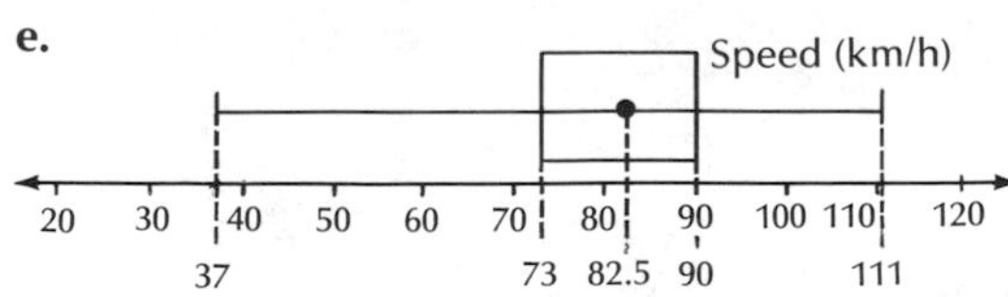

f. 50% of the cars are travelling between 73 km/h and 90 km/h inclusive.

9.

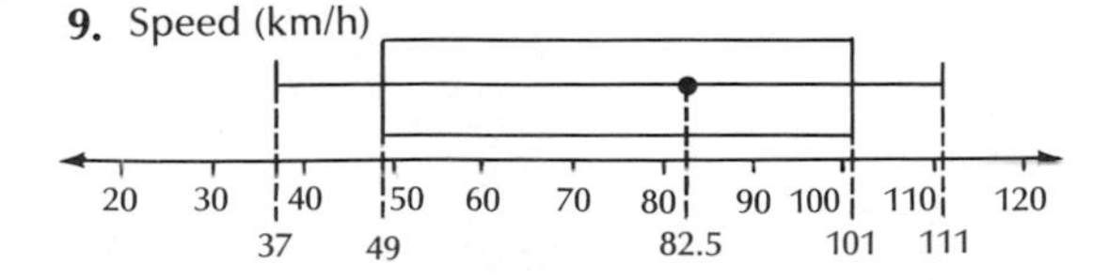

Review, page 331

1. a.

Number of Heads	Frequency
0	4
1	8
2	26
3	9
4	3

b. mean = 2, median = 2, mode = 2

c. mean = 1.98, median = 2, mode = 2

d. range = 4, mean deviation = 0.63, standard deviation = 0.95

f.

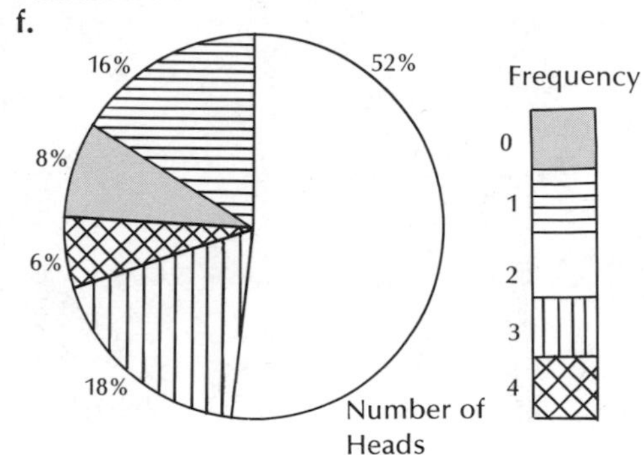

g. yes

2. a.

Number of Absences	
0	0, 0, 0, 0, 1, 1, 1, 2, 2, 3, 3, 3, 4, 5, 5, 5, 6, 7, 8, 8, 8
1	0, 1, 1, 2, 2, 3, 6
2	1, 5

b.

Absences	Frequency (f)	Cumulative Frequency	Midpoint (x)	Subtotal (fx)
0-4	13	13	2	26
5-9	8	21	7	56
10-14	6	27	12	72
15-19	1	28	17	17
20-24	1	29	22	22
25-29	1	30	27	27
	$n = 30$			$\Sigma fx = 220$

d. mean = 7.3
median = 7
mode = 2

e. range = 29
mean deviation = 4.8
standard deviation = 6.3

f. 90 **g.** $Q_L = 2$; $Q_u = 11$

h.

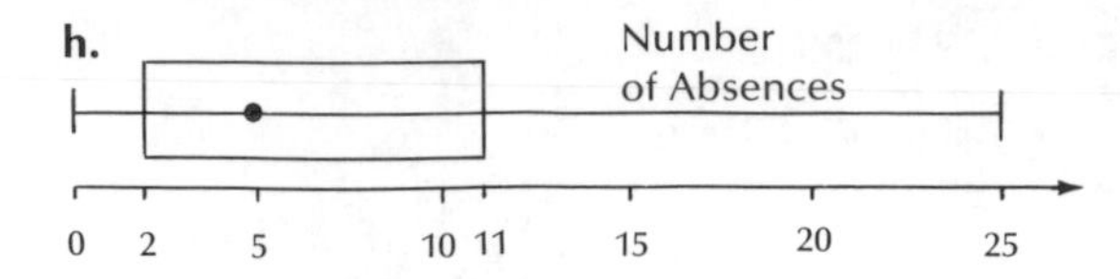

3. 0.297

4. a.

Period	Moving Average
Jan.-Mar.	692
Feb.-April	560
Mar.-May	372
April-June	205
May-July	128
June-Aug.	106
July-Sept.	98
Aug.-Oct.	184
Sept.-Nov.	360
Oct.-Dec.	562

b. c.

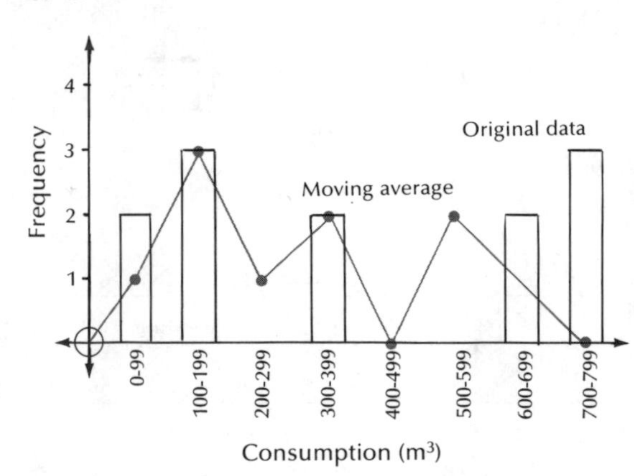

d. The moving average graph shows the consumption of gas over the year to be more consistent.

Exercise 9-4, page 333

1. d. In general, Math and Science grades have a positive correlation. Those with high Math grades have low Music grades. There doesn't appear to be a correlation between Math and English grades. **e.** 85 **2. c.** 7 minutes **d.** $y = x - 5$ **e.** 211 minutes. An 18-year-old would not play with a baby's toy. **3. c.** $y = 2^x$ **d.** 11.3 million **e.** $332 000

Exercise 9-5, page 337

1. a. positive **b.** positive **c.** zero **d.** negative **e.** positive **f.** positive **g.** negative **h.** zero **2. a.** positive **b.** negative **c.** zero **3.** positive **4.** curvilinear **5. b. i.** 70 **ii.** About 60

Exercise 9-6, page 341

1. c. $y = 0.72x - 52.75$ **d.** 79 kg **e.** 186 cm **2. c.** $y = 0.54x + 74.35$ **d.** 166 cm **e.** Answers will vary. **3. a.** $y = 0.92x + 5.79$ **b.** $y = -0.62x + 107.35$ **c.** Science = 75.71 Music = 60.23 **d.** Science = 51.79 Music = 76.35 **4. a.** $y = 0.81x - 1.33$ **b.** $900 **c.** 7 years old **5. a.** $y = -3.1x + 23.1$ **b.** 4.5¢ **c.** 5500 widgets. **6. c.** $y = -22.47x + 132.62$ **d.** 54 km/h

Exercise 9-7, page 344

1. yes

2. a.

Restaurant	Critic's Ranking	Price Ranking	d	d^2
A	3	1	−7	49
B	4	4	−3	9
C	7	7	3	9
D	10	10	9	81
E	1	2	−8	64
F	9	9	7	49
G	5	6	0	0
H	2	3	−6	36
I	8	8	5	25
J	6	5	0	0

b. $r_{rank} = 0.95$ **c.** The higher the price, the better the restaurant. **3. a.** $r_{rank} = 0.89$ **b.** The daughters' heights are very close to their mothers' heights.

4. a.

Rear axle gear ratio rank	Speedometer reading rank
2	2
3	1
1	3

b. $r_{rank} = -1$ **c.** There is a perfect negative correlation.

5. a.

Student	Math Rank	English Rank	Music Rank	Science Rank
A	5	6	9	5
B	12	5	2	12
C	2	9	10.5	2
D	7	11	6	7
E	10	10	4.5	10
F	8	3	10.5	9
G	6	2	4.5	6
H	4	7	7	4
I	3	1	8	3
J	1	8	12	1
K	9	12	3	8
L	11	4	1	11

b. i. $r_{rank} = 0.03$ **ii.** $r_{rank} = -0.81$ **iii.** $r_{rank} = 0.99$ **c.** There is no correlation between Math and English. The correlation between Math and Music is negative. There is almost perfect positive correlation between Math and Science.

Review, page 345

1. b. positive **d.** $y = \frac{1}{2}x + \frac{1}{2}$ **e.** 3 minutes **f.** 7 slices. **2. b.** negative **d.** $y = -0.67x + 3.28$ **e.** 0.6 h **f.**

Student	Rank of TV hours	Rank of Homework Hours
Ann	7	2
Warren	5	3
Beth	2	5
Clarence	4	6
Joel	2	7
Anthony	1	8
Janet	8	1
Karen	5	4

g. $r_{rank} = -0.93$ **h.** The correlation between homework hours and TV hours is almost perfectly negative.

Test, page 346

1. a.

Stem	Leaf
3	7 1 3 6 5 2 0 2
4	3 1 0 2 3 7 7
5	2 8 7 8 0 1 8 9 6 8
6	4 2 7 1

b. $Q_L = 37$; median score $= 47$; $Q_U = 58$

c.

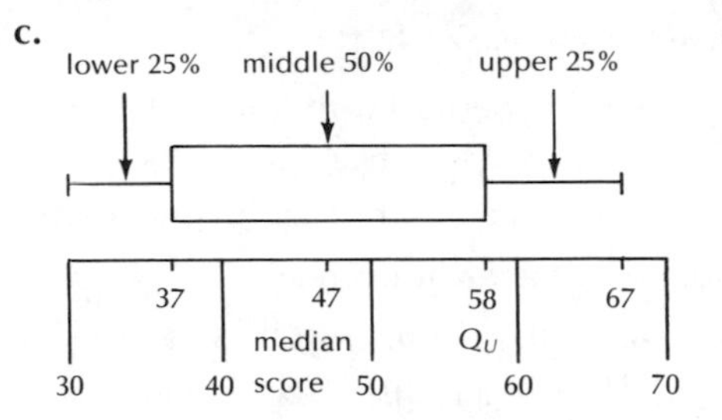

d. 37

e.

Number of Phone Calls	Frequency (f)	Midpoint of Interval (x)
30-39	9	34.5
40-49	7	44.5
50-59	10	54.5
60-69	4	64.5

Subtotal (fx)	Deviation (d)	d^2
310.5	−13	169
311.5	−3	9
545	7	49
258	17	289
1425		

g. mean = 47.5; median − 44.5; mode − 54.5; range = 39; mean deviation = 9.2; standard deviation = 10.39

h. Part **b** is the exact median, and part **g** is the approximate median.

2. b. positive **d.** $y = 13.42x - 367.47$ **e.** \$303.53 **f.** 72 calls **g.** between 53 and 80 calls per evening.

h.

Employee	Rank of Calls	Rank of Sales
Paul	8	9
Gale	6	6
Carl	7	7
Marsha	2	1
Nicole	1	2
Danny	3	3
Steve	10	10
Jennifer	9	8
Marla	3	4
Sheila	5	5

$r_{rank} = 0.97$ **i.** There is almost perfect positive correlation between the number of calls made and the amount of sales generated.

j. 132 minutes, \$7.90

Cumulative Review, page 347

1. $y = \frac{9}{2 - x}$ is a hyperbola with horizontal asymptote $x = 2$, vertical asymptote $y = 0$.
2. a. It increases by a factor of 2. **b.** It increases by a factor of $\frac{1}{2}$. (It actually decreases.)
3. $17 920 **4. a.** 0.8455 **b.** 0.5109 **5. a.** 64 **b.** 8 **6.** $k = \frac{10}{3}$ **7.** 3.49 rad/s
9. $x^2 + 16y^2 - 4x + 32y = 0$
10. circle with radius $r = 6$ that intersects hyperbola at $V_1\,(6,0)$ and $V_2\,(-6,0)$.
11. vertex (minimum point): $V(-2, 5)$, focus : $F(-2, 11)$, directrix : $y = -1$. **12.** 8.6 min

UNIT 10

Exercise 10-1, pages 351-353

1. Point: a single position in space which has no magnitude.
Line: a one-dimensional set of points.
Plane: a two-dimensional set of all points which can be formed by any three points or by any two distinct lines on the plane.
Space: a point, a line, a plane, or a set of planes. It can have any dimension.
3. a. This definition doesn't distinguish a circle from a sphere.
b. This doesn't distinguish the altitude from the angle bisector or the median of a triangle.
c. This definition doesn't place the figure in a known set.
d. This definition doesn't distinguish a square from a rhombus.
e. This definition doesn't place the object in a known set.
4. i. perpendicular bisector **ii.** reflex angle **iii.** perpendicular to a line **iv.** straight angle **v.** obtuse angle **vi.** acute angle **vii.** bisector of an angle
5. b. i. The midpoint of a side is the point on the side which is equidistant from each endpoint of the side.
ii. A line that joins a vertex to the midpoint of the opposite side is a median.
iii. The bisector of an angle is the line that divides an angle into two equal angles.
iv. An altitude is a line that joins a vertex to the opposite side, meeting the side at a right angle.
v. The perpendicular bisector of a side is a line that passes through the midpoint of the side, forming a 90° angle.

6. a. $\angle ACB$, $\angle BCG$; $\angle BCG$, $\angle GCE$; $\angle GCE$, $\angle ECD$; $\angle ECD$, $\angle DCA$
b. $\angle ACB$, $\angle DCE$; $\angle ACD$, $\angle BCE$
c. $\angle ACB$, $\angle BCE$; $\angle BCE$, $\angle ECD$; $\angle ECD$, $\angle DCA$; $\angle DCA$, $\angle ACB$ **d.** $\angle ACB$, $\angle BCG$
e. $\angle ACD$, $\angle BCE$
f. $\angle ACD$ (through point G), $\angle BCE$ (through point A) **g.** $\overline{CG}$, $\overline{AE}$ **h.** $\angle BCE$ or $\angle ACD$
i. A, C, F, E
7. a. triangle **b.** quadrilateral **c.** pentagon **d.** hexagon **e.** heptagon **f.** octagon **g.** nonogon **h.** decagon **8.** 45° **9.** 22.5°
10. 50° **11. a.** C, I, J **b.** L **c.** A **d.** $\overline{DB}$
e. $\overline{CD}$ **f.** the plane containing D, F, G, K, B
g. planes containing A, I, C, D, B, J; C, D, F, E, L; E, F, G, H; and A, J, B, K, G, H
12. figure $ABCD$ is a square
13. a. $AC = 12$ **b.** $AD = 6$ **c.** 20 **d.** 14
14. Let 2θ be the obtuse angle.
$$90° < 2\theta < 180°$$
$$\therefore 45° < \theta < 90°$$
15. Let 2θ be the reflex angle.
$$180° < 2\theta < 360°$$
$$\therefore 90° < \theta < 180°$$
$\therefore$ Two obtuse angles are formed.
16. a. false: Parallel planes do not intersect.
b. false: Intersecting planes may form a line.
c. false: A line on the plane intersects the plane in a line.
d. false: Two lines might not intersect (parallel), or they may intersect in a line (collinear).
e. false: If the points are the same they define a point; if they are collinear, they determine a line.
f. true **g.** true
h. false: They may be collinear.
17. AB bisects $\angle DBF$ and BC bisects $\angle FBE$.
$\angle DBF + \angle FBE = 180°$
$\angle ABF + \angle FBC = \frac{180°}{2}$; $\therefore \angle ABC = 90°$

Exercise 10-2, pages 355-357

1. a. If two sides of a parallelogram are opposite, then they are equal in length.
b. If a person is eighteen years of age or older, he can vote.
c. If two angles are supplementary, then their sum is 180°.
d. If a triangle is equilateral, then it has three equal angles.
e. If the temperature of water is 100°C, it will boil.
2. a. not necessarily true. **b.** not true **c.** not true **d.** not true **e.** true **f.** not true **g.** not true **h.** not true

3. e. A number ends in 0 or 5 if, and only if, it is divisible by 5.
4. a. The cost increase may be due to another factor such as insurance or maintenance.
b. The last statement is true, but it does not follow only from the first two statements.
c. Steve plays an instrument, but he may not play a saxophone.
d. Mr. Forest may be going to Vancouver on another train. Therefore, he would not need reservations on this train.
5. a. true **b.** true **c.** false **d.** true **e.** false **f.** true **g.** true **h.** false **i.** false **j.** true
6. b. Greg will be the quarter back.
e. Quadrilateral $ABCD$ is cyclic.
g. Angles P and Q are equal.
h. C is on the perpendicular bisector of $\overline{AB}$.
7. a. 0 **b.** 2 **c.** any real number divided by 0 **d.** rhombus **e.** $n = 10, 11$
8. a. $\frac{1}{1} + \frac{1}{2} \neq \frac{1}{3}$ **b.** $\frac{1}{1} + \frac{1}{2} \neq \frac{2}{3}$
c. $\frac{1}{2} \times \frac{3}{4} \neq \frac{4}{6}$ **d.** $\sqrt{3^2 + 4^2} \neq 7$
e. $\frac{2}{2+3} \neq \frac{1}{3}$ **f.** $\sqrt{-(-1)}$ is defined.
9. a. yes **b.** no **c.** yes **d.** yes

Application, page 358

p	q	Series Circuit	Parallel Circuit
T	T	T	T
T	F	F	T
F	T	F	T
F	F	F	F

p	T	T	F	F
q	T	F	T	F
$\sim p$	F	F	T	T
$\sim p$ and q	F	F	T	F
p and q	T	F	F	F
($\sim p$ and q) or (p and q)	T	F	T	F

Exercise 10-3, pages 360-361
1. a. $\angle A \neq \angle B$ **b.** $18 - x \leq 12$
c. $\angle\ PQR$ is not an acute angle.
d. $6 - 3x = 15$ **2. a.** $\angle\ ABC$ is not a right angle. **b.** $\triangle XYZ$ is not isosceles. **c.** It is not raining outside. **d.** T is not the midpoint of $\overline{RS}$.
3. No. $a = b$ is also a possibility. **4.** No. He must prove m and n do not intersect. **5.** $a = b$
6. a. Let $a = 2n + 1, n \in \mathbf{Z}$
Assume a^2 is even.
$a^2 = (2n + 1)^2$
$= 2(2n^2 + 2n) + 1$
Not even.
b. Assume $\sqrt{10} = 3$.
$\therefore 10 = 9$
Contradiction
7. $2n + 1$ = odd number of quarters;
d = number of dimes; $d, n \in \mathbf{Z}$
$10d + 25(2n + 1) = 340$
$d = \frac{157.5 - 25n}{5} \notin \mathbf{Z}$ and $n = \frac{157.5 - 5d}{25} \notin \mathbf{Z}$
Contradiction
8. Let $ABCD$ be a quadrilateral.
Assume $\angle A = \angle B = \angle C = 120°$. $\therefore \angle D = 0°$
This implies ABC is a triangle.
Contradiction
9. Assume $x = 2n + 1$,
$n \in \mathbf{Z}$
Then $5(2n + 1) + 6y = 142$
$5n + 3y = 68.5$
But $n, y \in \mathbf{Z}$, $5n + 3y \in \mathbf{Z}$
$\therefore 68.5 \in \mathbf{Z}$
Contradiction
10. Let $x = 2k$; $k, y \in \mathbf{Z}$
Assume $5x + 6y = 2n + 1, n \in \mathbf{Z}$
Implies $5k + 3y - n = \frac{1}{2}$.
But $k, y, n \in \mathbf{Z}$,
so $(5k + 3y - n) \in \mathbf{Z}$.
Contradiction.

Exercise 10-4, pages 365-367
1. a. A triangle is isosceles if the angles opposite the equal sides are equal. The angles opposite the equal sides are equal if the triangle is isosceles.
b. A point is on the perpendicular bisector of a line segment if it is equidistant from the end points of the segment. A point is equidistant from the end points of a line segment if it is on the perpendicular bisector.
c. A point is on the bisector of an angle if it is equidistant from the arms of the angle. A point is equidistant from the arms of an angle if it is on the bisector of the angle.
2. a. ASA **b.** SSS **c.** SAS **d.** SAS **e.** SSS **f.** not congruent **g.** HST **h.** HST **i.** not congruent **3. a.** $x = 25°, y = 100°, z = 17°$
b. $x = 58°, y = 64°, z = 24.4°$
c. $x = 14°, y = 14.4°$
4. Use ITT, subtraction, and substitution.
5. Use common side PR and SSS to prove $\triangle PQR = \triangle PSR$.
6. Show $\triangle AEB \cong \triangle AED$ and $\triangle BEC \cong \triangle DEC$ by SAS.

7. Show $\triangle ABD \cong \triangle CBD$ by SAS, then use the results to show $DB \perp AC$.
8. Show both P and R are on the perpendicular bisector of $\overline{QS}$ by PBT.
9. Construct: $\overline{DG} \perp \overline{AB}$, $\overline{DF} \perp \overline{AC}$, $\overline{DE} \perp \overline{BC}$. Then show $\triangle BDG \cong \triangle BDE$ and $\triangle CDE \cong \triangle CDF$ by AAS.
10. Construct D at the intersection of the perpendicular bisectors of $\overline{AB}$ and $\overline{AC}$. Then use PBT to prove.
11. Show $\triangle QPS \cong \triangle RSP$ by SAS; then use the results, ITT, and substitution to prove.
12. Construct: diagonals $\overline{BD}$, $\overline{CA}$. By PBT, there can only be one perpendicular bisector for $\overline{BD}$ and for $\overline{AC}$.
13. a. Use AST to show DAF, FCE, and EBD are straight edges.
b. Use the properties of an equilateral triangle, SAS, and transitivity to prove.
14. a. Prove $\triangle NBM \cong \triangle PMC$ by ASA.
b. Use the results of **a**, subtraction and ITT to prove.
15. Prove $\triangle XYZ$ is isosceles using OAT, substitution, subtraction, and SAS to show $\triangle SWY \cong \triangle TWZ$. Then use ITT, addition, and substitution.
Prove $\overline{XW}$ is a median of $\triangle XYZ$ by constructing $\overline{XA}$, the perpendicular bisector of $\overline{YZ}$, and show $W = A$.

Exercise 10-5, pages 370-371
1. a. largest: $\angle A$, smallest: $\angle B$
b. largest: $\angle E$, smallest: $\angle F$
c. largest: $\angle M$, smallest: $\angle L$
2. a. $\overline{AC}, \overline{BC}, \overline{AB}$ **b.** $\overline{YZ}, \overline{XY}, \overline{XZ}$ **c.** $\overline{EF}, \overline{DF}, \overline{DE}$
3. a. yes **b.** no **c.** yes **d.** no **e.** yes
4. 5 cm, 5 cm, 6 cm; 6 cm, 6 cm, 4 cm; 7 cm, 7 cm, 2 cm
5. Assume $AB = AC$. Use ITT to show a contradiction.
6. Assume $XY = XZ$. Use PBT to show a contradiction.
7. Assume $BD = DC$. Use PBT to show a contradiction.
8. Prove indirectly. Assume $\angle YWZ = 90°$. Use AST and substitution to show $\angle YXZ = 0°$. Contradiction.
9. Assume: $AE = EC$ and $DE = EB$. Use OAT, SAS, and the properties of congruent triangles to show the contradiction $\overline{AD} \parallel \overline{BC}$.
10. Use the triangle inequality, addition, and substitution to prove.
11. Let $\overline{PT}$ be a segment joining P to the opposite side at any angle $\angle PTR$. Use AST, subtraction, and the triangle inequality to prove.
12. Show that $\angle ABC \neq \angle DEF$ and $\angle ABC \not< \angle DEF$, by using SAS, congruent triangles, and triangle inequality.

Exercise 10-6, pages 375-376
1. a. corresponding **b.** alternate **c.** alternate
d. corresponding **e.** alternate **f.** none
g. none **h.** interior
2. $\angle 1 = \angle 3 = \angle 6 = \angle 8 = \angle 9 = \angle 11 = \angle 14 = \angle 16 = 125°$
$\angle 2 = \angle 4 = \angle 5 = \angle 7 = \angle 10 = \angle 12 = \angle 13 = \angle 15 = 55°$
3. a. $w = 75°, x = 75°, y = 30°, z = 75°$
b. $x = 85°, y = 95°, z = 85°$
c. $w = 25°, x = 70°, y = 110°, z = 25°$
d. $x = 66°, y = 24°$ **e.** $x = 35°, y = 35°$
f. $x = 50°, y = 50°$
4. Use OAT, ITT, and the properties of a straight angle.
5. Prove by PLT, substitution, and ITT.
6. Construct: $\overline{EF} \parallel \overline{CD}$. Use ITT, AST, the properties of a straight angle, and PLT: alternate angles to prove.
7. a. 360° **b.** 540° **c.** 720° **d.** 1440°
e. $(n - 2)180°, n \in \mathbf{N}$ **8. a.** 360°, 360°, 360°, 360°
b. For an n-gon:
Sum of interior angles $= (n - 2)180°$
Sum of exterior angles $= 180°n - (n - 2)180° = 360°$
9. a. 8 **b.** 13 **c.** 23 **d.** 27
10. a. angle sum of a regular n-gon $= 180°(n - 2)$
number of angles $=$ number of sides $= n$
All angles are equal in a regular n-gon.
b. 108°, 135°, 172.8° **c.** 15

Exercise 10-7, pages 378-380
1. a, c, d, e, f
2. a. Prove $\angle XYZ \cong \angle ZWX$ by PLT: alternate angles and ASA.
b. Use the proof from part **a**, addition, and substitution.
c. Use PLT: alternate angles and ASA to show $\triangle XWV \cong \triangle ZYV$.
3. Show each of P and R are on the perpendicular bisector of $\overline{QS}$.
4. Show $\triangle PQS = \triangle SQR$ by ITT, PLT: alternate angles, and substitution.
5. Show $\angle EDC + \angle ECD = 90°$ by PLT: interior angles, division, and substitution. Then use AST.
6. Show $\triangle XAW \cong \triangle ZBY$ by PLT and SAS. Then show $\angle WAZ = \angle YBX$ by subtraction from a straight angle.
7. a. Use SSS to show $\triangle ABC \cong \triangle CDA$. Use the results and PLT to show $\overline{AB} \parallel \overline{DC}$ and $\overline{AD} \parallel \overline{BC}$.
b. Show $\triangle ABE \cong \triangle CDE$ and $\triangle AED \cong \triangle CEB$ by OAT and SAS.

c. Use the fact the sum of interior angles of a quadrilateral is 360°, then substitution, division, and PLT: interior angles to show $\overline{AB} \parallel \overline{DC}$ and $\overline{AD} \parallel \overline{BC}$.
8. Show $\triangle AED \cong \triangle CEB$ by PLT and ASA, then show $\triangle EDC \cong \triangle EBC$ by SSS.
9. a. $AC = 10$; $BD = 24$ **b.** 5 **c.** 7
10. Construct extensions of $\overline{AD}$, $\overline{BC}$ to meet at E. Show $\triangle EDC$ is isosceles by supplementary angles such that $ED = EC$. Then, show $\triangle EDC \sim \triangle EAB$.
11. Show $\triangle ABD \cong \triangle CBD$ by AAS and a $AGD \cong \triangle CGD$ by SAS. Then use PLT: alternate angles and substitution.
12. Show $APCR$ and $SDQB$ are parallelograms by SAS and use the results to show $\overline{XY} \parallel \overline{WZ}$ and $\overline{XW} \parallel \overline{YZ}$.
13. Construct $\overline{CB} \parallel \overline{QA}$. Show $CBAQ$ is a parallelogram and then use PLT, substitution, and AAS to show $\triangle PAB \cong \triangle BCR$.
14. Prove $\triangle AXY \cong \triangle CZY$ by OAT, PLT, and ASA. Then use the results and POP to show $2XY = BC$.
15. Use the results of exercise 14 to show $2FE = BC$ and $2XY = BC$. Then use OAT, PLT, and AAS to show $\triangle FGE \cong \triangle YGX$. Show $FC = FG + GY + YC$ and use $FG = GY = YC$.

Exercise 10-8, pages 382-383
1. a. $T'(0, 1)$ **b.** $R'(-6, 9)$ **c.** $U'(1, -2)$
d. $S'(-4, -6)$ **e.** $W'(-5, -2)$ **2.** $(9, -5)$
4. Use the definition of a translation to show $AH = DG$.
5. Show $A \to D$ and $H \to G$. A translation is an isometry.
6. Let $P \to Q$, $S \to R$, $T \to U$ under a given translation. Show $\triangle QUR$ is the image of $\triangle PTS$ by POP.
7. Show $XZ = YW$ by definition of a translation. Use substitution to show $ZW = XY$, and show $\overline{ZP} \parallel \overline{WQ}$ by definition of a translation.
8. Use the definition of a translation to prove $\overline{CD}$ is the image of $\overline{BA}$. Then use PLT and ASA to show $\triangle ABD \cong \triangle CDB$.
9. Show $M \to N$ and $P \to S$.
10. a. Show each is a line segment by showing A, P, C and A, M, B and B, N, C are each collinear points.
b. Show $MB = PN$ and $MP = BN$.
c. Use the definition of a translation.
d. Show $MP = BN = NC$ and $BC = BN + NC$.
e. Show $\triangle NPM \cong \triangle AMP \cong \triangle MBN \cong \triangle PNC$ by SSS and use addition to prove.

Exercise 10-9, pages 385-386
2. a. $P'(4, -3)$ **b.** $P'(-4, 3)$ **c.** $P'(3, 4)$
d. $P'(-3, -4)$ **3. a.** $P'(a, -b)$ **b.** $P'(-a, b)$
c. $P'(b, a)$ **d.** $P'(-b, -a)$
4. Construct $\overline{AB} \parallel l$. Label the point of intersection as D. Then use ASA to show $\triangle ADC \cong \triangle BDC$. Show $A \to B$, $D \to D$, and thus $n \to m$ under reflection in l.
5. Let $\overline{AB}$ be any diameter of a circle with centre C. Then construct $\overline{DE} \perp \overline{AB}$, through a point F on $\overline{AB}$. Show $\triangle CFE \cong \triangle CFD$ by HST, and use the properties of a reflection to prove.
6. One circle is the image of the other under a reflection. $\overline{PQ}$ is the line of reflection. Show $\overline{AQ} \to \overline{BQ}$.
7. Use PBT and the fact $PX = PY = r$.
8. $ABCD$ must be a rhombus.
9. a. Given, $\overline{AB} \to \overline{A'B'}$ show $P' = P$. Then show the perpendicular distance from P to l is 0.
b. Show l is the perpendicular bisector of $\overline{AA'}$ by definition of a reflection. Then use SSS and $\angle APC = \angle A'PC$ to show l bisects $\angle APA'$.
10. Use SAS and PBT to show $\overline{BD}$ is the perpendicular bisector of $\overline{AC}$. Then show $\overline{AB} \to \overline{CB}$ under reflection in $\overline{BD}$.
11. Extend $\overline{BA}$ and $\overline{CD}$ to intersect at point E. Construct median $\overline{EF}$. Show $\overline{EF}$ is the perpendicular bisector of $\overline{BC}$ and show $\triangle EAD \sim \triangle EBC$. Conclude $\angle BAG \to \angle CDG$ so $\angle BAD = \angle BAG = \angle CDG = \angle CDA$.

Application, page 387
1. d. If a mirror was placed along the edge of the table where the ball is cushioned, the image of the ball in the mirror continues along the straight path it was originally making.
2. d. Place mirrors along the two edges the ball is to bounce against. View the reflection of the first mirror's image in the second mirror. The ball seems to continue on its original course after hitting the second cushion.
3. d. Several possibilities

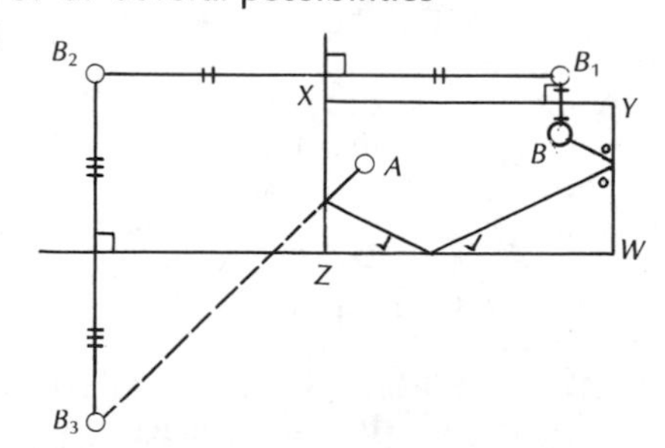

Exercise 10-10, pages 390-391
2. a. negative half-turn about O
b. negative three-quarter turn about O.
c. 315° about O **d.** $-210°$ about O

3. a. $A'(-3, 2)$, $B'(1, 4)$, $C'(0, 5)$, $D'(3, 6)$
b. $A'(-2, -3)$, $B'(-4, 1)$, $C'(-5, 0)$, $D'(-6, 3)$
c. $A'(3, -2)$, $B'(-1, -4)$, $C'(0, -5)$, $D'(-3, -6)$
d. $A'(-3, 2)$, $B'(1, 4)$, $C'(0, 5)$, $D'(3, 6)$
4. a. $(-a, -b)$ **b.** $(-b, a)$
5. Construct a circle with centre C and two equal sector angles $\angle ACB = \angle ECD$. Use the properties of a rotation to show $\overline{AB} \to \overline{ED}$.
6. Prove $\overline{AD} \to \overline{CB}$ and $\overline{AB} \to \overline{CD}$.
7. Use the fact the sum of angles of a quadrilateral is 360° and show $\angle PQP' = 180° - \theta$.
8. a. $+30°$ rotation **b.** Under a $+30°$ rotation, $\overline{BD} \to \overline{CE}$. $\therefore BD = CE$ **c.** 30°
9. Show $\triangle PRT \equiv \triangle QST$ by SSS. Then show $\overline{PR} \to \overline{QS}$ under a 180° rotation.
10. Show $\triangle XUZ \cong \triangle WVZ$ by PLT, OAT, and ASA Use the results and properties of a half-turn.
11. a. $\triangle DCG$ **b.** Use the results of part **a** to show $\triangle BCE \cong \triangle DCB$. **c.** Use part **a** to show $\overline{BE} \to \overline{DG}$.
12. b. $C(4.5, 4.5)$ **c.** 90°

Review, pages 392–393

1. a. Congruent lines are lines that pass through a common point.
b. A median of a triangle is a line that extends from a vertex to the opposite side, bisecting that side.
c. A trapezoid is a quadrilateral with two parallel sides.
d. Supplementary angles are two angles whose measures add to 180°.
2. a. If the angles opposite the equal sides are equal, the triangle is isosceles. True.
b. If $x^2 = 36$, then $x = 6$. Not true **3. a.** yes
b. no
4. Show $\triangle ACE \cong \triangle DBC$ by supplementary angles and SAS.

5. a. Construct the altitude $\overline{AD}$ to the unequal third side $\overline{BC}$ of an isosceles triangle. Show $\triangle ADB \cong \triangle ADC$ by HST and use reflection properties to show.
Prove that if $\triangle ABC$ is isosceles with $AB = AC$, then $\angle ABC = \angle ACB$ by constructing altitude $\overline{AD}$ to $\overline{BC}$ and by showing $\triangle ADB \cong \triangle ADC$.
b. Prove that if $\triangle ABC$ is isosceles such that $\angle ABC = \angle ACB$ then $AB = AC$ by constructing altitude $\overline{AD}$ to $\overline{BC}$ and by using AAS and reflection properties.
6. Show $\angle PZW = \angle XZP$ and $\angle PZW = YXZ$ by ITT, PLT, and substitution. Then use angle addition.
7. Construct $\overline{AE}$ and $\overline{DF}$ each perpendicular to $\overline{BC}$. Use PLT: interior angles to show $AEFD$ is a parallelogram and then use HST and congruent angles.

8. a. Assume x is even. Show that L.S. is even and R.S. is odd.
b. Let: number of triangles $= x$, number of squares $= y$; $x, y \in \mathbf{Z}$. Assume $y = 2n$, $n \in \mathbf{Z}$. Show this implies $937.5 \in \mathbf{Z}$.
9. Use half-turn rotations to show $XW = ZY$ and $XY = ZW$.
10. a. Assume $XZ = WZ$, and show indirectly that $\angle WYX = 0°$. Contradiction. Then assume $XZ < WZ$ and use an indirect proof to show $\angle WYX < 0°$. Contradiction.
b. Use the same method as part **a**. That is, show $XY \not< YW$ and $XY \neq YW$.
c. Use the results of parts **a** and **b** and addition.
11. Use ITT and AST to show $\angle AOB = 2\angle OAB$ and $\angle COD = 2\angle OCD$. Then use common angle $\angle O$, substitution, and PLT.
12. Use the triangle inequality theorem and the transitive property.
13. Use the law of cosines and $PZ = WY$ to show $PY^2 > WZ^2$ so $PY > WZ$.
14. a. Show $\triangle EAB \cong \triangle CBA$ by PLT, ITT, addition, and SAS.
b. Use the results of part **a**, ITT, OAT, and AST to show $\angle XEC = \angle XBA = 90° - \frac{1}{2}\angle EXC$. Then use PLT: alternate angles.

Test, page 394

1. b. Yes. **2. a.** $x = 65°$, $y = 45°$, $z = 50°$
b. $w = 125°$, $x = 55°$, $y = 53°$, $z = 53°$
c. $x = 69°$, $y = 69°$, $z = 55.5°$
3. Assume $\angle A = \angle B$, and prove indirectly with ITT. **4. a.** Wendy is at least 16 years old.
b. no conclusion **c.** no conclusion
d. Neil is not in 12C.
5. Use the triangle inequality and subtraction.
6. Use POP, substitution, and PLT to show $STQU$ is a parallelogram.
7. Assume $WZ \neq WY$ and $WZ \neq WX$. Construct $\overline{WQ}$ to $\overline{YZ}$ with $WQ = WY$ and $\overline{WP}$ to $\overline{XZ}$ with $WP = WX$. Show $\triangle PWX$ and $\triangle QWY$ are isosceles such that $XW = PW = QW = YW$ and then show that $\overline{PW}$, $\overline{ZW}$ and $\overline{QW}$ are the same line.
8. Show this is true by an indirect proof. Assume the bisectors of two angles are perpendicular. Use OAT, AST, and supplementary angles to show the third angle must measure 0°, a contradiction.
9. Construct $\overline{CF} \parallel \overline{BO}$. Show $\triangle AED \cong \triangle CEF$ and $CFDB$ is a parallelogram. Use POP and the results of the congruent triangles to show $BC = 2DE$.

Cumulative Review, page 395

1. $(x - 2)^2 + (y + 3)^2 = 5$ **2.** 0.044 g **3. a.** 9

b. $\frac{1}{8}$ **4.** \$4776.21 **5. a.** -2 **b.** 12
6. $(x + 3)(x + 4)$
7. $y^5 + 4y^4 + 2y^2 + 4$
$= (y + 4)(y^4 + 2y - 8) + 36$
8. a. $\sin \theta = -\frac{15}{17}$; $\cos \theta = \frac{8}{17}$
9. 3191 m **10.** $\frac{35}{5}\pi$ cm
11. a. period $= \frac{2\pi}{3}$; amplitude $= 2$

UNIT 11

Exercise 11-1, pages 398-399

1. a. false Two isosceles triangles are similar when the contained angles between the pairs of equal sides are equal. **b.** true **c.** false **d.** false **e.** true **2. a.** $\angle P = \angle I, \angle Q = \angle J, \angle R = \angle K, \frac{PQ}{IJ} = \frac{QR}{JK} = \frac{PR}{IK}$ **b.** $\angle P = \angle J, \angle Q = \angle K, \angle R = \angle L, \angle S = \angle M, \frac{PQ}{JK} = \frac{QR}{KL} = \frac{RS}{LM} = \frac{PS}{JM}$
3. a. The angles may be different.
b. Squares are not similar to rectangles.
4. $\overline{QR} = 7.5, \overline{ST} = 8.64$ **5.** $\angle ABC = 80°, \angle BAC = 65°, \angle YXZ = 65°$ **6. a.** $x = 3.6, y = 3.4$ **b.** $x = 25.6, y = 25$ **c.** $x = 9, y = 22.5$
7. $AM = 10, AB = 20$ **8.** The triangles are similar with scale factor 1 : 2. **9.** 12 cm
10. $\frac{x}{y} = \frac{ky}{x}$; $\therefore x = \sqrt{ky}$. Since x and y are integers, $\sqrt{k}$ must be an integer. Thus k is a perfect square.

Application, page 399

1. a. 6 m × 4.5 m **b.** 7.1 m **c.** 1.5 m × 1 m
2. a. 0.9 cm by 1.2 cm **b.** 0.8 cm wide
c. 1.22 cm wide

Exercise 11-2, pages 401-402

1. a. Proved by PLT and AA~. $\frac{WV}{XY} = \frac{VZ}{YZ} = \frac{WZ}{XZ}$
b. Proved by a common angle and AA~. $\frac{AB}{DB} = \frac{BC}{BE} = \frac{AC}{DE}$ **c.** Proved by a common angle and AA~. $\frac{XY}{TX} = \frac{YZ}{TZ} = \frac{XZ}{TZ}$
d. Proved by AST, substitution and AA~. $\frac{DE}{MN} = \frac{EF}{NO} = \frac{DF}{MO}$
2. a. $x = 9, y = 10, z = 15, q = 6$ **b.** $a = \frac{21}{11}$
c. $x = 2.5, y = 12.5$, **d.** $x = 7.5, y = 10$
e. $x = 10, y = 7.5$ **f.** $x = 11, y = 17.5$
3. Proof by PLT, OAT, and AA~.
4. Proof by common angles, AA~, AAA~, supplementary angles, and substitution.
5. Proof by AAA~ and AA~. **6.** 24 m
7. Show *XYZC* is a parallelogram. Then show *XZYB* is a parallelogram. Proof by AA~.
8. a. Proof by PLT, common angles, and AA~.
b. $\frac{MN}{QR} = \frac{1}{2}$ **9. a.** Proof by common angles and AA~. **b.** Proof by common angles and AA~.
c. Proof from **a** and **b** and substitution.

Extra, page 403

2. $(4\sqrt{5} - 4)$ cm **3.** $\frac{l}{w} = \frac{1 + \sqrt{5}}{2}$ **4.** $x = \frac{1 + \sqrt{5}}{2}$
5. a. 1.618 **b.** 2.618 **c.** 0.618 **d.** -0.618

Exercise 11-3, pages 405-406

1. a. ± 6 **b.** ± 10 **c.** $\pm 6\sqrt{2}$ **d.** $\pm 4a\sqrt{6}$
e. $\pm 5\sqrt{13}$ **f.** $\pm 16x^2$ **g.** $\pm a(a + b)$ **h.** ± 6
2. 45 **3.** $x = 10$ **4.** part **a.**
5. a. $(2ab)^2 + (a^2 - b^2)^2 = a^4 + 2a^2b^2 + b^4;$
$= (a^2 + b)^2$
b. $\{3, 4, 5\}; \{6, 8, 10\}; \{8, 15, 17\}; \{10, 24, 26\}; \{12, 35, 37\}; \{14, 48, 50\}$ **6. a.** $x = 6; y = 2\sqrt{13}; z = 3\sqrt{13}$ **b.** $x = \sqrt{2}; y = \sqrt{3}; z = 2$
c. $x = 3$ **6. d.** $x = 16; y = 8\sqrt{5}; z = 4\sqrt{5}$
e. $x = 12$ **f.** $h = 24$ **g.** $x = 4; y = 5\sqrt{21}$
h. $x = 9; y = 16; z = 12$ **7. a.** Use common angles, AA~, and AAA~. **b.** Use the same method as part **a.** **8.** Use PT, addition, and substitution. **9.** Use a common angle, AA~, AAA~, and substitution to show $\frac{BD}{AD} = \frac{AE}{CB}$.
10. Use MPT to show $\frac{(XY)^2}{(XW)^2} = \frac{(YZ)(YW)}{(YW)(WZ)}$.

Extra, page 407

1. Use MPT and substitution.
2. a. Use MPT to show $(BD)(DC) = 10$.

Exercise 11-4, pages 410-411

1. a. $x = 4.8$ **b.** $x = 6$ **c.** $x = 3$ **d.** $x = 6.25$
2. a. $\overline{DF} \parallel \overline{AC}$ by PPT; $\overline{EF} \parallel \overline{AB}$ by PPT **b.** $\overline{QV} \parallel \overline{RS}$; $\overline{VU} \parallel \overline{ST}$; Show $\Delta RST \sim \Delta QVU$, and show $\frac{PQ}{PR} = \frac{PU}{UT}$ to prove $\overline{RT} \parallel \overline{QU}$. **3.** Use PPT and substitution.
4. Use PPT, PLT: corresponding angles, PLT: alternate angles, and AA~. **5.** Use PPT to show $PN : NR = PL : LQ$ and $PL : LQ = MR : MQ$.
6. Use PLT: corresponding and alternate angles, substitution, ITT, and PPT. **7.** Construct $\overline{AF}$ and $\overline{DG}$ each perpendicular to $\overline{BC}$. Use PPT and POP to show *AHJD* and *HJFG* are parallelograms. Then, use POP and substitution.

8. Assume $\overline{XY}$ is not parallel to $\overline{DC}$, and prove indirectly by using the proof of exercise 7 and substitution. **9.** Use PPT and substitution. **10.** Use PPT and substitution to show $FLME$ is a parallelogram. Then use POP, OAT, PLT, AAS, and AAA ~. **11.** Use PLT, substitution, ITT, and PPT.

Extra, page 411

1. $AC : CG = XM : MY$ by PPT **2.** On $\overline{XZ}$, mark 5 equal segments. Construct $\overline{EY}$. Construct $\overline{BM}$ parallel to $\overline{EY}$, where M is on $\overline{XY}$ · **3.** On $\overline{XZ}$, mark 8 equal segments, Construct $\overline{HY}$. Construct $\overline{AM}$ and $\overline{DN}$ each parallel to $\overline{HY}$, where M and N are on $\overline{XY}$.

Exercise 11-5, page 414

1. a. Prove $EG : ED = EH : EF$ and use a common angle and SAS. **b.** Prove using OAT and SAS ~. **c.** Prove showing $PQ : US = QR : ST$ and use SAS ~. **2.** Use OAT, SAS ~, AAA ~, and PLT: alternate angles. **3.** Use a common angle, SAS ~, and AAA ~. **4.** $EC = \frac{32}{3}$; $DE = 10$; $BC = \frac{70}{3}$ **5.** Show $\overline{DE} \parallel \overline{BC}$ and use PLT: alternate angles, OAT, and AA ~. **6.** Use SAS ~, AAA ~, a common side, and POP to prove $ABCD$ is a parallelogram. **7.** Use common $\angle B$, AA ~, and AAA ~.

Review, page 415

1. a. Use common $\angle A$ and AA ~.
b. Use OAT and AA ~. **2.** Use common $\angle B$ and AA ~ to show $\frac{DB}{CB} = \frac{DE}{CA}$.
3. Use PLT: corresponding angles and AA ~.
4. Show $\Delta BAC \sim \Delta CAD$ and then use AAA ~, common $\angle B$, and substitution.
5. a. $x = 12$; $y = 15$; $z = 20$ **b.** $x = 10$; $y = 15$; $z = 9$ **c.** $x = 15$; $y = 48$
d. $x = \frac{112}{3}$ **e.** $x = 8$
6. Show $APCD$ is a parallelogram, then use POP, PPT, and substitution. **7.** Use PLT: corresponding angles and AA ~ to show $\Delta AGE \sim \Delta AFC$ and $\Delta ADE \sim \Delta ABC$. Then use AAA ~ and substitution. **8.** Use MPT to show $\frac{(AB)^2}{(AC)^2} = \frac{(CB)(DB)}{(BC)(DC)}$. **9.** Use AA ~, AAA ~, substitution, addition, and AST to show $ABCD \sim EFGH$.

Exercise 11-6, pages 416-418

1. The tree is 3.96 m tall.
2. The tree is 6.24 m tall. **3.** The distance is 3.2 m.
4. Consider $C' = C$ so $CC' = 0$;
Ratio of enlargement $= \frac{AA' - CC'}{BB' - CC'} = \frac{AA'}{BB'}$
5. a. 285 m **b.** 1.8 m **6. a.** Show $\angle ZVF = 90°$ and use OAT and AA ~. **b.** Show $\frac{AB}{VZ} = \frac{BF}{FV}$ and use substitution. **c.** Use the results of part **b** and AAA ~ to show $\frac{f}{d_i} = 1 - \frac{f}{d_o}$
7. a. $h_i = 10$ cm; $d_i = 60$ cm **b.** $d_o = 22.5$ cm

Exercise 11-7, pages 423-424

1. a. $\frac{4}{25}$; $\frac{4}{21}$ **b.** $\frac{3}{1}$; $\frac{1}{2}$ **c.** $\frac{25}{9}$ **d.** $\frac{4}{1}$; $\frac{3}{1}$
2. a. area ΔADE: area $\Delta ABC = 36 : 121$
b. $AD : DB = 3 : 1$
c. area $DBCE$: area $\Delta ABC = 153 : 169$
3. $HB = ED = 6$ cm; $HE = BD = \frac{66}{5}$ cm
4. a. 2 : 3 **b.** Moving clockwise around the patio, start at the top: 4.5 m, 3.4 m, 3.6 m, 1.5 m, 9.75 m, 7.8 m.
5. a. Use OAT, PLT: alternate angles, and AA ~.
b. The altitudes from each of $\angle A$ and $\angle D$ to $\overline{BC}$ form a rectangle $ABCD$. Show area ΔABC = area ΔDCB and use subtraction and substitution. **6. a.** $\frac{1}{4}$ **b.** $\frac{1}{2}$ **c.** $\frac{1}{4}$ **d.** $\frac{1}{1}$ **7. a.** $\frac{2}{5}$; $\frac{5}{7}$
b. $\frac{1}{1}$; $\frac{2}{1}$; $\frac{2}{3}$ **8. a.** $\frac{5}{8}$ **b.** $\frac{4}{9}$ **c.** $\frac{5}{18}$

9.
$$\begin{aligned} \text{area } \Delta ABD &= 4(\text{area } \Delta ECA) \text{ by SAS} \sim \\ \text{area } \Delta BDF &= 4(\text{area } \Delta CEG) \text{ by AAS} \sim \\ \therefore \text{area } \Delta ADF &= 4(\text{area } \Delta ECA + \text{area } \Delta CEG) \\ &= 4(\text{area } \Delta AEG) \end{aligned}$$

10. a. Prove by showing $\overline{QP} \parallel \overline{XY}$ and use OAT, PLT: alternate angles, AA ~, and the ratio of the areas of similar triangles. **b.** Use AAA ~ and RAT to find the individual ratios of area and multiply.

Exercise 11-8, pages 426-427

1. a. No. Ratio of radii is 4 : 3, but ratio of heights is 5 : 4. **b.** Yes. Both are spheres.
c. Yes. Ratio of all corresponding sides is 3 : 2.
d. Yes. Ratio of all corresponding sides is 3 : 2.
2. a. 125 : 343 **b.** 32.768 : 3.375 **c.** $7\sqrt{7} : 10\sqrt{10}$
3. a. 6 : 11 **b.** 4 : 5 **c.** 3 : 7 **4. a.** $x = \frac{32}{5}$; $h = \frac{15}{4}$ **b.** $V = 2187$ **c.** $V = 47.2$ **d.** $h = 8.4$
5. 21.6 L **6.** 5 m **7.** 42.5 cm × 42.5 cm × 74.4 cm
8. 19.8 cm **9.** 1.1 L **10.** 0.89 times as large
11. a. $\frac{25}{49}$ **b.** $\frac{125}{343}$ **12. a.** $\frac{7}{11}$ **b.** $\frac{343}{1331}$
13. 4.5 cm³ **14.** 175 cm²

Review, pages 428-429

1. a. $x = 16$ **b.** $x = 7.2; y = \frac{98}{9}$ **c.** $y = \frac{20}{3}$; $x = 7.5$ **d.** $x = \frac{28}{3}; y = 5; z = \frac{35}{3}$ **e.** $x = \frac{26}{3}$ **f.** $x = 12; y = 15; z = 20$
2. Show *ABCQ* and *ABRC* are parallelograms. Then use PLT: corresponding angles and AA~.
3. Join *A* to *C*. Show $\overline{NP} \parallel \overline{AC}$ and $\overline{MQ} \parallel \overline{AC}$. Then substitute and use the transitive property.
4. Use substitution. **5.** Use AAA~, the definition of an altitude, and substitution.
6. a. $\frac{9}{64}$ **b.** $\frac{2}{5}$ **c.** $\frac{2}{7}$ **d.** $\frac{9}{224}$ **7. a.** $\frac{PQ}{BC} = \frac{3}{8}$
b. $\frac{PQ}{RS} = \frac{3}{4}$ **c.** $\frac{\text{area}\,\Delta APQ}{\text{area}\,\Delta ABC} = \frac{9}{64}$
d. $\frac{\text{area}\,PQCB}{\text{area}\,\Delta APQ} = \frac{55}{9}$ **e.** $\frac{\text{area}\,\Delta PQT}{\text{area}\,\Delta SRT} = \frac{9}{16}$
8. 5.8 m **9. a.** $\frac{3}{5}$ **b.** $\frac{9}{25}$ **10. a.** $\frac{16}{25}$ **b.** $\frac{64}{125}$
11. 37.8 cm **12.** Assume $\overline{PQ}$ is not parallel to $\overline{AB}$ and prove indirectly. **13.** Use common $\angle A$, AA~ and AAA~ to show $(AD)(AO) = (AB)(AF)$ and $(AD)(AO) = (AC)(AE)$. **14.** Use MPT to show $(BA)^2 = (AC)(AD) = (BE)(BD)$.
15. Use PLT: corresponding and alternate angles, substitution, and ITT to show $PV = PR$. Then use $\overline{VR} \parallel \overline{PT}$ and substitution.

Test, page 430

1. a. $BY = 1$ **b.** 1 : 3 **2.** Show *MNXQ* is a parallelogram, then use POP and substitution.
3. a. $\frac{28}{5}$ **b.** $\frac{25}{49}$ **4. a.** 4 : 9 **b.** 4 : 25 **5. a.** 17.5 cm **b.** 29.2 cm **c.** 15 cm **6. a.** 27 : 64 **b.** 9 : 16
7. a. 3 : 2 **b.** 14 **c.** 9 : 4 **8.** Use MPT, PT, and substitution in each of ΔBAD and ΔBCD. **9.** Use PLT: corresponding angles, AA~, and AAA~ to show $AY : AD = AZ : AC$. Then use PLT, common $\angle A$, AA~, and AAA~ to show $XZ : BC = AZ : AC$. **10.** Use OAT, PLT: alternate angles, AA~, AAA~, and substitution to show $XM : MC = MZ : MB$ and $XM : AM = MZ : MB$.

Cumulative Review, page 431

1. a. $D_f = \{x \mid x \in \mathbf{R}\}; R_f = \{y \mid y \geq -2, y \in \mathbf{R}\}$
b. Parabola with *y*-intercept: -2 and *x*-intercepts: $\pm\sqrt{2}$. **c.** $f^{-1}: x \rightarrow +\sqrt{x + 2}$
d. Parabola with *x*-intercept: -2, *y*-intercept: $\sqrt{2}$, and $y \geq 0$.
2. $y + 2 = \frac{(x - 1)^2}{4} - 2(x - 1)$ **3.** 137 min
4. $x = -2.46$ **5.** If $x - 2$ is a factor, then 2 is a root. $\therefore 2^5 - 2^4 - 2^3 - 2^2 + 2 - 6 = 0$
6. 1144 m **7.** $(x, y) = (\pm 1, -3)$ or $(x, y) = (\pm\sqrt{5}, 1)$

8. a. Use POP and SAS to show $\Delta ABF \cong \Delta CDE$. Then use POP to prove $\overline{AF} \parallel \overline{EC}$.
b. Use PLT: corresponding angles, AA~, and AAA~.
c. Use PLT, substitution, ASA and congruent triangles to prove $DK = KM = MB$.

UNIT 12

Exercise 12-1, pages 434-435

1. a. an infinite number **b.** one (unless $P = 0$)
2. a. 201 cm² **b.** 112 cm² **c.** 391 cm² **d.** 223 cm² **3. a.** 25.1 cm **b.** 14.0 cm **c.** 48.8 cm **d.** 27.9 cm **4.** 20 units **5.** 30 units **6. a.** 100° **b.** 240° **c.** 40° **7. a.** 240° **b.** 22° **c.** 320°
8. 12 cm **9.** 514 m; 4827.4 m²
11. $\therefore \frac{s}{2} = \frac{\pi r\theta}{360}$; $A = \frac{r\pi r\theta}{360} = r\left(\frac{s}{2}\right)$
12. a. 178.4 cm² **b.** 80°
13. a. 29.3 cm **b.** 120° **14.** 20 012 km

Exercise 12-2, pages 438-439

1. a. Since every point on a circle is equidistant from its centre, the circle can be rotated about its centre and the image will always be the same circle, no matter what the magnitude of the rotation. **b.** Any diameter of a circle divides the circle into two equal semi-circles. **2.** 14 cm
3. a. 5 cm **b.** 23.1 cm **c.** 25 cm **d.** 6 cm
4. 17 cm **5.** 7 cm **6.** Construct radii $\overline{OX}$, $\overline{OY}$, $\overline{OP}$, $\overline{OQ}$. Show $\angle YOP = 180°$, then $\Delta OAY \cong \Delta ODP$ by OAT and SSS, and $\Delta ABY \cong \Delta DCP$ by OAT, PLT, and AAS.
7. Construct perpendicular bisectors from the centre to each chord. Then prove the right triangles formed are equal by SSA. **8.** $r = 25$ cm
9. Draw the perpendicular bisector of each side. Their point of intersection will be the centre of the circle and $OA = OB = OC = r$.
10. Construct $\overline{OA} \perp \overline{PQ}$. Use the chord property and subtraction to show $AP - AX = AQ - AY$. Substitute. **11.** Construct $\overline{OP} \perp \overline{XY}$ and $\overline{OQ} \perp \overline{YZ}$. Show $\Delta OPQ \cong \Delta OQY$ by the chord property and HST. Use ABT to show $\overline{YW}$ bisects $\angle XYZ$.
12. ΔQPR is equilateral. Prove using the results of exercise 7. **13.** Show $\Delta OFA \cong \Delta OGE$ and $\Delta OFC \cong \Delta OGC$ by ABT and HST. Add and substitute to conclude.

Application, page 441

1. Ottawa (45°N, 76° W); Vancouver (49°N, 123°W); Halifax (45°N, 64°W); Paris (49°N, 2°E); Tokyo (36°N, 140°E) **2. a.** 1800 nautical miles **b.** 2700 nautical miles **c.** 5700 nautical miles **d.** 7200 nautical miles **e.** 8100 nautical miles **3. a.** (40°S, 120°W) **b.** (50°S, 110°W)

c. (30°N, 50°W) **d.** (50°N, 110°W)
e. (48°S, 80°E) **f.** (50°N, 80°W)
4. a. 2580 nautical miles **b.** 4020 nautical miles

Exercise 12-3, pages 444-446
1. a. $\theta = 80°$; $\varphi = 105°$; $\phi = 25°$ **b.** $\theta = 82°$; $\varphi = 82°$; $\phi = 98°$ **c.** $\theta = 122°$; $\varphi = 58°$
d. $\theta = 120°$; $\varphi = 120°$ **e.** $\theta = 90°$; $\varphi = 90°$; $\phi = 30°$ **f.** $\theta = 69°$ **2.** Show equal chords subtend equal sector angles, and use IAT to prove.
3. Show equal sector angles subtend equal chords and use IAT and transitivity to prove.
4. $\angle AEB = 135°$ **5.** $\angle A = 90°$; $\angle B = 68°$; $\angle C = 90°$; $\angle D = 112°$ **6.** Use PLT: alternate angles and IAT to show each. **7.** Use IAT, ITT, addition, and substitution. **8.** Show $\angle QPS = \angle RPT$ and $\angle QSP = \angle RTP$ by IAT. Then use AAS. **9.** $\angle ABC = 130°$ **10.** Show *AXYB* and *DCYX* are parallelograms by IAT and PLT: alternate angles. **11.** Use common $\angle T$, IAT, and AST. **12.** Prove by SAS after showing $\angle PQS = \angle PRS$ by IAT. **13. a.** 360° **b.** 540° **c.** 180° $(n - 1)$ **14.** Show $PA^2 = PX^2 + AX^2$ and $PB^2 = PX^2 + XB^2$ by PT. Add $PA^2 + PB^2$ and solve in terms of $\overline{PO}$, $\overline{AB}$, $\overline{OB}$, and $\overline{OA}$.

Review, page 447
1. a. $\overline{OB}$, $\overline{OD}$, $\overline{OE}$ **b.** $\overline{BE}$ **c.** $\angle BOD$, $\angle DOE$, $\angle BOE$ **d.** $\angle BAD$, $\angle ADC$, $\angle ADB$, $\angle BDC$, $\angle DCB$, $\angle CBA$, $\angle CBE$, $\angle CBD$, $\angle EBD$, $\angle EBA$, $\angle DBA$ **e.** *ABCD* **f.** $\overline{BO}$, $\overline{OD}$, arc *BD*; $\overline{DO}$, $\overline{OE}$, arc *DE* **g.** $\overline{BE}$, arc *BAE* or arc *BCE* **h.** $\overline{BD}$, arc *BCD*; $\overline{BA}$, arc *BCA*; $\overline{BC}$, arc *BAC*; *AD*, arc *ABD*; $\overline{DC}$, arc *DBC* **2. a.** arc *AB* = 22.0 units; area *AOB* = 154 units^2 **b.** arc *AB* = 16.7 units; area *AOB* = 67.0 units^2 **c.** arc *AB* = 16.7 units; area *AOB* = 101 units^2 **d.** arc *AB* = 68.1 units; area *AOB* = 510.5 units^2 **3. a.** $OB = 10$ **b.** $AB = 24$ **c.** $DO = 7$ **d.** $AB = 6$ **4.** 28 cm **5.** 4 cm **6. a.** $\theta = 35°$; $\varphi = 40°$; $\phi = 35°$ **b.** $\theta = 132.5°$; $\varphi = 47.5°$; **c.** $\varphi = 90°$; $\phi = 65°$ **d.** $\theta = 28°$; $\varphi = 28°$; $\phi = 28°$ **7.** Use OAT, IAT, and AAA to show $\triangle XTW \sim \triangle YTZ$. Use the results to show $(XT)(TZ) = (WT)(TY)$.

Exercise 12-4, pages 450-451
1. *S, W, Y, Q*; *S, W, T, P*; *T, W, Y, R*
2. a. $\angle A + \angle C = 180°$. Use CPT. $x = 92°$
b. $\angle SPT = 25° = \angle TRS$. By CPT, *PSTR* is cyclic; Show $\angle QSV + \angle QTV = 180°$. By CPT, *SVTQ* is cyclic. **c.** External angle at *Z* of $\overline{ZY}$ extended is 115°. $\angle WVZ = 115°$. By CPT, *W, V, Z, Y* are concyclic. $x = 65°$ **3.** For any two opposite angles, the sum is 180°. By CPT, the rectangle is cyclic. **4. a.** Construct right-angled $\triangle ABC$ with hypotenuse $\overline{BC}$, the diameter of a circle. Indirectly prove *A* is neither inside nor outside the circle. **b.** Construct quadrilateral *ABCD* with external angle $\angle ADE = \angle ABC$. Show the sum of internal angles is $\angle ADC + \angle ABC = 180°$, and by the proof of example 1 in lesson 12-4, *ABCD* must be cyclic. **5.** Use the results of exercise 4, part **a** to show the segments from the midpoint of the hypotenuse to each vertex are radii of the circle that the triangle can be inscribed in.
6. Use CPT, PLT, and substitution. **7.** Show $\angle TSR = \angle TPQ$ and use CPT. $\angle QRP = 33°$.
8. Show $\angle YAX = \angle YZW$ and use CPT.
9. Prove each by addition and CPT.
10. Use IAT and HST to show $\triangle XYW \cong \triangle XZW$. Use the results to show $\angle YXW = \angle ZXW$.
11. Use CPT, POP, PLT: alternate angles, and substitution to show *EFCD* is cyclic.
12. Use IAT, supplementary angles, and addition to show $\angle ABZ + \angle AYZ = 180°$. Then, use CPT.
13. Show $\triangle PSR \cong \triangle QRS$ by CPT, PLT, IAT, and AAS. **14.** Use CPT, PLT, IAT, and substitution to show $\angle ACD + \angle ABD = 180°$. Use CPT.

Exercise 12-5, pages 454-455
1. a. 6 **b.** 12 **c.** $AB = 6$; $AC = 6\sqrt{2}$ **d.** 12
2. Show *D* and *A* are each on the perpendicular bisector of $\overline{BC}$ by PBT. **3.** Use the fact that $OA = OB = r$, and use common side $\overline{OP}$, and HST to show $\triangle APO \cong \triangle BPO$. **4.** Show the centre *O* is on the bisector of each angle of the triangle by ABT. **5.** Show *O* is on the bisector of each exterior angle by ABT. **6.** $\overline{XY}$ and $\overline{PQ}$ are equidistant from the centre at their points of contact to the smaller circle. Thus, $\overline{XY}$ and $\overline{PQ}$ are chords equidistant from the centre of the large circle. See Lesson 12-2 exercise 7. **7.** Show $\angle AQO = \angle OAP$ by PBT, TST, and substitution. Then use substitution and AST to show $\angle APB = 2\angle CAB$. **8.** Show $\triangle OWP \cong \triangle OZP$ and $\triangle YOX \cong \triangle ZOX$ by HST. Use the sum $\angle OWP + \angle OZP + \angle YOX + \angle ZOX = 180°$ and substitute. **9.** Show $\angle OXY = \angle OYX = \angle WXY$ by ITT and substitution. Then add and use AST and substitution to prove. **10.** 48 cm
11. a. i. The two circles are distinct except common point of tangency *R*. **ii.** The smaller circle is contained in the larger circle.
b. i. Show $\angle PRS = \angle QRS = 90°$ and add.
ii. Show $\angle PRS = \angle QRS = 90°$ and they are the same angle. **c. i.** $PQ = PR + RQ = R_1 + R_2$
ii. $PQ = PR - RQ = R_1 - R_2$ **12.** $ST = 21.9$ cm
13. a. 84.2 cm **b.** 94.25 cm

Exercise 12-6, pages 457-459
1. a. $\theta = 70°$; $\varphi = 45°$; $\phi = 65°$ **b.** $\theta = 35°$; $\varphi = 65°$; $\phi = 85°$ **c.** $\alpha = 80°$; $\theta = 23°$; $\varphi = 32°$;

$\phi = 148^\circ$ **d.** $\theta = 70^\circ$ **e.** $\theta = 36^\circ$ **f.** $\theta = 90^\circ$; $\alpha = 65^\circ$; $\phi = 25^\circ$ **2.** Use ITT, TCT, and substitution. **3. a.** $\angle ABD = 33^\circ$ **b.** $\angle DAC = 62^\circ$ **c.** $\angle ABC = 95^\circ$ **d.** $\angle ADC = 85^\circ$ **4.** Show $\angle YZX = \angle XYZ$ by TCT, PLT, and substitution.
5. $\angle DEF = 72.5^\circ$; $\angle EFD = 50^\circ$; $\angle FDE = 57.5^\circ$
6. $\angle D = 60^\circ$; $\angle E = 90^\circ$; $\angle F = 30^\circ$, where $\angle D$ is opposite $\angle A$, $\angle E$ is opposite $\angle C$, and $\angle F$ is opposite $\angle B$. **7.** Show $\overline{AD}$ bisects $\angle BAC$ by TCT, ITT, and substitution. **8.** Show $\angle PQA = \angle RQC$ by PLT, TCT, and substitution. Then show $2\angle PQA + \angle AQC = \angle ABC + \angle AQC$ by CPT.
9. Use TCT and substitution to show $\angle ABD + \angle GFD = 180^\circ$. By CPT and subtraction, show $\angle ABD = \angle GED$, then use PLT.
10. a. Show $\angle BED = \angle ADB$ by IAT and substitution. Use TCT and AST to show $\angle ABD = \angle DBE$. **b.** Use EAT, TCT and substitution.
11. $\angle PQR = 22.5^\circ$; $\angle QRP = 29.5^\circ$; $\angle RPQ = 128^\circ$
12. Show $\angle ABD = \angle EBC$ by PLT, TCT, and substitution. Use CPT, sum of a straight-angle, and subtraction to show $\angle BAD = \angle ECB$. Use AST and substitution to finish.
13. Extend $\overline{CA}$ to E and construct $\overline{GAF}$, the tangent to both circles. Show $\angle FAC = \angle FCA$ and $\angle BAF = \angle ABF$ by TCT. Use AST, division, and subtraction to show $\angle DAC = 90^\circ$, and conclude with IAT.

Extra, page 459
The curve has an infinite radius. It is a straight line.

Exercise 12-7, pages 462-463
1. a. 16 **b.** 6 **c.** 10 **2.** 26.8 cm
3. $RW = 12$ cm; $RV = 9$ cm; $RT = 36$ cm
4. a. 5 **b.** 8 **c.** 3 **5.** Show $(AB)(AC) = AE^2$ and $(AF)(AG) = AE^2$ by TST. Use substitution.
6. Show $PE^2 = (PA)(PB)$ and $PE^2 = (PC)(PD)$ by TST. Substitute. **7.** Show $CX^2 = CY^2$ by TST and take the square root. **8.** Extend $\overline{AO}$ to D. Prove $(AB)(AC) = (AE)(AD)$ by TST and show $AE = OA - OB$ and $AD = OA + OB$. **9.** Show $SQRT$ is a cyclic quadrilateral by CPT and use the TST corollary. **10.** Show B, X, Y, C are concyclic and that $\overline{AXB}$ and $\overline{AYC}$ are secants through those points. Then use the corollary to TST. **11.** Show Y, B, A, Z are concyclic by ITT, AST and CPT. $\overline{XBY}$ and $\overline{XAZ}$ are secants as in exercise 10. Use TST. **12. a.** By IAT, show $\overline{AC}$ is a diameter of the circle containing A, C, and D. Show $\overline{BA}$ is perpendicular to a radius of the circle. **b.** Use the results of part **a** and TST.
13. Show $PE^2 - PD^2 = DE^2 = (2r)^2$, which is constant, by TST and PT. **14.** Show by TST that $\overline{ADE}$ and $\overline{ABC}$ are secants to the same circle so E, D, B, C are concyclic.

Review, pages 464-465
1. 27.8 cm^2 **2.** 36.6 mm **3.** 12 cm **4.** 26 cm
5. a. $\theta = 50^\circ$; $\varphi = 45^\circ$; $\phi = 45^\circ$ **b.** $\theta = 115^\circ$; $\varphi = 100^\circ$ **c.** $\theta = 136^\circ$ **d.** $\theta = 90^\circ$; $\varphi = 58^\circ$ **e.** $\theta = 115^\circ$; $\varphi = 115^\circ$; $\phi = 65^\circ$ **f.** $\theta = 70^\circ$; $\varphi = 25^\circ$; $\phi = 85^\circ$ **g.** $\theta = 75^\circ$; $\varphi = 40^\circ$; $\phi = 113^\circ$ **h.** $\beta = 90^\circ$; $\varphi = 26^\circ$; $\phi = 26^\circ$; $\alpha = 64^\circ$; $\theta = 90^\circ$
6. Show $\angle OPQ = \angle SRQ$ and $\angle PQO = \angle SQR$ so $\triangle POQ \sim \triangle RSQ$ by AA~. **7. a.** Show $\overline{OW}$ bisects $\angle RWS$ and $\overline{PW}$ bisects $\angle TWU$ by ABT. Use OAT. **b.** $RU = 10$ cm; $PT = 5.33$ cm; $OP = 16.67$ cm **8.** Use OAT, IAT and AA~ to show $\triangle AEB \sim \triangle CED$. Use the results.
9. a. Draw tangents $\overline{OA}$, $\overline{OB}$, and $\overline{OC}$. Show $\angle QCR = \angle RBP = \angle PAQ = 180^\circ$ by addition. **b.** 24 cm
10. 16 cm **11. a.** 1.33 cm **b.** $PE = 2\sqrt{2}$ cm
12. $\angle ABC = 52^\circ$; $\angle BCA = 68^\circ$; $\angle CAB = 60^\circ$
13. Show $\angle BAC = \angle BCA$ by IAT and ITT. Use TCT and PLT to finish the proof. **14.** Construct radii $\overline{OA}$ and $\overline{OB}$. Use the definition of a tangent and HST to show $\triangle POA \cong \triangle QOB$. Use the angle sum of a straight angle and ITT to show $\angle OAB = \angle OBA$. Then use AST and PLT.
15. Show $\triangle OXW \cong \triangle OYZ$ by SSS, $\angle OWZ = \angle OZW$ by ITT and then use CPT and PLT to show the result. **16.** Use TST to show $BC^2 = AC^2 - 2(AE)(AC)$. Then use PT. **17.** Show $\triangle AEC \sim \triangle DEB$ by OAT, IAT and AA~. Use the results and OAT to show $\triangle AEL \sim \triangle DEM$. $ALMD$ is cyclic by CPT. **18.** Show $\angle ODB = \angle OAB$ by the definition of a tangent. Use CPT. **19.** Show $\angle ABC = \angle ACM$, $\angle AMC = \angle ACB$ so $\triangle AMC \sim \triangle ACB$ by AA~. Then show $(AM)(AB) = AC^2$ which is constant.

Test, page 466
1. $\dfrac{2\pi r}{3}$ **2.** 18 cm **3. a.** $\theta = 90^\circ$; $\varphi = 53^\circ$ **b.** $\theta = 120^\circ$; $\varphi = 96^\circ$ **c.** $\theta = 90^\circ$; $\varphi = 26^\circ$; $\phi = 26^\circ$; $\beta = 90^\circ$; $\alpha = 64^\circ$ **d.** $\theta = 112^\circ$ **e.** $\theta = 108^\circ$; $\varphi = 108^\circ$; $\phi = 72^\circ$ **f.** $\theta = 52^\circ$; $\varphi = 46^\circ$; $\phi = 46^\circ$ **g.** $\theta = 78^\circ$; $\varphi = 41^\circ$; $\phi = 114^\circ$ **h.** $\theta = 22^\circ$; $\varphi = 75^\circ$; $\phi = 83^\circ$
4. a. 25 **b.** 8 **c.** 21 **d.** 24
5. $\angle A + \angle B + \angle C + \angle D = 540^\circ$
6. Use common $\angle X$, and AST to prove.
7. $\angle DEF = 30^\circ$; $\angle EFD = 104^\circ$; $\angle FDE = 46^\circ$
8. Show $\triangle PAB \cong \triangle PCB$ and $\triangle ABE \cong \triangle CBE$ by HST and SAS. Use TCT to show $\angle CBD = \angle ECB$. By PLT, $\overline{BD} \parallel \overline{AC}$. **9.** Show $\angle BDE = \angle BCF$ by TCT, common $\angle B$, and substitution. Then use PLT.
10. Show $AB^2 = (AT)(AP) = (BT)(BQ)$ by TST. Substitute.

Cumulative Review, page 467

1. a. $x = \frac{5}{3}$ or $x = -3$ **b.** $-4 < x < 3$
2. $f \circ g(x) = 3x^2 + 1$; $g \circ f(x) = 9x^2 + 24x + 15$
3. a. 101.3 kPa **b.** 3.17 kPa **c.** 10.50 km above sea level **4. a.** 1.8587 **b.** 13.2011 **c.** 1.8226
5. $(x - 2)(x + 3)(x + 6)(x + 1)$
7. Yes. **8.** length = 16m; width = 15 m

9. a.

Size	Central Angle
0.5	15.8°
1	133.6°
2	113.05°
4	89.65°
6	7.9°

b. mean = 3.6L; median = 2L; mode = 1L **c.** range = 5.5L; mean deviation = 1.8; standard deviation = 2.0
10. a. $V(-2, 5)$ **b.** $F(-2, 11)$; $y = -1$

INDEX

Photograph Credits

Every effort has been made to ascertain proper ownership of copyrighted materials and obtain permission for their use. Any omission is unintentional and will be corrected in future printings upon proper notification.

Government of Canada, Department of Fisheries and Oceans: 1, 40
National Research Council of Canada: 7
Candive Services, Vancouver, BC: 25
Chapman Studios: 26
Library of Congress, Washington, DC: 48
Bettman Archive Galleries: 59, 85, 225, 348
Canapress Photo Services: 71, 105, 250, 282, 342, 387
Esso Research: 80
David Hamilton: 100
General Motors of Canada: 110
Ministry of Tourism, British Columbia: 156, 314
Allan Pollett, The Stock Market: 204, 452
BCS Electronics: 226
Bank of Canada Review, 1987: 326
The Image Bank: 334, 384
Miller Comstock: 381
Raleigh Bicycles: 388, 432
Designed by Home Planners, Inc.: reprinted courtesy *Home Beautiful's Houses and Plans*, 1986, the Hearst Corp.: 396
Fabergé: 425
Ted Bieler: 459

Photo Research: Debbie Brewer

8723 51